DEVELOPMENTAL MATH; A MODULAR CURRICULUM FOR THE NORTH CAROLINA COMMUNITY COLLEGE SYSTEM

ALAN S. TUSSY
CITRUS COLLEGE

R. DAVID GUSTAFSON
ROCK VALLEY COLLEGE

DIANE R. KOENIG
ROCK VALLEY COLLEGE

BROOKS/COLE
CENGAGE Learning

Brazil • Japan • Korea • Mexico • Singapore • Spain • United Kingdom • United States

Developmental Math A Modular Curriculum for The North Carolina Community College System
Alan S. Tussy, R. David Gustafson, Diane R. Koenig

Publisher: Charlie Van Wagner
Senior Developmental Editor: Danielle Derbenti
Senior Development Editor for Market Strategies: Rita Lombard
Assistant Editor: Stefanie Beeck
Editorial Assistant: Jennifer Cordoba
Media Editor: Heleny Wong
Marketing Manager: Gordon Lee
Marketing Assistant: Angela Kim
Marketing Communications Manager: Katy Malatesta
Content Project Manager: Jennifer Risden
Creative Director: Rob Hugel
Art Director: Vernon Boes
Print Buyer: Linda Hsu
Rights Acquisitions Account Manager, Text: Mardell Glinksi-Schultz
Rights Acquisitions Account Manager, Image: Don Schlotman
Production Service: Graphic World Inc.
Text Designer: Diane Beasley
Photo Researcher: Bill Smith Group
Illustrators: Lori Heckelman; Graphic World Inc.
Cover Designer: Terri Wright
Cover Image: Background: © Jason Edwards/Getty Images RF, Y Button: © Art Parts/Fotosearch RF
Compositor: Graphic World Inc.

Library of Congress Control Number: TBD

ISBN-13: 978-1-133-83584-4

ISBN-10: 1-133-83584-8

Brooks/Cole
20 Davis Drive
Belmont, CA 94002-3098
USA

Cengage Learning is a leading provider of customized learning solutions with office locations around the globe, including Singapore, the United Kingdom, Australia, Mexico, Brazil, and Japan. Locate your local office at **www.cengage.com/global**

Cengage Learning products are represented in Canada by Nelson Education, Ltd.

To learn more about Brooks/Cole, visit **www.cengage.com/brookscole**

Purchase any of our products at your local college store or at our preferred online store **www.cengagebrain.com**

Printed in the United States of America
1 2 3 4 5 6 7 14 13 12 11 10

To my lovely wife, Liz,

thank you for your insight and encouragement

ALAN S. TUSSY

■

To my grandchildren:

Daniel, Tyler, Spencer, Skyler, Garrett, and Jake Gustafson

R. DAVID GUSTAFSON

■

To my husband and my best friend, Brian Koenig

DIANE R. KOENIG

■

CONTENTS

© OJO Images Ltd/Alamy

iStockphoto.com/Monkeybusinessimages

MODULE 3 DMA 030

Proportion Ratios Rates and Percents 269

Nick White/Getty Images

MODULE 4 DMA 040

Expressions, Linear Equations, Linear Inequalities 415

MODULE 5 DMA 050

Graphs and Equations of Lines 495

Kim Steele/Photodisc/Getty Images

MODULE 6 DMA 060

Polynomials and Quadratic Applications 571

© Robert E. Daemmrich/Getty Images

MODULE 7 DMA 070

Rational Expressions and Equations 701

Reggie Casagrande/Getty Images

MODULE 8 DMA 080

Rational Expressions and Equations 757

© istockphoto.com/Sean Locke

APPENDIXES

PREFACE

Developmental Math a Modular Curriculum for the North Carolina Community College System was developed after reviewing the redesign principles put forth by the math redesign task force in North Carolina. The design principles match quite nicely with the pedagogical approach that the author team has refined over the years, an approach which they believe promotes sound mathematical learning. This book contains all eight modules as described by the task force. Each module lists the content and shows how it aligns with the North Carolina student learning outcomes. While all eight modules are presented here as one book, because of the modular development we can provide them packaged any way that the adopting school would like them. In addition to the print book we can provide a superior technology package that provides instant feedback to the student with Enhanced WebAssign.

Mathematics, for many of today's developmental math students, is like a foreign language. They have difficulty translating the words, their meanings, and how they apply to problem solving. With these needs in mind (and as educational research suggests), our fundamental goal is to have students read, write, think, and speak using the *language of mathematics.* Instructional approaches that include vocabulary, practice, and well-defined pedagogy, along with an emphasis on reasoning, modeling, communication, and technology skills have been blended to address this need.

The most common question that students ask as they watch their instructors solve problems and as they read the textbook is … *Why?* Experience teaches us that it's not enough to know *how* a problem is solved. Students gain a deeper understanding of algebraic concepts if they know *why* a particular approach is taken. This instructional truth was the motivation for adding a **Strategy** and **Why** explanation to the solution of each worked example.

Proportion/Ratios/Rates/
Percents

3

3.1 An Introduction to Fractions
3.2 Multiplying Fractions
3.3 Dividing Fractions
3.4 Adding and Subtracting Fractions
3.5 Multiplying and Dividing Mixed Numbers
3.6 Adding and Subtracting Mixed Numbers
3.7 Order of Operations and Complex Fractions
Chapter Summary and Review
Chapter Test
Cumulative Review

from Campus to Careers

School Guidance Counselor

School guidance counselors plan academic programs and help students choose the best courses to take to achieve their educational goals. Counselors often meet with students to discuss the life skills needed for personal and social growth. To prepare for this career, guidance counselors take classes in an area of mathematics called *statistics*, where they learn how to collect, analyze, explain, and present data.

In **Problem 109** of **Study Set 3.4,** you will see how a counselor must be able to add fractions to better understand a graph that shows students' study habits.

JOB TITLE: School Guidance Counselor
EDUCATION: A master's degree is usually required to be licensed as a counselor. However, some schools accept a bachelor's degree with the appropriate counseling courses.
JOB OUTLOOK: Excellent.
ANNUAL EARNINGS: The average (median) salary in 2006 was $53,750.
FOR MORE INFORMATION:

207

Chapter Openers That Answer the Question: When Will I Use This?

Instructors are asked this question time and again by students. In response, we have written chapter openers called *From Campus to Careers.* This feature highlights vocations that require various algebraic skills. Designed to inspire career exploration, each includes job outlook, educational requirements, and annual earnings information. Careers presented in the openers are tied to an exercise found later in the *Study Sets.*

Examples That Tell Students Not Just How, But WHY

Why? That question is often asked by students as they watch their instructor solve problems in class and as they are working on problems at home. It's not enough to know *how* a problem is solved. Students gain a deeper understanding of the algebraic concepts if they know *why* a particular approach was taken. This instructional truth was the motivation for adding a *Strategy* and *Why* explanation to each worked example.

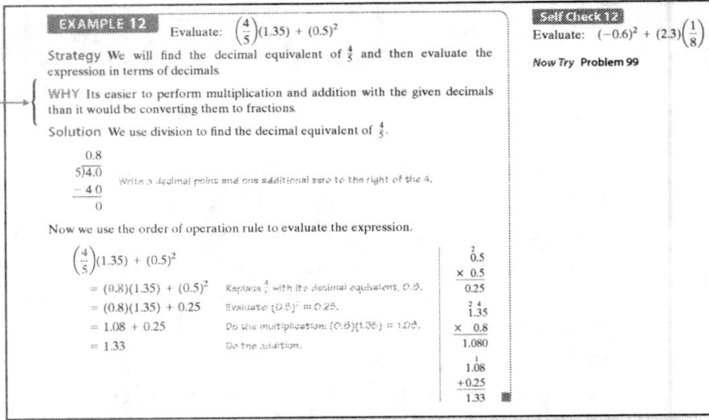

EXAMPLE 12 Evaluate: $\left(\frac{4}{5}\right)(1.35) + (0.5)^2$

Strategy We will find the decimal equivalent of $\frac{4}{5}$ and then evaluate the expression in terms of decimals.

WHY Its easier to perform multiplication and addition with the given decimals than it would be converting them to fractions.

Solution We use division to find the decimal equivalent of $\frac{4}{5}$.

$5\overline{)4.0}$ = 0.8; -40; 0 — Write a decimal point and one additional zero to the right of the 4.

Now we use the order of operation rule to evaluate the expression.

$\left(\frac{4}{5}\right)(1.35) + (0.5)^2$

$= (0.8)(1.35) + (0.5)^2$ — Replace $\frac{4}{5}$ with its decimal equivalent, 0.8.

$= (0.8)(1.35) + 0.25$ — Evaluate: $(0.5)^2 = 0.25$.

$= 1.08 + 0.25$ — Do the multiplication: $(0.8)(1.35) = 1.08$.

$= 1.33$ — Do the addition.

$0.5 \times 0.5 = 0.25$; $1.35 \times 0.8 = 1.080$; $1.08 + 0.25 = 1.33$

Self Check 12 Evaluate: $(-0.6)^2 + (2.3)\left(\frac{1}{8}\right)$

Now Try Problem 99

Examples That Offer Immediate Feedback

Each worked example includes a *Self Check.* These can be completed by students on their own or as classroom lecture examples, which is how Alan Tussy uses them. Alan asks selected students to read aloud the *Self Check* problems as he writes what the student says on the board. The other students, with their books open to that page, can quickly copy the *Self Check* problem to their notes. This speeds up the note-taking process and encourages student participation in his lectures. It also teaches students how to read mathematical symbols. Each *Self Check* answer is printed adjacent to the corresponding problem in the *Annotated Instructor's Edition* for easy reference. *Self Check* solutions can be found at the end of each section in the student edition before each *Study Set.*

Examples That Ask Students to Work Independently

Each worked example ends with a *Now Try* problem. These are the final step in the learning process. Each one is linked to a similar problem found within the *Guided Practice* section of the *Study Sets.*

Examples That Show the Behind-the-Scenes Calculations

Some steps of the solutions to worked examples involve arithmetic calculations that are too complicated to be performed mentally. In these instances, we have shown the actual computations that must be made to complete the formal solution. These computations appear directly to the right of the author notes and are separated from them by a thin, gray rule. The necessary addition, subtraction, multiplication, or division (usually done on scratch paper) is placed at the appropriate stage of the solution where such a computation is required. Rather than simply list the steps of a solution horizontally, making no mention of how the numerical values within the solution are obtained, this unique feature will help answer the often-heard question from a struggling student, "How did you get that answer?" It also serves as a model for the calculations that students must perform independently to solve the problems in the Study Sets.

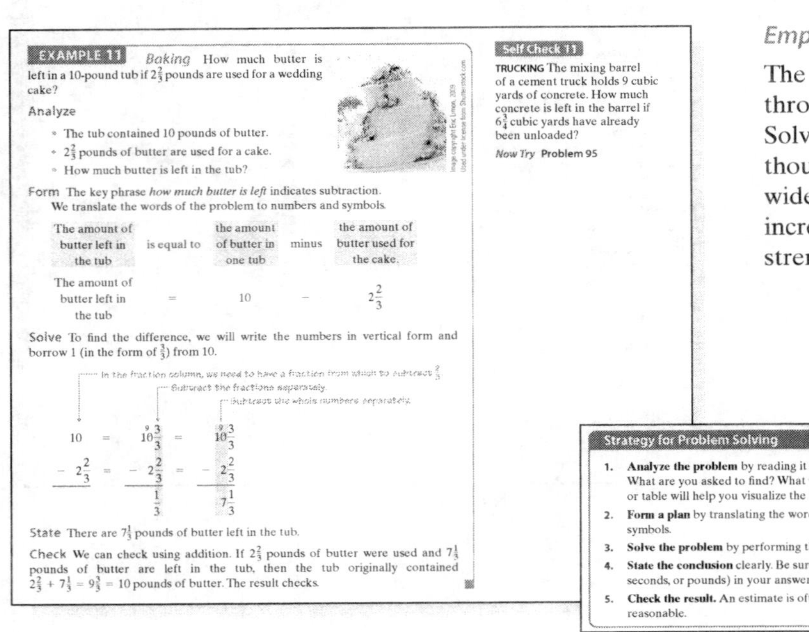

EXAMPLE 11 *Baking* How much butter is left in a 10-pound tub if $2\frac{2}{3}$ pounds are used for a wedding cake?

Analyze

- The tub contained 10 pounds of butter.
- $2\frac{2}{3}$ pounds of butter are used for a cake.
- How much butter is left in the tub?

Image copyright Eric Limon, 2009. Used under license from Shutterstock.com

Form The key phrase *how much butter is left* indicates subtraction. We translate the words of the problem to numbers and symbols.

The amount of butter left in the tub	is equal to	the amount of butter in one tub	minus	the amount of butter used for the cake.
The amount of butter left in the tub	=	10	−	$2\frac{2}{3}$

Solve To find the difference, we will write the numbers in vertical form and borrow 1 (in the form of $\frac{3}{3}$) from 10.

In the fraction column, we need to have a fraction from which to subtract $\frac{2}{3}$. Subtract the fractions separately. Subtract the whole numbers separately.

$$10 - 2\frac{2}{3} = 9\frac{3}{3} - 2\frac{2}{3}: \quad \frac{3}{3}-\frac{2}{3}=\frac{1}{3}, \quad 9\frac{3}{3}-2\frac{2}{3}=7\frac{1}{3}$$

State There are $7\frac{1}{3}$ pounds of butter left in the tub.

Check We can check using addition. If $2\frac{2}{3}$ pounds of butter were used and $7\frac{1}{3}$ pounds of butter are left in the tub, then the tub originally contained $2\frac{2}{3} + 7\frac{1}{3} = 9\frac{3}{3} = 10$ pounds of butter. The result checks.

Self Check 11 TRUCKING The mixing barrel of a cement truck holds 9 cubic yards of concrete. How much concrete is left in the barrel if $6\frac{3}{4}$ cubic yards have already been unloaded?

Now Try Problem 95

Emphasis on Problem-Solving

The five-step problem-solving strategy guides students through applied worked examples using the Analyze, Form, Solve, State, and Check process. This approach clarifies the thought process and mathematical skills necessary to solve a wide variety of problems. As a result, students' confidence is increased and their problem-solving abilities are strengthened.

Strategy for Problem Solving

1. **Analyze the problem** by reading it carefully. What information is given? What are you asked to find? What vocabulary is given? Often, a diagram or table will help you visualize the facts of the problem.
2. **Form a plan** by translating the words of the problem to numbers and symbols.
3. **Solve the problem** by performing the calculations.
4. **State the conclusion** clearly. Be sure to include the units (such as feet, seconds, or pounds) in your answer.
5. **Check the result.** An estimate is often helpful to see whether an answer is reasonable.

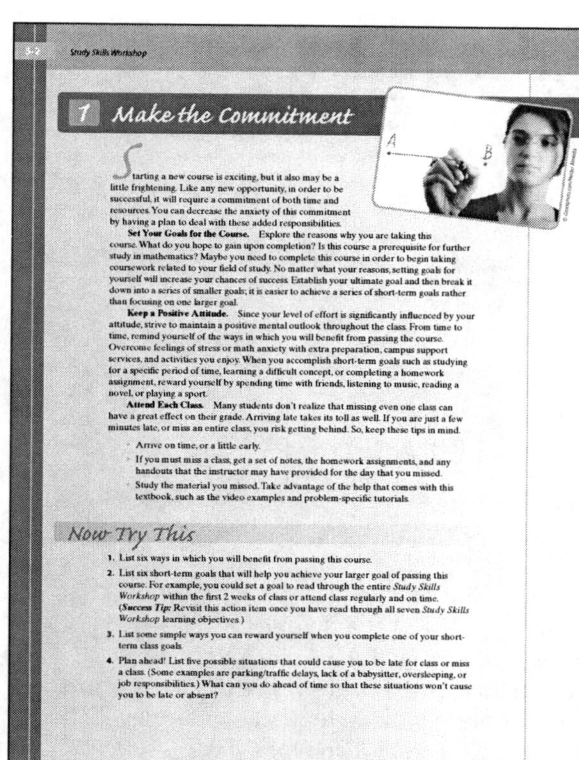

S-2 Study Skills Workshop

1 Make the Commitment

Starting a new course is exciting, but it also may be a little frightening. Like any new opportunity, in order to be successful, it will require a commitment of both time and resources. You can decrease the anxiety of this commitment by having a plan to deal with these added responsibilities.

Set Your Goals for the Course. Explore the reasons why you are taking this course. What do you hope to gain upon completion? Is this course a prerequisite for further study in mathematics? Maybe you need to complete this course in order to begin taking coursework related to your field of study. No matter what your reasons, setting goals for yourself will increase your chances of success. Establish your ultimate goal and then break it down into a series of smaller goals; it is easier to achieve a series of short-term goals rather than focusing on one larger goal.

Keep a Positive Attitude. Since your level of effort is significantly influenced by your attitude, strive to maintain a positive mental outlook throughout the class. From time to time, remind yourself of the ways in which you will benefit from passing the course. Overcome feelings of stress or math anxiety with extra preparation, campus support services, and activities you enjoy. When you accomplish short-term goals such as studying for a specific period of time, learning a difficult concept, or completing a homework assignment, reward yourself by spending time with friends, listening to music, reading a novel, or playing a sport.

Attend Each Class. Many students don't realize that missing even one class can have a great effect on their grade. Arriving late takes its toll as well. If you are just a few minutes late, or miss an entire class, you risk getting behind. So, keep these tips in mind.

- Arrive on time, or a little early.
- If you must miss a class, get a set of notes, the homework assignments, and any handouts that the instructor may have provided for the day that you missed.
- Study the material you missed. Take advantage of the help that comes with this textbook, such as the video examples and problem-specific tutorials.

Now Try This

1. List six ways in which you will benefit from passing this course.
2. List six short-term goals that will help you achieve your larger goal of passing this course. For example, you could set a goal to read through the entire *Study Skills Workshop* within the first 2 weeks of class or attend class regularly and on time. (***Success Tip:*** Revisit this action item once you have read through all seven *Study Skills Workshop* learning objectives.)
3. List some simple ways you can reward yourself when you complete one of your short-term class goals.
4. Plan ahead! List five possible situations that could cause you to be late for class or miss a class. (Some examples are parking/traffic delays, lack of a babysitter, oversleeping, or job responsibilities.) What can you do ahead of time so that these situations won't cause you to be late or absent?

Emphasis on Study Skills

This book begins with a *Study Skills Workshop* module. Instead of simple, unrelated suggestions printed in the margins, this module contains one-page discussions of study skills topics followed by a *Now Try This* section offering students actionable skills, assignments, and projects that will impact their study habits throughout the course.

The Language of Mathematics The word *fraction* comes from the Latin word *fractio* meaning "breaking in pieces."

Integrated Focus on the Language of Mathematics

Language of Mathematics boxes draw connections between mathematical terms and everyday references to reinforce the language of mathematics approach that runs throughout the text.

Guidance When Students Need It Most

Appearing at key teaching moments, *Success Tips* and *Caution* boxes improve students' problem-solving abilities, warn students of potential pitfalls, and increase clarity.

Success Tip In the newspaper example, we found a *part of a part* of a page. Multiplying proper fractions can be thought of in this way. When taking a *part of a part* of something, the result is always smaller than the original part that you began with.

Caution! In Example 5, it was very helpful to prime factor and simplify when we did (the third step of the solution). If, instead, you find the product of the numerators and the product of the denominators, the resulting fraction is difficult to simplify because the numerator, 126, and the denominator, 420, are large.

$$\frac{2}{3} \cdot \frac{9}{14} \cdot \frac{7}{10} = \frac{2 \cdot 9 \cdot 7}{3 \cdot 14 \cdot 10} = \frac{126}{420}$$

↑ Factor and simplify at this stage, before multiplying in the numerator and denominator.

↑ Don't multiply in the numerator and denominator and then try to simplify the result. You will get the same answer, but it takes much more work.

Useful Objectives Help Keep Students Focused

Each section begins with a set of numbered *Objectives* that focus students' attention on the skills that they will learn. As each objective is discussed in the section, the number and heading reappear to the reader to remind them of the objective at hand.

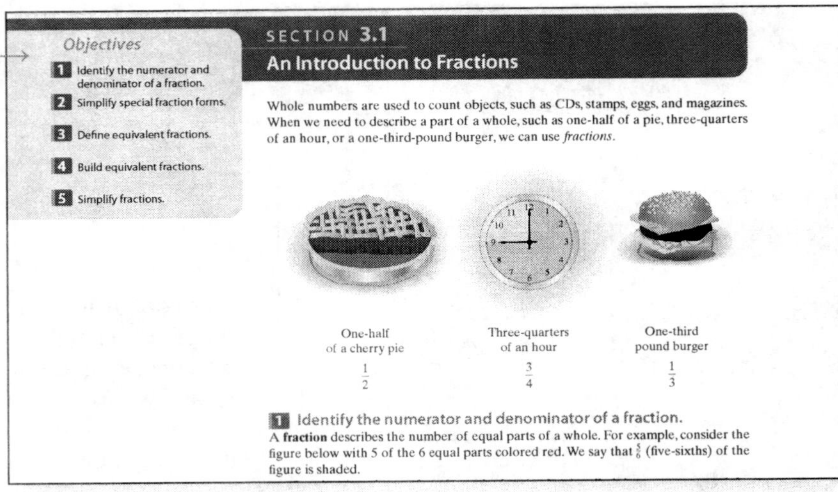

Objectives

1 Identify the numerator and denominator of a fraction.

2 Simplify special fraction forms.

3 Define equivalent fractions.

4 Build equivalent fractions.

5 Simplify fractions.

SECTION 3.1

An Introduction to Fractions

Whole numbers are used to count objects, such as CDs, stamps, eggs, and magazines. When we need to describe a part of a whole, such as one-half of a pie, three-quarters of an hour, or a one-third-pound burger, we can use *fractions*.

One-half of a cherry pie $\frac{1}{2}$ | Three-quarters of an hour $\frac{3}{4}$ | One-third pound burger $\frac{1}{3}$

1 Identify the numerator and denominator of a fraction.

A **fraction** describes the number of equal parts of a whole. For example, consider the figure below with 5 of the 6 equal parts colored red. We say that $\frac{5}{6}$ (five-sixths) of the figure is shaded.

GUIDED PRACTICE

Perform each operation and simplify, if possible. See Example 1.

17. $\frac{4}{9}+\frac{1}{9}$ 18. $\frac{3}{7}+\frac{1}{7}$

19. $\frac{3}{8}+\frac{1}{8}$ 20. $\frac{7}{12}+\frac{1}{12}$

21. $\frac{11}{15}-\frac{7}{15}$ 22. $\frac{10}{21}-\frac{5}{21}$

23. $\frac{11}{20}-\frac{3}{20}$ 24. $\frac{7}{18}-\frac{5}{18}$

Subtract and simplify, if possible. See Example 2.

25. $-\frac{11}{5}-\left(-\frac{8}{5}\right)$ 26. $-\frac{15}{9}-\left(-\frac{11}{9}\right)$

27. $-\frac{7}{21}-\left(-\frac{2}{21}\right)$ 28. $-\frac{21}{25}-\left(-\frac{9}{25}\right)$

Perform the operations and simplify, if possible. See Example 3.

29. $\frac{19}{40}-\frac{3}{40}-\frac{1}{40}$ 30. $\frac{11}{24}-\frac{1}{24}-\frac{7}{24}$

31. $\frac{13}{33}+\frac{1}{33}+\frac{7}{33}$ 32. $\frac{21}{50}+\frac{1}{50}+\frac{13}{50}$

49. $\frac{1}{6}+\frac{5}{8}$ 50. $\frac{7}{12}+\frac{3}{8}$

51. $\frac{4}{9}+\frac{5}{12}$ 52. $\frac{1}{9}+\frac{5}{6}$

Subtract and simplify, if possible. See Example 9.

53. $\frac{9}{10}-\frac{3}{14}$ 54. $\frac{11}{12}-\frac{11}{30}$

55. $\frac{11}{12}-\frac{7}{15}$ 56. $\frac{7}{15}-\frac{5}{12}$

Determine which fraction is larger. See Example 10.

57. $\frac{3}{8}$ or $\frac{5}{16}$ 58. $\frac{5}{6}$ or $\frac{7}{12}$

59. $\frac{4}{5}$ or $\frac{2}{3}$ 60. $\frac{7}{9}$ or $\frac{4}{5}$

61. $\frac{7}{9}$ or $\frac{11}{12}$ 62. $\frac{3}{8}$ or $\frac{5}{12}$

63. $\frac{23}{20}$ or $\frac{7}{6}$ 64. $\frac{19}{15}$ or $\frac{5}{4}$

Add and simplify, if possible. See Example 11.

Thoroughly Revised Study Sets

The *Study Sets* have been thoroughly revised to ensure that every example type covered in the section is represented in the *Guided Practice* problems. Particular attention was paid to developing a gradual level of progression within problem types.

Guided Practice Problems

All of the problems in the *Guided Practice* portion of the *Study Sets* are linked to an associated worked example or objective from that section. This feature promotes student success by referring them to the proper worked example(s) or objective(s) if they encounter difficulties solving homework problems.

Try It Yourself

To promote problem recognition, the *Study Sets* include a collection of *Try It Yourself* problems that *do not* link to worked examples. These problem types are thoroughly mixed, giving students an opportunity to practice decision making and strategy selection as they would when taking a test or quiz.

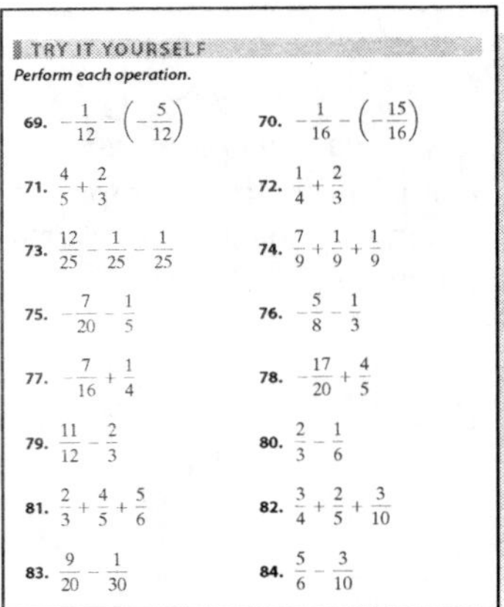

TRY IT YOURSELF

Perform each operation.

69. $-\frac{1}{12}-\left(-\frac{5}{12}\right)$ 70. $-\frac{1}{16}-\left(-\frac{15}{16}\right)$

71. $\frac{4}{5}+\frac{2}{3}$ 72. $\frac{1}{4}+\frac{2}{3}$

73. $\frac{12}{25}-\frac{1}{25}-\frac{1}{25}$ 74. $\frac{7}{9}+\frac{1}{9}+\frac{1}{9}$

75. $-\frac{7}{20}-\frac{1}{5}$ 76. $-\frac{5}{8}-\frac{1}{3}$

77. $-\frac{7}{16}+\frac{1}{4}$ 78. $-\frac{17}{20}+\frac{4}{5}$

79. $\frac{11}{12}-\frac{2}{3}$ 80. $\frac{2}{3}-\frac{1}{6}$

81. $\frac{2}{3}+\frac{4}{5}+\frac{5}{6}$ 82. $\frac{3}{4}+\frac{2}{5}+\frac{3}{10}$

83. $\frac{9}{20}-\frac{1}{30}$ 84. $\frac{5}{6}-\frac{3}{10}$

Study Skills That Point Out Common Student Mistakes

These *Study Skills Checklists* warn students of common errors, giving them time to consider these pitfalls before taking their exam.

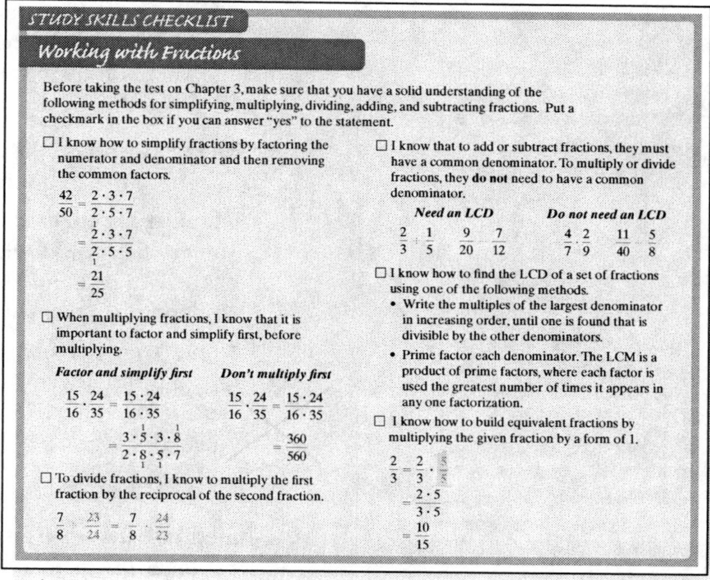

STUDY SKILLS CHECKLIST

Working with Fractions

Before taking the test on Chapter 3, make sure that you have a solid understanding of the following methods for simplifying, multiplying, dividing, adding, and subtracting fractions. Put a checkmark in the box if you can answer "yes" to the statement.

☐ I know how to simplify fractions by factoring the numerator and denominator and then removing the common factors.

$$\frac{42}{50} = \frac{2 \cdot 3 \cdot 7}{2 \cdot 5 \cdot 7} = \frac{\overset{1}{\cancel{2}} \cdot 3 \cdot 7}{\underset{1}{\cancel{2}} \cdot 5 \cdot 5} = \frac{21}{25}$$

☐ When multiplying fractions, I know that it is important to factor and simplify first, before multiplying.

Factor and simplify first

$$\frac{15}{16} \cdot \frac{24}{35} = \frac{15 \cdot 24}{16 \cdot 35} = \frac{3 \cdot \overset{1}{\cancel{5}} \cdot 3 \cdot \overset{1}{\cancel{8}}}{2 \cdot \underset{1}{\cancel{8}} \cdot \underset{1}{\cancel{5}} \cdot 7}$$

Don't multiply first

$$\frac{15}{16} \cdot \frac{24}{35} = \frac{15 \cdot 24}{16 \cdot 35} = \frac{360}{560}$$

☐ To divide fractions, I know to multiply the first fraction by the reciprocal of the second fraction.

$$\frac{7}{8} \div \frac{23}{24} = \frac{7}{8} \cdot \frac{24}{23}$$

☐ I know that to add or subtract fractions, they must have a common denominator. To multiply or divide fractions, they **do not** need to have a common denominator.

Need an LCD

$$\frac{2}{3} + \frac{1}{5} \qquad \frac{9}{20} - \frac{7}{12}$$

Do not need an LCD

$$\frac{4}{7} \cdot \frac{2}{9} \qquad \frac{11}{40} \div \frac{5}{8}$$

☐ I know how to find the LCD of a set of fractions using one of the following methods.

- Write the multiples of the largest denominator in increasing order, until one is found that is divisible by the other denominators.
- Prime factor each denominator. The LCM is a product of prime factors, where each factor is used the greatest number of times it appears in any one factorization.

☐ I know how to build equivalent fractions by multiplying the given fraction by a form of 1.

$$\frac{2}{3} = \frac{2}{3} \cdot \frac{5}{5} = \frac{2 \cdot 5}{3 \cdot 5} = \frac{10}{15}$$

TRUSTED FEATURES

- **Study Sets** found in each section offer a multifaceted approach to practicing and reinforcing the concepts taught in each section. They are designed for students to methodically build their knowledge of the section concepts, from basic recall to increasingly complex problem solving, through reading, writing, and thinking mathematically.

  Vocabulary—Each *Study Set* begins with the important *Vocabulary* discussed in that section. The fill-in-the-blank vocabulary problems emphasize the main concepts taught in the chapter and provide the foundation for learning and communicating the language of algebra.

  Concepts—In *Concepts,* students are asked about the specific subskills and procedures necessary to successfully complete the *Guided Practice* and *Try It Yourself* problems that follow.

  Notation—In *Notation,* the students review the new symbols introduced in a section. Often, they are asked to fill in steps of a sample solution. This strengthens their ability to read and write mathematics and prepares them for the *Guided Practice* problems by modeling solution formats.

  Guided Practice—The problems in *Guided Practice* are linked to an associated worked example or objective from that section. This feature promotes student success by referring them to the proper examples if they encounter difficulties solving homework problems.

  Try It Yourself—To promote problem recognition, the *Try It Yourself* problems are thoroughly mixed and are *not* linked to worked examples, giving students an opportunity to practice decision-making and strategy selection as they would when taking a test or quiz.

  Applications—The *Applications* provide students the opportunity to apply their newly acquired algebraic skills to relevant and interesting real-life situations.

  Writing—The *Writing* problems help students build mathematical communication skills.

Review—The *Review* problems consist of randomly selected problems from previous chapters. These problems are designed to keep students' successfully mastered skills up-to-date before they move on to the next section.

- **Detailed Author Notes** that guide students along in a step-by-step process appear in the solutions to every worked example.
- **Think It Through** features make the connection between mathematics and student life. These relevant topics often require algebra skills from the chapter to be applied to a real-life situation. Topics include tuition costs, student enrollment, job opportunities, credit cards, and many more.
- **Using Your Calculator** is an optional feature that is designed for instructors who wish to use calculators as part of the instruction in this course. This feature introduces keystrokes and shows how scientific and graphing calculators can be used to solve problems. In the *Study Sets,* icons are used to denote problems that may be solved using a calculator.

Annotated Instructor's Edition
The *Annotated Instructor's Edition* provides the complete student text with answers next to each respective exercise. Teaching Examples have been added for each worked example.

Electronic Ancillaries

Enhanced WebAssign
Instant feedback and ease of use are just two reasons why WebAssign is the most widely used homework system in higher education. WebAssign's homework delivery system allows you to assign, collect, grade, and record homework assignments via the web. Personal Study Plans provide diagnostic quizzing for each chapter that identifies concepts that students still need to master, and directs them to the appropriate review material. And now, this proven system has been enhanced to include links to textbook sections, video examples, and problem-specific tutorials. Enhanced WebAssign is more than a homework system—it is a complete learning system for math students. Contact your local representative for ordering details.

Solution Builder
Easily build solution sets for homework or exams using *Solution Builder's* online solutions manual. Visit www.cengage.com/solutionbuilder

Website ***www.cengage.com/math/tussy***
Visit us on the web for access to a wealth of learning resources, including tutorials, final exams, chapter outlines, chapter reviews, web links, videos, flashcards, study skills handouts, and more!

ACKNOWLEDGMENTS

We want to express our gratitude to all those who helped with this project: Steve Odrich, Mary Lou Wogan, Paul McCombs, Maria H. Andersen, Sheila Pisa, Laurie McManus, Alexander Lee, Ed Kavanaugh, Karl Hunsicker, Cathy Gong, Dave Ryba, Terry Damron, Marion Hammond, Lin Humphrey, Doug Keebaugh, Robin Carter, Tanja Rinkel, Bob Billups, Jeff Cleveland, Jo Morrison, Sheila White, Jim McClain, Paul Swatzel, Matt Stevenson, Carole Carney, Joyce Low, Rob Everest, David Casey, Heddy Paek, Ralph Tippins, Mo Trad, Eagle Zhuang, and the Citrus College library staff (including Barbara Rugeley) for their help with this project. Your encouragement, suggestions, and insight have been invaluable to us.

We would also like to express our thanks to the Cengage Learning editorial, marketing, production, and design staff for helping us craft this new edition: Charlie

Van Wagner, Danielle Derbenti, Gordon Lee, Rita Lombard, Greta Kleinert, Stefanie Beeck, Jennifer Cordoba, Angela Kim, Maureen Ross, Heleny Wong, Jennifer Risden, Vernon Boes, Diane Beasley, Carol O'Connell, and Graphic World.

Additionally, we would like to say that authoring a textbook is a tremendous undertaking. A revision of this scale would not have been possible without the thoughtful feedback and support from the following colleagues listed below. Their contributions to this edition have shaped this revision in countless ways.

Alan S. Tussy
R. David Gustafson
Diane R. Koenig

Advisory Board

J. Donato Fortin, *Johnson and Wales University*
Geoff Hagopian, *College of the Desert*
Jane Wampler, *Housatonic Community College*
Mary Lou Wogan, *Klamath Community College*
Kevin Yokoyama, *College of the Redwoods*

Reviewers

Darla Aguilar, *Pima Community College*
Sheila Anderson, *Housatonic Community College*
David Behrman, *Somerset Community College*
Michael Branstetter, *Hartnell College*
Joseph A. Bruno, Jr., *Community College of Allegheny County*
Joy Conner, *Tidewater Community College*
Ruth Dalrymple, *Saint Philip's College*
John D. Driscoll, *Middlesex Community College*
LaTonya Ellis, *Bishop State Community College*
Steven Felzer, *Lenoir Community College*
Rhoderick Fleming, *Wake Technical Community College*
Heather Gallacher, *Cleveland State University*
Kathirave Giritharan, *John A. Logan College*
Marilyn Green, *Merritt College and Diablo Valley College*
Joseph Guiciardi, *Community College of Allegheny County*
Deborah Hanus, *Brookhaven College*
A.T. Hayashi, *Oxnard College*
Susan Kautz, *Cy-Fair College*
Sandy Lofstock, *Saint Petersburg College–Tarpon Springs*
Mikal McDowell, *Cedar Valley College*
Gregory Perkins, *Hartnell College*
Euguenia Peterson, *City Colleges of Chicago–Richard Daley*
Carol Ann Poore, *Hinds Community College*
Christopher Quarles, *Shoreline Community College*
George Reed, *Angelina College*
John Squires, *Cleveland State Community College*
Sharon Testone, *Onondaga Community College*
Bill Thompson, *Red Rocks Community College*
Donna Tupper, *Community College of Baltimore County–Essex*
Andreana Walker, *Calhoun Community College*
Jane Wampler, *Housatonic Community College*
Mary Young, *Brookdale Community College*

Focus Groups

David M. Behrman, *Somerset Community College*
Eric Compton, *Brookdale Community College*

Nathalie Darden, *Brookdale Community College*
Joseph W. Giuciardi, *Community College of Allegheny County*
Cheryl Hobneck, *Illinois Valley Community College*
Todd J. Hoff, *Wisconsin Indianhead Technical College*
Jack Keating, *Massasoit Community College*
Russ Alan Killingsworth, *Seattle Pacific University*
Lynn Marecek, *Santa Ana College*
Lois Martin, *Massasoit Community College*
Chris Mirbaha, *The Community College of Baltimore County*
K. Maggie Pasqua, *Brookdale Community College*
Patricia C. Rome, *Delgado Community College*
Patricia B. Roux, *Delgado Community College*
Rebecca Rozario, *Brookdale Community College*
Barbara Tozzi, *Brookdale Community College*
Arminda Wey, *Brookdale Community College*
Valerie Wright, *Central Piedmont Community College*

ABOUT THE AUTHORS

Alan S. Tussy

Alan Tussy teaches all levels of developmental mathematics at Citrus College in Glendora, California. He has written nine math books—a paperback series and a hardcover series. A meticulous, creative, and visionary teacher who maintains a keen focus on his students' greatest challenges, Alan Tussy is an extraordinary author, dedicated to his students' success. Alan received his Bachelor of Science degree in Mathematics from the University of Redlands and his Master of Science degree in Applied Mathematics from California State University, Los Angeles. He has taught up and down the curriculum from Prealgebra to Differential Equations. He is currently focusing on the developmental math courses. Professor Tussy is a member of the American Mathematical Association of Two-Year Colleges.

R. David Gustafson

R. David Gustafson is Professor Emeritus of Mathematics at Rock Valley College in Illinois and coauthor of several best-selling math texts, including Gustafson/Frisk's *Beginning Algebra, Intermediate Algebra, Beginning and Intermediate Algebra: A Combined Approach, College Algebra,* and the Tussy/Gustafson developmental mathematics series. His numerous professional honors include Rock Valley Teacher of the Year and Rockford's Outstanding Educator of the Year. He earned a Master of Arts from Rockford College in Illinois, as well as a Master of Science from Northern Illinois University.

Diane R. Koenig

Diane Koenig received a Bachelor of Science degree in Secondary Math Education from Illinois State University in 1980. She began her career at Rock Valley College in 1981, when she became the Math Supervisor for the newly formed Personalized Learning Center. Earning her Master's Degree in Applied Mathematics from Northern Illinois University, Ms. Koenig in 1984 had the distinction of becoming the

first full-time woman mathematics faculty member at Rock Valley College. In addition to being nominated for AMATYC's Excellence in Teaching Award, Diane Koenig was chosen as the Rock Valley College Faculty of the Year by her peers in 2005, and, in 2006, she was awarded the NISOD Teaching Excellence Award as well as the Illinois Mathematics Association of Community Colleges Award for Teaching Excellence. In addition to her teaching, Ms. Koenig has been an active member of the Illinois Mathematics Association of Community Colleges (IMACC). As a member, she has served on the board of directors, on a state-level task force rewriting the course outlines for the developmental mathematics courses, and as the association's newsletter editor.

Study Skills Workshop

© iStockphoto.com/Aldo Murillo

OBJECTIVES

1 Make the Commitment

2 Prepare to Learn

3 Manage Your Time

4 Listen and Take Notes

5 Build a Support System

6 Do Your Homework

7 Prepare for the Test

SUCCESS IN YOUR COLLEGE COURSES requires more than just mastery of the content. The development of strong study skills and disciplined work habits plays a crucial role as well. Good note-taking, listening, test-taking, team-building, and time management skills are habits that can serve you well, not only in this course, but throughout your life and into your future career. Students often find that the approach to learning that they used for their high school classes no longer works when they reach college. In this Study Skills Workshop, *we will discuss ways of improving and fine-tuning your study skills, providing you with the best chance for a successful college experience.*

1 Make the Commitment

© iStockphoto.com/Helder Almeida

Starting a new course is exciting, but it also may be a little frightening. Like any new opportunity, in order to be successful, it will require a commitment of both time and resources. You can decrease the anxiety of this commitment by having a plan to deal with these added responsibilities.

Set Your Goals for the Course. Explore the reasons why you are taking this course. What do you hope to gain upon completion? Is this course a prerequisite for further study in mathematics? Maybe you need to complete this course in order to begin taking coursework related to your field of study. No matter what your reasons, setting goals for yourself will increase your chances of success. Establish your ultimate goal and then break it down into a series of smaller goals; it is easier to achieve a series of short-term goals rather than focusing on one larger goal.

Keep a Positive Attitude. Since your level of effort is significantly influenced by your attitude, strive to maintain a positive mental outlook throughout the class. From time to time, remind yourself of the ways in which you will benefit from passing the course. Overcome feelings of stress or math anxiety with extra preparation, campus support services, and activities you enjoy. When you accomplish short-term goals such as studying for a specific period of time, learning a difficult concept, or completing a homework assignment, reward yourself by spending time with friends, listening to music, reading a novel, or playing a sport.

Attend Each Class. Many students don't realize that missing even one class can have a great effect on their grade. Arriving late takes its toll as well. If you are just a few minutes late, or miss an entire class, you risk getting behind. So, keep these tips in mind.

- Arrive on time, or a little early.
- If you must miss a class, get a set of notes, the homework assignments, and any handouts that the instructor may have provided for the day that you missed.
- Study the material you missed. Take advantage of the help that comes with this textbook, such as the video examples and problem-specific tutorials.

Now Try This

1. List six ways in which you will benefit from passing this course.
2. List six short-term goals that will help you achieve your larger goal of passing this course. For example, you could set a goal to read through the entire *Study Skills Workshop* within the first 2 weeks of class or attend class regularly and on time. (***Success Tip:*** Revisit this action item once you have read through all seven *Study Skills Workshop* learning objectives.)
3. List some simple ways you can reward yourself when you complete one of your short-term class goals.
4. Plan ahead! List five possible situations that could cause you to be late for class or miss a class. (Some examples are parking/traffic delays, lack of a babysitter, oversleeping, or job responsibilities.) What can you do ahead of time so that these situations won't cause you to be late or absent?

2 Prepare to Learn

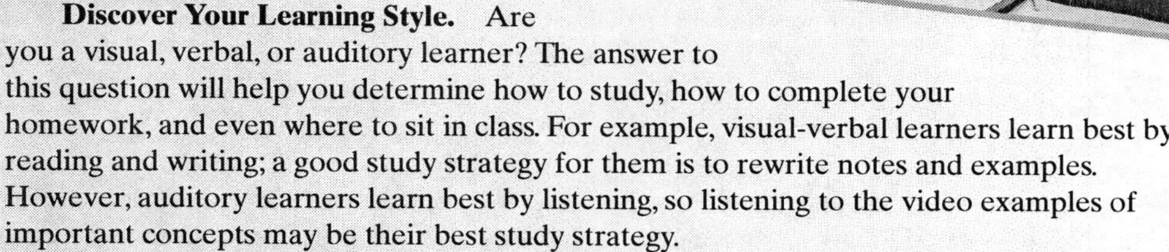

© iStockphoto.com/Yobro10

Many students believe that there are two types of people—those who are good at math and those who are not—and that this cannot be changed. This is not true! You can increase your chances for success in mathematics by taking time to prepare and taking inventory of your skills and resources.

Discover Your Learning Style. Are you a visual, verbal, or auditory learner? The answer to this question will help you determine how to study, how to complete your homework, and even where to sit in class. For example, visual-verbal learners learn best by reading and writing; a good study strategy for them is to rewrite notes and examples. However, auditory learners learn best by listening, so listening to the video examples of important concepts may be their best study strategy.

Get to Know Your Textbook and Its Resources. You have made a significant investment in your education by purchasing this book and the resources that accompany it. It has been designed with you in mind. Use as many of the features and resources as possible in ways that best fit your learning style.

Know What Is Expected. Your course syllabus maps out your instructor's expectations for the course. Read the syllabus completely and make sure you understand all that is required. If something is not clear, contact your instructor for clarification.

Organize Your Notebook. You will definitely appreciate a well-organized notebook when it comes time to study for the final exam. So let's start now! Refer to your syllabus and create a separate section in the notebook for each chapter (or unit of study) that your class will cover this term. Now, set a standard order within each section. One recommended order is to begin with your class notes, followed by your completed homework assignments, then any study sheets or handouts, and, finally, all graded quizzes and tests.

Now Try This

1. To determine what type of learner you are, take the *Learning Style Survey* at http://www.metamath.com/multiple/multiple_choice_questions.html. You may also wish to take the *Index of Learning Styles Questionnaire* at http://www.engr.ncsu.edu/learningstyles/ilsweb.html, which will help you determine your learning type and offer study suggestions by type. List what you learned from taking these surveys. How will you use this information to help you succeed in class?
2. Complete the *Study Skills Checklists* found at the end of sections 1–4 of Chapter 1 in order to become familiar with the many features that can enhance your learning experience using this book.
3. Read through the list of Student Resources found in the Preface of this book. Which ones will you use in this class?
4. Read through your syllabus and write down any questions that you would like to ask your instructor.
5. Organize your notebook using the guidelines given above. Place your syllabus at the very front of your notebook so that you can see the dates over which the material will be covered and for easy reference throughout the course.

3 Manage Your Time

© iStockphoto.com/Yiannos Ioannou

Now that you understand the importance of attending class, how will you make time to study what you have learned while attending? Much like learning to play the piano, math skills are best learned by practicing a little every day.

Make the Time. In general, 2 hours of independent study time is recommended for every hour in the classroom. If you are in class 3 hours per week, plan on 6 hours per week for reviewing your notes and completing your homework. It is best to schedule this time over the length of a week rather than to try to cram everything into one or two marathon study days.

Prioritize and Make a Calendar. Because daily practice is so important in learning math, it is a good idea to set up a calendar that lists all of your time commitments, as well as the time you will need to set aside for studying and doing your homework. Consider how you spend your time each week and prioritize your tasks by importance. During the school term, you may need to reduce or even eliminate certain nonessential tasks in order to meet your goals for the term.

Maximize Your Study Efforts. Using the information you learned from determining your learning style, set up your blocks of study time so that you get the most out of these sessions. Do you study best in groups or do you need to study alone to get anything done? Do you learn best when you schedule your study time in 30-minute time blocks or do you need at least an hour before the information kicks in? Consider your learning style to set up a schedule that truly suits your needs.

Avoid Distractions. Between texting and social networking, we have so many opportunities for distraction and procrastination. On top of these, there are the distractions of TV, video games, and friends stopping by to hang out. Once you have set your schedule, honor your study times by turning off any electronic devices and letting your voicemail take messages for you. After this time, you can reward yourself by returning phone calls and messages or spending time with friends after the pressure of studying has been lifted.

Now Try This

1. Keep track of how you spend your time for a week. Rate each activity on a scale from 1 (not important) to 5 (very important). Are there any activities that you need to reduce or eliminate in order to have enough time to study this term?
2. List three ways that you learn best according to your learning style. How can you use this information when setting up your study schedule?
3. Download the *Weekly Planner Form* from www.cengage.com/math/tussy and complete your schedule. If you prefer, you may set up a schedule in Google Calendar (calendar.google.com), www.rememberthemilk.com, your cell, or your email system. Many of these have the ability to set up useful reminders and to-do lists in addition to a weekly schedule.
4. List three ways in which you are most often distracted. What can you do to avoid these distractions during your scheduled study times?

4 Listen and Take Notes

© iStockphoto.com/Jacob Wackerhausen

Make good use of your class time by listening and taking notes. Because your instructor will be giving explanations and examples that may not be found in your textbook, as well as other information about your course (test dates, homework assignments, and so on), it is important that you keep a written record of what was said in class.

Listen Actively. Listening in class is different from listening in social situations because it requires that you be an *active* listener. Since it is impossible to write down everything that is said in class, you need to exercise your active listening skills to learn to write down what is *important.* You can spot important material by listening for cues from your instructor. For instance, pauses in lectures or statements from your instructor such as "This is really important" or "This is a question that shows up frequently on tests" are indications that you should be paying special attention. Listen with a pencil (or highlighter) in hand, ready to record or highlight (in your textbook) any examples, definitions, or concepts that your instructor discusses.

Take Notes You Can Use. Don't worry about making your notes really neat. After class you can rework them into a format that is more useful to you. However, you should organize your notes as much as possible as you write them. Copy the examples your instructor uses in class. Circle or star any key concepts or definitions that your instructor mentions while explaining the example. Later, your homework problems will look a lot like the examples given in class, so be sure to copy each of the steps in detail.

Listen with an Open Mind. Even if there are concepts presented that you feel you already know, keep tuned in to the presentation of the material and look for a deeper understanding of the material. If the material being presented is something that has been difficult for you in the past, listen with an open mind; your new instructor may have a fresh presentation that works for you.

Avoid Classroom Distractions. Some of the same things that can distract you from your study time can distract you, and others, during class. Because of this, be sure to turn off your cell phone during class. If you take notes on a laptop, log out of your email and social networking sites during class. In addition to these distractions, avoid getting into side conversations with other students. Even if you feel you were only distracted for a few moments, you may have missed important verbal or body language cues about an upcoming exam or hints that will aid in your understanding of a concept.

Now Try This

1. Before your next class, refer to your syllabus and read the section(s) that will be covered. Make a list of the terms that you predict your instructor will think are most important.
2. During your next class, bring your textbook and keep it open to the sections being covered. If your instructor mentions a definition, concept, or example that is found in your text, highlight it.
3. Find at least one classmate with whom you can review notes. Make an appointment to compare your class notes as soon as possible after the class. Did you find differences in your notes?
4. Go to www.cengage.com/math/tussy and read the *Reworking Your Notes* handout. Complete the action items given in this document.

5 Build a Support System

© iStockphoto.com/Chris Schmidt

Have you ever had the experience where you understand everything that your instructor is saying in class, only to go home and try a homework problem and be completely stumped? This is a common complaint among math students. The key to being a successful math student is to take care of these problems before you go on to tackle new material. That is why you should know what resources are available outside of class.

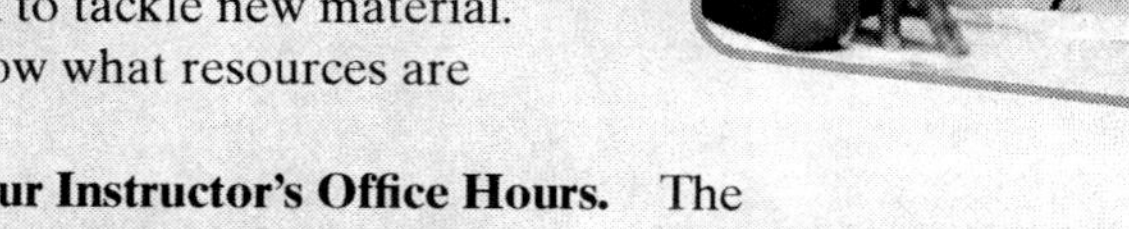

Make Good Use of Your Instructor's Office Hours. The purpose of your instructor's office hours is to be available to help students with questions. Usually these hours are listed in your syllabus and no appointment is needed. When you visit your instructor, have a list of questions and try to pinpoint exactly where in the process you are getting stuck. This will help your instructor answer your questions efficiently.

Use Your Campus Tutoring Services. Many colleges offer tutorial services for free. Sometimes tutorial assistance is available in a lab setting where you are able to drop in at your convenience. In some cases, you need to make an appointment to see a tutor in advance. Make sure to seek help as soon as you recognize the need, and come to see your tutor with a list of identified problems.

Form a Study Group. Study groups are groups of classmates who meet outside of class to discuss homework problems or study for tests. Get the most out of your study group by following these guidelines:

- Keep the group small—a maximum of four committed students. Set a regularly scheduled meeting day, time, and place.
- Find a place to meet where you can talk and spread out your work.
- Members should attempt all homework problems before meeting.
- All members should contribute to the discussion.
- When you meet, practice verbalizing and explaining problems and concepts to each other. The best way to really learn a topic is by teaching it to someone else.

Now Try This

1. Refer to your syllabus. Highlight your instructor's office hours and location. Next, pay a visit to your instructor during office hours this week and introduce yourself. (***Success Tip:*** Program your instructor's office phone number and email address into your cell phone or email contact list.)
2. Locate your campus tutoring center or math lab. Write down the office hours, phone number, and location on your syllabus. Drop by or give them a call and find out how to go about making an appointment with a tutor.
3. Find two to three classmates who are available to meet at a time that fits your schedule. Plan to meet 2 days before your next homework assignment is due and follow the guidelines given above. After your group has met, evaluate how well it worked. Is there anything that the group can do to make it better next time you meet?
4. Download the *Support System Worksheet* at www.cengage.com/math/tussy. Complete the information and keep it at the front of your notebook following your syllabus.

6 Do Your Homework

© iStockphoto.com/djordje zivaljevic

Attending class and taking notes are important, but the only way that you are really going to learn mathematics is by completing your homework. Sitting in class and listening to lectures will help you to place concepts in short-term memory, but in order to do well on tests and in future math classes, you want to put these concepts in long-term memory. When completed regularly, homework assignments will help with this.

Give Yourself Enough Time. In Objective 3, you made a study schedule, setting aside 2 hours for study and homework for every hour that you spend in class. If you are not keeping this schedule, make changes to ensure that you can spend enough time outside of class to learn new material.

Review Your Notes and the Worked Examples from Your Text. In Objective 4, you learned how to take useful notes. Before you begin your homework, review or rework your notes. Then, read the sections in your textbook that relate to your homework problems, paying special attention to the worked examples. With a pencil in hand, work the *Self Check* and *Now Try* problems that are listed next to the examples in your text. Using the worked example as a guide, solve these problems and try to understand each step. As you read through your notes and your text, keep a list of anything that you don't understand.

Now Try Your Homework Problems. Once you have reviewed your notes and the textbook worked examples, you should be able to successfully manage the bulk of your homework assignment easily. When working on your homework, keep your textbook and notes close by for reference. If you have trouble with a homework question, look through your textbook and notes to see if you can identify an example that is similar to the homework question. See if you can apply the same steps to your homework problem. If there are places where you get stuck, add these to your list of questions.

Get Answers to Your Questions. At least one day before your assignment is due, seek help with the questions you have been listing. You can contact a classmate for assistance, make an appointment with a tutor, or visit your instructor during office hours.

Now Try This

1. Review your study schedule. Are you following it? If not, what changes can you make to adhere to the rule of 2 hours of homework and study for every hour of class?
2. Find five homework problems that are similar to the worked examples in your textbook. Were there any homework problems in your assignment that didn't have a worked example that was similar? (***Success Tip:*** Look for the *Now Try* and *Guided Practice* features for help linking problems to worked examples.)
3. As suggested in this Objective, make a list of questions while completing your homework. Visit your tutor or your instructor with your list of questions and ask one of them to work through these problems with you.
4. Go to www.cengage.com/math/tussy and read the *Study and Memory Techniques* handout. List the techniques that will be most helpful to you in your math course.

7 Prepare for the Test

Taking a test does not need to be an unpleasant experience. Use your time management, organization, and these test-taking strategies to make this a learning experience and improve your score.

Make Time to Prepare. Schedule at least four daily 1-hour sessions to prepare specifically for your test.

Four days before the test: Create your own study sheet using your reworked notes. Imagine you could bring one $8\frac{1}{2} \times 11$ sheet of paper to your test. What would you write on that sheet? Include all the key definitions, rules, steps, and formulas that were discussed in class or covered in your reading. Whenever you have the opportunity, pull out your study sheet and review your test material.

Three days before the test: Create a sample test using the in-class examples from your notes and reading material. As you review and work these examples, make sure you understand how each example relates to the rules or definitions on your study sheet. While working through these examples, you may find that you forgot a concept that should be on your study sheet. Update your study sheet and continue to review it.

Two days before the test: Use the *Chapter Test* from your textbook or create one by matching problems from your text to the example types from your sample test. Now, with your book closed, take a timed trial test. When you are done, check your answers. Make a list of the topics that were difficult for you and review or add these to your study sheet.

One day before the test: Review your study sheet once more, paying special attention to the material that was difficult for you when you took your practice test the day before. Be sure you have all the materials that you will need for your test laid out ahead of time (two sharpened pencils, a good eraser, possibly a calculator or protractor, and so on). The most important thing you can do today is get a good night's rest.

Test day: Review your study sheet, if you have time. Focus on how well you have prepared and take a moment to relax. When taking your test, complete the problems that you are sure of first. Skip the problems that you don't understand right away, and return to them later. Bring a watch or make sure there will be some kind of time-keeping device in your test room so that you can keep track of your time. Try not to spend too much time on any one problem.

Now Try This

1. Create a study schedule using the guidelines given above.
2. Read the *Preparing for a Test* handout at www.cengage.com/math/tussy.
3. Read the *Taking the Test* handout at www.cengage.com/math/tussy.
4. After your test has been returned and scored, read the *Analyzing Your Test Results* handout at www.cengage.com/math/tussy.
5. Take time to reflect on your homework and study habits after you have received your test score. What actions are working well for you? What do you need to improve?
6. To prepare for your final exam, read the *Preparing for Your Final Exam* handout at www.cengage.com/math/tussy. Complete the action items given in this document.

Module 1: Operations with Integers

DMA 010

© OJO Images Ltd/Alamy

Note: The blue numbers in parentheses correspond to the North Carolina Student Learning Outcomes.

from ***Campus to Careers***

Personal Financial Advisor

Personal financial advisors help people manage their money and teach them how to make their money grow. They offer advice on how to budget for monthly expenses, as well as how to save for retirement. A bachelor's degree in business, accounting, finance, economics, or statistics provides good preparation for the occupation. Strong communication and problem-solving skills are equally important to achieve success in this field.

In **Problem 90** of **Study Set 1.2,** you will see how a personal financial planner uses integers to determine whether a duplex rental unit would be a money-making investment for a client.

JOB TITLE: Personal Financial Advisor
EDUCATION: Must have at least a bachelor's degree. Some states require a certificate or license.
JOB OUTLOOK: Excellent—Jobs are projected to grow by 41% over the next decade.
ANNUAL EARNINGS: In 2007, average yearly earnings were $89,220.
FOR MORE INFORMATION: http://www.collegeboard.com/csearch/majors_careers/profiles/careers/101000.html

Objectives

1. Define the set of integers.
2. Graph integers on a number line.
3. Use inequality symbols to compare integers.
4. Find the absolute value of an integer.
5. Find the opposite of an integer.

SECTION 1.1
An Introduction to the Integers

We have seen that whole numbers can be used to describe many situations that arise in everyday life. However, we cannot use whole numbers to express temperatures below zero, the balance in a checking account that is overdrawn, or how far an object is below sea level. In this section, we will see how negative numbers can be used to describe these three situations as well as many others.

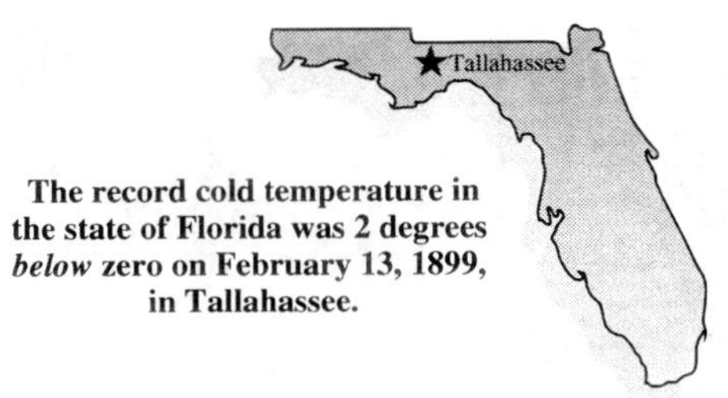

The record cold temperature in the state of Florida was 2 degrees *below* zero on February 13, 1899, in Tallahassee.

RECORD ALL CHARGES OR CREDITS THAT AFFECT YOUR ACCOUNT

NUMBER	DATE	DESCRIPTION OF TRANSACTION	PAYMENT/DEBIT (−)	√ T	FEE (IF ANY) (−)	DEPOSIT/CREDIT (+)	BALANCE $ 450 00
1207	5/2	Wood's Auto Repair Transmission	$ 500 00		$	$	

A check for $500 was written when there was only $450 in the account. The checking account is *overdrawn.*

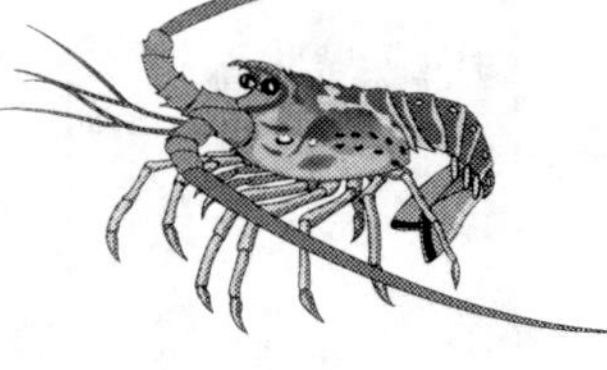

The American lobster is found off the East Coast of North America at depths as much as 600 feet *below* sea level.

1 Define the set of integers.

To describe a temperature of 2 degrees above zero, a balance of $50, or 600 feet above sea level, we can use numbers called **positive numbers.** All positive numbers are greater than 0, and we can write them with or without a **positive sign** +.

In words	In symbols	Read as
2 degrees above zero	+2 or 2	positive two
A balance of $50	+50 or 50	positive fifty
600 feet above sea level	+600 or 600	positive six hundred

To describe a temperature of 2 degrees below zero, $50 overdrawn, or 600 feet below sea level, we need to use negative numbers. **Negative numbers** are numbers less than 0, and they are written using a **negative sign** −.

In words	In symbols	Read as
2 degrees below zero	−2	negative two
$50 overdrawn	−50	negative fifty
600 feet below sea level	−600	negative six hundred

Together, positive and negative numbers are called **signed numbers.**

Positive and Negative Numbers

Positive numbers are greater than 0. **Negative numbers** are less than 0.

Caution! Zero is neither positive nor negative.

The collection of positive whole numbers, the negatives of the whole numbers, and 0 is called the set of **integers** (read as "in-ti-jers").

The Set of Integers

$\{\ldots, -5, -4, -3, -2, -1, 0, 1, 2, 3, 4, 5, \ldots\}$

The three dots on the right indicate that the list continues forever—there is no largest integer. The three dots on the left indicate that the list continues forever—there is no smallest integer. The set of **positive integers** is $\{1, 2, 3, 4, 5, \ldots\}$ and the set of **negative integers** is $\{\ldots, -5, -4, -3, -2, -1\}$.

The Language of Mathematics Since every whole number is an integer, we say that the set of whole numbers is a **subset** of the integers.

The set of integers → $\{\ldots, -5, -4, -3, -2, -1, \underbrace{0, 1, 2, 3, 4, 5, \ldots}\}$

The set of whole numbers

2 Graph integers on a number line.

Negative numbers can be represented on a number line by extending the line to the left and drawing an arrowhead. Beginning at the origin (the 0 point), we move to the left, marking equally spaced points as shown below. As we move to the right on the number line, the values of the numbers increase. As we move to the left, the values of the numbers decrease.

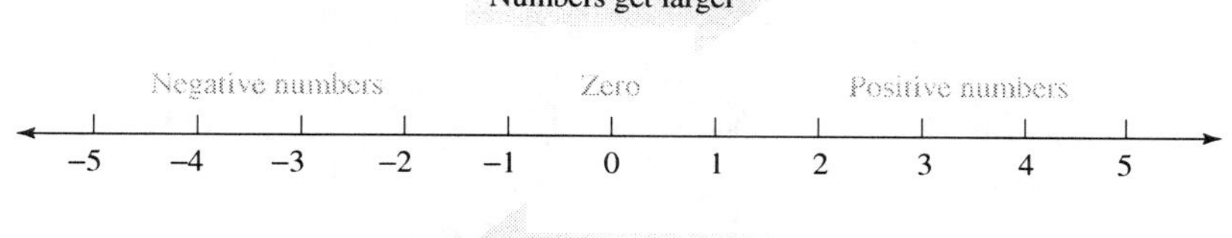

The thermometer shown on the next page is an example of a vertical number line. It is scaled in degrees and shows a temperature of $-10°$. The time line is an example of a horizontal number line. It is scaled in units of 500 years.

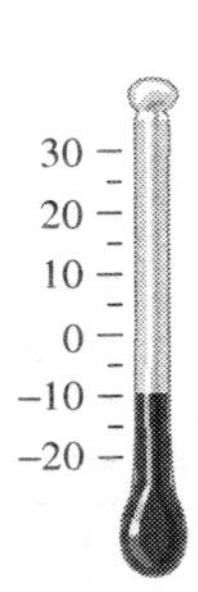

A vertical number line

MAYA CIVILIZATION

500 B.C. Maya culture begins

A.D. 300–A.D. 900 Classic period of Maya culture

A.D. 900–A.D. 1400 Maya culture declines

A.D. 1441 Mayapán falls to invaders

A.D. 1697 Last Maya city conquered by the Spanish

500 B.C. B.C./A.D. A.D. 500 A.D. 1000 A.D. 1500 A.D. 2000

Based on data from People in Time and Place, Western Hemisphere (Silver Burdett & Ginn., 1991), p. 129

A horizontal number line

Self Check 1

Graph −4, −2, 1, and 3 on a number line.

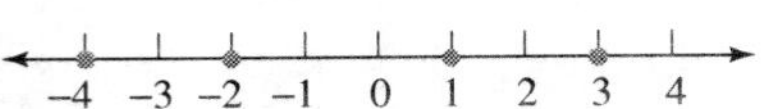

Now Try **Problem 23**

Teaching Example 1 Graph −4, −2, 0, and 3 on a number line.

Answer:

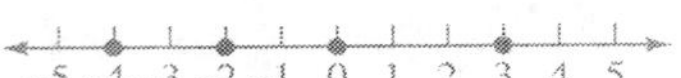

EXAMPLE 1 Graph −3, 2, −1, and 4 on a number line.

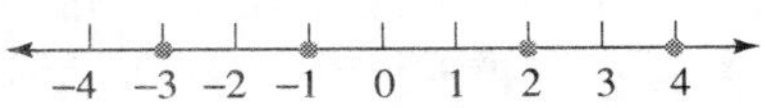

Strategy We will locate the position of each integer on the number line and draw a bold dot.

WHY To *graph a number* means to make a drawing that represents the number.

Solution

The position of each negative integer is to the left of 0. The position of each positive integer is to the right of 0.

By extending the number line to include negative numbers, we can represent more situations using bar graphs and line graphs. For example, the following bar graph shows the net income of the Eastman Kodak Company for the years 2000 through 2007. Since the net income in 2004 was positive \$556 million, the company made a *profit*. Since the net income in 2005 was −\$1,362 million, the company had a *loss*.

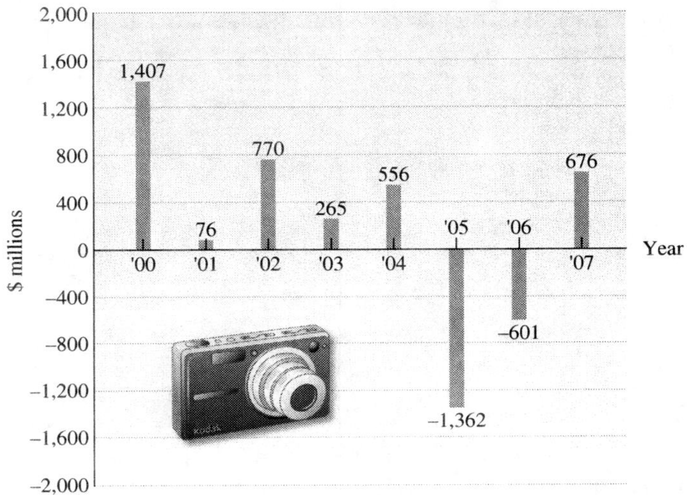

Source: Morningstar.com

The Language of Mathematics *Net* refers to what remains after all the deductions (losses) have been accounted for. **Net income** is a term used in business that often is referred to as the *bottom line*. Net income indicates what a company has earned (or lost) in a given period of time (usually 1 year).

THINK IT THROUGH ***Credit Card Debt***

"The most dangerous pitfall for many college students is the overuse of credit cards. Many banks do their best to entice new card holders with low or zero-interest cards."

Gary Schatsky, certified financial planner

Which numbers on the credit card statement below are actually debts and, therefore, could be represented using negative numbers? \$4,621, \$1,073, \$3,325

Account Summary

Previous Balance	New Purchases	Payments & Credits	New Balance
\$4,621	**\$1,073**	**\$2,369**	**\$3,325**

04/21/10 Billing Date	**05/16/10** Date Payment Due	**\$67** Minimum payment

BANK STAR **Periodic rates may vary. See reverse for explanation and important information. Please allow sufficient time for mail to reach Bank Star.**

3 Use inequality symbols to compare integers.

Recall that the symbol $<$ means "is less than" and that $>$ means "is greater than." The figure below shows the graph of the integers -2 and 1. Since -2 is to the left of 1 on the number line, $-2 < 1$. Since $-2 < 1$, it is also true that $1 > -2$.

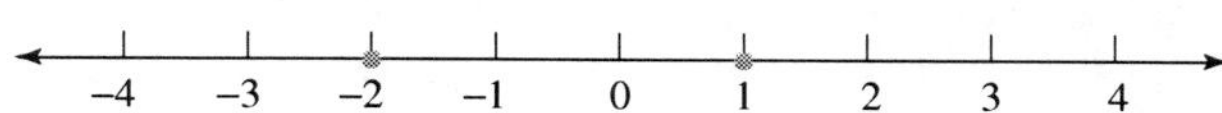

EXAMPLE 2 Place an $<$ or an $>$ symbol in the box to make a true statement. **a.** $4 \; \square \; -5$ **b.** $-8 \; \square \; -7$

Strategy To pick the correct inequality symbol to place between the pair of numbers, we will determine the position of each number on the number line.

WHY For any two numbers on a number line, the number to the *left* is the smaller number and the number on the *right* is the larger number.

Solution

a. Since 4 is to the right of -5 on the number line, $4 > -5$.

b. Since -8 is to the left of -7 on the number line, $-8 < -7$.

Self Check 2

Place an $<$ or an $>$ symbol in the box to make a true statement.

a. $6 \; \square \; -6$ $>$

b. $-11 \; \square \; -10$ $<$

Now Try **Problems 31 and 35**

Teaching Example 2 Place an $<$ or an $>$ symbol in the box to make a true statement.
a. $-15 \; \square \; 51$ b. $-3 \; \square \; -4$
Answers:
a. $<$ b. $>$

The Language of Mathematics Because the symbol $<$ requires one number to be strictly less than another number and the symbol $>$ requires one number to be strictly greater than another number, mathematical statements involving the symbols $<$ and $>$ are called *strict inequalities.*

There are three other commonly used inequality symbols.

Inequality Symbols

$\neq$ means *is not equal to*

$\geq$ means *is greater than or equal to*

$\leq$ means *is less than or equal to*

$-5 \neq -2$ Read as "-5 is not equal to -2."

$-6 \leq 10$ Read as "-6 is less than or equal to 10." This statement is true, because $-6 < 10$.

$12 \leq 12$ Read as "12 is less than or equal to 12." This statement is true, because $12 = 12$.

$-15 \geq -17$ Read as "-15 is greater than or equal to -17." This statement is true, because $-15 > -17$.

$-20 \geq -20$ Read as "-20 is greater than or equal to -20." This statement is true, because $-20 = -20$.

Self Check 3

Tell whether each statement is true or false.

a. $-17 \geq -15$ false

b. $-35 \leq -35$ true

c. $-2 \geq -2$ true

d. $-61 \leq -62$ false

Now Try **Problems 41 and 45**

Teaching Example 3 Tell whether each statement is true or false.

a. $-56 \leq -57$

b. $-3 \leq -3$

c. $-14 \geq -19$

d. $-8 \leq -8$

Answers:

a. false

b. true

c. true

d. true

EXAMPLE 3 Tell whether each statement is true or false.

a. $-9 \geq -9$ **b.** $-1 \leq -5$ **c.** $-27 \geq 6$ **d.** $-32 \leq -32$

Strategy We will determine if either the strict inequality or the equality that the symbols $\leq$ and $\geq$ allow is true.

WHY If either is true, then the given statement is true.

Solution

a. $-9 \geq -9$ This statement is true, because $-9 = -9$.

b. $-1 \leq -5$ This statement is false, because neither $-1 < -5$ nor $-1 = -5$ is true.

c. $-27 \geq 6$ This statement is false, because neither $-27 > 6$ nor $-27 = 6$ is true.

d. $-32 \leq -31$ This statement is true, because $-32 < -31$.

4 Find the absolute value of an integer.

Using a number line, we can see that the numbers 3 and -3 are both a distance of 3 units away from 0, as shown below.

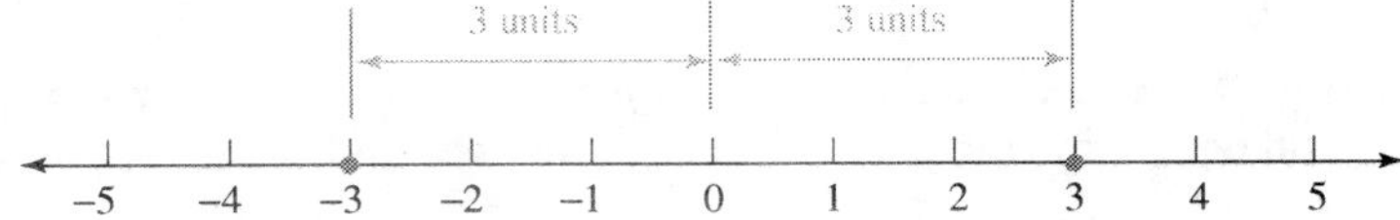

The **absolute value** of a number gives the distance between the number and 0 on the number line. To indicate absolute value, the number is inserted between two vertical bars, called the **absolute value symbol.** For example, we can write $|-3| = 3$. This is read as "The absolute value of negative 3 is 3," and it tells us that the distance between -3 and 0 on the number line is 3 units. From the figure, we also see that $|3| = 3$.

Absolute Value

The **absolute value** of a number is the distance on the number line between the number and 0.

Caution! Absolute value expresses distance. The absolute value of a number is always positive or 0. It is never negative.

EXAMPLE 4 Find each absolute value: **a.** $|8|$ **b.** $|-5|$ **c.** $|0|$

Strategy We need to determine the distance that the number within the vertical absolute value bars is from 0 on a number line.

WHY The absolute value of a number is the distance between 0 and the number on a number line.

Solution

a. On the number line, the distance between 8 and 0 is 8. Therefore,

$$|8| = 8$$

b. On the number line, the distance between -5 and 0 is 5. Therefore,

$$|-5| = 5$$

c. On the number line, the distance between 0 and 0 is 0. Therefore,

$$|0| = 0$$

Self Check 4

Find each absolute value:

a. $|-9|$ 9

b. $|4|$ 4

Now Try **Problems 47 and 49**

Teaching Example 4 Find each absolute value:
a. $|16|$
b. $|-7|$
c. $|0|$
Answers:
a. 16
b. 7
c. 0

5 Find the opposite of an integer.

Opposites or Negatives

Two numbers that are the same distance from 0 on the number line, but on opposite sides of it, are called **opposites** or **negatives.**

The figure below shows that for each whole number on the number line, there is a corresponding whole number, called its *opposite,* to the left of 0. For example, we see that 3 and -3 are opposites, as are -5 and 5. Note that 0 is its own opposite.

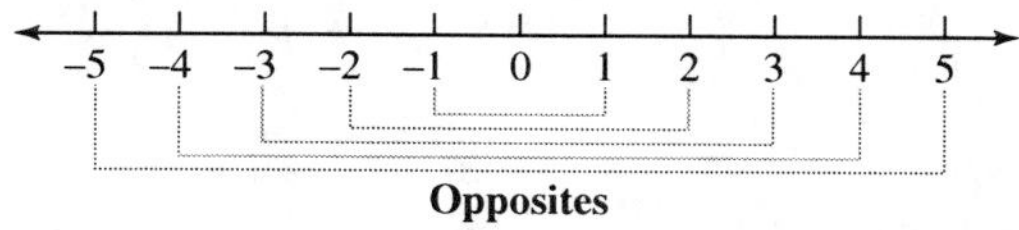

To write the opposite of a number, a $-$ symbol is used. For example, the opposite of 5 is -5 (read as "negative 5"). Parentheses are needed to express the opposite of a negative number. The opposite of -5 is written as $-(-5)$. Since 5 and -5 are the same distance from 0, the opposite of -5 is 5. Therefore, $-(-5) = 5$. This illustrates the following rule.

The Opposite of the Opposite Rule

The opposite of the opposite (or negative) of a number is that number.

Number	Opposite	
57	-57	Read as "negative fifty-seven."
-8	$-(-8) = 8$	Read as "the opposite of negative eight is eight."
0	$-0 = 0$	Read as "the opposite of 0 is 0."

The concept of opposite can also be applied to an absolute value. For example, the opposite of the absolute value of -8 can be written as $-|-8|$. Think of this as a two-step process, where the absolute value symbol serves as a grouping symbol. Find the absolute value first, and then attach a $-$ sign to that result.

First, find the absolute value.

$-|-8| = -8$ Read as "the opposite of the absolute value of negative eight is negative eight."

Then attach a $-$ sign.

Self Check 5

Simplify each expression:

a. $-(-1)$ 1

b. $-|4|$ -4

c. $-|-99|$ -99

Now Try **Problems 55, 65, and 67**

Teaching Example 5 Simplify each expression:

a. $-(-23)$

b. $-|200|$

c. $-|-81|$

Answers:

a. 23

a. -200

c. -81

EXAMPLE 5 Simplify each expression: **a.** $-(-44)$ **b.** $-|11|$ **c.** $-|-225|$

Strategy We will find the opposite of each number.

WHY In each case, the $-$ symbol written outside the grouping symbols means "the opposite of."

Solution

a. $-(-44)$ means the opposite of -44. Since the opposite of -44 is 44, we write

$$-(-44) = 44$$

b. $-|11|$ means the opposite of the absolute value of 11. Since $|11| = 11$, and the opposite of 11 is -11, we write

$$-|11| = -11$$

c. $-|-225|$ means the opposite of the absolute value of -225. Since $|-225| = 225$, and the opposite of 225 is -225, we write

$$-|-225| = -225$$

The $-$ symbol is used to indicate a negative number, the opposite of a number, and the operation of subtraction. The key to reading the $-$ symbol correctly is to examine the context in which it is used.

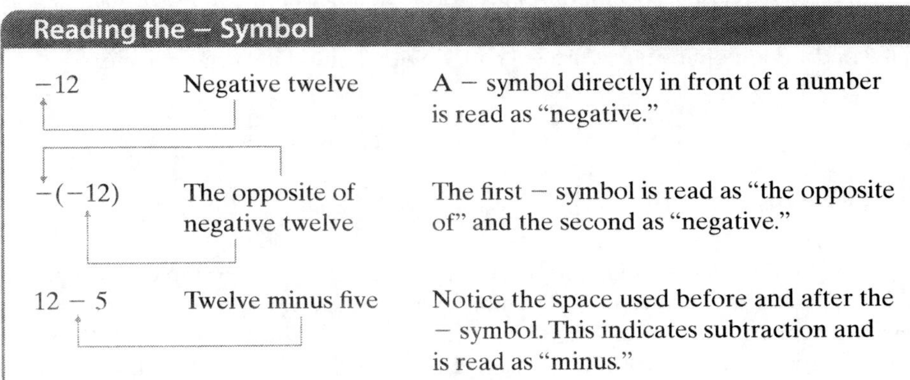

Reading the – Symbol

-12	Negative twelve	A $-$ symbol directly in front of a number is read as "negative."
$-(-12)$	The opposite of negative twelve	The first $-$ symbol is read as "the opposite of" and the second as "negative."
$12 - 5$	Twelve minus five	Notice the space used before and after the $-$ symbol. This indicates subtraction and is read as "minus."

ANSWERS TO SELF CHECKS

1. 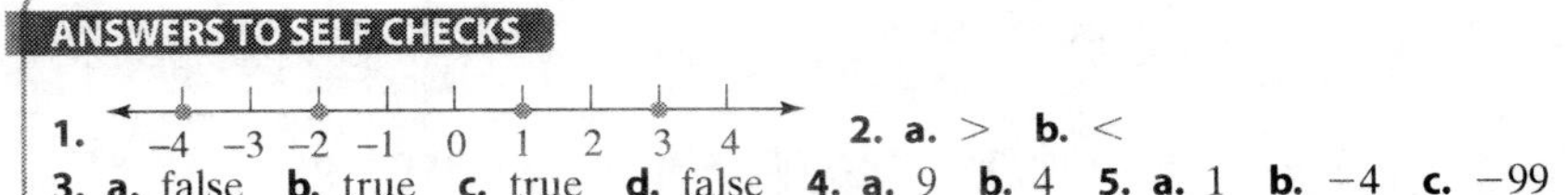

2. a. > **b.** < **3. a.** false **b.** true **c.** true **d.** false **4. a.** 9 **b.** 4 **5. a.** 1 **b.** -4 **c.** -99

SECTION 1.1 STUDY SET

VOCABULARY

Fill in the blanks.

1. Positive numbers are greater than 0 and negative numbers are less than 0.
2. {. . . , −5, −4, −3, −2, −1, 0, 1, 2, 3, 4, 5, . . .} is called the set of integers.
3. To graph an integer means to locate it on the number line and highlight it with a dot.
4. The symbols > and < are called inequality symbols.
5. The absolute value of a number is the distance between the number and 0 on the number line.
6. Two numbers that are the same distance from 0 on the number line, but on opposite sides of it, are called opposites.

CONCEPTS

7. Represent each of these situations using a signed number.
   a. $225 overdrawn −225
   b. 10 seconds before liftoff −10 sec
   c. 3 degrees below normal −3°
   d. A deficit of $12,000 −$12,000
   e. A 1-mile retreat by an army −1 mi
8. Represent each of these situations using a signed number, and then describe its opposite in words.
   a. A trade surplus of $3 million
   +3 million, $3 million deficit
   b. A bacteria count 70 more than the standard
   +70, 70 less than the standard
   c. A profit of $67
   +67, a loss of $67
   d. A business $1 million in the "black"
   +1 million, $1 million in the red
   e. 20 units over their quota
   +20, 20 units under quota
9. Determine what is wrong with each number line.
   a. −3 −2 −1 0 1 2 3 4
   The spacing is not uniform.
   b. −3 −2 −1 0 2 4 6 8
   The numbering is not uniform.
   c. −3 −2 −1 1 2 3 4 5
   Zero is missing.
   d. −3 −2 −1 0 1 2 3 4
   The arrowheads are not drawn.
10. a. If a number is less than 0, what type of number must it be? It is negative.
    b. If a number is greater than 0, what type of number must it be? It is positive.
11. On the number line, what number is
    a. 3 units to the right of −7? −4
    ▶ b. 4 units to the left of 2? −2
12. Name two numbers on the number line that are a distance of
    a. 5 away from −3. −8 and 2
    ▶ b. 4 away from 3. 7 and −1
13. a. Which number is closer to −3 on the number line: 2 or −7? −7
    b. Which number is farther from 1 on the number line: −5 or 8? 8
14. Is there a number that is both greater than 10 and less than 10 at the same time? no
15. a. Express the fact −12 < 15 using an > symbol.
    15 > −12
    b. Express the fact −4 > −5 using an < symbol.
    −5 < −4
16. Fill in the blank: The opposite of the opposite of a number is that number.
17. Complete the table by finding the opposite and the absolute value of the given numbers.

Number	Opposite	Absolute value
−25	25	25
39	−39	39
0	0	0

18. Is the absolute value of a number always positive? no, $|0| = 0$

NOTATION

19. Translate each phrase to mathematical symbols.
    a. The opposite of negative eight $-(-8)$
    b. The absolute value of negative eight $|-8|$
    c. Eight minus eight $8 - 8$
    d. The opposite of the absolute value of negative eight $-|-8|$

20. **a.** Write the set of integers.
$\{\ldots, -5, -4, -3, -2, -1, 0, 1, 2, 3, 4, 5, \ldots\}$

b. Write the set of positive integers. $\{1, 2, 3, 4, 5, \ldots\}$

c. Write the set of negative integers.
$\{\ldots, -5, -4, -3, -2, -1\}$

21. Fill in the blanks.

a. We read $\geq$ as "is _greater_ than or _equal_ to."

b. We read $\leq$ as "is _less_ than or _equal_ to."

22. Which of the following expressions contains a minus sign?
$15 - 8$ $\quad -(-15)$ $\quad -15$ $\quad 15 - 8$

GUIDED PRACTICE

Graph the following numbers on a number line. See Example 1.

23. $-3, 4, 3, 0, -1$

−5 −4 −3 −2 −1 0 1 2 3 4 5

24. $2, -4, 5, 1, -1$

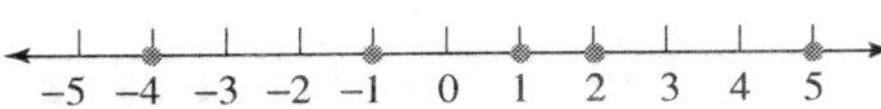

25. The integers that are less than 3 but greater than -5

−5 −4 −3 −2 −1 0 1 2 3 4 5

26. The integers that are less than 4 but greater than -3

−5 −4 −3 −2 −1 0 1 2 3 4 5

27. The opposite of -3, the opposite of 5, and the absolute value of -2

−5 −4 −3 −2 −1 0 1 2 3 4 5

28. The absolute value of 3, the opposite of 3, and the number that is 1 less than -3

−5 −4 −3 −2 −1 0 1 2 3 4 5

29. 2 more than 0, 4 less than 0, 2 more than negative 5, and 5 less than 4

−5 −4 −3 −2 −1 0 1 2 3 4 5

30. 4 less than 0, 1 more than 0, 2 less than -2, and 6 more than -4

−5 −4 −3 −2 −1 0 1 2 3 4 5

Place an < or an > symbol in the box to make a true statement. See Example 2.

31. $-5 < 5$ **32.** $0 > -1$

33. $-12 < -6$ **34.** $-7 < -6$

35. $-10 > -17$ **36.** $-11 > -20$

37. $-325 > -532$ **38.** $-401 < -104$

Tell whether each statement is true or false. See Example 3.

39. $-15 \leq -14$ true **40.** $-77 \leq -76$ true

41. $210 \geq 210$ true **42.** $37 \geq 37$ true

43. $-1{,}255 \geq -1{,}254$ false **44.** $-6{,}546 \geq -6{,}465$ false

45. $0 \leq -8$ false **46.** $-6 \leq -6$ true

Find each absolute value. See Example 4.

47. $|9|$ 9 **48.** $|12|$ 12

49. $|-8|$ 8 **50.** $|-1|$ 1

51. $|-14|$ 14 **52.** $|-85|$ 85

53. $|180|$ 180 **54.** $|371|$ 371

Simplify each expression. See Example 5.

55. $-(-11)$ 11 **56.** $-(-1)$ 1

57. $-(-4)$ 4 **58.** $-(-9)$ 9

59. $-(-102)$ 102 **60.** $-(-295)$ 295

61. $-(-561)$ 561 **62.** $-(-703)$ 703

63. $-|20|$ -20 **64.** $-|143|$ -143

65. $-|6|$ -6 **66.** $-|0|$ 0

67. $-|-253|$ -253 **68.** $-|-11|$ -11

69. $-|-0|$ 0 **70.** $-|97|$ -97

TRY IT YOURSELF

Place an < or an > symbol in the box to make a true statement.

71. $|-12| > -(-7)$ **72.** $|-50| > -(-40)$

73. $-|-71| < -|-65|$ **74.** $-|-163| < -|-150|$

75. $-(-343) > -(-161)$ **76.** $-(-999) > -(-998)$

77. $-|-30| < -|-(-8)|$ **78.** $-|-100| < -|-(-88)|$

Write the integers in order, from least to greatest.

79. $82, -52, 52, -22, 12, -12$ $\quad -52, -22, -12, 12, 52, 82$

80. $49, -9, 19, -39, 89, -49$ $\quad -49, -39, -9, 19, 49, 89$

Fill in the blanks to continue each pattern.

81. $5, 3, 1, -1, -3, -5, -7, \ldots$

82. $4, 2, 0, -2, -4, -6, -8, \ldots$

APPLICATIONS

83. HORSE RACING In the 1973 Belmont Stakes, *Secretariat* won by 31 lengths over second place finisher, *Twice a Prince.* Some experts call it the greatest performance by a thoroughbred in the history of racing. Express the position of *Twice a Prince* compared to *Secretariat* as a signed number. (Source: ezinearticles.com) −31 lengths

© Bettmann/Corbis

84. NASCAR In the NASCAR driver standings, negative numbers are used to tell how many points behind the leader a given driver is. Jimmie Johnson was the leading driver in 2008. The other drivers in the top ten were Greg Biffle (−217), Clint Bowyer (−303), Jeff Burton (−349), Kyle Busch (−498), Carl Edwards (−69), Jeff Gordon (−368), Denny Hamlin (−470), Kevin Harvick (−276), and Tony Stewart (−482). Use this information to rank the drivers in the table below.

AP Images

2008 NASCAR Final Driver Standings

Rank	Driver	Points behind leader
1	Jimmie Johnson	Leader
2	Carl Edwards	−69
3	Greg Biffle	−217
4	Kevin Harvick	−276
5	Clint Bowyer	−303
6	Jeff Burton	−349
7	Jeff Gordon	−368
8	Denny Hamlin	−470
9	Tony Stewart	−482
10	Kyle Busch	−498

(Source: NASCAR.com)

85. FREE FALL A boy launches a water balloon from the top of a building, as shown in the next column. At that instant, his friend starts a stopwatch and keeps track of the time as the balloon sails above the building and then falls to the ground. Use the number line to estimate the position of the balloon at each time listed in the table below.

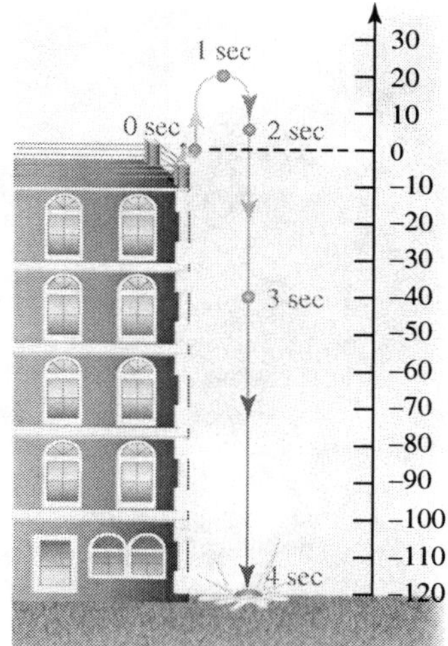

Time	Position of balloon
0 sec	0
1 sec	20
2 sec	5
3 sec	−40
4 sec	−120

86. CARNIVAL GAMES At a carnival shooting gallery, players aim at moving ducks. The path of one duck is shown, along with the time it takes the duck to reach certain positions on the gallery wall. Use the number line to estimate the position of the duck at each time listed in the table below.

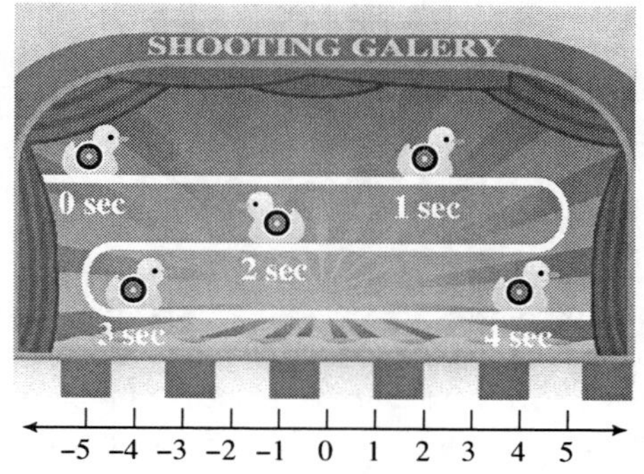

Time	Position of duck
0 sec	−5
1 sec	2
2 sec	−1
3 sec	−4
4 sec	4

87. TECHNOLOGY The readout from a testing device is shown. Use the number line to find the height of each of the peaks and the depth of each of the valleys. peaks: 2, 4, 0; valleys: −3, −5, −2

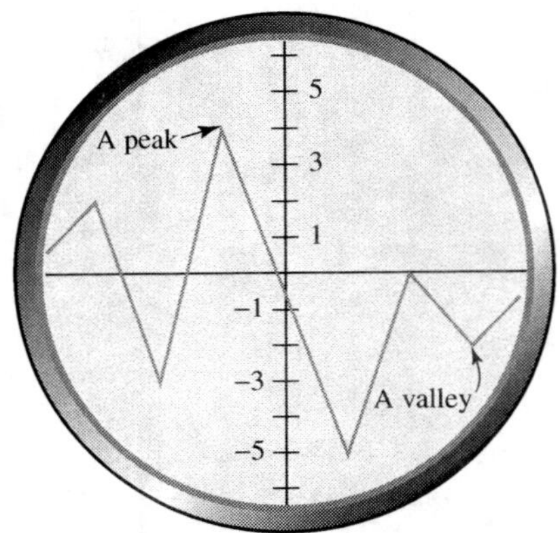

88. FLOODING A week of daily reports listing the height of a river in comparison to flood stage is given in the table. Complete the bar graph shown below.

Flood Stage Report

Sun.	2 ft below
Mon.	3 ft over
Tue.	4 ft over
Wed.	2 ft over
Thu.	1 ft below
Fri.	3 ft below
Sat.	4 ft below

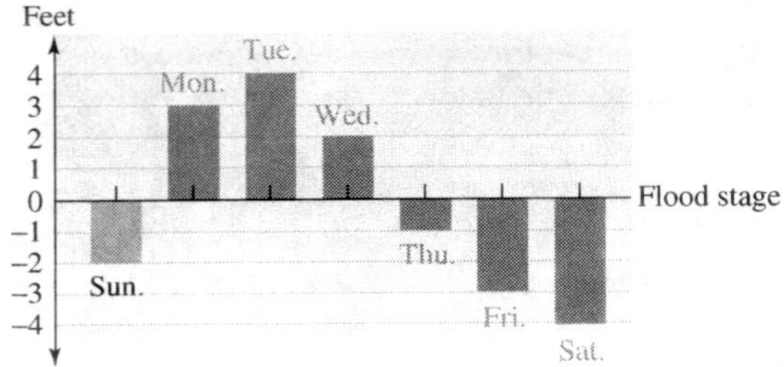

89. GOLF In golf, *par* is the standard number of strokes considered necessary on a given hole. A score of −2 indicates that a golfer used 2 strokes less than par. A score of +2 means 2 more strokes than par were used. In the graph in the next column, each golf ball represents the score of a professional golfer on the 16th hole of a certain course.

a. What score was shot most often on this hole? −1 (1 below par)

b. What was the best score on this hole? −3 (3 below par)

c. Explain why this hole appears to be too easy for a professional golfer. Most of the scores are below par.

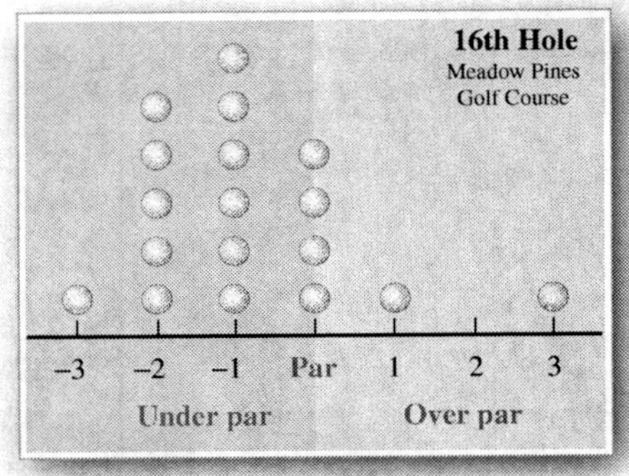

90. PAYCHECKS Examine the items listed on the following paycheck stub. Then write two columns on your paper—one headed "positive" and the other "negative." List each item under the proper heading. positives: gross pay, overtime, Christmas bonus; negatives: all others

Tom Dryden Dec. 09		Christmas bonus	$100
Gross pay	$2,000	**Reductions**	
Overtime	$300	Retirement	$200
Deductions		**Taxes**	
Union dues	$30	Federal withholding	$160
U.S. Bonds	$100	State withholding	$35

91. WEATHER MAPS The illustration shows the predicted Fahrenheit temperatures for a day in mid-January.

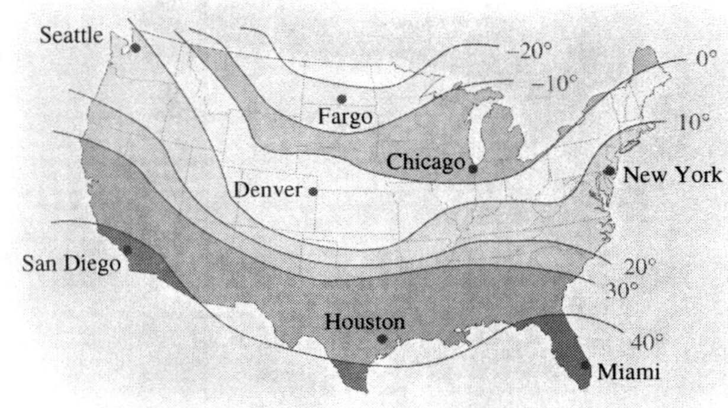

a. What is the temperature range for the region including Fargo, North Dakota? −20° to −10°

b. According to the prediction, what is the warmest it should get in Houston? 40°

c. According to this prediction, what is the coldest it should get in Seattle? 10°

92. INTERNET COMPANIES The graph on the next page shows the net income of Amazon.com for the years 1998–2007. (Source: Morningstar)

a. In what years did Amazon suffer a loss? Estimate each loss. 1998: −$120 million, 1999: −$720 million, 2000: −$1,410 million, 2001: −$570 million, 2002: −$150 million

b. In what year did Amazon first turn a profit? Estimate it. 2003: $30 million

c. In what year did Amazon have the greatest profit? Estimate it. 2004: $590 million

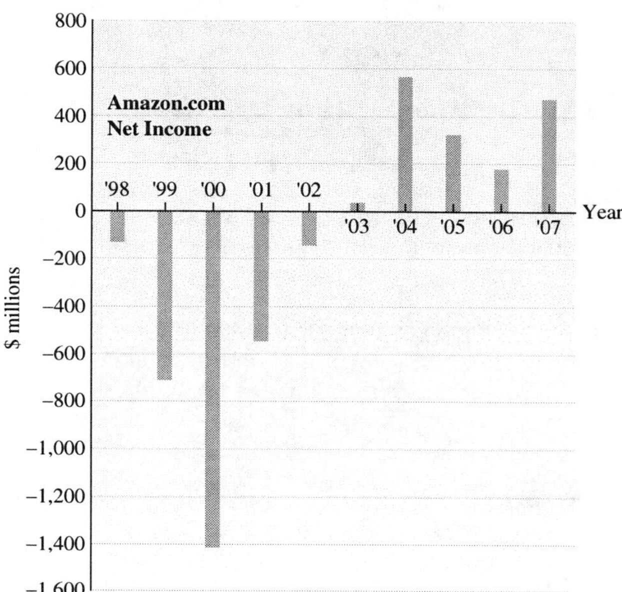

93. HISTORY Number lines can be used to display historical data. Some important world events are shown on the time line below.

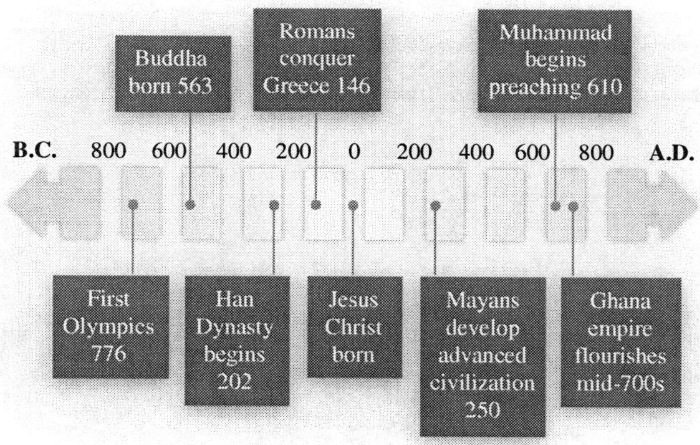

a. What basic unit is used to scale this time line? 200 yr

b. What can be thought of as positive numbers? A.D.

c. What can be thought of as negative numbers? B.C.

d. What important event distinguishes the positive from the negative numbers? the birth of Christ

94. ASTRONOMY Astronomers use an inverted vertical number line called the *apparent magnitude scale* to denote the brightness of objects in the sky. The brighter an object appears to an observer on Earth, the more negative is its apparent magnitude. Graph each of the following on the scale to the right.

- Visual limit of binoculars +10
- Visual limit of large telescope +20
- Visual limit of naked eye +6
- Full moon −12
- Pluto +15
- Sirius (a bright star) −2
- Sun −26
- Venus −4

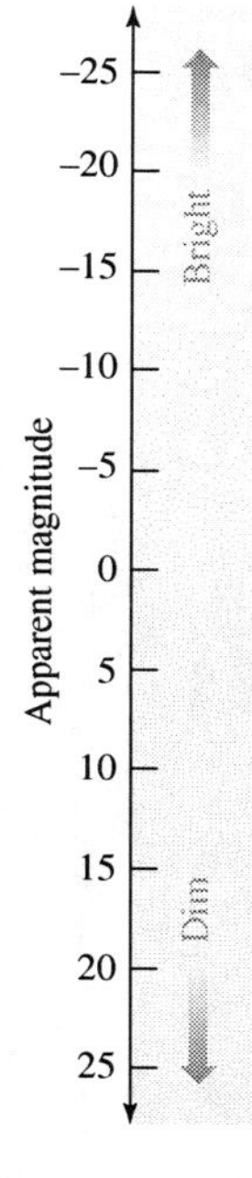

95. LINE GRAPHS Each thermometer in the illustration gives the daily high temperature in degrees Fahrenheit. Use the data to complete the line graph below.

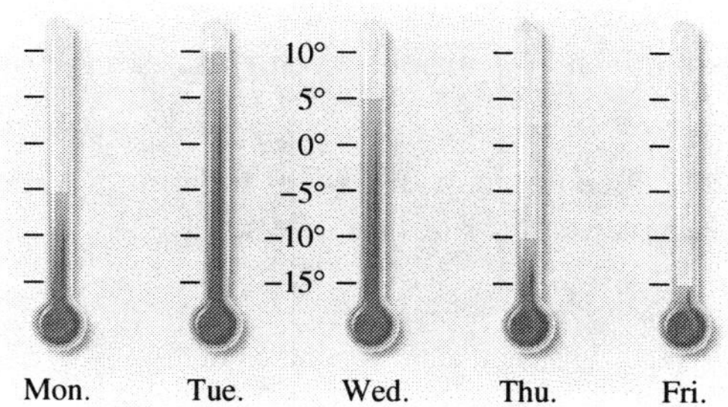

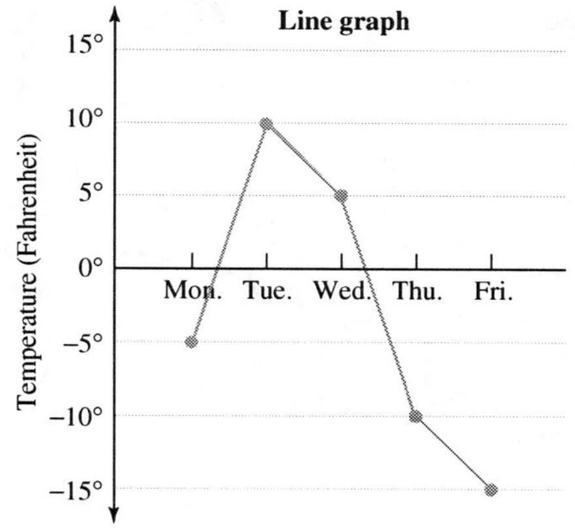

96. GARDENING The illustration shows the depths at which the bottoms of various types of flower bulbs should be planted. (The symbol " represents inches.)

a. At what depth should a tulip bulb be planted? 8" below the surface (−8")

b. How much deeper are hyacinth bulbs planted than gladiolus bulbs? 3"

c. Which bulb must be planted the deepest? How deep? daffodil, 11" below the surface (−11")

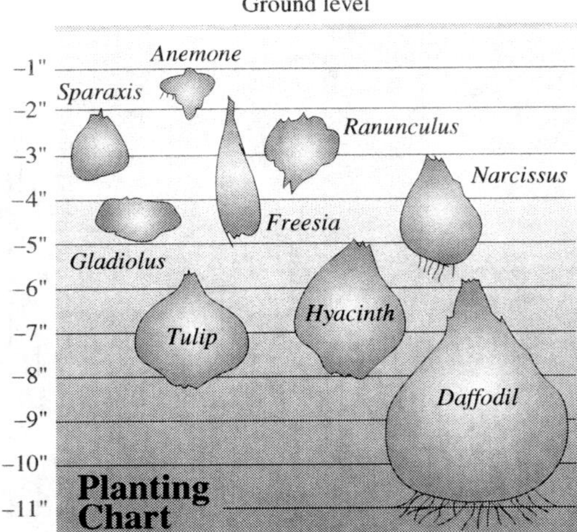

WRITING

97. Explain the concept of *the opposite of a number.*

98. What real-life situation do you think gave rise to the concept of a negative number?

99. Explain why the absolute value of a number is never negative.

100. Give an example of the use of the number line that you have seen in another course.

101. DIVING Divers use the terms *positive buoyancy, neutral buoyancy,* and *negative buoyancy* as shown. What do you think each of these terms means?

102. GEOGRAPHY Much of the Netherlands is low-lying, with half of the country below sea level. Explain why it is not under water.

103. Suppose integer A is greater than integer B. Is the opposite of integer A greater than integer B? Explain why or why not. Use an example.

104. Explain why -11 is less than -10.

REVIEW

105. Round 23,456 to the nearest hundred. 23,500

106. Evaluate: $19 - 2 \cdot 3$ 13

107. Subtract 2,081 from 2,842. 761

108. Divide 346 by 15. 23 R 1

109. Give the name of the property shown below:

$$(13 \cdot 2) \cdot 5 = 13 \cdot (2 \cdot 5)$$ associative property of multiplication

110. Write *four times five* using three different symbols. 4×5, $4 \cdot 5$, $4(5)$

SECTION 1.2 Adding Integers

Objectives

1. Add two integers that have the same sign.
2. Add two integers that have different signs.
3. Perform several additions to evaluate expressions.
4. Identify opposites (additive inverses) when adding integers.
5. Solve application problems by adding integers.

An amazing change in temperature occurred in 1943 in Spearfish, South Dakota. On January 22, at 7:30 A.M., the temperature was −4 degrees Fahrenheit. Strong warming winds suddenly kicked up and, in just 2 minutes, the temperature rose 49 degrees! To calculate the temperature at 7:32 A.M., we need to add 49 to −4.

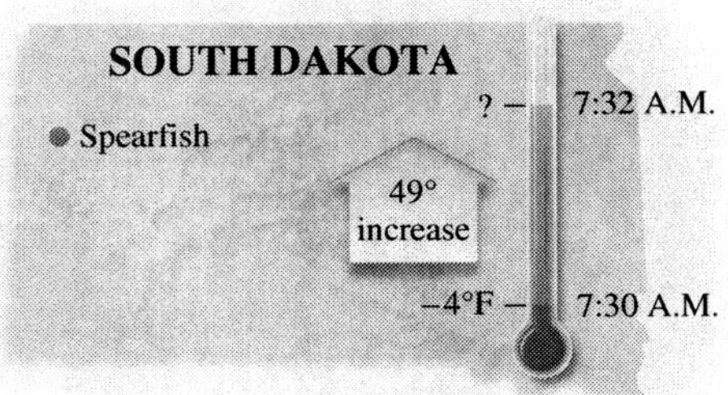

$$-4 + 49$$

To perform this addition, we must know how to add positive and negative integers. In this section, we develop rules to help us make such calculations.

> ***The Language of Mathematics*** In 1724, Daniel Gabriel *Fahrenheit,* a German scientist, introduced the temperature scale that bears his name. The United States is one of the few countries that still use this scale. The temperature -4 degrees Fahrenheit can be written in more compact form as $-4°$F.

1 Add two integers that have the same sign.

We can use the number line to explain addition of integers. For example, to find $4 + 3$, we begin at 0 and draw an arrow 4 units long that points to the right. It represents positive 4. From the tip of that arrow, we draw a second arrow, 3 units long, that points to the right. It represents positive 3. Since we end up at 7, it follows that $4 + 3 = 7$.

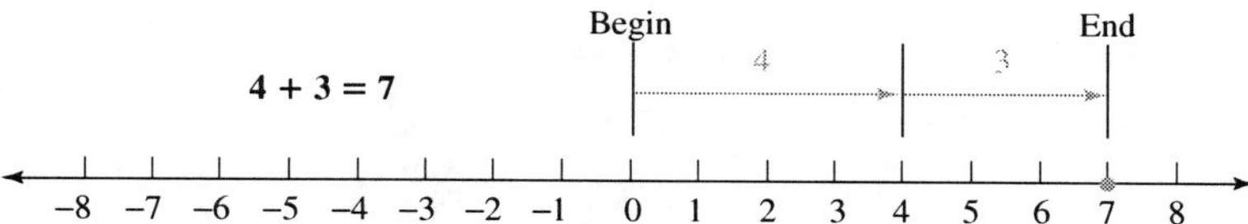

To check our work, let's think of the problem in terms of money. If you had \$4 and earned \$3 more, you would have a total of \$7.

To find $-4 + (-3)$ on a number line, we begin at 0 and draw an arrow 4 units long that points to the left. It represents -4. From the tip of that arrow, we draw a second arrow, 3 units long, that points to the left. It represents -3. Since we end up at -7, it follows that $-4 + (-3) = -7$.

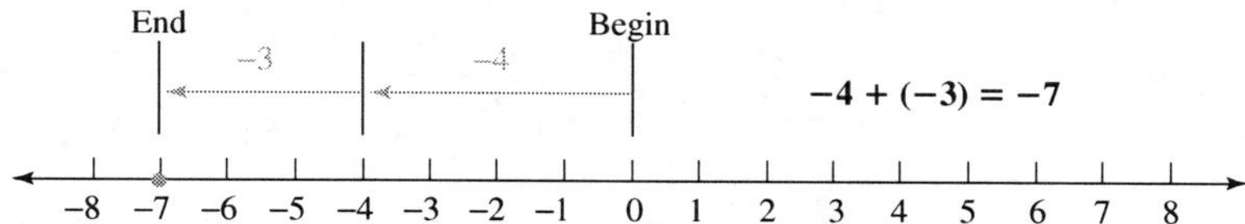

Let's think of this problem in terms of money. If you lost \$4 (-4) and then lost another \$3 (-3), overall, you would have lost a total of \$7 (-7).

Here are some observations about the process of adding two numbers that have the same sign on a number line.

- The arrows representing the integers point in the same direction and they build upon each other.
- The answer has the same sign as the integers that we added.

These observations illustrate the following rules.

Adding Two Integers That Have the Same (Like) Signs

1. To add two positive integers, add them as usual. The final answer is positive.
2. To add two negative integers, add their absolute values and make the final answer negative.

The Language of Mathematics When writing additions that involve integers, write negative integers within parentheses to separate the negative sign − from the plus symbol +.

$9 + (-4)$ ~~$9 + -4$~~ and $-9 + (-4)$ ~~$-9 + -4$~~

Self Check 1

Add:

a. $-7 + (-2)$ −9

b. $-25 + (-48)$ −73

c. $-325 + (-169)$ −494

Now Try **Problems 19, 23, and 27**

Teaching Example 1 Add:
a. $-4 + (-3)$
b. $-38 + (-25)$
c. $-502 + (-189)$

Answers:
a. −7 b. −63 c. −691

EXAMPLE 1 Add: **a.** $-3 + (-5)$ **b.** $-26 + (-65)$ **c.** $-456 + (-177)$

Strategy We will use the rule for adding two integers that have the *same sign.*

WHY In each case, we are asked to add two negative integers.

Solution

a. To add two negative integers, we add the absolute values of the integers and make the final answer negative. Since $|-3| = 3$ and $|-5| = 5$, we have

$-3 + (-5) = -8$ Add their absolute values, 3 and 5, to get 8. Then make the final answer negative.

b. Find the absolute values: $|-26| = 26$ and $|-65| = 65$

$-26 + (-65) = -91$ Add their absolute values, 26 and 65, to get 91. Then make the final answer negative.

$$\begin{array}{r} \overset{1}{2}6 \\ +65 \\ \hline 91 \end{array}$$

c. Find the absolute values: $|-456| = 456$ and $|-177| = 177$

$-456 + (-177) = -633$ Add their absolute values, 456 and 177, to get 633. Then make the final answer negative.

$$\begin{array}{r} \overset{1}{4}\overset{1}{5}6 \\ +177 \\ \hline 633 \end{array}$$

Success Tip Calculations that you cannot perform in your head should be shown outside the steps of your solution.

The Language of Mathematics Two negative integers, as well as two positive integers, are said to have *like* signs.

2 Add two integers that have different signs.

To find $4 + (-3)$ on a number line, we begin at 0 and draw an arrow 4 units long that points to the right. This represents positive 4. From the tip of that arrow, we draw a second arrow, 3 units long, that points to the left. It represents −3. Since we end up at 1, it follows that $4 + (-3) = 1$.

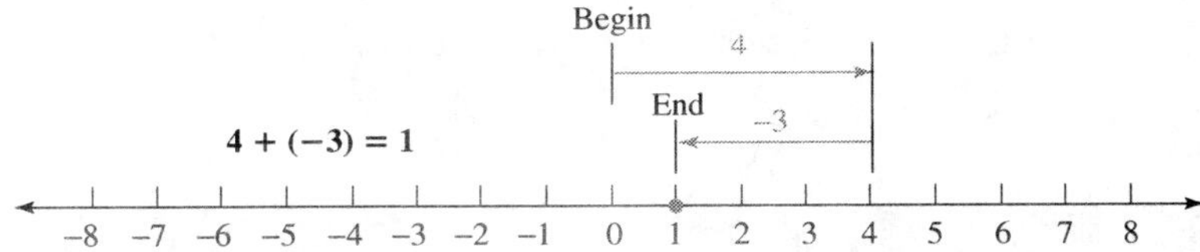

In terms of money, if you won \$4 and then lost \$3 (−3), overall, you would have \$1 left.

To find $-4 + 3$ on a number line, we begin at 0 and draw an arrow 4 units long that points to the left. It represents −4. From the tip of that arrow, we draw a second arrow, 3 units long, that points to the right. It represents positive 3. Since we end up at -1, it follows that $-4 + 3 = -1$.

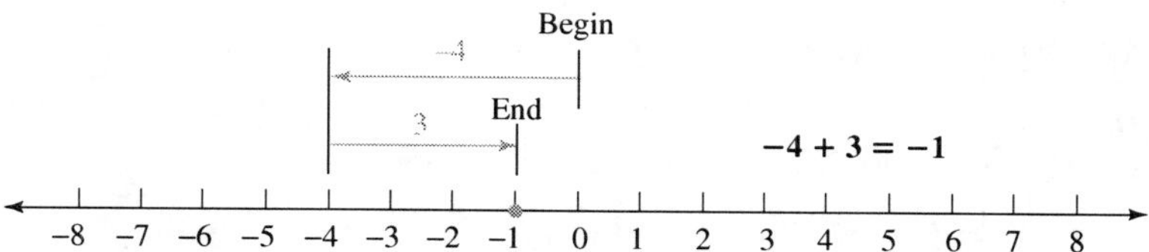

In terms of money, if you lost \$4 (-4) and then won \$3, overall, you have lost \$1 (-1).

Here are some observations about the process of adding two integers that have different signs on a number line.

- The arrows representing the integers point in opposite directions.
- The longer of the two arrows determines the sign of the answer. If the longer arrow represents a positive integer, the sum is positive. If it represents a negative integer, the sum is negative.

These observations suggest the following rules.

Adding Two Integers That Have Different (Unlike) Signs

To add a positive integer and a negative integer, subtract the smaller absolute value from the larger.

1. If the positive integer has the larger absolute value, the final answer is positive.
2. If the negative integer has the larger absolute value, make the final answer negative.

EXAMPLE 2 Add: $5 + (-7)$

Strategy We will use the rule for adding two integers that have different signs.

WHY The addend 5 is positive and the addend -7 is negative.

Solution

Step 1 To add two integers with different signs, we first subtract the smaller absolute value from the larger absolute value. Since $|5|$, which is 5, is smaller than $|-7|$, which is 7, we begin by subtracting 5 from 7.

$$7 - 5 = 2$$

Step 2 Since the negative number, -7, has the larger absolute value, we attach a negative sign $-$ to the result from step 1. Therefore,

$$5 + (-7) = -2$$

Make the final answer negative.

Self Check 2

Add: $6 + (-9)$ -3

Now Try **Problem 31**

Teaching Example 2 Add: $3 + (-8)$
Answer:
-5

The Language of Mathematics A positive integer and a negative integer are said to have *unlike* signs.

Self Check 3

Add:

a. $7 + (-2)$ 5

b. $-53 + 39$ -14

c. $-506 + 888$ 382

Now Try **Problems 33, 35, and 39**

Teaching Example 3 Add:
a. $6 + (-3)$
b. $-43 + 18$
c. $-301 + 566$

Answers:
a. 3
b. -25
c. 265

EXAMPLE 3 Add: **a.** $8 + (-4)$ **b.** $-41 + 17$ **c.** $-206 + 568$

Strategy We will use the rule for adding two integers that have different signs.

WHY In each case, we are asked to add a positive integer and a negative integer.

Solution

a. Find the absolute values: $|8| = 8$ and $|-4| = 4$

$8 + (-4) = 4$ Subtract the smaller absolute value from the larger: $8 - 4 = 4$. Since the positive number, 8, has the larger absolute value, the final answer is positive.

b. Find the absolute values: $|-41| = 41$ and $|17| = 17$

$-41 + 17 = -24$ Subtract the smaller absolute value from the larger: $41 - 17 = 24$. Since the negative number, -41, has the larger absolute value, make the final answer negative.

$$\begin{array}{r} \overset{3\,11}{\cancel{4}\cancel{1}} \\ -17 \\ \hline 24 \end{array}$$

c. Find the absolute values: $|-206| = 206$ and $|568| = 568$

$-206 + 568 = 362$ Subtract the smaller absolute value from the larger: $568 - 206 = 362$. Since the positive number, 568, has the larger absolute value, the answer is positive.

$$\begin{array}{r} 568 \\ -206 \\ \hline 362 \end{array}$$

Caution! Did you notice that the answers to the addition problems in Examples 2 and 3 were found using subtraction? This is the case when the addition involves two integers that have *different signs.*

THINK IT THROUGH *Cash Flow*

"College can be trial by fire — a test of how to cope with pressure, freedom, distractions, and a flood of credit card offers. It's easy to get into a cycle of overspending and unnecessary debt as a student."

Planning for College, Wells Fargo Bank

If your income is less than your expenses, you have a *negative* cash flow. A negative cash flow can be a red flag that you should increase your income and/or reduce your expenses. Which of the following activities can increase income and which can decrease expenses?

- Buy generic or store-brand items. decrease expenses
- Get training and/or more education. increase income
- Use your student ID to get discounts at stores, events, etc. decrease expenses
- Work more hours. increase income
- Turn a hobby or skill into a money-making business. increase income
- Tutor young students. increase income
- Stop expensive habits, like smoking, buying snacks every day, etc decrease expenses
- Attend free activities and free or discounted days at local attractions. decrease expenses
- Sell rarely used items, like an old CD player. increase income
- Compare the prices of at least three products or at three stores before buying. decrease expenses

Based on the *Building Financial Skills* by National Endowment for Financial Education.

3 Perform several additions to evaluate expressions.

To evaluate expressions that contain several additions, we make repeated use of the rules for adding two integers.

EXAMPLE 4 Evaluate: $-3 + 5 + (-12) + 2$

Strategy Since there are no calculations within parentheses, no exponential expressions, and no multiplication or division, we will perform the additions, working from the left to the right.

Solution

$-3 + 5 + (-12) + 2 = 2 + (-12) + 2$ Use the rule for adding two integers that have different signs: $-3 + 5 = 2$.

$= -10 + 2$ Use the rule for adding two integers that have different signs: $2 + (-12) = -10$.

$= -8$ Use the rule for adding two integers that have different signs.

Self Check 4

Evaluate:
$-12 + 8 + (-6) + 1$ -9

Now Try **Problem 43**

Teaching Example 4 Evaluate:
$-7 + 3 + (-15) + 6$
Answer:
-13

Commutative Property of Addition

The order in which integers are added does not change their sum.

Associative Property of Addition

The way in which integers are grouped does not change their sum.

Another way to evaluate an expression like that in Example 4 is to use these properties to reorder and regroup the integers in a helpful way.

EXAMPLE 5 Use the commutative and/or associative properties of addition to help evaluate the expression: $-3 + 5 + (-12) + 2$

Strategy We will use the commutative and/or associative properties of addition so that we can add the positives and add the negatives separately. Then we will add those results to obtain the final answer.

WHY It is easier to add integers that have the same sign than integers that have different signs. This approach lessens the possibility of an error, because we only have to add integers that have different signs once.

Solution

$-3 + 5 + (-12) + 2$

$= -3 + (-12) + 5 + 2$ Use the commutative property of addition to reorder the integers.

Negatives Positives

$= [-3 + (-12)] + (5 + 2)$ Use the associative property of addition to group the negatives and group the positives.

$= -15 + 7$ Use the rule for adding two integers that have the same sign twice. Add the negatives within the brackets. Add the positives within the parentheses.

$= -8$ Use the rule for adding two integers that have different signs. This is the same result as in Example 4.

Self Check 5

Use the commutative and/or associative properties of addition to help evaluate the expression:
$-12 + 8 + (-6) + 1$ -9

Now Try **Problem 45**

Teaching Example 5 Use the commutative and/or associative properties of addition to help evaluate the expression from Teaching Example 4 in a different way: $-7 + 3 + (-15) + 6$
Answer:
-13

Self Check 6

Evaluate:
$(-6 + 8) + [10 + (-17)]$ -5

***Now Try* Problem 47**

Teaching Example 6 Evaluate:
$[-8 + (-4)] + (-9 + 3)$
Answer:
-18

EXAMPLE 6 Evaluate: $[-21 + (-5)] + (-17 + 6)$

Strategy We will perform the addition within the brackets and the addition within the parentheses first. Then we will add those results.

WHY By the order of operations rule, we must perform the calculations within the grouping symbols first.

Solution Use the rule for adding two integers that have the same sign to do the addition within the brackets and the rule for adding two integers that have different signs to do the addition within parentheses.

$$[-21 + (-5)] + (-17 + 6) = -26 + (-11)$$ Add within each pair of grouping symbols.

$$= -37$$ Use the rule for adding two integers that have the same sign.

4 Identify opposites (additive inverses) when adding integers.

When 0 is added to a whole number, the whole number remains the same. This is also true for integers. For example, $-5 + 0 = -5$ and $0 + (-43) = -43$. Because of this, we call 0 the **additive identity.**

The Language of Mathematics *Identity* is a form of the word *identical,* meaning the same. You have probably seen *identical* twins.

Addition Property of 0

The sum of any integer and 0 is that integer. For example,

$-3 + 0 = -3,$ $-19 + 0 = -19,$ and $0 + (-76) = -76$

There is another important fact about the operation of addition and 0. To illustrate it, we use the number line below to add 6 and its opposite, -6. Notice that $6 + (-6) = 0$.

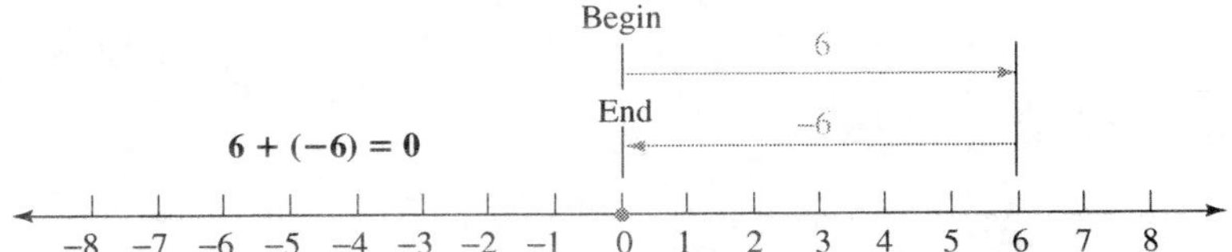

If the sum of two numbers is 0, the numbers are said to be **additive inverses** of each other. Since $6 + (-6) = 0$, we say that 6 and -6 are additive inverses. Likewise, -7 is the additive inverse of 7, and 51 is the additive inverse of -51.

We can now classify a pair of integers such as 6 and -6 in three ways: as opposites, negatives, or additive inverses.

Addition Property of Opposites

The sum of an integer and its opposite (additive inverse) is 0. For example,

$4 + (-4) = 0, \quad -53 + 53 = 0, \quad \text{and} \quad 710 + (-710) = 0$

At certain times, the addition property of opposites can be used to make addition of several integers easier.

EXAMPLE 7 Evaluate: $12 + (-5) + 6 + 5 + (-12)$

Strategy Instead of working from left to right, we will use the commutative and associative properties of addition to add *pairs of opposites.*

WHY Since the sum of an integer and its opposite is 0, it is helpful to identify such pairs in an addition.

Solution

$$12 + (-5) + 6 + 5 + (-12) = 0 + 0 + 6$$ Locate pairs of opposites and add them to get 0. (opposites: 12 and −12; −5 and 5)

$$= 6$$ The sum of any integer and 0 is that integer.

Self Check 7

Evaluate:
$8 + (-1) + 6 + (-8) + 1$ 6

Now Try **Problem 51**

Teaching Example 7 Evaluate:
$16 + (-3) + 9 + 3 + (-16)$
Answer:
9

5 Solve application problems by adding integers.

Since application problems are almost always written in words, the ability to understand what you read is very important. Recall from Chapter 1 that words and phrases such as *gained, increased by,* and *rise* indicate addition.

EXAMPLE 8 *Record Temperature Change* At the beginning of this section, we learned that at 7:30 A.M. on January 22, 1943, in Spearfish, South Dakota, the temperature was −4°F. The temperature then rose 49 degrees in just 2 minutes. What was the temperature at 7:32 A.M.?

Strategy We will carefully read the problem looking for a key word or phrase.

WHY Key words and phrases indicate what arithmetic operations should be used to solve the problem.

Solution The phrase *rose 49 degrees* indicates addition. With that in mind, we translate the words of the problem to numbers and symbols.

The temperature at 7:32 A.M.	was	the temperature at 7:30 A.M.	plus	49 degrees.
The temperature at 7:32 A.M.	=	−4	+	49

To find the sum, we will use the rule for adding two integers that have different signs. First, we find the absolute values: $|-4| = 4$ and $|49| = 49$.

$-4 + 49 = 45$ Subtract the smaller absolute value from the larger absolute value: $49 - 4 = 45$. Since the positive number, 49, has the larger absolute value, the final answer is positive.

At 7:32 A.M., the temperature was 45°F.

Self Check 8

TEMPERATURE CHANGE On the morning of February 21, 1918, in Granville, North Dakota, the morning low temperature was −33°F. By the afternoon, the temperature had risen a record 83 degrees. What was the afternoon high temperature in Granville? (Source: *Extreme Weather* by Christopher C. Burt)

Now Try **Problem 83**

Self Check 8 Answer
50°F

Teaching Example 8
RECORD TEMPERATURE CHANGE The greatest temperature change ever recorded in a 24-hour period occurred in Loma, Montana, in 1972. On January 14, the low temperature there was −54°F. By the next day, the temperature had risen 103°F. What was the high temperature in Loma on January 15? (Source: *Extreme Weather* by Christopher C. Burt)
Answer:
49°F

Using Your CALCULATOR **Entering Negative Numbers**

Canada is the largest U.S. trading partner. To calculate the 2007 U.S. trade balance with Canada, we add the $249 billion worth of U.S. exports *to* Canada (considered positive) to the $317 billion worth of U.S. imports *from* Canada (considered negative). We can use a calculator to perform the addition: $249 + (-317)$

We do not have to do anything special to enter a positive number. Negative numbers are entered using either **direct** or **reverse entry,** depending on the type of calculator you have.

To enter -317 using reverse entry, press the change-of-sign key [+/−] *after entering* 317. To enter -317 using direct entry, press the negative key [(−)] *before* entering 317. In either case, note that [+/−] and the [(−)] keys are different from the subtraction key [−].

Reverse entry: 249 [+] 317 [+/−] [=]

Direct entry: 249 [+] [(−)] 317 [ENTER]   −68

In 2007, the United States had a trade balance of −$68 billion with Canada. Because the result is negative, it is called a trade *deficit.*

ANSWERS TO SELF CHECKS

1. a. −9 **b.** −73 **c.** −494 **2.** −3 **3. a.** 5 **b.** −14 **c.** 382 **4.** −9 **5.** −9 **6.** −5 **7.** 6 **8.** 50°F

SECTION 1.2 STUDY SET

VOCABULARY

Fill in the blanks.

1. Two negative integers, as well as two positive integers, are said to have the same or _like_ signs.

2. A positive integer and a negative integer are said to have different or _unlike_ signs.

3. When 0 is added to a number, the number remains the same. We call 0 the additive _identity_.

▶ **4.** Since $-5 + 5 = 0$, we say that 5 is the additive _inverse_ of -5. We can also say that 5 and -5 are _opposites_.

5. _Commutative_ property of addition: The order in which integers are added does not change their sum.

6. _Associative_ property of addition: The way in which integers are grouped does not change their sum.

CONCEPTS

7. a. What is the absolute value of 10? What is the absolute value of -12? $|10| = 10$, $|-12| = 12$

b. Which number has the larger absolute value, 10 or -12? -12

c. Using your answers to part a, subtract the smaller absolute value from the larger absolute value. What is the result? 2

8. a. If you lost $6 and then lost $8, overall, what amount of money was lost? $14 was lost.

b. If you lost $6 and then won $8, overall, what amount of money have you won? $2 was won.

Fill in the blanks.

9. To add two integers with unlike signs, _subtract_ their absolute values, the smaller from the larger. Then attach to that result the sign of the number with the _larger_ absolute value.

10. To add two integers with like signs, add their _absolute_ values and attach their common _sign_ to the sum.

11. a. Is the sum of two positive integers always positive? yes

b. Is the sum of two negative integers always negative? yes

c. Is the sum of a positive integer and a negative integer always positive? no

d. Is the sum of a positive integer and a negative integer always negative? no

12. Complete the table by finding the additive inverse, opposite, and absolute value of the given numbers.

Number	Additive inverse	Opposite	Absolute value
19	−19	−19	19
−2	2	2	2
0	0	0	0

▶ **13. a.** What is the sum of an integer and its additive inverse? 0

b. What is the sum of an integer and its opposite? 0

14. a. What number must be added to −5 to obtain 0? 5

b. What number must be added to 8 to obtain 0? −8

NOTATION

Complete each solution to evaluate the expression.

15. $-16 + (-2) + (-1) = -18 + (-1)$
$= -19$

▶ **16.** $-8 + (-2) + 6 = -10 + 6$
$= -4$

17. $(-3 + 8) + (-3) = 5 + (-3)$
$= 2$

18. $-5 + [2 + (-9)] = -5 + (-7)$
$= -12$

GUIDED PRACTICE

Add. See Example 1.

19. $-6 + (-3)$ −9

▶ **20.** $-2 + (-3)$ −5

21. $-5 + (-5)$ −10

22. $-8 + (-8)$ −16

23. $-51 + (-11)$ −62

24. $-43 + (-12)$ −55

25. $-69 + (-27)$ −96

▶ **26.** $-55 + (-36)$ −91

27. $-248 + (-131)$ −379

28. $-423 + (-164)$ −587

29. $-565 + (-309)$ −874

30. $-709 + (-187)$ −896

Add. See Examples 2 and 3.

31. $-8 + 5$ −3

32. $-9 + 3$ −6

33. $7 + (-6)$ 1

34. $4 + (-2)$ 2

35. $20 + (-42)$ −22

▶ **36.** $-18 + 10$ −8

37. $71 + (-23)$ 48

38. $75 + (-56)$ 19

39. $479 + (-122)$ 357

40. $589 + (-242)$ 347

41. $-339 + 279$ −60

42. $-704 + 649$ −55

Evaluate each expression. See Examples 4 and 5.

43. $9 + (-3) + 5 + (-4)$ 7

▶ **44.** $-3 + 7 + (-4) + 1$ 1

45. $6 + (-4) + (-13) + 7$ −4

46. $8 + (-5) + (-10) + 6$ −1

Evaluate each expression. See Example 6.

▶ **47.** $[-3 + (-4)] + (-5 + 2)$ −10

48. $[9 + (-10)] + (-7 + 9)$ 1

49. $(-1 + 34) + [16 + (-8)]$ 41

50. $(-32 + 13) + [5 + (-14)]$ −28

Evaluate each expression. See Example 7.

51. $23 + (-5) + 3 + 5 + (-23)$ 3

52. $41 + (-1) + 9 + 1 + (-41)$ 9

▶ **53.** $-10 + (-1) + 10 + (-6) + 1$ −6

54. $-14 + (-30) + 14 + (-9) + 9$ −30

TRY IT YOURSELF

Add.

55. $-2 + 6 + (-1)$ 3

56. $4 + (-3) + (-2)$ −1

57. $-7 + 0$ −7

58. $0 + (-15)$ −15

59. $24 + (-15)$ 9

60. $-4 + 14$ 10

61. $-435 + (-127)$ −562

62. $-346 + (-273)$ −619

63. $-7 + 9$ 2

▶ **64.** $-3 + 6$ 3

65. $2 + (-2)$ 0

66. $-10 + 10$ 0

67. $2 + (-10 + 8)$ 0

▶ **68.** $(-9 + 12) + (-4)$ −1

69. $-9 + 1 + (-2) + (-1) + 9$ −2

70. $5 + 4 + (-6) + (-4) + (-5)$ −6

71. $[6 + (-4)] + [8 + (-11)]$ −1

72. $[5 + (-8)] + [9 + (-15)]$ −9

73. $(-4 + 8) + (-11 + 4)$ −3

▶ **74.** $(-12 + 6) + (-6 + 8)$ −4

75. $-675 + (-456) + 99$ −1,032

76. $-9{,}750 + (-780) + 2{,}345$ −8,185

77. Find the sum of −6, −7, and −8. −21

▶ **78.** Find the sum of −11, −12, and −13. −36

79. $-2 + [789 + (-9{,}135)]$ −8,348

80. $-8 + [2{,}701 + (-4{,}089)]$ −1,396

81. What is 25 more than −45? −20

82. What is 31 more than −65? −34

APPLICATIONS

Use signed numbers to solve each problem.

83. RECORD TEMPERATURES The lowest recorded temperatures for Michigan and Minnesota are shown below. Use the given information to find the highest recorded temperature for each state. 112°F, 114°F

State	Lowest temperature	Highest temperature
Michigan	Feb. 9, 1934: −51°F	July 13, 1936: 163°F warmer than the record low
Minnesota	Feb. 2, 1996: −60°F	July 6, 1936: 174°F warmer than the record low

(Source: *The World Almanac Book of Facts*, 2009)

84. ELEVATIONS The lowest point in the United States is Death Valley, California, with an elevation of −282 feet (282 feet below sea level). Mt. McKinley (Alaska) is the highest point in the United States. Its elevation is 20,602 feet higher than Death Valley. What is the elevation of Mt. McKinley? (Source: *The World Almanac Book of Facts,* 2009) 20,320 ft

85. SUNKEN SHIPS Refer to the map below.

a. The German battleship *Bismarck,* one of the most feared warships of World War II, was sunk by the British in 1941. It lies on the ocean floor 15,720 feet below sea level off the west coast of France. Represent that depth using a signed number. −15,720 ft

b. In 1912, the famous cruise ship *Titanic* sank after striking an iceberg. It lies on the North Atlantic ocean floor, 3,220 feet higher than the *Bismarck.* At what depth is the *Titanic* resting? −12,500 ft

86. JOGGING A businessman's lunchtime workout includes jogging up ten stories of stairs in his high-rise office building. He starts the workout on the fourth level below ground in the underground parking garage.

a. Represent that level using a signed number. −4

b. On what story of the building will he finish his workout? 6th story

87. FLOODING After a heavy rainstorm, a river that had been 9 feet under flood stage rose 11 feet in a 48-hour period.

a. Represent that level of the river before the storm using a signed number. −9 ft

b. Find the height of the river after the storm in comparison to flood stage. 2 ft above flood stage

88. ATOMS An atom is composed of protons, neutrons, and electrons. A proton has a positive charge (represented by +1), a neutron has no charge, and an electron has a negative charge (−1). Two simple models of atoms are shown below.

a. How many protons does the atom in figure (a) have? How many electrons? 8, 10

b. What is the net charge of the atom in figure (a)? −2

c. How many protons does the atom in figure (b) have? How many electrons? 4, 4

d. What is the net charge of the atom in figure (b)? 0

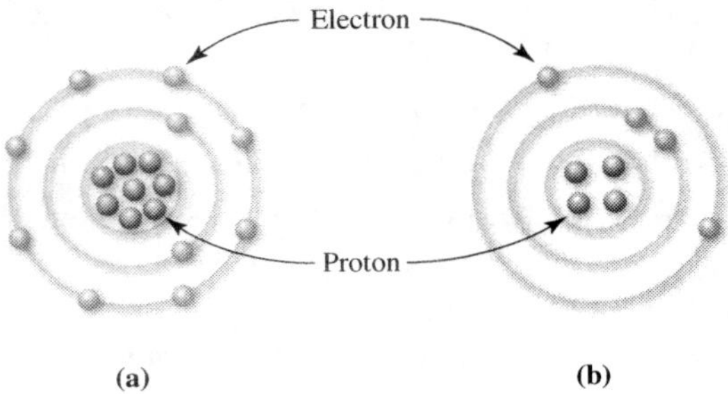

89. CHEMISTRY The three steps of a chemistry lab experiment are listed here. The experiment begins with a compound that is stored at −40°F.

Step 1 Raise the temperature of the compound 200°.

Step 2 Add sulfur and then raise the temperature 10°.

Step 3 Add 10 milliliters of water, stir, and raise the temperature 25°.

What is the resulting temperature of the mixture after step 3? 195°

90. Suppose as a personal financial advisor, your clients are considering purchasing income property. You find a duplex apartment unit that is for sale and learn that the maintenance costs, utilities, and taxes on it total \$900 per month. If the current owner receives monthly rental payments of \$450 and \$380 from the tenants, does the duplex produce a positive cash flow each month? no, \$70 shortfall each month (−\$70)

from Campus to Careers
Personal Financial Advisor

91. HEALTH Find the point total for the six risk factors (shown with blue headings) on the medical questionnaire below. Then use the table at the bottom of the form (under the red heading) to determine the risk of contracting heart disease for the man whose responses are shown. 5, 4% risk

Age		**Total Cholesterol**	
Age	Points	Reading	Points
35	*−4*	*280*	*3*

Cholesterol		**Blood Pressure**	
HDL	Points	Systolic/Diastolic	Points
62	*−3*	*124/100*	*3*

Diabetic		**Smoker**	
	Points		Points
Yes	*4*	*Yes*	*2*

10-Year Heart Disease Risk

Total Points	Risk	Total Points	Risk
−2 or less	1%	5	4%
−1 to 1	2%	6	6%
2 to 3	3%	7	6%
4	4%	8	7%

Source: National Heart, Lung, and Blood Institute

92. POLITICAL POLLS Six months before a general election, the incumbent senator found himself trailing the challenger by 18 points. To overtake his opponent, the campaign staff decided to use a four-part strategy. Each part of this plan is shown below, with the anticipated point gain.

Part 1 Intense TV ad blitz: gain 10 points

Part 2 Ask for union endorsement: gain 2 points

Part 3 Voter mailing: gain 3 points

Part 4 Get-out-the-vote campaign: gain 1 point

With these gains, will the incumbent overtake the challenger on election day?
No, he will still be behind by 2 points.

93. MILITARY SCIENCE During a battle, an army retreated 1,500 meters, regrouped, and advanced 3,500 meters. The next day, it advanced 1,250 meters. Find the army's net gain. 3,250 m

94. AIRLINES The graph in the next column shows the annual net income for Delta Air Lines during the years 2004–2007.

a. Estimate the company's total net income over this span of four years in millions of dollars. about −$13,000 million

b. Express your answer from part a in billions of dollars. about −$13 billion

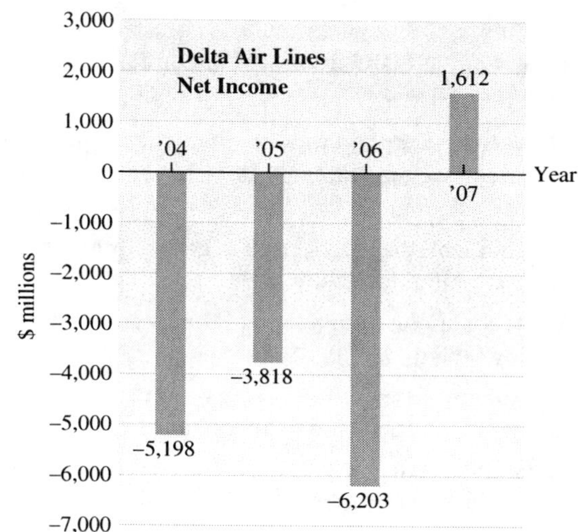

(Source: *The Wall Street Journal*)

95. ACCOUNTING On a financial balance sheet, debts (considered negative numbers) are written within parentheses. Assets (considered positive numbers) are written without parentheses. What is the 2009 fund balance for the preschool whose financial records are shown below? ($967)

ABC Preschool Balance Sheet, June 2009

Fund	Balance $
Classroom supplies	$5,889
Emergency needs	$927
Holiday program	($2,928)
Insurance	$1,645
Janitorial	($894)
Licensing	$715
Maintenance	($6,321)
BALANCE	?

96. SPREADSHEETS Monthly rain totals for four counties are listed in the spreadsheet below. The −1 entered in cell B1 means that the rain total for Suffolk County for a certain month was 1 inch *below* average. We can analyze this data by asking the computer to perform various operations.

Book 1

File Edit View Insert Format Tools Data Window Help

	A	B	C	D	E	F
1	Suffolk	−1	−1	0	+1	+1
2	Marin	0	−2	+1	+1	−1
3	Logan	−1	+1	+2	+1	+1
4	Tipton	−2	−2	+1	−1	−3
5						

a. To ask the computer to add the numbers in cells B1, B2, B3, and B4, we type SUM(B1:B4). Find this sum. −4

b. Find SUM(F1:F4). −2

WRITING

97. Is the sum of a positive and a negative number always positive? Explain why or why not.

98. How do you explain the fact that when asked to *add* −4 and 8, we must actually *subtract* to obtain the result?

99. Explain why the sum of two negative numbers is a negative number.

100. Write an application problem that will require adding −50 and −60.

101. If the sum of two integers is 0, what can be said about the integers? Give an example.

102. Explain why the expression −6 + −5 is not written correctly. How should it be written?

REVIEW

103. **a.** Find the perimeter of the rectangle shown below. 16 ft

b. Find the area of the rectangle shown below. 15 ft^2

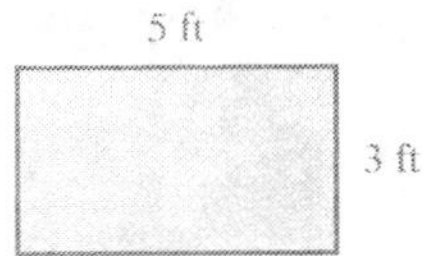

104. What property is illustrated by the statement $5 \cdot 15 = 15 \cdot 5$? commutative property of multiplication

105. Prime factor 250. Use exponents to express the result. $2 \cdot 5^3$

106. Divide: $\frac{144}{12}$ 12

Objectives

1 Use the subtraction rule.

2 Evaluate expressions involving subtraction and addition.

3 Solve application problems by subtracting integers.

SECTION 1.3 Subtracting Integers

In this section, we will discuss a rule that is helpful when subtracting signed numbers.

1 Use the subtraction rule.

The subtraction problem 6 − 4 can be thought of as taking away 4 from 6. We can use a number line to illustrate this. Beginning at 0, we draw an arrow of length 6 units long that points to the right. It represents positive 6. From the tip of that arrow, we draw a second arrow, 4 units long, that points to the left. It represents taking away 4. Since we end up at 2, it follows that 6 − 4 = 2.

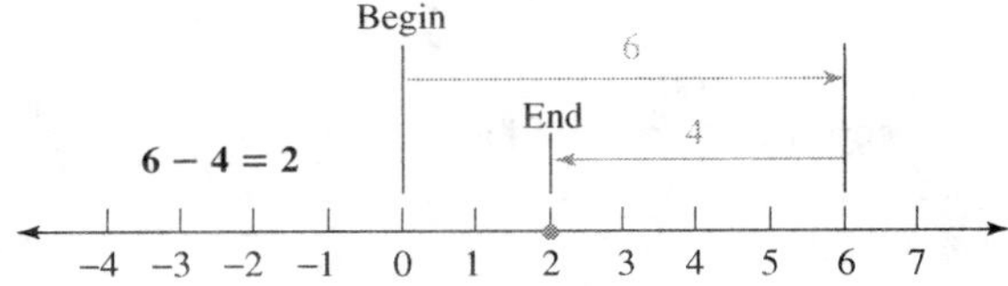

Note that the illustration above also represents the *addition* 6 + (−4) = 2. We see that

Subtracting 4 from 6 . . . is the same as . . . adding the opposite of 4 to 6.

$6 - 4 = 2$ $\qquad$ $6 + (-4) = 2$

The results are the same.

This observation suggests the following rule.

Rule for Subtraction

To subtract two integers, add the first integer to the opposite (additive inverse) of the integer to be subtracted.

Put more simply, this rule says that *subtraction is the same as adding the opposite.*

After rewriting a subtraction as addition of the opposite, we then use one of the rules for the addition of signed numbers to find the result.

You won't need to use this rule for every subtraction problem. For example, $6 - 4$ is obviously 2; it does not need to be rewritten as adding the opposite. But for more complicated problems such as $-6 - 4$ or $3 - (-5)$, where the result is not obvious, the subtraction rule will be quite helpful.

EXAMPLE 1 Subtract and check the result:

a. $-6 - 4$ **b.** $3 - (-5)$ **c.** $7 - 23$

Strategy To find each difference, we will apply the rule for subtraction: Add the first integer to the opposite of the integer to be subtracted.

WHY It is easy to make an error when subtracting signed numbers. We will probably be more accurate if we write each subtraction as addition of the opposite.

Solution

a. We read $-6 - 4$ as "negative six *minus* four." Thus, the number to be subtracted is 4. Subtracting 4 is the same as adding its opposite, -4.

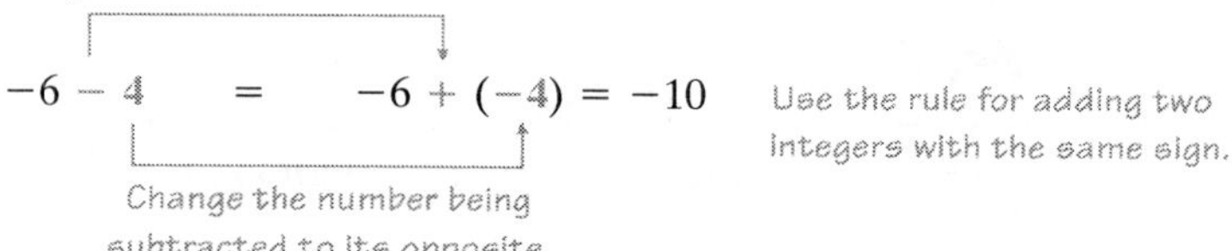

To check, we add the *difference*, -10, and the *subtrahend*, 4. We should get the *minuend*, -6.

Check: $-10 + 4 = -6$ The result checks.

Caution! Don't forget to write the opposite of the number to be subtracted within parentheses if it is negative.

$$-6 - 4 = -6 + (-4)$$

b. We read $3 - (-5)$ as "three *minus* negative five." Thus, the number to be subtracted is -5. Subtracting -5 is the same as adding its opposite, 5.

Add . . .

$$3 - (-5) = 3 + 5 = 8$$

. . . the opposite

Check: $8 + (-5) = 3$ The result checks.

Self Check 1

Subtract and check the result:

a. $-2 - 3$ -5

b. $4 - (-8)$ 12

c. $6 - 85$ -79

Now Try **Problems 21, 25, and 29**

Teaching Example 1 Subtract and check the result:

a. $-5 - 3$

b. $9 - (-2)$

c. $4 - 67$

Answers:

a. -8

b. 11

c. -63

c. We read $7 - 23$ as "seven *minus* twenty-three." Thus, the number to be subtracted is 23. Subtracting 23 is the same as adding its opposite, -23.

Add . . .

$$7 - 23 = 7 + (-23) = -16$$ Use the rule for adding two integers with different signs.

. . . the opposite

Check: $-16 + 23 = 7$ The result checks.

Caution! When applying the subtraction rule, *do not change* the first number.

$$-6 - 4 = -6 + (-4) \qquad 3 - (-5) = 3 + 5$$

Self Check 2

a. Subtract -10 from -7. 3

b. Subtract -7 from -10. -3

Now Try **Problem 33**

Teaching Example 2
a. Subtract -14 from -2.
b. Subtract -2 from -14.
Answers:
a. 12
b. -12

EXAMPLE 2 **a.** Subtract -12 from -8. **b.** Subtract -8 from -12.

Strategy We will translate each phrase to mathematical symbols and then perform the subtraction. We must be careful when translating the instruction to subtract one number *from* another number.

WHY The order of the numbers in each word phrase must be reversed when we translate it to mathematical symbols.

Solution

a. Since -12 is the number to be subtracted, we reverse the order in which -12 and -8 appear in the sentence when translating to symbols.

Subtract -12 from -8

$$-8 - (-12)$$ Write -12 within parentheses.

To find this difference, we write the subtraction as addition of the opposite:

Add . . .

$$-8 - (-12) = -8 + 12 = 4$$ Use the rule for adding two integers with different signs.

. . . the opposite

b. Since -8 is the number to be subtracted, we reverse the order in which -8 and -12 appear in the sentence when translating to symbols.

Subtract -8 from -12

$$-12 - (-8)$$ Write -8 within parentheses.

To find this difference, we write the subtraction as addition of the opposite:

Add . . .

$$-12 - (-8) = -12 + 8 = -4$$ Use the rule for adding two integers with different signs.

. . . the opposite

The Language of Mathematics When we change a number to its opposite, we say we have *changed* (or *reversed*) its sign.

Remember that any subtraction problem can be rewritten as an equivalent addition. We just add the opposite of the number that is to be subtracted. Here are four examples:

- $4 - 8 = 4 + (-8) = -4$
- $4 - (-8) = 4 + 8 = 12$
- $-4 - 8 = -4 + (-8) = -12$
- $-4 - (-8) = -4 + 8 = 4$

Any subtraction can be written as addition of the opposite of the number to be subtracted.

2 Evaluate expressions involving subtraction and addition.

Expressions can involve repeated subtraction or combinations of subtraction and addition. To evaluate them, we use the order of operations rule.

EXAMPLE 3 Evaluate: $-1 - (-2) - 10$

Strategy This expression involves two subtractions. We will write each subtraction as addition of the opposite and then evaluate the expression using the order of operations rule.

WHY It is easy to make an error when subtracting signed numbers. We will probably be more accurate if we write each subtraction as addition of the opposite.

Solution We apply the rule for subtraction twice and then perform the additions, working from left to right. (We could also add the positives and the negatives separately, and then add those results.)

$-1 - (-2) - 10 = -1 + 2 + (-10)$ Add the opposite of −2, which is 2. Add the opposite of 10, which is −10.

$= 1 + (-10)$ Work from left to right. Add −1 + 2 using the rule for adding integers that have different signs.

$= -9$ Use the rule for adding integers that have different signs.

Self Check 3

Evaluate: $-3 - 5 - (-1)$ −7

Now Try **Problem 37**

Teaching Example 3 Evaluate: $-4 - (-9) - 12$

Answer: −7

EXAMPLE 4 Evaluate: $-80 - (-2 - 24)$

Strategy We will consider the subtraction within the parentheses first and rewrite it as addition of the opposite.

WHY By the order of operations rule, we must perform all calculations within parentheses first.

Solution

$-80 - (-2 - 24) = -80 - [-2 + (-24)]$ Add the opposite of 24, which is −24. Since −24 must be written within parentheses, we write −2 + (−24) within brackets.

$= -80 - (-26)$ Within the brackets, add −2 and −24. Since only one set of grouping symbols is now needed, we can write the answer, −26, within parentheses.

$$\begin{array}{r} \overset{7\,10}{\cancel{8}\cancel{0}} \\ -26 \\ \hline 54 \end{array}$$

$= -80 + 26$ Add the opposite of −26, which is 26.

$= -54$ Use the rule for adding integers that have different signs.

Self Check 4

Evaluate: $-72 - (-6 - 51)$ −15

Now Try **Problem 49**

Teaching Example 4 Evaluate: $-61 - (-1 - 22)$

Answer: −38

EXAMPLE 5 Evaluate: $-(-6) + (-18) - 4 - (-51)$

Strategy This expression involves one addition and two subtractions. We will write each subtraction as addition of the opposite and then evaluate the expression.

Self Check 5

Evaluate: $-(-3) + (-16) - 9 - (-28)$ 6

Now Try **Problem 55**

Teaching Example 5 Evaluate: $-(-6) + (-7) - 14 - (-39)$

Answer:
24

WHY It is easy to make an error when subtracting signed numbers. We will probably be more accurate if we write each subtraction as addition of the opposite.

Solution We apply the rule for subtraction twice. Then we will add the positives and the negatives separately, and add those results. (By the commutative and associative properties of addition, we can add the integers in any order.)

$-(-6) + (-18) - 4 - (-51)$

$= 6 + (-18) + (-4) + 51$ Simplify: $-(-6) = 6$. Add the opposite of 4, which is -4, and add the opposite of -51, which is 51.

$= (6 + 51) + [(-18) + (-4)]$ Reorder the integers. Then group the positives together and group the negatives together.

$= 57 + (-22)$ Add the positives within the parentheses. Add the negatives within the brackets.

$= 35$ Use the rule for adding integers that have different signs.

3 Solve application problems by subtracting integers.

Subtraction finds the *difference* between two numbers. When we find the difference between the maximum value and the minimum value of a collection of measurements, we are finding the **range** of the values.

Self Check 6

THE GATEWAY CITY The record high temperature for St. Louis, Missouri, is 107°F. The record low temperature is −18°F. Find the temperature range for these extremes. (Source: *The World Almanac and Book of Facts,* 2009) 125°F

Now Try **Problem 101**

Teaching Example 6
THE STEEL CITY The record high temperature for Pittsburgh, Pennsylvania, is 103°F. The record low is −22°F. Find the temperature range for these extremes. (Source: *The World Almanac and Book of Facts,* 2009)

Answer:
125°F

EXAMPLE 6 *The Windy City* The record high temperature for Chicago, Illinois, is 104°F. The record low is −27°F. Find the temperature range for these extremes. (Source: *The World Almanac and Book of Facts,* 2009)

Strategy We will subtract the lowest temperature (−27°F) from the highest temperature (104°F).

WHY The *range* of a collection of data indicates the spread of the data. It is the difference between the largest and smallest values.

Solution We apply the rule for subtraction and add the opposite of −27.

$104 - (-27) = 104 + 27$ 104° is the highest temperature and −27° is the lowest.

$= 131$

The temperature range for these extremes is 131°F.

Things are constantly changing in our daily lives. The amount of money we have in the bank, the price of gasoline, and our ages are examples. In mathematics, the operation of subtraction is used to measure change. To find the **change** in a quantity, we subtract the earlier value from the later value.

Change = later value − earlier value

EXAMPLE 7

Water Management On Monday, the water level in a city storage tank was 16 feet above normal. By Friday, the level had fallen to a mark 14 feet below normal. Find the change in the water level from Monday to Friday.

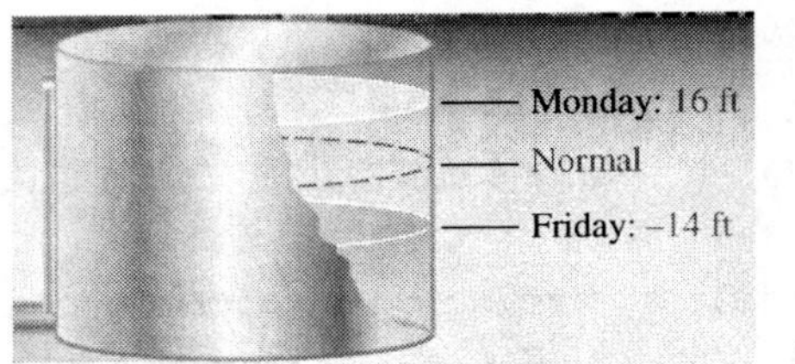

Analyze It is helpful to list the given facts and what you are to find.

- On Monday, the water level was 16 feet above normal. *Given*
- On Friday, the water level was 14 feet below normal. *Given*
- Find the change in the water level. *Find*

Form To find the change in the water level, we *subtract the earlier value from the later value.* The water levels of 16 feet above normal (the earlier value) and 14 feet below normal (the later value) can be represented by 16 and −14.

We translate the words of the problem to numbers and symbols.

The change in the water level	is equal to	the later water level (Friday)	minus	the earlier water level (Monday).
The change in the water level	=	−14	−	16

Solve We can use the rule for subtraction to find the difference.

$-14 - 16 = -14 + (-16)$ *Add the opposite of 16, which is −16.*

$= -30$ *Use the rule for adding integers with the same sign.*

State The negative result means the water level *fell* 30 feet from Monday to Friday.

Check If we represent the change in water level on a horizontal number line, we see that the water level fell 16 + 14 = 30 units. The result checks.

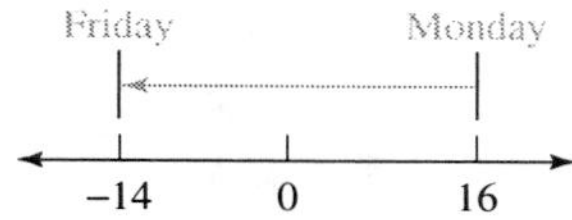

Self Check 7

CRUDE OIL On Wednesday, the level of crude oil in a storage tank was 5 feet above standard capacity. Thursday, after a large refining session, the level fell to a mark 76 feet below standard capacity. Find the change in the crude oil level from Wednesday to Thursday. The crude oil level fell 81 ft.

Now Try **Problem 103**

Teaching Example 7
WATER MANAGEMENT On Monday, the water level in a city storage tank was 19 feet above normal. By the following Monday, the level had fallen to a mark 15 feet below normal. Find the change in the water level that week.

Answer:
The water level fell 34 ft.

Using Your CALCULATOR Subtraction with Negative Numbers

The world's highest peak is Mount Everest in the Himalayas. The greatest ocean depth yet measured lies in the Mariana Trench near the island of Guam in the western Pacific. To find the range between the highest peak and the greatest depth, we must subtract:

$$29{,}035 - (-36{,}025)$$

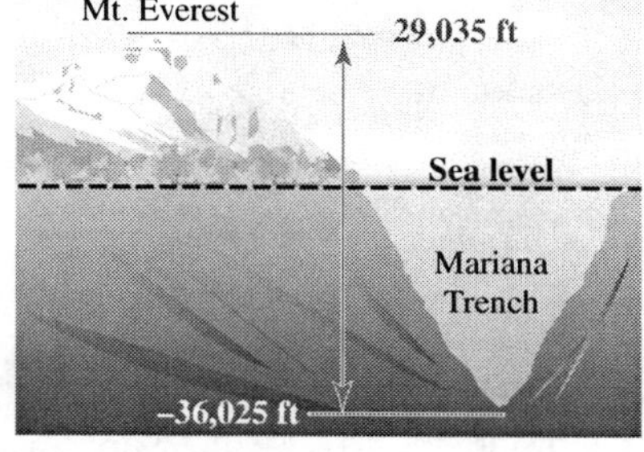

To perform this subtraction on a calculator, we enter the following:

Reverse entry: 29035 [−] 36025 [+/−] [=]

Direct entry: 29035 [−] [(−)] 36025 [ENTER] [65060]

The range is 65,060 feet between the highest peak and the lowest depth. (We could also write 29,035 − (−36,025) as 29,035 + 36,025 and then use the addition key [+] to find the answer.)

ANSWERS TO SELF CHECKS

1. a. −5 **b.** 12 **c.** −79 **2. a.** 3 **b.** −3 **3.** −7 **4.** −15 **5.** 6 **6.** 125°F
7. The crude oil level fell 81 ft.

SECTION 1.3 STUDY SET

VOCABULARY

Fill in the blanks.

1. -8 is the opposite (or additive inverse) of 8.
2. When we change a number to its opposite, we say we have *changed* (or *reversed*) its sign.
3. To evaluate an expression means to find its value.
4. The difference between the maximum and the minimum value of a collection of measurements is called the range of the values.

CONCEPTS

Fill in the blanks.

5. To subtract two integers, add the first integer to the opposite (additive inverse) of the integer to be subtracted.
6. Subtracting is the same as adding the opposite.
7. Subtracting 3 is the same as adding -3.
8. Subtracting -6 is the same as adding 6.
9. We can find the change in a quantity by subtracting the earlier value from the later value.
10. After rewriting a subtraction as addition of the opposite, we then use one of the rules for the addition of signed numbers to find the result.
11. In each case, determine what number is being subtracted.
    a. $-7 - 3$ 3
    b. $1 - (-12)$ -12
12. Fill in the blanks to rewrite each subtraction as addition of the opposite of the number being subtracted.
    a. $2 - 7 = 2 + (-7)$
    b. $2 - (-7) = 2 + 7$
    c. $-2 - 7 = -2 + (-7)$
    d. $-2 - (-7) = -2 + 7$
13. Apply the rule for subtraction and fill in the three blanks.

    $3 - (-6) = 3 + 6 = 9$

14. Use addition to check this subtraction: $14 - (-2) = 12$. Is the result correct? no, $12 + (-2) \neq 14$

NOTATION

15. Write each phrase using symbols.
    a. negative eight minus negative four $-8 - (-4)$
    b. negative eight subtracted from negative four $-4 - (-8)$
16. Write each phrase in words.
    a. $7 - (-2)$ seven minus negative two
    b. $-2 - (-7)$ negative two minus negative seven

Complete each solution to evaluate each expression.

17. $1 - 3 - (-2) = 1 + (-3) + 2$
    $= -2 + 2$
    $= 0$

▶ 18. $-6 + 5 - (-5) = -6 + 5 + 5$
    $= -1 + 5$
    $= 4$

19. $(-8 - 2) - (-6) = [-8 + (-2)] - (-6)$
    $= -10 - (-6)$
    $= -10 + 6$
    $= -4$

20. $-(-5) - (-1 - 4) = 5 - [-1 + (-4)]$
    $= 5 - (-5)$
    $= 5 + 5$
    $= 10$

GUIDED PRACTICE

Subtract. See Example 1.

21. $-4 - 3$ -7
▶ 22. $-4 - 1$ -5
23. $-5 - 5$ -10
24. $-7 - 7$ -14
▶ 25. $8 - (-1)$ 9
▶ 26. $3 - (-8)$ 11
27. $11 - (-7)$ 18
28. $10 - (-5)$ 15
29. $3 - 21$ -18
30. $8 - 32$ -24
31. $15 - 65$ -50
32. $12 - 82$ -70

Perform the indicated operation. See Example 2.

▶ 33. a. Subtract -1 from -11. -10
    b. Subtract -11 from -1. 10
34. a. Subtract -2 from -19. -17
    b. Subtract -19 from -2. 17
35. a. Subtract -41 from -16. 25
    b. Subtract -16 from -41. -25
36. a. Subtract -57 from -15. 42
    b. Subtract -15 from -57. -42

Evaluate each expression. See Example 3.

37. $-4 - (-4) - 15$ -15
▶ 38. $-3 - (-3) - 10$ -10
39. $10 - 9 - (-8)$ 9
40. $16 - 14 - (-9)$ 11

41. $-1 - (-3) - 4$ −2
42. $-2 - 4 - (-1)$ −5
43. $-5 - 8 - (-3)$ −10
44. $-6 - 5 - (-1)$ −10

Evaluate each expression. See Example 4.

45. $-1 - (-4 - 6)$ 9
46. $-7 - (-2 - 14)$ 9
47. $-42 - (-16 - 14)$ −12
48. $-45 - (-8 - 32)$ −5
49. $-9 - (6 - 7)$ −8
50. $-13 - (6 - 12)$ −7
51. $-8 - (4 - 12)$ 0
52. $-9 - (1 - 10)$ 0

Evaluate each expression. See Example 5.

53. $-(-5) + (-15) - 6 - (-48)$ 32
54. $-(-2) + (-30) - 3 - (-66)$ 35
55. $-(-3) + (-41) - 7 - (-19)$ −26
56. $-(-1) + (-52) - 4 - (-21)$ −34

Use a calculator to perform each subtraction. See *Using Your Calculator.*

57. $-1{,}557 - 890$ −2,447
58. $20{,}007 - (-496)$ 20,503
59. $-979 - (-44{,}879)$ 43,900
60. $-787 - 1{,}654 - (-232)$ −2,209

TRY IT YOURSELF

Evaluate each expression.

61. $5 - 9 - (-7)$ 3
62. $6 - 8 - (-4)$ 2
63. Subtract -3 from 7. 10
64. Subtract 8 from -2. −10
65. $-2 - (-10)$ 8
66. $-6 - (-12)$ 6
67. $0 - (-5)$ 5
68. $0 - 8$ −8
69. $(6 - 4) - (1 - 2)$ 3
70. $(5 - 3) - (4 - 6)$ 4
71. $-5 - (-4)$ −1
72. $-9 - (-1)$ −8
73. $-3 - 3 - 3$ −9
74. $-1 - 1 - 1$ −3
75. $-(-9) + (-20) - 14 - (-3)$ −22
76. $-(-8) + (-33) - 7 - (-21)$ −11
77. $[-4 + (-8)] - (-6) + 15$ 9
78. $[-5 + (-4)] - (-2) + 22$ 15
79. Subtract -6 from -10. −4
80. Subtract -4 from -9. −5
81. $-3 - (-3)$ 0
82. $-5 - (-5)$ 0
83. $-8 - [4 - (-6)]$ −18
84. $-1 - [5 - (-2)]$ −8
85. $4 - (-4)$ 8
86. $-3 - 3$ −6
87. $(-6 - 5) - 3 + (-11)$ −25
88. $(-2 - 1) - 5 + (-19)$ −27

APPLICATIONS

Use signed numbers to solve each problem.

89. SUBMARINES A submarine was traveling 2,000 feet below the ocean's surface when the radar system warned of a possible collision with another sub. The captain ordered the navigator to dive an additional 200 feet and then level off. Find the depth of the submarine after the dive. −2,200 ft

90. SCUBA DIVING A diver jumps from his boat into the water and descends to a depth of 50 feet. He pauses to check his equipment and then descends an additional 70 feet. Use a signed number to represent the diver's final depth. −120 ft

91. GEOGRAPHY Death Valley, California, is the lowest land point in the United States, at 282 feet below sea level. The lowest land point on the Earth is the Dead Sea, which is 1,348 feet below sea level. How much lower is the Dead Sea than Death Valley? 1,066 ft

92. HISTORY Two of the greatest Greek mathematicians were Archimedes (287–212 B.C.) and Pythagoras (569–500 B.C.).
   a. Express the year of Archimedes' birth as a negative number. −287
   b. Express the year of Pythagoras' birth as a negative number. −569
   c. How many years apart were they born? 282 yr

93. AMPERAGE During normal operation, the ammeter on a car reads +5. If the headlights are turned on, they lower the ammeter reading 7 amps. If the radio is turned on, it lowers the reading 6 amps. What number will the ammeter register if they are both turned on? −8

94. GIN RUMMY After a losing round, a card player must deduct the value of each of the cards left in his hand from his previous point total of 21. If face cards are counted as 10 points, what is his new score? −8

95. FOOTBALL A college football team records the outcome of each of its plays during a game on a stat sheet. Find the net gain (or loss) after the third play. −4 yd

Down	Play	Result
1st	Run	Lost 1 yd
2nd	Pass—sack!	Lost 6 yd
Penalty	Delay of game	Lost 5 yd
3rd	Pass	Gained 8 yd

▶ **96.** ACCOUNTING Complete the balance sheet below. Then determine the overall financial condition of the company by subtracting the total debts from the total assets. $86,514; $99,218; −$12,704

Walker Corporation Balance Sheet 2010	
Assets	
Cash	$11,109
Supplies	7,862
Land	67,543
Total assets	$
Debts	
Accounts payable	$79,037
Income taxes	20,181
Total debts	$

97. OVERDRAFT PROTECTION A student forgot that she had only $15 in her bank account and wrote a check for $25, used an ATM to get $40 cash, and used her debit card to buy $30 worth of groceries. On each of the three transactions, the bank charged her a $20 overdraft protection fee. Find the new account balance. −$140

98. CHECKING ACCOUNTS Michael has $1,303 in his checking account. Can he pay his car insurance premium of $676, his utility bills of $121, and his rent of $750 without having to make another deposit? Explain. No, he will be $244 overdrawn (−244).

99. TEMPERATURE EXTREMES The highest and lowest temperatures ever recorded in several cities are shown below. List the cities in order, from the largest to smallest range in temperature extremes. Portland, Barrow, Kansas City, Atlantic City, Norfolk

Extreme Temperatures

City	Highest	Lowest
Atlantic City, NJ	106	−11
Barrow, AK	79	−56
Kansas City, MO	109	−23
Norfolk, VA	104	−3
Portland, ME	103	−39

100. EYESIGHT *Nearsightedness,* the condition where near objects are clear and far objects are blurry, is measured using negative numbers. Farsightedness, the condition where far objects are clear and near objects are blurry, is measured using positive numbers. Find the range in the measurements shown in the next column. 6

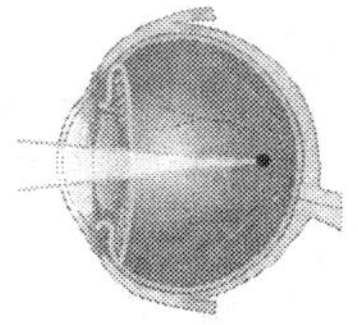
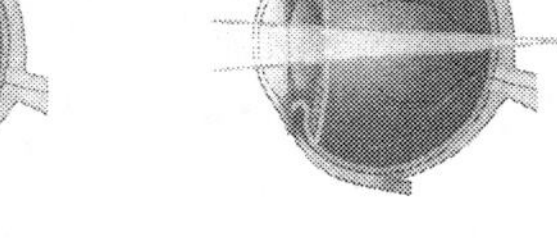

Nearsighted −2

Farsighted +4

101. FREEZE DRYING To make freeze-dried coffee, the coffee beans are roasted at a temperature of 360°F and then the ground coffee bean mixture is frozen at a temperature of −110°F. What is the temperature range of the freeze-drying process? 470°F

▶ **102.** WEATHER Rashawn flew from his New York home to Hawaii for a week of vacation. He left blizzard conditions and a temperature of −6°F, and stepped off the airplane into 85°F weather. What temperature change did he experience? 91°F increase

▶ **103.** READING PROGRAMS In a state reading test given at the start of a school year, an elementary school's performance was 23 points below the county average. The principal immediately began a special tutorial program. At the end of the school year, retesting showed the students to be only 7 points below the average. How did the school's reading score change over the year? 16-point increase

▶ **104.** LIE DETECTOR TESTS On one lie detector test, a burglar scored −18, which indicates deception. However, on a second test, he scored −1, which is inconclusive. Find the change in his scores. 17

WRITING

105. Explain what is meant when we say that subtraction is the same as addition of the opposite.

▶ **106.** Give an example showing that it is possible to subtract something from nothing.

107. Explain how to check the result: $-7 - 4 = -11$

108. Explain why students don't need to change every subtraction they encounter to an addition of the opposite. Give some examples.

REVIEW

109. **a.** Round 24,085 to the nearest ten. 24,090

b. Round 5,999 to the nearest hundred. 6,000

110. List the factors of 20 from least to greatest. 1, 2, 4, 5, 10, 20

▶ **111.** It takes 13 oranges to make one can of orange juice. Find the number of oranges used to make 12 cans. 156

112. **a.** Find the LCM of 15 and 18. 90

b. Find the GCF of 15 and 18. 3

SECTION 1.4 Multiplying Integers

Objectives

1. Multiply two integers that have different signs.
2. Multiply two integers that have the same sign.
3. Perform several multiplications to evaluate expressions.
4. Evaluate exponential expressions that have negative bases.
5. Solve application problems by multiplying integers.

Multiplication of integers is very much like multiplication of whole numbers. The only difference is that we must determine whether the answer is positive or negative.

When we multiply two nonzero integers, they either have different signs or they have the same sign. This means that there are two possibilities to consider.

1 Multiply two integers that have different signs.

To develop a rule for multiplying two integers that have different signs, we will find $4(-3)$, which is the product of a positive integer and negative integer. We say that the signs of the factors are *unlike*. By the definition of multiplication, $4(-3)$ means that we are to add -3 four times.

$4(-3) = (-3) + (-3) + (-3) + (-3)$ Write -3 as an addend four times.

$= -12$ Use the rule for adding two integers that have the same sign.

The result is negative. As a check, think in terms of money. If you lose \$3 four times, you have lost a total of \$12, which is written $-\$12$. This example illustrates the following rule.

Multiplying Two Integers That Have Different (Unlike) Signs

To multiply a positive integer and a negative integer, multiply their absolute values. Then make the final answer negative.

EXAMPLE 1

Multiply:

a. $7(-5)$ **b.** $20(-8)$ **c.** $-93 \cdot 16$ **d.** $-34(1{,}000)$

Strategy We will use the rule for multiplying two integers that have different (unlike) signs.

WHY In each case, we are asked to multiply a positive integer and a negative integer.

Solution

a. Find the absolute values: $|7| = 7$ and $|-5| = 5$.

$7(-5) = -35$ Multiply the absolute values, 7 and 5, to get 35. Then make the final answer negative.

b. Find the absolute values: $|20| = 20$ and $|-8| = 8$.

$20(-8) = -160$ Multiply the absolute values, 20 and 8, to get 160. Then make the final answer negative.

c. Find the absolute values: $|-93| = 93$ and $|16| = 16$.

$-93 \cdot 16 = -1{,}488$ Multiply the absolute values, 93 and 16, to get 1,488. Then make the final answer negative.

$$\begin{array}{r} 93 \\ \times\ 16 \\ \hline 558 \\ 930 \\ \hline 1{,}488 \end{array}$$

d. To find the product of a whole number and 10, 100, 1,000, and so on, *attach the number of zeros in that number to the right of the whole number.* This rule can be extended to products of integers and 10, 100, 1,000, and so on.

$-34(1{,}000) = -34{,}000$ Since 1,000 has three zeros, attach three 0's after -34.

Self Check 1

Multiply:

a. $2(-6)$ -12

b. $30(-4)$ -120

c. $-75 \cdot 17$ $-1{,}275$

d. $-98(1{,}000)$ $-98{,}000$

Now Try **Problems 21, 25, 29, and 31**

Teaching Example 1 Multiply:
a. $9(-4)$
b. $30(-6)$
c. $-57 \cdot 18$
d. $-29(1{,}000)$

Answers:
a. -36
b. -180
c. $-1{,}026$
d. $-29{,}000$

> ***Caution!*** When writing multiplication involving signed numbers, do not write a negative sign − next to a raised dot · (the multiplication symbol). Instead, use parentheses to show the multiplication.
>
> $6(-2)$ $\quad 6 \cdot -2$ $\quad$ and $\quad -6(-2)$ $\quad -6 \cdot -2$

2 Multiply two integers that have the same sign.

To develop a rule for multiplying two integers that have the same sign, we will first consider 4(3), which is the product of two positive integers. We say that the signs of the factors are *like.* By the definition of multiplication, 4(3) means that we are to add 3 four times.

$$4(3) = 3 + 3 + 3 + 3 \qquad \text{Write 3 as an addend four times.}$$
$$= 12 \qquad \text{The result is 12, which is a positive number.}$$

As expected, the result is positive.

To develop a rule for multiplying two negative integers, consider the following list, where we multiply −4 by factors that decrease by 1. We know how to find the first four products. Graphing those results on a number line is helpful in determining the last three products.

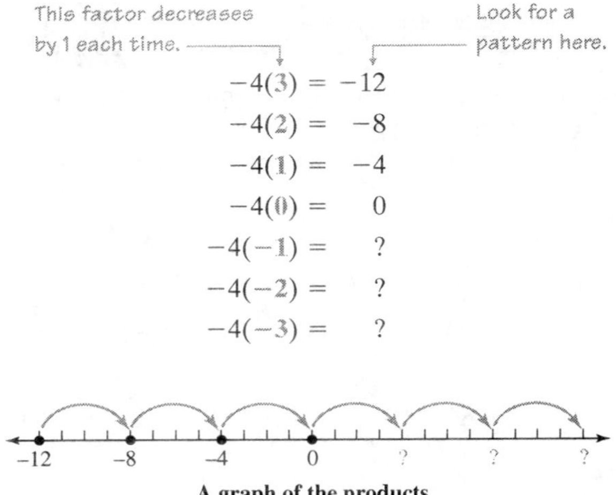

A graph of the products

From the pattern, we see that the product increases by 4 each time. Thus,

$$-4(-1) = 4, \qquad -4(-2) = 8, \qquad \text{and} \qquad -4(-3) = 12$$

These results illustrate that *the product of two negative integers is positive.* As a check, think of it as losing four debts of \$3. This is equivalent to gaining \$12. Therefore, $-4(-\$3) = \$12$.

We have seen that the product of two positive integers is positive, and the product of two negative integers is also positive. Those results illustrate the following rule.

> **Multiplying Two Integers That Have the Same (Like) Signs**
>
> To multiply two integers that have the same sign, multiply their absolute values. The final answer is positive.

EXAMPLE 2 Multiply:

a. $-5(-9)$ **b.** $-8(-10)$ **c.** $-23(-42)$ **d.** $-2{,}500(-30{,}000)$

Strategy We will use the rule for multiplying two integers that have the same (like) signs.

WHY In each case, we are asked to multiply two negative integers.

Solution

a. Find the absolute values: $|-5| = 5$ and $|-9| = 9$.

$-5(-9) = 45$ Multiply the absolute values, 5 and 9, to get 45. The final answer is positive.

b. Find the absolute values: $|-8| = 8$ and $|-10| = 10$.

$-8(-10) = 80$ Multiply the absolute values, 8 and 10, to get 80. The final answer is positive.

c. Find the absolute values: $|-23| = 23$ and $|-42| = 42$.

$-23(-42) = 966$ Multiply the absolute values, 23 and 42, to get 966. The final answer is positive.

$$\begin{array}{r} 42 \\ \times\ 23 \\ \hline 126 \\ 840 \\ \hline 966 \end{array}$$

d. We can extend the method for multiplying whole-number factors with trailing zeros to products of integers with trailing zeros.

$-2{,}500(-30{,}000) = 75{,}000{,}000$ Attach six 0's after 75.

Multiply −25 and −3 to get 75.

Self Check 2

Multiply:

a. $-9(-7)$ 63

b. $-12(-2)$ 24

c. $-34(-15)$ 510

d. $-4{,}100(-20{,}000)$ 82,000,000

Now Try **Problems 33, 37, 41, and 43**

Teaching Example 2 Multiply:
a. $-3(-7)$
b. $-9(-9)$
c. $-46(-24)$
d. $-1{,}200(-40{,}000)$

Answers:
a. 21
b. 81
c. 1,104
d. 48,000,000

We now summarize the multiplication rules for two integers.

Multiplying Two Integers

To multiply two nonzero integers, multiply their absolute values.

1. The product of two integers that have the same (*like*) signs is positive.
2. The product of two integers that have different (*unlike*) signs is negative.

Using Your CALCULATOR **Multiplication with Negative Numbers**

At Thanksgiving time, a large supermarket chain offered customers a free turkey with every grocery purchase of \$200 or more. Each turkey cost the store \$8, and 10,976 people took advantage of the offer. Since each of the 10,976 turkeys given away represented a loss of \$8 (which can be expressed as −\$8), the company lost a total of 10,976(−\$8). To perform this multiplication using a calculator, we enter the following:

Reverse entry: 10976 [×] 8 [+/−] [=] → −87808

Direct entry: 10976 [×] [(−)] 8 [ENTER] → −87808

The negative result indicates that with the turkey giveaway promotion, the supermarket chain lost \$87,808.

3 Perform several multiplications to evaluate expressions.

To evaluate expressions that contain several multiplications, we make repeated use of the rules for multiplying two integers.

Self Check 3

Evaluate each expression:

a. $3(-12)(-2)$ 72

b. $-1(9)(-6)$ 54

c. $-4(-5)(8)(-3)$ -480

Now Try **Problems 45, 47, and 49**

Teaching Example 3 Evaluate each expression:

a. $4(-9)(-3)$

b. $-5(12)(-1)$

c. $-6(-3)(2)(-7)$

Answers:

a. 108

b. 60

c. -252

EXAMPLE 3 Evaluate each expression:

a. $6(-2)(-7)$ **b.** $-9(8)(-1)$ **c.** $-3(-5)(2)(-4)$

Strategy Since there are no calculations within parentheses and no exponential expressions, we will perform the multiplications, working from the left to the right.

Solution

a. $6(-2)(-7) = -12(-7)$ Use the rule for multiplying two integers that have different signs: $6(-2) = -12$.

$= 84$ Use the rule for multiplying two integers that have the same sign.

$$\begin{array}{r} \overset{1}{1}2 \\ \times 7 \\ \hline 84 \end{array}$$

b. $-9(8)(-1) = -72(-1)$ Use the rule for multiplying two integers that have different signs: $-9(8) = -72$.

$= 72$ Use the rule for multiplying two integers that have the same sign.

c. $-3(-5)(2)(-4) = 15(2)(-4)$ Use the rule for multiplying two integers that have the same sign: $-3(-5) = 15$.

$= 30(-4)$ Use the rule for multiplying two integers that have the same sign: $15(2) = 30$.

$= -120$ Use the rule for multiplying two integers that have different signs.

Properties of Multiplication

Commutative property of multiplication: The order in which integers are multiplied does not change their product.

Associative property of multiplication: The way in which integers are grouped does not change their product.

Multiplication property of 0: The product of any integer and 0 is 0.

Multiplication property of 1: The product of any integer and 1 is that integer.

Another approach to evaluate expressions like those in Example 3 is to use the properties of multiplication to reorder and regroup the factors in a helpful way.

Self Check 4

Use the commutative and/or associative properties of multiplication to evaluate each expression from Self Check 3 in a different way:

a. $3(-12)(-2)$ 72

b. $-1(9)(-6)$ 54

c. $-4(-5)(8)(-3)$ -480

Now Try **Problems 45, 47, and 49**

EXAMPLE 4 Use the commutative and/or associative properties of multiplication to evaluate each expression from Example 3 in a different way:

a. $6(-2)(-7)$ **b.** $-9(8)(-1)$ **c.** $-3(-5)(2)(-4)$

Strategy When possible, we will use the commutative and/or associative properties of multiplication to multiply pairs of negative factors.

WHY The product of two negative factors is positive. With this approach, we work with fewer negative numbers, and that lessens the possibility of an error.

Solution

a. $6(-2)(-7) = 6(14)$ Multiply the last two negative factors to produce a positive product: $-7(-2) = 14$.

$= 84$

$$\begin{array}{r} \overset{2}{1}4 \\ \times 6 \\ \hline 84 \end{array}$$

b. $-9(8)(-1) = 9(8)$ Multiply the negative factors to produce a positive product: $-9(-1) = 9$.

$= 72$

c. $-3(-5)(2)(-4) = 15(-8)$ Multiply the first two negative factors to produce a positive product. Multiply the last two factors.

$$\begin{array}{r} \overset{4}{1}5 \\ \times 8 \\ \hline 120 \end{array}$$

$= -120$ Use the rule for multiplying two integers that have different signs.

Teaching Example 4 Use the commutative and/or associative properties of multiplication to evaluate each expression from Teaching Example 3 in a different way:
a. $4(-9)(-3)$
b. $-5(12)(-1)$
c. $-6(-3)(2)(-7)$
Answers:
a. 108 b. 60 c. -252

EXAMPLE 5 Evaluate: **a.** $-2(-4)(-5)$ **b.** $-3(-2)(-6)(-5)$

Strategy When possible, we will use the commutative and/or associative properties of multiplication to multiply pairs of negative factors.

WHY The product of two negative factors is positive. With this approach, we work with fewer negative numbers, and that lessens the possibility of an error.

Solution

a. Note that this expression is the product of three (an odd number) negative integers.

$-2(-4)(-5) = 8(-5)$ Multiply the first two negative factors to produce a positive product.

$= -40$ The product is negative.

b. Note that this expression is the product of four (an even number) negative integers.

$-3(-2)(-6)(-5) = 6(30)$ Multiply the first two negative factors and the last two negative factors to produce positive products.

$= 180$ The product is positive.

Self Check 5

Evaluate each expression:

a. $-1(-2)(-5)$ -10

b. $-2(-7)(-1)(-2)$ 28

Now Try **Problems 53 and 57**

Teaching Example 5 Evaluate each expression:
a. $-3(-6)(-5)$
b. $-2(-1)(-3)(-8)$
Answers:
a. -90
b. 48

Example 5, part a, illustrates that a product is negative when there is an odd number of negative factors. Example 5, part b, illustrates that a product is positive when there is an even number of negative factors.

Multiplying an Even and an Odd Number of Negative Integers

The product of an even number of negative integers is positive.
The product of an odd number of negative integers is negative.

4 Evaluate exponential expressions that have negative bases.

Recall that exponential expressions are used to represent repeated multiplication. For example, 2 to the third power, or 2^3, is a shorthand way of writing $2 \cdot 2 \cdot 2$. In this expression, the *exponent* is 3 and the base is *positive* 2. In the next example, we evaluate exponential expressions with bases that are negative numbers.

EXAMPLE 6 Evaluate each expression: **a.** $(-2)^4$ **b.** $(-5)^3$ **c.** $(-1)^5$

Strategy We will write each exponential expression as a product of repeated factors and then perform the multiplication. This requires that we identify the base and the exponent.

WHY The exponent tells the number of times the base is to be written as a factor.

Self Check 6

Evaluate each expression:

a. $(-3)^4$ 81

b. $(-4)^3$ -64

c. $(-1)^7$ -1

Now Try **Problems 61, 65, and 67**

Teaching Example 6 Evaluate each expression:
a. $(-4)^4$
b. $(-6)^3$
c. $(-1)^9$

Answers:
a. 256
b. -216
c. -1

Solution

a. We read $(-2)^4$ as "negative two raised to the fourth power" or as "the fourth power of negative two." Note that the exponent is even.

$(-2)^4 = (-2)(-2)(-2)(-2)$ Write the base, −2, as a factor 4 times.

$= 4(4)$ Multiply the first two negative factors and the last two negative factors to produce positive products.

$= 16$ The result is positive.

b. We read $(-5)^3$ as "negative five raised to the third power" or as "the third power of negative five," or as " negative five, cubed." Note that the exponent is odd.

$(-5)^3 = (-5)(-5)(-5)$ Write the base, −5, as a factor 3 times.

$= 25(-5)$ Multiply the first two negative factors to produce a positive product.

$= -125$ The result is negative.

$$\begin{array}{r} \overset{2}{2}5 \\ \times 5 \\ \hline 125 \end{array}$$

c. We read $(-1)^5$ as "negative one raised to the fifth power" or as "the fifth power of negative one." Note that the exponent is odd.

$(-1)^5 = (-1)(-1)(-1)(-1)(-1)$ Write the base, −1, as a factor 5 times.

$= 1(1)(-1)$ Multiply the first and second negative factors and multiply the third and fourth negative factors to produce positive products.

$= -1$ The result is negative.

In Example 6, part a, −2 was raised to an even power, and the answer was positive. In parts b and c, −5 and −1 were raised to odd powers, and, in each case, the answer was negative. These results suggest a general rule.

Even and Odd Powers of a Negative Integer

When a negative integer is raised to an even power, the result is positive.
When a negative integer is raised to an odd power, the result is negative.

Although the exponential expressions $(-3)^2$ and -3^2 look similar, they are not the same. We read $(-3)^2$ as "negative 3 squared" and -3^2 as "the opposite of the square of three." When we evaluate them, it becomes clear that they are not equivalent.

$(-3)^2 = (-3)(-3)$ Because of the parentheses, the base is −3. The exponent is 2.

$= 9$

$-3^2 = -(3 \cdot 3)$ Since there are no parentheses around −3, the base is 3. The exponent is 2.

$= -9$

Different results

Caution! The base of an exponential expression *does not include* the negative sign unless parentheses are used.

-7^3 Positive base: 7

$(-7)^3$ Negative base: −7

EXAMPLE 7 Evaluate: -2^2

Strategy We will rewrite the expression as a product of repeated factors, and then perform the multiplication. We must be careful when identifying the base. It is 2, not -2.

WHY Since there are no parentheses around -2, the base is 2.

Solution

$-2^2 = -(2 \cdot 2)$ Read as "the opposite of the square of two."

$= -4$ Do the multiplication within the parentheses to get 4. Then write the opposite of that result.

Self Check 7

Evaluate: -4^2 -16

Now Try **Problem 71**

Teaching Example 7 Evaluate: -5^2

Answer: -25

Using Your CALCULATOR Raising a Negative Number to a Power

We can find powers of negative integers, such as $(-5)^6$, using a calculator. The keystrokes that are used to evaluate such expressions vary from model to model, as shown below. You will need to determine which keystrokes produce the positive result that we would expect when raising a negative number to an even power.

5 [+/−] [y^x] 6 [=] Some calculators don't require the parentheses to be entered.

[(] 5 [+/−] [)] [y^x] 6 [=] Other calculators require the parentheses to be entered.

[(] [(−)] 5 [)] [^] 6 [ENTER] 15625

From the calculator display, we see that $(-5)^6 = 15{,}625$.

5 Solve application problems by multiplying integers.

Problems that involve repeated addition are often more easily solved using multiplication.

EXAMPLE 8 *Oceanography*

Scientists lowered an underwater vessel called a *submersible* into the Pacific Ocean to record the water temperature. The first measurement was made 75 feet below sea level, and more were made every 75 feet until it reached the ocean floor. Find the depth of the submersible when the 25th measurement was made.

Emory Kristof/National Geographic/Getty Images

Analyze

- The first measurement was made 75 feet below sea level. Given
- More measurements were made every 75 feet. Given
- Find the depth of the submersible when it made the 25th measurement. Find

Form If we use negative numbers to represent the depths at which the measurements were made, then the first was at -75 feet. The depth (in feet) of the submersible when the 25th measurement was made can be found by adding -75 twenty-five times. This repeated addition can be calculated more simply by multiplication.

Self Check 8

GASOLINE LEAKS To determine how badly a gasoline tank was leaking, inspectors used a drilling process to take soil samples nearby. The first sample was taken 6 feet below ground level, and more were taken every 6 feet after that. The 14th sample was the first one that did not show signs of gasoline. How far below ground level was that?

Now Try **Problem 97**

Self Check 8 Answer

It was 84 ft below ground level (-84 ft).

Teaching Example 8
FORESTRY To determine the moisture content of the ground in a forest, rangers took soil samples at various depths. The first sample was taken 18 inches below ground, and more were taken every 18 inches after that. Find the depth of the 12th sample.
Answer:
216 in. below ground level (−216 in.)

We translate the words of the problem to numbers and symbols.

The depth of the submersible when it made the 25th measurement	is equal to	the number of measurements made	times	the amount it was lowered each time.
The depth of the submersible when it made the 25th measurement	=	25	·	(−75)

Solve To find the product, we use the rule for multiplying two integers that have different signs. First, we find the absolute values: $|25| = 25$ and $|-75| = 75$.

$25(-75) = -1{,}875$ Multiply the absolute values, 25 and 75, to get 1,875. Since the integers have different signs, make the final answer negative.

$$\begin{array}{r} 75 \\ \times\ 25 \\ \hline 375 \\ 1\ 500 \\ \hline 1{,}875 \end{array}$$

State The depth of the submersible was 1,875 feet below sea level (−1,875 feet) when the 25th temperature measurement was taken.

Check We can use estimation or simply perform the actual multiplication again to see if the result seems reasonable.

ANSWERS TO SELF CHECKS

1. a. −12 **b.** −120 **c.** −1,275 **d.** −98,000 **2. a.** 63 **b.** 24 **c.** 510 **d.** 82,000,000 **3. a.** 72 **b.** 54 **c.** −480 **4. a.** 72 **b.** 54 **c.** −480 **5. a.** −10 **b.** 28 **6. a.** 81 **b.** −64 **c.** −1 **7.** −16 **8.** 84 ft below ground level (−84 ft)

SECTION 1.4 STUDY SET

VOCABULARY

Fill in the blanks.

1. In the multiplication problem shown below, label each *factor* and the *product*.

−5	·	10	=	−50
↑		↑		↑
factor		factor		product

2. Two negative integers, as well as two positive integers, are said to have the same signs or _like_ signs.
3. A positive integer and a negative integer are said to have different signs or _unlike_ signs.
4. _Commutative_ property of multiplication: The order in which integers are multiplied does not change their product.
5. _Associative_ property of multiplication: The way in which integers are grouped does not change their product.
6. In the expression $(-3)^5$, the _base_ is −3, and 5 is the _exponent_.

CONCEPTS

Fill in the blanks.

7. Multiplication of integers is very much like multiplication of whole numbers. The only difference is that we must determine whether the answer is _positive_ or _negative_.
8. When we multiply two nonzero integers, they either have _unlike/different_ signs or _like/the same_ sign.
9. To multiply a positive integer and a negative integer, multiply their absolute values. Then make the final answer _negative_.
10. To multiply two integers that have the same sign, multiply their absolute values. The final answer is _positive_.
11. The product of two integers with _unlike/different_ signs is negative.
12. The product of two integers with _like/the same_ signs is positive.
13. ▶ The product of any integer and 0 is _0_.

14. The product of an even number of negative integers is positive and the product of an odd number of negative integers is negative.

15. Find each absolute value.

a. $|-3|$ 3 b. $|12|$ 12

16. If each of the following expressions were evaluated, what would be the *sign* of the result?

a. $(-5)^{13}$ negative b. $(-3)^{20}$ positive

NOTATION

17. For each expression, identify the base and the exponent.

a. -8^4 base: 8, exponent: 4 b. $(-7)^9$ base: −7, exponent: 9

18. Translate to mathematical symbols.

a. negative three times negative two $-3(-2)$

b. negative five squared $(-5)^2$

c. the opposite of the square of five -5^2

Complete each solution to evaluate the expression.

19. $-3(-2)(-4) = 6(-4)$
$= -24$

20. $(-3)^4 = (-3)(-3)(-3)(-3)$
$= 9(9)$
$= 81$

GUIDED PRACTICE

Multiply. See Example 1.

21. $5(-3)$ −15
22. $4(-6)$ −24
23. $9(-2)$ −18
24. $5(-7)$ −35
25. $18(-4)$ −72
26. $17(-8)$ −136
27. $21(-6)$ −126
28. $39(-3)$ −117
29. $-45 \cdot 37$ −1,665
30. $-42 \cdot 24$ −1,008
31. $-94 \cdot 1{,}000$ −94,000
32. $-76 \cdot 1{,}000$ −76,000

Multiply. See Example 2.

33. $(-8)(-7)$ 56
34. $(-9)(-3)$ 27
35. $-7(-1)$ 7
36. $-5(-1)$ 5
37. $-3(-52)$ 156
38. $-4(-73)$ 292
39. $-6(-46)$ 276
40. $-8(-48)$ 384
41. $-59(-33)$ 1,947
42. $-61(-29)$ 1,769
43. $-60{,}000(-1{,}200)$ 72,000,000
44. $-20{,}000(-3{,}200)$ 64,000,000

Evaluate each expression. See Examples 3 and 4.

45. $6(-3)(-5)$ 90
46. $9(-3)(-4)$ 108
47. $-5(10)(-3)$ 150
48. $-8(7)(-2)$ 112
49. $-2(-4)(6)(-8)$ −384
50. $-3(-5)(2)(-9)$ −270
51. $-8(-3)(7)(-2)$ −336
52. $-9(-3)(4)(-2)$ −216

Evaluate each expression. See Example 5.

53. $-4(-2)(-6)$ −48
54. $-4(-6)(-3)$ −72
55. $-3(-9)(-3)$ −81
56. $-5(-2)(-5)$ −50
57. $-1(-3)(-2)(-6)$ 36
58. $-1(-4)(-2)(-4)$ 32
59. $-9(-4)(-1)(-4)$ 144
60. $-6(-3)(-6)(-1)$ 108

Evaluate each expression. See Example 6.

61. $(-3)^3$ −27
62. $(-6)^3$ −216
63. $(-2)^5$ −32
64. $(-3)^5$ −243
65. $(-5)^4$ 625
66. $(-7)^4$ 2,401
67. $(-1)^8$ 1
68. $(-1)^{10}$ 1

Evaluate each expression. See Example 7.

69. $(-7)^2$ and -7^2 49, −49
70. $(-5)^2$ and -5^2 25, −25
71. $(-12)^2$ and -12^2 144, −144
72. $(-11)^2$ and -11^2 121, −121

TRY IT YOURSELF

Evaluate each expression.

73. $6(-5)(2)$ −60
74. $4(-2)(2)$ −16
75. $-8(0)$ 0
76. $0(-27)$ 0
77. $(-4)^3$ −64
78. $(-8)^3$ −512
79. $(-2)10$ −20
80. $(-3)8$ −24
81. $-2(-3)(3)(-1)$ −18
82. $5(-2)(3)(-1)$ 30
83. Find the product of −6 and the opposite of 10. 60
84. Find the product of the opposite of 9 and the opposite of 8. 72
85. $-6(-4)(-2)$ −48
86. $-3(-2)(-3)$ −18
87. $-42 \cdot 200{,}000$ −8,400,000
88. $-56 \cdot 10{,}000$ −560,000
89. -5^4 −625
90. -2^4 −16
91. $-12(-12)$ 144
92. $-5(-5)$ 25
93. $(-1)^6$ 1
94. $(-1)^5$ −1
95. $(-1)(-2)(-3)(-4)(-5)$ −120
96. $(-10)(-8)(-6)(-4)(-2)$ −3,840

APPLICATIONS

Use signed numbers to solve each problem.

97. SUBMARINES As part of a training exercise, the captain of a submarine ordered it to descend 250 feet, level off for 5 minutes, and then repeat the process several times. If the sub was on the ocean's surface at the beginning of the exercise, find its depth after the 8th dive. −2,000 ft

98. BUILDING A PIER A *pile driver* uses a heavy weight to pound tall poles into the ocean floor. If each strike of a pile driver on the top of a pole sends it 6 inches deeper, find the depth of the pole after 20 strikes. −120 in

99. MAGNIFICATION A mechanic used an electronic testing device to check the smog emissions of a car. The results of the test are displayed on a screen.

a. Find the high and low values for this test as shown on the screen. high: 2, low: −3

b. By switching a setting, the picture on the screen can be magnified. What would be the new high and new low if every value were doubled? high: 4, low: −6

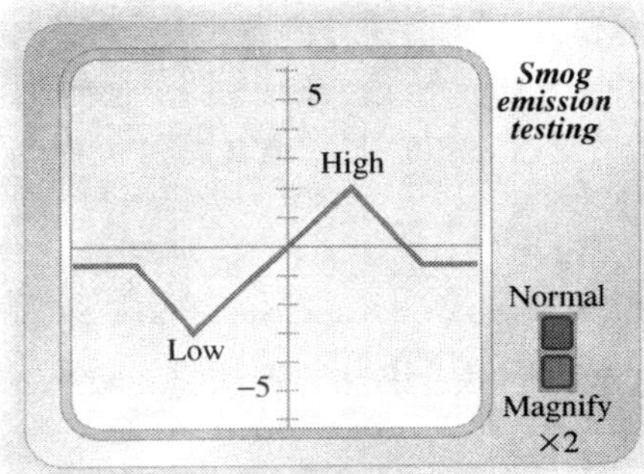

100. LIGHT Sunlight is a mixture of all colors. When sunlight passes through water, the water absorbs different colors at different rates, as shown.

a. Use a signed number to represent the depth to which red light penetrates water. −15 ft

b. Green light penetrates 4 times deeper than red light. How deep is this? −60 ft

c. Blue light penetrates 3 times deeper than orange light. How deep is this? −75 ft

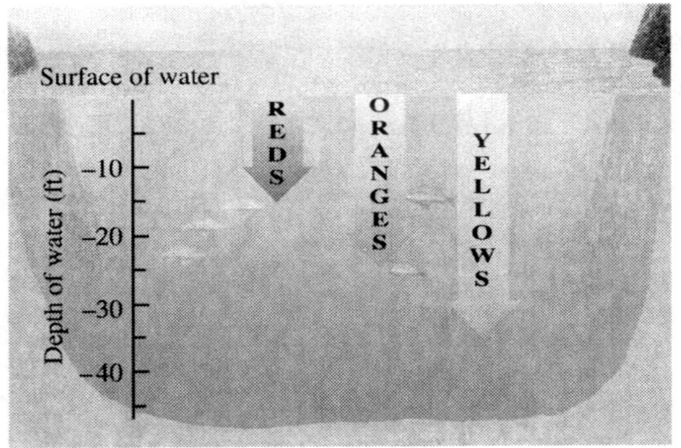

101. JOB LOSSES Refer to the bar graph. Find the number of jobs lost in . . .

a. September 2008 if it was about 6 times the number lost in April. −402,000 jobs

b. October 2008 if it was about 9 times the number lost in May. −423,000 jobs

c. November 2008 if it was about 7 times the number lost in February. −581,000 jobs

d. December if it was about 6 times the number lost in March. −528,000 jobs

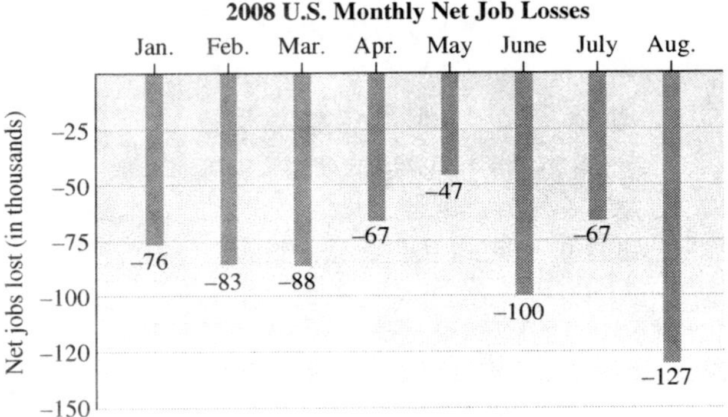

Source: Bureau of Labor Statistics

102. RUSSIA The U.S. Census Bureau estimates that Russia's population is decreasing by about 700,000 per year because of high death rates and low birth rates. If this pattern continues, what will be the total decline in Russia's population over the next 30 years? (Source: About.com) −21,000,000

103. PLANETS The average surface temperature of Mars is −81°F. Find the average surface temperature of Uranus if it is four times colder than Mars. (Source: *The World Almanac and Book of Facts,* 2009) −324°F

104. CROP LOSS A farmer, worried about his fruit trees suffering frost damage, calls the weather service for temperature information. He is told that temperatures will be decreasing approximately 5 degrees every hour for the next five hours. What signed number represents the total change in temperature expected over the next five hours? −25°

105. TAX WRITE-OFF For each of the last six years, a businesswoman has filed a $200 depreciation allowance on her income tax return for an office computer system. What signed number represents the total amount of depreciation written off over the six-year period? −$1,200

106. EROSION A levee protects a town in a low-lying area from flooding. According to geologists, the banks of the levee are eroding at a rate of 2 feet per year. If something isn't done to correct the problem, what signed number indicates how much of the levee will erode during the next decade? −20 ft

107. DECK SUPPORTS After a winter storm, a homeowner has an engineering firm inspect his damaged deck. Their report concludes that the original foundation poles were not sunk deep enough, by a factor of 3. What signed number represents the depth to which the poles should have been sunk? −18 ft

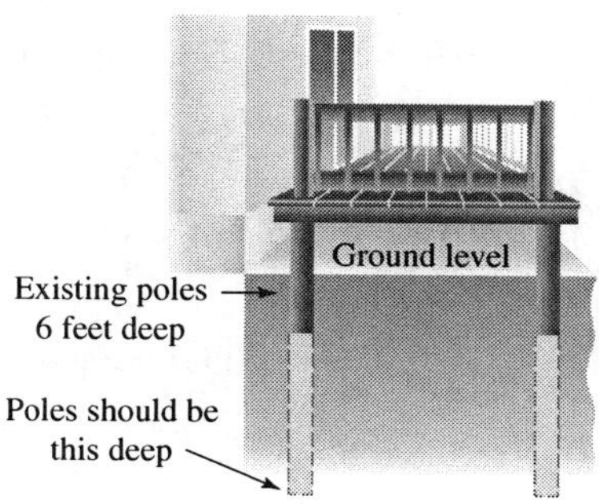

108. DIETING After giving a patient a physical exam, a physician felt that the patient should begin a diet. The two options that were discussed are shown in the following table.

	Plan #1	Plan #2
Length	10 weeks	14 weeks
Daily exercise	1 hr	30 min
Weight loss per week	3 lb	2 lb

a. Find the expected weight loss from Plan 1. Express the answer as a signed number. −30 lb

b. Find the expected weight loss from Plan 2. Express the answer as a signed number. −28 lb

c. With which plan should the patient expect to lose more weight? Explain why the patient might not choose it. plan #1, the workout time is double that of plan #2

109. ADVERTISING The paid attendance for the last night of the 2008 Rodeo Houston was 71,906. Suppose a local country music radio station gave a sports bag, worth \$3, to everyone that attended. Find the signed number that expresses the radio station's financial loss from this giveaway. −\$215,718

110. HEALTH CARE A health care provider for a company estimates that 75 hours per week are lost by employees suffering from stress-related or preventable illness. In a 52-week year, how many hours are lost? Use a signed number to answer. −3,900 hr

WRITING

111. Explain why the product of a positive number and a negative number is negative, using $5(-3)$ as an example.

112. Explain the multiplication rule for integers that is shown in the pattern of signs below.

$$(-)(-) = +$$
$$(-)(-)(-) = -$$
$$(-)(-)(-)(-) = +$$
$$(-)(-)(-)(-)(-) = -$$
$$\vdots$$

113. When a number is multiplied by -1, the result is the opposite of the original number. Explain why.

114. A student claimed, "A positive and a negative is negative." What is wrong with this statement?

REVIEW

115. List the first ten prime numbers. 2, 3, 5, 7, 11, 13, 17, 19, 23, 29

116. ENROLLMENT The number of students attending a college went from 10,250 to 12,300 in one year. What was the increase in enrollment? 2,050

117. Divide: $175 \div 4$ 43 R 3

118. What does the symbol $<$ mean? is less than

SECTION 1.5 Dividing Integers

Objectives

1. Divide two integers.
2. Identify *division of 0* and *division by 0*.
3. Solve application problems by dividing integers.

In this section, we will develop rules for division of integers, just as we did earlier for multiplication of integers.

1 Divide two integers.

Every division has a related multiplication statement. For example,

$$\frac{6}{3} = 2 \quad \text{because} \quad 2(3) = 6$$

and

$$\frac{20}{5} = 4 \qquad \text{because} \qquad 4(5) = 20$$

We can use the relationship between multiplication and division to help develop rules for dividing integers. There are four cases to consider.

Case 1: A positive integer divided by a positive integer
From years of experience, we already know that the result is positive. Therefore, *the quotient of two positive integers is positive.*

Case 2: A negative integer divided by a negative integer
As an example, consider the division $\frac{-12}{-2} = ?$. We can find ? by examining the related multiplication statement.

Related multiplication statement	**Division statement**
$?(-2) = -12$	$\frac{-12}{-2} = ?$
↑ This must be *positive* 6 if the product is to be *negative* 12.	↑ So the quotient is *positive* 6.

Therefore, $\frac{-12}{-2} = 6$. This example illustrates that *the quotient of two negative integers is positive.*

Case 3: A positive integer divided by a negative integer
Let's consider $\frac{12}{-2} = ?$. We can find ? by examining the related multiplication statement.

Related multiplication statement	**Division statement**
$?(-2) = 12$	$\frac{12}{-2} = ?$
↑ This must be -6 if the product is to be *positive* 12.	↑ So the quotient is -6.

Therefore, $\frac{12}{-2} = -6$. This example illustrates that *the quotient of a positive integer and a negative integer is negative.*

Case 4: A negative integer divided by a positive integer
Let's consider $\frac{-12}{2} = ?$. We can find ? by examining the related multiplication statement.

Related multiplication statement	**Division statement**
$?(2) = -12$	$\frac{-12}{2} = ?$
↑ This must be -6 if the product is to be -12.	↑ So the quotient is -6.

Therefore, $\frac{-12}{2} = -6$. This example illustrates that *the quotient of a negative integer and a positive integer is negative.*

We now summarize the results from the previous examples and note that they are similar to the rules for multiplication.

Dividing Two Integers

To divide two integers, divide their absolute values.

1. The quotient of two integers that have the same (*like*) signs is positive.
2. The quotient of two integers that have different (*unlike*) signs is negative.

EXAMPLE 1 Divide and check the result:

a. $\frac{-14}{7}$ **b.** $30 \div (-5)$ **c.** $\frac{176}{-11}$ **d.** $-24{,}000 \div 600$

Strategy We will use the rule for dividing two integers that have different (unlike) signs.

WHY Each division involves a positive and a negative integer.

Solution

a. Find the absolute values: $|-14| = 14$ and $|7| = 7$.

$\frac{-14}{7} = -2$ Divide the absolute values, 14 by 7, to get 2. Then make the final answer negative.

To check, we multiply the *quotient,* −2, and the *divisor,* 7. We should get the *dividend,* −14.

Check: $-2(7) = -14$ The result checks.

b. Find the absolute values: $|30| = 30$ and $|-5| = 5$.

$30 \div (-5) = -6$ Divide the absolute values, 30 by 5, to get 6. Then make the final answer negative.

Check: $-6(-5) = 30$ The result checks.

c. Find the absolute values: $|176| = 176$ and $|-11| = 11$.

$\frac{176}{-11} = -16$ Divide the absolute values, 176 by 11, to get 16. Then make the final answer negative.

$$\begin{array}{r} 16 \\ 11\overline{)176} \\ -11 \\ \hline 66 \\ -66 \\ \hline 0 \end{array}$$

Check: $-16(-11) = 176$ The result checks.

d. If a divisor has ending zeros, we can simplify the division by removing the same number of ending zeros in the divisor and dividend.

There are two zeros in the divisor.

$-24{,}000 \div 600 = -240 \div 6 = -40$ Divide the absolute values, 240 by 6, to get 40. Then make the final answer negative.

Remove two zeros from the dividend and the divisor, and divide.

Check: $-40(600) = -24{,}000$ Use the original divisor and dividend in the check.

Self Check 1

Divide and check the result:

a. $\frac{-45}{5}$ −9

b. $28 \div (-4)$ −7

c. $\frac{336}{-14}$ −24

d. $-18{,}000 \div 300$ −60

Now Try **Problems 13, 15, 21, and 27**

Teaching Example 1 Divide and check the result:

a. $\frac{-40}{5}$

b. $18 \div (-2)$

c. $\frac{468}{-18}$

d. $-56{,}000 \div 800$

Answers:

a. −8

b. −9

c. −26

d. −70

EXAMPLE 2 Divide and check the result:

a. $\frac{-12}{-3}$ **b.** $-48 \div (-6)$ **c.** $\frac{-315}{-9}$ **d.** $-200 \div (-40)$

Strategy We will use the rule for dividing two integers that have the same (like) signs.

WHY In each case, we are asked to find the quotient of two negative integers.

Solution

a. Find the absolute values: $|-12| = 12$ and $|-3| = 3$.

$\frac{-12}{-3} = 4$ Divide the absolute values, 12 by 3, to get 4. The final answer is positive.

Check: $4(-3) = -12$ The result checks.

Self Check 2

Divide and check the result:

a. $\frac{-27}{-3}$ 9

b. $-24 \div (-4)$ 6

c. $\frac{-301}{-7}$ 43

d. $-400 \div (-20)$ 20

Now Try **Problems 33, 37, 41, and 43**

Teaching Example 2 Divide and check the result:

a. $\frac{-36}{-6}$

b. $-63 \div (-9)$

c. $\frac{-624}{-16}$

d. $-600 \div (-30)$

Answers:

a. 6

b. 7

c. 39

d. 20

b. Find the absolute values: $|-48| = 48$ and $|-6| = 6$.

$-48 \div (-6) = 8$ Divide the absolute values, 48 by 6, to get 8. The final answer is positive.

Check: $8(-6) = -48$ The result checks.

c. Find the absolute values: $|-315| = 315$ and $|-9| = 9$.

$\frac{-315}{-9} = 35$ Divide the absolute values, 315 by 9, to get 35. The final answer is positive.

$$\begin{array}{r} 35 \\ 9\overline{)315} \\ -27 \\ \hline 45 \\ -45 \\ \hline 0 \end{array}$$

Check: $35(-9) = -315$ The result checks.

d. We can simplify the division by removing the same number of ending zeros in the divisor and dividend.

There is one zero in the divisor.

$-200 \div (-40) = -20 \div (-4) = 5$ Divide the absolute values, 20 by 4, to get 5. The final answer is positive.

Remove one zero from the dividend and the divisor, and divide.

Check: $5(-40) = -200$ The result checks.

2 Identify *division of 0* and *division by 0*.

To review the concept of division of 0, we consider $\frac{0}{-2} = ?$. We can attempt to find ? by examining the related multiplication statement.

Related multiplication statement	**Division statement**
$(?)(-2) = 0$ — This must be 0 if the product is to be 0.	$\frac{0}{-2} = ?$ — So the quotient is 0.

Therefore, $\frac{0}{-2} = 0$. This example illustrates that *the quotient of 0 divided by any nonzero integer is 0.*

To review division by 0, let's consider $\frac{-2}{0} = ?$. We can attempt to find ? by examining the related multiplication statement.

Related multiplication statement	**Division statement**
$(?)0 = -2$ — There is no number that gives −2 when multiplied by 0.	$\frac{-2}{0} = ?$ — There is no quotient.

Therefore, $\frac{-2}{0}$ does not have an answer and we say that $\frac{-2}{0}$ is undefined. This example illustrates that *the quotient of any nonzero integer divided by 0 is undefined.*

Division with 0

1. If 0 is divided by any nonzero integer, the quotient is 0.
2. Division of any nonzero integer by 0 is undefined.

EXAMPLE 3 Divide, if possible: **a.** $\frac{-4}{0}$ **b.** $0 \div (-8)$

Strategy In each case, we need to determine if we have division *of* 0 or division *by* 0.

WHY *Division of 0* by a nonzero integer is defined, and the answer is 0. However, *division of a nonzero integer by 0* is undefined; there is no answer.

Solution

a. $\frac{-4}{0}$ is undefined. This is division by 0.

b. $0 \div (-8) = 0$ because $0(-8) = 0$. This is division of 0.

Self Check 3

Divide, if possible:

a. $\frac{-12}{0}$ undefined **b.** $0 \div (-6)$ 0

Now Try **Problems 45 and 47**

Teaching Example 3 Divide, if possible:

a. $\frac{-15}{0}$

b. $0 \div (-9)$

Answers:

a. undefined.

b. 0

3 Solve application problems by dividing integers.

Problems that involve forming equal-sized groups can be solved by division.

EXAMPLE 4 *Real Estate* Over the course of a year, a homeowner reduced the price of his house by an equal amount each month, because it was not selling. By the end of the year, the price was \$11,400 less than at the beginning of the year. By how much was the price of the house reduced each month?

David McNew/Getty Images

Analyze

- The homeowner dropped the price \$11,400 in 1 year. *Given*
- The price was reduced by an equal amount each month. *Given*
- By how much was the price of the house reduced each month? *Find*

Form We can express the drop in the price of the house for the year as −\$11,400. The phrase *reduced by an equal amount each month* indicates division.

We translate the words of the problem to numbers and symbols.

The amount the price was reduced each month	is equal to	the drop in the price of the house for the year	divided by	the number of months in 1 year.
The amount the price was reduced each month	=	−11,400	÷	12

Solve To find the quotient, we use the rule for dividing two integers that have different signs. First, we find the absolute values: $|-11{,}400| = 11{,}400$ and $|12| = 12$.

$-11{,}400 \div 12 = -950$ Divide the absolute values, 11,400 and 12, to get 950. Then make the final answer negative.

$$\begin{array}{r} 950 \\ 12\overline{)11{,}400} \\ -10\,8 \\ 60 \\ -60 \\ 00 \\ -00 \\ 0 \end{array}$$

State The negative result indicates that the price of the house was *reduced* by \$950 each month.

Check We can use estimation to check the result. A reduction of \$1,000 each month would cause the price to drop \$12,000 in 1 year. It seems reasonable that a reduction of \$950 each month would cause the price to drop \$11,400 in a year.

Self Check 4

SELLING BOATS The owner of a sail boat reduced the price of the boat by an equal amount each month, because there were no interested buyers. After 8 months, and a \$960 reduction in price, the boat sold. By how much was the price of the boat reduced each month?

Now Try **Problem 81**

Self Check 4 Answer

The price was reduced by \$120 each month.

Teaching Example 4

PRICE REDUCTIONS For 1 year, an electronics store reduced the price of a television set by an equal amount each month, because it was not selling. By the end of the year, the price was \$132 less than at the beginning of the year. By how much was the price reduced each month?

Answer:

The price was reduced by \$11 each month.

Using Your CALCULATOR Division with Negative Numbers

The Bureau of Labor Statistics estimated that the United States lost 162,000 auto manufacturing jobs (motor vehicles and parts) in 2008. Because the jobs were lost, we write this as −162,000. To find the average number of manufacturing jobs lost each month, we divide: $\frac{-162{,}000}{12}$. We can use a calculator to perform the division.

Reverse entry: 162000 [+/−] [÷] 12 [=]

Direct entry: 162000 [÷] [(−)] 12 [ENTER] [−13500]

The average number of auto manufacturing jobs lost each month in 2008 was 13,500.

ANSWERS TO SELF CHECKS

1. a. −9 **b.** −7 **c.** −24 **d.** −60 **2. a.** 9 **b.** 6 **c.** 43 **d.** 20 **3. a.** undefined **b.** 0 **4.** The price was reduced by $120 each month.

SECTION 1.5 STUDY SET

VOCABULARY

Fill in the blanks.

1. In the division problems shown below, label the *dividend, divisor,* and *quotient.*

$12 \div (-4) = -3$
(12: dividend; −4: divisor; −3: quotient)

$\frac{12}{-4} = -3$
(12: dividend; −4: divisor; −3: quotient)

2. The related multiplication statement for $\frac{-6}{3} = -2$ is $-2(3) = -6$.

3. $\frac{-3}{0}$ is division by 0 and $\frac{0}{-3} = 0$ is division of 0.

4. Division of a nonzero integer by 0, such as $\frac{-3}{0}$, is undefined.

CONCEPTS

5. Write the related multiplication statement for each division.

a. $\frac{-25}{5} = -5$ $-5(5) = -25$ **b.** $-36 \div (-6) = 6$ $6(-6) = -36$ **c.** $\frac{0}{-15} = 0$ $0(-15) = 0$

6. Using multiplication, check to determine whether $-720 \div 45 = -12$. The answer is incorrect: $-12(45) \neq -720$

7. Fill in the blanks.
To divide two integers, divide their absolute values.

a. The quotient of two integers that have the same (*like*) signs is positive.

b. The quotient of two integers that have different (*unlike*) signs is negative.

8. If a divisor has ending zeros, we can simplify the division by removing the same number of ending zeros in the divisor and dividend. Fill in the blank: $-2{,}400 \div 60 = -240 \div 6$

9. Fill in the blanks.

a. If 0 is divided by any nonzero integer, the quotient is 0.

b. Division of any nonzero integer by 0 is undefined.

10. What operation can be used to solve problems that involve forming equal-sized groups? division

11. Determine whether each statement is always true, sometimes true, or never true.

a. The product of a positive integer and a negative integer is negative. always true

b. The sum of a positive integer and a negative integer is negative. sometimes true

c. The quotient of a positive integer and a negative integer is negative. always true

▶ **12.** Determine whether each statement is always true, sometimes true, or never true.

a. The product of two negative integers is positive. always true

b. The sum of two negative integers is negative. always true

c. The quotient of two negative integers is negative. never true

GUIDED PRACTICE

Divide and check the result. See Example 1.

13. $\frac{-14}{2}$ −7
14. $\frac{-10}{5}$ −2
15. $\frac{-20}{5}$ −4
16. $\frac{-24}{3}$ −8
17. $36 \div (-6)$ −6
18. $36 \div (-9)$ −4
19. $24 \div (-3)$ −8
20. $42 \div (-6)$ −7
21. $\frac{264}{-12}$ −22
22. $\frac{364}{-14}$ −26
23. $\frac{702}{-18}$ −39
24. $\frac{396}{-12}$ −33
25. $-9{,}000 \div 300$ −30
26. $-12{,}000 \div 600$ −20
27. $-250{,}000 \div 5{,}000$ −50
28. $-420{,}000 \div 7{,}000$ −60

Divide and check the result. See Example 2.

29. $\frac{-8}{-4}$ 2
30. $\frac{-12}{-4}$ 3
31. $\frac{-45}{-9}$ 5
32. $\frac{-81}{-9}$ 9
33. $-63 \div (-7)$ 9
34. $-21 \div (-3)$ 7
35. $-32 \div (-8)$ 4
36. $-56 \div (-7)$ 8
37. $\frac{-400}{-25}$ 16
38. $\frac{-490}{-35}$ 14
39. $\frac{-651}{-31}$ 21
40. $\frac{-736}{-32}$ 23
41. $-800 \div (-20)$ 40
42. $-800 \div (-40)$ 20
43. $-15{,}000 \div (-30)$ 500
44. $-36{,}000 \div (-60)$ 600

Divide, if possible. See Example 3.

45. a. $\frac{-3}{0}$ undefined b. $\frac{0}{-3}$ 0
46. a. $\frac{-5}{0}$ undefined b. $\frac{0}{-5}$ 0
47. a. $\frac{0}{-24}$ 0 b. $\frac{-24}{0}$ undefined
48. a. $\frac{0}{-32}$ 0 b. $\frac{-32}{0}$ undefined

TRY IT YOURSELF

Divide, if possible.

49. $-36 \div (-12)$ 3
50. $-45 \div (-15)$ 3
51. $\frac{425}{-25}$ −17
52. $\frac{462}{-42}$ −11
53. $0 \div (-16)$ 0
54. $0 \div (-6)$ 0
55. Find the quotient of −45 and 9. −5
56. Find the quotient of −36 and −4. 9
57. $-2{,}500 \div 500$ −5
58. $-52{,}000 \div 4{,}000$ −13
59. $\frac{-6}{0}$ undefined
60. $\frac{-8}{0}$ undefined
61. $\frac{-19}{1}$ −19
62. $\frac{-9}{1}$ −9
63. $-23 \div (-23)$ 1
64. $-11 \div (-11)$ 1
65. $\frac{40}{-2}$ −20
66. $\frac{35}{-7}$ −5
67. $9 \div (-9)$ −1
68. $15 \div (-15)$ −1
69. $\frac{-10}{-1}$ 10
70. $\frac{-12}{-1}$ 12
71. $\frac{-888}{37}$ −24
72. $\frac{-456}{24}$ −19
73. $\frac{3{,}000}{-100}$ −30
74. $\frac{-60{,}000}{-1{,}000}$ 60
75. Divide 8 by −2. −4
76. Divide −16 by −8. 2

Use a calculator to perform each division.

77. $\frac{-13{,}550}{25}$ −542
78. $\frac{3{,}876}{-19}$ −204
79. $\frac{27{,}778}{-17}$ −1,634
80. $\frac{-168{,}476}{-77}$ 2,188

APPLICATIONS

Use signed numbers to solve each problem.

81. LOWERING PRICES A furniture store owner reduced the price of an oak table an equal amount each week, because it was not selling. After six weeks, and a $210 reduction in price, the table was purchased. By how much was the price of the table reduced each week? −$35 per week

82. TEMPERATURE DROP During a five-hour period, the temperature steadily dropped 20°F. By how many degrees did the temperature change each hour? −4° per hour

83. SUBMARINES In a series of three equal dives, a submarine is programmed to reach a depth of 3,030 feet below the ocean surface. What signed number describes how deep each of the dives will be? −1,010 ft

84. GRAND CANYON A mule train is to travel from a stable on the rim of the Grand Canyon to a camp on the canyon floor, approximately 5,500 feet below the rim. If the guide wants the mules to be rested after every 500 feet of descent, how many stops will be made on the trip? 11

85. CHEMISTRY During an experiment, a solution was steadily chilled and the times and temperatures were recorded, as shown in the illustration below. By how many degrees did the temperature of the solution change each minute? $-7°$ per min

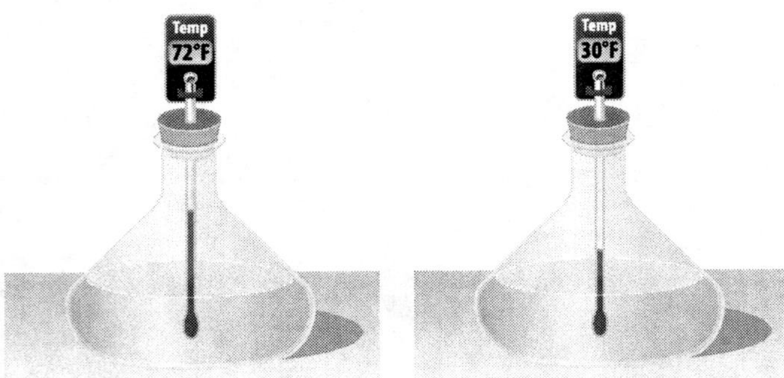

Beginning of experiment 8:00 A.M. End of experiment 8:06 A.M.

86. OCEAN EXPLORATION The Mariana Trench is the deepest part of the world's oceans. It is located in the North Pacific Ocean near the Philippines and has a maximum depth of 36,201 feet. If a remote-controlled vessel is sent to the bottom of the trench in a series of 11 equal descents, how far will the vessel descend on each dive? (Source: marianatrench.com) $-3{,}291$ ft

▶ **87.** BASEBALL TRADES At the midway point of the season, a baseball team finds itself 12 games behind the league leader. Team management decides to trade for a talented hitter, in hopes of making up at least half of the deficit in the standings by the end of the year. Where in the league standings does management expect to finish at season's end? -6 (6 games behind)

▶ **88.** BUDGET DEFICITS A politician proposed a two-year plan for cutting a county's \$20-million budget deficit, as shown. If this plan is put into effect, how will the deficit change in two years? The deficit will be reduced by \$15 million.

	Plan	Prediction
1st year	Raise taxes, drop failing programs	Will cut deficit in half
2nd year	Search out waste and fraud	Will cut remaining deficit in half

▶ **89.** MARKDOWNS The owner of a clothing store decides to reduce the price on a line of jeans that are not selling. She feels she can afford to lose \$300 of projected income on these pants. By how much can she mark down each of the 20 pairs of jeans? $-\$15$

▶ **90.** WATER STORAGE Over a week's time, engineers at a city water reservoir released enough water to lower the water level 105 feet. On average, how much did the water level change each day during this period? -15 ft

▶ **91.** THE STOCK MARKET On Monday, the value of Maria's 255 shares of stock was at an all-time high. By Friday, the value had fallen \$4,335. What was her per-share loss that week? $-\$17$

▶ **92.** CUTTING BUDGETS In a cost-cutting effort, a company decides to cut \$5,840,000 from its annual budget. To do this, all of the company's 160 departments will have their budgets reduced by an equal amount. By how much will each department's budget be reduced? $-\$36{,}500$

WRITING

93. Explain why the quotient of two negative integers is positive.

94. How do the rules for multiplying integers compare with the rules for dividing integers?

95. Use a specific example to explain how multiplication can be used as a check for division.

▶ **96.** Explain what it means when we say that division by 0 is undefined.

97. Explain the division rules for integers that are shown below using symbols.

$$\frac{+}{+} = + \qquad \frac{-}{-} = + \qquad \frac{-}{+} = - \qquad \frac{+}{-} = -$$

98. Explain the difference between *division of 0* and *division by 0.*

REVIEW

99. Evaluate: $5^2\left(\frac{2 \cdot 3^2}{6}\right)^2 - 7(2)$ 211

100. Find the prime factorization of 210. $2 \cdot 3 \cdot 5 \cdot 7$

101. The statement $(4 + 8) + 10 = 4 + (8 + 10)$ illustrates what property? associative property of addition

102. Is $17 \geq 17$ a true statement? yes

▶ **103.** Does $8 - 2 = 2 - 8$? no

104. Sharif has scores of 55, 70, 80, and 75 on four mathematics tests. What is his mean (average) score? 70

SECTION 1.6
Exponents and Order of Operations

Objectives

1. Evaluate exponential expressions.
2. Use the order of operations rules.
3. Evaluate expressions with no grouping symbols.
4. Evaluate expressions containing grouping symbols.
5. Find the mean (average).

In this course, we will perform six operations with real numbers: addition, subtraction, multiplication, division, raising to a power, and finding a root. Quite often, we will have to **evaluate** (find the value of) expressions containing more than one operation. In that case, we need to know the order in which the operations are to be performed. That is a topic of this section.

1 Evaluate exponential expressions.

In the expression $3 \cdot 3 \cdot 3 \cdot 3 \cdot 3$, the number 3 is used as a factor 5 times. We call 3 a *repeated factor.* To express a repeated factor, we can use an **exponent.**

Exponent and Base

An **exponent** is used to indicate repeated multiplication. It tells how many times the **base** is used as a factor.

$$\underbrace{3 \cdot 3 \cdot 3 \cdot 3 \cdot 3}_{} = 3^5$$

The exponent is 5.

Five repeated factors of 3. The base is 3.

In the **exponential expression** a^n, a is the base, and n is the exponent. The expression a^n is called a **power of *a*.** Some examples of powers are

5^2 Read as "5 to the second power" or "5 squared."

9^3 Read as "9 to the third power" or "9 cubed."

$(-2)^5$ Read as "-2 to the fifth power."

The Language of Algebra 5^2 represents the area of a square with sides 5 units long. 4^3 represents the volume of a cube with sides 4 units long.

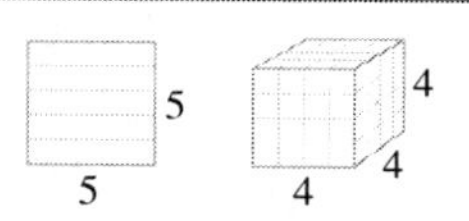

EXAMPLE 1 Write each expression using exponents: **a.** $4 \cdot 4 \cdot 4$ **b.** $(-5)(-5)(-5)(-5)(-5)$ **c.** sixteen cubed **d.** $8 \cdot 8 \cdot 15 \cdot 15 \cdot 15 \cdot 15$

Strategy We will count the number of repeated factors in each expression.

WHY An exponent can be used to represent repeated multiplication.

Solution

a. The factor 4 is repeated 3 times. We can represent this repeated multiplication with an exponential expression having a base of 4 and an exponent of 3: $4 \cdot 4 \cdot 4 = 4^3$.

b. The factor -5 is repeated 5 times: $(-5)(-5)(-5)(-5)(-5) = (-5)^5$.

c. Sixteen cubed can be written as 16^3.

d. $8 \cdot 8 \cdot 15 \cdot 15 \cdot 15 \cdot 15 = 8^2 \cdot 15^4$

Self Check 1

Write each expression using exponents:

a. $(12)(12)(12)(12)(12)(12)$ 12^6

b. $2 \cdot 9 \cdot 9 \cdot 9$ $2 \cdot 9^3$

c. fifty squared 50^2

d. $(-30)(-30)(-30)$ $(-30)^3$

Now Try **Problem 23**

Teaching Example 1 Write each expression using exponents:
a. $(-2)(-2)(-2)$ **b.** twelve squared
Answers:
a. $(-2)^3$
b. 12^2

In the next example, we use exponents to rewrite expressions involving repeated variable factors.

Self Check 2

Write each product using exponents:

a. $y \cdot y \cdot y \cdot y$ y^4

b. $12 \cdot b \cdot b \cdot b \cdot c$ $12b^3c$

Now Try **Problem 27**

Teaching Example 2 Write each product using exponents:
a. $xxxxx$ **b.** $xxyyyzzzz$
Answers:
a. x^5 **b.** $x^2y^3z^4$

EXAMPLE 2 Write each product using exponents:

a. $a \cdot a \cdot a \cdot a \cdot a \cdot a$ **b.** $4 \cdot \pi \cdot r \cdot r$

Strategy We will count the number of repeated factors in each expression.

WHY An exponent can be used to represent repeated multiplication.

Solution

a. $a \cdot a \cdot a \cdot a \cdot a \cdot a = a^6$ *a is repeated as a factor 6 times.*

b. $4 \cdot \pi \cdot r \cdot r = 4\pi r^2$ *r is repeated as a factor 2 times.*

Self Check 3

Find each power:

a. 2^5 32

b. $(-6)^2$ 36

c. $(-5)^3$ -125

Now Try **Problem 35**

Teaching Example 3 Find each power:
a. 3^2 **b.** $(-2)^5$ **c.** $(-5)^4$
Answers:
a. 9 **b.** -32 **c.** 625

EXAMPLE 3 Find each power: **a.** 5^3 **b.** 10^1 **c.** $(-3)^4$ **d.** $(-3)^5$

Strategy We will identify the base to determine the repeated factor and identify the exponent to determine the number of times the factor is repeated. Then we will multiply to evaluate the expression.

WHY Exponents represent repeated multiplication.

Solution

We write the base as a factor the number of times indicated by the exponent. Then we perform the multiplication.

a. $5^3 = 5 \cdot 5 \cdot 5 = 125$ *The base is 5, the exponent is 3.*

b. $10^1 = 10$ *The base is 10, the exponent is 1.*

c. $(-3)^4 = (-3)(-3)(-3)(-3)$ *Write −3 as a factor 4 times.*

$= 9(-3)(-3)$ *Work from left to right: (−3)(−3) = 9.*

$= -27(-3)$ *Work from left to right: 9(−3) = −27.*

$= 81$

d. $(-3)^5 = (-3)(-3)(-3)(-3)(-3)$ *Write −3 as a factor 5 times.*

$= 9(-3)(-3)(-3)$ *Work from left to right: (−3)(−3) = 9.*

$= -27(-3)(-3)$ *Work from left to right: 9(−3) = −27.*

$= 81(-3)$ *Work from left to right: −27(−3) = 81.*

$= -243$

Caution! Don't make the mistake of multiplying the base and the exponent.

Incorrect	Correct
~~$5^3 = 5 \cdot 3$~~	$5^3 = 5 \cdot 5 \cdot 5$
	$= 125$

We can now make some observations about raising a negative number to an *even power* (2, 4, 6, 8, and so on) and raising a negative number to an *odd power* (1, 3, 5, 7, and so on). In part c of Example 3, we raised −3 to an even power, and the result was positive. In part d, we raised −3 to an odd power, and the result was negative. These results illustrate the following general rule.

Even and Odd Powers of a Negative Number

When a negative number is raised to an even power, the result is positive.

When a negative number is raised to an odd power, the result is negative.

Caution! Although the expressions -4^2 and $(-4)^2$ look alike, they are not. In -4^2, the base is 4 and the exponent is 2. The $-$ sign in front of 4^2 means the opposite of 4^2. In $(-4)^2$, the base is -4 and the exponent is 2. When we find the value of each expression, it becomes clear that they are not equivalent.

$-4^2 = -(4 \cdot 4)$	Write 4 as a factor 2 times.	$(-4)^2 = (-4)(-4)$	Write -4 as a factor 2 times.
$= -16$	Multiply within the parentheses.	$= 16$	The product of two negative numbers is positive.

Different results

EXAMPLE 4 Find each power: **a.** $\left(-\frac{2}{3}\right)^3$ **b.** $(0.6)^2$ **c.** -2^6

Strategy We will write each exponential expression as a product and multiply the repeated factors.

WHY Exponents represent repeated multiplication.

Solution

a. $\left(-\frac{2}{3}\right)^3 = \left(-\frac{2}{3}\right)\left(-\frac{2}{3}\right)\left(-\frac{2}{3}\right)$ Since $-\frac{2}{3}$ is the base and 3 is the exponent, we write $-\frac{2}{3}$ as a factor 3 times.

$= \frac{4}{9}\left(-\frac{2}{3}\right)$ Multiply: $\left(-\frac{2}{3}\right)\left(-\frac{2}{3}\right) = \frac{4}{9}$.

$= -\frac{8}{27}$ Perform the multiplication.

b. $(0.6)^2 = (0.6)(0.6)$ Since 0.6 is the base and 2 is the exponent, we write 0.6 as a factor 2 times.

$= 0.36$ Perform the multiplication.

c. $-2^6 = -(2 \cdot 2 \cdot 2 \cdot 2 \cdot 2 \cdot 2)$ Since 2 is the base and 6 is the exponent, we write 2 as a factor 6 times. We use the opposite of the final value.

$= -64$ Perform the multiplication.

Self Check 4

Find each power:

a. $\left(-\frac{3}{4}\right)^3$ $-\frac{27}{64}$

b. $(-0.3)^2$ 0.09

c. -5^2 -25

Now Try **Problem 37**

Teaching Example 4 Find each power:
a. $\left(-\frac{2}{5}\right)^2$
b. $(-0.1)^3$
c. -3^2
Answers:
a. $\frac{4}{25}$ b. -0.001
c. -9

Using Your CALCULATOR **Finding a Power**

On a scientific calculator, we can use the squaring key $\boxed{x^2}$ to find the square of a number, and we can use the exponential key $\boxed{y^x}$ (on some calculators labeled x^y) to raise a number to a power. For example, to evaluate 125^2 and 2^{10} using a scientific calculator, we enter these numbers and press these keys.

125 $\boxed{x^2}$ 15625

2 $\boxed{y^x}$ 10 $\boxed{=}$ 1024

Using a graphing or direct-entry calculator, we can evaluate 125^2 and 2^{10} by pressing these keys.

125 $\boxed{x^2}$ $\boxed{\text{ENTER}}$ | 125^2 15625

2 $\boxed{\wedge}$ 10 $\boxed{\text{ENTER}}$ | 2^10 1024

We have found that $125^2 = 15{,}625$ and $2^{10} = 1{,}024$.

2 Use the order of operations rules.

Suppose you have been asked to contact a friend if you see a Rolex watch for sale when you are traveling in Europe. While in Switzerland, you find the watch and send the text message shown on the left. The next day, you get the response shown on the right.

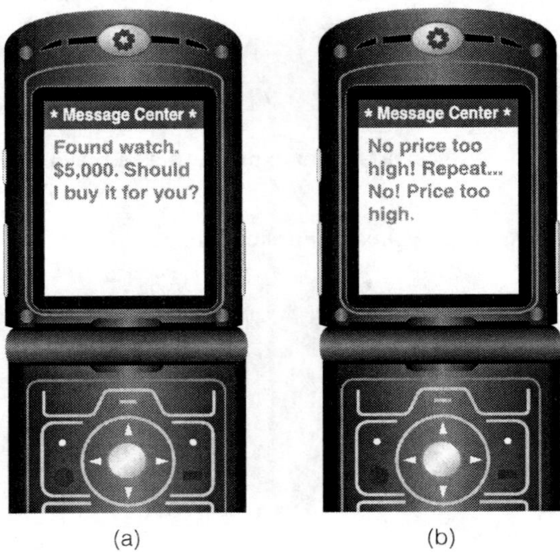

(a) (b)

Something is wrong. The first part of the response (No price too high!) says to buy the watch at any price. The second part (No! Price too high.) says not to buy it, because it's too expensive. The placement of the exclamation point makes us read the two parts of the response differently, resulting in different meanings. When reading a mathematical statement, the same kind of confusion is possible. For example, consider the expression

$$2 + 3 \cdot 6$$

which contains two operations: addition and multiplication. We can consider doing the calculations in two ways. We can add first and then multiply. Or we can multiply first and then add. However, we get different results.

Method 1: Add first

$2 + 3 \cdot 6 = 5 \cdot 6$ Add 2 and 3 first.

$= 30$ Multiply 5 and 6.

Method 2: Multiply first

$2 + 3 \cdot 6 = 2 + 18$ Multiply 3 and 6 first.

$= 20$ Add 2 and 18.

If we don't establish a uniform order of operations, the expression $2 + 3 \cdot 6$ has two different values. To avoid this possibility, we always use the following set of priority rules.

Order of Operations

1. Perform all calculations within parentheses and other grouping symbols following the order listed in steps 2–4 below, working from the innermost pair to the outermost pair.
2. Evaluate all exponential expressions.
3. Perform all multiplications and divisions as they occur from left to right.
4. Perform all additions and subtractions as they occur from left to right.

When grouping symbols have been removed, repeat steps 2–4 to complete the calculation.

If a fraction is present, evaluate the expression above and the expression below the bar separately. Then do the division indicated by the fraction bar, if possible.

It isn't necessary to apply all of these steps in every problem. For example, the expression $2 + 3 \cdot 6$ does not contain any parentheses, and there are no exponential expressions. So we look for multiplications and divisions to perform. To evaluate $2 + 3 \cdot 6$ correctly, we proceed as follows:

$2 + 3 \cdot 6 = 2 + 18$ Multiply first: $3 \cdot 6 = 18$.

$= 20$ Add.

Therefore, the correct result when evaluating $2 + 3 \cdot 6$ is 20.

3 Evaluate expressions with no grouping symbols.

EXAMPLE 5 Evaluate: $3 \cdot 2^3 - 4$

Strategy We will scan the expression to determine what operations need to be performed. Then we will perform those operations, one at a time, following the order of operations rules.

WHY The order of operations gives us the steps needed to find the correct result.

Solution

To find the value of this expression, we must perform the operations of multiplication, raising to a power, and subtraction. The rules for the order of operations tell us to begin by evaluating the exponential expression.

$3 \cdot 2^3 - 4 = 3 \cdot 8 - 4$ Evaluate the exponential expression: $2^3 = 8$.

$= 24 - 4$ Multiply: $3 \cdot 8 = 24$.

$= 20$ Subtract.

Self Check 5

Evaluate: $2 \cdot 3^2 + 17$ 35

Now Try **Problem 43**

Teaching Example 5 Evaluate: $4 + 3 \cdot 2^2 - 5$

Answer: 11

The Language of Algebra Sometimes, for problems like these, the instruction *Simplify* is used instead of *Evaluate*.

EXAMPLE 6 Evaluate: $-30 - 4 \cdot 5 + 9$

Strategy We will scan the expression to determine what operations need to be performed. Then we will perform those operations, one at a time, following the order of operations rules.

WHY The order of operations gives us the steps needed to find the correct result.

Self Check 6

Evaluate: $-40 - 9 \cdot 4 + 10$ −66

Now Try **Problem 49**

Teaching Example 6 Evaluate: $-10 - 5 \cdot 3 + 8$

Answer: −17

Solution

To evaluate this expression, we must perform the operations of subtraction, multiplication, and addition. The rules for the order of operations tell us to begin with the multiplication.

$$\begin{aligned} -30 - 4 \cdot 5 + 9 &= -30 - 20 + 9 && \text{Multiply: } 4 \cdot 5 = 20. \\ &= -50 + 9 && \text{Working from left to right, subtract } -30 - 20 = -30 + (-20) = -50. \\ &= -41 && \text{Add.} \end{aligned}$$

Caution! Some students think that additions are always done before subtractions. As you saw in Example 6, this is not true. Working from left to right, we do the additions or subtractions in the order in which they occur. The same is true for multiplications and divisions.

Self Check 7

Evaluate:
$240 \div (-8)(3) - 3(-2)4$ -66

Now Try **Problem 54**

Teaching Example 7 Evaluate:
$120 \div (-3)(2) - 4(-1)5$
Answer:
-60

EXAMPLE 7 Evaluate: $160 \div (-4)(3) - 6(-2)3$

Strategy We will scan the expression to determine what operations need to be performed. Then we will perform those operations, one at a time, following the order of operations rules.

WHY The order of operations gives us the steps needed to find the correct result.

Solution

Although this expression contains parentheses, there are no operations to perform within them. Since there are no exponents, we perform multiplications and divisions as they occur from left to right.

$$\begin{aligned} 160 \div (-4)(3) - 6(-2)3 &= -40(3) - 6(-2)3 && \text{Divide: } 160 \div (-4) = -40. \\ &= -120 - 6(-2)3 && \text{Multiply: } -40(3) = -120 \\ &= -120 - (-12)3 && \text{Multiply: } 6(-2) = -12. \\ &= -120 - (-36) && \text{Multiply: } (-12)3 = -36. \\ &= -120 + 36 && \text{Write the subtraction as addition of the opposite.} \\ &= -84 && \text{Add.} \end{aligned}$$

Caution! A common mistake is to forget to work from left to right and incorrectly perform the multiplication before the division.

4 Evaluate expressions containing grouping symbols.

Grouping symbols are mathematical punctuation marks. They help determine the order in which an expression is to be evaluated. Examples of grouping symbols are parentheses ( ), brackets [ ], absolute value symbols | |, and the fraction bar —.

Self Check 8

Evaluate: $(12 - 6)^3$ 216

Now Try **Problem 59**

EXAMPLE 8 Evaluate: $(6 - 3)^2$

Strategy We will perform the operation(s) within the parentheses first. When there is more than one operation to perform within the parentheses, we follow the order of operations rules.

WHY This is the first step of the order of operations.

Solution

This expression contains parentheses. By the rules for the order of operations, we must perform the operation within the parentheses first.

$(6 - 3)^2 = 3^2$ Subtract within the parentheses: $6 - 3 = 3$.

$= 9$ Evaluate the exponential expression.

Teaching Example 8 Evaluate: $(7 - 2)^3$
Answer: 125

EXAMPLE 9 Evaluate: $5^3 + 2(-8 - 3 \cdot 2)$

Strategy We will perform the operation(s) within the parentheses first. When there is more than one operation to perform within the parentheses, we follow the order of operations rules.

WHY This is the first step of the order of operations.

Solution

First, we perform the operations within the parentheses in the proper order.

$5^3 + 2(-8 - 3 \cdot 2) = 5^3 + 2(-8 - 6)$ Multiply within the parentheses: $3 \cdot 2 = 6$.

$= 5^3 + 2(-14)$ Subtract within the parentheses: $-8 - 6 = -8 + (-6) = -14$.

$= 125 + 2(-14)$ Evaluate the exponential expression: $5^3 = 125$.

$= 125 + (-28)$ Multiply: $2(-14) = -28$.

$= 97$ Add.

Self Check 9

Evaluate: $1^3 + 6(-6 - 3 \cdot 0)$

Now Try **Problem 63**

Self Check 9 Answers
-35

Teaching Example 9 Evaluate: $3^2 + 4(-5 - 2 \cdot 7)$
Answer: -67

Success Tip Multiplication is indicated when a number is next to a parentheses or bracket.

Expressions can contain two or more pairs of grouping symbols. To evaluate the following expression, we begin by working within the innermost pair of grouping symbols. Then we work within the outermost pair.

Innermost pair

$-4[-2 - 3(4 - 8^2)] - 2$

Outermost pair

The Language of Algebra When one pair of grouping symbols is inside another pair, we say that those grouping symbols are *nested,* or *embedded.*

EXAMPLE 10 Evaluate: $-4[-2 - 3(4 - 8^2)] - 2$

Strategy We will work within the parentheses first and then within the brackets. At each stage, we follow the order of operations rules.

WHY By the order of operations, we must work from the *innermost* pair of grouping symbols to the *outermost.*

Self Check 10

Evaluate:
$-5[2(5^2 - 15) + 4] - 10$ -130

Now Try **Problem 74**

Teaching Example 10 Evaluate: $-3[4(2^3 - 4) - 5] + 3$
Answer:
-30

Solution
We work within the innermost grouping symbols (the parentheses) first.

$-4[-2 - 3(4 - 8^2)] - 2$

$= -4[-2 - 3(4 - 64)] - 2$ — Evaluate the exponential expression within the parentheses: $8^2 = 64$.

$= -4[-2 - 3(-60)] - 2$ — Subtract within the parentheses: $4 - 64 = 4 + (-64) = -60$.

$= -4[-2 - (-180)] - 2$ — Multiply within the brackets: $3(-60) = -180$.

$= -4(178) - 2$ — Subtract within the brackets: $-2 - (-180) = -2 + 180 = 178$.

$= -712 - 2$ — Multiply.

$= -714$ — Subtract: $-712 - 2 = -712 + (-2) = -714$.

Self Check 11

Evaluate: $\dfrac{-4(-2 + 8) + 6}{8 - 5(-2)}$ -1

Now Try **Problem 75**

Teaching Example 11 Evaluate: $\dfrac{-2(-4 + 7) + 9}{6 - 3(-7)}$
Answer:
$\frac{1}{9}$

EXAMPLE 11 Evaluate: $\dfrac{-3(3 + 2) + 5}{17 - 3(-4)}$

Strategy We will evaluate the expression above and the expression below the fraction bar separately. Then we will simplify the fraction, if possible.

WHY Fraction bars are grouping symbols. They group the numerator and denominator. The expression could be written as $[-3(3 + 2) + 5] \div [17 - 3(-4)]$.

Solution
We simplify the numerator and the denominator separately.

$\dfrac{-3(3 + 2) + 5}{17 - 3(-4)} = \dfrac{-3(5) + 5}{17 - (-12)}$ — In the numerator, add within the parentheses. In the denominator, multiply.

$= \dfrac{-15 + 5}{17 + 12}$ — In the numerator, multiply. In the denominator, write the subtraction as addition of the opposite of -12, which is 12.

$= \dfrac{-10}{29}$ — Perform the additions.

$= -\dfrac{10}{29}$ — Write the $-$ sign in front of the fraction: $\frac{-10}{29} = -\frac{10}{29}$.

Success Tip The order of operations are built in to most calculators. A left parenthesis key (and a right parenthesis key) should be used when grouping symbols, including a fraction bar, are in the problem.

Self Check 12

Evaluate: $10^3 + 3|24 - 25|$ 1,003

Now Try **Problem 86**

Teaching Example 12 Evaluate: $4^2|6 - 8| - 12 \div 3(4)$
Answer:
16

EXAMPLE 12 Evaluate: $10|9 - 15| - 2^5$

Strategy The absolute value bars are grouping symbols. We will perform the calculation within them first.

WHY By the order of operations, we must perform all calculations within parentheses and other grouping symbols (such as absolute value bars) first.

Solution
Since the absolute value bars are grouping symbols, we perform the calculation within them first.

$$10|9 - 15| - 2^5 = 10|-6| - 2^5$$ Subtract: $9 - 15 = 9 + (-15) = -6$.

$$= 10(6) - 2^5$$ $10|-6|$ means 10 times $|-6|$. Find the absolute value: $|-6| = 6$.

$$= 10(6) - 32$$ Evaluate the exponential expression: $2^5 = 32$.

$$= 60 - 32$$ Multiply.

$$= 28$$

Caution! When a number is next to an absolute value symbol, multiplication is indicated.

5 Find the mean (average).

The **arithmetic mean** (or **average**) of a set of numbers is a value around which the values of the numbers are grouped.

Finding an Arithmetic Mean

To find the **mean** of a set of values, divide the sum of the values by the number of values.

EXAMPLE 13 *Hotel Reservations* In an effort to improve customer service, a hotel electronically recorded the number of times the reservation desk telephone rang before it was answered by a receptionist. The results of the week-long survey are shown in the table. Find the average number of times the phone rang before a receptionist answered.

Number of rings	Number of calls
1	11
2	46
3	45
4	28
5	20

Strategy First, we will determine the total number of times the reservation desk telephone rang during the week. Then we will divide that result by the total number of calls received.

WHY To find the *average* value of a set of values, we divide the sum of the values by the number of values.

Solution

To find the total number of rings, we multiply each *number of rings* (1, 2, 3, 4, and 5 rings) by the respective number of occurrences and add those subtotals.

$$\text{Total number of rings} = 11(1) + 46(2) + 45(3) + 28(4) + 20(5)$$

The total number of calls received was $11 + 46 + 45 + 28 + 20$. To find the average, we divide the total number of rings by the total number of calls.

$$\text{Average} = \frac{11(1) + 46(2) + 45(3) + 28(4) + 20(5)}{11 + 46 + 45 + 28 + 20}$$

$$= \frac{11 + 92 + 135 + 112 + 100}{150}$$ In the numerator, do the multiplications. In the denominator, do the additions.

$$= \frac{450}{150}$$ Do the addition.

$$= 3$$ Simplify the fraction.

The average number of times the phone rang before it was answered was 3.

Self Check 13

On an evaluation, students are to mark 1 for *strongly agree,* 2 for *agree,* 3 for *disagree,* and 4 for *strongly disagree.* If on a question 17 students marked 1, 5 students marked 2, and 2 students marked 4, find the average response for this question on the survey. 1.46

Now Try **Problem 133**

Teaching Example 13 For a recent survey, the responses of 1 = satisfied, 2 = no opinion, and 3 = dissatisfied were recorded. The results are shown in the table. Find the average rating of satisfaction for these responses.

Survey options	Number of responses
1	15
2	1
3	4

Answer:
1.45

ANSWERS TO SELF CHECKS

1. a. 12^6 **b.** $2 \cdot 9^3$ **c.** 50^2 **d.** $(-30)^3$ **2. a.** y^4 **b.** $12b^3c$ **3. a.** 32 **b.** 36 **c.** −125 **4. a.** $\frac{-27}{64}$ **b.** 0.09 **c.** −25 **5.** 35 **6.** −66 **7.** −66 **8.** 216 **9.** −35 **10.** −130 **11.** −1 **12.** 1,003 **13.** 1.46

SECTION 1.6 STUDY SET

VOCABULARY

Fill in the blanks.

1. In the exponential expression 3^2, 3 is the base, and 2 is the exponent.

2. 10^2 can be read as ten squared, and 10^3 can be read as ten cubed.

3. 7^5 is the fifth power of seven.

▶ **4.** An exponent is used to represent repeated multiplication.

5. The rules for the order of operations guarantee that an evaluation of a numerical expression will result in a single answer.

6. The arithmetic mean or average of a set of numbers is a value around which the values of the numbers are grouped.

CONCEPTS

7. Given: $4 + 5 \cdot 6$

a. What operations does this expression contain? addition and multiplication

b. Evaluate the expression in two different ways, and state the two possible results. 54, 34

c. Which result from part b is correct, and why? 34, multiplication is to be done before addition.

8. a. What repeated multiplication does 5^3 represent? $5 \cdot 5 \cdot 5$

b. Write a multiplication statement in which the factor x is repeated 4 times. Then write the expression in simpler form using an exponent. $x \cdot x \cdot x \cdot x = x^4$

c. How can we represent the repeated addition $3 + 3 + 3 + 3 + 3$ in a simpler form? 5(3)

9. a. How is the mean (or average) of a set of scores found? Divide the sum of the scores by the number of scores.

b. Find the average of 75, 81, 47, and 53. 64

10. In the expression $-8 + 2[15 - (-6 + 1)]$, which grouping symbols are innermost and which are outermost? innermost: parentheses, outermost: brackets

11. a. What operations does the expression $12 + 5^2(-3)$ contain? addition, power, multiplication

b. In what order should they be performed? power, multiplication, addition

12. a. What operations does the expression $20 - (-2)^2 + 3(-1)$ contain? subtraction, power, addition, multiplication

b. In what order should they be performed? power, multiplication, subtraction, addition

13. Consider the expression $\frac{36 - 4(7)}{2(10 - 8)}$. In the numerator, what operation should be done first? In the denominator, what operation should be done first? multiplication, subtraction

14. Explain the differences in evaluating $4 \cdot 2^2$ and $(4 \cdot 2)^2$. In $4 \cdot 2^2$, find the power, then multiply. In $(4 \cdot 2)^2$, multiply, then find the power.

15. To evaluate each expression, what operation should be performed first?

a. $-80 - 3 + 5 - 2^2$ power

b. $-80 - (3 + 5) - 2^2$ addition

c. $-80 + 3 + (5 - 2)^2$ subtraction

▶ **16.** To evaluate each expression, what operation should be performed first?

a. $(65 - 3)^3$ subtraction

b. $65 - 3^3$ power

c. $6(5) - (3)^3$ power

NOTATION

17. Write an exponential expression with a base of 12 and an exponent of 6. 12^6

18. Give the name of each grouping symbol: ( ), [ ], | |, and —. parentheses, brackets, absolute value symbols, fraction bar

Complete each evaluation.

19.
$$\begin{aligned} 50 + 6 \cdot 3^2 &= 50 + 6 \cdot 9 \\ &= 50 + 54 \\ &= 104 \end{aligned}$$

▶ **20.**
$$\begin{aligned} -100 - (25 - 8 \cdot 2) &= -100 - (25 - 16) \\ &= -100 - 9 \\ &= -109 \end{aligned}$$

21. $-19 - 2[(1 + 2) \cdot 3] = -19 - 2[\ 3\ \cdot 3]$
$= -19 - 2(\ 9\ )$
$= -19 - \ 18$
$= -37$

22. $\dfrac{46 - 2^3}{-3(5) - 4} = \dfrac{46 - \ 8}{-15\ - 4}$
$= \dfrac{38}{-19}$
$= -2$

GUIDED PRACTICE

Write each product using exponents. See Example 1.

23. $3 \cdot 3 \cdot 3 \cdot 3$ 3^4
24. $(-7)(-7)(-7)(-7)(-7)(-7)$ $(-7)^6$
25. $10 \cdot 10 \cdot 12 \cdot 12 \cdot 12$ $10^2 \cdot 12^3$
▶ 26. $5(5)(5)(11)(11)$ $5^3 \cdot 11^2$

Write each product using exponents. See Example 2.

27. $8 \cdot \pi \cdot r \cdot r \cdot r$ $8\pi r^3$
▶ 28. $4 \cdot \pi \cdot r \cdot r$ $4\pi r^2$
29. $6(x)(x)(y)(y)(y)$ $6x^2y^3$
30. $76 \cdot s \cdot s \cdot s \cdot s \cdot t$ $76s^4t$

Find each power. See Examples 3–4.

31. 7^2 49
32. 11^3 1,331
33. $(-6)^2$ 36
34. $(-4)^4$ 256
▶ 35. $(-2)^3$ −8
36. -5^3 −125
37. $\left(-\dfrac{2}{5}\right)^3$ $-\dfrac{8}{125}$
38. $\left(-\dfrac{1}{4}\right)^3$ $-\dfrac{1}{64}$
39. $(-0.4)^2$ 0.16
40. $(-0.5)^2$ 0.25
41. -6^2 −36
42. -4^4 −256

Evaluate each expression. See Example 5.

▶ 43. $3 \cdot 8^2 - 5$ 187
44. $3 \cdot 4^2 - 8$ 40
45. $3 - 5 \cdot 4^2$ −77
46. $-4 \cdot 6^2 + 5$ −139

Evaluate each expression. See Examples 6–7.

47. $8 \cdot 5 - 4 \div 2$ 38
▶ 48. $9 \cdot 5 - 6 \div 3$ 43
49. $100 - 8(10) + 60$ 80
50. $50 - 2(5) - 7$ 33
51. $-22 - 15(-3)$ 23
52. $-33 - 8(-10)$ 47
53. $-2(9) - 2(5)$ −28
54. $18 \div 9(-2) - 4(-3)$ 8
55. $5^2 + 13^2$ 194
▶ 56. $3^3 - 2^3$ 19
57. $2 \cdot 3^2 + 5 \cdot 2^3$ 58
58. $4 \cdot 2^5 - 3 \cdot 5^2$ 53

Evaluate each expression. See Example 8.

59. $(-5 - 2)^2$ 49
60. $(-3 - 5)^2$ 64
61. $(12 - 2)^3$ 1,000
▶ 62. $(10 - 3)^2$ 49

Evaluate each expression. See Example 9.

63. $175 - 2 \cdot 3^4$ 13
64. $75 - 3 \cdot 1^2$ 72
▶ 65. $200 - (-6 + 5)^3$ 201
66. $19 - (-45 + 41)^3$ 83
67. $-6(130 - 4^3)$ −396
68. $-5(150 - 3^3)$ −615
69. $5 \cdot 2^2 \cdot 4 - 30$ 50
70. $2 + (3 \cdot 2^2 \cdot 4)$ 50

Evaluate each expression. See Example 10.

▶ 71. $-3[5^2 - (7 - 3)^2]$ −27
72. $3 - [3^3 + (3 - 1)^3]$ −32
73. $5 + (4^2 - 2^3)^2$ 69
▶ 74. $(-5)^3[4(2^3 - 3^2)]^2$ −2,000

Evaluate each expression. See Example 11.

▶ 75. $\dfrac{5 \cdot 50 - 160}{-9}$ −10
76. $\dfrac{5(68 - 32)}{-9}$ −20
77. $\dfrac{(4^3 - 10) + (-4)}{5^2 - (-4)(-5)}$ 10
78. $\dfrac{(6 - 5)^4 - (-21)}{(-9)(-3) - 4^2}$ 2
79. $\dfrac{72 - (2 - 2 \cdot 1)}{10^2 - (90 + 2^2)}$ 12
▶ 80. $\dfrac{13^2 - 5^2}{-3(5 - 9)}$ 12
81. $\dfrac{40 \div 2 - 5 \cdot 2}{3^2 - (-1)}$ 1
82. $\dfrac{(5 - 2)^2 - (2 - (-1))}{5 \cdot 2 + (-7)}$ 2

Evaluate each expression. See Example 12.

83. $-2|4 - 8|$ −8
84. $-5|1 - 8|$ −35
85. $|7 - 8(4 - 7)|$ 31
▶ 86. $|9 - 5(1 - 8)|$ 44
87. $\dfrac{|6 - 4| + 2|-4|}{26 - 2^4}$ 1
88. $\dfrac{4|9 - 7| + |-7|}{3^2 - 2^2}$ 3
▶ 89. $\dfrac{(3 + 5)^2 + |-2|}{-2(5 - 8)}$ 11
90. $\dfrac{|-25| - 8(-5)}{2^4 - 29}$ −5

TRY IT YOURSELF

Evaluate each expression.

91. $-(-6)^4$ −1,296
92. $-(-7)^2$ −49
93. $-4(6 + 5)$ −44
94. $-3(5 - 4)$ −3
95. $4^2 - (-2)^2$ 12
96. $3 + (-5)^2$ 28
97. $12 + 2\left(-\dfrac{9}{3}\right) - (-2)$ 8
98. $2 + 3\left(-\dfrac{25}{5}\right) - (-4)$ −9
99. $1(2)(3)(-4)$ −24
100. $3(4)(5)(-6)$ −360
101. $[6(5) - 5(5)]4$ 20
102. $5[9(2) - 2(8)]$ 10
103. $(17 - 5 \cdot 2)^3$ 343
▶ 104. $(4 + 2 \cdot 3)^4$ 10,000
105. $-5(-2)^3(3)^2$ 360
106. $-3(-2)^5(2)^2$ 384
107. $-2\left(\dfrac{15}{-5}\right) - \dfrac{6}{2} + 9$ 12
108. $-6\left(\dfrac{25}{-5}\right) - \dfrac{36}{9} + 1$ 27
109. $5(10 + 2) - 1$ 59
110. $14 + 3(7 - 5)$ 20
111. $64 - 6[15 + (-3)3]$ 28
▶ 112. $4 + 2[26 + 5(-3)]$ 26
113. $(-2)^3\left(\dfrac{-6}{2}\right)(-1)$ −24
114. $(-3)^3\left(\dfrac{-4}{2}\right)(-1)$ −54

115. $\dfrac{-7 - 3^2}{2 \cdot 4}$ -2

▶ **116.** $\dfrac{-5 - 3^3}{2^3}$ -4

117. $\dfrac{1}{2}\left(\dfrac{1}{8}\right) + \left(-\dfrac{1}{4}\right)^2$ $\dfrac{1}{8}$

118. $-\dfrac{1}{9}\left(\dfrac{1}{4}\right) + \left(-\dfrac{1}{6}\right)^2$ 0

119. $3 + 2[-1 - 4(5)]$ -39

120. $4 + 2[-7 - 3(9)]$ -64

121. $-(2 \cdot 3 - 4)^3$ -8

122. $-(3 \cdot 5 - 2 \cdot 6)^2$ -9

123. $\dfrac{2[-4 - 2(3 - 1)]}{3(-3)(-2)}$ $-\dfrac{8}{9}$

124. $\dfrac{3[-9 + 2(7 - 3)]}{(5 - 8)(7 - 9)}$ $-\dfrac{1}{2}$

125. $-\left(\dfrac{40 - 1^3 - 2^4}{3(2 + 5) + 2}\right)$ -1

▶ **126.** $-\left(\dfrac{8^2 - 10}{2(3)(4) - 5(3)}\right)$ -6

127. $\dfrac{3(3{,}246 - 1{,}111)}{561 - 546}$ 427

128. $54^3 - 16^4 + 19(3)$ $91{,}985$

129. $(23.1)^2 - (14.7)(-61)^3$ $3{,}337{,}154.31$

130. $12 - 7\left(-\dfrac{85.684}{34.55}\right)^3$ 118.770944

APPLICATIONS

▶ **131.** LIGHT The illustration shows that the light energy that passes through the first unit of area, 1 yard away from the bulb, spreads out as it travels away from the source. How much area does that light energy cover 2 yards, 3 yards, and 4 yards from the bulb? Express each answer using exponents.
2^2 square units, 3^2 square units, 4^2 square units

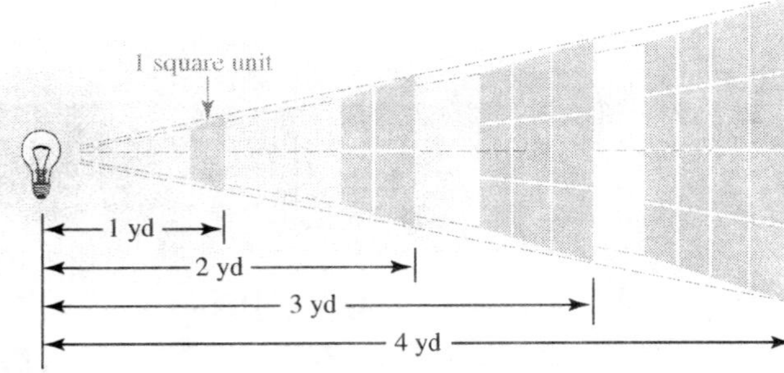

▶ **132.** CHAIN LETTERS A store owner sent two friends a letter advertising her store's low prices. The ad closed with the following request: "Please send a copy of this letter to two of your friends."

a. Assume that all those receiving letters respond and that everyone in the chain receives just one letter. Complete the table.

b. How many letters will be circulated in the tenth level of the mailing? $2^{10} = 1{,}024$

Level	Numbers of letters circulated
1st	$2 = 2^1$
2nd	$4 = 2^2$
3rd	$8 = 2^3$
4th	$16 = 2^4$

▶ **133.** AUTO INSURANCE See the premium comparison in the table. What is the average 6-month insurance premium? $2,106

Allstate	$2,672	Mercury	$1,370
Auto Club	$1,680	State Farm	$2,737
Farmers	$2,485	20th Century	$1,692

Criteria: Six-month premium. Husband, 45, drives a 1995 Explorer, 12,000 annual miles. Wife, 43, drives a 1996 Dodge Caravan, 12,000 annual miles. Son, 17, is an occasional operator. All have clean driving records.

▶ **134.** SWEEPS WEEK During sweeps week, television networks make a special effort to gain viewers by showing unusually flashy programming. Use the information in the illustration on the next page to determine the average daily gain (or loss) of ratings points by a network for the 7-day sweeps period.
a gain of 0.6 of a rating point

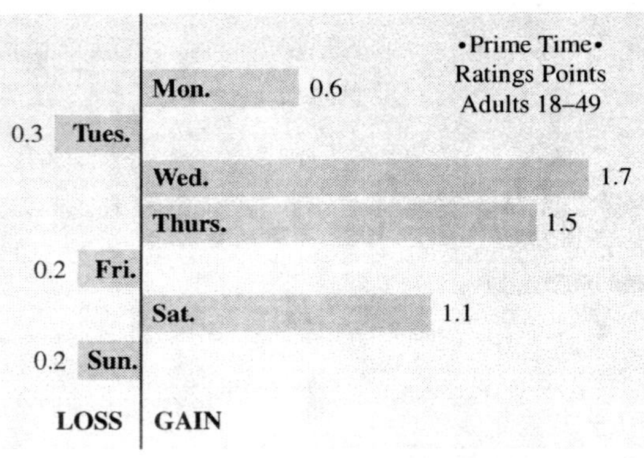

▶ **135.** YOUTUBE VIDEO CONTEST A video contest is to be part of a promotional kickoff for a new sports drink. The prizes to be awarded are shown.

YouTube Video Contest
Grand prize: Disney World vacation plus $2,500
Four 1st place prizes of $500
Thirty-five 2nd place prizes of $150
Eighty-five 3rd place prizes of $25

a. How much money will be awarded in the promotion? $11,875

b. What is the average cash prize? $95

136. ENERGY USAGE Refer to the illustration below. Find the average number of therms of natural gas used per month. Then draw a dashed line across the graph showing the average. 31.5 therms

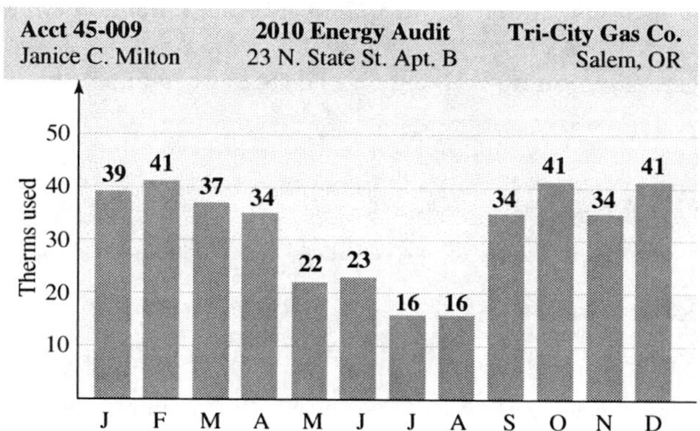

137. SCRABBLE Illustration (a) in the next column shows a portion of the game board before and illustration (b) shows it after the word *QUARTZY* is played. Determine the score. (The number on each tile gives the point value of the letter.)
$3(10 + 1 + 1 + 1 + 1 + 2 \cdot 10 + 4) = 114$

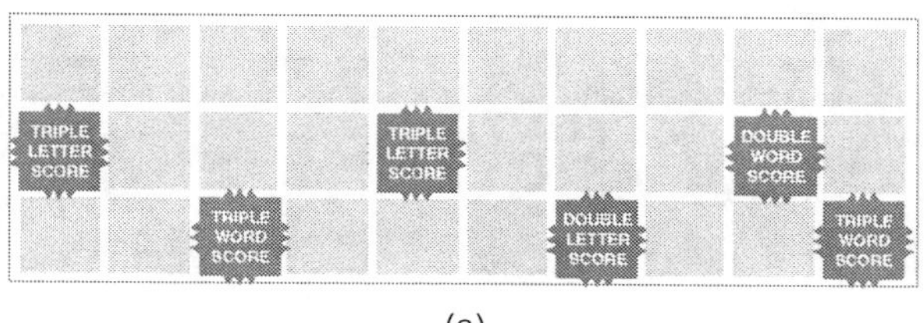

(a)

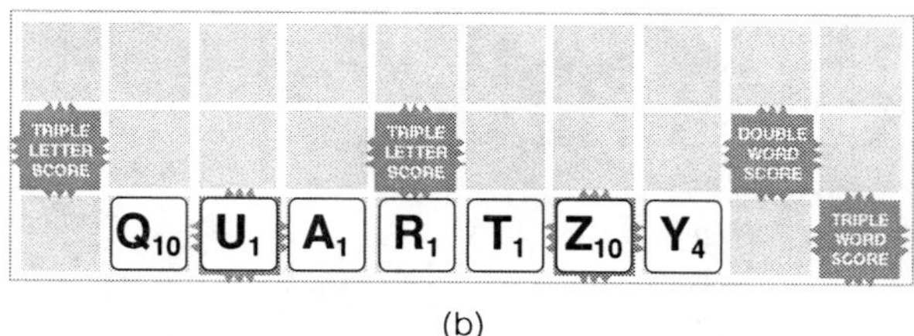

(b)

138. WRAPPING GIFTS How much ribbon is needed to wrap the package shown if 15 inches of ribbon are needed to make the bow? 81 in.

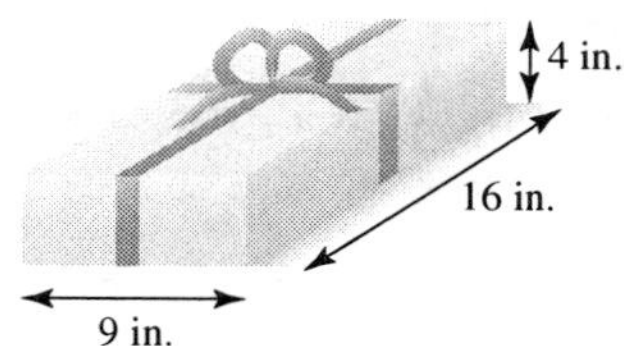

139. SPREADSHEETS This spreadsheet contains data collected by a chemist. For each row, the sum of the values in columns A and B is to be subtracted from the product of 6 and the value in column C. That result is then to be divided by 12 and entered in column D. Use this information to complete the spreadsheet.

	A	B	C	D
1	20	4	8	2
2	9	3	16	7
3	1	5	11	5

140. DOG SHOWS The final score for each dog competing in a toy breeds competition is computed by dividing the sum of the judges' marks, after the highest and lowest have been dropped, by 6. See the table.

a. What was their order of finish? pomeranian, terrier, pekingese

b. Did any judge rate all the dogs the same? yes, judge 6

Judge	1	2	3	4	5	6	7	8
Terrier	14	11	11	10	12	12	13	13
Pekingese	10	9	8	11	11	12	9	10
Pomeranian	15	14	13	11	14	12	10	14

WRITING

141. Explain the difference between 2^3 and 3^2.

142. Explain why rules for the order of operations are necessary.

143. What does it mean when we say perform all additions and subtractions *as they occur from left to right?*

144. In what settings do you encounter or use the concept of arithmetic mean (average) in your everyday life?

REVIEW

145. Match each term with the proper operation.

a. sum ii	**i.** division
b. difference iii	**ii.** addition
c. product iv	**iii.** subtraction
d. quotient i	**iv.** multiplication

146. What is the result when we add a number and its opposite? 0

147. What is the result when we divide a nonzero number by itself? 1

148. What is wrong with the following statement? Subtraction is the same as adding.
Subtraction is the same as adding the opposite.

SECTION 1.7
Square Roots

Objectives

1. Find the square root of a perfect square.
2. Find the square root of fractions and decimals.
3. Evaluate expressions that contain square roots.
4. Evaluate formulas involving square roots.
5. Approximate square roots.

We have discussed the relationships between addition and subtraction and between multiplication and division. In this section, we explore the relationship between raising a number to a power and finding a root. Decimals play an important role in this discussion.

1 Find the square root of a perfect square.

When we raise a number to the second power, we are squaring it, or finding its **square.**

The square of 6 is 36, because $6^2 = 36$.

The square of -6 is 36, because $(-6)^2 = 36$.

The **square root** of a given number is a number whose square is the given number. For example, the square roots of 36 are 6 and -6, because either number, when squared, is 36.

Every positive number has two square roots. The number 0 has only one square root. In fact, it is its own square root, because $0^2 = 0$.

Square Root

A number is a **square root** of a second number if the square of the first number equals the second number.

Self Check 1

Find the two square roots of 64. 8 and -8

Now Try **Problem 21**

Teaching Example 1 Find the two square roots of 4.

Answers:
2 and -2

EXAMPLE 1 Find the two square roots of 49.

Strategy We will ask "What positive number and what negative number, when squared, is 49?"

WHY The square root of 49 is a number whose square is 49.

Solution

7 is a square root of 49 because $7^2 = 49$

and

-7 is a square root of 49 because $(-7)^2 = 49$. ■

In Example 1, we saw that 49 has two square roots—one positive and one negative. The symbol $\sqrt{}$ is called a **radical symbol** and is used to indicate a positive square root of a nonnegative number. When reading this symbol, we usually drop the word *positive* and simply say *square root.* Since 7 is the positive square root of 49, we can write

$\sqrt{49} = 7$ $\quad$ $\sqrt{49}$ represents the positive number whose square is 49. Read as "the square root of 49 is 7."

When a number, called the **radicand,** is written under a radical symbol, we have a **radical expression.**

Radical symbol → $\sqrt{49}$ ← Radicand

Radical expression

Some other examples of radical expressions are:

$$\sqrt{36} \qquad \sqrt{100} \qquad \sqrt{144} \qquad \sqrt{81}$$

To evaluate (or simplify) a radical expression like those shown above, we need to find the positive square root of the radicand. For example, if we evaluate $\sqrt{36}$ (read as "the square root of 36"), the result is

$$\sqrt{36} = 6$$

because $6^2 = 36$.

> ***Caution!*** Remember that the radical symbol asks you to find only the *positive* square root of the radicand. It is incorrect, for example, to say that
>
> $$\sqrt{36} \text{ is } 6 \text{ and } -6$$

The symbol $-\sqrt{\ }$ is used to indicate the **negative square root** of a positive number. It is the opposite of the positive square root. Since –6 is the negative square root of 36, we can write

$$-\sqrt{36} = -6$$ Read as "the negative square root of 36 is −6" or "the opposite of the square root of 36 is −6." $-\sqrt{36}$ represents the negative number whose square is 36.

If the number under the radical symbol is 0, we have $\sqrt{0} = 0$.

Numbers, such as 36 and 49, that are squares of whole numbers, are called **perfect squares.** To evaluate square root radical expressions, it is helpful to be able to identify perfect square radicands. You need to memorize the following list of perfect squares, shown in red.

Perfect Squares

$0 = 0^2$	$16 = 4^2$	$64 = 8^2$	$144 = 12^2$
$1 = 1^2$	$25 = 5^2$	$81 = 9^2$	$169 = 13^2$
$4 = 2^2$	$36 = 6^2$	$100 = 10^2$	$196 = 14^2$
$9 = 3^2$	$49 = 7^2$	$121 = 11^2$	$225 = 15^2$

A calculator is helpful in finding the square root of a perfect square that is larger than 225.

EXAMPLE 2 Evaluate each square root: **a.** $\sqrt{81}$ **b.** $-\sqrt{100}$

Strategy In each case, we will determine what positive number, when squared, produces the radicand.

WHY The radical symbol $\sqrt{\ }$ indicates that the positive square root of the number written under it should be found.

Solution

a. $\sqrt{81} = 9$ Ask: What positive number, when squared, is 81? The answer is 9 because $9^2 = 81$.

b. $-\sqrt{100}$ is the opposite (or negative) of the square root of 100. Since $\sqrt{100} = 10$, we have

$$-\sqrt{100} = -10$$

Self Check 2

Evaluate each square root:

a. $\sqrt{144}$ 12

b. $-\sqrt{81}$ −9

Now Try **Problems 25 and 29**

Teaching Example 2 Evaluate each square root:
a. $\sqrt{25}$
b. $-\sqrt{121}$
Answers:
a. 5
b. −11

Caution! Radical expressions such as

$$\sqrt{-36} \quad \sqrt{-100} \quad \sqrt{-144} \quad \sqrt{-81}$$

do not represent real numbers, because there are no real numbers that when squared give a negative number.

Be careful to note the difference between expressions such as $-\sqrt{36}$ and $\sqrt{-36}$. We have seen that $-\sqrt{36}$ is a real number: $-\sqrt{36} = -6$. In contrast, $\sqrt{-36}$ is not a real number.

Using Your CALCULATOR **Finding a square root**

We use the [$\sqrt{\ }$] key (square root key) on a scientific calculator to find square roots. For example, to find $\sqrt{729}$, we enter these numbers and press these keys.

729 [$\sqrt{\ }$]   [27]

We have found that $\sqrt{729} = 27$. To check this result, we need to square 27. This can be done by entering 27 and pressing the [x^2] key. We obtain 729. Thus, 27 is the square root of 729.

Some calculator models require keystrokes of [2nd] and then [$\sqrt{\ }$] followed by the radicand to find a square root.

2 Find the square root of fractions and decimals.

So far, we have found square roots of whole numbers. We can also find square roots of fractions and decimals.

Self Check 3

Evaluate:

a. $\sqrt{\frac{16}{49}}$ $\frac{4}{7}$

b. $\sqrt{0.04}$ 0.2

Now Try **Problems 37 and 43**

Teaching Example 3 Evaluate each square root:

a. $\sqrt{\frac{81}{4}}$

b. $\sqrt{0.25}$

Answers:

a. $\frac{9}{2}$

b. 0.5

EXAMPLE 3 Evaluate each square root: **a.** $\sqrt{\frac{25}{64}}$ **b.** $\sqrt{0.81}$

Strategy In each case, we will determine what positive number, when squared, produces the radicand.

WHY The radical symbol $\sqrt{\ }$ indicates that the positive square root of the number written under it should be found.

Solution

a. $\sqrt{\frac{25}{64}} = \frac{5}{8}$ Ask: What positive fraction, when squared, is $\frac{25}{64}$? The answer is $\frac{5}{8}$ because $\left(\frac{5}{8}\right)^2 = \frac{25}{64}$.

b. $\sqrt{0.81} = 0.9$ Ask: What positive decimal, when squared, is 0.81? The answer is 0.9 because $(0.9)^2 = 0.81$.

3 Evaluate expressions that contain square roots.

In Chapters 1, 2, and 3, we used the order of operations rule to evaluate expressions that involve more than one operation. If an expression contains any square roots, they are to be evaluated at the same stage in your solution as exponential expressions. (See step 2 in the familiar order of operations rule on the next page.)

Order of Operations

1. Perform all calculations within parentheses and other grouping symbols following the order listed in Steps 2–4 below, working from the innermost pair of grouping symbols to the outermost pair.
2. Evaluate all exponential expressions and **square roots.**
3. Perform all multiplications and divisions as they occur from left to right.
4. Perform all additions and subtractions as they occur from left to right.

EXAMPLE 4 Evaluate: **a.** $\sqrt{64} + \sqrt{9}$ **b.** $-\sqrt{25} - \sqrt{225}$

Strategy We will scan the expression to determine what operations need to be performed. Then we will perform those operations, one-at-a-time, following the order of operations rule.

WHY If we don't follow the correct order of operations, the expression can have more than one value.

Solution Since the expression does not contain any parentheses, we begin with step 2 of the rules for the order of operations: Evaluate all exponential expressions and any square roots.

a. $\sqrt{64} + \sqrt{9} = 8 + 3$ *Evaluate each square root first.*

$= 11$ *Do the addition.*

b. $-\sqrt{25} - \sqrt{225} = -5 - 15$ *Evaluate each square root first.*

$= -20$ *Do the subtraction.*

Self Check 4

Evaluate:

a. $\sqrt{121} + \sqrt{1}$ 12

b. $-\sqrt{9} - \sqrt{196}$ −17

Now Try **Problems 49 and 53**

Teaching Example 4 Evaluate:
a. $\sqrt{81} + \sqrt{144}$
b. $-\sqrt{169} - \sqrt{100}$

Answers:
a. 21
b. −23

EXAMPLE 5 Evaluate: **a.** $6\sqrt{100}$ **b.** $-5\sqrt{16} + 3\sqrt{9}$

Strategy We will scan the expression to determine what operations need to be performed. Then we will perform those operations, one-at-a-time, following the order of operations rule.

WHY If we don't follow the correct order of operations, the expression can have more than one value.

Solution Since the expression does not contain any parentheses, we begin with step 2 of the rules for the order of operations: Evaluate all exponential expressions and any square roots.

a. We note that $6\sqrt{100}$ means $6 \cdot \sqrt{100}$.

$6\sqrt{100} = 6(10)$ *Evaluate the square root first.*

$= 60$ *Do the multiplication.*

b. $-5\sqrt{16} + 3\sqrt{9} = -5(4) + 3(3)$ *Evaluate each square root first.*

$= -20 + 9$ *Do the multiplication.*

$= -11$ *Do the addition.*

Self Check 5

Evaluate:

a. $8\sqrt{121}$ 88

b. $-6\sqrt{25} + 2\sqrt{36}$ −18

Now Try **Problems 57 and 61**

Teaching Example 5 Evaluate:
a. $5\sqrt{49}$
b. $-6\sqrt{1} + \sqrt{64}$

Answers:
a. 35
b. 2

EXAMPLE 6 Evaluate: $12 + 3[3^2 - (4 - 1)\sqrt{36}]$

Strategy We will work within the parentheses first and then within the brackets. Within each set of grouping symbols, we will follow the order of operations rule.

WHY By the order of operations rule, we must work from the *innermost* pair of grouping symbols to the *outermost.*

Self Check 6

Evaluate:
$10 - 4[2^2 - (3 + 2)\sqrt{4}]$ 34

Now Try **Problems 65 and 69**

Teaching Example 6 Evaluate: $15 + 2[4^2 - (4 + 1)\sqrt{25}]$

Answer: -3

Solution

$$12 + 3[3^2 - (4 - 1)\sqrt{36}] = 12 + 3[3^2 - 3\sqrt{36}]$$ Do the subtraction within the parentheses.

$$= 12 + 3[9 - 3(6)]$$ Within the brackets, evaluate the exponential expression and the square root.

$$= 12 + 3[9 - 18]$$ Do the multiplication within the brackets.

$$= 12 + 3[-9]$$ Do the subtraction within the brackets.

$$= 12 + (-27)$$ Do the multiplication.

$$= -15$$ Do the addition.

4 Evaluate formulas involving square roots.

To evaluate formulas that involve square roots, we replace the letters with specific numbers and the then use the order of operations rule.

Self Check 7

Evaluate $a = \sqrt{c^2 - b^2}$ for $c = 17$ and $b = 15$. 8

Now Try **Problem 81**

Teaching Example 7 Evaluate $c = \sqrt{a^2 + b^2}$ for $a = 5$ and $b = 12$.

Answer: 13

EXAMPLE 7 Evaluate $c = \sqrt{a^2 + b^2}$ for $a = 3$ and $b = 4$.

Strategy In the given formula, we will replace the letter a with 3 and b with 4. Then we will use the order of operations rule to find the value of the radicand.

WHY We need to know the value of the radicand before we can find its square root.

Solution

$$c = \sqrt{a^2 + b^2}$$ This is the formula to evaluate.

$$= \sqrt{3^2 + 4^2}$$ Replace a with 3 and b with 4.

$$= \sqrt{9 + 16}$$ Evaluate the exponential expressions.

$$= \sqrt{25}$$ Do the addition.

$$= 5$$ Evaluate the square root.

5 Approximate square roots.

In Examples 2–7, we have found square roots of perfect squares. If a number is not a perfect square, we can use the $\boxed{\sqrt{\ }}$ key on a calculator or a table of square roots to find its *approximate* square root. For example, to find $\sqrt{17}$ using a scientific calculator, we enter 17 and press the square root key:

17 $\boxed{\sqrt{\ }}$

The display reads

4.123105626

This result is an approximation, because the exact value of $\sqrt{17}$ is a **nonterminating decimal** that never repeats. If we round to the nearest thousandth, we have

$\sqrt{17} \approx 4.123$ Read ≈ as "is approximately equal to."

To check this approximation, we square 4.123.

$(4.123)^2 = 16.999129$

Since the result is close to 17, we know that $\sqrt{17} \approx 4.123$.

n	$\sqrt{n}$
11	3.317
12	3.464
13	3.606
14	3.742
15	3.873
16	4.000
17	4.123
18	4.243
19	4.359
20	4.472

A portion of the table of square roots from Appendix III on page A-00 is shown in the margin on the previous page. The table gives decimal approximations of square roots of whole numbers that are not perfect squares. To find an approximation of $\sqrt{17}$ to the nearest thousandth, we locate 17 in the n-column of the table and scan directly right, to the $\sqrt{n}$-column, to find that $\sqrt{17} \approx 4.123$.

EXAMPLE 8 Use a calculator to approximate each square root. Round to the nearest hundredth. **a.** $\sqrt{373}$ **b.** $\sqrt{56.2}$ **c.** $\sqrt{0.0045}$

Strategy We will identify the radicand and find the square root using the $\sqrt{}$ key. Then we will identify the digit in the thousandths column of the display.

WHY To round to the hundredths column, we must determine whether the digit in the thousandths column is less than 5, or greater than or equal to 5.

Solution

a. From the calculator, we get $\sqrt{373} \approx 19.31320792$. Rounded to the nearest hundredth, $\sqrt{373} \approx 19.31$.

b. From the calculator, we get $\sqrt{56.2} \approx 7.496665926$. Rounded to the nearest hundredth, $\sqrt{56.2} \approx 7.50$.

c. From the calculator, we get $\sqrt{0.0045} \approx 0.067082039$. Rounded to the nearest hundredth, $\sqrt{0.0045} \approx 0.07$.

Self Check 8

Use a calculator to approximate each square root. Round to the nearest hundredth.

a. $\sqrt{153}$ 12.37

b. $\sqrt{607.8}$ 24.65

c. $\sqrt{0.076}$ 0.28

Now Try **Problems 87 and 91**

Teaching Example 8 Use a calculator to approximate each square root. Round to the nearest hundredth.
a. $\sqrt{217}$
b. $\sqrt{89.1}$
c. $\sqrt{0.032}$

Answers:
a. 14.73
b. 9.44
c. 0.18

ANSWERS TO SELF CHECKS

1. 8 and −8 **2. a.** 12 **b.** −9 **3. a.** $\frac{4}{7}$ **b.** 0.2 **4. a.** 12 **b.** −17 **5. a.** 88 **b.** −18 **6.** 34 **7.** 8 **8. a.** 12.37 **b.** 24.65 **c.** 0.28

SECTION 1.7 STUDY SET

VOCABULARY

Fill in the blanks.

1. When we raise a number to the second power, we are squaring it, or finding its _square_.
2. The square _root_ of a given number is a number whose square is the given number.
3. The symbol $\sqrt{}$ is called a _radical_ symbol.
4. Label the *radicand,* the *radical expression,* and the *radical symbol* in the illustration below.

Radical symbol

$\sqrt{64}$ ← Radicand

Radical expression

5. Whole numbers such as 36 and 49, that are squares of whole numbers, are called _perfect_ squares.
6. The exact value of $\sqrt{17}$ is a _nonterminating_ decimal that never repeats.

CONCEPTS

Fill in the blanks.

7. **a.** The square of 5 is 25, because $5^2 = 25$.
   b. The square of $\frac{1}{4}$ is $\frac{1}{16}$, because $\left(\frac{1}{4}\right)^2 = \frac{1}{16}$.
8. Complete the list of perfect squares: 1, 4, 9, 16, 25, 36, 49, 64, 81, 100, 121, 144, 169, 196, 225.
9. **a.** $\sqrt{49} = 7$, because $7^2 = 49$.
   b. $\sqrt{4} = 2$, because $2^2 = 4$.
10. **a.** $\sqrt{\frac{9}{16}} = \frac{3}{4}$, because $\left(\frac{3}{4}\right)^2 = \frac{9}{16}$.
    b. $\sqrt{0.16} = 0.4$, because $(0.4)^2 = 0.16$.
11. Evaluate each square root.
    a. $\sqrt{1}$ 1 **b.** $\sqrt{0}$ 0
12. Evaluate each square root.
    a. $\sqrt{121}$ 11 **b.** $\sqrt{144}$ 12 **c.** $\sqrt{169}$ 13
    d. $\sqrt{196}$ 14 **e.** $\sqrt{225}$ 15

13. In what step of the order of operations rule are square roots to be evaluated? Step 2: Evaluate all exponential expressions and any square roots.

14. Graph $\sqrt{9}$ and $-\sqrt{4}$ on a number line.

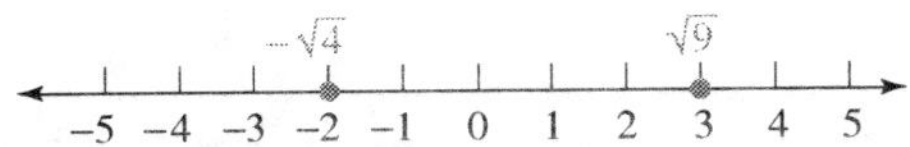

15. Graph $-\sqrt{3}$ and $\sqrt{7}$ on a number line. (*Hint:* Use a calculator or square root table to approximate each square root first.)

$-\sqrt{3}$ $\sqrt{7}$

−5 −4 −3 −2 −1 0 1 2 3 4 5

16. a. Between what two whole numbers would $\sqrt{19}$ be located when graphed on a number line? 4, 5

b. Between what two whole numbers would $\sqrt{50}$ be located when graphed on a number line? 7, 8

NOTATION

Fill in the blanks.

17. a. The symbol $\sqrt{}$ is used to indicate a positive square root.

b. The symbol $-\sqrt{}$ is used to indicate the negative square root of a positive number.

18. $4\sqrt{9}$ means $4 \cdot \sqrt{9}$.

Complete each solution to evaluate the expression.

19. $-\sqrt{49} + \sqrt{64} = -7 + 8$
$= 1$

▶ **20.** $2\sqrt{100} - 5\sqrt{25} = 2(10) - 5(5)$
$= 20 - 25$
$= -5$

GUIDED PRACTICE

Find the two square roots of each number. See Example 1.

21. 25 5 and −5 **22.** 1 1 and −1

23. 16 4 and −4 ▶ **24.** 144 12 and −12

Evaluate each square root without using a calculator. See Example 2.

25. $\sqrt{16}$ 4 ▶ **26.** $\sqrt{64}$ 8

27. $\sqrt{9}$ 3 **28.** $\sqrt{16}$ 4

29. $-\sqrt{144}$ −12 ▶ **30.** $-\sqrt{121}$ −11

31. $-\sqrt{49}$ −7 **32.** $-\sqrt{81}$ −9

Use a calculator to evaluate each square root. See Objective 1, Using Your Calculator.

33. $\sqrt{961}$ 31 **34.** $\sqrt{841}$ 29

35. $\sqrt{3{,}969}$ 63 ▶ **36.** $\sqrt{5{,}625}$ 75

Evaluate each square root without using a calculator. See Example 3.

37. $\sqrt{\frac{4}{25}}$ $\frac{2}{5}$ ▶ **38.** $\sqrt{\frac{36}{121}}$ $\frac{6}{11}$

39. $-\sqrt{\frac{16}{9}}$ $-\frac{4}{3}$ ▶ **40.** $-\sqrt{\frac{64}{25}}$ $-\frac{8}{5}$

41. $-\sqrt{\frac{1}{81}}$ $-\frac{1}{9}$ ▶ **42.** $-\sqrt{\frac{1}{4}}$ $-\frac{1}{2}$

43. $\sqrt{0.64}$ 0.8 ▶ **44.** $\sqrt{0.36}$ 0.6

45. $-\sqrt{0.81}$ −0.9 **46.** $-\sqrt{0.49}$ −0.7

47. $\sqrt{0.09}$ 0.3 **48.** $\sqrt{0.01}$ 0.1

Evaluate each expression without using a calculator. See Example 4.

49. $\sqrt{36} + \sqrt{1}$ 7 **50.** $\sqrt{100} + \sqrt{16}$ 14

51. $\sqrt{81} + \sqrt{49}$ 16 **52.** $\sqrt{4} + \sqrt{36}$ 8

53. $-\sqrt{144} - \sqrt{16}$ −16 ▶ **54.** $-\sqrt{1} - \sqrt{196}$ −15

55. $-\sqrt{225} + \sqrt{144}$ −3 **56.** $-\sqrt{169} + \sqrt{16}$ −9

Evaluate each expression without using a calculator. See Example 5.

▶ **57.** $4\sqrt{25}$ 20 **58.** $2\sqrt{81}$ 18

59. $-10\sqrt{196}$ −140 **60.** $-40\sqrt{4}$ −80

61. $-4\sqrt{169} + 2\sqrt{4}$ −48 ▶ **62.** $-6\sqrt{81} + 5\sqrt{1}$ −49

63. $-8\sqrt{16} + 5\sqrt{225}$ 43 **64.** $-3\sqrt{169} + 2\sqrt{225}$ −9

Evaluate each expression without using a calculator. See Example 6.

65. $15 + 4\left[5^2 - (6 - 1)\sqrt{4}\right]$ 75

▶ **66.** $18 + 2\left[4^2 - (7 - 3)\sqrt{9}\right]$ 26

67. $50 - \left[(6^2 - 24) + 9\sqrt{25}\right]$ −7

68. $40 - \left[(7^2 - 40) + 7\sqrt{64}\right]$ −25

69. $\sqrt{196} + 3\left(5^2 - 2\sqrt{225}\right)$ −1

70. $\sqrt{169} + 2\left(7^2 - 3\sqrt{144}\right)$ 39

71. $\dfrac{\sqrt{16} - 6(2^2)}{\sqrt{4}}$ −10 **72.** $\dfrac{\sqrt{49} - 3(1^6)}{\sqrt{16} - \sqrt{64}}$ −1

73. $\sqrt{\frac{1}{16}} - \sqrt{\frac{9}{25}}$ $-\frac{7}{20}$ **74.** $\sqrt{\frac{25}{9}} - \sqrt{\frac{64}{81}}$ $\frac{7}{9}$

75. $5\left(-\sqrt{49}\right)(-2)^2$ −140 ▶ **76.** $\left(-\sqrt{64}\right)(-2)(3)^3$ 432

77. $(6^2)\sqrt{0.04} + 2.36$ 9.56 **78.** $(5^2)\sqrt{0.25} + 4.7$ 17.2

79. $-\left(-3\sqrt{1.44} + 5\right)$ −1.4 ▶ **80.** $-\left(-2\sqrt{1.21} - 6\right)$ 8.2

Evaluate each formula without using a calculator. See Example 7.

81. Evaluate $c = \sqrt{a^2 + b^2}$ for $a = 9$ and $b = 12$. 15

▶ **82.** Evaluate $c = \sqrt{a^2 + b^2}$ for $a = 6$ and $b = 8$. 10

83. Evaluate $a = \sqrt{c^2 - b^2}$ for $c = 25$ and $b = 24$. 7

84. Evaluate $b = \sqrt{c^2 - a^2}$ for $c = 17$ and $a = 8$. 15

Use a calculator (or the square root table in Appendix III) to complete each square root table. Round to the nearest thousandth when an answer is not exact. See Example 8.

85.

Number	Square Root
1	1
2	1.414
3	1.732
4	2
5	2.236
6	2.449
7	2.646
8	2.828
9	3
10	3.162

86.

Number	Square Root
10	3.162
20	4.472
30	5.477
40	6.325
50	7.071
60	7.746
70	8.367
80	8.944
90	9.487
100	10

Use a calculator (or a square root table) to approximate each of the following to the nearest hundredth. See Example 8.

87. $\sqrt{15}$ 3.87

88. $\sqrt{51}$ 7.14

89. $\sqrt{66}$ 8.12

90. $\sqrt{204}$ 14.28

Use a calculator to approximate each of the following to the nearest thousandth. See Example 8.

91. $\sqrt{24.05}$ 4.904

92. $\sqrt{70.69}$ 8.408

93. $-\sqrt{11.1}$ −3.332

94. $\sqrt{0.145}$ 0.381

APPLICATIONS

In the following problems, some lengths are expressed as square roots. Solve each problem by evaluating any square roots. You may need to use a calculator. If so, round to the nearest tenth when an answer is not exact.

95. CARPENTRY Find the length of the slanted side of each roof truss shown below.

a. 5 ft

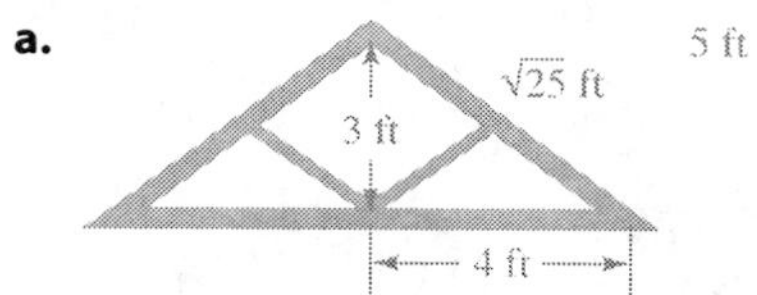

b. 10 ft

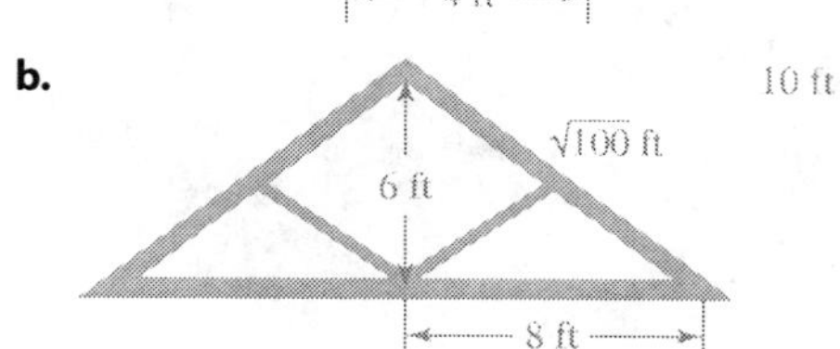

96. RADIO ANTENNAS Refer to the illustration below. How far from the base of the antenna is each guy wire anchored to the ground? (The measurements are in feet.) 12 ft, 4 ft, 6 ft

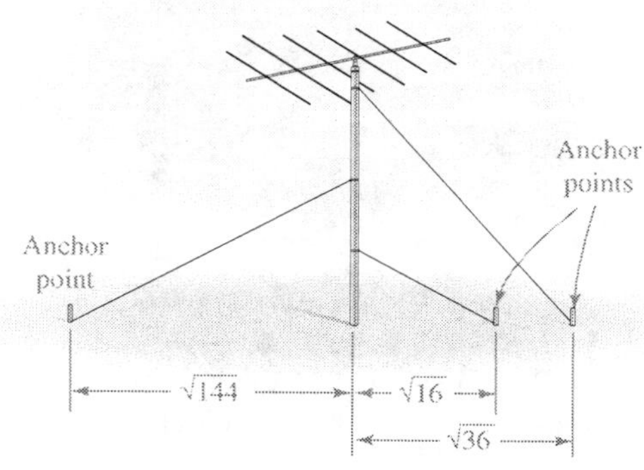

97. BASEBALL The illustration below shows some dimensions of a major league baseball field. How far is it from home plate to second base? 127.3 ft

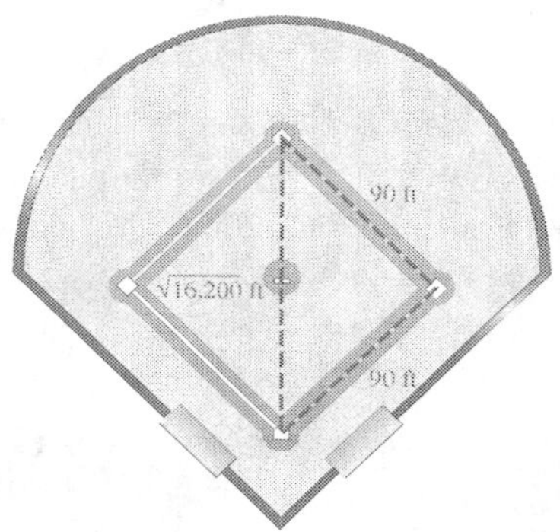

98. SURVEYING Refer to the illustration below. Use the imaginary triangles set up by a surveyor to find the length of each lake. (The measurements are in meters.)

a. 564 m

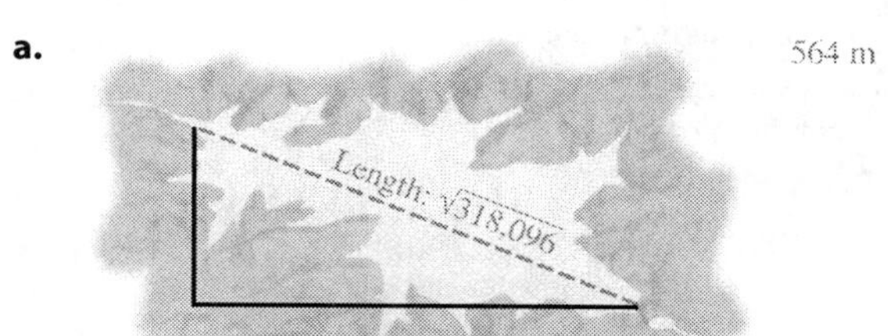

b. 305 m

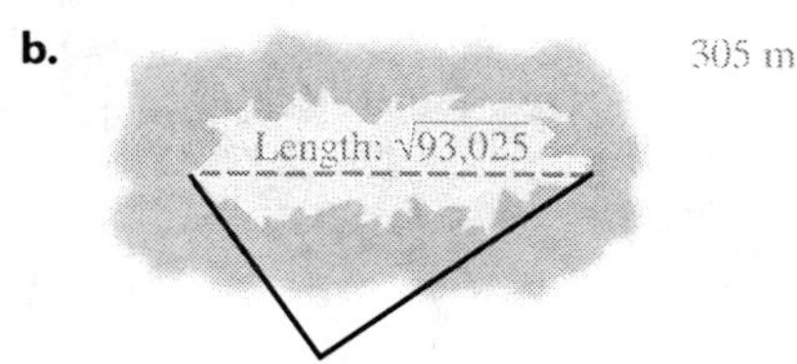

▶ **99.** FLATSCREEN TELEVISIONS The picture screen on a television set is measured diagonally. What size screen is shown below? 42-inch screen

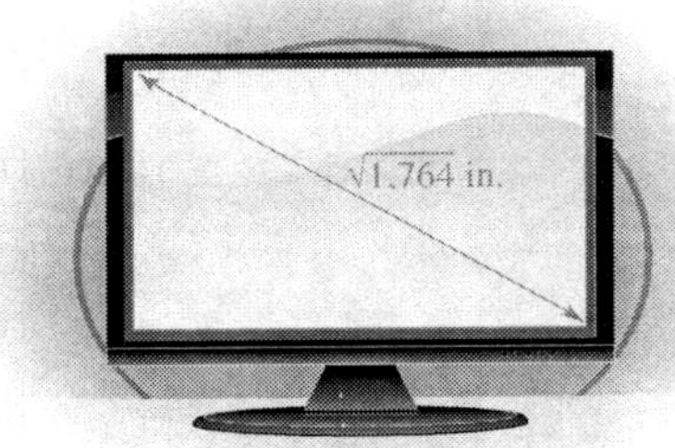

▶ **100.** LADDERS A painter's ladder is shown below. How long are the legs of the ladder? 15 ft, 13 ft

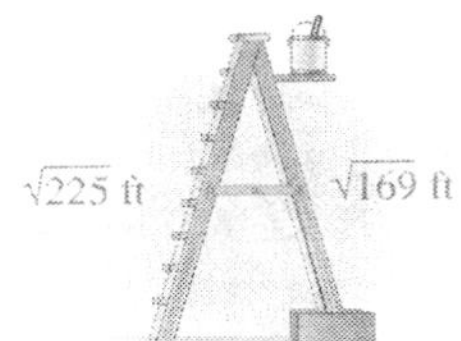

WRITING

101. When asked to find $\sqrt{16}$, a student answered 8. Explain his misunderstanding of the concept of square root.

▶ **102.** Explain the difference between the *square* and the *square root* of a number. Give an example.

103. What is a *nonterminating* decimal? Use an example in your explanation.

104. **a.** How would you check whether $\sqrt{389} = 17$?

b. How would you check whether $\sqrt{7} \approx 2.65$?

105. Explain why $\sqrt{-4}$ does not represent a real number.

106. Is there a difference between $-\sqrt{25}$ and $\sqrt{-25}$? Explain.

107. $\sqrt{6} \approx 2.449$. Explain why an $\approx$ symbol is used and not an $=$ symbol.

108. Without evaluating the following square roots, determine which is the largest and which is the smallest. Explain how you decided.

$$\sqrt{23}, \sqrt{27}, \sqrt{11}, \sqrt{6}, \sqrt{20}$$

REVIEW

109. Multiply: $6.75 \cdot 12.2$ 82.35

110. Divide: $5.7\overline{)18.525}$ 3.25

▶ **111.** Evaluate: $(3.4)^3$ 39.304

112. Add: $23.45 + 76 + 0.009 + 3.8$ 103.259

Objectives

1. Define scientific notation.
2. Write numbers in scientific notation.
3. Convert from scientific notation to standard notation.
4. Perform computations with scientific notation.

SECTION 1.8
Scientific Notation

Scientists often deal with extremely large and extremely small numbers. Two examples are shown below.

The distance from Earth to the sun is approximately 150,000,000 kilometers.

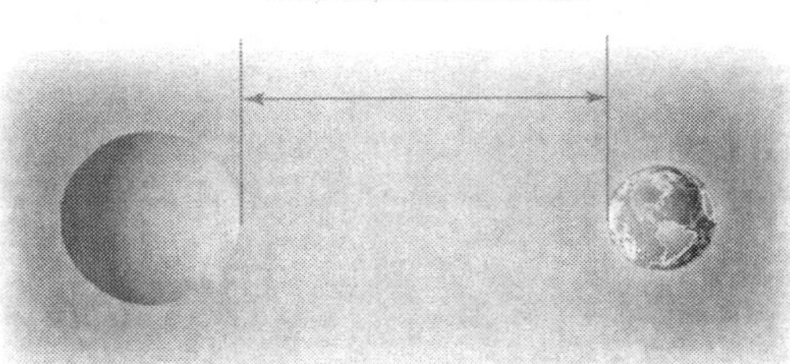

The influenza virus, which causes "flu" symptoms of cough, sore throat, headache, and congestion, has a diameter of 0.00000256 inch.

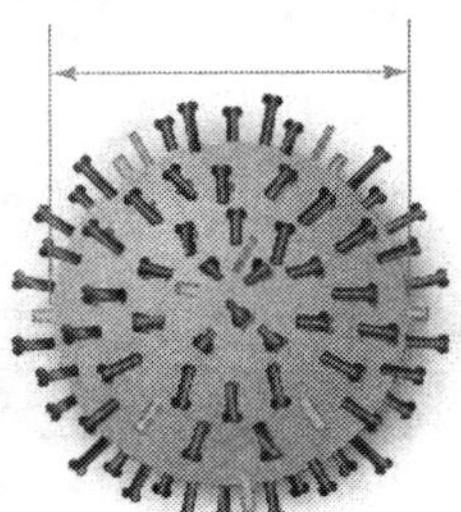

The large number of zeros in 150,000,000 and 0.00000256 makes them difficult to read and hard to remember. In this section, we will discuss a notation that will make such numbers easier to use.

1 Define scientific notation.

Scientific notation provides a compact way of writing large numbers, such as 5,213,000,000,000, and small numbers, such as 0.000000000000914.

Scientific Notation

A number is written in **scientific notation** when it is written as the product of a number between 1 (including 1) and 10, denoted N, and an integer power of 10, denoted n. In symbols, scientific notation has the form $N \times 10^n$.

These numbers are written in scientific notation:

3.9×10^6, 2.24×10^{-4}, and 9.875×10^{22}

Every number written in scientific notation has the following form:

An integer exponent

$\blacksquare.\blacksquare\blacksquare \times 10^{\blacksquare}$

A decimal between 1 and 10

2 Write numbers in scientific notation.

To write a number in scientific notation ($N \times 10^n$), we first determine N then n.

EXAMPLE 1 Change to scientific notation: 150,000,000

Strategy We will write the number as a product of a number between 1 and 10 and a power of 10.

WHY Numbers written in scientific notation have the form $N \times 10^n$.

Solution

We note that 1.5 lies between 1 and 10. To obtain 150,000,000, the decimal point in 1.5 must be moved eight places to the right.

1.50000000

8 places to the right

Because multiplying a number by 10 moves the decimal point one place to the right, we can accomplish this by multiplying 1.5 by 10 eight times. We can show the multiplication of 1.5 by 10 eight times using the notation 10^8. Thus, 150,000,000 written in scientific notation is 1.5×10^8.

Self Check 1

The distance from Earth to the sun is approximately 93,000,000 miles. Write this number in scientific notation. 9.3×10^7

Now Try **Problem 20**

Teaching Example 1 Change to scientific notation: 2,340,000,000
Answer:
2.34×10^9

EXAMPLE 2 Change to scientific notation: 0.00000256

Strategy We will write the number as a product of a number between 1 and 10 and a power of 10.

WHY Numbers written in scientific notation have the form $N \times 10^n$.

Solution

We note that 2.56 is between 1 and 10. To obtain 0.00000256, the decimal point in 2.56 must be moved six places to the left.

Self Check 2

The *Salmonella* bacterium, which causes food poisoning, is 0.00009055 inch long. Write this number in scientific notation. 9.055×10^{-5}

Now Try **Problem 26**

Teaching Example 2 Change 0.000000057 to scientific notation.
Answer:
5.7×10^{-8}

0 0 0 0 0 2 . 56
6 places to the left

We can accomplish this by dividing 2.56 by 10^6, which is equivalent to multiplying 2.56 by $\frac{1}{10^6}$ (or by 10^{-6}). Thus, 0.00000256 written in scientific notation is 2.56×10^{-6}.

Self Check 3

Write in scientific notation:

a. 17,500 1.75×10^4

b. 0.657 6.57×10^{-1}

Now Try **Problems 27 and 29**

Teaching Example 3 Write in scientific notation

a. 0.000042 b. 5,367,000,000

Answers:

a. 4.2×10^{-5} b. 5.367×10^9

EXAMPLE 3 Write in scientific notation: **a.** 235,000 **b.** 0.0000073

Strategy We will write each number as a product of a number between 1 and 10 and a power of 10.

WHY Numbers written in scientific notation have the form $N \times 10^n$.

Solution

a. $235{,}000 = 2.35 \times 10^5$ Because $2.35 \times 10^5 = 235{,}000$ and 2.35 is between 1 and 10

b. $0.0000073 = 7.3 \times 10^{-6}$ Because $7.3 \times 10^{-6} = 0.0000073$ and 7.3 is between 1 and 10

Sucess Tip From Examples 1, 2, and 3, we see that in scientific notation, a positive exponent is used when writing a number that is greater than 10. A negative exponent is used when writing a number that is between 0 and 1.

Using Your CALCULATOR **Calculators and Scientific Notation**

When displaying a very large or a very small number as an answer, most scientific calculators express it in scientific notation. To show this, we will find the values of $(453.46)^5$ and $(0.0005)^{12}$. We enter these numbers and press these keys.

453.46 [y^x] 5 [=] 1.917321395 13

.0005 [y^x] 12 [=] 2.44140625 −40

Since the answers in standard notation require more space than the calculator display has, the calculator gives each result in scientific notation. The first display represents $1.917321395 \times 10^{13}$, and the second represents $2.44140625 \times 10^{-40}$.

If we evaluate the same two expressions using a graphing or direct-entry calculator, we see that the letter E is used when displaying a number in scientific notation.

453.46 [^] 5 [ENTER] 453.46^5
1.917321395E13

.0005 [^] 12 [ENTER] .0005^12
2.44140625E − 40

Caution! When reading an answer such as [1.917321395 13] off the calculator, be careful to write $1.917321395 \times 10^{13}$, not 1.917321395^{13}.

EXAMPLE 4 Write in scientific notation: 432.0×10^5

Strategy We will write the number as a product of a number between 1 and 10 and a power of 10.

WHY Numbers written in scientific notation have the form $N \times 10^n$.

Solution

The number 432.0×10^5 is not written in scientific notation, because 432.0 is not a number between 1 and 10. To write this number in scientific notation, we proceed as follows:

$$432.0 \times 10^5 = 4.32 \times 10^2 \times 10^5 \quad \text{Write 432.0 in scientific notation.}$$
$$= 4.32 \times 10^7 \quad 10^2 \times 10^5 = 10^{2+5} = 10^7.$$

Self Check 4

Write in scientific notation: 85×10^{-3} 8.5×10^{-2}

Now Try **Problem 40**

Teaching Example 4 Write 0.026×10^5 in scientific notation.
Answer:
2.6×10^3

3 Convert from scientific notation to standard notation.

We can change a number written in scientific notation to **standard notation.** For example, to write 9.3×10^7 in standard notation, we multiply 9.3 by 10^7.

$$9.3 \times 10^7 = 9.3 \times 10{,}000{,}000 \quad 10^7 \text{ is equal to 1 followed by 7 zeros.}$$
$$= 93{,}000{,}000$$

The following numbers are written in both scientific and standard notation. In each case, the exponent gives the number of places that the decimal point moves, and the sign of the exponent indicates the direction that it moves.

$5.32 \times 10^5 = 532000.$ The decimal point moves 5 places to the right.

$8.95 \times 10^{-4} = 0.000895$ The decimal point moves 4 places to the left.

$9.77 \times 10^0 = 9.77$ There is no movement of the decimal point.

The following summarizes our observations.

Converting from Scientific to Standard Notation

1. If the exponent on 10 is positive, move the decimal point the same number of places to the right as the exponent.
2. If the exponent on 10 is negative, move the decimal point the same number of places to the left as the absolute value of the exponent.

EXAMPLE 5 Convert to standard notation: **a.** 3.4×10^5 **b.** 2.1×10^{-4}

Strategy We will identify the exponent on the 10 and consider its sign.

WHY The exponent gives the number of decimal places that we should move the decimal point. The sign of the exponent indicates whether it should be moved to the right or the left.

Solution

a. $3.4 \times 10^5 = 3.4 \times 100{,}000$
$= 340{,}000$

b. $2.1 \times 10^{-4} = 2.1 \times \frac{1}{10^4}$
$= 2.1 \times \frac{1}{10{,}000}$
$= 2.1 \times 0.0001$
$= 0.00021$

Self Check 5

Convert to standard notation:

a. 4.76×10^5 476,000

b. 9.8×10^{-3} 0.0098

Now Try **Problems 50 and 52**

Teaching Example 5 Convert to standard notation:
a. 2.47×10^{-5} b. 7.142×10^7
Answers:
a. 0.0000247
b. 71,420,000

4 Perform computations with scientific notation.

Another advantage of scientific notation becomes apparent when we evaluate products or quotients that contain very large or very small numbers.

Self Check 6

Use scientific notation to evaluate:
(2,540,000,000,000) (0.00041)

Now Try **Problem 55**

Self Check 6 Answer
1.0414×10^9

Teaching Example 6 Use scientific notation to evaluate:
(0.0000024) (5,310,000,000,000)
Answer:
1.2744×10^7 or 12,744,000

EXAMPLE 6 *Astronomy* Except for the sun, the nearest star visible to the naked eye from most parts of the United States is Sirius. Light from Sirius reaches Earth in about 70,000 hours. If light travels at approximately 670,000,000 mph, how far from Earth is Sirius?

NASA

Strategy We will use the formula $d = rt$ to find the distance from Sirius to Earth.

WHY We know the *rate* at which light travels and the *time* it takes to travel from Sirius to Earth. We want to know the distance.

Solution
We are given the rate at which light travels (670,000,000 mph) and the time it takes the light to travel from Sirius to Earth (70,000 hr). We can find the distance the light travels using the formula $d = rt$.

$d = rt$

$d = 670{,}000{,}000(70{,}000)$ Substitute 670,000,000 for r and 70,000 for t.

$= (6.7 \times 10^8)(7.0 \times 10^4)$ Write each number in scientific notation.

$= (6.7 \cdot 7.0) \times (10^8 \cdot 10^4)$ Group the numbers together and the powers of 10 together.

$= (6.7 \cdot 7.0) \times 10^{8+4}$ Keep the base and add the exponents.

$= 46.9 \times 10^{12}$ Perform the multiplication. Perform the addition.

We note that 46.9 is not between 0 and 1, so 46.9×10^{12} is not written in scientific notation. To answer in scientific notation, we proceed as follows.

$= 4.69 \times 10^1 \times 10^{12}$ Write 46.9 in scientific notation as 4.69×10^1.

$= 4.69 \times 10^{13}$ Keep the base of 10 and add the exponents.

Sirius is approximately 4.69×10^{13} or 46,900,000,000,000 miles from Earth. ■

THINK IT THROUGH ***Science Majors and Space Travel***

"The number of U.S. college students earning degrees in science, technology, engineering, and math has fallen over the last 15 years. What a better way to hook our children than with a new space exploration plan?"

Patricia Arnold, Space Foundation, 2004

It has been almost 40 years since a U.S. astronaut last walked on the moon. Many educators feel that manned flights to the moon and Mars would ignite a passion for space and science studies among young people. However, the minimum distance Mars is from Earth is 135 times further than the moon is from Earth. Traveling such a long way poses many problems. If the average distance from Earth to the moon is about 2.4×10^5 miles, what is the distance between Earth and Mars? Express the result in scientific notation. 3.24×10^7 mi.

EXAMPLE 7 *Atoms* Scientific notation is used in chemistry. As an example, we can approximate the weight (in grams) of one atom of the heaviest naturally occurring element, uranium, by evaluating the following expression.

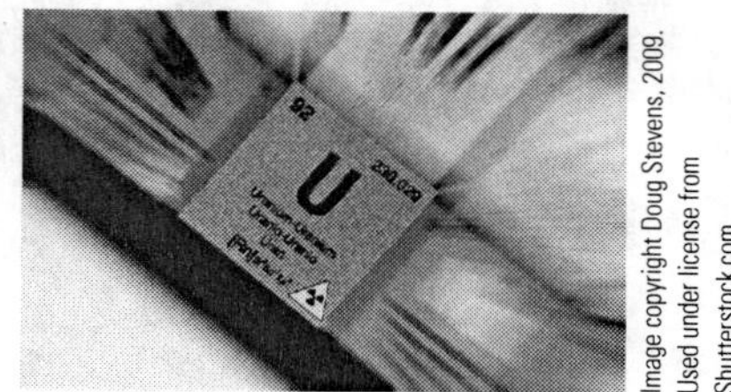

Image copyright Doug Stevens, 2009. Used under license from Shutterstock.com

$$\frac{2.4 \times 10^2}{6.0 \times 10^{23}}$$

Strategy We will divide the numbers and the powers of 10 separately.

WHY We can use the quotient rule for exponents to simplify the calculations.

Solution

$$\frac{2.4 \times 10^2}{6.0 \times 10^{23}} = \frac{2.4}{6.0} \times \frac{10^2}{10^{23}}$$ Divide the numbers and the powers of 10 separately.

$$= \frac{2.4}{6.0} \times 10^{2-23}$$ For the powers of 10, keep the base and subtract the exponents.

$$= 0.4 \times 10^{-21}$$ Perform the division. Then subtract the exponents.

$$= 4.0 \times 10^{-1} \times 10^{-21}$$ Write 0.4 in scientific notation as 4.0×10^{-1}.

$$= 4.0 \times 10^{-22}$$ Keep the base and add the exponents.

One atom of uranium weighs 4.0×10^{-22} gram. Written in standard notation, this is 0.00000000000000000000004 g.

Self Check 7

Find the approximate weight (in grams) of one atom of gold by evaluating: $\frac{1.98 \times 10^2}{6.0 \times 10^{23}}$

Now Try **Problem 58**

Self Check 7 Answer
3.3×10^{-22} g

Teaching Example 7 Evaluate: $\frac{5.2 \times 10^{15}}{4.0 \times 10^{6}}$
Answer:
1.3×10^{9}

Using Your CALCULATOR **Entering Numbers in Scientific Notation**

We can evaluate the expression from Example 7 by entering the numbers written in scientific notation, using the [EE] key on a scientific calculator.

2.4 [EE] 2 [÷] 6 [EE] 23 [=] 4. −22

The result shown in the display means 4.0×10^{-22}.

If we use a graphing calculator, the keystrokes are similar.

2.4 [2nd] [EE] 2 [÷] 6 [2nd] [EE] 23 [ENTER]

```
2.4E2/6E23
      4 E - 22
```

ANSWERS TO SELF CHECKS

1. 9.3×10^7 **2.** 9.055×10^{-5} **3. a.** 1.75×10^4 **b.** 6.57×10^{-1} **4.** 8.5×10^{-2}
5. a. 476,000 **b.** 0.0098 **6.** 1.0414×10^9 **7.** 3.3×10^{-22} g

SECTION 1.8 STUDY SET

VOCABULARY

Fill in the blanks.

1. A number is written in scientific notation when it is written as the product of a number between 1 (including 1) and 10 and an integer power of 10.

▶ 2. The number 125,000 is written in standard notation.

CONCEPTS

Fill in the blanks by writing the number in standard notation.

3. $2.5 \times 10^2 =$ 250
4. $2.5 \times 10^{-2} =$ 0.025
5. $2.5 \times 10^{-5} =$ 0.000025
6. $2.5 \times 10^5 =$ 250,000

Fill in the blanks with a power of 10.

7. $387{,}000 = 3.87 \times 10^5$
8. $38.7 = 3.87 \times 10^1$
9. $0.00387 = 3.87 \times 10^{-3}$
10. $0.000387 = 3.87 \times 10^{-4}$
11. When we multiply a decimal by 10^5, the decimal point moves 5 places to the right.
12. When we multiply a decimal by 10^{-7}, the decimal point moves 7 places to the left.
13. Dividing a decimal by 10^4 is equivalent to multiplying it by 10^{-4}.
14. Multiplying a decimal by 10^0 does not move the decimal point, because $10^0 =$ 1.
15. When a real number greater than 10 is written in scientific notation, the exponent on 10 is a positive number.

▶ 16. When a real number between 0 and 1 is written in scientific notation, the exponent on 10 is a negative number.

NOTATION

Complete each solution.

17. Write in scientific notation: 63.7×10^5

$$63.7 \times 10^5 = 6.37 \times 10^1 \times 10^5$$
$$= 6.37 \times 10^{1+5}$$
$$= 6.37 \times 10^6$$

▶ 18. Simplify: $\dfrac{64{,}000}{0.00004}$

$$\frac{64{,}000}{0.00004} = \frac{6.4 \times 10^4}{4 \times 10^{-5}}$$
$$= \frac{6.4}{4} \times \frac{10^4}{10^{-5}}$$
$$= 1.6 \times 10^{4-(-5)}$$
$$= 1.6 \times 10^9$$

GUIDED PRACTICE

Write each number in scientific notation. See Example 1.

19. 23,000 2.3×10^4
20. 4,750 4.75×10^3
21. 625,000 6.25×10^5
▶ 22. 320,000 3.2×10^5

Write each answer in scientific notation. See Example 2.

23. 0.062 6.2×10^{-2}
24. 0.75 7.5×10^{-1}
25. 0.00073 7.3×10^{-4}
▶ 26. 0.000057 5.7×10^{-5}

Write each number in scientific notation. See Example 3.

27. 543,000 5.43×10^5
28. 17,000,000 1.7×10^7
29. 0.00000875 8.75×10^{-6}
30. 0.000002 2×10^{-6}
31. 1,700,000 1.7×10^6
▶ 32. 290,000 2.9×10^5
33. 909,000,000 9.09×10^8
34. 7,007,000,000 7.007×10^9
35. 0.00502 5.02×10^{-3}
36. 0.0000081 8.1×10^{-6}
37. 0.0000051 5.1×10^{-6}
▶ 38. 0.04 4.0×10^{-2}

Write each number in scientific notation. See Example 4.

39. 42.5×10^2 4.25×10^3
▶ 40. 25.2×10^{-3} 2.52×10^{-2}
41. 0.25×10^{-2} 2.5×10^{-3}
▶ 42. 0.3×10^3 3.0×10^2
43. 201.8×10^{15} 2.018×10^{17}
44. 154.3×10^{17} 1.543×10^{19}
▶ 45. 0.073×10^{-3} 7.3×10^{-5}
46. 0.0017×10^{-4} 1.7×10^{-7}

Write each number in standard notation. See Example 5.

47. 2.3×10^2 230
▶ 48. 3.75×10^4 37,500
49. 8.12×10^5 812,000
50. 1.2×10^3 1,200
51. 1.15×10^{-3} 0.00115
▶ 52. 4.9×10^{-2} 0.049
53. 9.76×10^{-4} 0.000976
▶ 54. 7.63×10^{-5} 0.0000763

Use scientific notation and the rules for exponents to simplify each expression. Give all answers in standard notation. See Examples 6–7.

55. $(3.4 \times 10^2)(2.1 \times 10^3)$ 714,000
56. $(4.1 \times 10^{-3})(3.4 \times 10^4)$ 139.4
57. $\dfrac{9.3 \times 10^2}{3.1 \times 10^{-2}}$ 30,000
▶ 58. $\dfrac{7.2 \times 10^6}{1.2 \times 10^8}$ 0.06

▶ Selected exercises available online at **www.webassign.net/brookscole**

TRY IT YOURSELF

Simplify if necessary, then write the answer in standard notation.

59. 25×10^6 25,000,000

60. 0.07×10^3 70

61. 0.51×10^{-3} 0.00051

62. 2.37×10^{-4} 0.000237

63. 617×10^{-2} 6.17

64. $5{,}280 \times 10^{-3}$ 5.280

65. 0.699×10^3 699

66. 0.012×10^4 120

67. $\dfrac{0.00000129}{0.0003}$ 0.0043

68. $\dfrac{169{,}000{,}000{,}000}{26{,}000{,}000}$ 6,500

69. $\dfrac{96{,}000}{(12{,}000)(0.00004)}$ 200,000

70. $\dfrac{(0.48)(14{,}400{,}000)}{96{,}000{,}000}$ 0.072

71. $(456.4)^6$ 9,038,030,748,000,000

72. $(0.053)^4$ 0.000007890481

73. $(0.009)^{-6}$ 1,881,676,423,000

74. 225^{-3} 0.0000000877914952

75. $\left(\dfrac{1}{3}\right)^{-25}$ 847,288,609,400

76. $\left(\dfrac{8}{5}\right)^{50}$ 16,069,380,440

APPLICATIONS

77. ASTRONOMY The distance from Earth to Alpha Centauri (the nearest star outside our solar system) is about 25,700,000,000,000 miles. Express this number in scientific notation. 2.57×10^{13} mi

78. SPEED OF SOUND The speed of sound in air is 33,100 centimeters per second. Express this number in scientific notation. 3.31×10^4 cm/sec

79. GEOGRAPHY The largest ocean in the world is the Pacific Ocean, which covers 6.38×10^7 square miles. Express this number in standard notation. 63,800,000 mi^2

80. ATOMS The number of atoms in 1 gram of iron is approximately 1.08×10^{22}. Express this number in standard notation. 10,800,000,000,000,000,000,000

81. LENGTH OF A METER One meter is approximately 0.00622 mile. Use scientific notation to express this number. 6.22×10^{-3} mi

82. ANGSTROM One angstrom is 1.0×10^{-7} millimeter. Express this number in standard notation. 0.0000001 mm

83. WAVELENGTHS Transmitters, vacuum tubes, and lights emit energy that can be modeled as a wave, as shown. Examples of the most common types of electromagnetic waves are given in the table. List the wavelengths in order from shortest to longest. g, x, u, v, i, m, r

This distance between the two crests of the wave is called the wavelength.

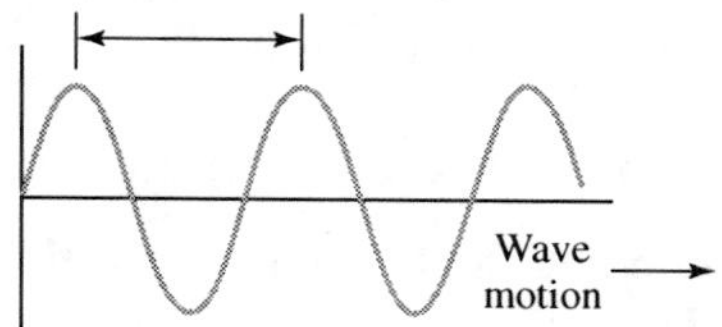

Type	Use	Wavelength (m)
visible light	lighting	9.3×10^{-6}
infrared	photography	3.7×10^{-5}
x-ray	medical	2.3×10^{-11}
radio wave	communication	3.0×10^{2}
gamma ray	treating cancer	8.9×10^{-14}
microwave	cooking	1.1×10^{-2}
ultraviolet	sun lamp	6.1×10^{-8}

84. SPACE EXPLORATION On July 4, 1997, the *Pathfinder,* carrying the rover vehicle called Sojourner, landed on Mars to perform a scientific investigation of the planet. The distance from Mars to Earth is approximately 3.5×10^7 miles. Use scientific notation to express this distance in feet. (*Hint:* 5,280 feet = 1 mile.) 1.848×10^{11} ft

Space Frontiers/Hulton Archive/Getty Images

85. PROTONS The mass of one proton is approximately 1.7×10^{-24} gram. Use scientific notation to express the mass of 1 million protons. 1.7×10^{-18} g

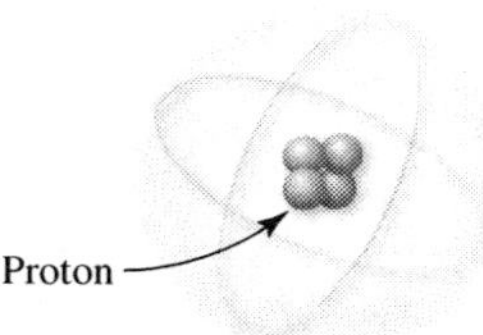

▶ **86.** SPEED OF SOUND The speed of sound in air is approximately 3.3×10^4 centimeters per second. Use scientific notation to express this speed in kilometers per second. (*Hint:* 100 centimeters = 1 meter and 1,000 meters = 1 kilometer.) 3.3×10^{-1} km/sec

▶ **87.** LIGHT YEARS One light year is about 5.87×10^{12} miles. Use scientific notation to express this distance in feet. (*Hint:* 5,280 feet = 1 mile.) 3.099363×10^{16} ft

▶ **88.** OIL RESERVES In 2006, Saudi Arabia had crude oil reserves of about 2.643×10^{11} barrels. A barrel contains 42 gallons of oil. Use scientific notation to express Saudi Arabia oil reserves in gallons. (Source: infoplease) 1.11006×10^{13} gal

89. INSURED DEPOSITS In 2006, the total insured deposits in U.S. banks and savings and loans was approximately 6.4×10^{12} dollars. If this money was invested at 4% simple annual interest, how much would it earn in 1 year? Use scientific notation to express the answer. (Source: Federal Deposit Insurance Corporation.) 2.56×10^{11} dollars

▶ **90.** CURRENCY In 2006, the number of \$20 bills in circulation was approximately 5.96×10^9. Find the total value of the currency. Use scientific notation to express the answer. (Source: The Federal Reserve.) 1.192×10^{11} dollars

▶ **91.** THE MILITARY The graph shows the number of U.S. troops for several years. Estimate each of the following and express your answers in scientific and standard notation.

a. The number of troops in 1993 1.7×10^6, 1,700,000

b. The largest numbers of troops during these years 1986: 2.05×10^6, 2,050,000

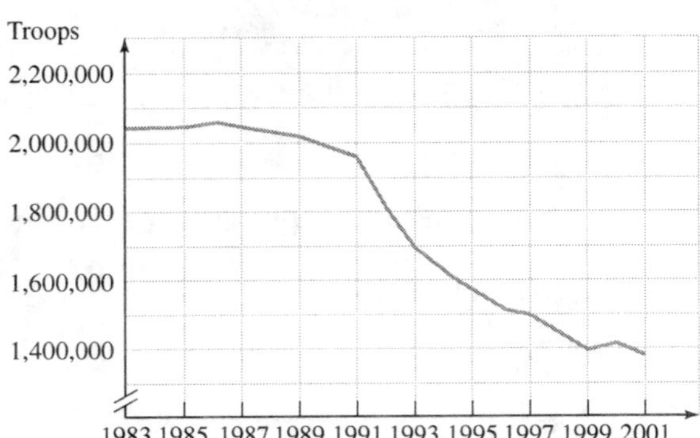

Based on data from the U.S. Department of Defense

92. SUPERCOMPUTERS In 2006, the world's fastest computer was IBM's BlueGene/L System. If it could make 2.81×10^{14} calculations in one second, how many could it make in one minute? Give the answer in scientific notation. 1.686×10^{16}

© Kimberly White/Reuters/Corbis

WRITING

93. In what situations would scientific notation be more convenient than standard notation?

▶ **94.** To multiply a number by a power of 10, we move the decimal point. Which way, and how far? Explain.

95. 2.3×10^{-3} contains a negative sign but represents a positive number. Explain.

▶ **96.** Is this a true statement? $2.0 \times 10^3 = 2 \times 10^3$ Explain.

REVIEW

97. If $y = -1$, find the value of $-5y^{55}$. 5

▶ **98.** What is the y-intercept of the graph of $y = -3x - 5$? $(0, -5)$

Determine which property of real numbers justifies each statement.

99. $5 + z = z + 5$ commutative property of addition

100. $7(u + 3) = 7u + 7 \cdot 3$ distributive property

Solve each equation.

101. $3(x - 4) - 6 = 0$ 6

102. $8(3x - 5) - 4(2x + 3) = 12$ 4

SECTION 1.9
Perimeters and Areas of Polygons

Objectives

1 Find the perimeter of a polygon.

2 Find the area of a polygon.

3 Find the area of figures that are combinations of polygons.

In this section, we will discuss how to find perimeters and areas of polygons. Finding perimeters is important when estimating the cost of fencing a yard or installing crown molding in a room. Finding area is important when calculating the cost of carpeting, painting a room, or fertilizing a lawn.

1 Find the perimeter of a polygon.

The **perimeter** of a polygon is the distance around it. To find the perimeter P of a polygon, we simply add the lengths of its sides.

Triangle

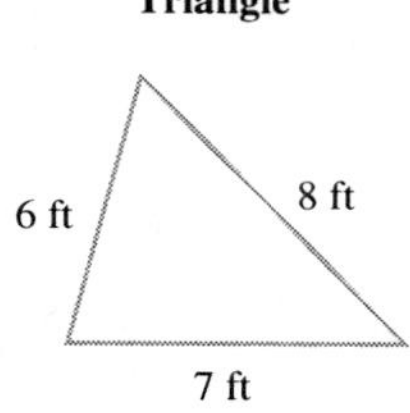

$P = 6 + 7 + 8$
$= 21$

The perimeter is 21 ft.

Quadrilateral

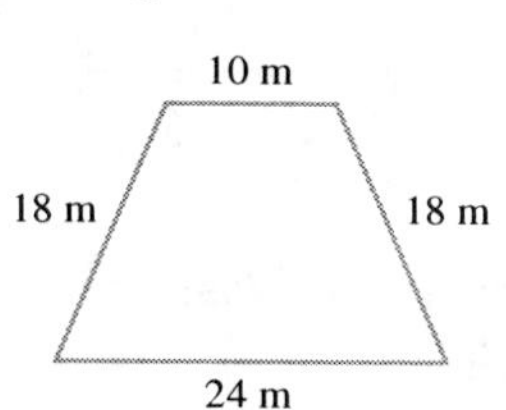

$P = 10 + 18 + 24 + 18$
$= 70$

The perimeter is 70 m.

Pentagon

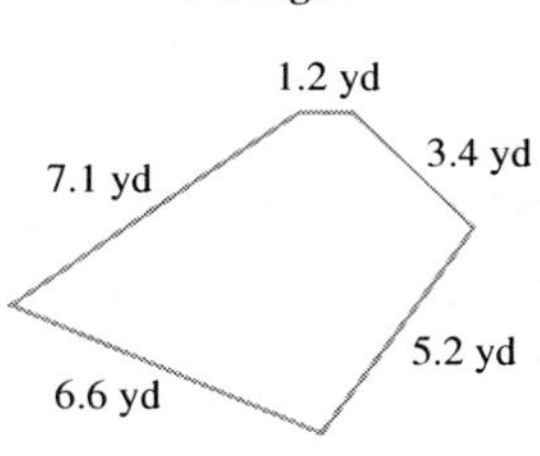

$P = 1.2 + 7.1 + 6.6 + 5.2 + 3.4$
$= 23.5$

The perimeter is 23.5 yd.

For some polygons, such as a square and a rectangle, we can simplify the computations by using a perimeter formula. Since a square has four sides of equal length s, its perimeter P is $s + s + s + s$, or $4s$.

Perimeter of a Square

If a square has a side of length s, its perimeter P is given by the formula

$$P = 4s$$

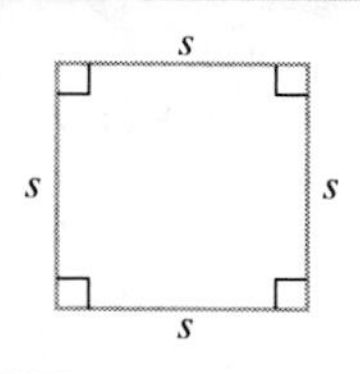

EXAMPLE 1 Find the perimeter of a square whose sides are 7.5 meters long.

Strategy We will substitute 7.5 for s in the formula $P = 4s$ and evaluate the right side.

WHY The variable P represents the unknown perimeter of the square.

Solution

$P = 4s$ This is the formula for the perimeter of a square.

$P = 4(7.5)$ Substitute 7.5 for s, the length of one side of the square.

$P = 30$ Do the multiplication.

$$\begin{array}{r} \overset{2}{7}.5 \\ \times\ 4 \\ \hline 30.0 \end{array}$$

The perimeter of the square is 30 meters.

Self Check 1

A Scrabble game board has a square shape with sides of length 38.5 cm. Find the perimeter of the game board. 154 cm

Now Try **Problems 17 and 19**

Teaching Example 1 Find the perimeter of a square whose sides are 2.5 miles long.

Answer:
10 mi

Since a rectangle has two lengths l and two widths w, its perimeter P is given by $l + w + l + w$, or $2l + 2w$.

Perimeter of a Rectangle

If a rectangle has length l and width w, its perimeter P is given by the formula

$$P = 2l + 2w$$

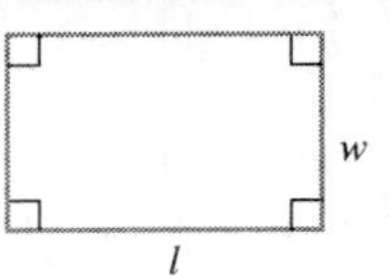

Caution! When finding the perimeter of a polygon, the lengths of the sides must be expressed in the same units.

Self Check 2

Find the perimeter of the triangle shown below, in inches. 50 in.

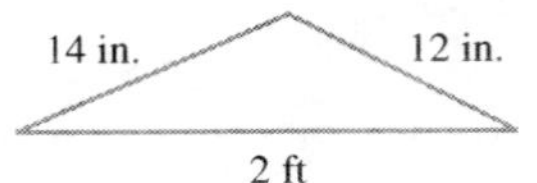

Now Try **Problem 21**

Teaching Example 2 Find the perimeter (in inches) of a rectangle that has a length of 4 feet and a width of 7 inches.

Answer:
110 in.

EXAMPLE 2 Find the perimeter of the rectangle shown on the right, in inches.

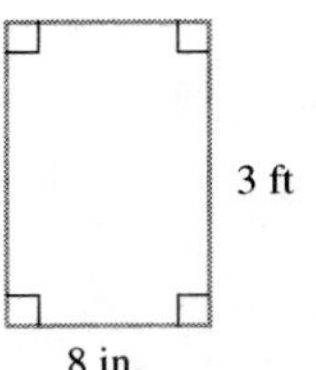

Strategy We will express the width of the rectangle in inches and then use the formula $P = 2l + 2w$ to find the perimeter of the figure.

WHY We can only add quantities that are measured in the same units.

Solution Since 1 foot = 12 inches, we can convert 3 feet to inches by multiplying 3 feet by the unit conversion factor $\frac{12 \text{ in.}}{1 \text{ foot}}$.

$3 \text{ ft} = 3 \text{ ft} \cdot \frac{12 \text{ in.}}{1 \text{ ft}}$ Multiply by 1: $\frac{12 \text{ in.}}{1 \text{ ft}} = 1$.

$= \frac{3 \text{ ft}}{1} \cdot \frac{12 \text{ in.}}{1 \text{ ft}}$ Write 3 ft as a fraction. Remove the common units of feet from the numerator and denominator. The units of inches remain.

$= 36 \text{ in.}$ Do the multiplication.

The width of the rectangle is 36 inches. We can now substitute 8 for l, the length, and 36 for w, the width, in the formula for the perimeter of a rectangle.

$P = 2l + 2w$ This is the formula for the perimeter of a rectangle.

$P = 2(8) + 2(36)$ Substitute 8 for l, the length, and 36 for w, the width.

$= 16 + 72$ Do the multiplication.

$= 88$ Do the addition.

$$\begin{array}{r} \overset{1}{3}6 \\ \times 2 \\ \hline 72 \end{array} \qquad \begin{array}{r} 16 \\ +72 \\ \hline 88 \end{array}$$

The perimeter of the rectangle is 88 inches.

Self Check 3

The perimeter of an isosceles triangle is 58 meters. If one of its sides of equal length is 15 meters long, how long is its base? 28 m

Now Try **Problem 25**

Teaching Example 3 The perimeter of an isosceles triangle is 150 yards. If one of its sides of equal length is 55 yards long, how long is its base?

Answer:
40 yd

EXAMPLE 3 *Structural Engineering* The truss shown below is made up of three parts that form an isosceles triangle. If 76 linear feet of lumber were used to make the truss, how long is the base of the truss?

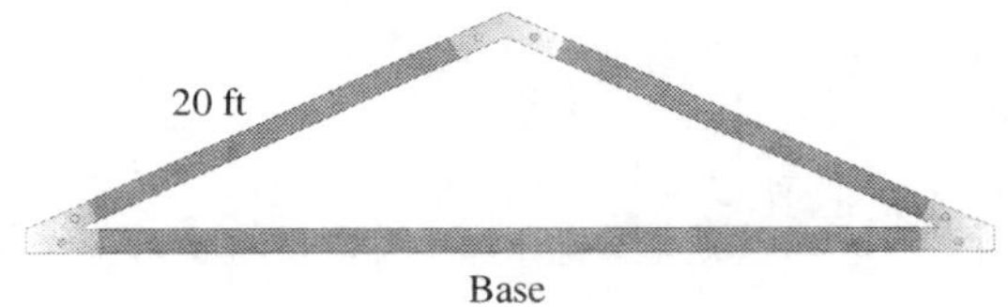

Analyze

- The truss is in the shape of an isosceles triangle. *Given*
- One of the sides of equal length is 20 feet long. *Given*
- The perimeter of the truss is 76 feet. *Given*
- What is the length of the base of the truss? *Find*

Form an Equation We can let b equal the length of the base of the truss (in feet). At this stage, it is helpful to draw a sketch. (See the figure on the right.) If one of the sides of equal length is 20 feet long, so is the other.

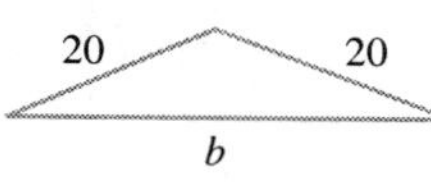

Because 76 linear feet of lumber were used to make the triangular-shaped truss,

The length of the base of the truss	plus	the length of one side	plus	the length of the other side	equals	the perimeter of the truss.
b	$+$	20	$+$	20	$=$	76

Solve

$$b + 20 + 20 = 76$$

$$b + 40 = 76 \quad \text{Combine like terms.}$$

$$b = 36 \quad \text{To isolate } b \text{, subtract 40 from both sides.}$$

$$\begin{array}{r} 76 \\ -\,40 \\ \hline 36 \end{array}$$

State The length of the base of the truss is 36 ft.

Check If we add the lengths of the parts of the truss, we get 36 ft + 20 ft + 20 ft = 76 ft. The result checks.

Using Your CALCULATOR **Perimeters of Figures That Are Combinations of Polygons**

To find the perimeter of the figure shown below, we need to know the values of x and y. Since the figure is a combination of two rectangles, we can use a calculator to see that

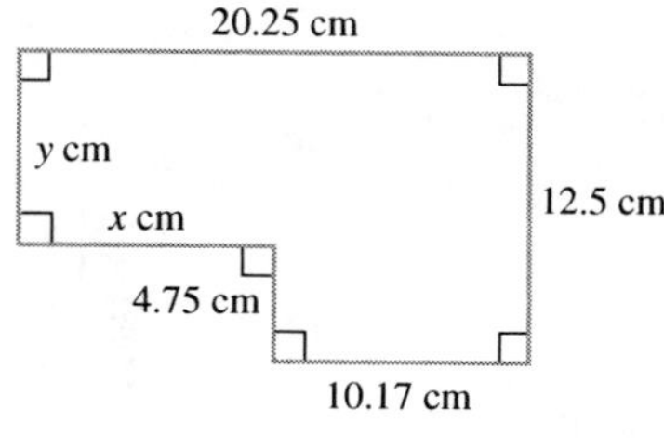

$$x = 20.25 - 10.17 \qquad \text{and} \qquad y = 12.5 - 4.75$$
$$= 10.08 \text{ cm} \qquad\qquad\qquad = 7.75 \text{ cm}$$

The perimeter P of the figure is

$$P = 20.25 + 12.5 + 10.17 + 4.75 + x + y$$
$$P = 20.25 + 12.5 + 10.17 + 4.75 + 10.08 + 7.75$$

We can use a scientific calculator to make this calculation.

20.25 [+] 12.5 [+] 10.17 [+] 4.75 [+] 10.08 [+] 7.75 [=] **65.5**

The perimeter is 65.5 centimeters.

2 Find the area of a polygon.

The **area** of a polygon is the measure of the amount of surface it encloses. Area is measured in square units, such as square inches or square centimeters, as shown below.

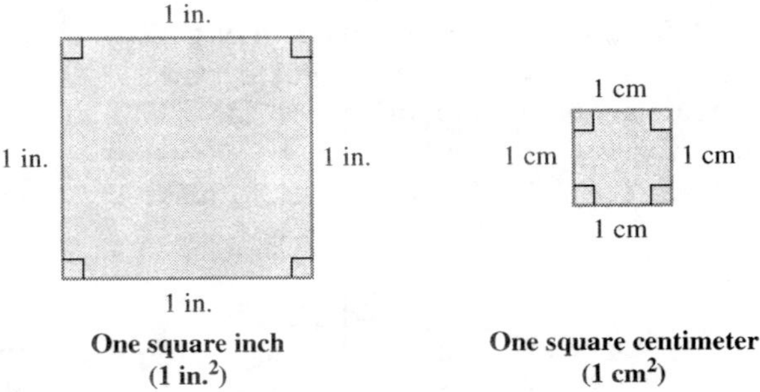

In everyday life, we often use areas. For example,

- To carpet a room, we buy square yards.
- A can of paint will cover a certain number of square feet.
- To measure vast amounts of land, we often use square miles.
- We buy house roofing by the "square." One square is 100 square feet.

The rectangle shown below has a length of 10 centimeters and a width of 3 centimeters. If we divide the rectangular region into square regions as shown in the figure, each square has an area of 1 square centimeter—a surface enclosed by a square measuring 1 centimeter on each side. Because there are 3 rows with 10 squares in each row, there are 30 squares. Since the rectangle encloses a surface area of 30 squares, its area is 30 square centimeters, which can be written as 30 cm^2.

This example illustrates that to find the area of a rectangle, we multiply its length by its width.

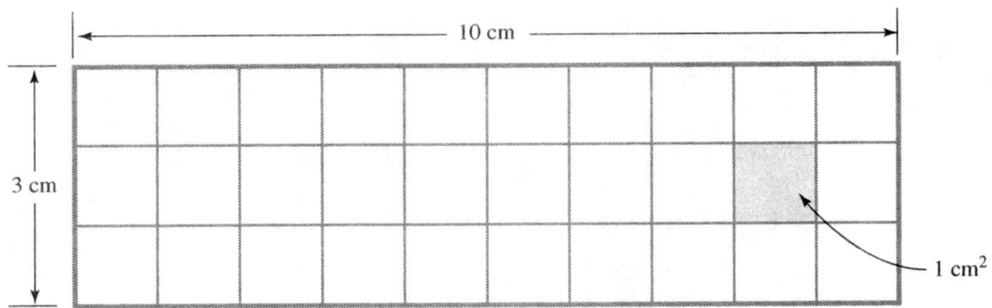

> ***Caution!*** Do not confuse the concepts of perimeter and area. Perimeter is the distance around a polygon. It is measured in linear units, such as centimeters, feet, or miles. Area is a measure of the surface enclosed within a polygon. It is measured in square units, such as square centimeters, square feet, or square miles.

In practice, we do not find areas of polygons by counting squares. Instead, we use formulas to find areas of geometric figures.

Figure	Name	Formula for Area
s, s, s, s	Square	$A = s^2$, where s is the length of one side.
l, w, w, l	Rectangle	$A = lw$, where l is the length and w is the width.
h, b	Parallelogram	$A = bh$, where b is the length of the base and h is the height. (A height is always perpendicular to the base.)
h, b; h, b	Triangle	$A = \frac{1}{2}bh$, where b is the length of the base and h is the height. The segment perpendicular to the base and representing the height (shown here using a dashed line) is called an **altitude.**
b_2, h, b_1	Trapezoid	$A = \frac{1}{2}h(b_1 + b_2)$, where h is the height of the trapezoid and b_1 and b_2 represent the lengths of the bases.

EXAMPLE 4 Find the area of the square shown on the right.

15 cm, 15 cm, 15 cm, 15 cm

Strategy We will substitute 15 for s in the formula $A = s^2$ and evaluate the right side.

WHY The variable A represents the unknown area of the square.

Solution

$A = s^2$ This is the formula for the area of a square.

$A = 15^2$ Substitute 15 for s, the length of one side of the square.

$A = 225$ Evaluate the exponential expression.

$$\begin{array}{r} 15 \\ \times 15 \\ \hline 75 \\ 150 \\ \hline 225 \end{array}$$

Recall that area is measured in square units. Thus, the area of the square is 225 square centimeters, which can be written as 225 cm^2.

Self Check 4

Find the area of the square shown below. 400 in.^{2}

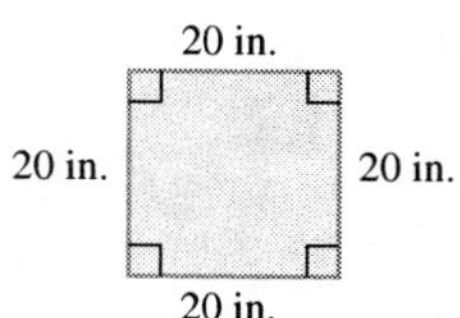

Now Try **Problems 29 and 31**

Teaching Example 4 Find the area of a square if the length of one of its sides is 16 feet.

Answer:
256 ft^2

EXAMPLE 5 Find the number of square feet in 1 square yard.

Strategy A figure is helpful to solve this problem. We will draw a square yard and divide each of its sides into 3 equally long parts.

WHY Since a square yard is a square with each side measuring 1 yard, each side also measures 3 feet.

Self Check 5

Find the number of square centimeters in 1 square meter.
10,000 cm^2

Now Try **Problems 33 and 39**

Teaching Example 5 Find the number of square inches in a square yard.

Answer:
1,296 in.^{2}

Solution

$$1\text{ yd}^2 = (\mathbf{1\text{ yd}})^2$$
$$= (\mathbf{3\text{ ft}})^2 \quad \text{Substitute 3 feet for 1 yard.}$$
$$= (3\text{ ft})(3\text{ ft})$$
$$= 9\text{ ft}^2$$

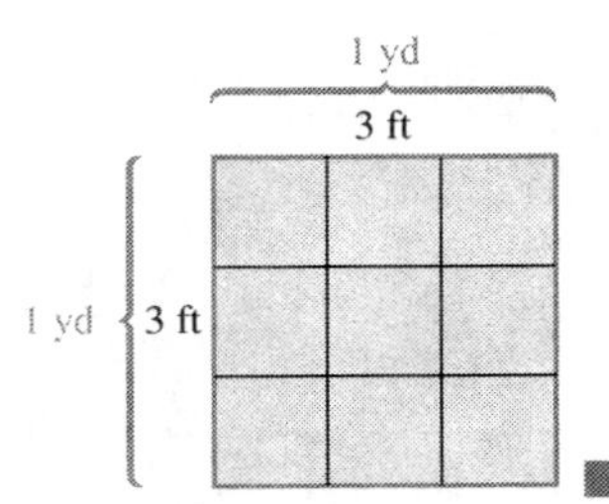

There are 9 square feet in 1 square yard.

Self Check 6

PING-PONG A regulation-size Ping-Pong table is 9 feet long and 5 feet wide. Find its area in square inches. 6,480 in.^{2}

Now Try **Problem 41**

Teaching Example 6
YOUTH SOCCER The recommended soccer field size for youth under 10 years old is 70 yards long by 40 yards wide. Find the area of the field in square feet.

Answer:
25,200 ft^2

EXAMPLE 6 *Women's Sports*

Field hockey is a team sport in which players use sticks to try to hit a ball into their opponents' goal. Find the area of the rectangular field shown on the right. Give the answer in square feet.

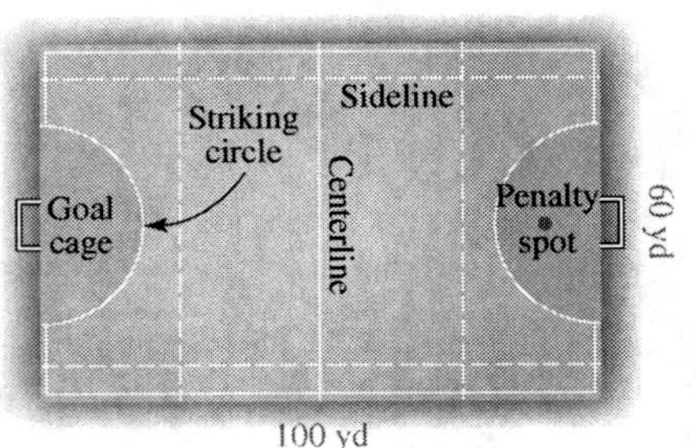

Strategy We will substitute 100 for l and 60 for w in the formula $A = lw$ and evaluate the right side.

WHY The variable A represents the unknown area of the rectangle.

Solution

$$A = lw \quad \text{This is the formula for the area of a rectangle.}$$
$$A = \mathbf{100}(\mathbf{60}) \quad \text{Substitute 100 for } l\text{, the length, and 60 for } w\text{, the width.}$$
$$= 6{,}000 \quad \text{Do the multiplication.}$$

The area of the rectangle is 6,000 square yards. Since there are 9 square feet per square yard, we can convert this number to square feet by multiplying 6,000 square yards by $\frac{9\text{ ft}^2}{1\text{ yd}^2}$.

$$6{,}000\text{ yd}^2 = 6{,}000\text{ yd}^2 \cdot \frac{\mathbf{9\text{ ft}^2}}{\mathbf{1\text{ yd}^2}} \quad \text{Multiply by the unit conversion factor: } \frac{9\text{ ft}^2}{1\text{ yd}^2} = 1.$$
$$= 6{,}000 \cdot 9\text{ ft}^2 \quad \text{Remove the common units of square yards in the numerator and denominator. The units of ft}^2\text{ remain.}$$
$$= 54{,}000\text{ ft}^2 \quad \text{Multiply: } 6{,}000 \cdot 9 = 54{,}000.$$

The area of the field is 54,000 ft^2.

THINK IT THROUGH *Dorm Rooms*

"The United States has more than 4,000 colleges and universities, with 2.3 million students living in college dorms."

The New York Times, 2007

The average dormitory room in a residence hall has about 180 square feet of floor space. The rooms are usually furnished with the following items having the given dimensions:

- 2 extra-long twin beds (each is 39 in. wide × 80 in. long × 24 in. high)
- 2 dressers (each is 18 in. wide × 36 in. long × 48 in. high)
- 2 bookcases (each is 12 in. wide × 24 in. long × 40 in. high)
- 2 desks (each is 24 in. wide × 48 in. long × 28 in. high)

How many square feet of floor space are left? about 108 ft^2

EXAMPLE 7 Find the area of the triangle shown on the right.

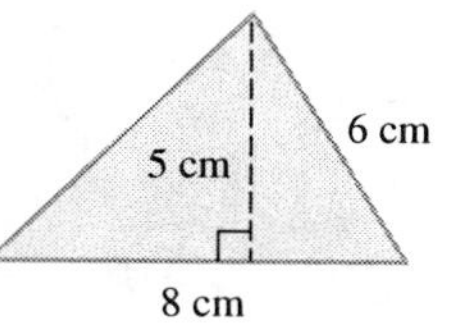

Strategy We will substitute 8 for b and 5 for h in the formula $A = \frac{1}{2}bh$ and evaluate the right side. (The side having length 6 cm is additional information that is not used to find the area.)

WHY The variable A represents the unknown area of the triangle.

Solution

$A = \frac{1}{2}bh$ This is the formula for the area of a triangle.

$A = \frac{1}{2}(8)(5)$ Substitute 8 for b, the length of the base, and 5 for h, the height.

$= 4(5)$ Do the first multiplication: $\frac{1}{2}(8) = 4$.

$= 20$ Complete the multiplication.

The area of the triangle is 20 cm^2.

Self Check 7

Find the area of the triangle shown below. $90\ mm^2$

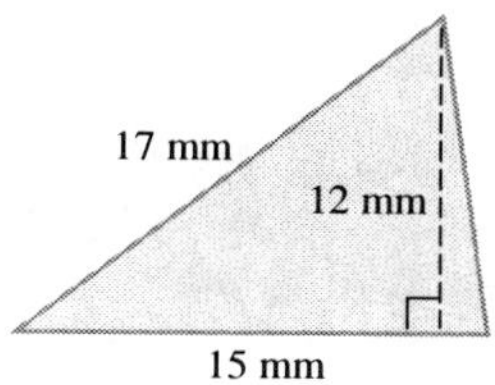

Now Try **Problem 45**

Teaching Example 7 Find the area of the triangle.

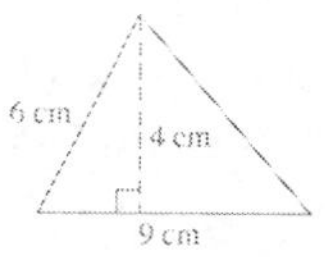

Answer:
$18\ cm^2$

EXAMPLE 8 Find the area of the triangle shown on the right.

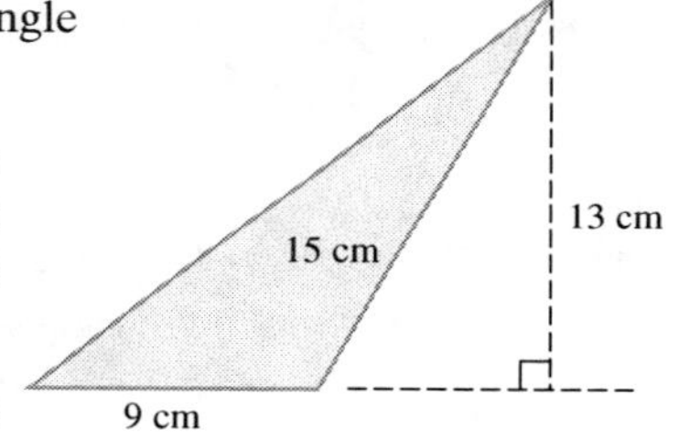

Strategy We will substitute 9 for b and 13 for h in the formula $A = \frac{1}{2}bh$ and evaluate the right side. (The side having length 15 cm is additional information that is not used to find the area.)

WHY The variable A represents the unknown area of the triangle.

Solution In this case, the altitude falls outside the triangle.

$A = \frac{1}{2}bh$ This is the formula for the area of a triangle.

$A = \frac{1}{2}(9)(13)$ Substitute 9 for b, the length of the base, and 13 for h, the height.

$= \frac{1}{2}\left(\frac{9}{1}\right)\left(\frac{13}{1}\right)$ Write 9 as $\frac{9}{1}$ and 13 as $\frac{13}{1}$.

$= \frac{117}{2}$ Multiply the fractions.

$= 58.5$ Do the division.

$$\begin{array}{r} \overset{2}{13} \\ \times 9 \\ \hline 117 \end{array} \qquad \begin{array}{r} 58.5 \\ 2\overline{)117.0} \\ -10 \\ \hline 17 \\ -16 \\ \hline 10 \\ -10 \\ \hline 0 \end{array}$$

The area of the triangle is 58.5 cm^2.

Self Check 8

Find the area of the triangle shown below. $10.5\ ft^2$

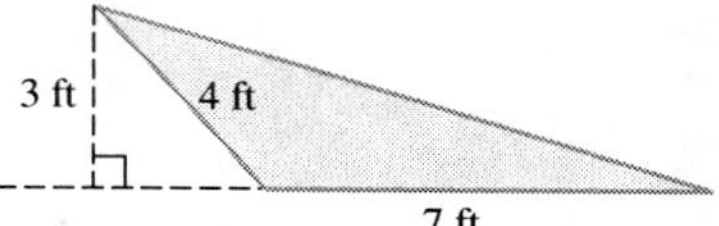

Now Try **Problem 49**

Teaching Example 8 Find the area of the triangle.

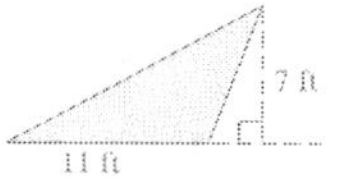

Answer:
$38.5\ ft^2$

EXAMPLE 9 Find the area of the trapezoid shown on the right.

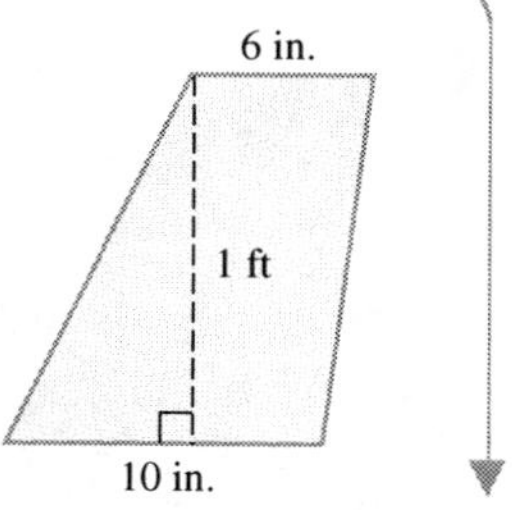

Strategy We will express the height of the trapezoid in inches and then use the formula $A = \frac{1}{2}h(b_1 + b_2)$ to find the area of the figure.

WHY The height of 1 foot must be expressed as 12 inches to be consistent with the units of the bases.

Self Check 9

Find the area of the trapezoid shown below. $54\ m^2$

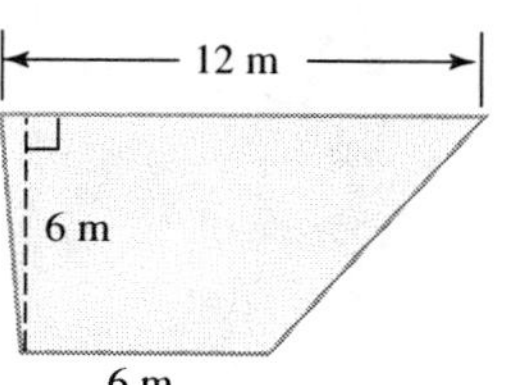

Now Try Problem 53

Teaching Example 9 Find the area of the trapezoid.

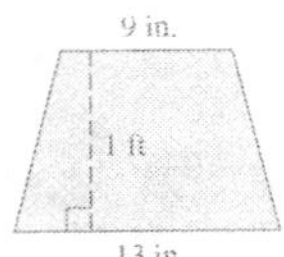

Answer:
132 in.^{2}

Solution

$A = \frac{1}{2}h(b_1 + b_2)$ — This is the formula for the area of a trapezoid.

$A = \frac{1}{2}(12)(10 + 6)$ — Substitute 12 for h, the height; 10 for b_1, the length of the lower base; and 6 for b_2, the length of the upper base.

$= \frac{1}{2}(12)(16)$ — Do the addition within the parentheses.

$= 6(16)$ — Do the first multiplication: $\frac{1}{2}(12) = 6$.

$= 96$ — Complete the multiplication.

$$\begin{array}{r} \overset{3}{1}6 \\ \times 6 \\ \hline 96 \end{array}$$

The area of the trapezoid is 96 in^2.

Self Check 10

The area of the parallelogram below is 96 cm^2. Find its height. 8 cm

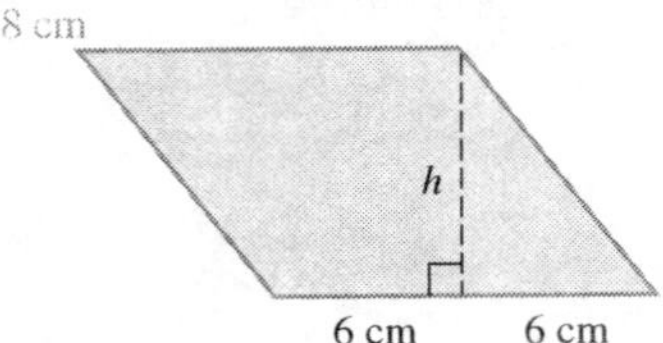

Now Try Problem 57

Teaching Example 10 The area of the parallelogram below is 32 ft^2. Find the height.

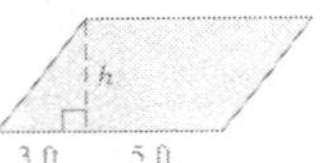

Answer:
4 ft

EXAMPLE 10 The area of the parallelogram shown on the right is 360 ft^2. Find the height.

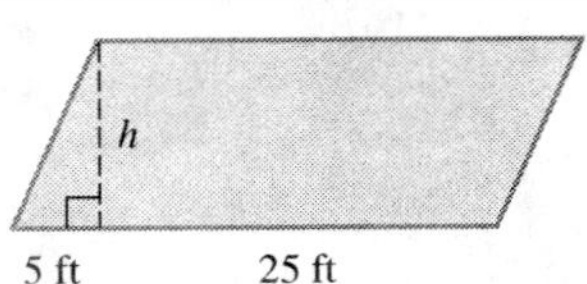

Strategy To find the height of the parallelogram, we will substitute the given values in the formula $A = bh$ and solve for h.

WHY The variable h represents the unknown height.

Solution From the figure, we see that the length of the base of the parallelogram is

5 feet + 25 feet = 30 feet

$A = bh$ — This is the formula for the area of a parallelogram.

$360 = 30h$ — Substitute 360 for A, the area, and 30 for b, the length of the base.

$\frac{360}{30} = \frac{30h}{30}$ — To isolate h, undo the multiplication by 30 by dividing both sides by 30.

$12 = h$ — Do the division.

$$\begin{array}{r} 12 \\ 30\overline{)360} \\ -30 \\ \hline 60 \\ 60 \\ \hline 0 \end{array}$$

The height of the parallelogram is 12 feet.

3 Find the area of figures that are combinations of polygons.

> ***Success Tip*** To find the area of an irregular shape, break up the shape into familiar polygons. Find the area of each polygon and then add the results.

Self Check 11

Find the area of the shaded figure below. 41 yd^2

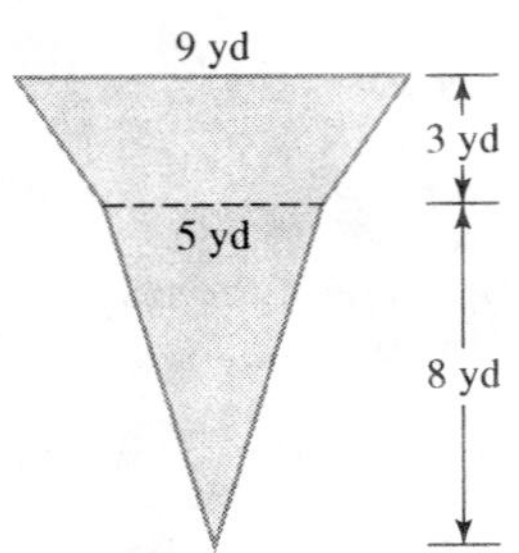

Now Try Problem 65

EXAMPLE 11 Find the area of one side of the tent shown below.

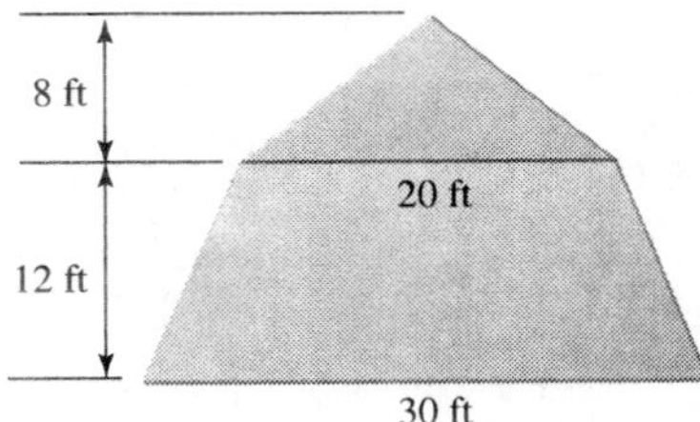

Strategy We will use the formula $A = \frac{1}{2}h(b_1 + b_2)$ to find the area of the lower portion of the tent and the formula $A = \frac{1}{2}bh$ to find the area of the upper portion of the tent. Then we will combine the results.

WHY A side of the tent is a combination of a trapezoid and a triangle.

Solution To find the area of the lower portion of the tent, we proceed as follows.

$A_{\text{trap.}} = \frac{1}{2}h(b_1 + b_2)$ This is the formula for the area of a trapezoid.

$A_{\text{trap.}} = \frac{1}{2}(12)(30 + 20)$ Substitute 30 for b_1, 20 for b_2, and 12 for h.

$= \frac{1}{2}(12)(50)$ Do the addition within the parentheses.

$= 6(50)$ Do the first multiplication: $\frac{1}{2}(12) = 6$.

$= 300$ Complete the multiplication.

The area of the trapezoid is 300 ft^2.

To find the area of the upper portion of the tent, we proceed as follows.

$A_{\text{triangle}} = \frac{1}{2}bh$ This is the formula for the area of a triangle.

$A_{\text{triangle}} = \frac{1}{2}(20)(8)$ Substitute 20 for b and 8 for h.

$= 80$ Do the multiplications, working from left to right: $\frac{1}{2}(20) = 10$ and then $10(8) = 80$.

The area of the triangle is 80 ft^2.

To find the total area of one side of the tent, we add:

$A_{\text{total}} = A_{\text{trap.}} + A_{\text{triangle}}$

$A_{\text{total}} = 300 \text{ ft}^2 + 80 \text{ ft}^2$

$= 380 \text{ ft}^2$

The total area of one side of the tent is 380 ft^2.

Teaching Example 11 Find the area of the shaded figure.

8 in.

7 in.

10 in.

17 in.

Answer:
148 in.^{2}

EXAMPLE 12

Find the area of the shaded region shown on the right.

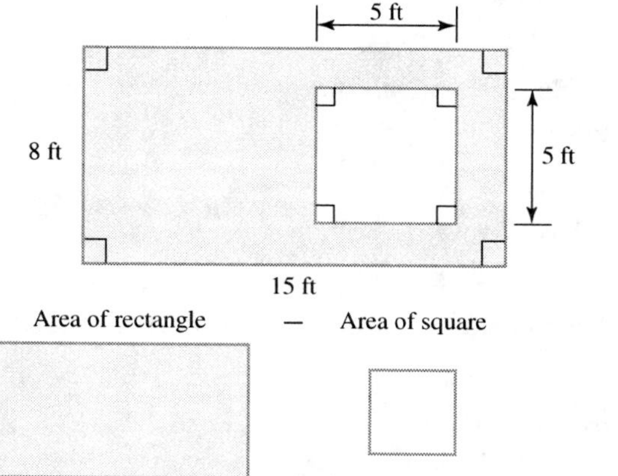

Strategy We will subtract the unwanted area of the square from the area of the rectangle.

Area of shaded region = Area of rectangle − Area of square

WHY The area of the rectangular-shaped shaded figure does not include the square region inside of it.

Solution

$A_{\text{shaded}} = lw - s^2$ The formula for the area of a rectangle is $A = lw$. The formula for the area of a square is $A = s^2$.

$A_{\text{shaded}} = 15(8) - 5^2$ Substitute 15 for the length l and 8 for the width w of the rectangle. Substitute 5 for the length s of a side of the square.

$= 120 - 25$

$= 95$

$$\begin{array}{r} \overset{4}{1}5 \\ \times 8 \\ \hline 120 \end{array} \qquad \begin{array}{r} \overset{11}{\cancel{1}}\overset{10}{\cancel{2}}\cancel{0} \\ -25 \\ \hline 95 \end{array}$$

The area of the shaded region is 95 ft^2.

Self Check 12

Find the area of the shaded region shown below. 119 ft^2

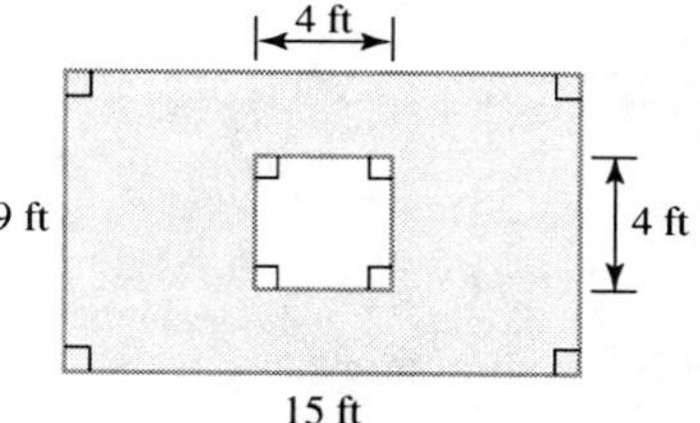

Now Try **Problem 69**

Teaching Example 12 Find the area of the shaded region.

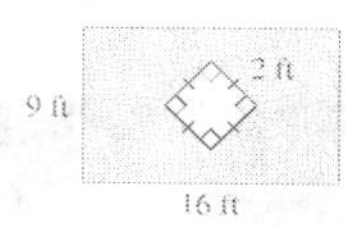

Answer:
140 ft^2

EXAMPLE 13 *Carpeting a Room* A living room/dining room has the floor plan shown in the figure. If carpet costs $29 per square yard, including pad and installation, how much will it cost to carpet both rooms? (Assume no waste.)

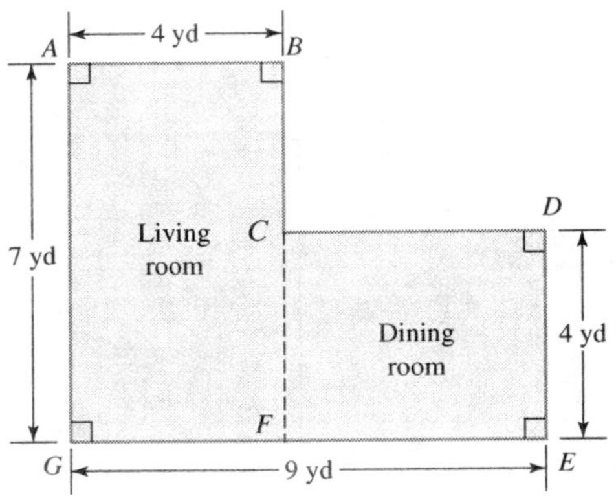

Strategy We will find the number of square yards of carpeting needed and multiply the result by $29.

WHY Each square yard costs $29.

Solution First, we must find the total area of the living room and the dining room:

$$A_{\text{total}} = A_{\text{living room}} + A_{\text{dining room}}$$

Since $\overline{CF}$ divides the space into two rectangles, the areas of the living room and the dining room are found by multiplying their respective lengths and widths. Therefore, the area of the living room is $4 \text{ yd} \cdot 7 \text{ yd} = 28 \text{ yd}^2$.

The width of the dining room is given as 4 yd. To find its length, we subtract:

$$m(\overline{CD}) = m(\overline{GE}) - m(\overline{AB}) = 9 \text{ yd} - 4 \text{ yd} = 5 \text{ yd}$$

Thus, the area of the dining room is $5 \text{ yd} \cdot 4 \text{ yd} = 20 \text{ yd}^2$. The total area to be carpeted is the sum of these two areas.

$$\begin{aligned} A_{\text{total}} &= A_{\text{living room}} + A_{\text{dining room}} \\ A_{\text{total}} &= 28 \text{ yd}^2 + 20 \text{ yd}^2 \\ &= 48 \text{ yd}^2 \end{aligned}$$

$$\begin{array}{r} 48 \\ \times 29 \\ \hline 432 \\ 960 \\ \hline 1{,}392 \end{array}$$

Now Try **Problem 73**

At $29 per square yard, the cost to carpet both rooms will be 48 · $29, or $1,392. ■

ANSWERS TO SELF CHECKS

1. 154 cm **2.** 50 in. **3.** 28 m **4.** 400 in.^{2} **5.** 10,000 cm^2 **6.** 6,480 in.^{2} **7.** 90 mm^2 **8.** 10.5 ft^2 **9.** 54 m^2 **10.** 8 cm **11.** 41 yd^2 **12.** 119 ft^2

SECTION 1.9 STUDY SET

VOCABULARY

Fill in the blanks.

1. The distance around a polygon is called the perimeter.
2. The perimeter of a polygon is measured in linear units such as inches, feet, and miles.
3. The measure of the surface enclosed by a polygon is called its area.
4. If each side of a square measures 1 foot, the area enclosed by the square is 1 square foot.
5. The area of a polygon is measured in square units.
6. ▶ The segment that represents the height of a triangle is called an altitude.

CONCEPTS

7. The figure below shows a kitchen floor that is covered with 1-foot-square tiles. Without counting *all* of the squares, determine the area of the floor.
$8 \text{ ft} \cdot 16 \text{ ft} = 128 \text{ ft}^2$

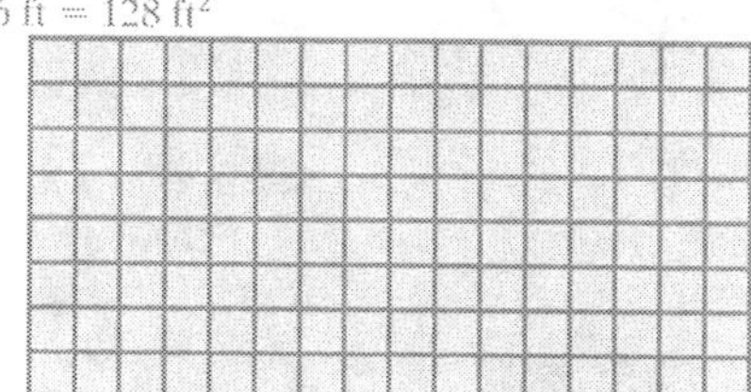

 8. Tell which concept applies, perimeter or area.
   a. The length of a walk around New York's Central Park perimeter
   b. The amount of office floor space in the White House area
   c. The amount of fence needed to enclose a playground perimeter
   d. The amount of land in Yellowstone National Park area

9. Give the formula for the perimeter of a
   a. square $p = 4s$
   b. rectangle $p = 2l + 2w$

10. Give the formula for the area of a
   a. square $A = s^2$
   b. rectangle $A = lw$
   c. triangle $A = \frac{1}{2}bh$
   d. trapezoid $A = \frac{1}{2}h(b_1 + b_2)$
   e. parallelogram $A = bh$

11. For each figure below, draw the altitude to the base b.

a.

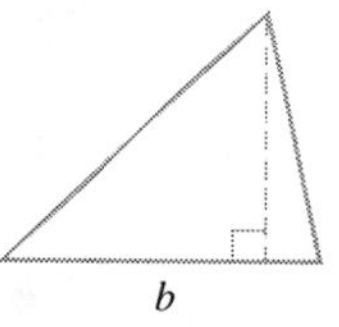

b.

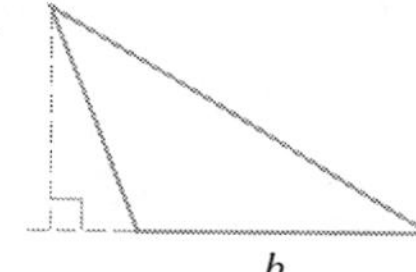

c.

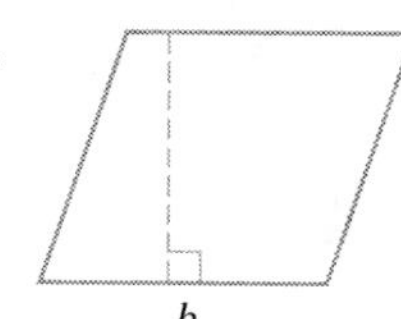

d.

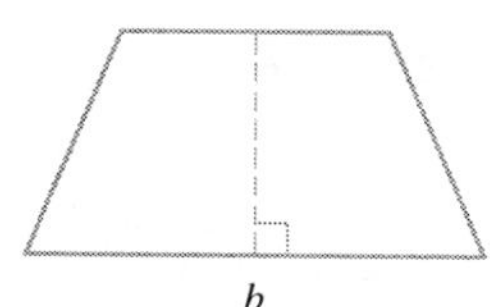

12. For each figure below, label the base b for the given altitude.

a.

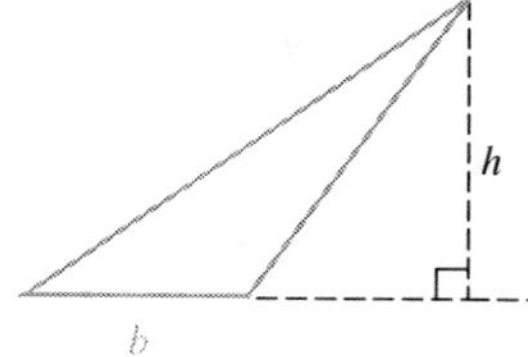

b.

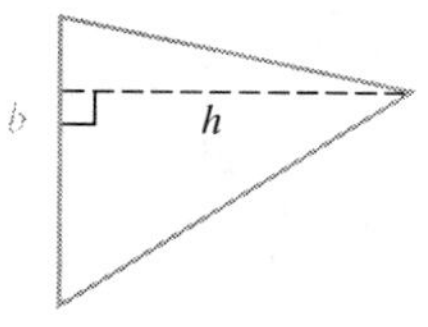

c.

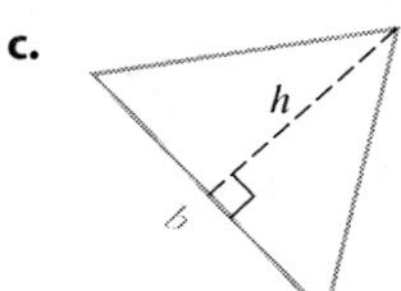

d.

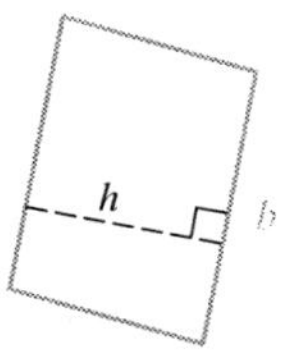

13. The shaded figure below is a combination of what two types of geometric figures? a rectangle and a triangle

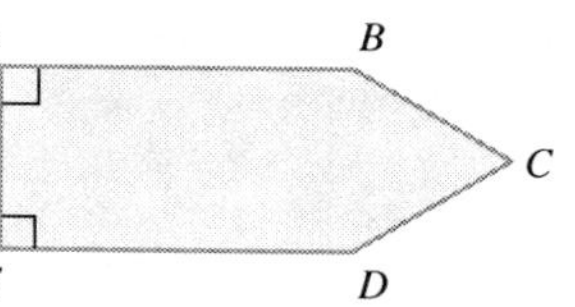

14. Explain how you would find the area of the following shaded figure. subtract the area of the triangle from the area of the parallelogram

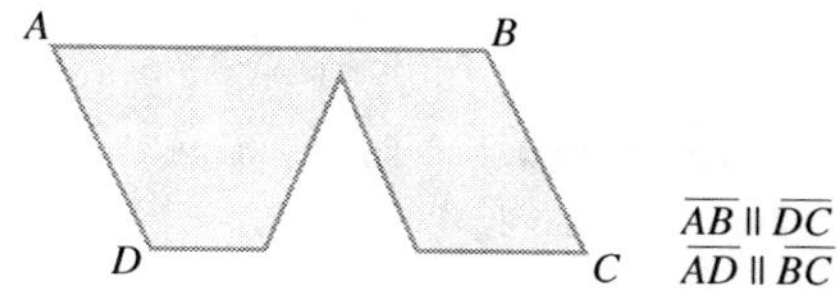

NOTATION

Fill in the blanks.

15. a. The symbol 1 in.^{2} means one square inch.
   b. One square meter is expressed as 1 m^2.

16. In the figure below, the symbol ⌉ indicates that the dashed line segment, called an *altitude*, is perpendicular to the base.

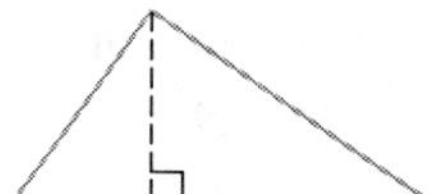

GUIDED PRACTICE

Find the perimeter of each square. See Example 1.

17.

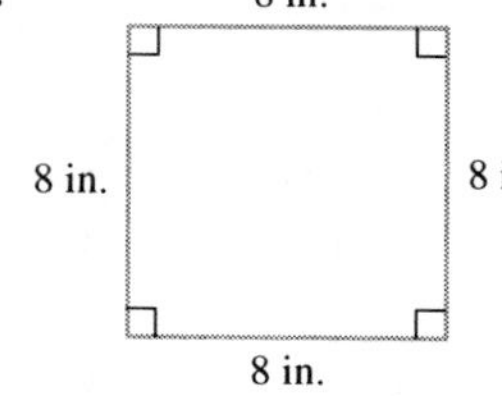

32 in.

18.

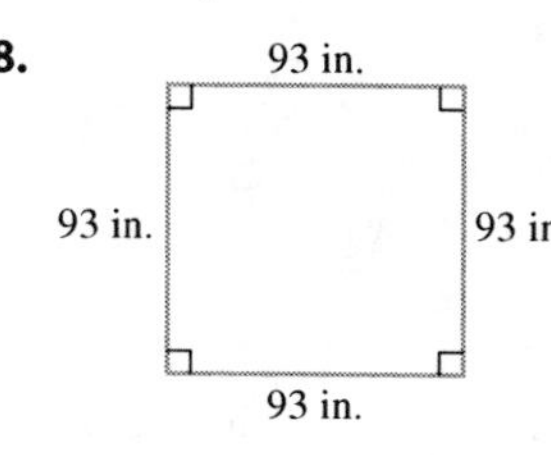

372 in.

19. A square with sides 5.75 miles long 23 mi
20. A square with sides 3.4 yards long 13.6 yd

Find the perimeter of each rectangle, in inches. See Example 2.

21.

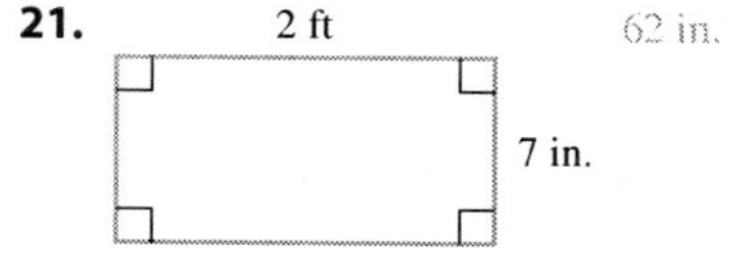

62 in.

22.

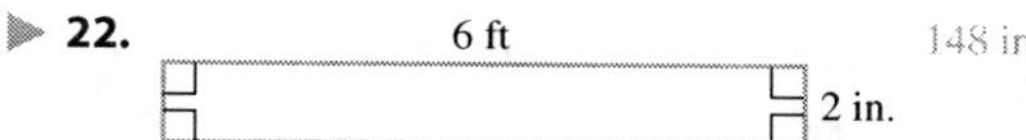

148 in.

23. **24.**

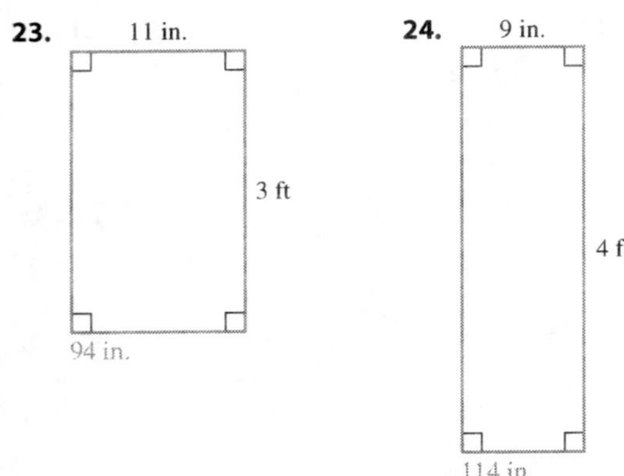

Write and then solve an equation to answer each problem. See Example 3.

25. The perimeter of an isosceles triangle is 35 feet. Each of the sides of equal length is 10 feet long. Find the length of the base of the triangle. 15 ft

26. The perimeter of an isosceles triangle is 94 feet. Each of the sides of equal length is 42 feet long. Find the length of the base of the triangle. 10 ft

▶ **27.** The perimeter of an isosceles trapezoid is 35 meters. The upper base is 10 meters long, and the lower base is 15 meters long. How long is each leg of the trapezoid? 5 m

28. The perimeter of an isosceles trapezoid is 46 inches. The upper base is 12 inches long, and the lower base is 16 inches long. How long is each leg of the trapezoid? 9 in.

Find the area of each square. See Example 4.

29. **30.**

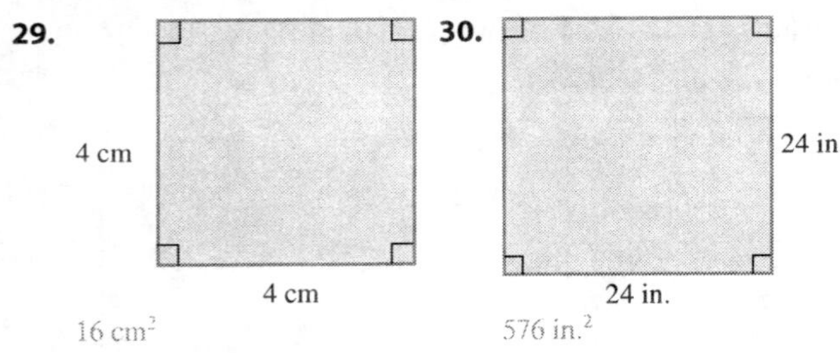

▶ **31.** A square with sides 2.5 meters long 6.25 m^2

32. A square with sides 6.8 feet long 46.24 ft^2

For Problems 33–40, see Example 5.

▶ **33.** How many square inches are in 1 square foot? 144 $in.^2$

▶ **34.** How many square inches are in 1 square yard? 1,296 $in.^2$

▶ **35.** How many square millimeters are in 1 square meter? 1,000,000 mm^2

▶ **36.** How many square decimeters are in 1 square meter? 100 dm^2

▶ **37.** How many square feet are in 1 square mile? 27,878,400 ft^2

▶ **38.** How many square yards are in 1 square mile? 3,097,600 yd^2

▶ **39.** How many square meters are in 1 square kilometer? 1,000,000 m^2

▶ **40.** How many square dekameters are in 1 square kilometer? 10,000 dam^2

Find the area of each rectangle. Give the answer in square feet. See Example 6.

41. **42.** ▶ **43.** **44.**

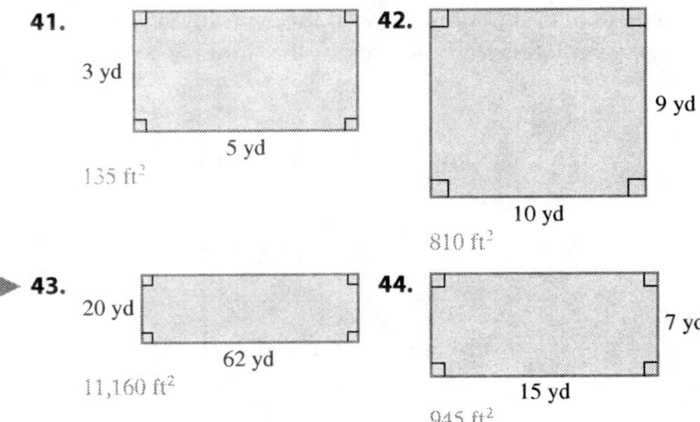

Find the area of each triangle. See Example 7.

45. ▶ **46.** **47.** **48.**

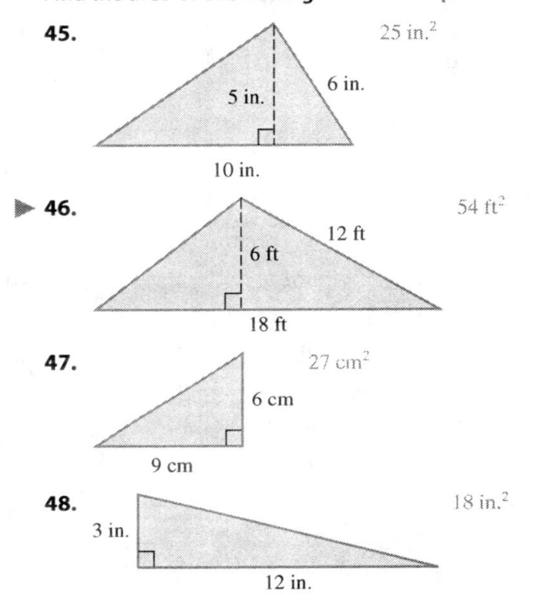

Find the area of each triangle. See Example 8.

49. **50.** ▶ **51.** **52.**

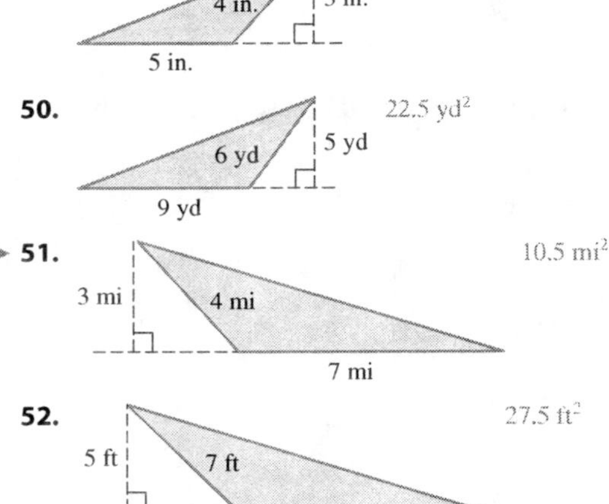

Find the area of each trapezoid. See Example 9.

53. 40 ft²

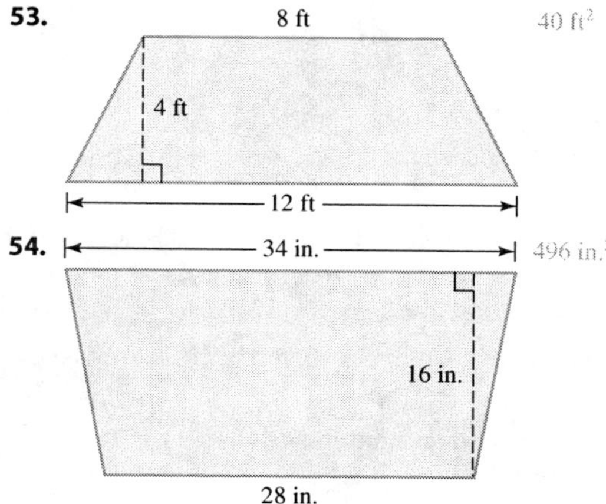

54. 496 in.²

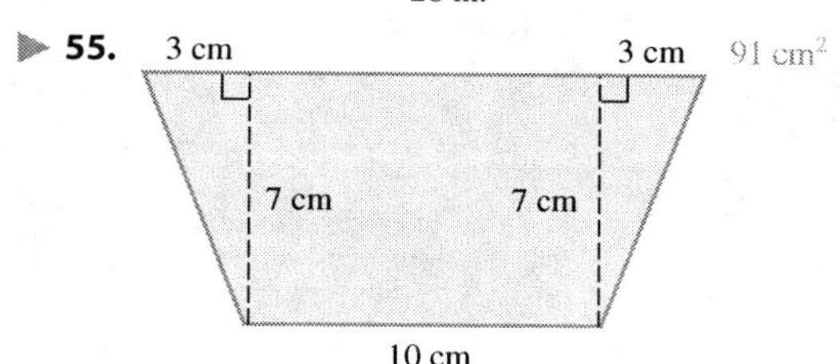

▶ **55.** 91 cm²

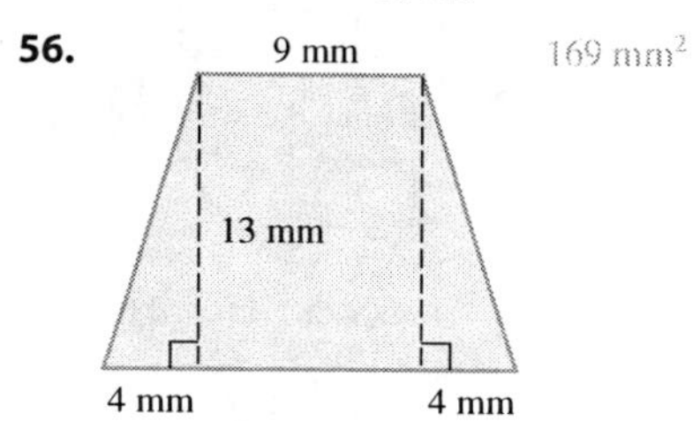

56. 169 mm²

Solve each problem. See Example 10.

57. The area of a parallelogram is 60 m², and its height is 15 m. Find the length of its base. 4 m

58. The area of a parallelogram is 95 in.², and its height is 5 in. Find the length of its base. 19 in.

▶ **59.** The area of a rectangle is 36 cm², and its length is 3 cm. Find its width. 12 cm

▶ **60.** The area of a rectangle is 144 mi², and its length is 6 mi. Find its width. 24 mi

▶ **61.** The area of a triangle is 54 m², and the length of its base is 3 m. Find the height. 36 m

▶ **62.** The area of a triangle is 270 ft², and the length of its base is 18 ft. Find the height. 30 ft

63. The perimeter of a rectangle is 64 mi, and its length is 21 mi. Find its width. 11 mi

64. The perimeter of a rectangle is 26 yd, and its length is 10.5 yd. Find its width. 2.5 yd

Find the area of each shaded figure. See Example 11.

65. 102 in.²

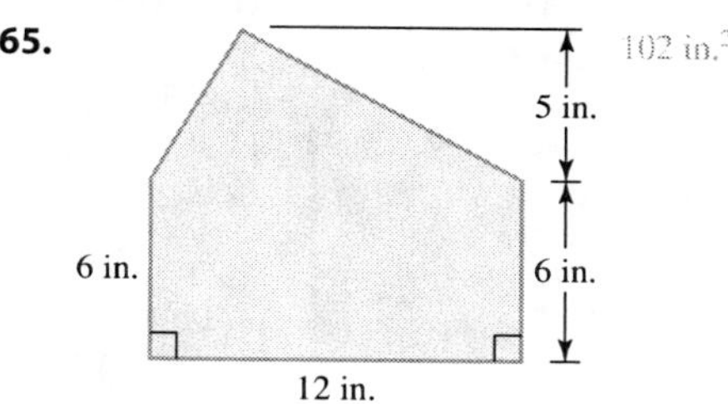

66. 80 m²

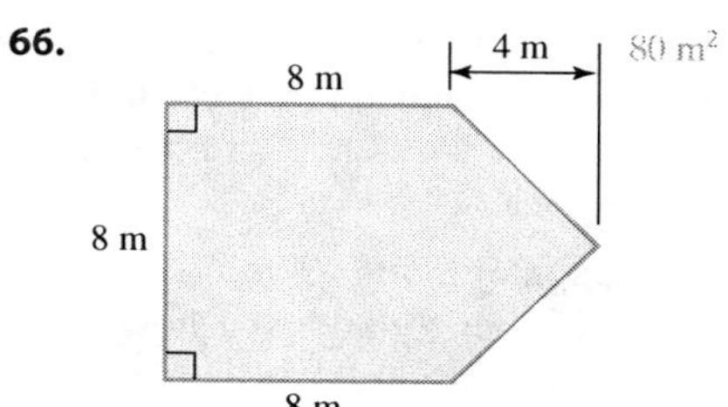

▶ **67.** 360 ft²

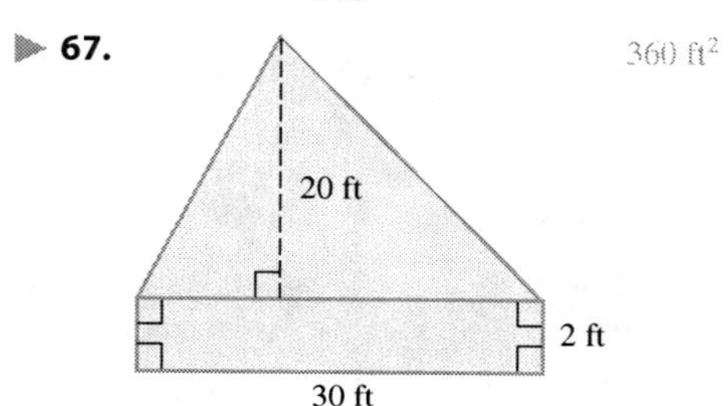

▶ **68.** 207 mm²

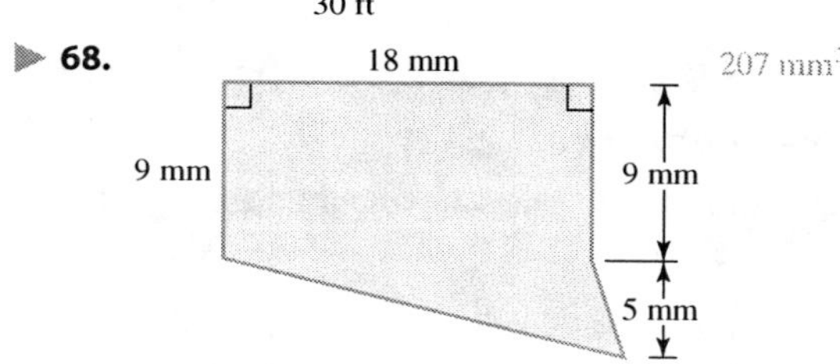

Find the area of each shaded figure. See Example 12.

69. 75 m²

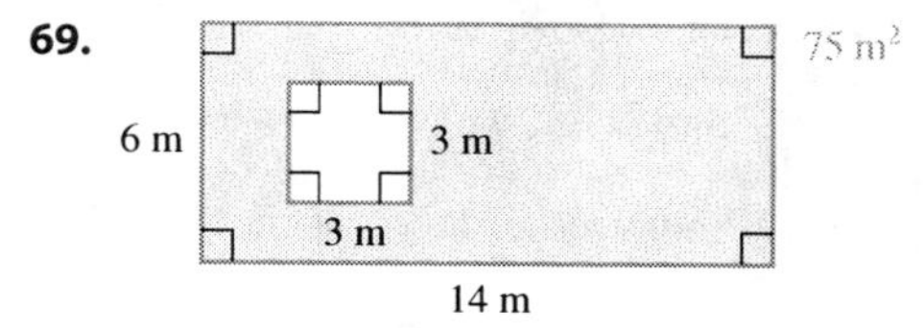

▶ **70.** 335 cm²

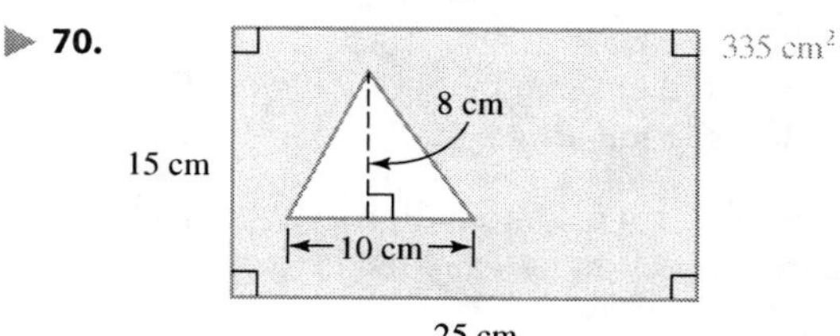

71. 75 yd²

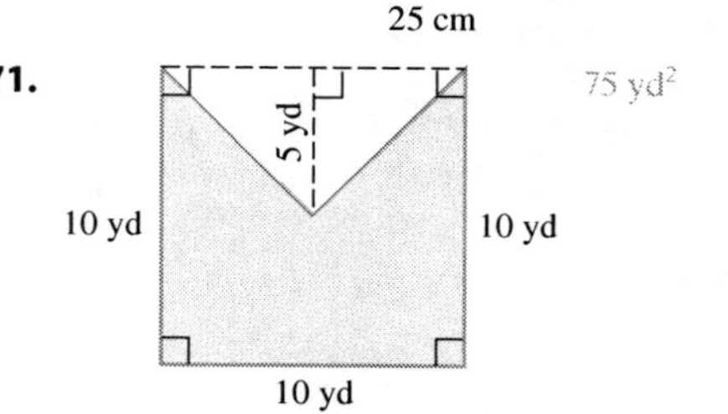

72. 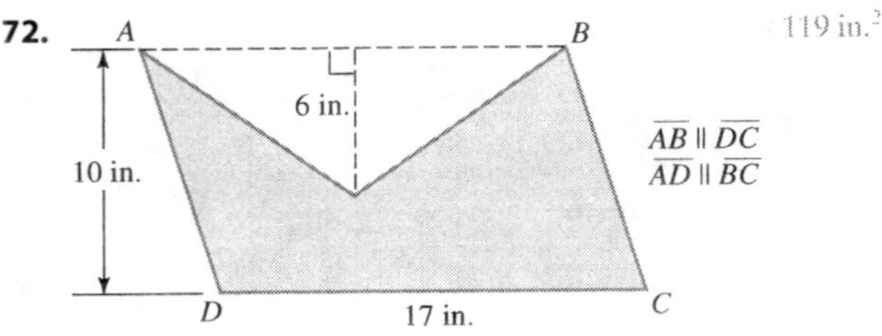

119 in.^{2}

Solve each problem. See Example 13.

73. FLOORING A rectangular family room is 8 yards long and 5 yards wide. At $30 per square yard, how much will it cost to put down vinyl sheet flooring in the room? (Assume no waste.) $1,200

74. CARPETING A rectangular living room measures 10 yards by 6 yards. At $32 per square yard, how much will it cost to carpet the room? (Assume no waste.) $1,920

75. FENCES A man wants to enclose a rectangular yard with fencing that costs $12.50 a foot, including installation. Find the cost of enclosing the yard if its dimensions are 110 ft by 85 ft. $4,875

76. FRAMES Find the cost of framing a rectangular picture with dimensions of 24 inches by 30 inches if framing material costs $0.75 per inch. $81

TRY IT YOURSELF

Sketch and label each of the figures.

77. Two different rectangles, each having a perimeter of 40 in. length 15 in. and width 5 in.; length 16 in. and width 4 in. (answers may vary)

78. Two different rectangles, each having an area of 40 in.^{2} length 10 in. and width 4 in.; length 20 in. and width 2 in. (answers may vary)

79. A square with an area of 25 m^2 sides of length 5 m

80. A square with a perimeter of 20 m sides of length 4 m

81. A parallelogram with an area of 15 yd^2 base 5 yd and height 3 yd (answers may vary)

82. A triangle with an area of 20 ft^2 base 5 ft and height 8 ft (answers may vary)

83. A figure consisting of a combination of two rectangles, whose total area is 80 ft^2 length 5 ft and width 4 ft; length 20 ft and width 3 ft (answers may vary)

84. A figure consisting of a combination of a rectangle and a square, whose total area is 164 ft^2 length 4 ft and width 25 ft; length 8 ft and width 8 ft (answers may vary)

Find the area of each parallelogram.

85. 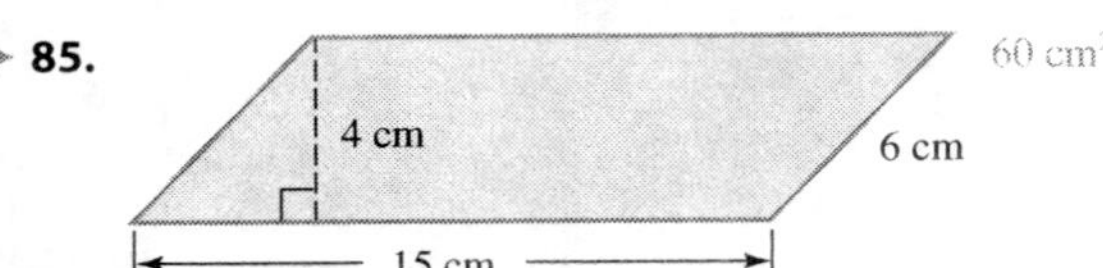

60 cm^2

86. 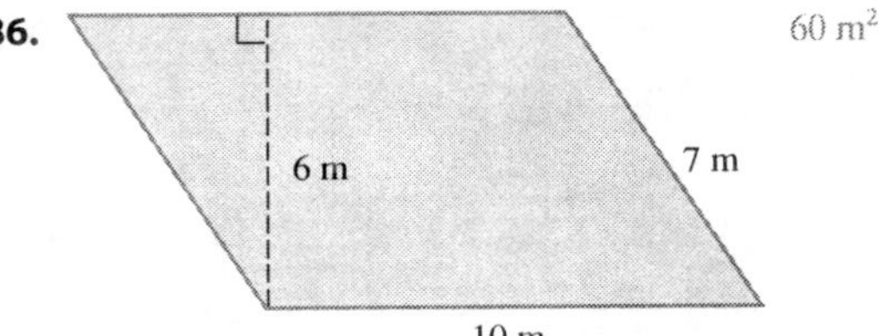

60 m^2

87. The perimeter of an isosceles triangle is 80 meters. If the length of one of the congruent sides is 22 meters, how long is the base? 36 m

88. The perimeter of a square is 35 yards. How long is a side of the square? 8.75 yd

89. The perimeter of an equilateral triangle is 85 feet. Find the length of each side. $28\frac{1}{3}$ ft

90. An isosceles triangle with congruent sides of length 49.3 inches has a perimeter of 121.7 inches. Find the length of the base. 23.1 in.

Find the perimeter of the figure.

91. **92.**

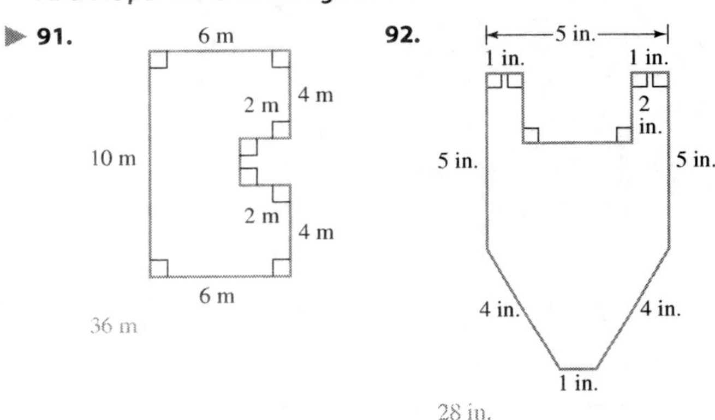

91. 36 m 92. 28 in.

Find x and y. Then find the perimeter of the figure.

93. 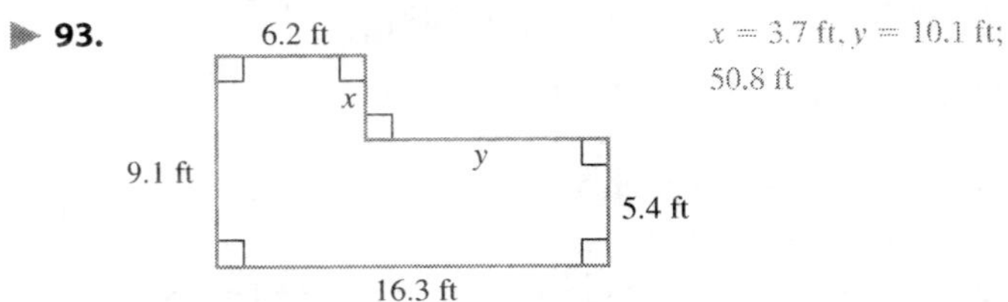

$x = 3.7$ ft, $y = 10.1$ ft; 50.8 ft

94. 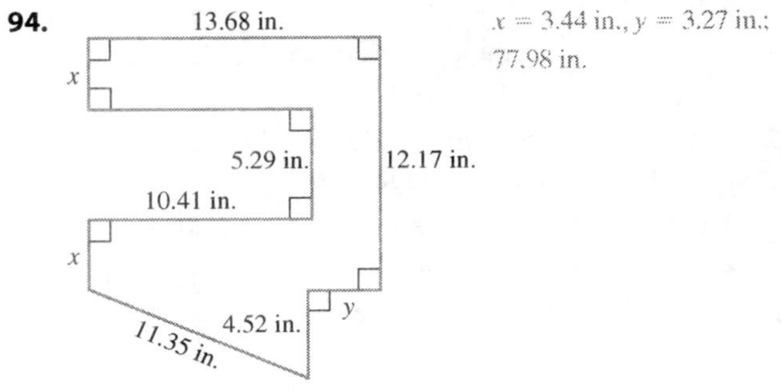

$x = 3.44$ in., $y = 3.27$ in.; 77.98 in.

APPLICATIONS

95. LANDSCAPING A woman wants to plant a pine-tree screen around three sides of her rectangular-shaped backyard. (See the figure below.) If she plants the trees 3 feet apart, how many trees will she need? 80 + 1 = 81 trees

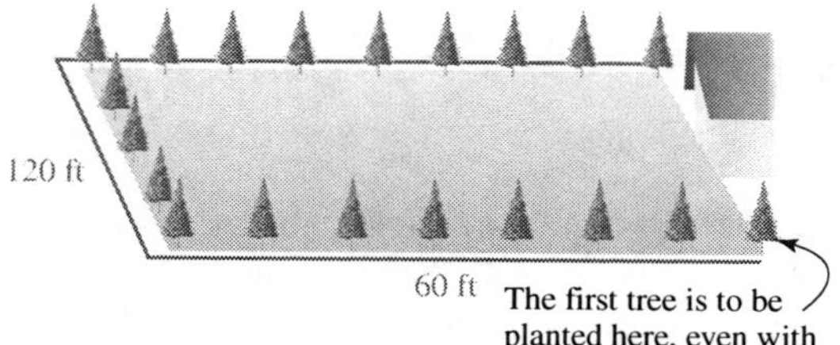

96. GARDENING A gardener wants to plant a border of marigolds around the garden shown below, to keep out rabbits. How many plants will she need if she allows 6 inches between plants? 144 plants

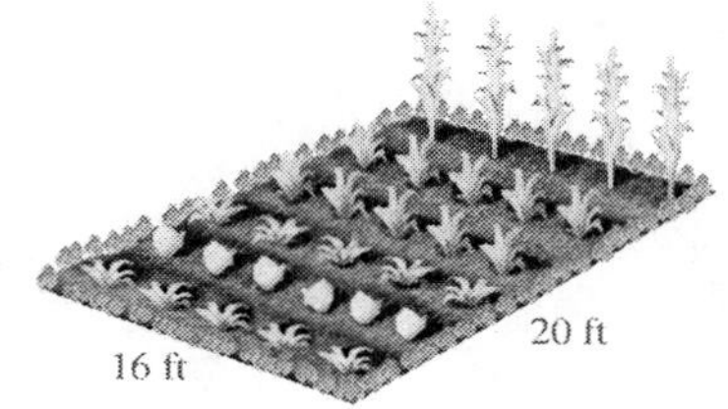

97. COMPARISON SHOPPING Which is more expensive: a ceramic-tile floor costing \$3.75 per square foot or vinyl costing \$34.95 per square yard? vinyl

98. COMPARISON SHOPPING Which is cheaper: a hardwood floor costing \$6.95 per square foot or a carpeted floor costing \$37.50 per square yard? carpeting

99. TILES A rectangular basement room measures 14 by 20 feet. Vinyl floor tiles that are 1 ft^2 cost \$1.29 each. How much will the tile cost to cover the floor? (Assume no waste.) \$361.20

▶ **100.** PAINTING The north wall of a barn is a rectangle 23 feet high and 72 feet long. There are five windows in the wall, each 4 by 6 feet. If a gallon of paint will cover 300 ft^2, how many gallons of paint must the painter buy to paint the wall? 6 gal

▶ **101.** SAILS If nylon is \$12 per square yard, how much would the fabric cost to make a triangular sail with a base of 12 feet and a height of 24 feet? \$192

102. REMODELING The gable end of a house is an isosceles triangle with a height of 4 yards and a base of 23 yards. It will require one coat of primer and one coat of finish to paint the triangle. Primer costs \$17 per gallon, and the finish paint costs \$23 per gallon. If one gallon of each type of paint covers 300 square feet, how much will it cost to paint the gable, excluding labor? \$80

103. GEOGRAPHY Use the dimensions of the trapezoid that is superimposed over the state of Nevada to estimate the area of the "Silver State." 111,825 mi^2

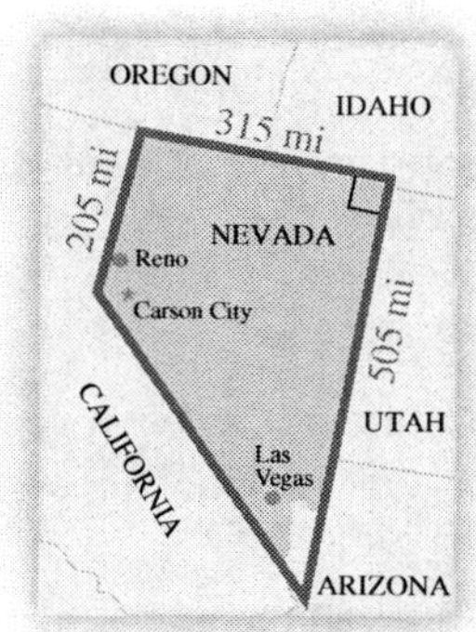

▶ **104.** SOLAR COVERS A swimming pool has the shape shown below. How many square feet of a solar blanket material will be needed to cover the pool? How much will the cover cost if it is \$1.95 per square foot? (Assume no waste.) 400 ft^2; \$780

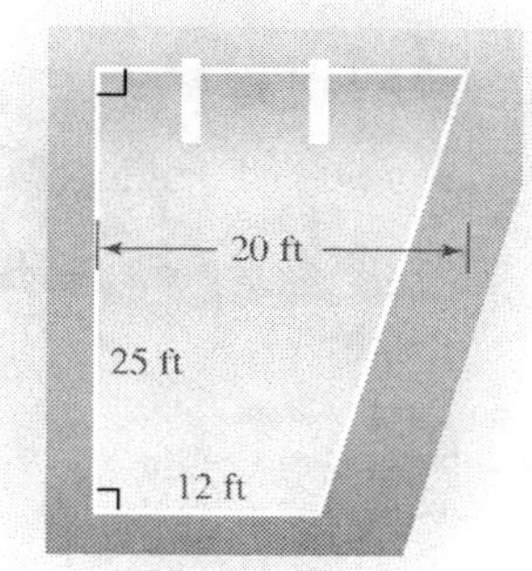

105. CARPENTRY How many sheets of 4-foot-by-8-foot sheetrock are needed to drywall the inside walls on the first floor of the barn shown below? (Assume that the carpenters will cover each wall entirely and then cut out areas for the doors and windows.) 51 sheets

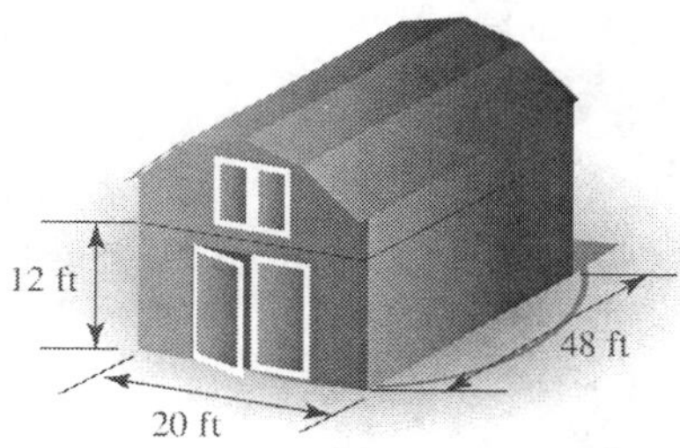

106. CARPENTRY If it costs \$90 per square foot to build a one-story home in northern Wisconsin, find the cost of building the house with the floor plan shown below. \$94,320

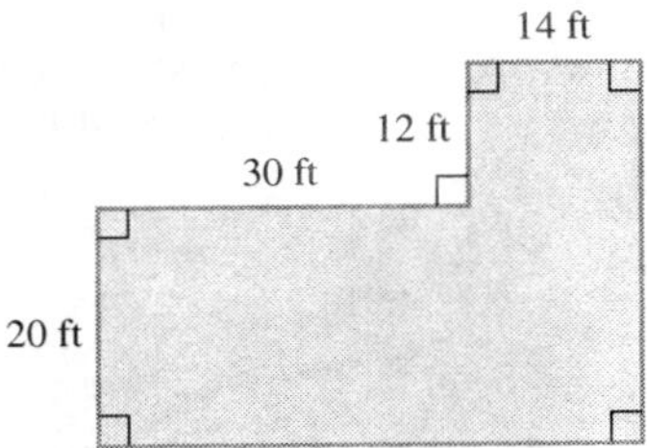

110. Refer to the figure below. What must be done before we can use the formula to find the area of this rectangle?

WRITING

107. Explain the difference between perimeter and area.

108. Why is it necessary that area be measured in square units?

109. A student expressed the area of the square in the figure below as 25^2 ft. Explain his error.

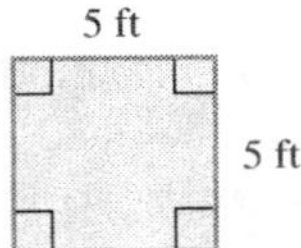

REVIEW

Simplify each expression.

111. $8\left(\frac{3}{4}t\right)$ $6t$

112. $27\left(\frac{2}{3}m\right)$ $18m$

113. $-\frac{2}{3}(3w - 6)$ $-2w + 4$

114. $\frac{1}{2}(2y - 8)$ $y - 4$

115. $-\frac{7}{16}x - \frac{3}{16}x$ $-\frac{5}{8}x$

116. $-\frac{5}{18}x - \frac{7}{18}x$ $-\frac{2}{3}x$

117. $60\left(\frac{3}{20}r - \frac{4}{15}\right)$ $9r - 16$

118. $72\left(\frac{7}{8}f - \frac{8}{9}\right)$ $63f - 64$

Objectives

1 Use the Pythagorean theorem to find the exact length of a side of a right triangle.

2 Use the Pythagorean theorem to approximate the length of a side of a right triangle.

3 Use the converse of the Pythagorean theorem.

SECTION 1.10 The Pythagorean Theorem

A **theorem** is a mathematical statement that can be proven. In this section, we will discuss one of the most widely used theorems of geometry—the Pythagorean theorem. It is named after Pythagoras, a Greek mathematician who lived about 2,500 years ago. He is thought to have been the first to develop a proof of it. The Pythagorean theorem expresses the relationship between the lengths of the sides of any right triangle.

Pythagoras

1 Use the Pythagorean theorem to find the exact length of a side of a right triangle.

Recall that a right triangle is a triangle that has a right angle (an angle with measure 90°). In a right triangle, the longest side is called the **hypotenuse.** It is the side opposite the right angle. The other two sides are called **legs.** It is common practice to let the variable c represent the length of the hypotenuse and the variables a and b represent the lengths of the legs, as shown on the right.

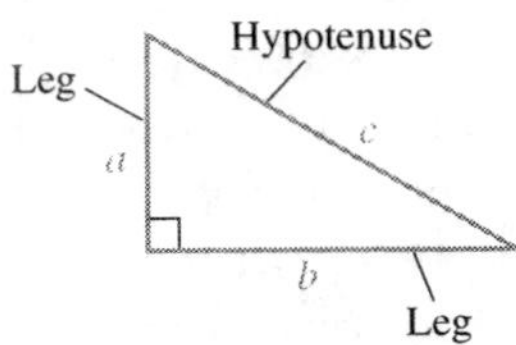

If we know the lengths of any two sides of a right triangle, we can find the length of the third side using the **Pythagorean theorem.**

Pythagorean Theorem

If a and b are the lengths of two legs of a right triangle and c is the length of the hypotenuse, then

$$a^2 + b^2 = c^2$$

In words, the Pythagorean theorem is expressed as follows:

In a right triangle, the sum of the squares of the lengths of the two legs is equal to the square of the length of the hypotenuse.

Caution! When using the **Pythagorean equation** $a^2 + b^2 = c^2$, we can let a represent the length of either leg of the right triangle. We then let b represent the length of the other leg. The variable c must always represent the length of the hypotenuse.

EXAMPLE 1 Find the length of the hypotenuse of the right triangle shown here.

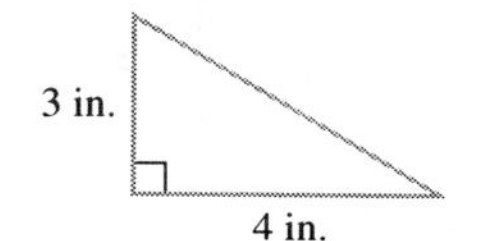

Strategy We will use the Pythagorean theorem to find the length of the hypotenuse.

WHY If we know the lengths of any two sides of a right triangle, we can find the length of the third side using the Pythagorean theorem.

Solution We will let $a = 3$ and $b = 4$, and substitute into the Pythagorean equation to find c.

$a^2 + b^2 = c^2$ This is the Pythagorean equation.

$3^2 + 4^2 = c^2$ Substitute 3 for a and 4 for b.

$9 + 16 = c^2$ Evaluate each exponential expression.

$25 = c^2$ Do the addition.

$c^2 = 25$ Reverse the sides of the equation so that c^2 is on the left.

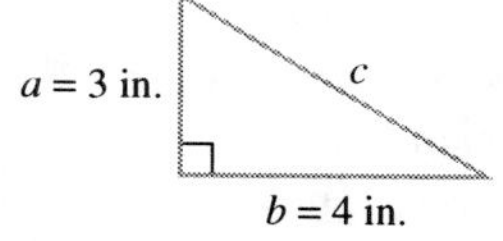

To find c, we must find a number that, when squared, is 25. There are two such numbers, one positive and one negative; they are the square roots of 25. Since c represents the length of a side of a triangle, c cannot be negative. For this reason, we need only find the positive square root of 25 to get c.

$c = \sqrt{25}$ The symbol $\sqrt{}$ is used to indicate the positive square root of a number.

$c = 5$ $\sqrt{25} = 5$ because $5^2 = 25$.

The length of the hypotenuse is 5 in.

Self Check 1

Find the length of the hypotenuse of the right triangle shown below.

13 ft

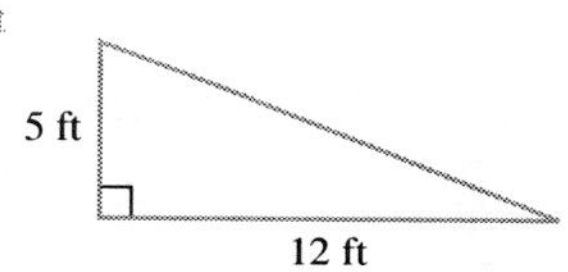

Now Try **Problem 15**

Teaching Example 1 Find the length of the hypotenuse of the right triangle.

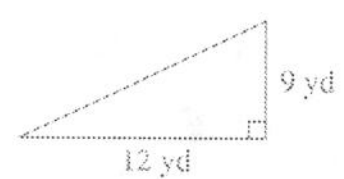

Answer:
15 yd

Success Tip The Pythagorean theorem is used to find the lengths of sides of right triangles. A calculator with a square root key $\boxed{\sqrt{}}$ is often helpful in the final step of the solution process when we must find the positive square root of a number.

Self Check 2

In Example 2, can the crews communicate by radio if the distance from point B to point C remains the same but the distance from point A to point C increases to 2,520 yards? no

Now Try **Problems 19 and 43**

Teaching Example 2
IRON WORKS Is a 120-inch-long iron bar long enough to cross brace the rectangular gate shown in the illustration?

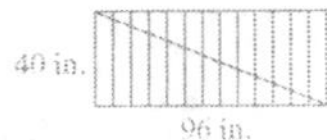

Answer:
yes

EXAMPLE 2 *Firefighting* To fight a forest fire, the forestry department plans to clear a rectangular fire break around the fire, as shown in the following figure. Crews are equipped with mobile communications that have a 3,000-yard range. Can crews at points A and B remain in radio contact?

Strategy We will use the Pythagorean theorem to find the distance between points A and B.

WHY If the distance is less than 3,000 yards, the crews can communicate by radio. If it is greater than 3,000 yards, they cannot.

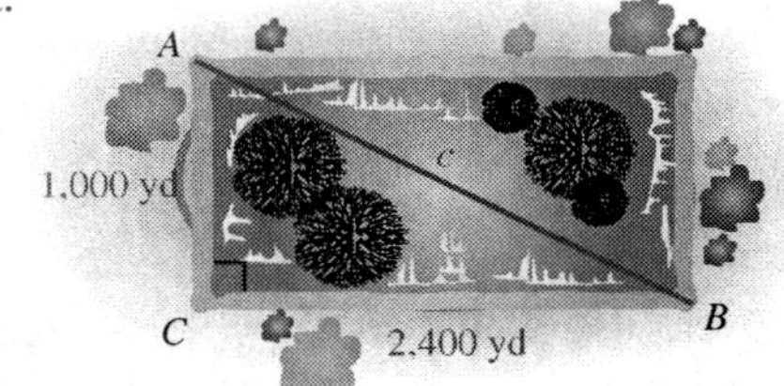

Solution The line segments connecting points A, B, and C form a right triangle. To find the distance c from point A to point B, we can use the Pythagorean equation, substituting 2,400 for a and 1,000 for b and solving for c.

$$a^2 + b^2 = c^2$$ This is the Pythagorean equation.

$$2{,}400^2 + 1{,}000^2 = c^2$$ Substitute for a and b.

$$5{,}760{,}000 + 1{,}000{,}000 = c^2$$ Evaluate each exponential expression.

$$6{,}760{,}000 = c^2$$ Do the addition.

$$c^2 = 6{,}760{,}000$$ Reverse the sides of the equation so that c^2 is on the left.

$$c = \sqrt{6{,}760{,}000}$$ If $c^2 = 6{,}760{,}000$, then c must be a square root of 6,760,000. Because c represents a length, it must be the positive square root of 6,760,000.

$$c = 2{,}600$$ Use a calculator to find the square root.

The two crews are 2,600 yards apart. Because this distance is less than the 3,000-yard range of the radios, they can communicate by radio.

Self Check 3

The lengths of two sides of a right triangle are given. Find the missing side length. 56 in.

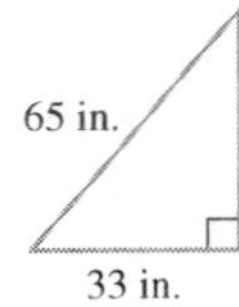

Now Try **Problem 23**

Teaching Example 3 Find the missing side length of the right triangle.

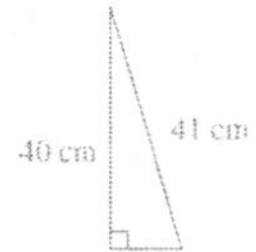

Answer:
9 cm

EXAMPLE 3 The lengths of two sides of a right triangle are given in the figure. Find the missing side length.

61 ft
11 ft

Strategy We will use the Pythagorean theorem to find the missing side length.

WHY If we know the lengths of any two sides of a right triangle, we can find the length of the third side using the Pythagorean theorem.

Solution We may substitute 11 for either a or b, but 61 must be substituted for the length c of the hypotenuse. If we choose to substitute 11 for b, we can find the unknown side length a as follows.

$c = 61$ ft
a
$b = 11$ ft

$$a^2 + b^2 = c^2$$ This is the Pythagorean equation.

$$a^2 + 11^2 = 61^2$$ Substitute 11 for b and 61 for c.

$$a^2 + 121 = 3{,}721$$ Evaluate each exponential expression.

$$a^2 + 121 - 121 = 3{,}721 - 121$$ To isolate a^2 on the left side, subtract 121 from both sides.

$$\begin{array}{r} 3{,}721 \\ -\ 121 \\ \hline 3{,}600 \end{array}$$

$$a^2 = 3{,}600$$ Do the subtraction.

$a = \sqrt{3{,}600}$ If $a^2 = 3{,}600$, then a must be a square root of 3,600. Because a represents a length, it must be the positive square root of 3,600.

$a = 60$ Use a calculator, if necessary, to find the square root.

The missing side length is 60 ft.

2 Use the Pythagorean theorem to approximate the length of a side of a right triangle.

When we use the Pythagorean theorem to find the length of a side of a right triangle, the solution is sometimes the square root of a number that is not a perfect square. In that case, we can use a calculator to *approximate* the square root.

EXAMPLE 4 Refer to the right triangle shown here. Find the missing side length. Give the exact answer and an approximation to the nearest hundredth.

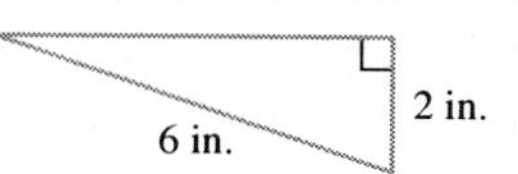

Strategy We will use the Pythagorean theorem to find the missing side length.

WHY If we know the lengths of any two sides of a right triangle, we can find the length of the third side using the Pythagorean theorem.

Solution We may substitute 2 for either a or b, but 6 must be substituted for the length c of the hypotenuse. If we choose to substitute 2 for a, we can find the unknown side length b as follows.

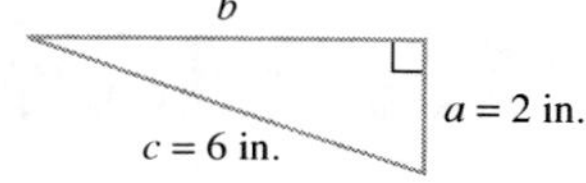

$a^2 + b^2 = c^2$ This is the Pythagorean equation.

$2^2 + b^2 = 6^2$ Substitute 2 for a and 6 for c.

$4 + b^2 = 36$ Evaluate each exponential expression.

$4 + b^2 - 4 = 36 - 4$ To isolate b^2 on the left side, undo the addition of 4 by subtracting 4 from both sides.

$b^2 = 32$ Do the subtraction.

We must find a number that, when squared, is 32. Since b represents the length of a side of a triangle, we consider only the positive square root.

$b = \sqrt{32}$ This is the exact length.

The missing side length is exactly $\sqrt{32}$ inches long. Since 32 is not a perfect square, its square root is not a whole number. We can use a calculator to *approximate* $\sqrt{32}$. To the nearest hundredth, the missing side length is 5.66 inches.

$\sqrt{32}$ in. $\approx$ 5.66 in.

Self Check 4

Refer to the triangle below. Find the missing side length. Give the exact answer and an approximation to the nearest hundredth. $\sqrt{24}$ m $\approx$ 4.90 m

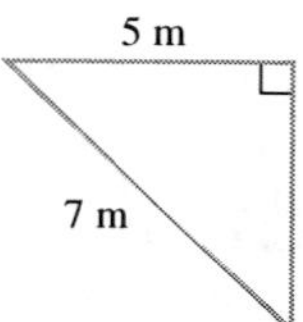

Now Try **Problem 35**

Teaching Example 4 Find the missing side length. Give the exact answer and an approximation to the nearest hundredth.

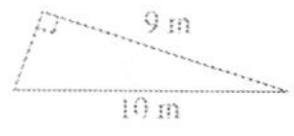

Answer:
$\sqrt{19}$ m $\approx$ 4.36 m

Using Your CALCULATOR Finding the Width of a TV Screen

The size of a television screen is the diagonal measure of its rectangular screen. To find the length of a 27-inch screen that is 17 inches high, we use the Pythagorean theorem with $c = 27$ and $b = 17$.

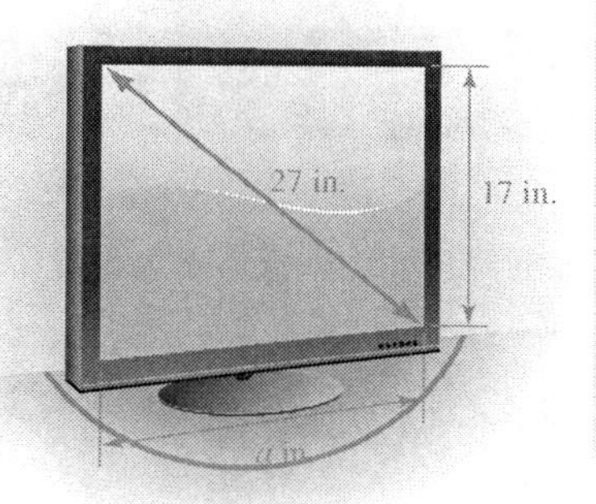

$$c^2 = a^2 + b^2$$
$$27^2 = a^2 + 17^2$$
$$27^2 - 17^2 = a^2$$

Since the variable a represents the length of the television screen, it must be positive. To find a, we find the positive square root of the result when 17^2 is subtracted from 27^2. Using a radical symbol to indicate this, we have

$$\sqrt{27^2 - 17^2} = a$$

We can evaluate the expression on the left side by entering:

(27 x^2 − 17 x^2) √ 20.97617696

To the nearest inch, the length of the television screen is 21 inches.

3 Use the converse of the Pythagorean theorem.

If a mathematical statement is written in the form *if p . . . , then q . . .* , we call the statement *if q . . . , then p . . .* its **converse.** The converses of some statements are true, while the converses of other statements are false. It is interesting to note that the converse of the Pythagorean theorem is true.

Converse of the Pythagorean Theorem

If a triangle has three sides of lengths a, b, and c, such that $a^2 + b^2 = c^2$, then the triangle is a right triangle.

Self Check 5

Is the triangle below a right triangle? yes

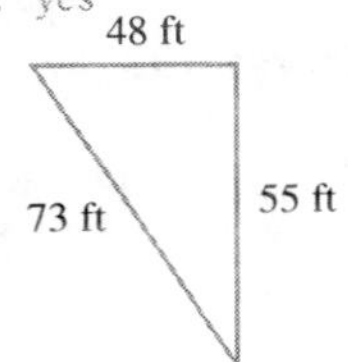

Now Try **Problem 39**

Teaching Example 5 Is the triangle a right triangle?

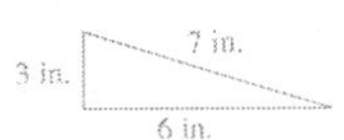

Answer: no

EXAMPLE 5 Is the triangle shown here a right triangle?

6 m, 11 m, 8 m

Strategy We will substitute the side lengths, 6, 8, and 11, into the Pythagorean equation $a^2 + b^2 = c^2$.

WHY By the converse of the Pythagorean theorem, the triangle is a right triangle if a true statement results. The triangle is not a right triangle if a false statement results.

Solution We must substitute the longest side length, 11, for c, because it is the possible hypotenuse. The lengths of 6 and 8 may be substituted for either a or b.

$a^2 + b^2 = c^2$ This is the Pythagorean equation.

$6^2 + 8^2 \stackrel{?}{=} 11^2$ Substitute 6 for a, 8 for b, and 11 for c.

$36 + 64 \stackrel{?}{=} 121$ Evaluate each exponential expression.

$100 = 121$ This is a false statement.

$$\begin{array}{r} \overset{1}{3}6 \\ +64 \\ \hline 100 \end{array}$$

Since $100 \neq 121$, the triangle is not a right triangle.

ANSWERS TO SELF CHECKS

1. 13 ft **2.** no **3.** 56 in. **4.** $\sqrt{24}$ m ≈ 4.90 m **5.** yes

SECTION 1.10 STUDY SET

VOCABULARY

Fill in the blanks.

1. In a right triangle, the side opposite the 90° angle is called the hypotenuse. The other two sides are called legs.

2. The Pythagorean theorem is named after the Greek mathematician, Pythagoras, who is thought to have been the first to prove it.

▶ 3. The Pythagorean theorem states that in any right triangle, the square of the length of the hypotenuse is equal to the sum of the squares of the lengths of the two legs.

4. $a^2 + b^2 = c^2$ is called the Pythagorean equation.

CONCEPTS

Fill in the blanks.

5. If a and b are the lengths of two legs of a right triangle and c is the length of the hypotenuse, then $a^2 + b^2 = c^2$.
6. The two solutions of $c^2 = 36$ are $c = -6$ or $c = 6$. If c represents the length of the hypotenuse of a right triangle, then we can discard the solution -6.
7. The converse of the Pythagorean theorem: If a triangle has three sides of lengths a, b, and c, such that $a^2 + b^2 = c^2$, then the triangle is a right triangle.
8. Use a protractor to draw an example of a right triangle.
9. Refer to the triangle on the right.
   a. What side is the hypotenuse? $\overline{BC}$
   b. What side is the longer leg? $\overline{AB}$
   c. What side is the shorter leg? $\overline{AC}$

C, 60°, 30°, B, A

10. What is the first step when solving the equation $25 + b^2 = 81$ for b? Subtract 25 from both sides.

NOTATION

Complete the solution to solve the equation, where $a > 0$ and $c > 0$.

▶ 11.
$$8^2 + 6^2 = c^2$$
$$64 + 36 = c^2$$
$$100 = c^2$$
$$\sqrt{100} = c$$
$$10 = c$$

12.
$$a^2 + 15^2 = 17^2$$
$$a^2 + 225 = 289$$
$$a^2 + 225 - 225 = 289 - 225$$
$$a^2 = 64$$
$$a = \sqrt{64}$$
$$a = 8$$

GUIDED PRACTICE

Find the length of the hypotenuse of the right triangle shown below if it has the given side lengths. See Examples 1 and 2.

▶ 13. $a = 6$ ft and $b = 8$ ft 10 ft
▶ 14. $a = 12$ mm and $b = 9$ mm 15 mm
▶ 15. $a = 5$ m and $b = 12$ m 13 m
▶ 16. $a = 16$ in. and $b = 12$ in. 20 in.
▶ 17. $a = 48$ mi and $b = 55$ mi 73 mi

a, c, b

▶ 18. $a = 80$ ft and $b = 39$ ft 89 ft
▶ 19. $a = 88$ cm and $b = 105$ cm 137 cm
▶ 20. $a = 132$ mm and $b = 85$ mm 157 mm

Refer to the right triangle below. See Example 3.

▶ 21. Find b if $a = 10$ cm and $c = 26$ cm. 24 cm
▶ 22. Find b if $a = 14$ in. and $c = 50$ in. 48 in.
▶ 23. Find a if $b = 18$ m and $c = 82$ m. 80 m
▶ 24. Find a if $b = 9$ yd and $c = 41$ yd. 40 yd
▶ 25. Find a if $b = 21$ m and $c = 29$ m. 20 m
▶ 26. Find a if $b = 16$ yd and $c = 34$ yd. 30 yd
▶ 27. Find b if $a = 180$ m and $c = 181$ m. 19 m
▶ 28. Find b if $a = 630$ ft and $c = 650$ ft. 160 ft

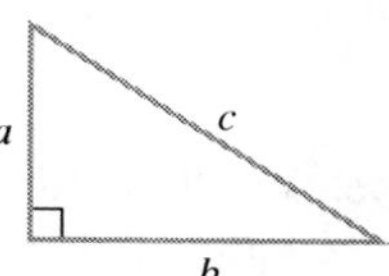

The lengths of two sides of a right triangle are given. Find the missing side length. Give the exact answer and an approximation to the nearest hundredth. See Example 4.

29. $a = 5$ cm and $c = 6$ cm
    $\sqrt{11}$ cm ≈ 3.32 cm
30. $a = 4$ in. and $c = 8$ in.
    $\sqrt{48}$ in. ≈ 6.93 in.
31. $a = 12$ m and $b = 8$ m
    $\sqrt{208}$ m ≈ 14.42 m
32. $a = 10$ ft and $b = 4$ ft
    $\sqrt{116}$ ft ≈ 10.77 ft
▶ 33. $a = 9$ in. and $b = 3$ in.
    $\sqrt{90}$ in. ≈ 9.49 in.
34. $a = 5$ mi and $b = 7$ mi
    $\sqrt{74}$ mi ≈ 8.60 mi
35. $b = 4$ in. and $c = 6$ in.
    $\sqrt{20}$ in. ≈ 4.47 in.
▶ 36. $b = 9$ mm and $c = 12$ mm
    $\sqrt{63}$ mm ≈ 7.94 mm

a, c, b

Is a triangle with the following side lengths a right triangle? See Example 5.

▶ 37. 12, 14, 15 no
▶ 38. 15, 16, 22 no
▶ 39. 33, 56, 65 yes
▶ 40. 20, 21, 29 yes

APPLICATIONS

41. ADJUSTING LADDERS A 20-foot ladder reaches a window 16 feet above the ground. How far from the wall is the base of the ladder? 12 ft
▶ 42. LENGTH OF GUY WIRES A 30-foot tower is to be fastened by three guy wires attached to the top of the tower and to the ground at positions 20 feet from its base. How much wire is needed? Round to the nearest tenth. $3\sqrt{1,300}$ ft ≈ 108.2 ft

43. PICTURE FRAMES After gluing and nailing two pieces of picture frame molding together, a frame maker checks her work by making a diagonal measurement. If the sides of the frame form a right angle, what measurement should the frame maker read on the yardstick? 25 in.

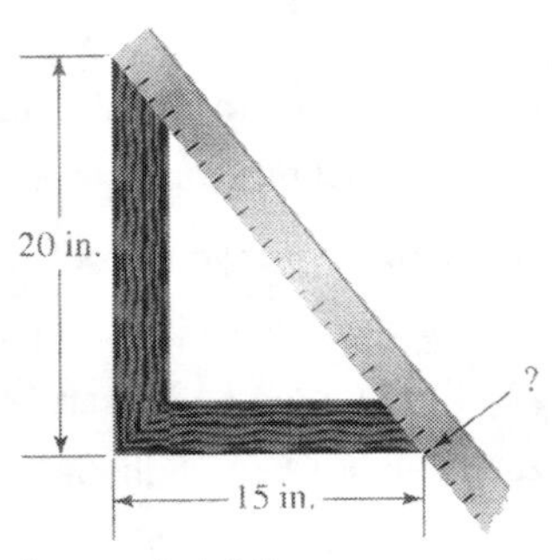

44. CARPENTRY The gable end of the roof shown is divided in half by a vertical brace, 8 feet in height. Find the length of the roof line. 17 ft

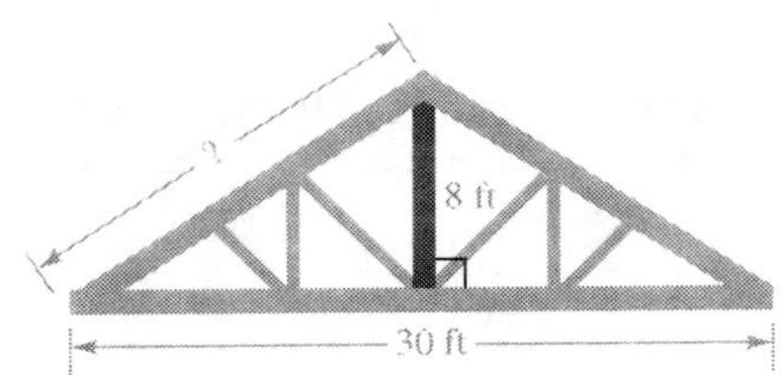

45. BASEBALL A baseball diamond is a square with each side 90 feet long. How far is it from home plate to second base? Round to the nearest hundredth. $\sqrt{16,200}$ ft ≈ 127.28 ft

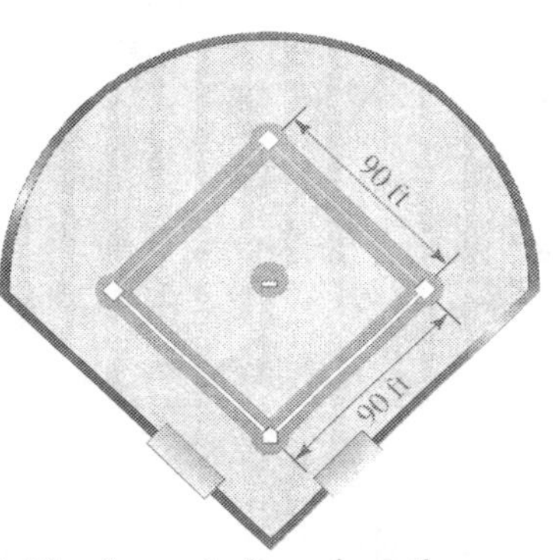

46. PAPER AIRPLANE The figure below gives the directions for making a paper airplane from a square piece of paper with sides 8 inches long. Find the length of the plane when it is completed in Step 3. Round to the nearest hundredth. $\sqrt{128}$ in. ≈ 11.31 in.

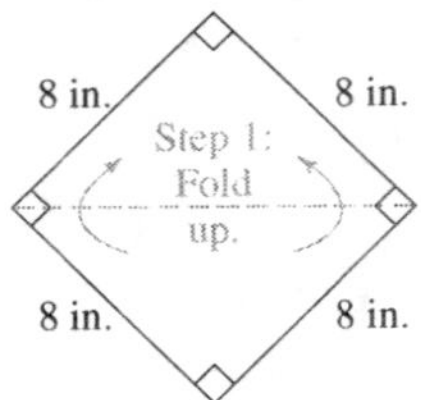

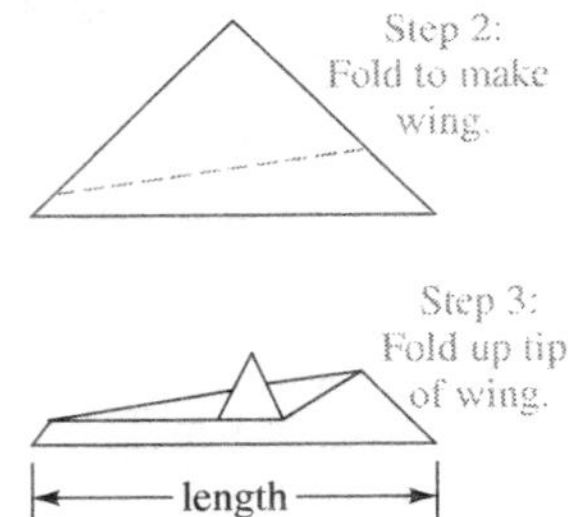

47. FIREFIGHTING The base of the 37-foot ladder shown in the figure below is 9 feet from the wall. Will the top reach a window ledge that is 35 feet above the ground? Explain how you arrived at your answer.
yes, $\sqrt{1,288}$ ft ≈ 35.89 ft

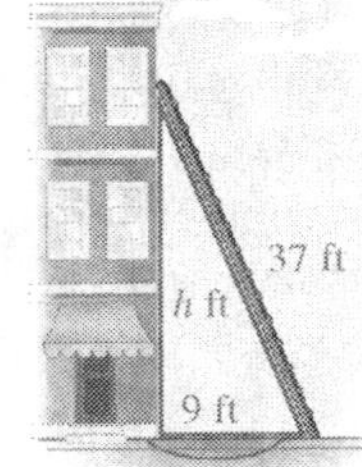

48. WIND DAMAGE A tree was blown over in a wind storm. Find the height of the tree when it was standing vertically upright. 81 ft

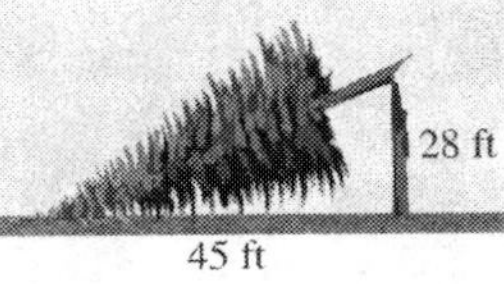

WRITING

49. State the Pythagorean theorem in your own words.

50. When the lengths of the sides of the triangle shown below are substituted into the equation $a^2 + b^2 = c^2$, the result is a false statement. Explain why.

$$a^2 + b^2 = c^2$$
$$2^2 + 4^2 = 5^2$$
$$4 + 16 = 25$$
$$20 = 25$$

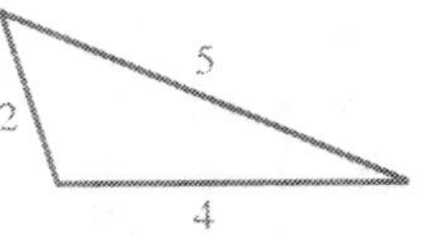

51. In the figure below, equal-sized squares have been drawn on the sides of right triangle $\triangle ABC$. Explain how this figure demonstrates that $3^2 + 4^2 = 5^2$.

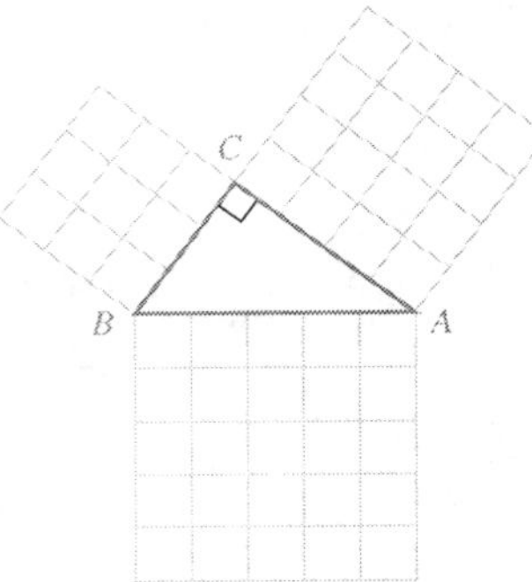

52. In the movie *The Wizard of Oz,* the scarecrow was in search of a brain. To prove that he had found one, he recited the following:

"The sum of the square roots of any two sides of an isosceles triangle is equal to the square root of the remaining side."

Unfortunately, this statement is not true. Correct it so that it states the Pythagorean theorem.

REVIEW

Use a check to determine whether the given number is a solution of the equation.

53. $2b + 3 = -15, -8$ no

54. $5t - 4 = -16, -2$ no

55. $0.5x = 2.9, 5$ no

56. $1.2 + x = 4.7, 3.5$ yes

57. $33 - \frac{x}{2} = 30, -6$ no

58. $\frac{x}{4} + 98 = 100, -8$ no

59. $3x - 2 = 4x - 5, 12$ no

60. $5y + 8 = 3y - 2, 5$ no

Module 2: Fractions and Decimals

DMA 020

iStockphoto.com/Monkeybusinessimages

from Campus to Careers

School Guidance Counselor

School guidance counselors plan academic programs and help students choose the best courses to take to achieve their educational goals. Counselors often meet with students to discuss the life skills needed for personal and social growth. To prepare for this career, guidance counselors take classes in an area of mathematics called *statistics,* where they learn how to collect, analyze, explain, and present data.

In **Problem 109** of **Study Set 2.4,** you will see how a counselor must be able to add fractions to better understand a graph that shows students' study habits.

JOB TITLE: School Guidance Counselor

EDUCATION: A master's degree is usually required to be licensed as a counselor. However, some schools accept a bachelor's degree with the appropriate counseling courses.

JOB OUTLOOK: Excellent.

ANNUAL EARNINGS: The average (median) salary in 2006 was $53,750.

FOR MORE INFORMATION: www.bls.gov/oco/ocos067.htm

Objectives

1 Identify the numerator and denominator of a fraction.

2 Simplify special fraction forms.

3 Define equivalent fractions.

4 Build equivalent fractions.

5 Simplify fractions.

SECTION 2.1
An Introduction to Fractions

Whole numbers are used to count objects, such as CDs, stamps, eggs, and magazines. When we need to describe a part of a whole, such as one-half of a pie, three-quarters of an hour, or a one-third-pound burger, we can use *fractions*.

One-half of a cherry pie	Three-quarters of an hour	One-third pound burger
$\frac{1}{2}$	$\frac{3}{4}$	$\frac{1}{3}$

1 Identify the numerator and denominator of a fraction.

A **fraction** describes the number of equal parts of a whole. For example, consider the figure below with 5 of the 6 equal parts colored red. We say that $\frac{5}{6}$ (five-sixths) of the figure is shaded.

In a fraction, the number above the **fraction bar** is called the **numerator,** and the number below is called the **denominator.**

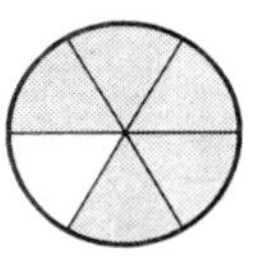

Fraction bar → $\frac{5}{6}$ ← numerator / ← denominator

The Language of Mathematics The word *fraction* comes from the Latin word *fractio* meaning "breaking in pieces."

Self Check 1

Identify the numerator and denominator of each fraction:

a. $\frac{7}{9}$ 7, 9

b. $\frac{21}{20}$ 21, 20

Now Try **Problem 21**

EXAMPLE 1 Identify the numerator and denominator of each fraction:

a. $\frac{11}{12}$ **b.** $\frac{8}{3}$

Strategy We will find the number above the fraction bar and the number below it.

WHY The number above the fraction bar is the numerator, and the number below is the denominator.

Solution

a. $\frac{11}{12}$ 11 ← numerator, 12 ← denominator

b. $\frac{8}{3}$ 8 ← numerator, 3 ← denominator

If the numerator of a fraction is less than its denominator, the fraction is called a **proper fraction.** A proper fraction is less than 1. If the numerator of a fraction is greater than or equal to its denominator, the fraction is called an **improper fraction.** An improper fraction is greater than or equal to 1.

Proper fractions

$$\frac{1}{4}, \frac{2}{3}, \text{ and } \frac{98}{99}$$

Improper fractions

$$\frac{7}{2}, \frac{98}{97}, \frac{16}{16}, \text{ and } \frac{5}{1}$$

Teaching Example 1 Identify the numerator and denominator of each fraction:

a. $\frac{31}{32}$ **b.** $\frac{12}{5}$

Answers:

a. numerator: 31, denominator: 32
b. numerator: 12, denominator: 5

The Language of Mathematics The phrase *improper fraction* is somewhat misleading. In algebra and other mathematics courses, we often use such fractions "properly" to solve many types of problems.

EXAMPLE 2 Write fractions that represent the shaded and unshaded portions of the figure below.

Strategy We will determine the number of equal parts into which the figure is divided. Then we will determine how many of those parts are shaded.

WHY The denominator of a fraction shows the number of equal parts in the whole. The numerator shows how many of those parts are being considered.

Solution

Since the figure is divided into 3 equal parts, the denominator of the fraction is 3. Since 2 of those parts are shaded, the numerator is 2, and we say that

$\frac{2}{3}$ of the figure is shaded. Write: $\frac{\text{number of parts shaded}}{\text{number of equal parts}}$

Since 1 of the 3 equal parts of the figure is not shaded, the numerator is 1, and we say that

$\frac{1}{3}$ of the figure is not shaded. Write: $\frac{\text{number of parts not shaded}}{\text{number of equal parts}}$

Self Check 2

Write fractions that represent the portion of the month that has passed and the portion that remains. $\frac{11}{31}, \frac{20}{31}$

DECEMBER

X	X	X	X	X	X	X
X	X	X	X	12	13	14
15	16	17	18	19	20	21
22	23	24	25	26	27	28
29	30	31				

Now Try **Problems 25 and 101**

Teaching Example 2 Write fractions to represent the shaded and unshaded portions of the figure.

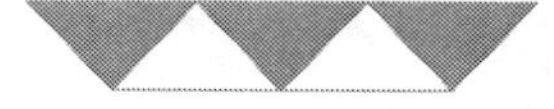

Answer:
$\frac{3}{5}, \frac{2}{5}$

There are times when a negative fraction is needed to describe a quantity. For example, if an earthquake causes a road to sink seven-eighths of an inch, the amount of downward movement can be represented by $-\frac{7}{8}$. Negative fractions can be written in three ways. The negative sign can appear in the numerator, in the denominator, or in front of the fraction.

$$\frac{-7}{8} = \frac{7}{-8} = -\frac{7}{8} \qquad \frac{-15}{4} = \frac{15}{-4} = -\frac{15}{4}$$

iStockphoto.com/Jamie VanBuskirk

Notice that the examples above agree with the rule from Chapter 2 for dividing integers with different (unlike) signs: *the quotient of a negative integer and a positive integer is negative.*

2 Simplify special fraction forms.

A fraction bar indicates division. This fact helps us simplify four special fraction forms.

- ***Fractions that have the same numerator and denominator:*** In this case, we have a number divided by itself. The result is 1 (provided the numerator and denominator are not 0). We call each of the following fractions a **form of 1.**

$$1 = \frac{1}{1} = \frac{2}{2} = \frac{3}{3} = \frac{4}{4} = \frac{5}{5} = \frac{6}{6} = \frac{7}{7} = \frac{8}{8} = \frac{9}{9} = \dots$$

- ***Fractions that have a denominator of 1:*** In this case, we have a number divided by 1. The result is simply the numerator.

$$\frac{5}{1} = 5 \qquad \frac{24}{1} = 24 \qquad \frac{-7}{1} = -7$$

- ***Fractions that have a numerator of 0:*** In this case, we have division of 0. The result is 0 (provided the denominator is not 0).

$$\frac{0}{8} = 0 \qquad \frac{0}{56} = 0 \qquad \frac{0}{-11} = 0$$

- ***Fractions that have a denominator of 0:*** In this case, we have division by 0. The division is undefined.

$$\frac{7}{0} \text{ is undefined} \qquad \frac{-18}{0} \text{ is undefined}$$

The Language of Mathematics Perhaps you are wondering about the fraction form $\frac{0}{0}$. It is said to be *undetermined*. This form is important in advanced mathematics courses.

Self Check 3

Simplify, if possible:

a. $\frac{4}{4}$ **b.** $\frac{51}{1}$ **c.** $\frac{45}{0}$ **d.** $\frac{0}{6}$

Now Try **Problem 33**

Self Check 3 Answers

a. 1 b. 51 c. undefined d. 0

Teaching Example 3 Simplify, if possible:

a. $\frac{10}{1}$ b. $\frac{9}{9}$ c. $\frac{0}{17}$ d. $\frac{21}{0}$

Answers:

a. 10 b. 1 c. 0 d. undefined

EXAMPLE 3 Simplify, if possible: **a.** $\frac{12}{12}$ **b.** $\frac{0}{24}$ **c.** $\frac{18}{0}$ **d.** $\frac{9}{1}$

Strategy To simplify each fraction, we will divide the numerator by the denominator, if possible.

WHY A fraction bar indicates division.

Solution

a. $\frac{12}{12} = 1$ This corresponds to dividing a quantity into 12 equal parts, and then considering all 12 of them. We would get 1 whole quantity.

b. $\frac{0}{24} = 0$ This corresponds to dividing a quantity into 24 equal parts, and then considering 0 (none) of them. We would get 0.

c. $\frac{18}{0}$ is undefined This corresponds to dividing a quantity into 0 equal parts, and then considering 18 of them. That is not possible.

d. $\frac{9}{1} = 9$ This corresponds to "dividing" a quantity into 1 equal part, and then considering 9 of them. We would get 9 of those quantities.

The Language of Mathematics Fractions are often referred to as **rational numbers.** All integers are rational numbers, because every integer can be written as a fraction with a denominator of 1. For example,

$$2 = \frac{2}{1}, \quad -5 = \frac{-5}{1}, \quad \text{and} \quad 0 = \frac{0}{1}$$

3 Define equivalent fractions.

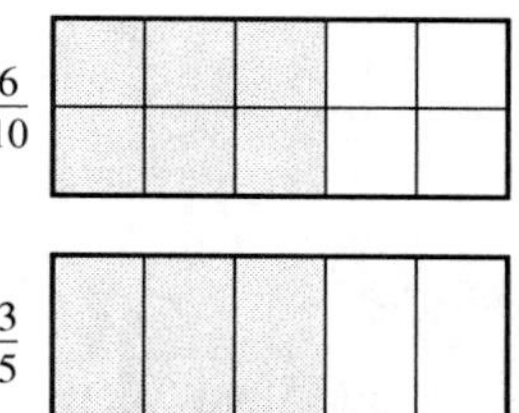

Fractions can look different but still represent the same part of a whole. To illustrate this, consider the identical rectangular regions on the right. The first one is divided into 10 equal parts. Since 6 of those parts are red, $\frac{6}{10}$ of the figure is shaded.

The second figure is divided into 5 equal parts. Since 3 of those parts are red, $\frac{3}{5}$ of the figure is shaded. We can conclude that $\frac{6}{10} = \frac{3}{5}$ because $\frac{6}{10}$ and $\frac{3}{5}$ represent the same shaded portion of the figure. We say that $\frac{6}{10}$ and $\frac{3}{5}$ are *equivalent fractions.*

Equivalent Fractions

Two fractions are **equivalent** if they represent the same number. **Equivalent fractions** represent the same portion of a whole.

4 Build equivalent fractions.

Writing a fraction as an equivalent fraction with a *larger* denominator is called **building** the fraction. To build a fraction, we use a familiar property from Chapter 1 that is also true for fractions:

Multiplication Property of 1

The product of any fraction and 1 is that fraction.

We also use the following rule for multiplying fractions.

Multiplying Fractions

To multiply two fractions, multiply the numerators and multiply the denominators.

To build an equivalent fraction for $\frac{1}{2}$ with a denominator of 8, we first ask, "What number times 2 equals 8?" To answer that question we *divide* 8 by 2 to get 4. Since we need to multiply the denominator of $\frac{1}{2}$ by 4 to obtain a denominator of 8, it follows that $\frac{4}{4}$ should be the form of 1 that is used to build an equivalent fraction for $\frac{1}{2}$.

$\frac{1}{2} = \frac{1}{2} \cdot \frac{4}{4}$ Multiply $\frac{1}{2}$ by 1 in the form of $\frac{4}{4}$. Note the form of 1 highlighted in red.

$= \frac{1 \cdot 4}{2 \cdot 4}$ Use the rule for multiplying two fractions. Multiply the numerators. Multiply the denominators.

$= \frac{4}{8}$

We have found that $\frac{4}{8}$ is equivalent to $\frac{1}{2}$. To build an equivalent fraction for $\frac{1}{2}$ with a denominator of 8, we *multiplied by a factor equal to 1* in the form of $\frac{4}{4}$. Multiplying $\frac{1}{2}$ by $\frac{4}{4}$ changes its appearance but does not change its value, because we are multiplying it by 1.

Building Fractions

To build a fraction, *multiply it by a factor of 1* in the form $\frac{2}{2}, \frac{3}{3}, \frac{4}{4}, \frac{5}{5}$, and so on.

The Language of Mathematics Building an equivalent fraction with a larger denominator is also called *expressing a fraction in higher terms.*

Self Check 4

Write $\frac{5}{8}$ as an equivalent fraction with a denominator of 24. $\frac{15}{24}$

Now Try **Problems 37 and 49**

Teaching Example 4 Write $\frac{5}{6}$ as an equivalent fraction with a denominator of 48.
Answer:
$\frac{40}{48}$

EXAMPLE 4 Write $\frac{3}{5}$ as an equivalent fraction with a denominator of 35.

Strategy We will compare the given denominator to the required denominator and ask, "What number times 5 equals 35?"

WHY The answer to that question helps us determine the form of 1 to use to build an equivalent fraction.

Solution

To answer the question "What number times 5 equals 35?" we *divide* 35 by 5 to get 7. Since we need to multiply the denominator of $\frac{3}{5}$ by 7 to obtain a denominator of 35, it follows that $\frac{7}{7}$ should be the form of 1 that is used to build an equivalent fraction for $\frac{3}{5}$.

$$\frac{3}{5} = \frac{3}{5} \cdot \frac{7}{7} \qquad \text{Multiply } \tfrac{3}{5} \text{ by a form of 1: } \tfrac{7}{7} = 1.$$

$$= \frac{3 \cdot 7}{5 \cdot 7} \qquad \text{Multiply the numerators. Multiply the denominators.}$$

$$= \frac{21}{35}$$

We have found that $\frac{21}{35}$ is equivalent to $\frac{3}{5}$.

Success Tip To build an equivalent fraction in Example 4, we multiplied $\frac{3}{5}$ by 1 in the form of $\frac{7}{7}$. As a result of that step, the numerator and the denominator of $\frac{3}{5}$ were multiplied by 7:

$$\frac{3 \cdot 7}{5 \cdot 7} \quad \begin{array}{l} \leftarrow \text{The numerator is multiplied by 7.} \\ \leftarrow \text{The denominator is multiplied by 7.} \end{array}$$

This process illustrates the following property of fractions.

The Fundamental Property of Fractions

If the numerator and denominator of a fraction are multiplied by the same nonzero number, the resulting fraction is equivalent to the original fraction.

Since multiplying the numerator and denominator of a fraction by the same nonzero number produces an equivalent fraction, your instructor may allow you to begin your solution to problems like Example 4 as shown in the Success Tip above.

EXAMPLE 5 Write 4 as an equivalent fraction with a denominator of 6.

Strategy We will express 4 as the fraction $\frac{4}{1}$ and build an equivalent fraction by multiplying it by $\frac{6}{6}$.

WHY Since we need to multiply the denominator of $\frac{4}{1}$ by 6 to obtain a denominator of 6, it follows that $\frac{6}{6}$ should be the form of 1 that is used to build an equivalent fraction for $\frac{4}{1}$.

Solution

$4 = \frac{4}{1}$ Write 4 as a fraction: $4 = \frac{4}{1}$.

$= \frac{4}{1} \cdot \frac{6}{6}$ Build an equivalent fraction by multiplying $\frac{4}{1}$ by a form of 1: $\frac{6}{6} = 1$.

$= \frac{4 \cdot 6}{1 \cdot 6}$ Multiply the numerators. Multiply the denominators.

$= \frac{24}{6}$

Self Check 5

Write 10 as an equivalent fraction with a denominator of 3. $\frac{30}{3}$

Now Try **Problem 57**

Teaching Example 5 Write 7 as an equivalent fraction with a denominator of 4.
Answer:
$\frac{28}{4}$

5 Simplify fractions.

Every fraction can be written in infinitely many equivalent forms. For example, some equivalent forms of $\frac{10}{15}$ are:

$$\frac{2}{3} = \frac{4}{6} = \frac{6}{9} = \frac{8}{12} = \frac{10}{15} = \frac{12}{18} = \frac{14}{21} = \frac{16}{24} = \frac{18}{27} = \frac{20}{30} = \cdots$$

Of all of the equivalent forms in which we can write a fraction, we often need to determine the one that is in *simplest form.*

Simplest Form of a Fraction

A fraction is in **simplest form,** or **lowest terms,** when the numerator and denominator have no common factors other than 1.

EXAMPLE 6 Are the following fractions in simplest form? **a.** $\frac{12}{27}$ **b.** $\frac{5}{8}$

Strategy We will determine whether the numerator and denominator have any common factors other than 1.

WHY If the numerator and denominator have no common factors other than 1, the fraction is in simplest form.

Solution

a. The factors of the numerator, 12, are: 1, 2, 3, 4, 6, 12
The factors of the denominator, 27, are: 1, 3, 9, 27

Since the numerator and denominator have a common factor of 3, the fraction $\frac{12}{27}$ is *not* in simplest form.

b. The factors of the numerator, 5, are: 1, 5
The factors of the denominator, 8, are: 1, 2, 4, 8

Since the only common factor of the numerator and denominator is 1, the fraction $\frac{5}{8}$ is in simplest form.

Self Check 6

Are the following fractions in simplest form?

a. $\frac{4}{21}$ yes

b. $\frac{6}{20}$ no

Now Try **Problem 61**

Teaching Example 6 Are the following fractions in simplest form?

a. $\frac{14}{18}$ b. $\frac{4}{9}$

Answers:
a. no b. yes

To **simplify a fraction,** we write it in simplest form by *removing a factor equal to 1.* For example, to simplify $\frac{10}{15}$, we note that the greatest factor common to the numerator and denominator is 5 and proceed as follows:

$$\frac{10}{15} = \frac{2 \cdot 5}{3 \cdot 5}$$ Factor 10 and 15. Note the form of 1 highlighted in red.

$$= \frac{2}{3} \cdot \frac{5}{5}$$ Use the rule for multiplying fractions in reverse: write $\frac{2 \cdot 5}{3 \cdot 5}$ as the product of two fractions, $\frac{2}{3}$ and $\frac{5}{5}$.

$$= \frac{2}{3} \cdot 1$$ A number divided by itself is equal to 1: $\frac{5}{5} = 1$.

$$= \frac{2}{3}$$ Use the multiplication property of 1: the product of any fraction and 1 is that fraction.

We have found that the simplified form of $\frac{10}{15}$ is $\frac{2}{3}$. To simplify $\frac{10}{15}$, we *removed a factor equal to 1* in the form of $\frac{5}{5}$. The result, $\frac{2}{3}$, is equivalent to $\frac{10}{15}$.

To streamline the simplifying process, we can replace pairs of factors common to the numerator and denominator with the equivalent fraction $\frac{1}{1}$.

Self Check 7

Simplify each fraction:

a. $\frac{10}{25}$ $\frac{2}{5}$

b. $\frac{3}{9}$ $\frac{1}{3}$

Now Try **Problems 65 and 69**

Teaching Example 7 Simplify each fraction:

a. $\frac{9}{15}$ b. $\frac{2}{18}$

Answers:

a. $\frac{3}{5}$ b. $\frac{1}{9}$

EXAMPLE 7

Simplify each fraction: **a.** $\frac{6}{10}$ **b.** $\frac{7}{21}$

Strategy We will factor the numerator and denominator. Then we will look for any factors common to the numerator and denominator and remove them.

WHY We need to make sure that the numerator and denominator have no common factors other than 1. If that is the case, then the fraction is in *simplest form.*

Solution

a. $$\frac{6}{10} = \frac{2 \cdot 3}{2 \cdot 5}$$ To prepare to simplify, factor 6 and 10. Note the form of 1 highlighted in red.

$$= \frac{\overset{1}{\cancel{2}} \cdot 3}{\underset{1}{\cancel{2}} \cdot 5}$$ Simplify by removing the common factor of 2 from the numerator and denominator. A slash / and the 1's are used to show that $\frac{2}{2}$ is replaced by the equivalent fraction $\frac{1}{1}$. A factor equal to 1 in the form of $\frac{2}{2}$ was removed.

$$= \frac{3}{5}$$ Multiply the remaining factors in the numerator: $1 \cdot 3 = 3$. Multiply the remaining factors in the denominator: $1 \cdot 5 = 5$.

Since 3 and 5 have no common factors (other than 1), $\frac{3}{5}$ is in simplest form.

b. $$\frac{7}{21} = \frac{7}{3 \cdot 7}$$ To prepare to simplify, factor 21.

$$= \frac{\overset{1}{\cancel{7}}}{3 \cdot \underset{1}{\cancel{7}}}$$ Simplify by removing the common factor of 7 from the numerator and denominator.

$$= \frac{1}{3}$$ Multiply the remaining factors in the denominator: $1 \cdot 3 = 3$.

Caution! Don't forget to write the 1's when removing common factors of the numerator and the denominator. Failure to do so can lead to the common mistake shown below.

$$\frac{7}{21} = \frac{\cancel{7}}{3 \cdot \cancel{7}} = \frac{0}{3}$$

We can easily identify common factors of the numerator and the denominator of a fraction if we write them in prime-factored form.

EXAMPLE 8 Simplify each fraction, if possible: **a.** $\frac{90}{105}$ **b.** $\frac{25}{27}$

Strategy We begin by prime factoring the numerator, 90, and denominator, 105. Then we look for any factors common to the numerator and denominator and remove them.

WHY When the numerator and/or denominator of a fraction are large numbers, such as 90 and 105, writing their prime factorizations is helpful in identifying any common factors.

Solution

a. $\frac{90}{105} = \frac{2 \cdot 3 \cdot 3 \cdot 5}{3 \cdot 5 \cdot 7}$ To prepare to simplify, write 90 and 105 in prime-factored form.

$= \frac{2 \cdot \overset{1}{\cancel{3}} \cdot 3 \cdot \overset{1}{\cancel{5}}}{\underset{1}{\cancel{3}} \cdot \underset{1}{\cancel{5}} \cdot 7}$ Remove the common factors of 3 and 5 from the numerator and denominator. Slashes and 1's are used to show that $\frac{3}{3}$ and $\frac{5}{5}$ are replaced by the equivalent fraction $\frac{1}{1}$. A factor equal to 1 in the form of $\frac{3 \cdot 5}{3 \cdot 5} = \frac{15}{15}$ was removed.

$= \frac{6}{7}$ Multiply the remaining factors in the numerator: $2 \cdot 1 \cdot 3 \cdot 1 = 6$. Multiply the remaining factors in the denominator: $1 \cdot 1 \cdot 7 = 7$.

90: 9, 10; 9: ③ ③; 10: ② ⑤
105: ⑤ 21; 21: ③ ⑦

Since 6 and 7 have no common factors (other than 1), $\frac{6}{7}$ is in simplest form.

b. $\frac{25}{27} = \frac{5 \cdot 5}{3 \cdot 3 \cdot 3}$ Write 25 and 27 in prime-factored form.

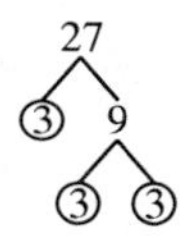

Since 25 and 27 have no common factors, other than 1, the fraction $\frac{25}{27}$ is in simplest form.

Self Check 8

Simplify each fraction, if possible:

a. $\frac{70}{126}$ $\frac{5}{9}$

b. $\frac{16}{81}$ in simplest form

Now Try **Problems 77 and 81**

Teaching Example 8 Simplify each fraction, if possible:

a. $\frac{75}{315}$ b. $\frac{8}{45}$

Answers:

a. $\frac{5}{21}$ b. in simplest form

EXAMPLE 9 Simplify: $\frac{63}{36}$

Strategy We will prime factor the numerator and denominator. Then we will look for any factors common to the numerator and denominator and remove them.

WHY We need to make sure that the numerator and denominator have no common factors other than 1. If that is the case, then the fraction is in *simplest form.*

Solution

$\frac{63}{36} = \frac{3 \cdot 3 \cdot 7}{2 \cdot 2 \cdot 3 \cdot 3}$ To prepare to simplify, write 63 and 36 in prime-factored form.

3⌊63	2⌊36
3⌊21	2⌊18
7	3⌊9
	3

$= \frac{\overset{1}{\cancel{3}} \cdot \overset{1}{\cancel{3}} \cdot 7}{2 \cdot 2 \cdot \underset{1}{\cancel{3}} \cdot \underset{1}{\cancel{3}}}$ Simplify by removing the common factors of 3 from the numerator and denominator.

$= \frac{7}{4}$ Multiply the remaining factors in the numerator: $1 \cdot 1 \cdot 7 = 7$. Multiply the remaining factors in the denominator: $2 \cdot 2 \cdot 1 \cdot 1 = 4$.

Success Tip If you recognized that 63 and 36 have a common factor of 9, you may remove that common factor from the numerator and denominator without writing the prime factorizations. However, make sure that the numerator and denominator of the resulting fraction do not have any common factors. If they do, continue to simplify.

$\frac{63}{36} = \frac{7 \cdot \overset{1}{\cancel{9}}}{4 \cdot \underset{1}{\cancel{9}}} = \frac{7}{4}$ Factor 63 as $7 \cdot 9$ and 36 as $4 \cdot 9$, and then remove the common factor of 9 from the numerator and denominator.

Self Check 9

Simplify: $\frac{162}{72}$ $\frac{9}{4}$

Now Try **Problem 89**

Teaching Example 9 Simplify: $\frac{132}{48}$

Answer:

$\frac{11}{4}$

Use the following steps to simplify a fraction.

Simplifying Fractions

To simplify a fraction, *remove factors equal to 1* of the form $\frac{2}{2}, \frac{3}{3}, \frac{4}{4}, \frac{5}{5}$, and so on, using the following procedure:

1. Factor (or prime factor) the numerator and denominator to determine their common factors.
2. Remove factors equal to 1 by replacing each pair of factors common to the numerator and denominator with the equivalent fraction $\frac{1}{1}$.
3. Multiply the remaining factors in the numerator and in the denominator.

Negative fractions are simplified in the same way as positive fractions. Just remember to write a negative sign − in front of each step of the solution. For example, to simplify $-\frac{15}{33}$ we proceed as follows:

$$-\frac{15}{33} = -\frac{\overset{1}{\cancel{3}} \cdot 5}{\underset{1}{\cancel{3}} \cdot 11}$$

$$= -\frac{5}{11}$$

ANSWERS TO SELF CHECKS

1. a. numerator: 7; denominator: 9 **b.** numerator: 21; denominator: 20 **2. a.** $\frac{11}{31}$ **b.** $\frac{20}{31}$ **3. a.** 1 **b.** 51 **c.** undefined **d.** 0 **4.** $\frac{15}{24}$ **5.** $\frac{30}{3}$ **6. a.** yes **b.** no **7. a.** $\frac{2}{5}$ **b.** $\frac{1}{3}$ **8. a.** $\frac{5}{9}$ **b.** in simplest form **9.** $\frac{9}{4}$

SECTION 2.1 STUDY SET

VOCABULARY

Fill in the blanks.

1. A _fraction_ describes the number of equal parts of a whole.
2. For the fraction $\frac{7}{8}$, the _numerator_ is 7 and the _denominator_ is 8.
3. If the numerator of a fraction is less than its denominator, the fraction is called a _proper_ fraction. If the numerator of a fraction is greater than or equal to its denominator it is called an _improper_ fraction.
4. Each of the following fractions is a form of _1_.

$$\frac{1}{1} = \frac{2}{2} = \frac{3}{3} = \frac{4}{4} = \frac{5}{5} = \frac{6}{6} = \frac{7}{7} = \frac{8}{8} = \frac{9}{9} = \dots$$

5. Two fractions are _equivalent_ if they represent the same number.
6. _Equivalent_ fractions represent the same portion of a whole.
7. Writing a fraction as an equivalent fraction with a larger denominator is called _building_ the fraction.
8. A fraction is in _simplest_ form, or lowest terms, when the numerator and denominator have no common factors other than 1.

CONCEPTS

9. What concept studied in this section is shown on the right?
equivalent fractions: $\frac{2}{6} = \frac{1}{3}$

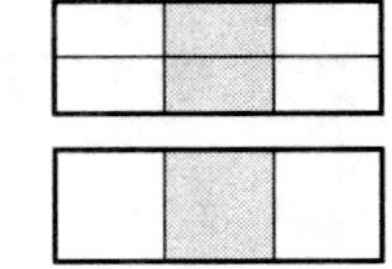

10. What concept studied in this section does the following statement illustrate?

$$\frac{1}{2} = \frac{2}{4} = \frac{3}{6} = \frac{4}{8} = \frac{5}{10} = \dots$$ equivalent fractions

Selected exercises available online at **www.webassign.net/brookscole**

11. Classify each fraction as a proper fraction or an improper fraction.

a. $\frac{37}{24}$ improper fraction **b.** $\frac{1}{3}$ proper fraction

c. $\frac{71}{100}$ proper fraction **d.** $\frac{9}{9}$ improper fraction

12. Remove the common factors of the numerator and denominator to simplify the fraction:

$$\frac{2 \cdot 3 \cdot 3 \cdot 5}{2 \cdot 3 \cdot 5 \cdot 7} \quad \frac{3}{7}$$

13. What common factor (other than 1) do the numerator and the denominator of the fraction $\frac{10}{15}$ have? 5

Fill in the blank.

14. Multiplication property of 1: The product of any fraction and 1 is that _fraction_.

15. Multiplying fractions: To multiply two fractions, multiply the _numerators_ and multiply the denominators.

16. a. Consider the following solution: $\frac{2}{3} = \frac{2}{3} \cdot \frac{4}{4}$

$$= \frac{8}{12}$$

To build an equivalent fraction for $\frac{2}{3}$ with a denominator of 12, _multiply_ it by a factor equal to 1 in the form of $\frac{4}{4}$.

b. Consider the following solution: $\frac{15}{27} = \frac{\overset{1}{\cancel{3}} \cdot 5}{\underset{1}{\cancel{3}} \cdot 9}$

$$= \frac{5}{9}$$

To simplify the fraction $\frac{15}{27}$, _remove_ a factor equal to 1 of the form $\frac{3}{3}$.

NOTATION

17. Write the fraction $\frac{7}{-8}$ in two other ways. $\frac{-7}{8}, -\frac{7}{8}$

18. Write each integer as a fraction.

a. 8 $\frac{8}{1}$ **b.** −25 $-\frac{25}{1}$

Complete each solution.

19. Build an equivalent fraction for $\frac{1}{6}$ with a denominator of 18.

$$\frac{1}{6} = \frac{1}{6} \cdot \frac{3}{3}$$

$$= \frac{1 \cdot 3}{6 \cdot 3}$$

$$= \frac{3}{18}$$

20. Simplify: $\frac{18}{24}$

$$\frac{18}{24} = \frac{2 \cdot 3 \cdot 3}{2 \cdot 2 \cdot 2 \cdot 3}$$

$$= \frac{\overset{1}{\cancel{2}} \cdot 3 \cdot \overset{1}{\cancel{3}}}{\underset{1}{\cancel{2}} \cdot 2 \cdot 2 \cdot \underset{1}{\cancel{3}}}$$

$$= \frac{3}{4}$$

GUIDED PRACTICE

Identify the numerator and denominator of each fraction. See Example 1.

21. $\frac{4}{5}$ numerator: 4; denominator: 5 ▶ **22.** $\frac{7}{8}$ numerator: 7; denominator: 8

23. $\frac{17}{10}$ numerator: 17; denominator: 10 **24.** $\frac{29}{21}$ numerator: 29; denominator: 21

Write a fraction to describe what part of the figure is shaded. Write a fraction to describe what part of the figure is not shaded. See Example 2.

25. $\frac{3}{4}, \frac{1}{4}$ ▶ **26.** $\frac{2}{3}, \frac{1}{3}$

27. $\frac{5}{8}, \frac{3}{8}$ **28.** $\frac{7}{12}, \frac{5}{12}$

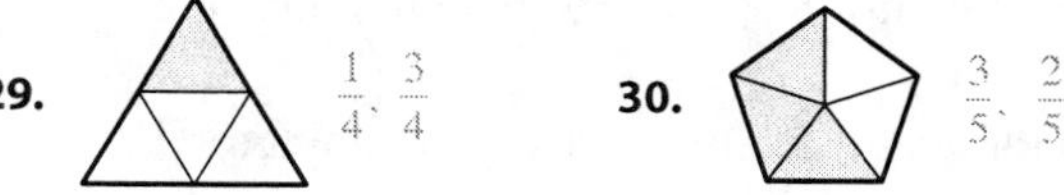

29. $\frac{1}{4}, \frac{3}{4}$ **30.** $\frac{3}{5}, \frac{2}{5}$

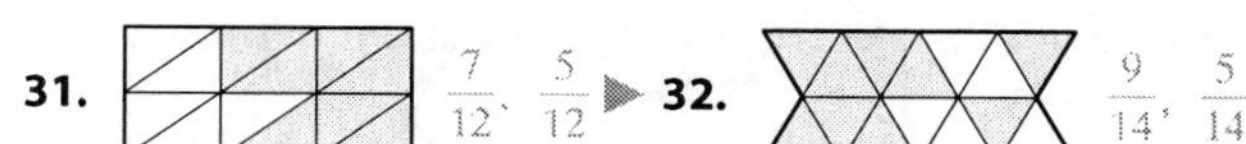

31. $\frac{7}{12}, \frac{5}{12}$ ▶ **32.** $\frac{9}{14}, \frac{5}{14}$

Simplify, if possible. See Example 3.

33. a. $\frac{4}{1}$ 4 **b.** $\frac{8}{8}$ 1

c. $\frac{0}{12}$ 0 **d.** $\frac{1}{0}$ undefined

34. a. $\frac{25}{1}$ 25 **b.** $\frac{14}{14}$ 1

c. $\frac{0}{1}$ 0 **d.** $\frac{83}{0}$ undefined

▶ **35. a.** $\frac{5}{0}$ undefined **b.** $\frac{0}{50}$ 0

c. $\frac{33}{33}$ 1 **d.** $\frac{75}{1}$ 75

36. **a.** $\frac{0}{64}$ 0 **b.** $\frac{27}{0}$ undefined

c. $\frac{125}{125}$ 1 **d.** $\frac{98}{1}$ 98

Write each fraction as an equivalent fraction with the indicated denominator. See Example 4.

37. $\frac{7}{8}$, denominator 40 $\frac{35}{40}$ **38.** $\frac{3}{4}$, denominator 24 $\frac{18}{24}$

39. $\frac{4}{9}$, denominator 27 $\frac{12}{27}$ ▶ **40.** $\frac{5}{7}$, denominator 49 $\frac{35}{49}$

41. $\frac{5}{6}$, denominator 54 $\frac{45}{54}$ **42.** $\frac{2}{3}$, denominator 27 $\frac{18}{27}$

43. $\frac{2}{7}$, denominator 14 $\frac{4}{14}$ **44.** $\frac{3}{10}$, denominator 50 $\frac{15}{50}$

45. $\frac{1}{2}$, denominator 30 $\frac{15}{30}$ **46.** $\frac{1}{3}$, denominator 60 $\frac{20}{60}$

47. $\frac{11}{16}$, denominator 32 $\frac{22}{32}$ ▶ **48.** $\frac{9}{10}$, denominator 60 $\frac{54}{60}$

49. $\frac{5}{4}$, denominator 28 $\frac{35}{28}$ **50.** $\frac{9}{4}$, denominator 44 $\frac{99}{44}$

51. $\frac{16}{15}$, denominator 45 $\frac{48}{45}$ **52.** $\frac{13}{12}$, denominator 36 $\frac{39}{36}$

Write each whole number as an equivalent fraction with the indicated denominator. See Example 5.

53. 4, denominator 9 $\frac{36}{9}$ **54.** 4, denominator 3 $\frac{12}{3}$

55. 6, denominator 8 $\frac{48}{8}$ ▶ **56.** 3, denominator 6 $\frac{18}{6}$

57. 3, denominator 5 $\frac{15}{5}$ **58.** 7, denominator 4 $\frac{28}{4}$

59. 14, denominator 2 $\frac{28}{2}$ **60.** 10, denominator 9 $\frac{90}{9}$

Are the following fractions in simplest form? See Example 6.

61. **a.** $\frac{12}{16}$ no **b.** $\frac{3}{25}$ yes

▶ **62.** **a.** $\frac{9}{24}$ no **b.** $\frac{7}{36}$ yes

63. **a.** $\frac{35}{36}$ yes **b.** $\frac{18}{21}$ no

64. **a.** $\frac{22}{45}$ yes **b.** $\frac{21}{56}$ no

Simplify each fraction, if possible. See Example 7.

65. $\frac{6}{9}$ $\frac{2}{3}$ **66.** $\frac{15}{20}$ $\frac{3}{4}$

67. $\frac{16}{20}$ $\frac{4}{5}$ **68.** $\frac{25}{35}$ $\frac{5}{7}$

69. $\frac{5}{15}$ $\frac{1}{3}$ ▶ **70.** $\frac{6}{30}$ $\frac{1}{5}$

71. $\frac{2}{48}$ $\frac{1}{24}$ **72.** $\frac{2}{42}$ $\frac{1}{21}$

Simplify each fraction, if possible. See Example 8.

73. $\frac{36}{96}$ $\frac{3}{8}$ ▶ **74.** $\frac{48}{120}$ $\frac{2}{5}$

75. $\frac{16}{17}$ in simplest form ▶ **76.** $\frac{14}{25}$ in simplest form

77. $\frac{55}{62}$ in simplest form **78.** $\frac{41}{51}$ in simplest form

79. $\frac{50}{55}$ $\frac{10}{11}$ **80.** $\frac{22}{88}$ $\frac{1}{4}$

81. $\frac{60}{108}$ $\frac{5}{9}$ **82.** $\frac{75}{275}$ $\frac{3}{11}$

83. $\frac{180}{210}$ $\frac{6}{7}$ **84.** $\frac{90}{120}$ $\frac{3}{4}$

Simplify each fraction. See Example 9.

85. $\frac{306}{234}$ $\frac{17}{13}$ **86.** $\frac{208}{117}$ $\frac{16}{9}$

87. $\frac{15}{6}$ $\frac{5}{2}$ **88.** $\frac{24}{16}$ $\frac{3}{2}$

89. $\frac{420}{144}$ $\frac{35}{12}$ ▶ **90.** $\frac{216}{189}$ $\frac{8}{7}$

91. $-\frac{4}{68}$ $-\frac{1}{17}$ **92.** $-\frac{3}{42}$ $-\frac{1}{14}$

93. $-\frac{90}{105}$ $-\frac{6}{7}$ **94.** $-\frac{98}{126}$ $-\frac{7}{9}$

95. $-\frac{16}{26}$ $-\frac{8}{13}$ **96.** $-\frac{81}{132}$ $-\frac{27}{44}$

TRY IT YOURSELF

Tell whether each pair of fractions are equivalent by simplifying each fraction.

97. $\frac{2}{14}$ and $\frac{6}{36}$ not equivalent **98.** $\frac{3}{12}$ and $\frac{4}{24}$ not equivalent

99. $\frac{22}{34}$ and $\frac{33}{51}$ equivalent **100.** $\frac{4}{30}$ and $\frac{12}{90}$ equivalent

APPLICATIONS

101. DENTISTRY Refer to the dental chart.

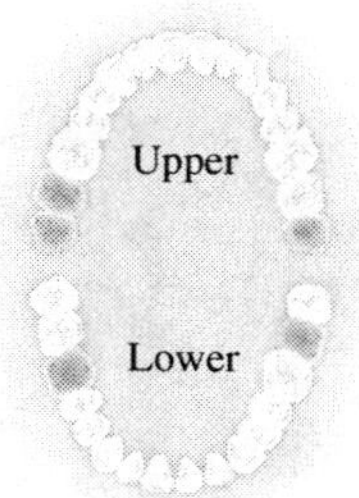

a. How many teeth are shown on the chart? 32

b. What fraction of this set of teeth have fillings? $\frac{5}{32}$

102. TIME CLOCKS For each clock, what fraction of the hour has passed? Write your answers in simplified form. (*Hint:* There are 60 minutes in an hour.)

a.  $\frac{15}{60} = \frac{1}{4}$ 

b.  $\frac{45}{60} = \frac{3}{4}$ 

c.  $\frac{25}{60} = \frac{5}{12}$ 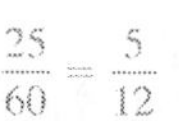

d.  $\frac{40}{60} = \frac{2}{3}$ 

103. RULERS The illustration below shows a ruler.

a. How many spaces are there between the numbers 0 and 1? 16

b. To what fraction is the arrow pointing? Write your answer in simplified form. $\frac{5}{8}$

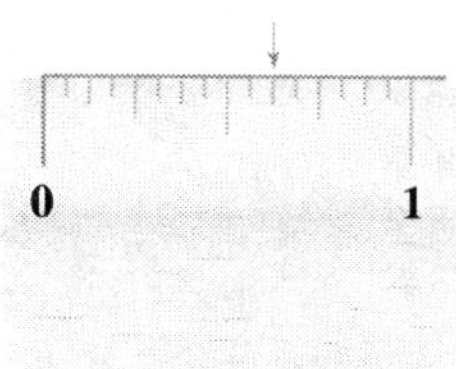

104. SINKHOLES The illustration below shows a side view of a drop in the sidewalk near a sinkhole. Describe the movement of the sidewalk using a signed fraction. $-\frac{15}{16}$ in.

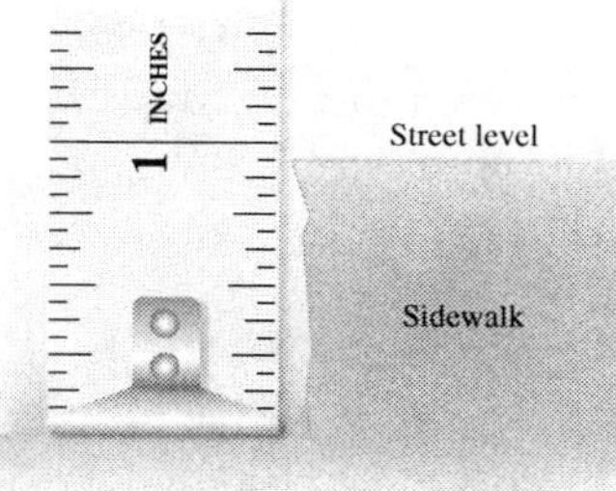

105. POLITICAL PARTIES The graph shows the number of Democrat and Republican governors of the 50 states, as of February 1, 2009.

a. How many Democrat governors are there? How many Republican governors are there? 28, 22

b. What fraction of the governors are Democrats? Write your answer in simplified form. $\frac{28}{50} = \frac{14}{25}$

c. What fraction of the governors are Republicans? Write your answer in simplified form. $\frac{22}{50} = \frac{11}{25}$

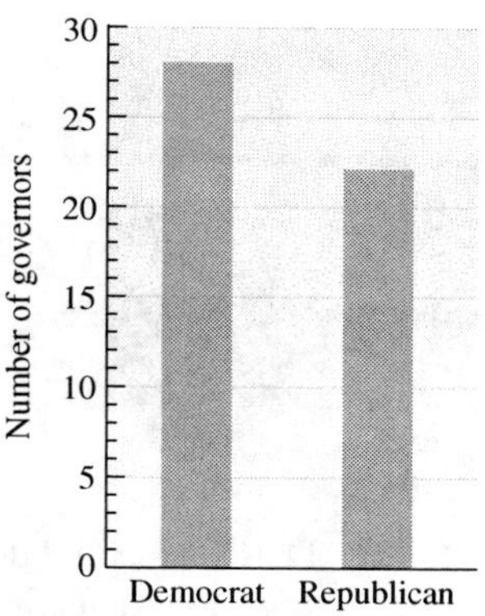

Source: thegreenpapers.com

106. GAS TANKS Write fractions to describe the amount of gas left in the tank and the amount of gas that has been used. $\frac{5}{8}, \frac{3}{8}$

107. SELLING CONDOS The model below shows a new condominium development. The condos that have been sold are shaded.

a. How many units are there in the development? 20

b. What fraction of the units in the development have been sold? What fraction have not been sold? Write your answers in simplified form. $\frac{2}{5}, \frac{3}{5}$

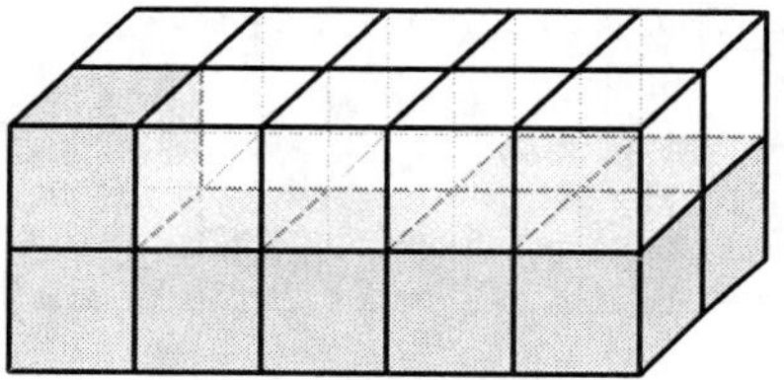

108. MUSIC The illustration shows a side view of the finger position needed to produce a length of string (from the bridge to the fingertip) that gives low C on a violin. To play other notes, fractions of that length are used. Locate these finger positions on the illustration.

a. $\frac{1}{2}$ of the length gives middle C.

b. $\frac{3}{4}$ of the length gives F above low C.

c. $\frac{2}{3}$ of the length gives G.

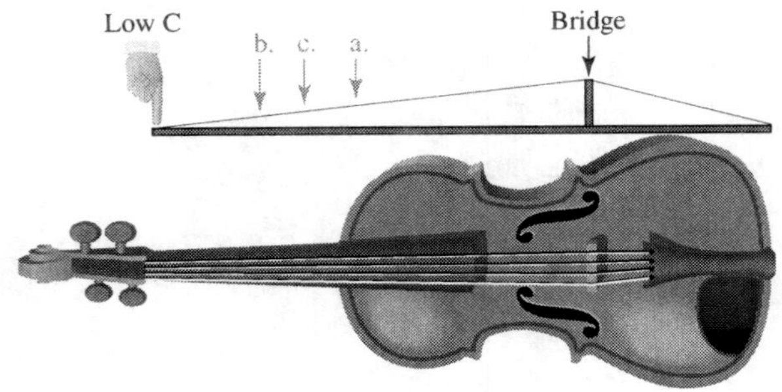

109. MEDICAL CENTERS Hospital designers have located a nurse's station at the center of a circular building. Show how to divide the surrounding office space (shaded in grey) so that each medical department has the fractional amount assigned to it. Label each department.

$\frac{2}{12}$: Radiology

$\frac{5}{12}$: Pediatrics

$\frac{1}{12}$: Laboratory

$\frac{3}{12}$: Orthopedics

$\frac{1}{12}$: Pharmacy

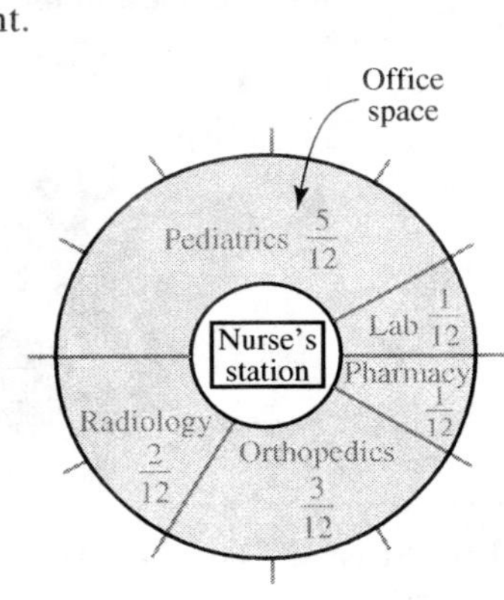

Medical Center

110. GDP The gross domestic product (GDP) is the official measure of the size of the U.S. economy. It represents the market value of all goods and services that have been bought during a given period of time. The GDP for the second quarter of 2008 is listed below. What is meant by the phrase *second quarter of 2008*? the months of April, May, and June of 2008

Second quarter of 2008	$14,294,500,000,000

Source: *The World Almanac and Book of Facts,* 2009

WRITING

111. Explain the concept of equivalent fractions. Give an example.

112. What does it mean for a fraction to be in simplest form? Give an example.

113. Why can't we say that $\frac{2}{5}$ of the figure below is shaded?

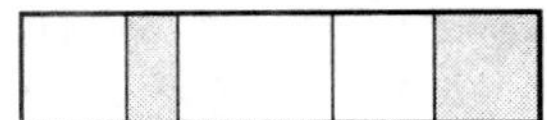

114. Perhaps you have heard the following joke:

> *A pizza parlor waitress asks a customer if he wants the pizza cut into four pieces or six pieces or eight pieces. The customer then declares that he wants either four or six pieces of pizza "because I can't eat eight."*

Explain what is wrong with the customer's thinking.

115. **a.** What type of problem is shown below? Explain the solution.

$$\frac{1}{2} = \frac{1}{2} \cdot \frac{4}{4} = \frac{4}{8}$$

b. What type of problem is shown below? Explain the solution.

$$\frac{15}{35} = \frac{3 \cdot \overset{1}{\cancel{5}}}{\underset{1}{\cancel{5}} \cdot 7} = \frac{3}{7}$$

116. Explain the difference in the two approaches used to simplify $\frac{20}{28}$. Are the results the same?

$$\frac{\overset{1}{\cancel{4}} \cdot 5}{\underset{1}{\cancel{4}} \cdot 7} \quad \text{and} \quad \frac{\overset{1}{\cancel{2}} \cdot \overset{1}{\cancel{2}} \cdot 5}{\underset{1}{\cancel{2}} \cdot \underset{1}{\cancel{2}} \cdot 7}$$

REVIEW

117. PAYCHECKS *Gross pay* is what a worker makes before deductions and *net pay* is what is left after taxes, health benefits, union dues, and other deductions are taken out. Suppose a worker's monthly gross pay is $3,575. If deductions of $235, $782, $148, and $103 are taken out of his check, what is his monthly net pay? $2,307

118. HORSE RACING One day, a man bet on all eight horse races at Santa Anita Racetrack. He won $168 on the first race and he won $105 on the fourth race. He lost his $50-bets on each of the other races. Overall, did he win or lose money betting on the horses? How much? He lost $27 (−$27)

SECTION 2.2
Multiplying Fractions

Objectives

1 Multiply fractions.

2 Simplify answers when multiplying fractions.

3 Evaluate exponential expressions that have fractional bases.

4 Solve application problems by multiplying fractions.

5 Find the area of a triangle.

In the next three sections, we discuss how to add, subtract, multiply, and divide fractions. We begin with the operation of multiplication.

1 Multiply fractions.

To develop a rule for multiplying fractions, let's consider a real-life application.

Suppose $\frac{3}{5}$ of the last page of a school newspaper is devoted to campus sports coverage. To show this, we can divide the page into fifths, and shade 3 of them red.

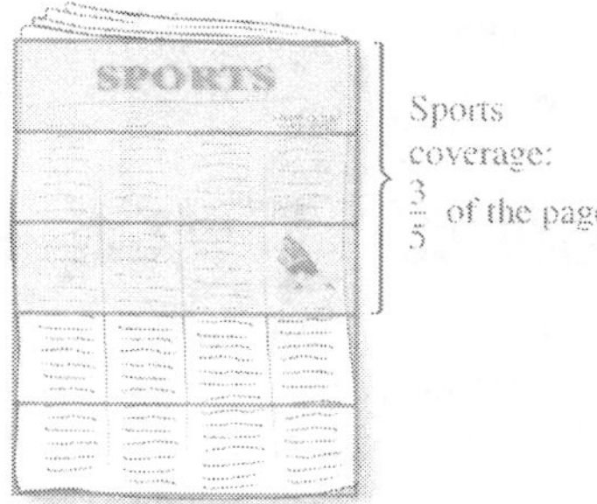

Furthermore, suppose that $\frac{1}{2}$ of the sports coverage is about women's teams. We can show that portion of the page by dividing the already colored region into two halves, and shading one of them in purple.

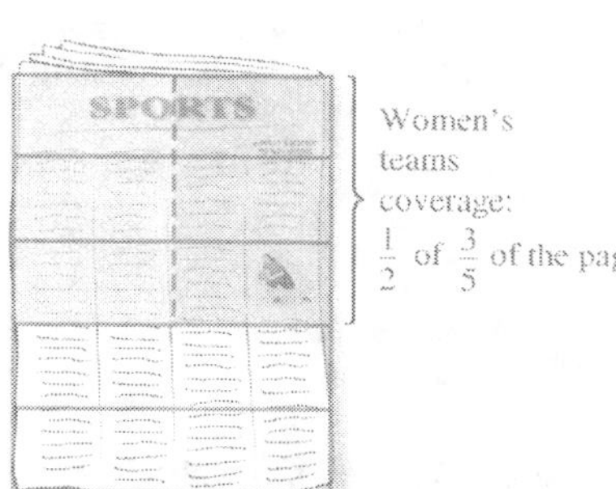

To find the fraction represented by the purple shaded region, the page needs to be divided into equal-size parts. If we extend the dashed line downward, we see there are 10 equal-sized parts. The purple shaded parts are 3 out of 10, or $\frac{3}{10}$, of the page. Thus, $\frac{3}{10}$ of the last page of the school newspaper is devoted to women's sports.

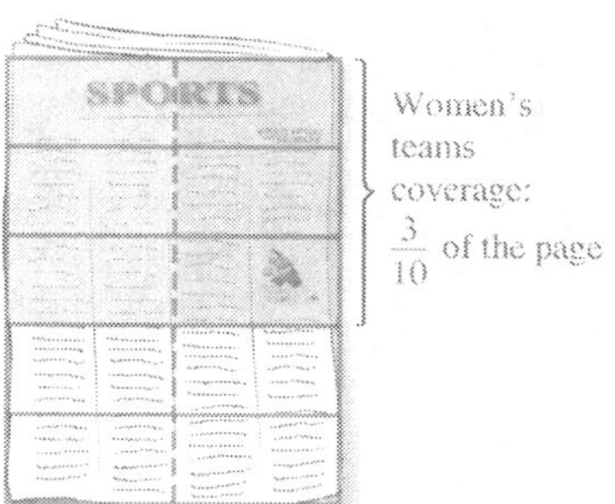

In this example, we have found that

$$\frac{1}{2} \text{ of } \frac{3}{5} \text{ is } \frac{3}{10}$$
$$\downarrow \qquad \downarrow$$
$$\frac{1}{2} \cdot \frac{3}{5} = \frac{3}{10}$$

Since the key word *of* indicates multiplication, and the key word *is* means equals, we can translate this statement to symbols.

Two observations can be made from this result.

- The numerator of the answer is the product of the numerators of the original fractions.

$1 \cdot 3 = 3$

$$\frac{1}{2} \cdot \frac{3}{5} = \frac{3}{10} \quad \text{Answer}$$

$2 \cdot 5 = 10$

- The denominator of the answer is the product of the denominators of the original fractions.

These observations illustrate the following rule for multiplying two fractions.

Multiplying Fractions

To multiply two fractions, multiply the numerators and multiply the denominators. Simplify the result, if possible.

Success Tip In the newspaper example, we found a *part of a part* of a page. Multiplying proper fractions can be thought of in this way. When taking a *part of a part* of something, the result is always smaller than the original part that you began with.

Self Check 1

Multiply:

a. $\frac{1}{2} \cdot \frac{1}{8}$ $\frac{1}{16}$

b. $\frac{5}{9} \cdot \frac{2}{3}$ $\frac{10}{27}$

Now Try **Problems 17 and 21**

Teaching Example 1
Multiply:

a. $\frac{1}{3} \cdot \frac{1}{4}$ b. $\frac{4}{7} \cdot \frac{2}{5}$

Answers:

a. $\frac{1}{12}$ b. $\frac{8}{35}$

EXAMPLE 1 Multiply: **a.** $\frac{1}{6} \cdot \frac{1}{4}$ **b.** $\frac{7}{8} \cdot \frac{3}{5}$

Strategy We will multiply the numerators and denominators, and make sure that the result is in simplest form.

WHY This is the rule for multiplying two fractions.

Solution

a. $\frac{1}{6} \cdot \frac{1}{4} = \frac{1 \cdot 1}{6 \cdot 4}$ Multiply the numerators. Multiply the denominators.

$= \frac{1}{24}$ Since 1 and 24 have no common factors other than 1, the result is in simplest form.

b. $\frac{7}{8} \cdot \frac{3}{5} = \frac{7 \cdot 3}{8 \cdot 5}$ Multiply the numerators. Multiply the denominators.

$= \frac{21}{40}$ Since 21 and 40 have no common factors other than 1, the result is in simplest form.

The sign rules for multiplying integers also hold for multiplying fractions. When we multiply two fractions with *like* signs, the product is positive. When we multiply two fractions with *unlike* signs, the product is negative.

EXAMPLE 2 Multiply: $-\frac{3}{4}\left(\frac{1}{8}\right)$

Strategy We will use the rule for multiplying two fractions that have different (unlike) signs.

WHY One fraction is positive and one is negative.

Solution

$$-\frac{3}{4}\left(\frac{1}{8}\right) = -\frac{3 \cdot 1}{4 \cdot 8}$$ Multiply the numerators. Multiply the denominators. Since the fractions have unlike signs, make the answer negative.

$$= -\frac{3}{32}$$ Since 3 and 32 have no common factors other than 1, the result is in simplest form.

Self Check 2

Multiply: $\frac{5}{6}\left(-\frac{1}{3}\right)$ $-\frac{5}{18}$

Now Try Problem 25

Teaching Example 2

Multiply: $-\frac{5}{8}\left(\frac{1}{9}\right)$

Answer:

$-\frac{5}{72}$

EXAMPLE 3 Multiply: $\frac{1}{2} \cdot 3$

Strategy We will begin by writing the integer 3 as a fraction.

WHY Then we can use the rule for multiplying two fractions to find the product.

Solution

$$\frac{1}{2} \cdot 3 = \frac{1}{2} \cdot \frac{3}{1}$$ Write 3 as a fraction: $3 = \frac{3}{1}$.

$$= \frac{1 \cdot 3}{2 \cdot 1}$$ Multiply the numerators. Multiply the denominators.

$$= \frac{3}{2}$$ Since 3 and 2 have no common factors other than 1, the result is in simplest form.

Self Check 3

Multiply: $\frac{1}{3} \cdot 7$ $\frac{7}{3}$

Now Try Problem 29

Teaching Example 3 Multiply: $\frac{1}{4} \cdot 9$

Answer:

$\frac{9}{4}$

2 Simplify answers when multiplying fractions.

After multiplying two fractions, we need to simplify the result, if possible. To do that, we can use the procedure of removing pairs of common factors of the numerator and denominator.

EXAMPLE 4 Multiply and simplify: $\frac{5}{8} \cdot \frac{4}{5}$

Strategy We will multiply the numerators and denominators, and make sure that the result is in simplest form.

WHY This is the rule for multiplying two fractions.

Solution

$$\frac{5}{8} \cdot \frac{4}{5} = \frac{5 \cdot 4}{8 \cdot 5}$$ Multiply the numerators. Multiply the denominators.

$$= \frac{5 \cdot 2 \cdot 2}{2 \cdot 2 \cdot 2 \cdot 5}$$ To prepare to simplify, write 4 and 8 in prime-factored form.

$$= \frac{\overset{1}{\cancel{5}} \cdot \overset{1}{\cancel{2}} \cdot \overset{1}{\cancel{2}}}{\underset{1}{\cancel{2}} \cdot \underset{1}{\cancel{2}} \cdot 2 \cdot \underset{1}{\cancel{5}}}$$ To simplify, remove the common factors of 2 and 5 from the numerator and denominator.

$$= \frac{1}{2}$$ Multiply the remaining factors in the numerator: 1·1·1 = 1. Multiple the remaining factors in the denominator: 1·1·2·1 = 2.

Factor trees: 4 → ② ②; 8 → ② 4, 4 → ② ②

Self Check 4

Multiply and simplify: $\frac{11}{25} \cdot \frac{10}{11}$ $\frac{2}{5}$

Now Try Problem 33

Teaching Example 4

Multiply and simplify: $\frac{7}{12} \cdot \frac{4}{7}$

Answer:

$\frac{1}{3}$

Success Tip If you recognized that 4 and 8 have a common factor of 4, you may remove that common factor from the numerator and denominator of the product without writing the prime factorizations. However, make sure that the numerator and denominator of the resulting fraction do not have any common factors. If they do, continue to simplify.

$$\frac{5}{8} \cdot \frac{4}{5} = \frac{5 \cdot 4}{8 \cdot 5} = \frac{\overset{1}{\cancel{5}} \cdot \overset{1}{\cancel{4}}}{2 \cdot \underset{1}{\cancel{4}} \cdot \underset{1}{\cancel{5}}} = \frac{1}{2}$$

Factor 8 as 2 · 4, and then remove the common factors of 4 and 5 in the numerator and denominator.

The rule for multiplying two fractions can be extended to find the product of three or more fractions.

Self Check 5

Multiply and simplify:

$\frac{2}{5}\left(-\frac{15}{22}\right)\left(-\frac{11}{26}\right)$ $\frac{3}{26}$

Now Try **Problem 37**

Teaching Example 5
Multiply and simplify:
$\frac{3}{5}\left(-\frac{25}{22}\right)\left(-\frac{11}{12}\right)$
Answer:
$\frac{5}{8}$

EXAMPLE 5 Multiply and simplify: $\frac{2}{3}\left(-\frac{9}{14}\right)\left(-\frac{7}{10}\right)$

Strategy We will multiply the numerators and denominators, and make sure that the result is in simplest form.

WHY This is the rule for multiplying three (or more) fractions.

Solution A product is positive when there are an even number of negative factors. Since $\frac{2}{3}\left(-\frac{9}{14}\right)\left(-\frac{7}{10}\right)$ has *two* negative factors, the product is positive.

$$\frac{2}{3}\left(-\frac{9}{14}\right)\left(-\frac{7}{10}\right) = \frac{2}{3}\left(\frac{9}{14}\right)\left(\frac{7}{10}\right)$$ Since the answer is positive, drop both − signs and continue.

$$= \frac{2 \cdot 9 \cdot 7}{3 \cdot 14 \cdot 10}$$ Multiply the numerators. Multiply the denominators.

$$= \frac{2 \cdot 3 \cdot 3 \cdot 7}{3 \cdot 2 \cdot 7 \cdot 2 \cdot 5}$$ To prepare to simplify, write 9, 14, and 10 in prime-factored form.

$$= \frac{\overset{1}{\cancel{2}} \cdot \overset{1}{\cancel{3}} \cdot 3 \cdot \overset{1}{\cancel{7}}}{\underset{1}{\cancel{3}} \cdot \underset{1}{\cancel{2}} \cdot \underset{1}{\cancel{7}} \cdot 2 \cdot 5}$$ To simplify, remove the common factors of 2, 3, and 7 from the numerator and denominator.

$$= \frac{3}{10}$$ Multiply the remaining factors in the numerator. Multiply the remaining factors in the denominator.

Caution! In Example 5, it was very helpful to prime factor and simplify when we did (the third step of the solution). If, instead, you find the product of the numerators and the product of the denominators, the resulting fraction is difficult to simplify because the numerator, 126, and the denominator, 420, are large.

$$\frac{2}{3} \cdot \frac{9}{14} \cdot \frac{7}{10} = \frac{2 \cdot 9 \cdot 7}{3 \cdot 14 \cdot 10} = \frac{126}{420}$$

↑ Factor and simplify at this stage, before multiplying in the numerator and denominator.

↑ Don't multiply in the numerator and denominator and then try to simplify the result. You will get the same answer, but it takes much more work.

3 Evaluate exponential expressions that have fractional bases.

We have evaluated exponential expressions that have whole-number bases and integer bases. If the base of an exponential expression is a fraction, the exponent tells us how many times to write that fraction as a factor. For example,

$$\left(\frac{2}{3}\right)^2 = \frac{2}{3} \cdot \frac{2}{3} = \frac{2 \cdot 2}{3 \cdot 3} = \frac{4}{9}$$ Since the exponent is 2, write the base, $\frac{2}{3}$, as a factor 2 times.

EXAMPLE 6 Evaluate each expression: **a.** $\left(\frac{1}{4}\right)^3$ **b.** $\left(-\frac{2}{3}\right)^2$ **c.** $-\left(\frac{2}{3}\right)^2$

Strategy We will write each exponential expression as a product of repeated factors, and then perform the multiplication. This requires that we identify the base and the exponent.

WHY The exponent tells the number of times the base is to be written as a factor.

Solution

Recall that exponents are used to represent repeated multiplication.

a. We read $\left(\frac{1}{4}\right)^3$ as "one-fourth raised to the third power," or as "one-fourth, cubed."

$$\left(\frac{1}{4}\right)^3 = \frac{1}{4} \cdot \frac{1}{4} \cdot \frac{1}{4}$$ Since the exponent is 3, write the base, $\frac{1}{4}$, as a factor 3 times.

$$= \frac{1 \cdot 1 \cdot 1}{4 \cdot 4 \cdot 4}$$ Multiply the numerators. Multiply the denominators.

$$= \frac{1}{64}$$

b. We read $\left(-\frac{2}{3}\right)^2$ as "negative two-thirds raised to the second power," or as "negative two-thirds, squared."

$$\left(-\frac{2}{3}\right)^2 = \left(-\frac{2}{3}\right)\left(-\frac{2}{3}\right)$$ Since the exponent is 2, write the base, $-\frac{2}{3}$, as a factor 2 times.

$$= \frac{2 \cdot 2}{3 \cdot 3}$$ The product of two fractions with like signs is positive: Drop the − signs. Multiply the numerators. Multiply the denominators.

$$= \frac{4}{9}$$

c. We read $-\left(\frac{2}{3}\right)^2$ as "the opposite of two-thirds squared." Recall that if the − symbol is not within the parantheses, it is not part of the base.

$$-\left(\frac{2}{3}\right)^2 = -\frac{2}{3} \cdot \frac{2}{3}$$ Since the exponent is 2, write the base, $\frac{2}{3}$, as a factor 2 times.

$$= -\frac{2 \cdot 2}{3 \cdot 3}$$ Multiply the numerators. Multiply the denominators.

$$= -\frac{4}{9}$$

Self Check 6

Evaluate each expression:

a. $\left(\frac{2}{5}\right)^3$ $\frac{8}{125}$

b. $\left(-\frac{3}{4}\right)^2$ $\frac{9}{16}$

c. $-\left(\frac{3}{4}\right)^2$ $-\frac{9}{16}$

Now Try **Problem 43**

Teaching Example 6 Evaluate each expression:

a. $\left(\frac{4}{5}\right)^3$ b. $\left(-\frac{3}{7}\right)^2$ c. $-\left(\frac{3}{7}\right)^2$

Answers:

a. $\frac{64}{125}$ b. $\frac{9}{49}$ c. $-\frac{9}{49}$

4 Solve application problems by multiplying fractions.

The key word *of* often appears in application problems involving fractions. When a fraction is followed by the word *of*, such as $\frac{1}{2}$ *of* or $\frac{3}{4}$ *of*, it indicates that we are to find a part of some quantity using multiplication.

EXAMPLE 7 *How a Bill Becomes Law* If the President vetoes (refuses to sign) a bill, it takes $\frac{2}{3}$ of those voting in the House of Representatives (and the Senate) to override the veto for it to become law. If all 435 members of the House cast a vote, how many of their votes does it take to override a presidential veto?

Analyze

- It takes $\frac{2}{3}$ *of* those voting to override a veto. *Given*
- All 435 members of the House cast a vote. *Given*
- How many votes does it take to override a Presidential veto? *Find*

Self Check 7

HOW A BILL BECOMES LAW If only 96 Senators are present and cast a vote, how many of their votes does it takes to override a Presidential veto? 64 votes

Now Try **Problems 45 and 87**

Teaching Example 7 COLLEGE LIFE It takes $\frac{3}{4}$ of the active members of Alpha Gamma Sigma to vote to accept a pledge into their fraternity. How many votes are needed if the fraternity has 84 active members?
Answer:
63 votes

Form The key phrase $\frac{2}{3}$ *of* suggests that we are to find a part of the 435 possible votes using multiplication.

We translate the words of the problem to numbers and symbols.

The number of votes needed in the House to override a veto	is equal to	$\frac{2}{3}$	of	the number of House members that vote.
The number of votes needed in the House to override a veto	=	$\frac{2}{3}$	$\cdot$	435

Solve To find the product, we will express 435 as a fraction and then use the rule for multiplying two fractions.

$$\frac{2}{3} \cdot 435 = \frac{2}{3} \cdot \frac{435}{1}$$ Write 435 as a fraction: $435 = \frac{435}{1}$.

$$= \frac{2 \cdot 435}{3 \cdot 1}$$ Multiply the numerators. Multiply the denominators.

$$= \frac{2 \cdot 3 \cdot 5 \cdot 29}{3 \cdot 1}$$ To prepare to simplify, write 435 in prime-factored form: $3 \cdot 5 \cdot 29$.

$$= \frac{2 \cdot \overset{1}{\cancel{3}} \cdot 5 \cdot 29}{\underset{1}{\cancel{3}} \cdot 1}$$ Remove the common factor of 3 from the numerator and denominator.

$$= \frac{290}{1}$$ Multiply the remaining factors in the numerator: $2 \cdot 1 \cdot 5 \cdot 29 = 290$. Multiply the remaining factors in the denominator: $1 \cdot 1 = 1$.

$$= 290$$ Any whole number divided by 1 is equal to that number.

Factor tree: 435 → ③ 145; 145 → ⑤ ㉙

State It would take 290 votes in the House to override a veto.

Check We can estimate to check the result. We will use 440 to approximate the number of House members voting. Since $\frac{1}{2}$ of 440 is 220, and since $\frac{2}{3}$ is a greater part than $\frac{1}{2}$, we would expect the number of votes needed to be *more than* 220. The result of 290 seems reasonable.

5 Find the area of a triangle.

As the figures below show, a triangle has three sides. The length of the base of the triangle can be represented by the letter b and the height by the letter h. The height of a triangle is always perpendicular (makes a square corner) to the base. This is shown by using the symbol ⌝.

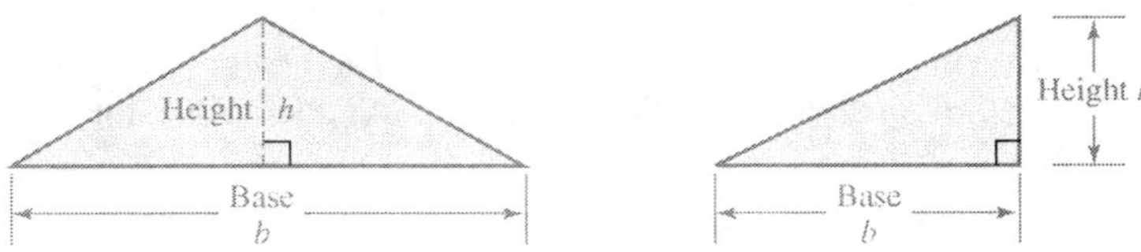

Recall that the area of a figure is the amount of surface that it encloses. The area of a triangle can be found by using the following formula.

Area of a Triangle

The area A of a triangle is one-half the product of its base b and its height h.

$$\text{Area} = \frac{1}{2}(\text{base})(\text{height}) \quad \text{or} \quad A = \frac{1}{2} \cdot b \cdot h$$

The Language of Mathematics The formula $A = \frac{1}{2} \cdot b \cdot h$ can be written more simply as $A = \frac{1}{2}bh$. The formula for the area of a triangle can also be written as $A = \frac{bh}{2}$.

EXAMPLE 8 *Geography* Approximate the area of the state of Virginia (in square miles) using the triangle shown below.

Strategy We will find the product of $\frac{1}{2}$, 405, and 200.

WHY The formula for the area of a triangle is $A = \frac{1}{2}$ (base)(height).

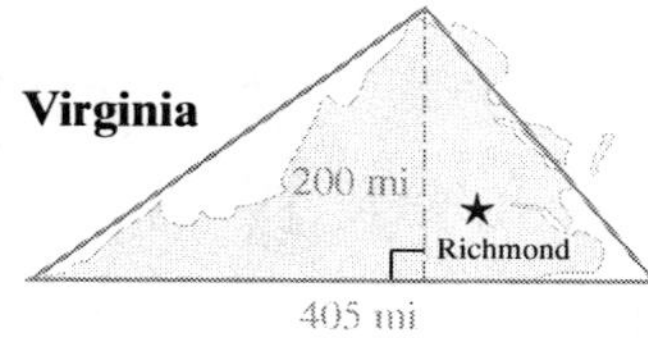

Solution

$A = \frac{1}{2}bh$ — This is the formula for the area of a triangle.

$= \frac{1}{2} \cdot 405 \cdot 200$ — $\frac{1}{2}bh$ means $\frac{1}{2} \cdot b \cdot h$. Substitute 405 for b and 200 for h.

$= \frac{1}{2} \cdot \frac{405}{1} \cdot \frac{200}{1}$ — Write 405 and 200 as fractions.

$= \frac{1 \cdot 405 \cdot 200}{2 \cdot 1 \cdot 1}$ — Multiply the numerators. Multiply the denominators.

$= \frac{1 \cdot 405 \cdot \overset{1}{\cancel{2}} \cdot 100}{\underset{1}{\cancel{2}} \cdot 1 \cdot 1}$ — Factor 200 as $2 \cdot 100$. Then remove the common factor of 2 from the numerator and denominator.

$= 40{,}500$ — In the numerator, multiply: $405 \cdot 100 = 40{,}500$.

The area of the state of Virginia is approximately 40,500 square miles. This can be written as 40,500 mi^2.

Caution! Remember that area is measured in square units, such as $in.^2$, ft^2, and cm^2. Don't forget to write the units in your answer when finding the area of a figure.

Self Check 8

Find the area of the triangle shown below. 216 in.^2

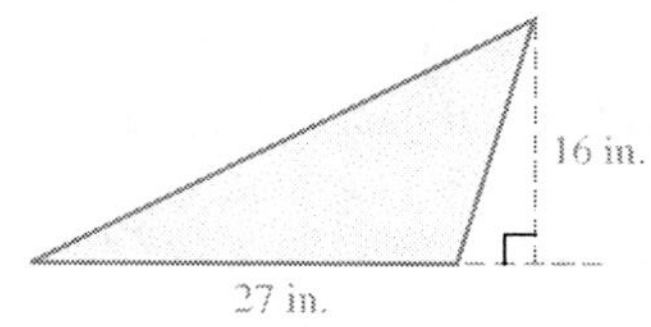

Now Try **Problems 49 and 99**

Teaching Example 8 Find the area of the triangle shown below.

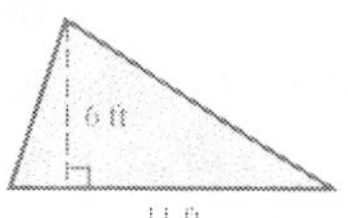

Answer:
33 ft^2

ANSWERS TO SELF CHECKS

1. a. $\frac{1}{16}$ **b.** $\frac{10}{27}$ **2.** $-\frac{5}{18}$ **3.** $\frac{7}{3}$ **4.** $\frac{2}{5}$ **5.** $\frac{3}{26}$ **6. a.** $\frac{8}{125}$ **b.** $\frac{9}{16}$ **c.** $-\frac{9}{16}$
7. 64 votes **8.** 216 in.^2

SECTION 2.2 STUDY SET

VOCABULARY

Fill in the blanks.

1. When a fraction is followed by the word *of*, such as $\frac{1}{3}$ *of*, it indicates that we are to find a part of some quantity using multiplication.
2. The answer to a multiplication is called the product.
3. To simplify a fraction, we remove common factors of the numerator and denominator.
4. In the expression $\left(\frac{1}{4}\right)^3$, the base is $\frac{1}{4}$ and the exponent is 3.
5. The area of a triangle is the amount of surface that it encloses.
6. Label the *base* and the *height* of the triangle shown below.

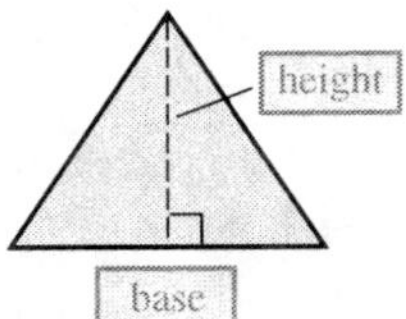

CONCEPTS

7. Fill in the blanks: To multiply two fractions, multiply the numerators and multiply the denominators. Then simplify, if possible.
8. Use the following rectangle to find $\frac{1}{3} \cdot \frac{1}{4}$.

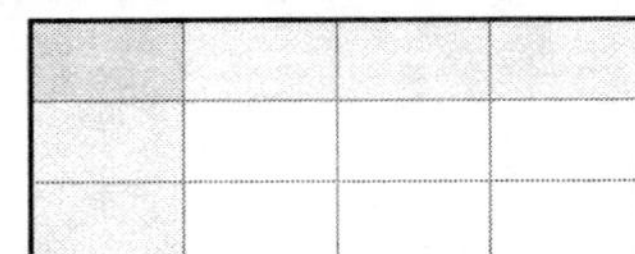

a. Draw three vertical lines that divide the given rectangle into four equal parts and lightly shade one part. What fractional part of the rectangle did you shade? $\frac{1}{4}$

b. To find $\frac{1}{3}$ of the shaded portion, draw two horizontal lines to divide the given rectangle into three equal parts and lightly shade one part. Into how many equal parts is the rectangle now divided? How many parts have been shaded twice? 12, 1

c. What is $\frac{1}{3} \cdot \frac{1}{4}$? $\frac{1}{12}$

9. Determine whether each product is positive or negative. *You do not have to find the answer.*

a. $-\frac{1}{8} \cdot \frac{3}{5}$ negative

b. $-\frac{7}{16}\left(-\frac{2}{21}\right)$ positive

c. $-\frac{4}{5}\left(\frac{1}{3}\right)\left(-\frac{1}{8}\right)$ positive

d. $-\frac{3}{4}\left(-\frac{8}{9}\right)\left(-\frac{1}{2}\right)$ negative

10. Translate each phrase to symbols. *You do not have to find the answer.*

a. $\frac{7}{10}$ of $\frac{4}{9}$ $\frac{7}{10} \cdot \frac{4}{9}$

b. $\frac{1}{5}$ of 40 $\frac{1}{5} \cdot 40$

11. Fill in the blanks: Area of a triangle = $\frac{1}{2}$(base)(height) or $A = \frac{1}{2}bh$
12. Fill in the blank: Area is measured in square units, such as in.^{2} and ft^2.

NOTATION

13. Write each of the following integers as a fraction.

a. 4 $\frac{4}{1}$

b. –3 $-\frac{3}{1}$

14. Fill in the blanks: $\left(\frac{1}{2}\right)^2$ represents the repeated multiplication $\frac{1}{2} \cdot \frac{1}{2}$.

Fill in the blanks to complete each solution.

15.
$$\frac{5}{8} \cdot \frac{7}{15} = \frac{5 \cdot 7}{8 \cdot 15} = \frac{5 \cdot 7}{2 \cdot 2 \cdot 2 \cdot 3 \cdot 5} = \frac{\overset{1}{\cancel{5}} \cdot 7}{2 \cdot 2 \cdot 2 \cdot 3 \cdot \underset{1}{\cancel{5}}} = \frac{7}{24}$$

16.
$$\frac{7}{12} \cdot \frac{4}{21} = \frac{7 \cdot 4}{12 \cdot 21} = \frac{7 \cdot 4}{3 \cdot 4 \cdot 3 \cdot 7} = \frac{\overset{1}{\cancel{7}} \cdot \overset{1}{\cancel{4}}}{3 \cdot \underset{1}{\cancel{4}} \cdot 3 \cdot \underset{1}{\cancel{7}}} = \frac{1}{9}$$

GUIDED PRACTICE

Multiply. Write the product in simplest form. See Example 1.

17. $\frac{1}{4} \cdot \frac{1}{2}$ $\frac{1}{8}$

18. $\frac{1}{3} \cdot \frac{1}{5}$ $\frac{1}{15}$

19. $\frac{1}{9} \cdot \frac{1}{5}$ $\frac{1}{45}$

20. $\frac{1}{2} \cdot \frac{1}{8}$ $\frac{1}{16}$

21. $\frac{2}{3} \cdot \frac{7}{9}$ $\frac{14}{27}$

▶ 22. $\frac{3}{4} \cdot \frac{5}{7}$ $\frac{15}{28}$

23. $\frac{8}{11} \cdot \frac{3}{7}$ $\frac{24}{77}$

24. $\frac{11}{13} \cdot \frac{2}{3}$ $\frac{22}{39}$

Multiply. See Example 2.

25. $-\frac{4}{5} \cdot \frac{1}{3}$ $-\frac{4}{15}$

▶ 26. $-\frac{7}{9} \cdot \frac{1}{4}$ $-\frac{7}{36}$

27. $\frac{5}{6}\left(-\frac{7}{12}\right)$ $-\frac{35}{72}$

28. $\frac{2}{15}\left(-\frac{4}{3}\right)$ $-\frac{8}{45}$

Multiply. See Example 3.

29. $\frac{1}{8} \cdot 9$ $\frac{9}{8}$

30. $\frac{1}{6} \cdot 11$ $\frac{11}{6}$

31. $\frac{1}{2} \cdot 5$ $\frac{5}{2}$

▶ 32. $\frac{1}{2} \cdot 21$ $\frac{21}{2}$

Multiply. Write the product in simplest form. See Example 4.

33. $\frac{11}{10} \cdot \frac{5}{11}$ $\frac{1}{2}$

34. $\frac{5}{4} \cdot \frac{2}{5}$ $\frac{1}{2}$

35. $\frac{6}{49} \cdot \frac{7}{6}$ $\frac{1}{7}$

▶ 36. $\frac{13}{4} \cdot \frac{4}{39}$ $\frac{1}{3}$

Multiply. Write the product in simplest form. See Example 5.

37. $\frac{3}{4}\left(-\frac{8}{35}\right)\left(-\frac{7}{12}\right)$ $\frac{1}{10}$

38. $\frac{9}{10}\left(-\frac{4}{15}\right)\left(-\frac{5}{18}\right)$ $\frac{1}{15}$

39. $-\frac{5}{8}\left(\frac{16}{27}\right)\left(-\frac{9}{25}\right)$ $\frac{2}{15}$

▶ 40. $-\frac{15}{28}\left(\frac{7}{9}\right)\left(-\frac{18}{35}\right)$ $\frac{3}{14}$

Evaluate each expression. See Example 6.

41. a. $\left(\frac{3}{5}\right)^2$ $\frac{9}{25}$ b. $\left(-\frac{3}{5}\right)^2$ $\frac{9}{25}$

42. a. $\left(\frac{4}{9}\right)^2$ $\frac{16}{81}$ b. $\left(-\frac{4}{9}\right)^2$ $\frac{16}{81}$

43. a. $-\left(-\frac{1}{6}\right)^2$ $-\frac{1}{36}$ b. $\left(-\frac{1}{6}\right)^3$ $-\frac{1}{216}$

▶ 44. a. $-\left(-\frac{2}{5}\right)^2$ $-\frac{4}{25}$ b. $\left(-\frac{2}{5}\right)^3$ $-\frac{8}{125}$

Find each product. Write your answer in simplest form. See Example 7.

45. $\frac{3}{4}$ of $\frac{5}{8}$ $\frac{15}{32}$

46. $\frac{4}{5}$ of $\frac{3}{7}$ $\frac{12}{35}$

47. $\frac{1}{6}$ of 54 9

▶ 48. $\frac{1}{9}$ of 36 4

Find the area of each triangle. See Example 8.

49. 15 ft²

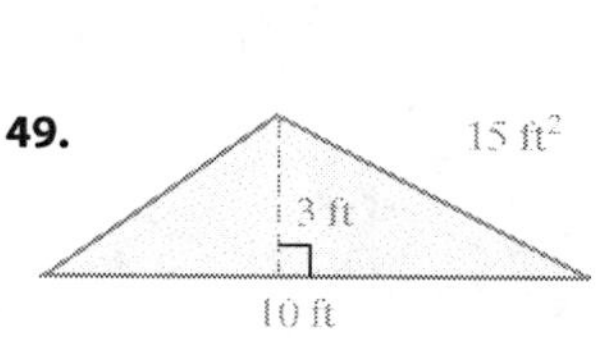

50. 10 yd²

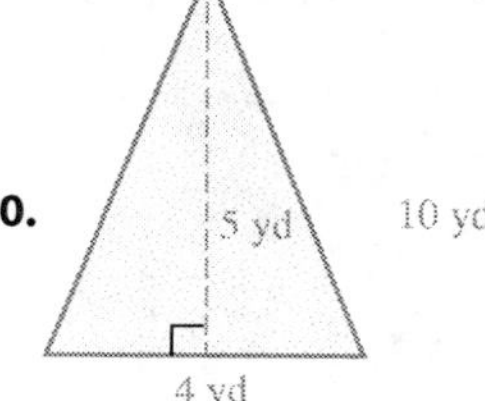

51. 63 in.²

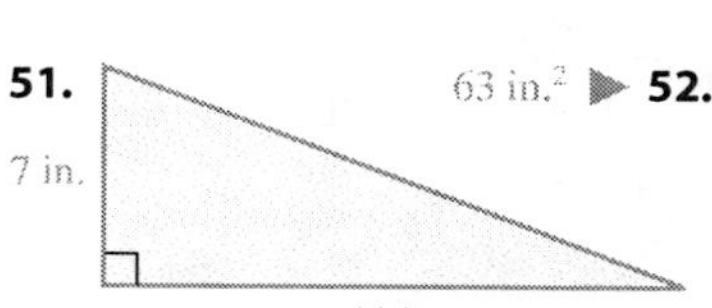

▶ 52. 6 cm²

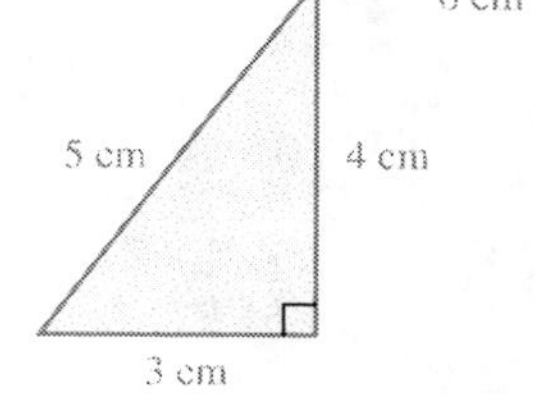

▶ 53. 6 m²

54. 102 in.²

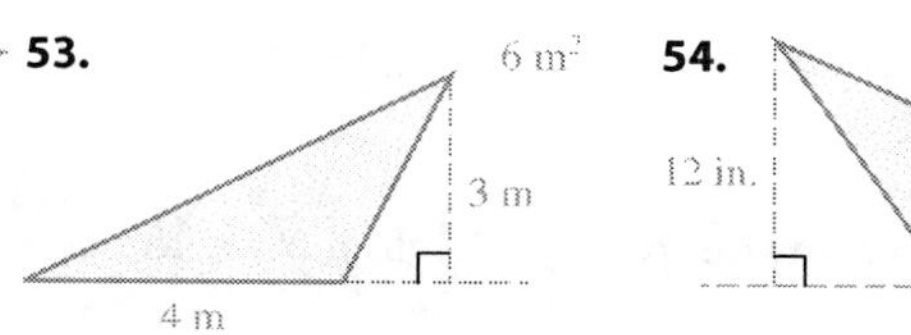

55. 60 ft²

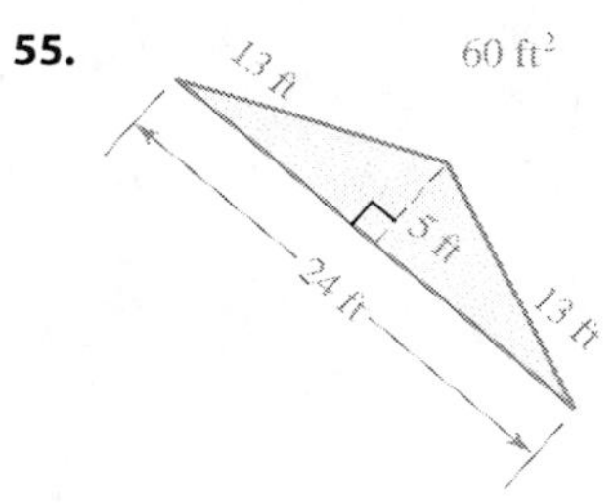

56. 420 mi²

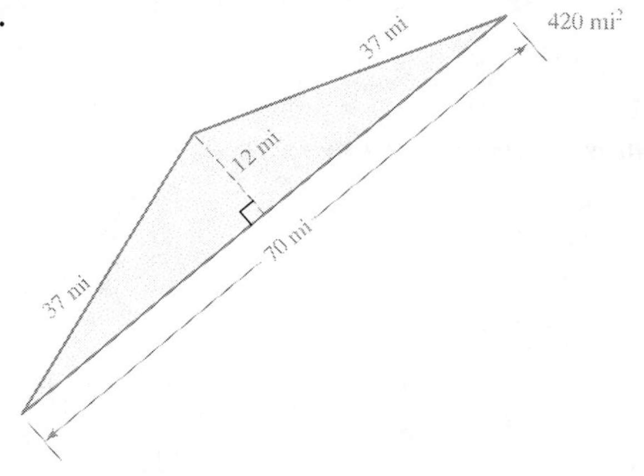

TRY IT YOURSELF

57. Complete the multiplication table of fractions.

$\cdot$	$\frac{1}{2}$	$\frac{1}{3}$	$\frac{1}{4}$	$\frac{1}{5}$	$\frac{1}{6}$
$\frac{1}{2}$	$\frac{1}{4}$	$\frac{1}{6}$	$\frac{1}{8}$	$\frac{1}{10}$	$\frac{1}{12}$
$\frac{1}{3}$	$\frac{1}{6}$	$\frac{1}{9}$	$\frac{1}{12}$	$\frac{1}{15}$	$\frac{1}{18}$
$\frac{1}{4}$	$\frac{1}{8}$	$\frac{1}{12}$	$\frac{1}{16}$	$\frac{1}{20}$	$\frac{1}{24}$
$\frac{1}{5}$	$\frac{1}{10}$	$\frac{1}{15}$	$\frac{1}{20}$	$\frac{1}{25}$	$\frac{1}{30}$
$\frac{1}{6}$	$\frac{1}{12}$	$\frac{1}{18}$	$\frac{1}{24}$	$\frac{1}{30}$	$\frac{1}{36}$

▶ **58.** Complete the table by finding the original fraction, given its square.

Original fraction squared	Original fraction
$\frac{1}{9}$	$\frac{1}{3}$
$\frac{1}{100}$	$\frac{1}{10}$
$\frac{4}{25}$	$\frac{2}{5}$
$\frac{16}{49}$	$\frac{4}{7}$
$\frac{81}{36}$	$\frac{9}{6}$
$\frac{9}{121}$	$\frac{3}{11}$

Multiply. Write the product in simplest form.

59. $-\frac{15}{24}\cdot\frac{8}{25}$ $-\frac{1}{5}$

60. $-\frac{20}{21}\cdot\frac{7}{16}$ $-\frac{5}{12}$

61. $\frac{3}{8}\cdot\frac{7}{16}$ $\frac{21}{128}$

62. $\frac{5}{9}\cdot\frac{2}{7}$ $\frac{10}{63}$

63. $\left(\frac{2}{3}\right)\left(-\frac{1}{16}\right)\left(-\frac{4}{5}\right)$ $\frac{1}{30}$

▶ **64.** $\left(\frac{3}{8}\right)\left(-\frac{2}{3}\right)\left(-\frac{12}{27}\right)$ $\frac{1}{9}$

65. $-\frac{5}{6}\cdot 18$ -15

66. $6\left(-\frac{2}{3}\right)$ -4

67. $\left(-\frac{3}{4}\right)^3$ $-\frac{27}{64}$

▶ **68.** $\left(-\frac{2}{5}\right)^3$ $-\frac{8}{125}$

69. $\frac{3}{4}\cdot\frac{4}{3}$ 1

70. $\frac{4}{5}\cdot\frac{5}{4}$ 1

71. $\frac{5}{3}\left(-\frac{6}{15}\right)(-4)$ $\frac{8}{3}$

72. $\frac{5}{6}\left(-\frac{2}{3}\right)(-12)$ $\frac{20}{3}$

73. $-\frac{11}{12}\cdot\frac{18}{55}\cdot 5$ $-\frac{3}{2}$

▶ **74.** $-\frac{24}{5}\cdot\frac{7}{12}\cdot\frac{1}{14}$ $-\frac{1}{5}$

75. $\left(-\frac{11}{21}\right)\left(-\frac{14}{33}\right)$ $\frac{2}{9}$

76. $\left(-\frac{16}{35}\right)\left(-\frac{25}{48}\right)$ $\frac{5}{21}$

77. $-\left(-\frac{5}{9}\right)^2$ $-\frac{25}{81}$

▶ **78.** $-\left(-\frac{5}{6}\right)^2$ $-\frac{25}{36}$

79. $\frac{7}{10}\left(\frac{20}{21}\right)$ $\frac{2}{3}$

80. $\left(\frac{7}{6}\right)\frac{9}{49}$ $\frac{3}{14}$

81. $\frac{3}{4}\left(\frac{5}{7}\right)\left(\frac{2}{3}\right)\left(\frac{7}{3}\right)$ $\frac{5}{6}$

82. $-\frac{5}{4}\left(\frac{8}{15}\right)\left(\frac{2}{3}\right)\left(\frac{7}{2}\right)$ $-\frac{14}{9}$

83. $-\frac{14}{15}\left(-\frac{11}{8}\right)$ $\frac{77}{60}$

84. $-\frac{5}{16}\left(-\frac{8}{3}\right)$ $\frac{5}{6}$

85. $\frac{3}{16}\cdot 4\cdot\frac{2}{3}$ $\frac{1}{2}$

86. $5\cdot\frac{7}{5}\cdot\frac{3}{14}$ $\frac{3}{2}$

APPLICATIONS

87. SENATE RULES A *filibuster* is a method U.S. Senators sometimes use to block passage of a bill or appointment by talking endlessly. It takes $\frac{3}{5}$ of those voting in the Senate to break a filibuster. If all 100 Senators cast a vote, how many of their votes does it take to break a filibuster? 60 votes

▶ **88.** GENETICS Gregor Mendel (1822–1884), an Augustinian monk, is credited with developing a model that became the foundation of modern genetics. In his experiments, he crossed purple-flowered plants with white-flowered plants and found that $\frac{3}{4}$ of the offspring plants had purple flowers and $\frac{1}{4}$ of them had white flowers. Refer to the illustration below, which shows a group of offspring plants. According to this concept, when the plants begin to flower, how many will have purple flowers? 9

89. BOUNCING BALLS A tennis ball is dropped from a height of 54 inches. Each time it hits the ground, it rebounds one-third of the previous height that it fell. Find the three missing rebound heights in the illustration. 18 in., 6 in., and 2 in.

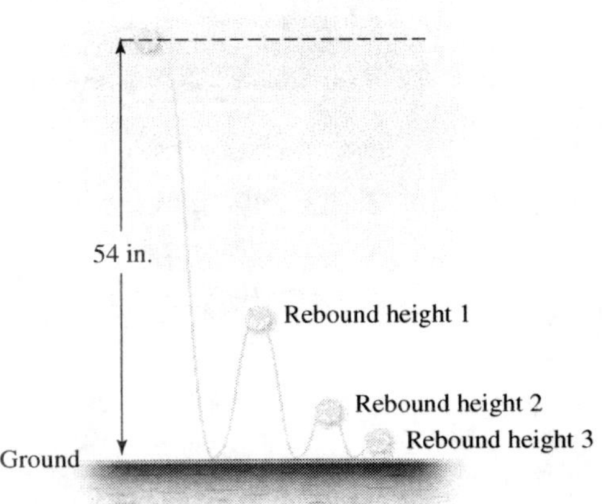

90. ELECTIONS The final election returns for a city bond measure are shown below.

a. Find the total number of votes cast. 188,400

b. Find two-thirds of the total number of votes cast. 125,600

c. Did the bond measure pass? It failed to pass by 1 vote.

MEASURE 1
100% of the precincts reporting

Fire–Police–Paramedics General Obligation Bonds
(Requires two-thirds vote)

YES	NO
125,599	62,801

91. COOKING Use the recipe below, along with the concept of multiplication of fractions, to find how much sugar and how much molasses are needed to make *one dozen* cookies. (*Hint:* this recipe is for *two dozen* cookies.) $\frac{3}{8}$ cup sugar, $\frac{1}{6}$ cup molasses

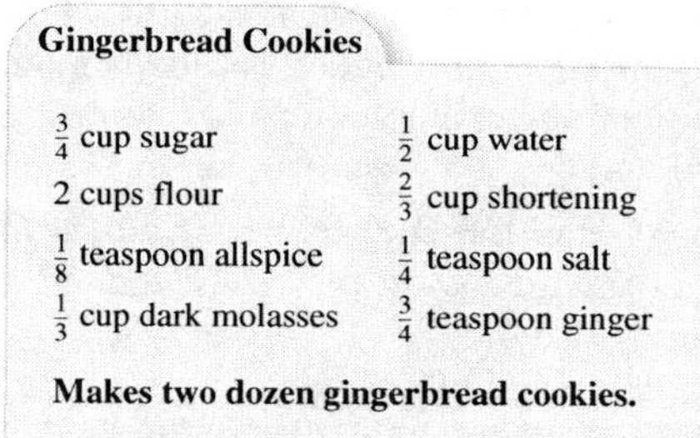
Gingerbread Cookies

$\frac{3}{4}$ cup sugar	$\frac{1}{2}$ cup water
2 cups flour	$\frac{2}{3}$ cup shortening
$\frac{1}{8}$ teaspoon allspice	$\frac{1}{4}$ teaspoon salt
$\frac{1}{3}$ cup dark molasses	$\frac{3}{4}$ teaspoon ginger

Makes two dozen gingerbread cookies.

92. THE EARTH'S SURFACE The surface of Earth covers an area of approximately 196,800,000 square miles. About $\frac{3}{4}$ of that area is covered by water. Find the number of square miles of the surface covered by water. 147,600,000 mi^2

93. BOTANY In an experiment, monthly growth rates of three types of plants doubled when nitrogen was added to the soil. Complete the graph by drawing the improved growth rate bar next to each normal growth rate bar.

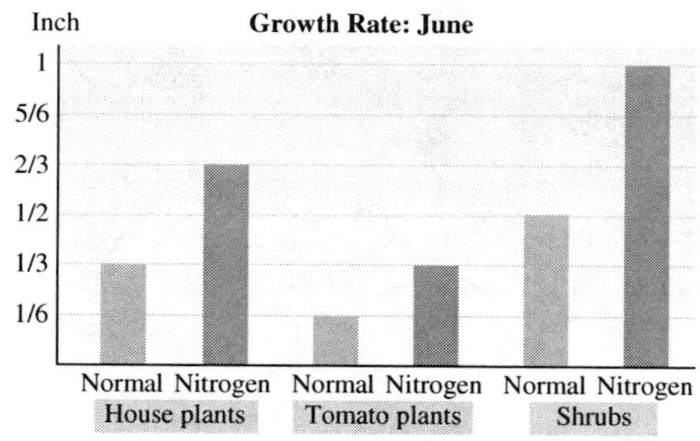

94. ICEBERGS About $\frac{9}{10}$ of the volume of an iceberg is below the water line.

a. What fraction of the volume of an iceberg is *above* the water line? $\frac{1}{10}$

b. Suppose an iceberg has a total volume of 18,700 cubic meters. What is the volume of the part of the iceberg that is above the water line? 1,870 cubic meters

© Ralph A. Clevenger/Corbis

95. KITCHEN DESIGN Find the area of the *kitchen work triangle* formed by the paths between the refrigerator, the range, and the sink shown below. 27 ft^2

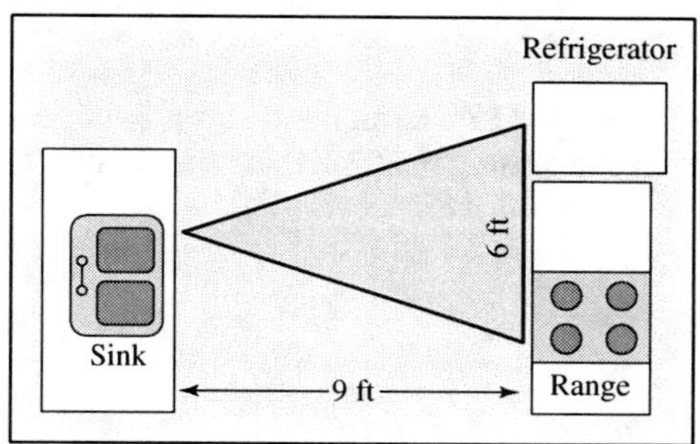

96. STARS AND STRIPES The illustration shows a folded U.S. flag. When it is placed on a table as part of an exhibit, how much area will it occupy? 121 in.^{2}

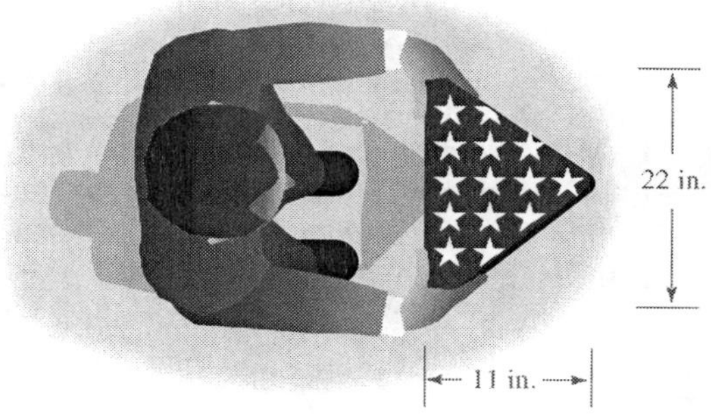

▶ **97.** WINDSURFING Estimate the area of the sail on the windsurfing board. 42 ft^2

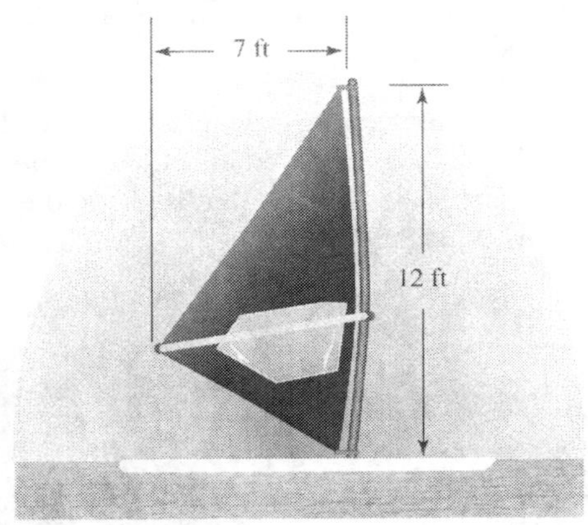

▶ **98.** TILE DESIGN A design for bathroom tile is shown. Find the amount of area on a tile that is blue. 18 in.^2

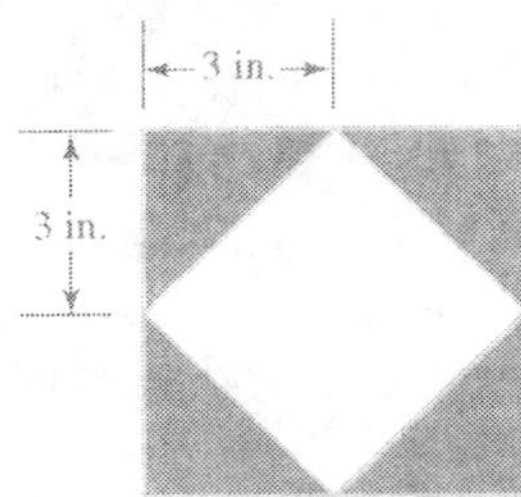

▶ **99.** GEOGRAPHY Estimate the area of the state of New Hampshire, using the triangle in the illustration. $9{,}646 \text{ mi}^2$

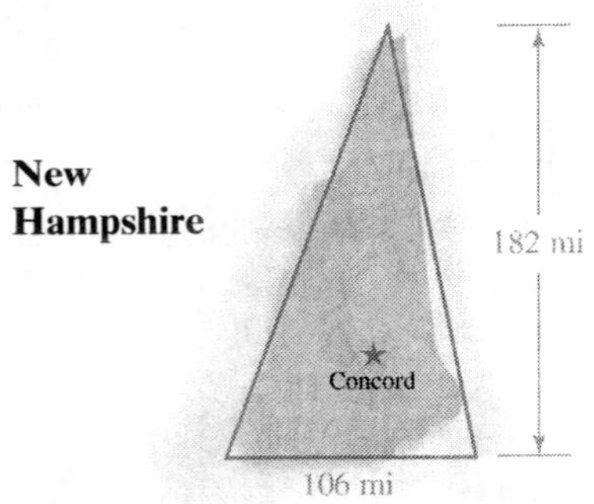

▶ **100.** STAMPS The best designs in a contest to create a wildlife stamp are shown. To save on paper costs, the postal service has decided to choose the stamp that has the smaller area. Which one did the postal service choose? (*Hint:* use the formula for the area of a rectangle.) the natural beauty stamp

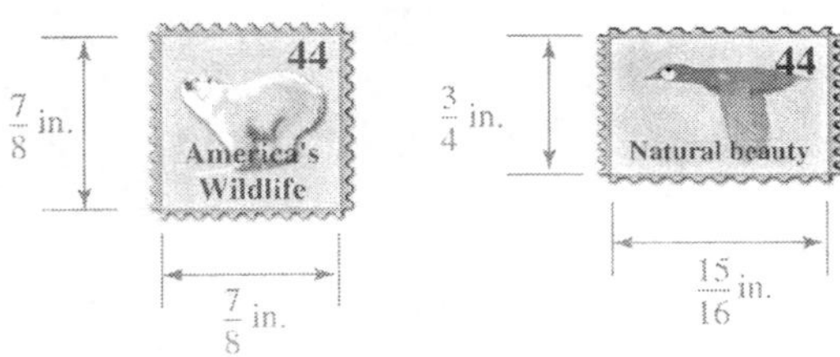

101. VISES Each complete turn of the handle of the bench vise shown below tightens its jaws exactly $\frac{1}{16}$ of an inch. How much tighter will the jaws of the vice get if the handle is turned 12 complete times? $\frac{3}{4}$ in.

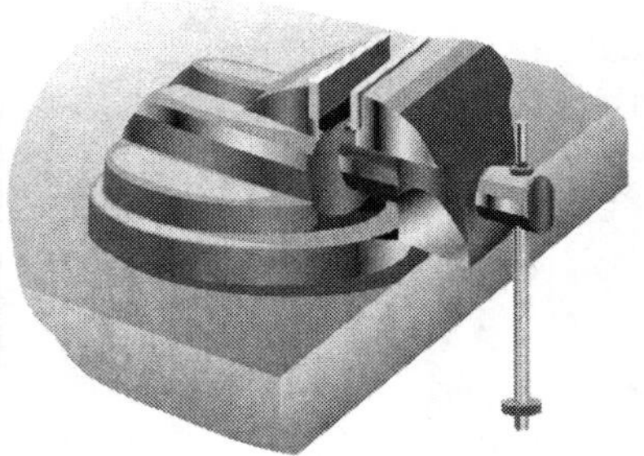

102. WOODWORKING Each time a board is passed through a power sander, the machine removes $\frac{1}{64}$ of an inch of thickness. If a rough pine board is passed through the sander 6 times, by how much will its thickness change? It will lose $\frac{3}{32}$ of an inch of thickness $\left(-\frac{3}{32}\right)$

WRITING

103. In a word problem, when a fraction is followed by the word *of,* multiplication is usually indicated. Give three real-life examples of this type of use of the word *of.*

104. Can you multiply the number 5 and another number and obtain an answer that is less than 5? Explain why or why not.

105. A MAJORITY The definition of the word *majority* is as follows: "a number greater than *one-half of* the total." Explain what it means when a teacher says, "A majority of the class voted to postpone the test until Monday." Give an example.

▶ **106.** What does area measure? Give an example.

107. In the following solution, what step did the student forget to use that caused him to have to work with such large numbers?

Multiply. Simplify the product, if possible.

$$\frac{44}{63} \cdot \frac{27}{55} = \frac{44 \cdot 27}{63 \cdot 55}$$
$$= \frac{1{,}188}{3{,}465}$$

108. Is the product of two proper fractions always smaller than either of those fractions? Explain why or why not.

REVIEW

Divide and check each result.

109. $\frac{-8}{4}$ -2

110. $21 \div (-3)$ -7

111. $-736 \div (-32)$ 23

112. $\frac{-400}{-25}$ 16

SECTION 2.3

Dividing Fractions

Objectives

1. Find the reciprocal of a fraction.
2. Divide fractions.
3. Solve application problems by dividing fractions.

We will now discuss how to divide fractions.

1 Find the reciprocal of a fraction.

Division with fractions involves working with *reciprocals.* To present the concept of reciprocal, we consider the problem $\frac{7}{8} \cdot \frac{8}{7}$.

$\frac{7}{8} \cdot \frac{8}{7} = \frac{7 \cdot 8}{8 \cdot 7}$ Multiply the numerators. Multiply the denominators.

$= \frac{\overset{1}{\cancel{7}} \cdot \overset{1}{\cancel{8}}}{\underset{1}{\cancel{8}} \cdot \underset{1}{\cancel{7}}}$ To simplify, remove the common factors of 7 and 8 from the numerator and denominator.

$= \frac{1}{1}$ Multiply the remaining factors in the numerator. Multiply the remaining factors in the denominator.

$= 1$ Any whole number divided by 1 is equal to that number.

The product of $\frac{7}{8}$ and $\frac{8}{7}$ is 1.

Whenever the product of two numbers is 1, we say that those numbers are *reciprocals.* Therefore, $\frac{7}{8}$ and $\frac{8}{7}$ are reciprocals. To find the reciprocal of a fraction, *we invert the numerator and the denominator.*

Reciprocals

Two numbers are called **reciprocals** if their product is 1.

Caution! Zero does not have a reciprocal, because the product of 0 and a number can never be 1.

EXAMPLE 1 For each number, find its reciprocal and show that their product is 1: **a.** $\frac{2}{3}$ **b.** $-\frac{3}{4}$ **c.** 5

Strategy To find each reciprocal, we will invert the numerator and denominator.

WHY This procedure will produce a new fraction that, when multiplied by the original fraction, gives a result of 1.

Solution

a. Fraction **Reciprocal**

$\frac{2}{3}$ → $\frac{3}{2}$ (invert)

The reciprocal of $\frac{2}{3}$ is $\frac{3}{2}$.

Check: $\frac{2}{3} \cdot \frac{3}{2} = \frac{\overset{1}{\cancel{2}} \cdot \overset{1}{\cancel{3}}}{\underset{1}{\cancel{3}} \cdot \underset{1}{\cancel{2}}} = 1$

Self Check 1

For each number, find its reciprocal and show that their product is 1.

a. $\frac{3}{5}$ $\frac{5}{3}$ **b.** $-\frac{5}{6}$ $-\frac{6}{5}$ **c.** 8 $\frac{1}{8}$

Now Try **Problem 13**

Teaching Example 1 For each number, find its reciprocal and show that their product is 1.

a. $\frac{11}{12}$ b. $-\frac{4}{5}$ c. 2

Answers:

a. $\frac{12}{11}$ b. $-\frac{5}{4}$ c. $\frac{1}{2}$

b. Fraction **Reciprocal**

$-\frac{3}{4}$ → $-\frac{4}{3}$

invert

The reciprocal of $-\frac{3}{4}$ is $-\frac{4}{3}$.

Check: $-\frac{3}{4}\left(-\frac{4}{3}\right) = \frac{\overset{1}{\cancel{3}} \cdot \overset{1}{\cancel{4}}}{\underset{1}{\cancel{4}} \cdot \underset{1}{\cancel{3}}} = 1$ The product of two fractions with like signs is positive.

c. Since $5 = \frac{5}{1}$, the reciprocal of 5 is $\frac{1}{5}$.

Check: $5 \cdot \frac{1}{5} = \frac{5}{1} \cdot \frac{1}{5} = \frac{\overset{1}{\cancel{5}} \cdot 1}{1 \cdot \underset{1}{\cancel{5}}} = 1$

Caution! Don't confuse the concepts of the *opposite* of a negative number and the *reciprocal* of a negative number. For example:

The reciprocal of $-\frac{9}{16}$ is $-\frac{16}{9}$.

The opposite of $-\frac{9}{16}$ is $\frac{9}{16}$.

2 Divide fractions.

To develop a rule for dividing fractions, let's consider a real-life application.

Suppose that the manager of a candy store buys large bars of chocolate and divides each one into four equal parts to sell. How many fourths can be obtained from 5 bars?

We are asking, "How many $\frac{1}{4}$'s are there in 5?" To answer the question, we need to use the operation of division. We can represent this division as $5 \div \frac{1}{4}$.

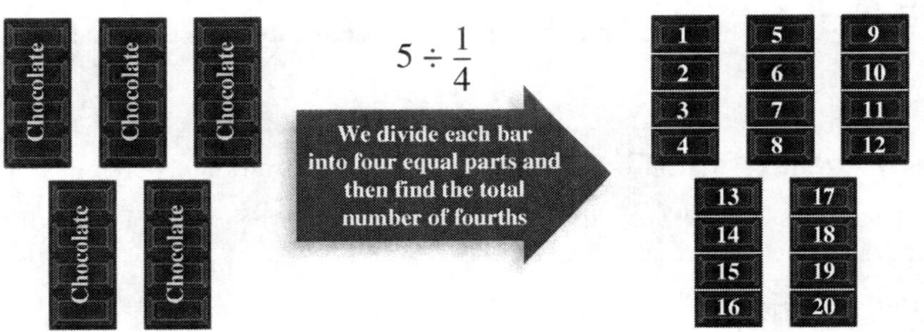

5 bars of chocolate

Total number of fourths = 5 • 4 = 20

There are 20 fourths in the 5 bars of chocolate. Two observations can be made from this result.

- This division problem involves a fraction: $5 \div \frac{1}{4}$.
- Although we were asked to find $5 \div \frac{1}{4}$, we solved the problem using *multiplication* instead of *division:* $5 \cdot 4 = 20$. That is, division by $\frac{1}{4}$ (a fraction) is the same as multiplication by 4 (its reciprocal).

$$5 \div \frac{1}{4} = 5 \cdot 4$$

These observations suggest the following rule for dividing two fractions.

Dividing Fractions

To divide two fractions, multiply the first fraction by the reciprocal of the second fraction. Simplify the result, if possible.

For example, to find $\frac{5}{7} \div \frac{3}{4}$, we multiply $\frac{5}{7}$ by the reciprocal of $\frac{3}{4}$.

Change the division to multiplication.

$$\frac{5}{7} \div \frac{3}{4} = \frac{5}{7} \cdot \frac{4}{3}$$

The reciprocal of $\frac{3}{4}$ is $\frac{4}{3}$.

$$= \frac{5 \cdot 4}{7 \cdot 3}$$ Multiply the numerators. Multiply the denominators.

$$= \frac{20}{21}$$

Thus, $\frac{5}{7} \div \frac{3}{4} = \frac{20}{21}$. We say that the *quotient* of $\frac{5}{7}$ and $\frac{3}{4}$ is $\frac{20}{21}$.

EXAMPLE 2 Divide: $\frac{1}{3} \div \frac{4}{5}$

Strategy We will multiply the first fraction, $\frac{1}{3}$, by the reciprocal of the second fraction, $\frac{4}{5}$. Then, if possible, we will simplify the result.

WHY This is the rule for dividing two fractions.

Solution

$$\frac{1}{3} \div \frac{4}{5} = \frac{1}{3} \cdot \frac{5}{4}$$ Multiply $\frac{1}{3}$ by the reciprocal of $\frac{4}{5}$, which is $\frac{5}{4}$.

$$= \frac{1 \cdot 5}{3 \cdot 4}$$ Multiply the numerators. Multiply the denominators.

$$= \frac{5}{12}$$

Since 5 and 12 have no common factors other than 1, the result is in simplest form. ■

Self Check 2

Divide: $\frac{2}{3} \div \frac{7}{8}$ $\frac{16}{21}$

Now Try **Problem 17**

Teaching Example 2 Divide: $\frac{1}{6} \div \frac{2}{5}$
Answer:
$\frac{5}{12}$

EXAMPLE 3 Divide and simplify: $\frac{9}{16} \div \frac{3}{20}$

Strategy We will multiply the first fraction, $\frac{9}{16}$, by the reciprocal of the second fraction, $\frac{3}{20}$. Then, if possible, we will simplify the result.

WHY This is the rule for dividing two fractions.

Self Check 3

Divide and simplify: $\frac{4}{5} \div \frac{8}{25}$ $\frac{5}{2}$

Now Try **Problem 21**

Teaching Example 3 Divide and simplify: $\frac{3}{7} \div \frac{9}{28}$

Answer: $\frac{4}{3}$

Solution

$\frac{9}{16} \div \frac{3}{20} = \frac{9}{16} \cdot \frac{20}{3}$ Multiply $\frac{9}{16}$ by the reciprocal of $\frac{3}{20}$, which is $\frac{20}{3}$.

$= \frac{9 \cdot 20}{16 \cdot 3}$ Multiply the numerators. Multiply the denominators.

$= \frac{\overset{1}{\cancel{3}} \cdot 3 \cdot \overset{1}{\cancel{4}} \cdot 5}{\underset{1}{\cancel{4}} \cdot 4 \cdot \underset{1}{\cancel{3}}}$ To simplify, factor 9 as $3 \cdot 3$, factor 20 as $4 \cdot 5$, and factor 16 as $4 \cdot 4$. Then remove out the common factors of 3 and 4 from the numerator and denominator.

$= \frac{15}{4}$ Multiply the remaining factors in the numerator: $1 \cdot 3 \cdot 1 \cdot 5 = 15$. Multiply the remaining factors in the denominator: $1 \cdot 4 \cdot 1 = 4$.

Self Check 4

Divide and simplify:

$80 \div \frac{20}{11}$ 44

Now Try **Problem 27**

Teaching Example 4 Divide and simplify: $90 \div \frac{30}{17}$

Answer: 51

EXAMPLE 4 Divide and simplify: $120 \div \frac{10}{7}$

Strategy We will write 120 as a fraction and then multiply the first fraction by the reciprocal of the second fraction.

WHY This is the rule for dividing two fractions.

Solution

$120 \div \frac{10}{7} = \frac{120}{1} \div \frac{10}{7}$ Write 120 as a fraction: $120 = \frac{120}{1}$.

$= \frac{120}{1} \cdot \frac{7}{10}$ Multiply $\frac{120}{1}$ by the reciprocal of $\frac{10}{7}$, which is $\frac{7}{10}$.

$= \frac{120 \cdot 7}{1 \cdot 10}$ Multiply the numerators. Multiply the denominators.

$= \frac{\overset{1}{\cancel{10}} \cdot 12 \cdot 7}{1 \cdot \underset{1}{\cancel{10}}}$ To simplify, factor 120 as $10 \cdot 12$, then remove the common factor of 10 from the numerator and denominator.

$= \frac{84}{1}$ Multiply the remaining factors in the numerator: $1 \cdot 12 \cdot 7 = 84$. Multiply the remaining factors in the denominator: $1 \cdot 1 = 1$.

$= 84$ Any whole number divided by 1 is the same number.

Because of the relationship between multiplication and division, the sign rules for *dividing* fractions are the same as those for *multiplying* fractions.

Self Check 5

Divide and simplify:

$\frac{2}{3} \div \left(-\frac{7}{6}\right)$ $-\frac{4}{7}$

Now Try **Problem 29**

EXAMPLE 5 Divide and simplify: $\frac{1}{6} \div \left(-\frac{1}{18}\right)$

Strategy We will multiply the first fraction, $\frac{1}{6}$, by the reciprocal of the second fraction, $-\frac{1}{18}$. To determine the sign of the result, we will use the rule for multiplying two fractions that have different (unlike) signs.

WHY One fraction is positive and one is negative.

Solution

$$\frac{1}{6} \div \left(-\frac{1}{18}\right) = \frac{1}{6}\left(-\frac{18}{1}\right)$$ Multiply $\frac{1}{6}$ by the reciprocal of $-\frac{1}{18}$, which is $-\frac{18}{1}$.

$$= -\frac{1 \cdot 18}{6 \cdot 1}$$ Multiply the numerators. Multiply the denominators. Since the fractions have unlike signs, make the answer negative.

$$= -\frac{1 \cdot 3 \cdot \overset{1}{\cancel{6}}}{\underset{1}{\cancel{6}} \cdot 1}$$ To simplify, factor 18 as 3 · 6. Then remove the common factor of 6 from the numerator and denominator.

$$= -\frac{3}{1}$$ Multiply the remaining factors in the numerator. Multiply the remaining factors in the denominator.

$$= -3$$

Teaching Example 5 Divide and simplify: $\frac{2}{9} \div \left(-\frac{25}{18}\right)$

Answer: $-\frac{4}{25}$

EXAMPLE 6 Divide and simplify: $-\frac{21}{36} \div (-3)$

Strategy We will multiply the first fraction, $-\frac{21}{36}$, by the reciprocal of -3. To determine the sign of the result, we will use the rule for multiplying two fractions that have the same (like) signs.

WHY Both fractions are negative.

Solution

$$-\frac{21}{36} \div (-3) = -\frac{21}{36}\left(-\frac{1}{3}\right)$$ Multiply $-\frac{21}{36}$ by the reciprocal of -3, which is $-\frac{1}{3}$.

$$= \frac{21}{36}\left(\frac{1}{3}\right)$$ Since the product of two negative fractions is positive, drop both − signs and continue.

$$= \frac{21 \cdot 1}{36 \cdot 3}$$ Multiply the numerators. Multiply the denominators.

$$= \frac{\overset{1}{\cancel{3}} \cdot 7 \cdot 1}{36 \cdot \underset{1}{\cancel{3}}}$$ To simplify, factor 21 as 3 · 7. Then remove the common factor of 3 from the numerator and denominator.

$$= \frac{7}{36}$$ Multiply the remaining factors in the numerator: $1 \cdot 7 \cdot 1 = 7$. Multiply the remaining factors in the denominator: $36 \cdot 1 = 36$.

Self Check 6

Divide and simplify:

$$-\frac{35}{16} \div (-7) \quad \frac{5}{16}$$

Now Try **Problem 33**

Teaching Example 6 Divide and simplify: $-\frac{64}{35} \div (-8)$

Answer: $\frac{8}{35}$

3 Solve application problems by dividing fractions.

Problems that involve forming equal-sized groups can be solved by division.

EXAMPLE 7 *Surfboard Designs* Most surfboards are made of a foam core covered with several layers of fiberglass to keep them water-tight. How many layers are needed to build up a finish $\frac{3}{8}$ of an inch thick if each layer of fiberglass has a thickness of $\frac{1}{16}$ of an inch?

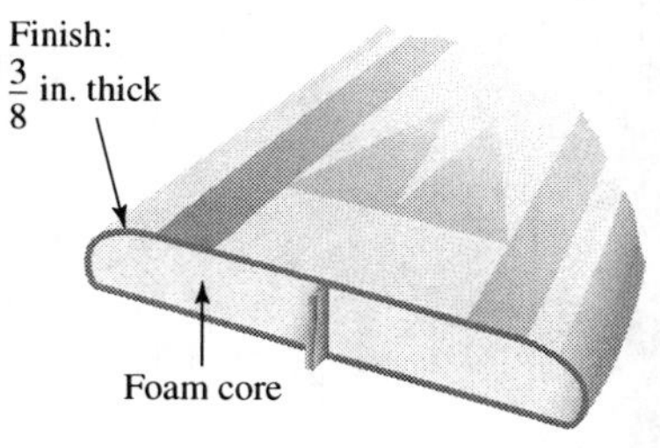

Self Check 7

COOKING A recipe calls for 4 cups of sugar, and the only measuring container you have holds $\frac{1}{3}$ cup. How many $\frac{1}{3}$ cups of sugar would you need to add to follow the recipe? 12

Now Try **Problem 77**

Teaching Example 7 GOLD COINS
How many $\frac{1}{16}$-ounce coins can be cast from a $\frac{7}{8}$-ounce bar of gold?
Answer:
14 coins

Analyze

- The surfboard is to have a $\frac{3}{8}$-inch-thick fiberglass finish. *Given*
- Each layer of fiberglass is $\frac{1}{16}$ of an inch thick. *Given*
- How many layers of fiberglass need to be applied? *Find*

Form Think of the $\frac{3}{8}$-inch-thick finish separated into an unknown number of equally thick layers of fiberglass. This indicates division.

We translate the words of the problem to numbers and symbols.

The number of layers of fiberglass that are needed	is equal to	the thickness of the finish	divided by	the thickness of 1 layer of fiberglass.
The number of layers of fiberglass that are needed	$=$	$\frac{3}{8}$	$\div$	$\frac{1}{16}$

Solve To find the quotient, we will use the rule for dividing two fractions.

$$\frac{3}{8} \div \frac{1}{16} = \frac{3}{8} \cdot \frac{16}{1}$$ Multiply $\frac{3}{8}$ by the reciprocal of $\frac{1}{16}$, which is $\frac{16}{1}$.

$$= \frac{3 \cdot 16}{8 \cdot 1}$$ Multiply the numerators. Multiply the denominators.

$$= \frac{3 \cdot 2 \cdot \overset{1}{\cancel{8}}}{\underset{1}{\cancel{8}} \cdot 1}$$ To simplify, factor 16 as $2 \cdot 8$. Then remove the common factor of 8 from the numerator and denominator.

$$= \frac{6}{1}$$ Multiply the remaining factors in the numerator. Multiply the remaining factors in the denominator.

$$= 6$$ Any whole number divided by 1 is the same number.

State The number of layers of fiberglass needed is 6.

Check If 6 layers of fiberglass, each $\frac{1}{16}$ of an inch thick, are used, the finished thickness will be $\frac{6}{16}$ of an inch. If we simplify $\frac{6}{16}$, we see that it is equivalent to the desired finish thickness:

$$\frac{6}{16} = \frac{\overset{1}{\cancel{2}} \cdot 3}{\underset{1}{\cancel{2}} \cdot 8} = \frac{3}{8}$$

The result checks. ■

ANSWERS TO SELF CHECKS

1. a. $\frac{5}{3}$ **b.** $-\frac{6}{5}$ **c.** $\frac{1}{8}$ **2.** $\frac{16}{21}$ **3.** $\frac{5}{2}$ **4.** 44 **5.** $-\frac{4}{7}$ **6.** $\frac{5}{16}$ **7.** 12

SECTION 2.3 STUDY SET

VOCABULARY

Fill in the blanks.

1. The reciprocal of $\frac{5}{12}$ is $\frac{12}{5}$.
2. To find the reciprocal of a fraction, invert the numerator and denominator.
3. The answer to a division is called the quotient.
4. To simplify $\frac{2 \cdot 2 \cdot 3}{2 \cdot 3 \cdot 5 \cdot 7}$, we remove common factors of the numerator and denominator.

CONCEPTS

5. Fill in the blanks.
   a. To divide two fractions, multiply the first fraction by the reciprocal of the second fraction.
   b. $\frac{1}{2} \div \frac{2}{3} = \frac{1}{2} \cdot \frac{3}{2}$
6. a. What division problem is illustrated below? $4 \div \frac{1}{3}$
   b. What is the answer? 12

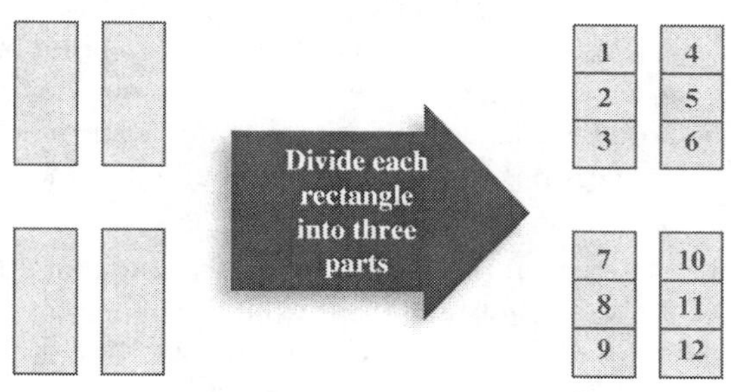

7. Determine whether each quotient is positive or negative. *You do not have to find the answer.*
   a. $-\frac{1}{4} \div \frac{3}{4}$ negative
   b. $-\frac{7}{8} \div \left(-\frac{21}{32}\right)$ positive
8. Complete the table.

Number	Opposite	Reciprocal
$\frac{3}{10}$	$-\frac{3}{10}$	$\frac{10}{3}$
$-\frac{7}{11}$	$\frac{7}{11}$	$-\frac{11}{7}$
6	-6	$\frac{1}{6}$

9. a. Multiply $\frac{4}{5}$ and its reciprocal. What is the result? 1
   b. Multiply $-\frac{3}{5}$ and its reciprocal. What is the result? 1
10. a. Find: $15 \div 3$ 5
    b. Rewrite $15 \div 3$ as multiplication by the reciprocal of 3, and find the result. $15 \cdot \frac{1}{3} = 5$
    c. Complete this statement: Division by 3 is the same as multiplication by $\frac{1}{3}$.

NOTATION

Fill in the blanks to complete each solution.

11. $\frac{4}{9} \div \frac{8}{27} = \frac{4}{9} \cdot \frac{27}{8}$

$= \frac{4 \cdot 27}{9 \cdot 8}$

$= \frac{4 \cdot 3 \cdot 9}{9 \cdot 2 \cdot 4}$

$= \frac{\overset{1}{\cancel{4}} \cdot 3 \cdot \overset{1}{\cancel{9}}}{\underset{1}{\cancel{9}} \cdot 2 \cdot \underset{1}{\cancel{4}}}$

$= \frac{3}{2}$

12. $\frac{25}{31} \div 10 = \frac{25}{31} \div \frac{10}{1}$

$= \frac{25}{31} \cdot \frac{1}{10}$

$= \frac{25 \cdot 1}{31 \cdot 10}$

$= \frac{5 \cdot 5 \cdot 1}{31 \cdot 2 \cdot 5}$

$= \frac{\overset{1}{\cancel{5}} \cdot 5 \cdot 1}{31 \cdot 2 \cdot \underset{1}{\cancel{5}}}$

$= \frac{5}{62}$

GUIDED PRACTICE

Find the reciprocal of each number. See Example 1.

13. a. $\frac{6}{7}$ $\frac{7}{6}$ b. $-\frac{15}{8}$ $-\frac{8}{15}$ c. 10 $\frac{1}{10}$
14. a. $\frac{2}{9}$ $\frac{9}{2}$ b. $-\frac{9}{4}$ $-\frac{4}{9}$ c. 7 $\frac{1}{7}$
15. a. $\frac{11}{8}$ $\frac{8}{11}$ b. $-\frac{1}{14}$ -14 c. -63 $-\frac{1}{63}$
16. a. $\frac{13}{2}$ $\frac{2}{13}$ b. $-\frac{1}{5}$ -5 c. -21 $-\frac{1}{21}$

Divide. Simplify each quotient, if possible. See Example 2.

17. $\frac{1}{8} \div \frac{2}{3}$ $\frac{3}{16}$
18. $\frac{1}{2} \div \frac{8}{9}$ $\frac{9}{16}$
19. $\frac{2}{23} \div \frac{1}{7}$ $\frac{14}{23}$
20. $\frac{4}{21} \div \frac{1}{5}$ $\frac{20}{21}$

Divide. Simplify each quotient, if possible. See Example 3.

21. $\frac{25}{32} \div \frac{5}{28}$ $\frac{35}{8}$

▶ **22.** $\frac{4}{25} \div \frac{2}{35}$ $\frac{14}{5}$

23. $\frac{27}{32} \div \frac{9}{8}$ $\frac{3}{4}$

24. $\frac{16}{27} \div \frac{20}{21}$ $\frac{28}{45}$

Divide. Simplify each quotient, if possible. See Example 4.

25. $50 \div \frac{10}{9}$ 45

▶ **26.** $60 \div \frac{10}{3}$ 18

27. $150 \div \frac{15}{32}$ 320

28. $170 \div \frac{17}{6}$ 60

Divide. Simplify each quotient, if possible. See Example 5.

29. $\frac{1}{8} \div \left(-\frac{1}{32}\right)$ -4

30. $\frac{1}{9} \div \left(-\frac{1}{27}\right)$ -3

31. $\frac{2}{5} \div \left(-\frac{4}{35}\right)$ $-\frac{7}{2}$

▶ **32.** $\frac{4}{9} \div \left(-\frac{16}{27}\right)$ $-\frac{3}{4}$

Divide. Simplify each quotient, if possible. See Example 6.

33. $-\frac{28}{55} \div (-7)$ $\frac{4}{55}$

▶ **34.** $-\frac{32}{45} \div (-8)$ $\frac{4}{45}$

35. $-\frac{33}{23} \div (-11)$ $\frac{3}{23}$

36. $-\frac{21}{31} \div (-7)$ $\frac{3}{31}$

TRY IT YOURSELF

Divide. Simplify each quotient, if possible.

37. $120 \div \frac{12}{5}$ 50

▶ **38.** $360 \div \frac{36}{5}$ 50

39. $\frac{1}{2} \div \frac{3}{5}$ $\frac{5}{6}$

40. $\frac{1}{7} \div \frac{5}{6}$ $\frac{6}{35}$

41. $\left(-\frac{7}{4}\right) \div \left(-\frac{21}{8}\right)$ $\frac{2}{3}$

42. $\left(-\frac{15}{16}\right) \div \left(-\frac{5}{8}\right)$ $\frac{3}{2}$

43. $\frac{4}{5} \div \frac{4}{5}$ 1

▶ **44.** $\frac{2}{3} \div \frac{2}{3}$ 1

45. Divide $-\frac{15}{32}$ by $\frac{3}{4}$ $-\frac{5}{8}$

46. Divide $-\frac{7}{10}$ by $\frac{4}{5}$ $-\frac{7}{8}$

47. $3 \div \frac{1}{12}$ 36

48. $9 \div \frac{3}{4}$ 12

49. $-\frac{4}{5} \div (-6)$ $\frac{2}{15}$

50. $-\frac{7}{8} \div (-14)$ $\frac{1}{16}$

51. $\frac{15}{16} \div 180$ $\frac{1}{192}$

▶ **52.** $\frac{7}{8} \div 210$ $\frac{1}{240}$

53. $-\frac{9}{10} \div \frac{4}{15}$ $-\frac{27}{8}$

54. $-\frac{3}{4} \div \frac{3}{2}$ $-\frac{1}{2}$

55. $\frac{9}{10} \div \left(-\frac{3}{25}\right)$ $-\frac{15}{2}$

▶ **56.** $\frac{11}{16} \div \left(-\frac{9}{16}\right)$ $-\frac{11}{9}$

57. $\frac{3}{16} \div \frac{1}{9}$ $\frac{27}{16}$

58. $\frac{5}{8} \div \frac{2}{9}$ $\frac{45}{16}$

59. $-\frac{1}{8} \div 8$ $-\frac{1}{64}$

60. $-\frac{1}{15} \div 15$ $-\frac{1}{225}$

The following problems involve multiplication and division. Perform each operation. Simplify the result, if possible.

61. $\frac{7}{6} \cdot \frac{9}{49}$ $\frac{3}{14}$

62. $\frac{7}{10} \cdot \frac{20}{21}$ $\frac{2}{3}$

63. $-\frac{4}{5} \div \left(-\frac{3}{2}\right)$ $\frac{8}{15}$

▶ **64.** $-\frac{2}{3} \div \left(-\frac{3}{2}\right)$ $\frac{4}{9}$

65. $\frac{13}{16} \div 2$ $\frac{13}{32}$

66. $\frac{7}{8} \div 6$ $\frac{7}{48}$

67. $\left(-\frac{11}{21}\right)\left(-\frac{14}{33}\right)$ $\frac{2}{9}$

68. $\left(-\frac{16}{35}\right)\left(-\frac{25}{48}\right)$ $\frac{5}{21}$

69. $-\frac{15}{32} \div \frac{5}{64}$ -6

▶ **70.** $-\frac{28}{15} \div \frac{21}{10}$ $-\frac{8}{9}$

71. $11 \cdot \frac{1}{6}$ $\frac{11}{6}$

72. $9 \cdot \frac{1}{8}$ $\frac{9}{8}$

73. $\frac{3}{4} \cdot \frac{5}{7}$ $\frac{15}{28}$

74. $\frac{2}{3} \cdot \frac{7}{9}$ $\frac{14}{27}$

75. $\frac{25}{7} \div \left(-\frac{30}{21}\right)$ $-\frac{5}{2}$

▶ **76.** $\frac{39}{25} \div \left(-\frac{13}{10}\right)$ $-\frac{6}{5}$

APPLICATIONS

▶ **77.** PATIO FURNITURE A production process applies several layers of a clear plastic coat to outdoor furniture to help protect it from the weather. If each protective coat is $\frac{3}{32}$-inch thick, how many applications will be needed to build up $\frac{3}{8}$ inch of clear finish? 4 applications

78. MARATHONS Each lap around a stadium track is $\frac{1}{4}$ mile. How many laps would a runner have to complete to get a 26-mile workout? 104 laps

▶ **79.** COOKING A recipe calls for $\frac{3}{4}$ cup of flour, and the only measuring container you have holds $\frac{1}{8}$ cup. How many $\frac{1}{8}$ cups of flour would you need to add to follow the recipe? 6 cups

▶ **80.** LASERS A technician uses a laser to slice thin pieces of aluminum off the end of a rod that is $\frac{7}{8}$-inch long. How many $\frac{1}{64}$-inch-wide slices can be cut from this rod? (Assume that there is no waste in the process.) 56 slices

81. UNDERGROUND CABLES Refer to the illustration and table on the next page.

a. How many days will it take to install underground TV cable from the broadcasting station to the new homes using route 1? 30 days

b. How long is route 2? 15 mi

c. How many days will it take to install the cable using route 2? 25 days

d. Which route will require the fewer number of days to install the cable? route 2

Proposal	Amount of cable installed per day	Comments
Route 1	$\frac{2}{5}$ of a mile	Ground very rocky
Route 2	$\frac{3}{5}$ of a mile	Longer than Route 1

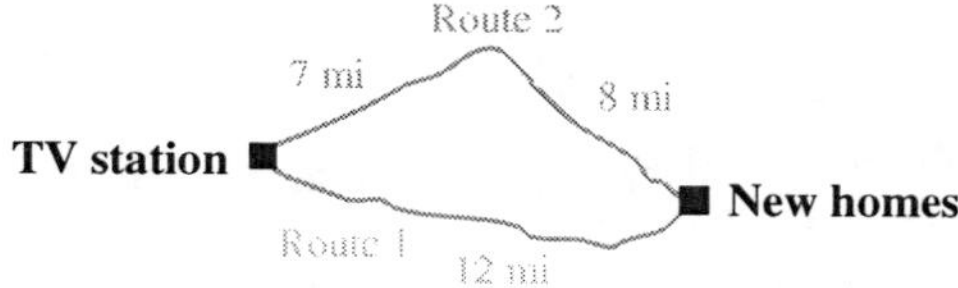

82. PRODUCTION PLANNING The materials used to make a pillow are shown. Examine the inventory list to decide how many pillows can be manufactured in one production run with the materials in stock. 147 pillows

$\frac{7}{8}$ yd corduroy fabric

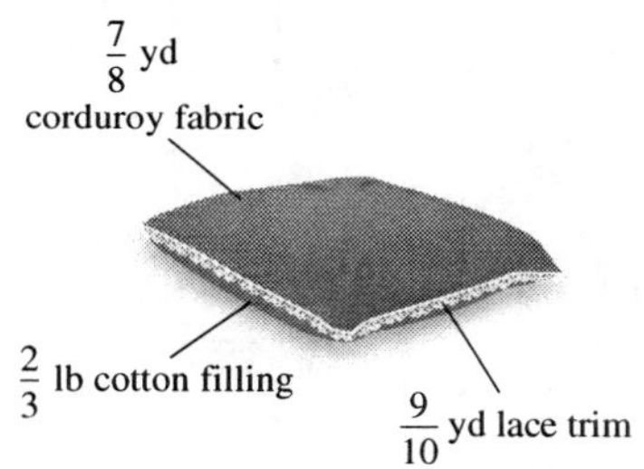

$\frac{2}{3}$ lb cotton filling

$\frac{9}{10}$ yd lace trim

Factory Inventory List

Materials	Amount in stock
Lace trim	135 yd
Corduroy fabric	154 yd
Cotton filling	98 lb

83. NOTE CARDS Ninety 3 × 5 cards are stacked next to a ruler as shown.

a. Into how many parts is 1 inch divided on the ruler? 16

b. How thick is the stack of cards? $\frac{3}{4}$ in.

c. How thick is one 3 × 5 card? $\frac{1}{120}$ in.

84. COMPUTER PRINTERS The illustration shows how the letter E is formed by a dot matrix printer. What is the height of one dot? $\frac{3}{224}$ in.

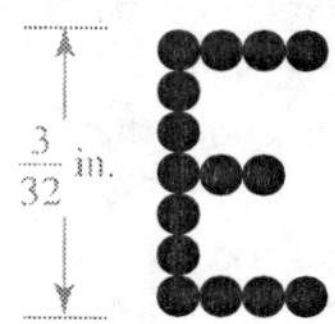

85. FORESTRY A set of forestry maps divides the 6,284 acres of an old-growth forest into $\frac{4}{5}$-acre sections. How many sections do the maps contain? 7,855 sections

86. HARDWARE A hardware chain purchases large amounts of nails and packages them in $\frac{9}{16}$-pound bags for sale. How many of these bags of nails can be obtained from 2,871 pounds of nails? 5,104 bags

WRITING

87. Explain how to divide two fractions.

88. Why do you need to know how to multiply fractions to be able to divide fractions?

89. Explain why 0 does not have a reciprocal.

90. What number is its own reciprocal? Explain why this is so.

91. Write an application problem that could be solved by finding $10 \div \frac{1}{5}$.

92. Explain why dividing a fraction by 2 is the same as finding $\frac{1}{2}$ of it. Give an example.

REVIEW

Fill in the blanks.

93. The symbol < means is less than.

94. The statement $9 \cdot 8 = 8 \cdot 9$ illustrates the commutative property of multiplication.

95. Zero is neither positive nor negative.

96. The sum of two negative numbers is negative.

97. Graph each of these numbers on a number line: –2, 0, $|-4|$, and the opposite of 1

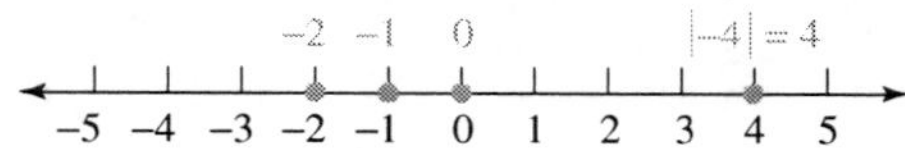

98. Evaluate each expression.

a. 3^5 243 **b.** $(-2)^5$ −32

Objectives

1. Add and subtract fractions that have the same denominator.
2. Add and subtract fractions that have different denominators.
3. Find the LCD to add and subtract fractions.
4. Identify the greater of two fractions.
5. Solve application problems by adding and subtracting fractions.

SECTION 2.4 Adding and Subtracting Fractions

In mathematics and everyday life, we can only add (or subtract) objects that are similar. For example, we can add dollars to dollars, but we cannot add dollars to oranges. This concept is important when adding or subtracting fractions.

1 Add and subtract fractions that have the same denominator.

Consider the problem $\frac{3}{5} + \frac{1}{5}$. When we write it in words, it is apparent that we are adding similar objects.

three-**fifths** + one-**fifth**

Similar objects

Because the denominators of $\frac{3}{5}$ and $\frac{1}{5}$ are the same, we say that they have a **common denominator.** Since the fractions have a common denominator, we can add them. The following figure explains the addition process.

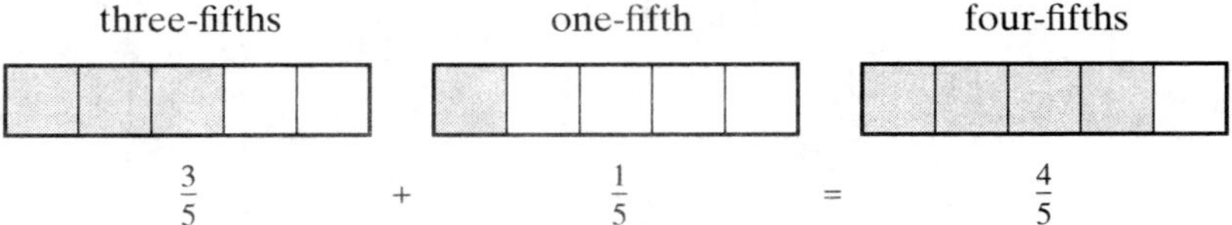

$$\frac{3}{5} + \frac{1}{5} = \frac{4}{5}$$

We can make some observations about the addition shown in the figure.

The sum of the numerators is the numerator of the answer.

$$\frac{3}{5} + \frac{1}{5} = \frac{4}{5}$$

The answer is a fraction that has the same denominator as the two fractions that were added.

These observations illustrate the following rule.

Adding and Subtracting Fractions That Have the Same Denominator

To add (or subtract) fractions that have the same denominator, add (or subtract) their numerators and write the sum (or difference) over the common denominator. Simplify the result, if possible.

Caution! We **do not** add fractions by adding the numerators and adding the denominators!

$$\frac{3}{5} + \frac{1}{5} = \frac{3+1}{5+5} = \frac{4}{10}$$

The same caution applies when subtracting fractions.

EXAMPLE 1 Perform each operation and simplify the result, if possible.

a. Add: $\frac{1}{8} + \frac{5}{8}$ **b.** Subtract: $\frac{11}{15} - \frac{4}{15}$

Strategy We will use the rule for adding and subtracting fractions that have *the same* denominator.

WHY In part a, the fractions have the same denominator, 8. In part b, the fractions have the same denominator, 15.

Solution

a. $\frac{1}{8} + \frac{5}{8} = \frac{1+5}{8}$ Add the numerators and write the sum over the common denominator 8.

$= \frac{6}{8}$ This fraction can be simplified.

$= \frac{\overset{1}{\cancel{2}} \cdot 3}{\underset{1}{\cancel{2}} \cdot 4}$ To simplify, factor 6 as $2 \cdot 3$ and 8 as $2 \cdot 4$. Then remove the common factor of 2 from the numerator and denominator.

$= \frac{3}{4}$ Multiply the remaining factors in the numerator: $1 \cdot 3 = 3$. Multiply the remaining factors in the denominator: $1 \cdot 4 = 4$.

b. $\frac{11}{15} - \frac{4}{15} = \frac{11-4}{15}$ Subtract the numerators and write the difference over the common denominator 15.

$= \frac{7}{15}$

Since 7 and 15 have no common factors other than 1, the result is in simplest form. ■

Self Check 1

Perform each operation and simplify the result, if possible.

a. Add: $\frac{5}{12} + \frac{1}{12}$ $\frac{1}{2}$

b. Subtract: $\frac{8}{9} - \frac{1}{9}$ $\frac{7}{9}$

Now Try **Problems 17 and 21**

Teaching Example 1 Perform each operation and simplify the result, if possible.

a. Add: $\frac{3}{10} + \frac{1}{10}$

b. Subtract: $\frac{6}{7} - \frac{2}{7}$

Answers:

a. $\frac{2}{5}$ b. $\frac{4}{7}$

To subtract two fractions, add the first to the opposite of the fraction to be subtracted.

EXAMPLE 2 Subtract: $-\frac{7}{3} - \left(-\frac{2}{3}\right)$

Strategy To find the difference, we will apply the rule for subtraction.

WHY It is easy to make an error when subtracting signed fractions. We will probably be more accurate if we write the subtraction as addition of the opposite.

Solution

We read $-\frac{7}{3} - \left(-\frac{2}{3}\right)$ as "negative seven-thirds *minus* negative two-thirds." Thus, the number to be subtracted is $-\frac{2}{3}$. Subtracting $-\frac{2}{3}$ is the same as adding its opposite, $\frac{2}{3}$.

$-\frac{7}{3} - \left(-\frac{2}{3}\right) = -\frac{7}{3} + \frac{2}{3}$ Add the opposite of $-\frac{2}{3}$, which is $\frac{2}{3}$. (Add; the opposite)

$= \frac{-7}{3} + \frac{2}{3}$ Write $-\frac{7}{3}$ as $\frac{-7}{3}$.

$= \frac{-7+2}{3}$ Add the numerators and write the sum over the common denominator 3.

$= \frac{-5}{3}$ Use the rule for adding two integers with different signs: $-7 + 2 = -5$.

$= -\frac{5}{3}$ Rewrite the result with the − sign in front: $\frac{-5}{3} = -\frac{5}{3}$. This fraction is in simplest form. ■

Self Check 2

Subtract: $-\frac{9}{11} - \left(-\frac{3}{11}\right)$ $-\frac{6}{11}$

Now Try **Problem 25**

Teaching Example 2

Subtract: $-\frac{9}{5} - \left(-\frac{2}{5}\right)$

Answer:

$-\frac{7}{5}$

Self Check 3

Perform the operations and simplify:

$$\frac{2}{9} + \frac{2}{9} + \frac{2}{9} \quad \frac{2}{3}$$

Now Try **Problem 29**

Teaching Example 3 Perform the operations and simplify:

$$\frac{23}{30} - \frac{11}{30} - \frac{7}{30}$$

Answer:

$$\frac{1}{6}$$

EXAMPLE 3 Perform the operations and simplify: $\frac{18}{25} - \frac{2}{25} - \frac{1}{25}$

Strategy We will use the rule for subtracting fractions that have *the same* denominator.

WHY All three fractions have the same denominator, 25.

Solution

$$\frac{18}{25} - \frac{2}{25} - \frac{1}{25} = \frac{18 - 2 - 1}{25}$$ Subtract the numerators and write the difference over the common denominator 25.

$$= \frac{15}{25}$$ This fraction can be simplified.

$$= \frac{3 \cdot \overset{1}{\cancel{5}}}{\underset{1}{\cancel{5}} \cdot 5}$$ To simplify, factor 15 as $3 \cdot 5$ and 25 as $5 \cdot 5$. Then remove the common factor of 5 from the numerator and denominator.

$$= \frac{3}{5}$$ Multiply the remaining factors in the numerator: $3 \cdot 1 = 3$. Multiply the remaining factors in the denominator: $1 \cdot 5 = 5$.

2 Add and subtract fractions that have different denominators.

Now we consider the problem $\frac{3}{5} + \frac{1}{3}$. Since the denominators are different, we cannot add these fractions in their present form.

three-**fifths** + one-**third**

Not similar objects

To add (or subtract) fractions with different denominators, we express them as equivalent fractions that have a common denominator. The smallest common denominator, called the **least** or **lowest common denominator,** is usually the easiest common denominator to use.

Least Common Denominator

The **least common denominator (LCD)** for a set of fractions is the smallest number each denominator will divide exactly (divide with no remainder).

The denominators of $\frac{3}{5}$ and $\frac{1}{3}$ are 5 and 3. The numbers 5 and 3 divide many numbers exactly (30, 45, and 60, to name a few), but the smallest number that they divide exactly is 15. Thus, 15 is the LCD for $\frac{3}{5}$ and $\frac{1}{3}$.

To find $\frac{3}{5} + \frac{1}{3}$, we *build* equivalent fractions that have denominators of 15. Then we use the rule for adding fractions that have the same denominator.

$$\frac{3}{5} + \frac{1}{3} = \frac{3}{5} \cdot \frac{3}{3} + \frac{1}{3} \cdot \frac{5}{5}$$

We need to multiply this denominator by 5 to obtain 15. It follows that $\frac{5}{5}$ should be the form of 1 used to build $\frac{1}{3}$.

We need to multiply this denominator by 3 to obtain 15. It follows that $\frac{3}{3}$ should be the form of 1 that is used to build $\frac{3}{5}$.

$$= \frac{9}{15} + \frac{5}{15}$$ Multiply the numerators. Multiply the denominators. Note that the denominators are now the same.

$$= \frac{9 + 5}{15}$$ Add the numerators and write the sum over the common denominator 15.

$$= \frac{14}{15}$$ Since 14 and 15 have no common factors other than 1, this fraction is in simplest form.

The figure below shows $\frac{3}{5}$ and $\frac{1}{3}$ expressed as equivalent fractions with a denominator of 15. Once the denominators are the same, the fractions are similar objects and can be added easily.

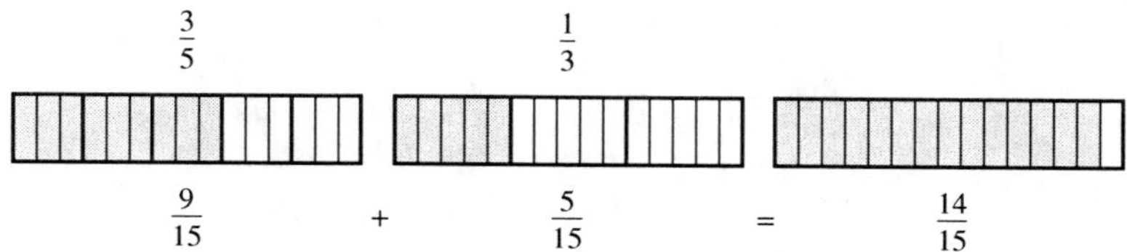

We can use the following steps to add or subtract fractions with different denominators.

Adding and Subtracting Fractions That Have Different Denominators

1. Find the LCD.
2. Rewrite each fraction as an equivalent fraction with the LCD as the denominator. To do so, build each fraction using a form of 1 that involves any factors needed to obtain the LCD.
3. Add or subtract the numerators and write the sum or difference over the LCD.
4. Simplify the result, if possible.

EXAMPLE 4 Add: $\frac{1}{7} + \frac{2}{3}$

Strategy We will express each fraction as an equivalent fraction that has the LCD as its denominator. Then we will use the rule for adding fractions that have the same denominator.

WHY To add (or subtract) fractions, the fractions must have *like* denominators.

Solution

Since the smallest number the denominators 7 and 3 divide exactly is 21, the LCD is 21.

$$\frac{1}{7} + \frac{2}{3} = \frac{1}{7} \cdot \frac{3}{3} + \frac{2}{3} \cdot \frac{7}{7}$$ To build $\frac{1}{7}$ and $\frac{2}{3}$ so that their denominators are 21, multiply each by a form of 1.

$$= \frac{3}{21} + \frac{14}{21}$$ Multiply the numerators. Multiply the denominators. The denominators are now the same.

$$= \frac{3 + 14}{21}$$ Add the numerators and write the sum over the common denominator 21.

$$= \frac{17}{21}$$ Since 17 and 21 have no common factors other than 1, this fraction is in simplest form.

Self Check 4

Add: $\frac{1}{2} + \frac{2}{5}$ $\frac{9}{10}$

Now Try **Problem 35**

Teaching Example 4

Add: $\frac{1}{2} + \frac{3}{7}$

Answer:

$\frac{13}{14}$

EXAMPLE 5 Subtract: $\frac{5}{2} - \frac{7}{3}$

Strategy We will express each fraction as an equivalent fraction that has the LCD as its denominator. Then we will use the rule for subtracting fractions that have the same denominator.

Self Check 5

Subtract: $\frac{6}{7} - \frac{3}{5}$ $\frac{9}{35}$

Now Try **Problem 37**

Teaching Example 5

Subtract: $\frac{4}{5} - \frac{2}{3}$

Answer:

$\frac{2}{15}$

WHY To add (or subtract) fractions, the fractions must have *like* denominators.

Solution

Since the smallest number the denominators 2 and 3 divide exactly is 6, the LCD is 6.

$$\frac{5}{2} - \frac{7}{3} = \frac{5}{2} \cdot \frac{3}{3} - \frac{7}{3} \cdot \frac{2}{2}$$ To build $\frac{5}{2}$ and $\frac{7}{3}$ so that their denominators are 6, multiply each by a form of 1.

$$= \frac{15}{6} - \frac{14}{6}$$ Multiply the numerators. Multiply the denominators. The denominators are now the same.

$$= \frac{15 - 14}{6}$$ Subtract the numerators and write the difference over the common denominator 6.

$$= \frac{1}{6}$$ This fraction is in simplest form.

Self Check 6

Subtract: $\frac{2}{3} - \frac{13}{6}$ $-\frac{3}{2}$

Now Try **Problem 41**

Teaching Example 6

Subtract: $\frac{1}{3} - \frac{17}{6}$

Answer:

$-\frac{5}{2}$

EXAMPLE 6 Subtract: $\frac{2}{5} - \frac{11}{15}$

Strategy Since the smallest number the denominators 5 and 15 divide exactly is 15, the LCD is 15. We will only need to build an equivalent fraction for $\frac{2}{5}$.

WHY We do not have to build the fraction $\frac{11}{15}$ because it already has a denominator of 15.

Solution

$$\frac{2}{5} - \frac{11}{15} = \frac{2}{5} \cdot \frac{3}{3} - \frac{11}{15}$$ To build $\frac{2}{5}$ so that its denominator is 15, multiply it by a form of 1.

$$= \frac{6}{15} - \frac{11}{15}$$ Multiply the numerators. Multiply the denominators. The denominators are now the same.

$$= \frac{6 - 11}{15}$$ Subtract the numerators and write the difference over the common denominator 15.

$$= -\frac{5}{15}$$ If it is helpful, use the subtraction rule and add the opposite in the numerator: $6 + (-11) = -5$. Write the $-$ sign in front of the fraction.

$$= -\frac{\overset{1}{\cancel{5}}}{3 \cdot \underset{1}{\cancel{5}}}$$ To simplify, factor 15 as $3 \cdot 5$. Then remove the common factor of 5 from the numerator and denominator.

$$= -\frac{1}{3}$$ Multiply the remaining factors in the denominator: $3 \cdot 1 = 3$.

Success Tip In Example 6, did you notice that the denominator 5 is a factor of the denominator 15, and that the LCD is 15. In general, when adding (or subtracting) two fractions with different denominators, *if the smaller denominator is a factor of the larger denominator, the larger denominator is the LCD.*

Caution! You might not have to build each fraction when adding or subtracting fractions with different denominators. For instance, the step in blue shown below is unnecessary when solving Example 6.

$$\frac{2}{5} - \frac{11}{15} = \frac{2}{5} \cdot \frac{3}{3} - \frac{11}{15} \cdot \frac{1}{1}$$

EXAMPLE 7

Add: $-5 + \frac{3}{4}$

Strategy We will write -5 as the fraction $\frac{-5}{1}$. Then we will follow the steps for adding fractions that have different denominators.

WHY The fractions $\frac{-5}{1}$ and $\frac{3}{4}$ have different denominators.

Solution

Since the smallest number the denominators 1 and 4 divide exactly is 4, the LCD is 4.

$$-5 + \frac{3}{4} = \frac{-5}{1} + \frac{3}{4}$$ Write -5 as $\frac{-5}{1}$.

$$= \frac{-5}{1} \cdot \frac{4}{4} + \frac{3}{4}$$ To build $\frac{-5}{1}$ so that its denominator is 4, multiply it by a form of 1.

$$= \frac{-20}{4} + \frac{3}{4}$$ Multiply the numerators. Multiply the denominators. The denominators are now the same.

$$= \frac{-20 + 3}{4}$$ Add the numerators and write the sum over the common denominator 4.

$$= \frac{-17}{4}$$ Use the rule for adding two integers with different signs: $-20 + 3 = -17$.

$$= -\frac{17}{4}$$ Write the result with the $-$ sign in front: $\frac{-17}{4} = -\frac{17}{4}$. This fraction is in simplest form.

Self Check 7

Add: $-6 + \frac{3}{8}$ $-\frac{45}{8}$

Now Try **Problem 45**

Teaching Example 7

Add: $-3 + \frac{11}{12}$

Answer:

$-\frac{25}{12}$

3 Find the LCD to add and subtract fractions.

When we add or subtract fractions that have different denominators, the least common denominator is not always obvious. We can use a concept studied earlier to determine the LCD for more difficult problems that involve larger denominators. To illustrate this, let's find the least common denominator of $\frac{3}{8}$ and $\frac{1}{10}$. (Note, the LCD *is not* 80.)

We have learned that both 8 and 10 must divide the LCD exactly.

The Least Common Multiple (LCM)

The **least common multiple (LCM)** of two whole numbers is the smallest whole number that is divisible by both of those numbers.

Thus, the least common denominator of $\frac{3}{8}$ and $\frac{1}{10}$ is simply the *least common multiple* of 8 and 10.

We can find the LCM of 8 and 10 by listing multiples of the larger number, 10, until we find one that is divisible by the smaller number, 8.

Multiples of 10: 10, 20, 30, 40, 50, 60, . . .

This is the first multiple of 10 that is divisible by 8 (no remainder).

Since the LCM of 8 and 10 is 40, it follows that the LCD of $\frac{3}{8}$ and $\frac{1}{10}$ is 40.

We can also find the LCM of 8 and 10 using prime factorization. We begin by prime factoring 8 and 10.

$$8 = (2 \cdot 2 \cdot 2)$$
$$10 = 2 \cdot (5)$$

The LCM of 8 and 10 is a product of prime factors, where each factor is used the greatest number of times it appears in any one factorization.

- We will use the factor 2 three times, because 2 appears three times in the factorization of 8. Circle $2 \cdot 2 \cdot 2$, as shown on the previous page.
- We will use the factor 5 once, because it appears one time in the factorization of 10. Circle 5 as shown on the previous page.

Since there are no other prime factors in either prime factorization, we have

Use 2 three times.
Use 5 one time.

$$\text{LCM}(8, 10) = 2 \cdot 2 \cdot 2 \cdot 5 = 40$$

Finding the LCD

The least common denominator (LCD) of a set of fractions is the least common multiple (LCM) of the denominators of the fractions. Two ways to find the LCM of the denominators are as follows:

- Write the multiples of the largest denominator in increasing order, until one is found that is divisible by the other denominators.
- Prime factor each denominator. The LCM is a product of prime factors, where each factor is used the greatest number of times it appears in any one factorization.

Self Check 8

Add: $\frac{1}{8} + \frac{5}{6}$ $\frac{23}{24}$

Now Try **Problem 49**

Teaching Example 8

Add: $\frac{3}{8} + \frac{5}{12}$

Answer:

$\frac{19}{24}$

EXAMPLE 8 Add: $\frac{7}{15} + \frac{3}{10}$

Strategy We begin by expressing each fraction as an equivalent fraction that has the LCD for its denominator. Then we use the rule for adding fractions that have the same denominator.

WHY To add (or subtract) fractions, the fractions must have *like* denominators.

Solution

To find the LCD, we find the prime factorization of both denominators and use each prime factor the *greatest* number of times it appears in any one factorization:

$$\left.\begin{aligned} 15 &= \textcircled{3} \cdot \textcircled{5} \\ 10 &= \textcircled{2} \cdot 5 \end{aligned}\right\} \text{LCD} = 2 \cdot 3 \cdot 5 = 30$$

2 appears once in the factorization of 10.
3 appears once in the factorization of 15.
5 appears once in the factorizations of 15 and 10.

The LCD for $\frac{7}{15}$ and $\frac{3}{10}$ is 30.

$\frac{7}{15} + \frac{3}{10} = \frac{7}{15} \cdot \frac{2}{2} + \frac{3}{10} \cdot \frac{3}{3}$ — To build $\frac{7}{15}$ and $\frac{3}{10}$ so that their denominators are 30, multiply each by a form of 1.

$= \frac{14}{30} + \frac{9}{30}$ — Multiply the numerators. Multiply the denominators. The denominators are now the same.

$= \frac{14 + 9}{30}$ — Add the numerators and write the sum over the common denominator 30.

$= \frac{23}{30}$ — Since 23 and 30 have no common factors other than 1, this fraction is in simplest form.

EXAMPLE 9 Subtract and simplify: $\frac{13}{28} - \frac{1}{21}$

Strategy We begin by expressing each fraction as an equivalent fraction that has the LCD for its denominator. Then we use the rule for subtracting fractions with *like* denominators.

WHY To add (or subtract) fractions, the fractions must have like denominators.

Solution

To find the LCD, we find the prime factorization of both denominators and use each prime factor the *greatest* number of times it appears in any one factorization:

$$\left.\begin{aligned} 28 &= 2 \cdot 2 \cdot 7 \\ 21 &= 3 \cdot 7 \end{aligned}\right\} \text{LCD} = 2 \cdot 2 \cdot 3 \cdot 7 = 84$$

2 appears twice in the factorization of 28.
3 appears once in the factorization of 21.
7 appears once in the factorizations of 28 and 21.

The LCD for $\frac{13}{28}$ and $\frac{1}{21}$ is 84.

We will compare the prime factorizations of 28, 21, and the prime factorization of the LCD, 84, to determine what forms of 1 to use to build equivalent fractions for $\frac{13}{28}$ and $\frac{1}{21}$ with a denominator of 84.

$\text{LCD} = 2 \cdot 2 \cdot 3 \cdot 7$	$\text{LCD} = 2 \cdot 2 \cdot 3 \cdot 7$
Cover the prime factorization of 28. Since 3 is left uncovered, use $\frac{3}{3}$ to build $\frac{13}{28}$.	Cover the prime factorization of 21. Since $2 \cdot 2 = 4$ is left uncovered, use $\frac{4}{4}$ to build $\frac{1}{21}$.

$$\frac{13}{28} - \frac{1}{21} = \frac{13}{28} \cdot \frac{3}{3} - \frac{1}{21} \cdot \frac{4}{4}$$
To build $\frac{13}{28}$ and $\frac{1}{21}$ so that their denominators are 84, multiply each by a form of 1.

$$= \frac{39}{84} - \frac{4}{84}$$
Multiply the numerators. Multiply the denominators. The denominators are now the same.

$$= \frac{39 - 4}{84}$$
Subtract the numerators and write the difference over the common denominator.

$$= \frac{35}{84}$$
This fraction is not in simplest form.

$$= \frac{5 \cdot \overset{1}{\cancel{7}}}{2 \cdot 2 \cdot 3 \cdot \underset{1}{\cancel{7}}}$$
To simplify, factor 35 and 84. Then remove the common factor of 7 from the numerator and denominator.

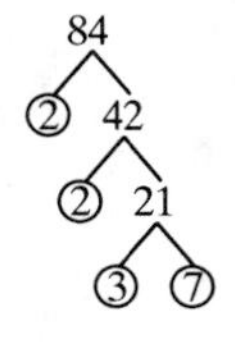

$$= \frac{5}{12}$$
Multiply the remaining factors in the numerator: $5 \cdot 1 = 5$. Multiply the remaining factors in the denominator: $2 \cdot 2 \cdot 3 \cdot 1 = 12$.

Self Check 9

Subtract and simplify: $\frac{21}{56} - \frac{9}{40}$ $\frac{3}{20}$

Now Try **Problem 53**

Teaching Example 9

Subtract and simplify: $\frac{13}{24} - \frac{3}{40}$

Answer: $\frac{7}{15}$

4 Identify the greater of two fractions.

If two fractions have the same denominator, the fraction with the greater numerator is the greater fraction.

For example,

$$\frac{7}{8} > \frac{3}{8} \quad \text{because } 7 > 3 \qquad -\frac{1}{3} > -\frac{2}{3} \quad \text{because } -1 > -2$$

If the denominators of two fractions are different, we need to write the fractions with a common denominator (preferably the LCD) before we can make a comparison.

Self Check 10

Which fraction is larger:

$\frac{7}{12}$ or $\frac{3}{5}$? $\frac{3}{5}$

Now Try **Problem 61**

Teaching Example 10

Which fraction is larger: $\frac{3}{7}$ or $\frac{1}{2}$?

Answer:

$\frac{1}{2}$

EXAMPLE 10 Which fraction is larger: $\frac{5}{6}$ or $\frac{7}{8}$?

Strategy We will express each fraction as an equivalent fraction that has the LCD for its denominator. Then we will compare their numerators.

WHY We cannot compare the fractions as given. They are not similar objects.

five-sixths   seven-eighths

Solution

Since the smallest number the denominators will divide exactly is 24, the LCD for $\frac{5}{6}$ and $\frac{7}{8}$ is 24.

$\frac{5}{6} = \frac{5}{6} \cdot \frac{4}{4}$	$\frac{7}{8} = \frac{7}{8} \cdot \frac{3}{3}$	To build $\frac{5}{6}$ and $\frac{7}{8}$ so that their denominators are 24, multiply each by a form of 1.
$= \frac{20}{24}$	$= \frac{21}{24}$	Multiply the numerators. Multiply the denominators.

Next, we compare the numerators. Since $21 > 20$, it follows that $\frac{21}{24}$ is greater than $\frac{20}{24}$. Thus, $\frac{7}{8} > \frac{5}{6}$.

5 Solve application problems by adding and subtracting fractions.

Self Check 11

Refer to the circle graph for Example 11. Find the fraction of the student body that watches 2 or more hours of television daily. $\frac{7}{12}$

Now Try **Problems 65 and 109**

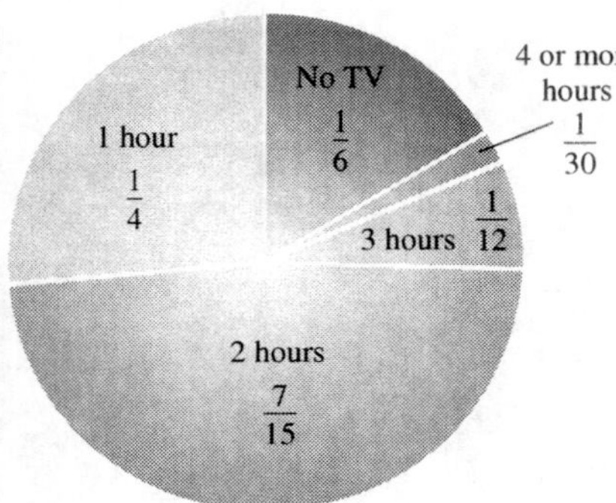

Teaching Example 11 Refer to the circle graph for Example 11. Find the fraction of the student body that watches from 1 to 3 hours of television daily.

Answer:

$\frac{4}{5}$

EXAMPLE 11 *Television Viewing Habits* Students on a college campus were asked to estimate to the nearest hour how much television they watched each day. The results are given in the **circle graph** below (also called a **pie chart**). For example, the chart tells us that $\frac{1}{4}$ of those responding watched 1 hour per day. What fraction of the student body watches from 0 to 2 hours daily?

Analyze

- $\frac{1}{6}$ of the student body watches no TV daily. *Given*
- $\frac{1}{4}$ of the student body watches 1 hour of TV daily. *Given*
- $\frac{7}{15}$ of the student body watches 2 hours of TV daily. *Given*
- What fraction of the student body watches 0 to 2 hours of TV daily? *Find*

Form We translate the words of the problem to numbers and symbols.

The fraction of the student body that watches from 0 to 2 hours of TV daily	is equal to	the fraction that watches no TV daily	plus	the fraction that watches 1 hour of TV daily	plus	the fraction that watches 2 hours of TV daily.
The fraction of the student body that watches from 0 to 2 hours of TV daily	$=$	$\frac{1}{6}$	$+$	$\frac{1}{4}$	$+$	$\frac{7}{15}$

Solve We must find the sum of three fractions with different denominators. To find the LCD, we prime factor the denominators and use each prime factor the *greatest* number of times it appears in any one factorization:

$$\left.\begin{aligned} 6 &= 2 \cdot \textcircled{3} \\ 4 &= \textcircled{2 \cdot 2} \\ 15 &= 3 \cdot \textcircled{5} \end{aligned}\right\} \text{LCD} = 2 \cdot 2 \cdot 3 \cdot 5 = 60$$

2 appears twice in the factorization of 4.
3 appears once in the factorization of 6 and 15.
5 appears once in the factorization of 15.

The LCD for $\frac{1}{6}$, $\frac{1}{4}$, and $\frac{7}{15}$ is 60.

$$\frac{1}{6} + \frac{1}{4} + \frac{7}{15} = \frac{1}{6} \cdot \frac{10}{10} + \frac{1}{4} \cdot \frac{15}{15} + \frac{7}{15} \cdot \frac{4}{4}$$ Build each fraction so that its denominator is 60.

$$= \frac{10}{60} + \frac{15}{60} + \frac{28}{60}$$ Multiply the numerators. Multiply the denominators. The denominators are now the same.

$$= \frac{10 + 15 + 28}{60}$$ Add the numerators and write the sum over the common denominator 60.

$$= \frac{53}{60}$$ This fraction is in simplest form.

$$\begin{array}{r} \overset{1}{1}0 \\ 15 \\ +\,28 \\ \hline 53 \end{array}$$

State The fraction of the student body that watches 0 to 2 hours of TV daily is $\frac{53}{60}$.

Check We can check by estimation. The result, $\frac{53}{60}$, is approximately $\frac{50}{60}$, which simplifies to $\frac{5}{6}$. The red, yellow, and blue shaded areas appear to shade about $\frac{5}{6}$ of the pie chart. The result seems reasonable.

ANSWERS TO SELF CHECKS

1. a. $\frac{1}{2}$ **b.** $\frac{7}{9}$ **2.** $-\frac{6}{11}$ **3.** $\frac{2}{3}$ **4.** $\frac{9}{10}$ **5.** $\frac{9}{35}$ **6.** $-\frac{3}{2}$ **7.** $-\frac{45}{8}$ **8.** $\frac{23}{24}$ **9.** $\frac{3}{20}$ **10.** $\frac{3}{5}$ **11.** $\frac{7}{12}$

THINK IT THROUGH *Budgets*

"Putting together a budget is crucial if you don't want to spend your way into serious problems. You're also developing a habit that can serve you well throughout your life."

Liz Pulliam Weston, MSN Money

The circle graph below shows a suggested budget for new college graduates as recommended by Springboard, a nonprofit consumer credit counseling service. What fraction of net take-home pay should be spent on housing? $\frac{7}{20}$

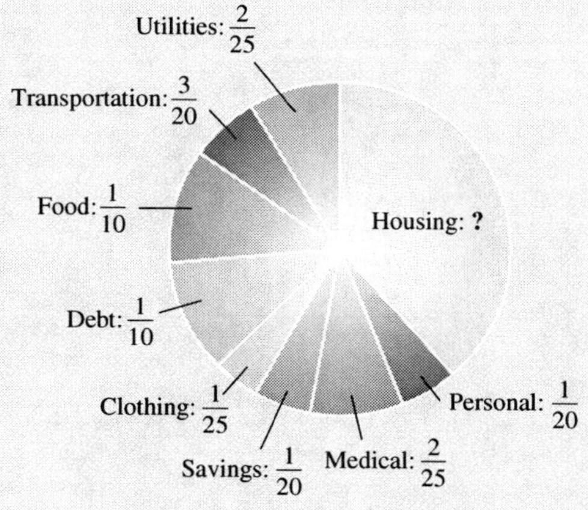

SECTION 2.4 STUDY SET

VOCABULARY

Fill in the blanks.

1. Because the denominators of $\frac{3}{8}$ and $\frac{7}{8}$ are the same number, we say that they have a _common_ denominator.
2. The _least_ common denominator for a set of fractions is the smallest number each denominator will divide exactly (no remainder).
3. Consider the solution below. To _build_ an equivalent fraction with a denominator of 18, we multiply $\frac{4}{9}$ by a 1 in the form of $\frac{2}{2}$.

$$\frac{4}{9} = \frac{4}{9} \cdot \frac{2}{2}$$
$$= \frac{8}{18}$$

4. Consider the solution below. To _simplify_ the fraction $\frac{15}{27}$, we factor 15 and 27, and then remove the common factor of 3 from the _numerator_ and the _denominator_.

$$\frac{15}{27} = \frac{\overset{1}{\cancel{3}} \cdot 5}{\underset{1}{\cancel{3}} \cdot 3 \cdot 3}$$
$$= \frac{5}{9}$$

CONCEPTS

Fill in the blanks.

5. To add (or subtract) fractions that have the same denominator, add (or subtract) their _numerators_ and write the sum (or difference) over the _common_ denominator. _Simplify_ the result, if possible.
6. To add (or subtract) fractions that have different denominators, we express each fraction as an equivalent fraction that has the _LCD_ for its denominator. Then we use the rule for adding (subtracting) fractions that have the _same_ denominator.
7. When adding (or subtracting) two fractions with different denominators, if the smaller denominator is a factor of the larger denominator, the _larger_ denominator is the LCD.

8. Write the subtraction as addition of the opposite:

$$-\frac{1}{8} - \left(-\frac{5}{8}\right) = -\frac{1}{8} + \frac{5}{8}$$

▶ 9. Consider $\frac{3}{4}$. By what form of 1 should we multiply the numerator and denominator to express it as an equivalent fraction with a denominator of 36? $\frac{9}{9}$

10. The *denominators* of two fractions are given. Find the least common denominator.
    - **a.** 2 and 3 6
    - **b.** 3 and 5 15
    - **c.** 4 and 8 8
    - **d.** 6 and 36 36

11. Consider the following prime factorizations:

$$24 = 2 \cdot 2 \cdot 2 \cdot 3$$
$$90 = 2 \cdot 3 \cdot 3 \cdot 5$$

For any one factorization, what is the greatest number of times
   - **a.** a 5 appears? once
   - **b.** a 3 appears? twice
   - **c.** a 2 appears? three times

12. The *denominators* of two fractions have their prime-factored forms shown below. Fill in the blanks to find the LCD for the fractions.

$$\left.\begin{aligned} 20 &= 2 \cdot 2 \cdot 5 \\ 30 &= 2 \cdot 3 \cdot 5 \end{aligned}\right\} \text{LCD} = 2 \cdot 2 \cdot 3 \cdot 5 = 60$$

13. The *denominators* of three fractions have their prime-factored forms shown below. Fill in the blanks to find the LCD for the fractions.

$$\left.\begin{aligned} 20 &= 2 \cdot 2 \cdot 5 \\ 30 &= 2 \cdot 3 \cdot 5 \\ 90 &= 2 \cdot 3 \cdot 3 \cdot 5 \end{aligned}\right\} \text{LCD} = 2 \cdot 2 \cdot 3 \cdot 3 \cdot 5 = 180$$

14. Place a > or < symbol in the blank to make a true statement.
    - **a.** $\frac{32}{35} > \frac{31}{35}$
    - **b.** $-\frac{13}{17} < -\frac{11}{17}$

▶ Selected exercises available online at **www.webassign.net/brookscole**

NOTATION

Fill in the blanks to complete each solution.

15. $\frac{2}{5}+\frac{1}{7}=\frac{2}{5}\cdot\frac{7}{\square}+\frac{1}{7}\cdot\frac{5}{5}$

$=\frac{\square}{35}+\frac{5}{35}$

$=\frac{\square+\square}{35}$

$=\frac{\square}{35}$

▶ **16.** $\frac{7}{8}-\frac{2}{3}=\frac{7}{8}\cdot\frac{3}{3}-\frac{2}{3}\cdot\frac{\square}{\square}$

$=\frac{21}{\square}-\frac{16}{\square}$

$=\frac{21-16}{\square}$

$=\frac{\square}{24}$

GUIDED PRACTICE

Perform each operation and simplify, if possible. See Example 1.

17. $\frac{4}{9}+\frac{1}{9}$ $\frac{5}{9}$

▶ **18.** $\frac{3}{7}+\frac{1}{7}$ $\frac{4}{7}$

19. $\frac{3}{8}+\frac{1}{8}$ $\frac{1}{2}$

20. $\frac{7}{12}+\frac{1}{12}$ $\frac{2}{3}$

21. $\frac{11}{15}-\frac{7}{15}$ $\frac{4}{15}$

▶ **22.** $\frac{10}{21}-\frac{5}{21}$ $\frac{5}{21}$

23. $\frac{11}{20}-\frac{3}{20}$ $\frac{2}{5}$

24. $\frac{7}{18}-\frac{5}{18}$ $\frac{1}{9}$

Subtract and simplify, if possible. See Example 2.

25. $-\frac{11}{5}-\left(-\frac{8}{5}\right)$ $-\frac{3}{5}$

26. $-\frac{15}{9}-\left(-\frac{11}{9}\right)$ $-\frac{4}{9}$

27. $-\frac{7}{21}-\left(-\frac{2}{21}\right)$ $-\frac{5}{21}$

▶ **28.** $-\frac{21}{25}-\left(-\frac{9}{25}\right)$ $-\frac{12}{25}$

Perform the operations and simplify, if possible. See Example 3.

29. $\frac{19}{40}-\frac{3}{40}-\frac{1}{40}$ $\frac{3}{8}$

30. $\frac{11}{24}-\frac{1}{24}-\frac{7}{24}$ $\frac{1}{8}$

31. $\frac{13}{33}+\frac{1}{33}+\frac{7}{33}$ $\frac{7}{11}$

▶ **32.** $\frac{21}{50}+\frac{1}{50}+\frac{13}{50}$ $\frac{7}{10}$

Add and simplify, if possible. See Example 4.

33. $\frac{1}{3}+\frac{1}{7}$ $\frac{10}{21}$

34. $\frac{1}{4}+\frac{1}{5}$ $\frac{9}{20}$

35. $\frac{2}{5}+\frac{1}{2}$ $\frac{9}{10}$

▶ **36.** $\frac{2}{7}+\frac{1}{2}$ $\frac{11}{14}$

Subtract and simplify, if possible. See Example 5.

37. $\frac{4}{5}-\frac{3}{4}$ $\frac{1}{20}$

▶ **38.** $\frac{2}{3}-\frac{3}{5}$ $\frac{1}{15}$

39. $\frac{3}{4}-\frac{2}{7}$ $\frac{13}{28}$

40. $\frac{6}{7}-\frac{2}{3}$ $\frac{4}{21}$

Subtract and simplify, if possible. See Example 6.

41. $\frac{11}{12}-\frac{2}{3}$ $\frac{1}{4}$

42. $\frac{11}{18}-\frac{1}{6}$ $\frac{4}{9}$

43. $\frac{9}{14}-\frac{1}{7}$ $\frac{1}{2}$

▶ **44.** $\frac{13}{15}-\frac{2}{3}$ $\frac{1}{5}$

Add and simplify, if possible. See Example 7.

45. $-2+\frac{5}{9}$ $-\frac{13}{9}$

46. $-3+\frac{5}{8}$ $-\frac{19}{8}$

47. $-3+\frac{9}{4}$ $-\frac{3}{4}$

▶ **48.** $-1+\frac{7}{10}$ $-\frac{3}{10}$

Add and simplify, if possible. See Example 8.

49. $\frac{1}{6}+\frac{5}{8}$ $\frac{19}{24}$

50. $\frac{7}{12}+\frac{3}{8}$ $\frac{23}{24}$

51. $\frac{4}{9}+\frac{5}{12}$ $\frac{31}{36}$

▶ **52.** $\frac{1}{9}+\frac{5}{6}$ $\frac{17}{18}$

Subtract and simplify, if possible. See Example 9.

53. $\frac{9}{10}-\frac{3}{14}$ $\frac{24}{35}$

54. $\frac{11}{12}-\frac{11}{30}$ $\frac{11}{20}$

55. $\frac{11}{12}-\frac{7}{15}$ $\frac{9}{20}$

▶ **56.** $\frac{7}{15}-\frac{5}{12}$ $\frac{1}{20}$

Determine which fraction is larger. See Example 10.

57. $\frac{3}{8}$ or $\frac{5}{16}$ $\frac{3}{8}$

▶ **58.** $\frac{5}{6}$ or $\frac{7}{12}$ $\frac{5}{6}$

59. $\frac{4}{5}$ or $\frac{2}{3}$ $\frac{4}{5}$

60. $\frac{7}{9}$ or $\frac{4}{5}$ $\frac{4}{5}$

61. $\frac{7}{9}$ or $\frac{11}{12}$ $\frac{11}{12}$

62. $\frac{3}{8}$ or $\frac{5}{12}$ $\frac{5}{12}$

63. $\frac{23}{20}$ or $\frac{7}{6}$ $\frac{7}{6}$

▶ **64.** $\frac{19}{15}$ or $\frac{5}{4}$ $\frac{19}{15}$

Add and simplify, if possible. See Example 11.

65. $\frac{1}{6}+\frac{5}{18}+\frac{2}{9}$ $\frac{2}{3}$

▶ **66.** $\frac{1}{10}+\frac{1}{8}+\frac{1}{5}$ $\frac{17}{40}$

67. $\frac{4}{15}+\frac{2}{3}+\frac{1}{6}$ $\frac{11}{10}$

68. $\frac{1}{2}+\frac{3}{5}+\frac{3}{20}$ $\frac{5}{4}$

TRY IT YOURSELF

Perform each operation.

69. $-\frac{1}{12}-\left(-\frac{5}{12}\right)$ $\frac{1}{3}$

70. $-\frac{1}{16}-\left(-\frac{15}{16}\right)$ $\frac{7}{8}$

71. $\frac{4}{5}+\frac{2}{3}$ $\frac{22}{15}$

72. $\frac{1}{4}+\frac{2}{3}$ $\frac{11}{12}$

73. $\frac{12}{25}-\frac{1}{25}-\frac{1}{25}$ $\frac{2}{5}$

74. $\frac{7}{9}+\frac{1}{9}+\frac{1}{9}$ 1

75. $-\frac{7}{20}-\frac{1}{5}$ $-\frac{11}{20}$

76. $-\frac{5}{8}-\frac{1}{3}$ $-\frac{23}{24}$

77. $-\frac{7}{16}+\frac{1}{4}$ $-\frac{3}{16}$

▶ **78.** $-\frac{17}{20}+\frac{4}{5}$ $-\frac{1}{20}$

79. $\frac{11}{12}-\frac{2}{3}$ $\frac{1}{4}$

80. $\frac{2}{3}-\frac{1}{6}$ $\frac{1}{2}$

81. $\frac{2}{3}+\frac{4}{5}+\frac{5}{6}$ $\frac{23}{10}$

82. $\frac{3}{4}+\frac{2}{5}+\frac{3}{10}$ $\frac{29}{20}$

83. $\frac{9}{20}-\frac{1}{30}$ $\frac{5}{12}$

84. $\frac{5}{6}-\frac{3}{10}$ $\frac{8}{15}$

85. $\frac{27}{50}+\frac{5}{16}$ $\frac{341}{400}$

86. $\frac{49}{50}-\frac{15}{16}$ $\frac{17}{400}$

87. $\frac{13}{20}-\frac{1}{5}$ $\frac{9}{20}$

▶ **88.** $\frac{71}{100}-\frac{1}{10}$ $\frac{61}{100}$

89. $\frac{37}{103}-\frac{17}{103}$ $\frac{20}{103}$

▶ **90.** $\frac{54}{53}-\frac{52}{53}$ $\frac{2}{53}$

91. $-\frac{3}{4}-5$ $-\frac{23}{4}$

▶ **92.** $-2-\frac{7}{8}$ $-\frac{23}{8}$

93. $\frac{4}{27}+\frac{1}{6}$ $\frac{17}{54}$

94. $\frac{8}{9}-\frac{7}{12}$ $\frac{11}{36}$

95. $\frac{7}{30}-\frac{19}{75}$ $-\frac{1}{50}$

▶ **96.** $\frac{73}{75}-\frac{31}{30}$ $-\frac{3}{50}$

97. Find the difference of $\frac{11}{60}$ and $\frac{2}{45}$. $\frac{5}{36}$

98. Find the sum of $\frac{9}{48}$ and $\frac{7}{40}$. $\frac{29}{80}$

99. Subtract $\frac{5}{12}$ from $\frac{2}{15}$. $-\frac{17}{60}$

100. What is the sum of $\frac{11}{24}$ and $\frac{7}{36}$ increased by $\frac{5}{48}$? $\frac{109}{144}$

APPLICATIONS

101. BOTANY To determine the effects of smog on tree development, a scientist cut down a pine tree and measured the width of the growth rings for the last two years.

a. What was the growth over this two-year period? $\frac{7}{32}$ in.

b. What is the difference in the widths of the two rings? $\frac{3}{32}$ in.

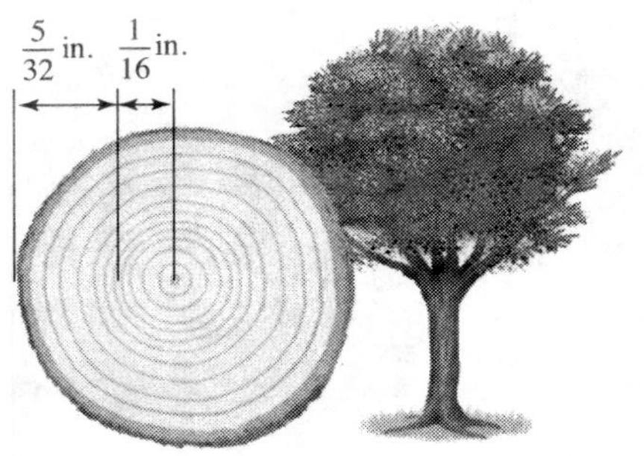

▶ **102.** GARAGE DOOR OPENERS What is the difference in strength between a $\frac{1}{3}$-hp and a $\frac{1}{2}$-hp garage door opener? $\frac{1}{6}$ hp

103. MAGAZINE COVERS The page design for the magazine cover shown below includes a blank strip at the top, called a *header*, and a blank strip at the bottom of the page, called a *footer*. How much page length is lost because of the header and footer? $\frac{11}{16}$ in.

▶ **104.** DELIVERY TRUCKS A truck can safely carry a one-ton load. Should it be used to deliver one-half ton of sand, one-third ton of gravel, and one-fifth ton of cement in one trip to a job site? No

105. DINNERS A family bought two large pizzas for dinner. Some pieces of each pizza were not eaten, as shown.

a. What fraction of the first pizza was not eaten? $\frac{3}{8}$

b. What fraction of the second pizza was not eaten? $\frac{2}{6} = \frac{1}{3}$

c. What fraction of a pizza was left? $\frac{17}{24}$ of a pizza was left

d. Could the family have been fed with just one pizza? no

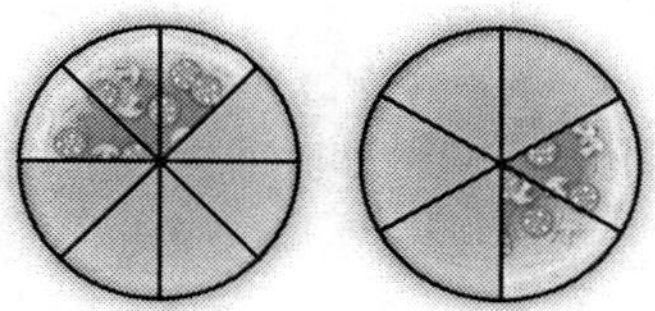

106. GASOLINE BARRELS Three identical-sized barrels are shown below. If their contents of the two of the barrels are poured into the empty third barrel, what fraction of the third barrel will be filled? $\frac{17}{20}$

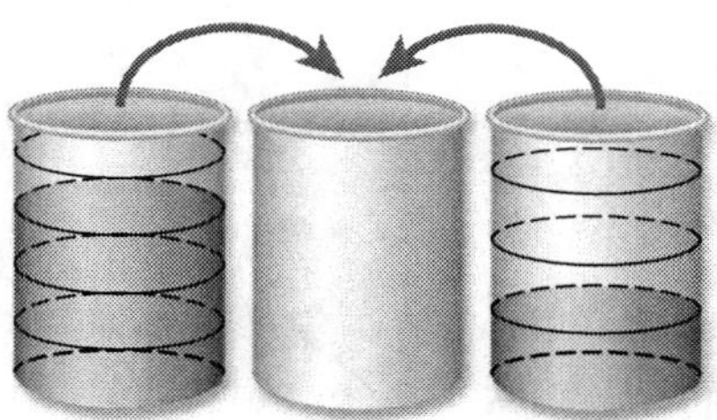

107. WEIGHTS AND MEASURES A consumer protection agency determines the accuracy of butcher shop scales by placing a known three-quarter-pound weight on the scale and then comparing that to the scale's readout. According to the illustration, by how much is this scale off? Does it result in undercharging or overcharging customers on their meat purchases? $\frac{1}{16}$ lb, undercharge

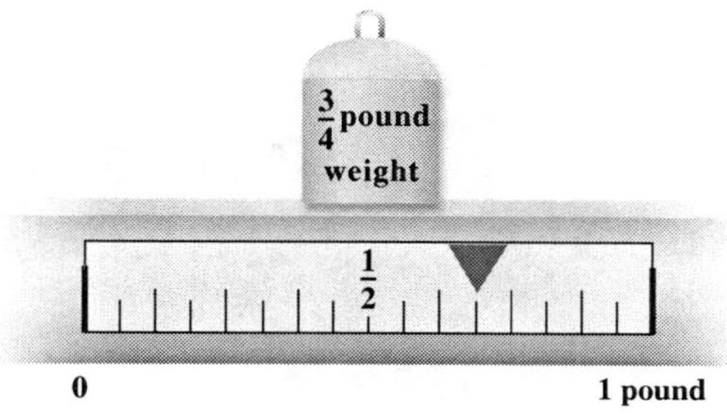

108. FIGURE DRAWING As an aid in drawing the human body, artists divide the body into three parts. Each part is then expressed as a fraction of the total body height. For example, the torso is $\frac{4}{15}$ of the body height. What fraction of body height is the head? $\frac{2}{15}$

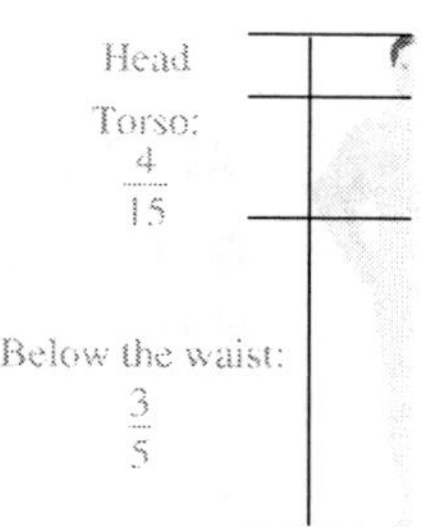

109. Suppose you work as a school guidance counselor at a community college and your department has conducted a survey of the full-time students to learn more about their study habits. As part of a *Power Point* presentation of the survey results to the school board, you show the following circle graph. At that time, you are asked, "What fraction of the full-time students study 2 hours or more daily?" What would you answer? $\frac{7}{10}$ of the full-time students study 2 or more hours a day.

from Campus to Careers

School Guidance Counselor

iStockphoto.com/Monkeybusinessimages

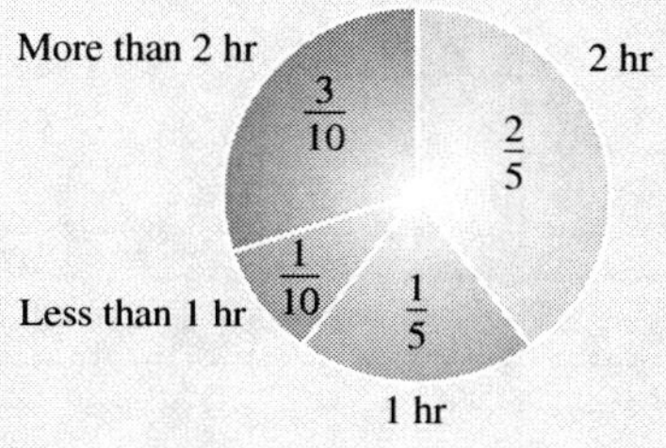

110. HEALTH STATISTICS The circle graph below shows the leading causes of death in the United States for 2006. For example, $\frac{13}{50}$ of all of the deaths that year were caused by heart disease. What fraction of all the deaths were caused by heart disease, cancer, or stroke, combined? $\frac{14}{25}$

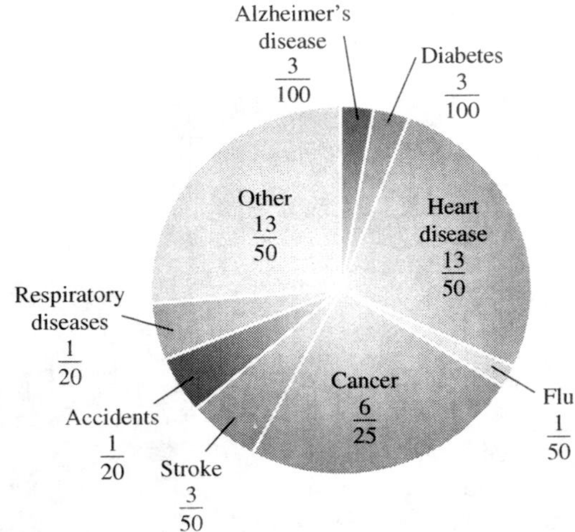

Source: National Center for Health Statistics

111. MUSICAL NOTES The notes used in music have fractional values. Their names and the symbols used to represent them are shown in illustration (a). In common time, the values of the notes in each measure must add to 1. Is the measure in illustration (b) complete? no

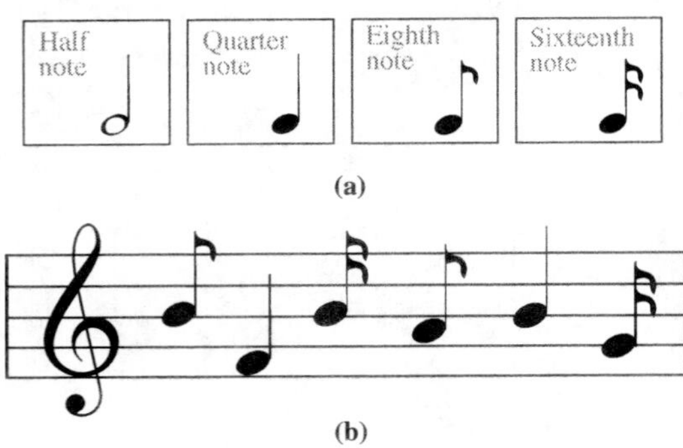

(a)

(b)

112. TOOLS A mechanic likes to hang his wrenches above his tool bench in order of narrowest to widest. What is the proper order of the wrenches in the illustration? $\frac{5}{32}, \frac{3}{16}, \frac{1}{4}, \frac{3}{8}$

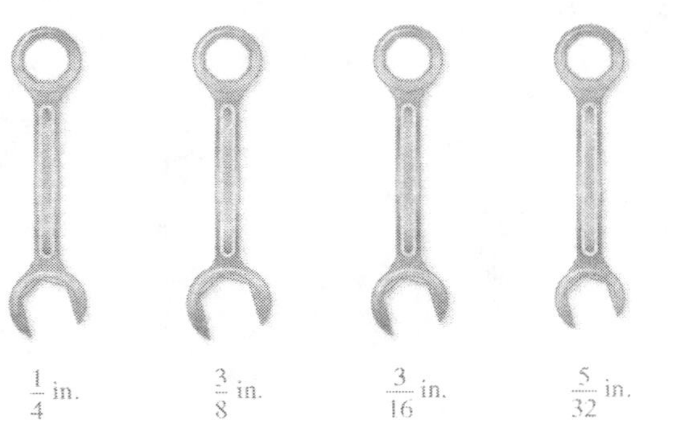

113. TIRE TREAD A mechanic measured the tire tread depth on each of the tires on a car and recorded them on the form shown below. (The letters LF stand for *left front*, RR stands for *right rear*, and so on.)

a. Which tire has the most tread? RR: right rear

b. Which tire has the least tread? LR: left rear

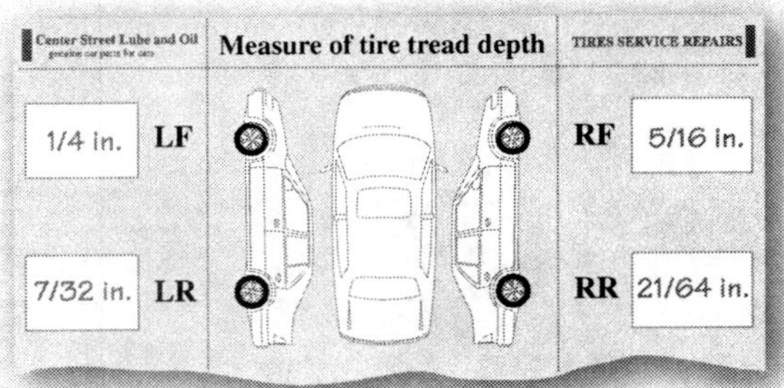

114. HIKING The illustration below shows the length of each part of a three-part hike. Rank the lengths of the parts from longest to shortest. $\frac{4}{5}, \frac{3}{4}, \frac{5}{8}$

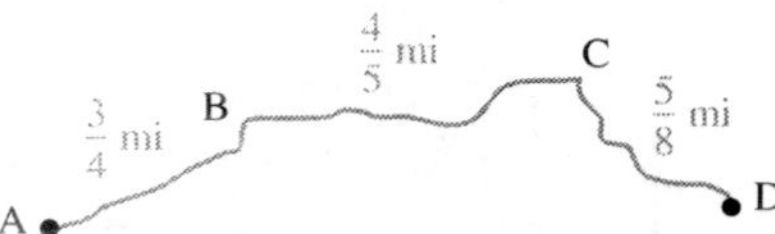

WRITING

115. Explain why we cannot add or subtract the fractions $\frac{2}{9}$ and $\frac{2}{5}$ as they are written.

116. To multiply fractions, must they have the same denominators? Explain why or why not. Give an example.

REVIEW

Perform each operation and simplify, if possible.

117. a. $\frac{1}{4} + \frac{1}{8}$ $\frac{3}{8}$ **b.** $\frac{1}{4} - \frac{1}{8}$ $\frac{1}{8}$

c. $\frac{1}{4} \cdot \frac{1}{8}$ $\frac{1}{32}$ **d.** $\frac{1}{4} \div \frac{1}{8}$ 2

118. a. $\frac{5}{21} + \frac{3}{14}$ $\frac{19}{42}$ **b.** $\frac{5}{21} - \frac{3}{14}$ $\frac{1}{42}$

c. $\frac{5}{21} \cdot \frac{3}{14}$ $\frac{5}{98}$ **d.** $\frac{5}{21} \div \frac{3}{14}$ $\frac{10}{9}$

SECTION 2.5

Multiplying and Dividing Mixed Numbers

Objectives

1. Identify the whole-number and fractional parts of a mixed number.
2. Write mixed numbers as improper fractions.
3. Write improper fractions as mixed numbers.
4. Graph fractions and mixed numbers on a number line.
5. Multiply and divide mixed numbers.
6. Solve application problems by multiplying and dividing mixed numbers.

In the next two sections, we show how to add, subtract, multiply, and divide *mixed numbers*. These numbers are widely used in daily life.

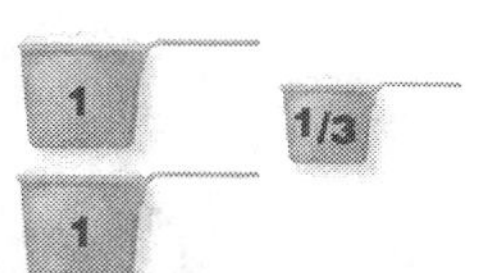

The recipe calls for $2\frac{1}{3}$ cups of flour.
(Read as "two and one-third.")

It took $3\frac{3}{4}$ hours to paint the living room.
(Read as "three and three-fourths.")

The entrance to the park is $1\frac{1}{2}$ miles away.
(Read as "one and one-half.")

1 Identify the whole-number and fractional parts of a mixed number.

A **mixed number** is the *sum* of a whole number and a proper fraction. For example, $3\frac{3}{4}$ is a mixed number.

$$3\frac{3}{4} = 3 + \frac{3}{4}$$

Mixed number — Whole-number part — Fractional part

Mixed numbers can be represented by shaded regions. In the illustration below, each rectangular region outlined in black represents one whole. To represent $3\frac{3}{4}$, we shade 3 *whole* rectangular regions and 3 out of 4 *parts* of another.

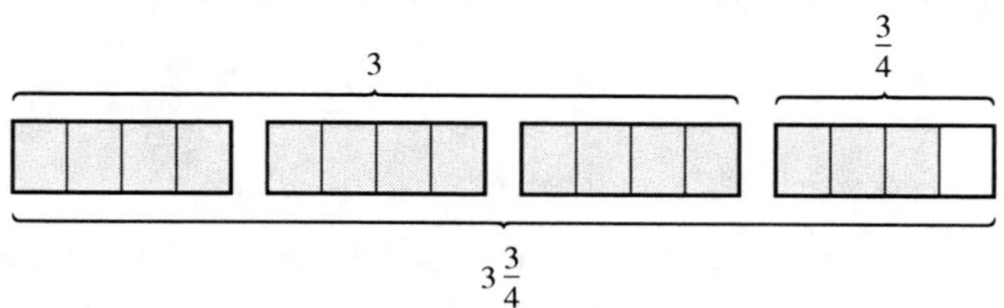

> ***Caution!*** Note that $3\frac{3}{4}$ means $3 + \frac{3}{4}$, even though the + symbol is not written. Do not confuse $3\frac{3}{4}$ with $3 \cdot \frac{3}{4}$ or $3\left(\frac{3}{4}\right)$, which indicate the multiplication of 3 by $\frac{3}{4}$.

EXAMPLE 1 In the illustration below, each disk represents one whole. Write an improper fraction and a mixed number to represent the shaded portion.

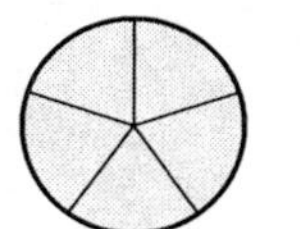 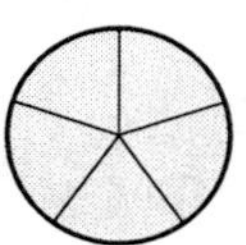 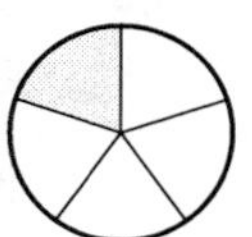

Strategy We will determine the number of equal parts into which a disk is divided. Then we will determine how many of those *parts* are shaded and how many of the *whole* disks are shaded.

Self Check 1

In the illustration below, each oval region represents one whole. Write an improper fraction and a mixed number to represent the shaded portion. $\frac{9}{2}$, $4\frac{1}{2}$

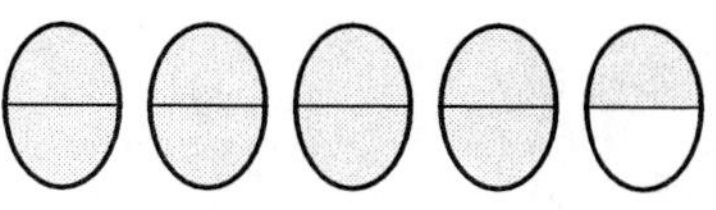

Now Try **Problem 19**

Teaching Example 1 In the illustration below, each disk represents one whole. Write an improper fraction and a mixed number to represent the shaded portion.

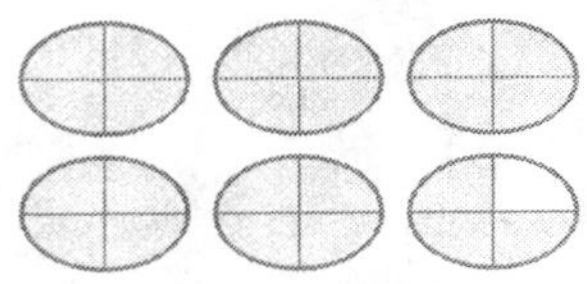

Answer:
$\frac{23}{4}$, $5\frac{3}{4}$

WHY To write an improper fraction, we need to find its numerator and its denominator. To write a mixed number, we need to find its whole number part and its fractional part.

Solution

Since each disk is divided into 5 equal parts, the denominator of the improper fraction is 5. Since a total of 11 of those parts are shaded, the numerator is 11, and we say that

$\frac{11}{5}$ is shaded. Write: $\frac{\text{total number of parts shaded}}{\text{number of equal parts in one disk}}$

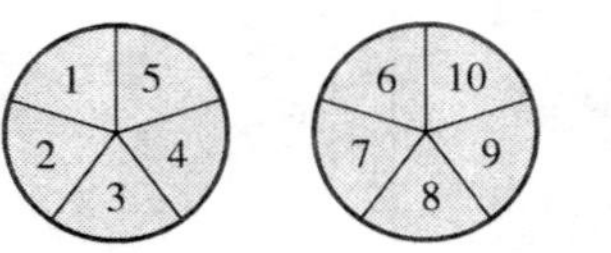

Since 2 whole disks are shaded, the whole number part of the mixed number is 2. Since 1 out of 5 of the parts of the last disk is shaded, the fractional part of the mixed number is $\frac{1}{5}$, and we say that

$2\frac{1}{5}$ is shaded.

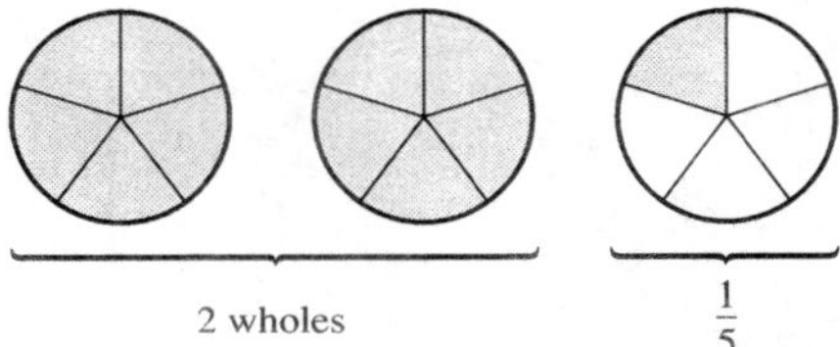

In this section, we will work with negative as well as positive mixed numbers. For example, the negative mixed number $-3\frac{3}{4}$ could be used to represent $3\frac{3}{4}$ feet below sea level. Think of $-3\frac{3}{4}$ as $-3 - \frac{3}{4}$ or as $-3 + \left(-\frac{3}{4}\right)$.

2 Write mixed numbers as improper fractions.

In Example 1, we saw that the shaded portion of the illustration can be represented by the mixed number $2\frac{1}{5}$ and by the improper fraction $\frac{11}{5}$. To develop a procedure to write any mixed number as an improper fraction, consider the following steps that show how to do this for $2\frac{1}{5}$. The objective is to find how many *fifths* that the mixed number $2\frac{1}{5}$ represents.

$$2\frac{1}{5} = 2 + \frac{1}{5}$$ Write the mixed number $2\frac{1}{5}$ as a sum.

$$= \frac{2}{1} + \frac{1}{5}$$ Write 2 as a fraction: $2 = \frac{2}{1}$.

$$= \frac{2}{1} \cdot \frac{5}{5} + \frac{1}{5}$$ To build $\frac{2}{1}$ so that its denominator is 5, multiply it by a form of 1.

$$= \frac{10}{5} + \frac{1}{5}$$ Multiply the numerators. Multiply the denominators.

$$= \frac{11}{5}$$ Add the numerators and write the sum over the common denominator 5.

Thus, $2\frac{1}{5} = \frac{11}{5}$.

We can obtain the same result with far less work. To change $2\frac{1}{5}$ to an improper fraction, we simply multiply 5 by 2 and add 1 to get the numerator, and keep the denominator of 5.

$$2\frac{1}{5} = \frac{5 \cdot 2 + 1}{5} = \frac{10 + 1}{5} = \frac{11}{5}$$

This example illustrates the following procedure.

Writing a Mixed Number as an Improper Fraction

To write a mixed number as an improper fraction:

1. Multiply the denominator of the fraction by the whole-number part.
2. Add the numerator of the fraction to the result from Step 1.
3. Write the sum from Step 2 over the original denominator.

EXAMPLE 2 Write the mixed number $7\frac{5}{6}$ as an improper fraction.

Strategy We will use the 3-step procedure to find the improper fraction.

WHY It's faster than writing $7\frac{5}{6}$ as $7 + \frac{5}{6}$, building to get an LCD, and adding.

Solution

To find the numerator of the improper fraction, multiply 6 by 7, and add 5 to that result. The denominator of the improper fraction is the same as the denominator of the fractional part of the mixed number.

Step 2: add

$$7\frac{5}{6} = \frac{6 \cdot 7 + 5}{6} = \frac{42 + 5}{6} = \frac{47}{6}$$

Step 1: multiply Step 3: Use the same denominator

By the order of operations rule, multiply first, and then add in the numerator.

Self Check 2

Write the mixed number $3\frac{3}{8}$ as an improper fraction. $\frac{27}{8}$

Now Try **Problems 23 and 27**

Teaching Example 2

Write the mixed number $4\frac{3}{9}$ as an improper fraction.

Answer:

$\frac{39}{9}$

To write a *negative mixed number* in fractional form, ignore the − sign and use the method shown in Example 2 on the positive mixed number. Once that procedure is completed, write a − sign in front of the result. For example,

$$-6\frac{1}{4} = -\frac{25}{4} \qquad -1\frac{9}{10} = -\frac{19}{10} \qquad -12\frac{3}{8} = -\frac{99}{8}$$

3 Write improper fractions as mixed numbers.

To write an improper fraction as a mixed number, we must find two things: the *whole-number part* and the *fractional part* of the mixed number. To develop a procedure to do this, let's consider the improper fraction $\frac{7}{3}$. To find the number of groups of 3 in 7, we can divide 7 by 3. This will find the whole-number part of the mixed number. The remainder is the numerator of the fractional part of the mixed number.

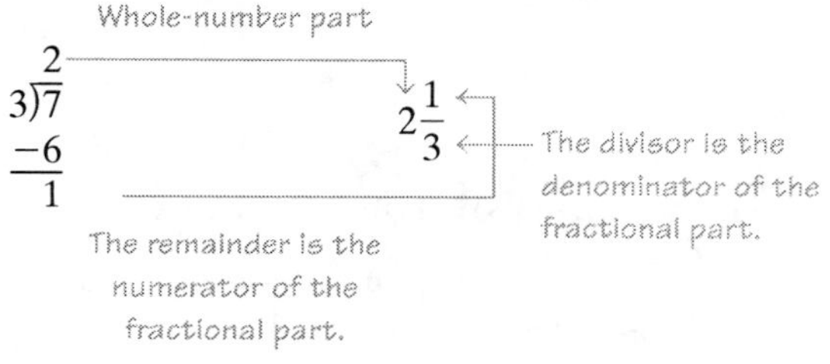

This example suggests the following procedure.

Writing an Improper Fraction as a Mixed Number

To write an improper fraction as a mixed number:

1. Divide the numerator by the denominator to obtain the whole-number part.
2. The remainder over the divisor is the fractional part.

Self Check 3

Write each improper fraction as a mixed number or a whole number:

a. $\frac{31}{7}$ $4\frac{3}{7}$ **b.** $\frac{50}{26}$ $1\frac{12}{13}$

c. $\frac{51}{3}$ 17 **d.** $-\frac{10}{3}$ $-3\frac{1}{3}$

Now Try **Problems 31, 35, 39, and 43**

Teaching Example 3

Write each improper fraction as a mixed number or a whole number:

a. $\frac{31}{9}$ b. $\frac{33}{6}$ c. $\frac{81}{3}$ d. $-\frac{9}{4}$

Answers:

a. $3\frac{4}{9}$ b. $5\frac{1}{2}$ c. 27 d. $-2\frac{1}{4}$

EXAMPLE 3 Write each improper fraction as a mixed number or a whole number: **a.** $\frac{29}{6}$ **b.** $\frac{40}{16}$ **c.** $\frac{84}{3}$ **d.** $-\frac{9}{5}$

Strategy We will divide the numerator by the denominator and write the remainder over the divisor.

WHY A fraction bar indicates division.

Solution

a. To write $\frac{29}{6}$ as a mixed number, divide 29 by 6:

$$\begin{array}{r} 4 \\ 6\overline{)29} \\ -24 \\ \hline 5 \end{array}$$

4 ← The whole-number part is 4.

5 ← Write the remainder 5 over the divisor 6 to get the fractional part.

Thus, $\frac{29}{6} = 4\frac{5}{6}$.

b. To write $\frac{40}{16}$ as a mixed number, divide 40 by 16:

$$\begin{array}{r} 2 \\ 16\overline{)40} \\ -32 \\ \hline 8 \end{array}$$

Thus, $\frac{40}{16} = 2\frac{8}{16} = 2\frac{1}{2}$. Simplify the fractional part: $\frac{8}{16} = \frac{\overset{1}{\cancel{8}}}{2 \cdot \underset{1}{\cancel{8}}} = \frac{1}{2}$.

c. For $\frac{84}{3}$, divide 84 by 3:

$$\begin{array}{r} 28 \\ 3\overline{)84} \\ -6 \\ \hline 24 \\ -24 \\ \hline 0 \end{array}$$

Thus, $\frac{84}{3} = 28$.

0 ← Since the remainder is 0, the improper fraction represents a whole number.

d. To write $-\frac{9}{5}$ as a mixed number, ignore the – sign, and use the method for the positive improper fraction $\frac{9}{5}$. Once that procedure is completed, write a – sign in front of the result.

$$\begin{array}{r} 1 \\ 5\overline{)9} \\ -5 \\ \hline 4 \end{array}$$

Thus, $-\frac{9}{5} = -1\frac{4}{5}$.

4 Graph fractions and mixed numbers on a number line.

In Chapters 1 and 2, we graphed whole numbers and integers on a number line. Fractions and mixed numbers can also be graphed on a number line.

EXAMPLE 4 Graph $-2\frac{3}{4}, -1\frac{1}{2}, -\frac{1}{8}$, and $\frac{13}{5}$ on a number line.

Strategy We will locate the position of each fraction and mixed number on the number line and draw a bold dot.

WHY To *graph a number* means to make a drawing that represents the number.

Solution

- Since $-2\frac{3}{4} < -2$, the graph of $-2\frac{3}{4}$ is to the left of -2 on the number line.
- The number $-1\frac{1}{2}$ is between -1 and -2.
- The number $-\frac{1}{8}$ is less than 0.
- Expressed as a mixed number, $\frac{13}{5} = 2\frac{3}{5}$.

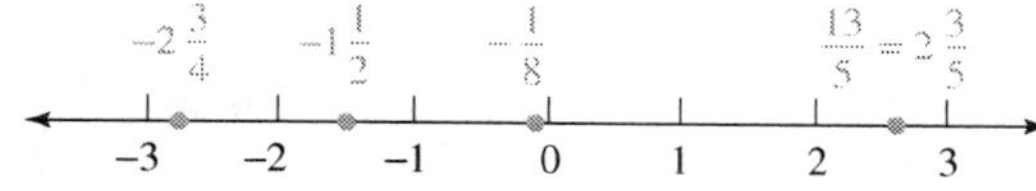

Self Check 4

Graph $-1\frac{7}{8}, -\frac{2}{3}, \frac{3}{5}$, and $\frac{9}{4}$ on a number line.

$-1\frac{7}{8}$ $-\frac{2}{3}$ $\frac{3}{5}$ $\frac{9}{4} = 2\frac{1}{4}$

−3 −2 −1 0 1 2 3

Now Try **Problem 47**

Teaching Example 4
Graph $-2\frac{1}{8}, \frac{9}{10}, -\frac{3}{4}$, and $\frac{8}{3}$ on a number line.
Answer:

$-2\frac{1}{8}$ $-\frac{3}{4}$ $\frac{9}{10}$ $\frac{8}{3} = 2\frac{2}{3}$

−3 −2 −1 0 1 2 3

5 Multiply and divide mixed numbers.

We will use the same procedures for multiplying and dividing mixed numbers as those that were used in Sections 2.2 and 2.3 to multiply and divide fractions. However, we must write the mixed numbers as improper fractions before we actually multiply or divide.

Multiplying and Dividing Mixed Numbers

To multiply or divide mixed numbers, first change the mixed numbers to improper fractions. Then perform the multiplication or division of the fractions. Write the result as a mixed number or a whole number in simplest form.

The sign rules for multiplying and dividing integers also hold for multiplying and dividing mixed numbers.

EXAMPLE 5 Multiply and simplify, if possible.

a. $1\frac{3}{4} \cdot 2\frac{1}{3}$ **b.** $5\frac{1}{5} \cdot \left(1\frac{2}{13}\right)$ **c.** $-4\frac{1}{9}(3)$

Strategy We will write the mixed numbers and whole numbers as improper fractions.

WHY Then we can use the rule for multiplying two fractions from Section 2.2.

Solution

a. $1\frac{3}{4} \cdot 2\frac{1}{3} = \frac{7}{4} \cdot \frac{7}{3}$ Write $1\frac{3}{4}$ and $2\frac{1}{3}$ as improper fractions.

$= \frac{7 \cdot 7}{4 \cdot 3}$ Use the rule for multiplying two fractions. Multiply the numerators and the denominators.

$= \frac{49}{12}$ Since there are no common factors to remove, perform the multiplication in the numerator and in the denominator. The result is an improper fraction.

$$\begin{array}{r} 4 \\ 12\overline{)49} \\ -48 \\ \hline 1 \end{array}$$

$= 4\frac{1}{12}$ Write the improper fraction $\frac{49}{12}$ as a mixed number.

Self Check 5

Multiply and simplify, if possible.

a. $3\frac{1}{3} \cdot 2\frac{1}{3}$ $7\frac{7}{9}$ **b.** $9\frac{3}{5} \cdot \left(3\frac{3}{4}\right)$ 36

c. $-4\frac{5}{6}(2)$ $-9\frac{2}{3}$

Now Try **Problems 51, 55, and 57**

Teaching Example 5
Multiply and simplify, if possible.

a. $2\frac{1}{3} \cdot 1\frac{1}{4}$ b. $3\frac{1}{2}\left(5\frac{3}{7}\right)$ c. $-4\frac{5}{6}(3)$

Answers:

a. $2\frac{11}{12}$ b. 19 c. $-14\frac{1}{2}$

b. $5\frac{1}{5}\left(1\frac{2}{13}\right) = \frac{26}{5} \cdot \frac{15}{13}$ Write $5\frac{1}{5}$ and $1\frac{2}{13}$ as improper fractions.

$= \frac{26 \cdot 15}{5 \cdot 13}$ Multiply the numerators. Multiply the denominators.

$= \frac{2 \cdot 13 \cdot 3 \cdot 5}{5 \cdot 13}$ To prepare to simplify, factor 26 as $2 \cdot 13$ and 15 as $3 \cdot 5$.

$= \frac{2 \cdot \overset{1}{\cancel{13}} \cdot 3 \cdot \overset{1}{\cancel{5}}}{\underset{1}{\cancel{5}} \cdot \underset{1}{\cancel{13}}}$ Remove the common factors of 13 and 5 from the numerator and denominator.

$= \frac{6}{1}$ Multiply the remaining factors in the numerator: $2 \cdot 1 \cdot 3 \cdot 1 = 6$. Multiply the remaining factors in the denominator: $1 \cdot 1 = 1$.

$= 6$ Any whole number divided by 1 remains the same.

c. $-4\frac{1}{9} \cdot 3 = -\frac{37}{9} \cdot \frac{3}{1}$ Write $-4\frac{1}{9}$ as an improper fraction and write 3 as a fraction.

$= -\frac{37 \cdot 3}{9 \cdot 1}$ Multiply the numerators and multiply the denominators. Since the fractions have unlike signs, make the answer negative.

$= -\frac{37 \cdot \overset{1}{\cancel{3}}}{\underset{1}{\cancel{3}} \cdot 3 \cdot 1}$ To simplify, factor 9 as $3 \cdot 3$, and then remove the common factor of 3 from the numerator and denominator.

$= -\frac{37}{3}$ Multiply the remaining factors in the numerator and in the denominator. The result is an improper fraction.

$= -12\frac{1}{3}$ Write the negative improper fraction $-\frac{37}{3}$ as a negative mixed number.

$$\begin{array}{r} 12 \\ 3\overline{)37} \\ \underline{-3} \\ 7 \\ \underline{-6} \\ 1 \end{array}$$

Success Tip We can use rounding to check the results when multiplying mixed numbers. If the fractional part of the mixed number is $\frac{1}{2}$ *or greater,* round up by adding 1 to the whole-number part and dropping the fraction. If the fractional part of the mixed number is less than $\frac{1}{2}$, round down by dropping the fraction and using only the whole-number part. To check the answer $4\frac{1}{12}$ from Example 5, part a, we proceed as follows:

$1\frac{3}{4} \cdot 2\frac{1}{3} \approx 2 \cdot 2 = 4$ Since $\frac{3}{4}$ is greater than $\frac{1}{2}$, round $1\frac{3}{4}$ up to 2. Since $\frac{1}{3}$ is less than $\frac{1}{2}$, round $2\frac{1}{3}$ down to 2.

Since $4\frac{1}{12}$ is close to 4, it is a reasonable answer.

Self Check 6

Divide and simplify, if possible:

a. $-3\frac{4}{15} \div \left(-2\frac{1}{10}\right)$ $1\frac{5}{9}$

b. $5\frac{3}{5} \div \frac{7}{8}$ $6\frac{2}{5}$

Now Try **Problems 59 and 65**

EXAMPLE 6

Divide and simplify, if possible:

a. $-3\frac{3}{8} \div \left(-2\frac{1}{4}\right)$ **b.** $1\frac{11}{16} \div \frac{3}{4}$

Strategy We will write the mixed numbers as improper fractions.

WHY Then we can use the rule for dividing two fractions from Section 2.3.

Solution

a. $-3\frac{3}{8} \div \left(-2\frac{1}{4}\right) = -\frac{27}{8} \div \left(-\frac{9}{4}\right)$ Write $-3\frac{3}{8}$ and $-2\frac{1}{4}$ as improper fractions.

$= -\frac{27}{8}\left(-\frac{4}{9}\right)$ Use the rule for dividing two fractions.: Multiply $-\frac{27}{8}$ by the reciprocal of $-\frac{9}{4}$, which is $-\frac{4}{9}$.

$= \frac{27}{8}\left(\frac{4}{9}\right)$ Since the product of two negative fractions is positive, drop both − signs and continue.

$= \frac{27 \cdot 4}{8 \cdot 9}$ Multiply the numerators. Multiply the denominators.

$= \frac{3 \cdot \overset{1}{\cancel{9}} \cdot \overset{1}{\cancel{4}}}{2 \cdot \underset{1}{\cancel{4}} \cdot \underset{1}{\cancel{9}}}$ To simplify, factor 27 as 3 · 9 and 8 as 2 · 4. Then remove the common factors of 9 and 4 from the numerator and denominator.

$= \frac{3}{2}$ Multiply the remaining factors in the numerator: 3 · 1 · 1 = 3. Multiply the remaining factors in the denominator: 2 · 1 · 1 = 2.

$= 1\frac{1}{2}$ Write the improper fraction $\frac{3}{2}$ as a mixed number by dividing 3 by 2.

b. $1\frac{11}{16} \div \frac{3}{4} = \frac{27}{16} \div \frac{3}{4}$ Write $1\frac{11}{16}$ as an improper fraction.

$= \frac{27}{16} \cdot \frac{4}{3}$ Multiply $\frac{27}{16}$ by the reciprocal of $\frac{3}{4}$, which is $\frac{4}{3}$.

$= \frac{27 \cdot 4}{16 \cdot 3}$ Multiply the numerators. Multiply the denominators.

$= \frac{\overset{1}{\cancel{3}} \cdot 9 \cdot \overset{1}{\cancel{4}}}{\underset{1}{\cancel{4}} \cdot 4 \cdot \underset{1}{\cancel{3}}}$ To simplify, factor 27 as 3 · 9 and 16 as 4 · 4. Then remove the common factors of 3 and 4 from the numerator and denominator.

$= \frac{9}{4}$ Multiply the remaining factors in the numerator and in the denominator. The result is an improper fraction.

$= 2\frac{1}{4}$ Write the improper fraction $\frac{9}{4}$ as a mixed number by dividing 9 by 4.

Teaching Example 6
Divide and simplify, if possible:

a. $-8\frac{1}{3} \div \left(-4\frac{4}{9}\right)$ b. $2\frac{11}{12} \div \frac{5}{6}$

Answers:

a. $1\frac{7}{8}$ b. $3\frac{1}{2}$

6 Solve application problems by multiplying and dividing mixed numbers.

EXAMPLE 7 *Toys* The dimensions of the rectangular-shaped screen of an Etch-a-Sketch are shown in the illustration below. Find the area of the screen.

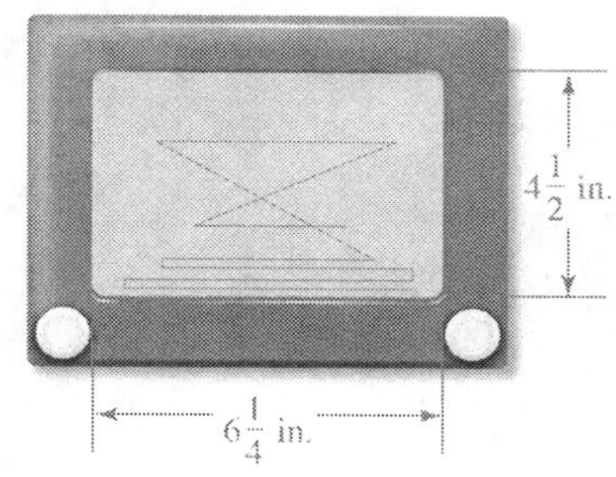

Strategy To find the area, we will multiply $6\frac{1}{4}$ by $4\frac{1}{2}$.

WHY The formula for the area of a rectangle is Area = length · width.

Self Check 7

BUMPER STICKERS A rectangular-shaped bumper sticker is $8\frac{1}{4}$ inches long by $3\frac{1}{4}$ inches wide. Find its area. $26\frac{13}{16}$ in.^{2}

Now Try **Problem 99**

Teaching Example 7 KLEENEX When unfolded and laid flat, a standard sheet of Kleenex brand tissue is $8\frac{1}{3}$ inches wide by $8\frac{2}{5}$ inches long. Find the area of a sheet of Kleenex.

Answer:

$68\frac{22}{25}$ in.^{2}

Solution

$A = lw$ — This is the formula for the area of a rectangle.

$= 6\frac{1}{4} \cdot 4\frac{1}{2}$ — Substitute $6\frac{1}{4}$ for l and $4\frac{1}{2}$ for w.

$= \frac{25}{4} \cdot \frac{9}{2}$ — Write $6\frac{1}{4}$ and $4\frac{1}{2}$ as improper fractions.

$= \frac{25 \cdot 9}{4 \cdot 2}$ — Multiply the numerators. Multiply the denominators.

$= \frac{225}{8}$ — Since there are no common factors to remove, perform the multiplication in the numerator and in the denominator. The result is an improper fraction.

$= 28\frac{1}{8}$ — Write the improper fraction $\frac{225}{8}$ as a mixed number.

$$\begin{array}{r} 28 \\ 8\overline{)225} \\ -16 \\ \hline 65 \\ -64 \\ \hline 1 \end{array}$$

The area of the screen of an Etch-a-Sketch is $28\frac{1}{8}$ in.^{2}.

Self Check 8

TV INTERVIEWS An $18\frac{3}{4}$-minute taped interview with an actor was played in equally long segments over 5 consecutive nights on a celebrity news program. How long was each interview segment? $3\frac{3}{4}$ min

Now Try **Problem 107**

Teaching Example 8 HIGHWAYS It took workers 3 days to paint the yellow centerline on a new $17\frac{1}{2}$-mile stretch of highway. If they covered the same distance each day, how much did they do in one day?
Answer:
$5\frac{5}{6}$ mi

EXAMPLE 8 *Government Grants* If $\$12\frac{1}{2}$ million is to be split equally among five cities to fund recreation programs, how much will each city receive?

Analyze

- There is $\$12\frac{1}{2}$ million in grant money. — *Given*
- 5 cities will split the money equally. — *Given*
- How much grant money will each city receive? — *Find*

Form The key phrase *split equally* suggests division.

We translate the words of the problem to numbers and symbols.

The amount of money that each city will receive (in millions of dollars)	is equal to	the total amount of grant money (in millions of dollars)	divided by	the number of cities receiving money.
The amount of money that each city will receive (in millions of dollars)	=	$12\frac{1}{2}$	÷	5

Solve To find the quotient, we will express $12\frac{1}{2}$ and 5 as fractions and then use the rule for dividing two fractions.

$12\frac{1}{2} \div 5 = \frac{25}{2} \div \frac{5}{1}$ — Write $12\frac{1}{2}$ as an improper fraction, and write 5 as a fraction.

$= \frac{25}{2} \cdot \frac{1}{5}$ — Multiply by the reciprocal of $\frac{5}{1}$, which is $\frac{1}{5}$.

$= \frac{25 \cdot 1}{2 \cdot 5}$ — Multiply the numerators. Multiply the denominators.

$= \frac{\overset{1}{\cancel{5}} \cdot 5 \cdot 1}{2 \cdot \underset{1}{\cancel{5}}}$ — To simplify, factor 25 as $5 \cdot 5$. Then remove the common factor of 5 from the numerator and denominator.

$= \frac{5}{2}$ — Multiply the remaining factors in the numerator. Multiply the remaining factors in the denominator.

$= 2\frac{1}{2}$ — Write the improper fraction $\frac{5}{2}$ as a mixed number by dividing 5 by 2. The units are in millions of dollars.

State Each city will receive $\$2\frac{1}{2}$ million in grant money.

Check We can estimate to check the result. If there was $10 million in grant money, each city would receive $\frac{\$10 \text{ million}}{5}$, or $2 million. Since there is actually $\$12\frac{1}{2}$ million in grant money, the answer that each city would receive $\$2\frac{1}{2}$ million seems reasonable.

ANSWERS TO SELF CHECKS

1. $\frac{9}{2}, 4\frac{1}{2}$ **2.** $\frac{27}{8}$ **3. a.** $4\frac{3}{7}$ **b.** $1\frac{12}{13}$ **c.** 17 **d.** $-3\frac{1}{3}$ **4.** Number line from −3 to 3 with points $-1\frac{7}{8}$, $-\frac{2}{3}$, $\frac{3}{5}$, $\frac{9}{4} = 2\frac{1}{4}$
5. a. $7\frac{7}{9}$ **b.** 36 **c.** $-9\frac{2}{3}$ **6. a.** $1\frac{5}{9}$ **b.** $6\frac{2}{5}$ **7.** $26\frac{13}{16}$ in.^{2} **8.** $3\frac{3}{4}$ min

SECTION 2.5 STUDY SET

VOCABULARY

Fill in the blanks.

1. A mixed number, such as $8\frac{4}{5}$, is the sum of a whole number and a proper fraction.

2. In the mixed number $8\frac{4}{5}$, the whole-number part is 8 and the fractional part is $\frac{4}{5}$.

▶ **3.** The numerator of an improper fraction is greater than or equal to its denominator.

4. To graph a number means to locate its position on the number line and highlight it using a dot.

CONCEPTS

5. What signed mixed number could be used to describe each situation?

a. A temperature of five and one-third degrees above zero $5\frac{1}{3}°$

b. The depth of a sprinkler pipe that is six and seven-eighths inches below the sidewalk $-6\frac{7}{8}$ in.

6. What signed mixed number could be used to describe each situation?

a. A rain total two and three-tenths of an inch lower than the average $-2\frac{3}{10}$ in.

b. Three and one-half minutes after the liftoff of a rocket $3\frac{1}{2}$ min

Fill in the blanks.

7. To write a mixed number as an improper fraction:

1. Multiply the denominator of the fraction by the whole-number part.

2. Add the numerator of the fraction to the result from Step 1.

3. Write the sum from Step 2 over the original denominator.

8. To write an improper fraction as a mixed number:

1. Divide the numerator by the denominator to obtain the whole-number part.

2. The remainder over the divisor is the fractional part.

9. What fractions have been graphed on the number line? $-\frac{4}{5}, -\frac{2}{5}, \frac{1}{5}$

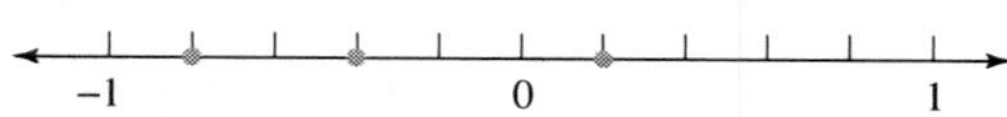

10. What mixed numbers have been graphed on the number line? $-1\frac{3}{4}, 1\frac{1}{4}$

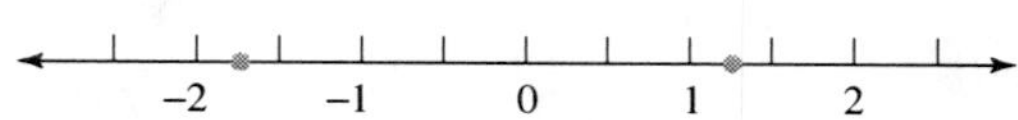

11. Fill in the blank: To multiply or divide mixed numbers, first change the mixed numbers to improper fractions. Then perform the multiplication or division of the fractions as usual.

12. Simplify the fractional part of each mixed number.

a. $11\frac{2}{4}$ $11\frac{1}{2}$

b. $1\frac{3}{9}$ $1\frac{1}{3}$

c. $7\frac{15}{27}$ $7\frac{5}{9}$

13. Use *estimation* to determine whether the following answer seems reasonable:

$$4\frac{1}{5} \cdot 2\frac{5}{7} = 7\frac{2}{35}$$ not reasonable: $4\frac{1}{5} \cdot 2\frac{5}{7} \approx 4 \cdot 3 = 12$

14. What is the formula for the

a. area of a rectangle? Area = (length)(width)

b. area of a triangle? Area = $\frac{1}{2}$(base)(height)

NOTATION

15. Fill in the blanks.

a. We read $5\frac{11}{16}$ as "five _and_ eleven-_sixteenths_."

b. We read $-4\frac{2}{3}$ as "_negative_ four and _two_-thirds."

16. Determine the sign of the result. *You do not have to find the answer.*

a. $1\frac{1}{9}\left(-7\frac{3}{14}\right)$ negative

b. $-3\frac{4}{15} \div \left(-1\frac{5}{6}\right)$ positive

Fill in the blanks to complete each solution.

17. Multiply: $5\frac{1}{4} \cdot 1\frac{1}{7}$

$$5\frac{1}{4} \cdot 1\frac{1}{7} = \frac{21}{4} \cdot \frac{8}{7}$$

$$= \frac{21 \cdot 8}{4 \cdot 7}$$

$$= \frac{3 \cdot \overset{1}{\cancel{7}} \cdot 2 \cdot \overset{1}{\cancel{4}}}{\underset{1}{\cancel{4}} \cdot \underset{1}{\cancel{7}}}$$

$$= \frac{6}{1}$$

$$= 6$$

▶ 18. Divide: $-5\frac{5}{6} \div 2\frac{1}{12}$

$$-5\frac{5}{6} \div 2\frac{1}{12} = -\frac{35}{6} \div \frac{25}{12}$$

$$= -\frac{35}{6} \cdot \frac{12}{25}$$

$$= -\frac{35 \cdot 12}{6 \cdot 25}$$

$$= -\frac{\overset{1}{\cancel{5}} \cdot 7 \cdot 2 \cdot \overset{1}{\cancel{6}}}{\underset{1}{\cancel{6}} \cdot \underset{1}{\cancel{5}} \cdot 5}$$

$$= -\frac{14}{5}$$

$$= -2\frac{4}{5}$$

GUIDED PRACTICE

Each region outlined in black represents one whole. Write an improper fraction and a mixed number to represent the shaded portion. See Example 1.

19. $\frac{19}{8}, 2\frac{3}{8}$

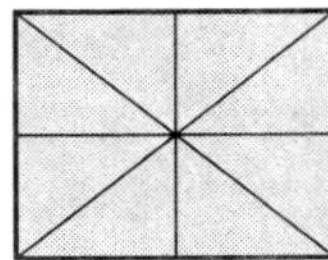
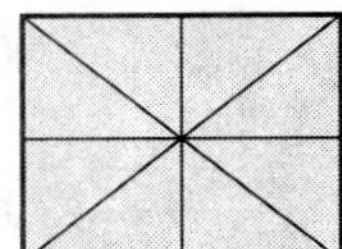
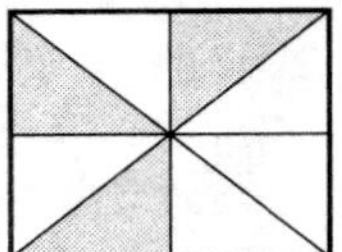

▶ 20. $\frac{29}{6}, 4\frac{5}{6}$

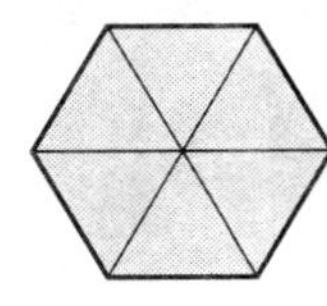
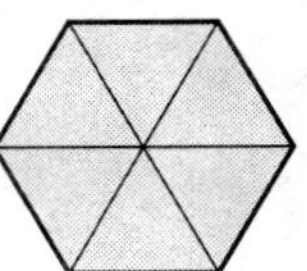
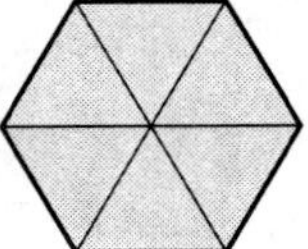
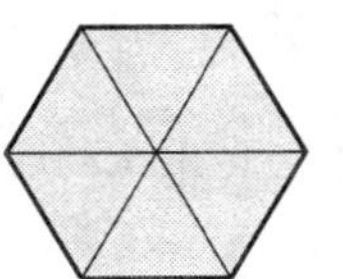
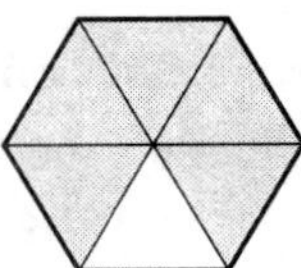

21. 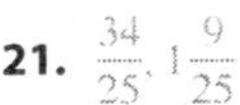 $\frac{34}{25}, 1\frac{9}{25}$

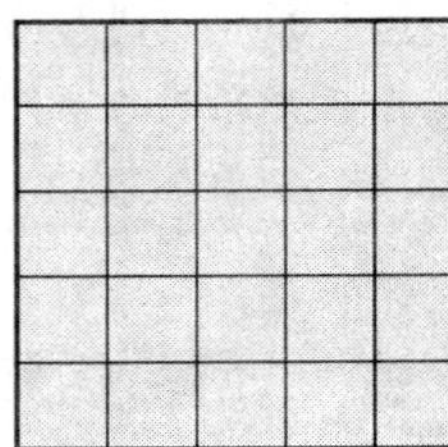
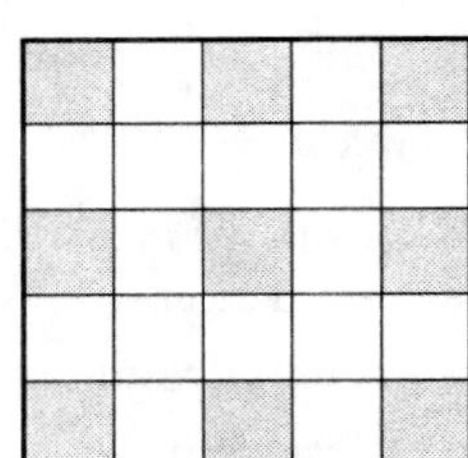

22. $\frac{51}{16}, 3\frac{3}{16}$

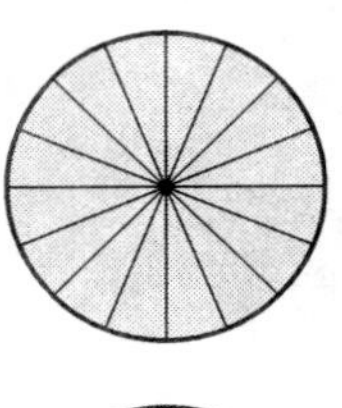
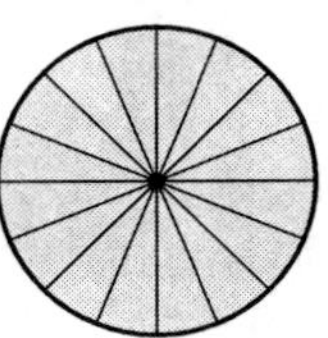
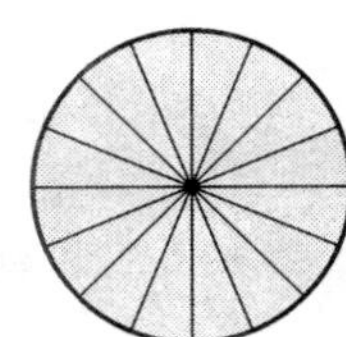
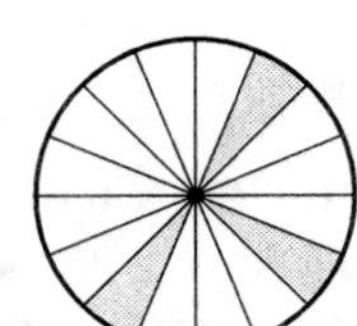

Write each mixed number as an improper fraction. See Example 2.

23. $6\frac{1}{2}$ $\frac{13}{2}$

24. $8\frac{2}{3}$ $\frac{26}{3}$

25. $20\frac{4}{5}$ $\frac{104}{5}$

▶ **26.** $15\frac{3}{8}$ $\frac{123}{8}$

27. $-7\frac{5}{9}$ $-\frac{68}{9}$

28. $-7\frac{1}{12}$ $-\frac{85}{12}$

29. $-8\frac{2}{3}$ $-\frac{26}{3}$

▶ **30.** $-9\frac{3}{4}$ $-\frac{39}{4}$

Write each improper fraction as a mixed number or a whole number. Simplify the result, if possible. See Example 3.

31. $\frac{13}{4}$ $3\frac{1}{4}$

32. $\frac{41}{6}$ $6\frac{5}{6}$

33. $\frac{28}{5}$ $5\frac{3}{5}$

▶ **34.** $\frac{28}{3}$ $9\frac{1}{3}$

35. $\frac{42}{9}$ $4\frac{2}{3}$

36. $\frac{62}{8}$ $7\frac{3}{4}$

37. $\frac{84}{8}$ $10\frac{1}{2}$

38. $\frac{93}{9}$ $10\frac{1}{3}$

39. $\frac{52}{13}$ 4

40. $\frac{80}{16}$ 5

41. $\frac{34}{17}$ 2

▶ **42.** $\frac{38}{19}$ 2

43. $-\frac{58}{7}$ $-8\frac{2}{7}$

44. $-\frac{33}{7}$ $-4\frac{5}{7}$

45. $-\frac{20}{6}$ $-3\frac{1}{3}$

▶ **46.** $-\frac{28}{8}$ $-3\frac{1}{2}$

Graph the given numbers on a number line. See Example 4.

47. $-2\frac{8}{9}, 1\frac{2}{3}, \frac{16}{5}, -\frac{1}{2}$

$-2\frac{8}{9}$ $-\frac{1}{2}$ $1\frac{2}{3}$ $\frac{16}{5}=3\frac{1}{5}$

▶ **48.** $-\frac{3}{4}, -3\frac{1}{4}, \frac{5}{2}, 4\frac{3}{4}$

$-3\frac{1}{4}$ $-\frac{3}{4}$ $\frac{5}{2}=2\frac{1}{2}$ $4\frac{3}{4}$

49. $3\frac{1}{7}, -\frac{98}{99}, -\frac{10}{3}, \frac{3}{2}$

$-\frac{10}{3}=-3\frac{1}{3}$ $-\frac{98}{99}$ $\frac{3}{2}=1\frac{1}{2}$ $3\frac{1}{7}$

50. $-2\frac{1}{5}, \frac{4}{5}, -\frac{11}{3}, \frac{17}{4}$

$-\frac{11}{3}=-3\frac{2}{3}$ $-2\frac{1}{5}$ $\frac{4}{5}$ $\frac{17}{4}=4\frac{1}{4}$

Multiply and simplify, if possible. See Example 5.

51. $3\frac{1}{2}\cdot 2\frac{1}{3}$ $8\frac{1}{6}$

52. $1\frac{5}{6}\cdot 1\frac{1}{2}$ $2\frac{3}{4}$

53. $2\frac{2}{5}\left(3\frac{1}{12}\right)$ $7\frac{2}{5}$

▶ **54.** $\frac{40}{16}\left(\frac{26}{5}\right)$ 16

55. $6\frac{1}{2}\cdot 1\frac{3}{13}$ 8

56. $12\frac{3}{5}\cdot 1\frac{3}{7}$ 18

57. $-2\frac{1}{2}(4)$ -10

▶ **58.** $-3\frac{3}{4}(8)$ -30

Divide and simplify, if possible. See Example 6.

59. $-1\frac{13}{15} \div \left(-4\frac{1}{5}\right)$ $\frac{4}{9}$

60. $-2\frac{5}{6} \div \left(-8\frac{1}{2}\right)$ $\frac{1}{3}$

61. $15\frac{1}{3} \div 2\frac{2}{9}$ $6\frac{9}{10}$

▶ **62.** $6\frac{1}{4} \div 3\frac{3}{4}$ $1\frac{2}{3}$

63. $1\frac{3}{4} \div \frac{3}{4}$ $2\frac{1}{3}$

64. $5\frac{3}{5} \div \frac{9}{10}$ $6\frac{2}{9}$

65. $1\frac{7}{24} \div \frac{7}{8}$ $1\frac{10}{21}$

66. $4\frac{1}{2} \div \frac{3}{17}$ $25\frac{1}{2}$

TRY IT YOURSELF

Perform each operation and simplify, if possible.

67. $-6\cdot 2\frac{7}{24}$ $-13\frac{3}{4}$

68. $-7\cdot 1\frac{3}{28}$ $-7\frac{3}{4}$

69. $-6\frac{3}{5} \div 7\frac{1}{3}$ $-\frac{9}{10}$

70. $-4\frac{1}{4} \div 4\frac{1}{2}$ $-\frac{17}{18}$

71. $\left(1\frac{2}{3}\right)^2$ $\frac{25}{9}=2\frac{7}{9}$

72. $\left(3\frac{1}{2}\right)^2$ $\frac{49}{4}=12\frac{1}{4}$

73. $8 \div 3\frac{1}{5}$ $2\frac{1}{2}$

▶ **74.** $15 \div 3\frac{1}{3}$ $4\frac{1}{2}$

75. $-20\frac{1}{4} \div \left(-1\frac{11}{16}\right)$ 12

76. $-2\frac{7}{10} \div \left(-1\frac{1}{14}\right)$ $2\frac{13}{25}$

77. $3\frac{1}{16}\cdot 4\frac{4}{7}$ 14

▶ **78.** $5\frac{3}{5}\cdot 1\frac{11}{14}$ 10

79. Find the quotient of $-4\frac{1}{2}$ and $2\frac{1}{4}$. -2

80. Find the quotient of 25 and $-10\frac{5}{7}$. $-2\frac{1}{3}$

81. $2\frac{1}{2}\left(-3\frac{1}{3}\right)$ $-8\frac{1}{3}$

▶ **82.** $\left(-3\frac{1}{4}\right)\left(1\frac{1}{5}\right)$ $-3\frac{9}{10}$

83. $2\frac{5}{8}\cdot\frac{5}{27}$ $\frac{35}{72}$

84. $3\frac{1}{9}\cdot\frac{3}{32}$ $\frac{7}{24}$

85. $6\frac{1}{4}\div 20$ $\frac{5}{16}$

▶ **86.** $4\frac{2}{5}\div 11$ $\frac{2}{5}$

87. Find the product of $1\frac{2}{3}$, 6, and $-\frac{1}{8}$. $-1\frac{1}{4}$

88. Find the product of $-\frac{5}{6}$, -8, and $-2\frac{1}{10}$. -14

89. $\left(-1\frac{1}{3}\right)^3$ $-\frac{64}{27}=-2\frac{10}{27}$

90. $\left(-1\frac{1}{5}\right)^3$ $-\frac{216}{125}=-1\frac{91}{125}$

APPLICATIONS

91. In the illustration below, each barrel represents one whole.

a. Write a mixed number to represent the shaded portion. $3\frac{2}{3}$

b. Write an improper fraction to represent the shaded portion. $\frac{11}{3}$

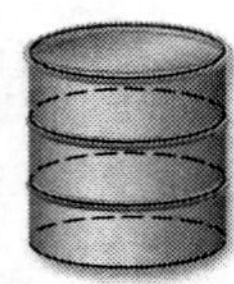

92. Draw $\frac{17}{8}$ pizzas.

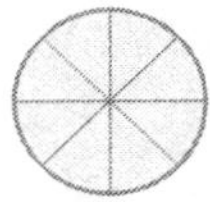
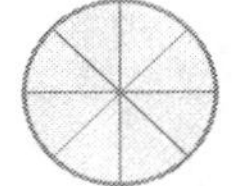
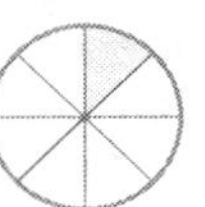

93. DIVING Fill in the blank with a mixed number to describe the dive shown below: forward $2\frac{1}{2}$ somersaults

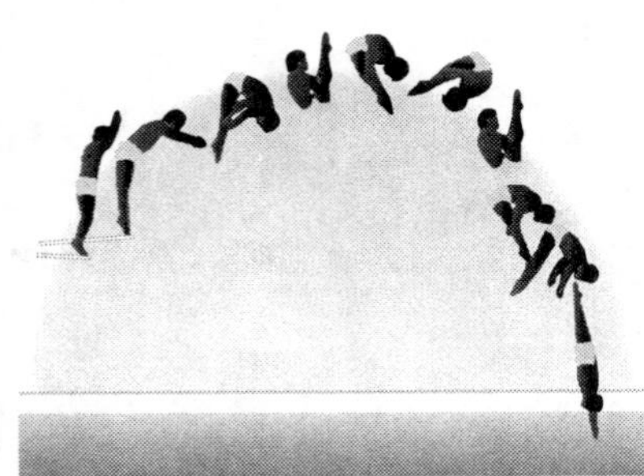

94. PRODUCT LABELING Several mixed numbers appear on the label shown below. Write each mixed number as an improper fraction. $1\frac{3}{4}=\frac{7}{4}$, $23\frac{1}{4}=\frac{93}{4}$, $18\frac{7}{8}=\frac{151}{8}$, $10\frac{1}{2}=\frac{21}{2}$

Laundry Basket
1 3/4 Bushel
•Easy-grip rim is reinforced to handle the biggest loads
23 1/4" L X 18 7/8" W X 10 1/2" H

95. READING METERS

a. Use a mixed number to describe the value to which the arrow is currently pointing. $2\frac{2}{3}$

b. If the arrow moves twelve tick marks to the left, to what value will it be pointing? $-1\frac{1}{3}$

▶ **96.** READING METERS

a. Use a mixed number to describe the value to which the arrow is currently pointing. $-2\frac{1}{2}$

b. If the arrow moves up six tick marks, to what value will it be pointing? $\frac{1}{2}$

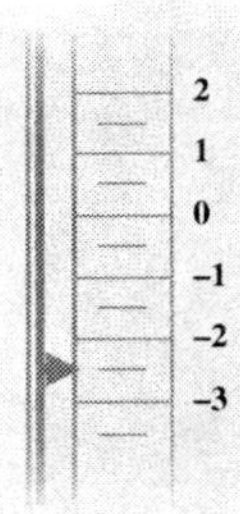

97. ONLINE SHOPPING A mother is ordering a pair of jeans for her daughter from the screen shown below. If the daughter's height is $60\frac{3}{4}$ in. and her waist is $24\frac{1}{2}$ in., on what size and what cut (regular or slim) should the mother point and click? size 14, slim cut

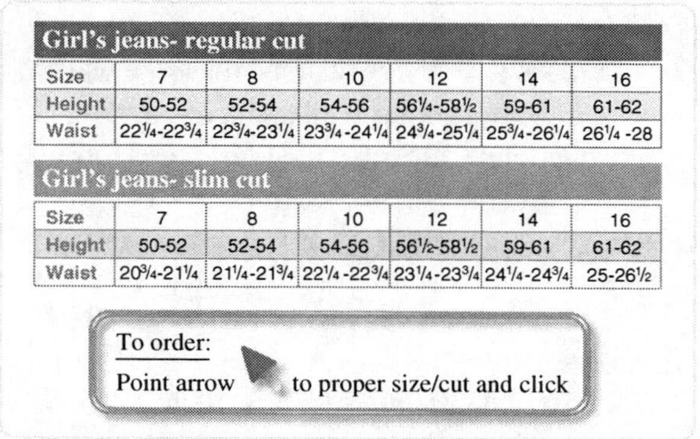

Girl's jeans- regular cut

Size	7	8	10	12	14	16
Height	50-52	52-54	54-56	56¼-58½	59-61	61-62
Waist	22¼-22¾	22¾-23¼	23¾-24¼	24¾-25¼	25¾-26¼	26¼-28

Girl's jeans- slim cut

Size	7	8	10	12	14	16
Height	50-52	52-54	54-56	56½-58½	59-61	61-62
Waist	20¾-21¼	21¼-21¾	22¼-22¾	23¼-23¾	24¼-24¾	25-26½

To order:

Point arrow to proper size/cut and click

98. SEWING Use the following table to determine the number of yards of fabric needed . . .

a. to make a size 16 top if the fabric to be used is 60 inches wide. $2\frac{1}{8}$ yd

b. to make size 18 pants if the fabric to be used is 45 inches wide. $2\frac{5}{8}$ yd

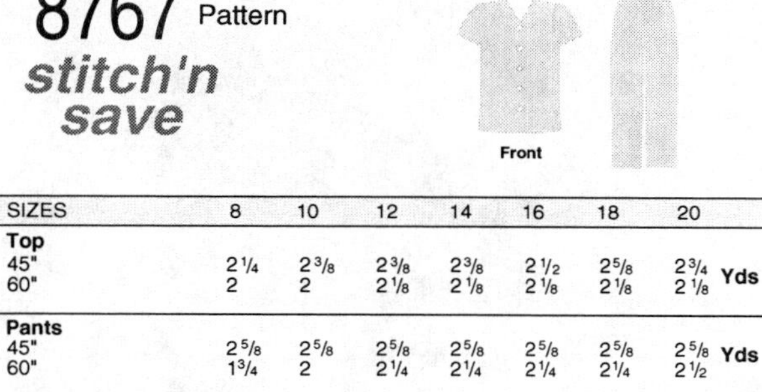

SIZES	8	10	12	14	16	18	20	
Top								
45"	2¼	2⅜	2⅜	2⅜	2½	2⅝	2¾	Yds
60"	2	2	2⅛	2⅛	2⅛	2⅛	2⅛	
Pants								
45"	2⅝	2⅝	2⅝	2⅝	2⅝	2⅝	2⅝	Yds
60"	1¾	2	2¼	2¼	2¼	2¼	2½	

99. LICENSE PLATES Find the area of the license plate shown below. $76\frac{9}{16}$ in.^{2}

100. GRAPH PAPER Mathematicians use specially marked paper, called graph paper, when drawing figures. It is made up of squares that are $\frac{1}{4}$-inch long by $\frac{1}{4}$-inch high.

a. Find the length of the piece of graph paper shown below. $2\frac{3}{4}$ in.

b. Find its height. $1\frac{1}{4}$ in.

c. What is the area of the piece of graph paper? $3\frac{7}{16}$ in.^{2}

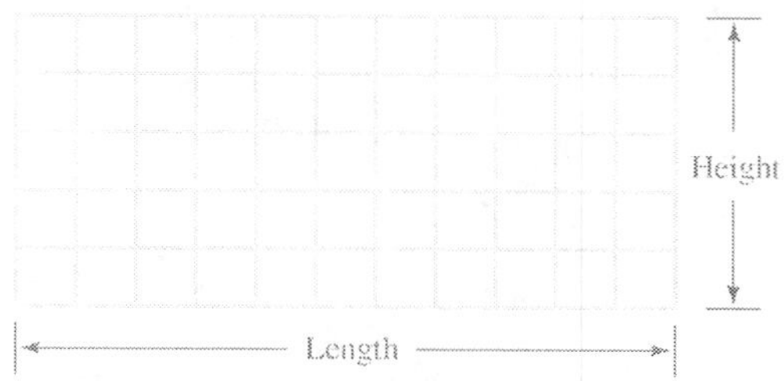

101. EMERGENCY EXITS The following sign marks the emergency exit on a school bus. Find the area of the sign. $42\frac{5}{8}$ in.^{2}

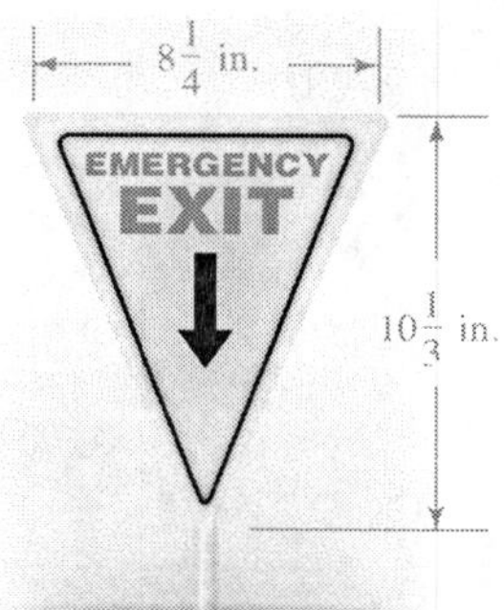

102. CLOTHING DESIGN Find the number of square yards of material needed to make the triangular-shaped shawl shown in the illustration. $1\frac{1}{9}$ yd^2

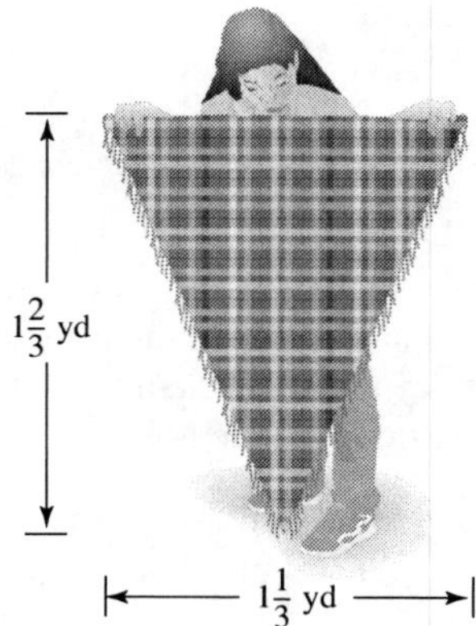

103. CALORIES A company advertises that its mints contain only $3\frac{1}{5}$ calories a piece. What is the calorie intake if you eat an entire package of 20 mints? 64 calories

104. CEMENT MIXERS A cement mixer can carry $9\frac{1}{2}$ cubic yards of concrete. If it makes 8 trips to a job site, how much concrete will be delivered to the site? 76 yd^3

105. SHOPPING In the illustration, what is the cost of buying the fruit in the scale? Give your answer in cents and in dollars. 357¢ = \$3.57

106. PICTURE FRAMES How many inches of molding is needed to make the square picture frame below? $40\frac{1}{2}$ in.

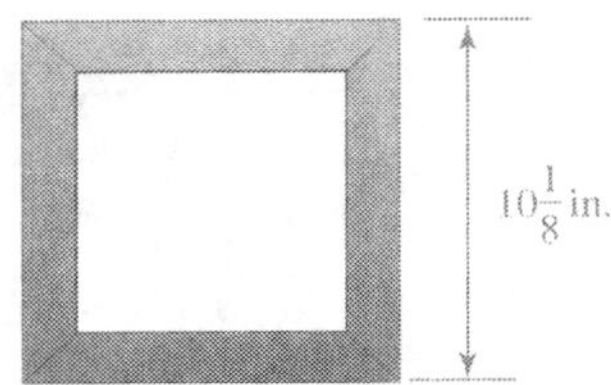

107. BREAKFAST CEREAL A box of cereal contains about $13\frac{3}{4}$ cups. Refer to the nutrition label shown below and determine the recommended size of one serving. $1\frac{1}{4}$ cups

108. BREAKFAST CEREAL A box of cereal contains about $14\frac{1}{4}$ cups. Refer to the nutrition label shown below. Determine how many servings there are for children under 4 in one box. 19 servings

Nutrition Facts
Serving size
Children under 4: $\frac{3}{4}$ cup

Servings per Container
Children Under 4: ?

109. CATERING How many people can be served $\frac{1}{3}$-pound hamburgers if a caterer purchases 200 pounds of ground beef? 600 people

110. SUBDIVISIONS A developer donated to the county 100 of the 1,000 acres of land she owned. She divided the remaining acreage into $1\frac{1}{3}$-acre lots. How many lots were created? 675 lots

111. HORSE RACING The race tracks on which thoroughbred horses run are marked off in $\frac{1}{8}$-mile-long segments called *furlongs*. How many furlongs are there in a $1\frac{1}{16}$-mile race? $8\frac{1}{2}$ furlongs

112. FIRE ESCAPES Part of the fire escape stairway for one story of an office building is shown below. Each riser is $7\frac{1}{2}$ inches high and each story of the building is 105 inches high.

a. How many stairs are there in one story of the fire escape stairway? 14 stairs

b. If the building has 43 stories, how many stairs are there in the entire fire escape stairway? 602 stairs

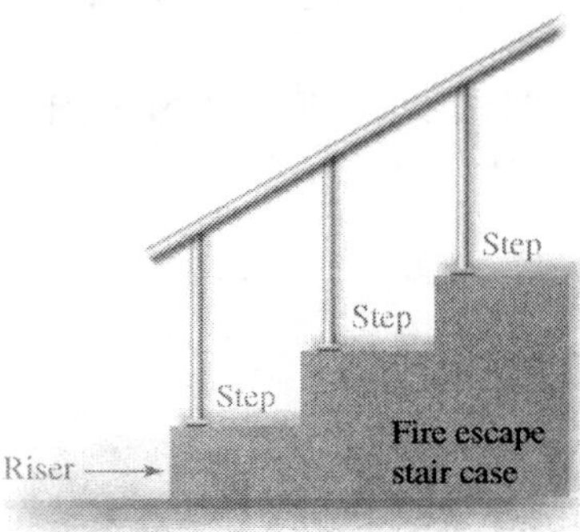

WRITING

113. Explain the difference between $2\frac{3}{4}$ and $2\left(\frac{3}{4}\right)$.

114. Give three examples of how you use mixed numbers in daily life.

REVIEW

Find the LCM of the given numbers.

115. 5, 12, 15 60

116. 8, 12, 16 48

Find the GCF of the given numbers.

117. 12, 68, 92 4

118. 24, 36, 40 4

SECTION 2.6
Adding and Subtracting Mixed Numbers

Objectives

1. Add mixed numbers.
2. Add mixed numbers in vertical form.
3. Subtract mixed numbers.
4. Solve application problems by adding and subtracting mixed numbers.

In this section, we discuss several methods for adding and subtracting mixed numbers.

1 Add mixed numbers.

We can add mixed numbers by writing them as improper fractions. To do so, we follow these steps.

Adding Mixed Numbers: Method 1

1. Write each mixed number as an improper fraction.
2. Write each improper fraction as an equivalent fraction with a denominator that is the LCD.
3. Add the fractions.
4. Write the result as a mixed number, if desired.

Method 1 works well when the whole-number parts of the mixed numbers are small.

EXAMPLE 1 Add: $4\frac{1}{6} + 2\frac{3}{4}$

Strategy We will write each mixed number as an improper fraction, and then use the rule for adding two fractions that have different denominators.

WHY We cannot add the mixed numbers as they are; their fractional parts are not similar objects.

$$4\frac{1}{6} + 2\frac{3}{4}$$

Four and one-sixth ↑ ↑ Two and three-fourths

Solution

$4\frac{1}{6} + 2\frac{3}{4} = \frac{25}{6} + \frac{11}{4}$ Write $4\frac{1}{6}$ and $2\frac{3}{4}$ as improper fractions.

By inspection, we see that the lowest common denominator is 12.

$= \frac{25 \cdot 2}{6 \cdot 2} + \frac{11 \cdot 3}{4 \cdot 3}$ To build $\frac{25}{6}$ and $\frac{11}{4}$ so that their denominators are 12, multiply each by a form of 1.

$= \frac{50}{12} + \frac{33}{12}$ Multiply the numerators. Multiply the denominators.

$= \frac{83}{12}$ Add the numerators and write the sum over the common denominator 12. The result is an improper fraction.

$= 6\frac{11}{12}$ Write the improper fraction $\frac{83}{12}$ as a mixed number.

$$\begin{array}{r} 6 \\ 12\overline{)83} \\ -\ 72 \\ \hline 11 \end{array}$$

Self Check 1

Add: $3\frac{2}{3} + 1\frac{1}{5}$ $4\frac{13}{15}$

Now Try **Problem 13**

Teaching Example 1

Add: $1\frac{5}{6} + 2\frac{1}{4}$

Answer:

$4\frac{1}{12}$

Success Tip We can use rounding to check the results when adding (or subtracting) mixed numbers. To check the answer $6\frac{11}{12}$ from Example 1, we proceed as follows:

$$4\frac{1}{6} + 2\frac{3}{4} \approx 4 + 3 = 7$$

Since $\frac{1}{6}$ is less than $\frac{1}{2}$, round $4\frac{1}{6}$ down to 4.
Since $\frac{3}{4}$ is greater than $\frac{1}{2}$, round $2\frac{3}{4}$ up to 3.

Since $6\frac{11}{12}$ is close to 7, it is a reasonable answer.

Self Check 2

Add: $-4\frac{1}{12} + 2\frac{1}{4}$ $-1\frac{5}{6}$

Now Try **Problem 17**

Teaching Example 2

Add: $-3\frac{1}{10} + 1\frac{2}{5}$

Answer:

$-1\frac{7}{10}$

EXAMPLE 2

Add: $-3\frac{1}{8} + 1\frac{1}{2}$

Strategy We will write each mixed number as an improper fraction, and then use the rule for adding two fractions that have different denominators.

WHY We cannot add the mixed numbers as they are; their fractional parts are not similar objects.

$$-3\frac{1}{8} + 1\frac{1}{2}$$

Negative three and one-eighth ($-3\frac{1}{8}$); One and one-half ($1\frac{1}{2}$)

Solution

$$-3\frac{1}{8} + 1\frac{1}{2} = -\frac{25}{8} + \frac{3}{2}$$ Write $-3\frac{1}{8}$ and $1\frac{1}{2}$ as improper fractions.

Since the smallest number the denominators 8 and 2 divide exactly is 8, the LCD is 8. We will only need to build an equivalent fraction for $\frac{3}{2}$.

$= -\frac{25}{8} + \frac{3}{2} \cdot \frac{4}{4}$ To build $\frac{3}{2}$ so that its denominator is 8, multiply it by a form of 1.

$= -\frac{25}{8} + \frac{12}{8}$ Multiply the numerators. Multiply the denominators.

$= \frac{-25 + 12}{8}$ Add the numerators and write the sum over the common denominator 8.

$= \frac{-13}{8}$ Use the rule for adding integers that have different signs: $-25 + 12 = -13$.

$= -1\frac{5}{8}$ Write $\frac{-13}{8}$ as a negative mixed number by dividing 13 by 8. ■

We can also add mixed numbers by adding their whole-number parts and their fractional parts. To do so, we follow these steps.

Adding Mixed Numbers: Method 2

1. Write each mixed number as the sum of a whole number and a fraction.
2. Use the commutative property of addition to write the whole numbers together and the fractions together.
3. Add the whole numbers and the fractions separately.
4. Write the result as a mixed number, if necessary.

Method 2 works well when the whole number parts of the mixed numbers are large.

EXAMPLE 3 Add: $168\frac{3}{7} + 85\frac{2}{9}$

Strategy We will write each mixed number as the sum of a whole number and a fraction. Then we will add the whole numbers and the fractions separately.

WHY If we change each mixed number to an improper fraction, build equivalent fractions, and add, the resulting numerators will be very large and difficult to work with.

Solution

We will write the solution in *horizontal* form.

$168\frac{3}{7} + 85\frac{2}{9} = 168 + \frac{3}{7} + 85 + \frac{2}{9}$ Write each mixed number as the sum of a whole number and a fraction.

$=$ + Use the commutative property of addition to change the order of the addition so that the whole numbers are together and the fractions are together.

$= 253 + \frac{3}{7} + \frac{2}{9}$ Add the whole numbers. $\begin{array}{r} {}^{1\,1}\\ 168 \\ +\ 85 \\ \hline 253 \end{array}$

$= 253 + \frac{3}{7} \cdot \frac{9}{9} + \frac{2}{9} \cdot \frac{7}{7}$ Prepare to add the fractions. To build $\frac{3}{7}$ and $\frac{2}{9}$ so that their denominators are 63, multipy each by a form of 1.

$= 253 + \frac{27}{63} + \frac{14}{63}$ Multiply the numerators. Multiply the denominators.

$= 253 + \frac{41}{63}$ Add the numerators and write the sum over the common denominator 63. $\begin{array}{r} {}^{1}\\ 27 \\ +\ 14 \\ \hline 41 \end{array}$

$= 253\frac{41}{63}$ Write the sum as a mixed number.

Self Check 3

Add: $275\frac{1}{6} + 81\frac{3}{5}$ $356\frac{23}{30}$

Now Try **Problem 21**

Teaching Example 3 Add: $353\frac{3}{7} + 71\frac{1}{9}$

Answer: $424\frac{34}{63}$

Caution! If we use method 1 to add the mixed numbers in Example 3, the numbers we encounter are very large. As expected, the result is the same: $253\frac{41}{63}$.

$168\frac{3}{7} + 85\frac{2}{9} = \frac{1{,}179}{7} + \frac{767}{9}$ Write $168\frac{3}{7}$ and $85\frac{2}{9}$ as improper fractions.

$= \frac{1{,}179}{7} \cdot \frac{9}{9} + \frac{767}{9} \cdot \frac{7}{7}$ The LCD is 63.

$= \frac{10{,}611}{63} + \frac{5{,}369}{63}$ Note how large the numerators are.

$= \frac{15{,}980}{63}$ Add the numerators and write the sum over the common denominator 63.

$= 253\frac{41}{63}$ To write the improper fraction as a mixed number, divide 15,980 by 63.

Generally speaking, the larger the whole-number parts of the mixed numbers, the more difficult it becomes to add those mixed numbers using method 1.

2 Add mixed numbers in vertical form.

We can add mixed numbers quickly when they are written in **vertical form** by working in columns. The strategy is the same as in Example 2: Add whole numbers to whole numbers and fractions to fractions.

Self Check 4

Add: $71\frac{5}{8} + 23\frac{1}{3}$ $94\frac{23}{24}$

Now Try **Problem 25**

Teaching Example 4

Add: $62\frac{2}{5} + 15\frac{1}{3}$

Answer:

$77\frac{11}{15}$

EXAMPLE 4

Add: $25\frac{3}{4} + 31\frac{1}{5}$

Strategy We will perform the addition in *vertical form* with the fractions in a column and the whole numbers lined up in columns. Then we will add the fractional parts and the whole-number parts separately.

WHY It is often easier to add the fractional parts and the whole-number parts of mixed numbers vertically—especially if the whole-number parts contain two or more digits, such as 25 and 31.

Solution

Write the mixed numbers in vertical form.
Build $\frac{3}{4}$ and $\frac{1}{5}$ so that their denominators are 20.
Add the fractions separately.
Add the whole numbers separately.

$$\begin{array}{rcrcrcr} 25\frac{3}{4} & = & 25\frac{3}{4}\cdot\frac{5}{5} & = & 25\frac{15}{20} & = & 25\frac{15}{20} \\ +\ 31\frac{1}{5} & = & +\ 31\frac{1}{5}\cdot\frac{4}{4} & = & +\ 31\frac{4}{20} & = & +\ 31\frac{4}{20} \\ \hline & & & & \frac{19}{20} & & 56\frac{19}{20} \end{array}$$

The sum is $56\frac{19}{20}$.

Self Check 5

Add and simplify, if possible:

$68\frac{1}{6} + 37\frac{5}{18} + 52\frac{1}{9}$ $157\frac{5}{9}$

Now Try **Problem 29**

Teaching Example 5

Add and simplify, if possible:

$44\frac{1}{3} + 91\frac{1}{5} + 27\frac{2}{15}$

Answer:

$162\frac{2}{3}$

EXAMPLE 5

Add and simplify, if possible: $75\frac{1}{12} + 43\frac{1}{4} + 54\frac{1}{6}$

Strategy We will write the problem in *vertical form*. We will make sure that the fractional part of the answer is in simplest form.

WHY When adding, subtracting, multiplying, or dividing fractions or mixed numbers, the answer should always be written in simplest form.

Solution

The LCD for $\frac{1}{12}, \frac{1}{4}$, and $\frac{1}{6}$ is 12.

Write the mixed numbers in vertical form.
Build $\frac{1}{4}$ and $\frac{1}{6}$ so that their denominators are 12.
Add the fractions separately.
Add the whole numbers separately.

$$\begin{array}{rcrcrcr} 75\frac{1}{12} & = & 75\frac{1}{12} & = & 75\frac{1}{12} & = & \overset{11}{75}\frac{1}{12} \\ 43\frac{1}{4} & = & 43\frac{1}{4}\cdot\frac{3}{3} & = & 43\frac{3}{12} & = & 43\frac{3}{12} \\ +\ 54\frac{1}{6} & = & +\ 54\frac{1}{6}\cdot\frac{2}{2} & = & +\ 54\frac{2}{12} & = & +\ 54\frac{2}{12} \\ \hline & & & & \frac{6}{12} & & 172\frac{6}{12} = 172\frac{1}{2} \end{array}$$

Simplify: $\frac{6}{12} = \frac{\overset{1}{\cancel{6}}}{2\cdot\underset{1}{\cancel{6}}} = \frac{1}{2}$.

The sum is $172\frac{1}{2}$.

When we add mixed numbers, sometimes the sum of the fractions is an improper fraction.

EXAMPLE 6

Add: $45\frac{2}{3} + 96\frac{4}{5}$

Strategy We will write the problem in *vertical form*. We will make sure that the fractional part of the answer is in simplest form.

WHY When adding, subtracting, multiplying, or dividing fractions or mixed numbers, the answer should always be written in simplest form.

Solution

The LCD for $\frac{2}{3}$ and $\frac{4}{5}$ is 15.

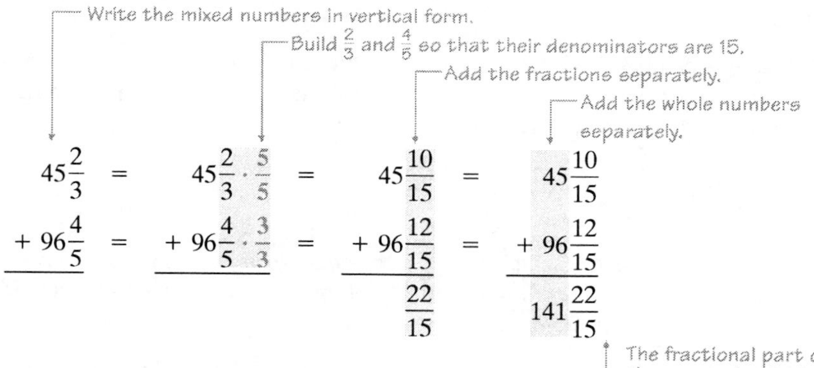

Since we don't want an improper fraction in the answer, we write $\frac{22}{15}$ as a mixed number. Then we *carry* 1 from the fraction column to the whole-number column.

$141\frac{22}{15} = 141 + \frac{22}{15}$ Write the mixed number as the sum of a whole number and a fraction.

$= 141 + 1\frac{7}{15}$ To write the improper fraction as a mixed number divide 22 by 15.

$= 142\frac{7}{15}$ Carry the 1 and add it to 141 to get 142.

$$\begin{array}{r} 1 \\ 15\overline{)22} \\ -\,15 \\ \hline 7 \end{array}$$

Self Check 6

Add: $76\frac{11}{12} + 49\frac{5}{8}$ $126\frac{13}{24}$

Now Try **Problem 33**

Teaching Example 6

Add: $83\frac{7}{8} + 39\frac{3}{5}$

Answer:

$123\frac{19}{40}$

3 Subtract mixed numbers.

Subtracting mixed numbers is similar to adding mixed numbers.

EXAMPLE 7

Subtract and simplify, if possible: $16\frac{7}{10} - 9\frac{8}{15}$

Strategy We will perform the subtraction in *vertical form* with the fractions in a column and the whole numbers lined up in columns. Then we will subtract the fractional parts and the whole-number parts separately.

WHY It is often easier to subtract the fractional parts and the whole-number parts of mixed numbers vertically.

Self Check 7

Subtract and simplify, if possible:

$12\frac{9}{20} - 8\frac{1}{30}$ $4\frac{5}{12}$

Now Try **Problem 37**

Teaching Example 7
Subtract and simplify, if possible:
$15\frac{2}{3} - 7\frac{5}{12}$
Answer:
$8\frac{1}{4}$

Solution

The LCD for $\frac{7}{10}$ and $\frac{8}{15}$ is 30.

Write the mixed numbers in vertical form.
Build $\frac{7}{10}$ and $\frac{8}{15}$ so that their denominators are 30.
Subtract the fractions separately.
Subtract the whole numbers separately.

$$\begin{array}{rcrcrcr} 16\frac{7}{10} & = & 16\frac{7}{10}\cdot\frac{3}{3} & = & 16\frac{21}{30} & = & 16\frac{21}{30} \\ -\ 9\frac{8}{15} & = & -\ 9\frac{8}{15}\cdot\frac{2}{2} & = & -\ 9\frac{16}{30} & = & -\ 9\frac{16}{30} \\ \hline & & & & \frac{5}{30} & & 7\frac{5}{30} = 7\frac{1}{6} \end{array}$$

Simplify: $\frac{5}{30} = \frac{\overset{1}{\cancel{5}}}{\underset{1}{\cancel{5}} \cdot 6} = \frac{1}{6}$.

The difference is $7\frac{1}{6}$.

Subtraction of mixed numbers (like subtraction of whole numbers) sometimes involves borrowing. When the fraction we are subtracting is greater than the fraction we are subtracting it from, it is necessary to borrow.

Self Check 8
Subtract: $258\frac{3}{4} - 175\frac{15}{16}$ $82\frac{13}{16}$

Now Try **Problem 41**

Teaching Example 8
Subtract: $219\frac{1}{4} - 63\frac{10}{11}$
Answer:
$155\frac{15}{44}$

EXAMPLE 8

Subtract: $34\frac{1}{8} - 11\frac{2}{3}$

Strategy We will perform the subtraction in *vertical form* with the fractions in a column and the whole numbers lined up in columns. Then we will subtract the fractional parts and the whole-number parts separately.

WHY It is often easier to subtract the fractional parts and the whole-number parts of mixed numbers vertically.

Solution

The LCD for $\frac{1}{8}$ and $\frac{2}{3}$ is 24.

Write the mixed number in vertical form.
Build $\frac{1}{8}$ and $\frac{2}{3}$ so that their denominators are 24.

$$\begin{array}{rcrcr} 34\frac{1}{8} & = & 34\frac{1}{8}\cdot\frac{3}{3} & = & 34\frac{3}{24} \\ -\ 11\frac{2}{3} & = & -\ 11\frac{2}{3}\cdot\frac{8}{8} & = & -\ 11\frac{16}{24} \\ \hline \end{array}$$

Note that $\frac{16}{24}$ is greater than $\frac{3}{24}$.

Since $\frac{16}{24}$ is greater than $\frac{3}{24}$, borrow 1 (in the form of $\frac{24}{24}$) from 34 and add it to $\frac{3}{24}$ to get $\frac{27}{24}$.
Subtract the fractions separately.
Subtract the whole numbers separately.

$$\begin{array}{rcrcr} \overset{33}{\cancel{34}}\frac{3}{24} + \frac{24}{24} & = & 33\frac{27}{24} & = & 33\frac{27}{24} \\ -\ 11\frac{16}{24} & = & -\ 11\frac{16}{24} & = & -\ 11\frac{16}{24} \\ \hline & & \frac{11}{24} & & 22\frac{11}{24} \end{array}$$

The difference is $22\frac{11}{24}$.

Success Tip We can use rounding to check the results when subtracting mixed numbers. To check the answer $22\frac{11}{24}$ from Example 8, we proceed as follows:

$$34\frac{1}{8} - 11\frac{2}{3} \approx 34 - 12 = 22$$

Since $\frac{1}{8}$ is less than $\frac{1}{2}$, round $34\frac{1}{8}$ down to 34.
Since $\frac{2}{3}$ is greater than $\frac{1}{2}$, round $11\frac{2}{3}$ up to 12.

Since $22\frac{11}{24}$ is close to 22, it is a reasonable answer.

EXAMPLE 9 Subtract: $419 - 53\frac{11}{16}$

Strategy We will write the numbers in vertical form and borrow 1 (in the form of $\frac{16}{16}$) from 419.

WHY In the fraction column, we need to have a fraction from which to subtract $\frac{11}{16}$.

Solution

Write the mixed number in vertical form.
Borrow 1 (in the form of $\frac{16}{16}$) from 419. Then subtract the fractions separately.
Subtract the whole numbers separately. This also requires borrowing.

$$\begin{array}{r} 419 \\ -\ 53\frac{11}{16} \\ \hline \end{array} = \begin{array}{r} 418\frac{16}{16} \\ -\ 53\frac{11}{16} \\ \hline 365\frac{5}{16} \end{array} = \begin{array}{r} \overset{3\,11}{\cancel{4}\cancel{1}}8\frac{16}{16} \\ -\ 53\frac{11}{16} \\ \hline 365\frac{5}{16} \end{array}$$

The difference is $365\frac{5}{16}$.

Self Check 9

Subtract: $2,300 - 129\frac{31}{32}$ $2,170\frac{1}{32}$

Now Try **Problem 45**

Teaching Example 9

Subtract: $643 - 81\frac{3}{28}$

Answer:

$561\frac{25}{28}$

4 Solve application problems by adding and subtracting mixed numbers.

EXAMPLE 10 *Horse Racing* In order to become the *Triple Crown Champion,* a thoroughbred horse must win three races: the Kentucky Derby ($1\frac{1}{4}$ miles long), the Preakness Stakes ($1\frac{3}{16}$ miles long), and the Belmont Stakes ($1\frac{1}{2}$ miles long). What is the combined length of the three races of the Triple Crown?

Focus on Sport/Getty Images

Affirmed, in 1978, was the last of only 11 horses in history to win the Triple Crown.

Analyze

- The Kentucky Derby is $1\frac{1}{4}$ miles long.
- The Preakness Stakes is $1\frac{3}{16}$ miles long.
- The Belmont Stakes is $1\frac{1}{2}$ miles long.
- What is the combined length of the three races?

Self Check 10

SALADS A three-bean salad calls for one can of green beans ($14\frac{1}{2}$ ounces), one can of garbanzo beans ($10\frac{3}{4}$ ounces), and one can of kidney beans ($15\frac{7}{8}$ ounces). How many ounces of beans are called for in the recipe? $41\frac{1}{8}$ oz

Now Try **Problem 89**

Teaching Example 10 BAKING A baker wants to make a cookie recipe that calls for $1\frac{1}{8}$ cups of flour, a bread recipe that calls for $3\frac{3}{4}$ cups of flour, and a cake recipe that calls for $2\frac{1}{2}$ cups. How many cups of flour does she need to make all three recipes?

Answer:

$7\frac{3}{8}$ cups

Form The key phrase *combined length* indicates addition. We translate the words of the problem to numbers and symbols.

The combined length of the three races	is equal to	the length of the Kentucky Derby	plus	the length of the Preakness Stakes	plus	the length of the Belmont Stakes.
The combined length of the three races	=	$1\frac{1}{4}$	+	$1\frac{3}{16}$	+	$1\frac{1}{2}$

Solve To find the sum, we will write the mixed numbers in vertical form. To add in the fraction column, the LCD for $\frac{1}{4}$, $\frac{3}{16}$, and $\frac{1}{2}$ is 16.

Build $\frac{1}{4}$ and $\frac{1}{2}$ so that their denominators are 16.
Add the fractions separately.
Add the whole numbers separately.

$$\begin{array}{rcrcrcr} 1\frac{1}{4} & = & 1\frac{1}{4}\cdot\frac{4}{4} & = & 1\frac{4}{16} & = & 1\frac{4}{16} \\ 1\frac{3}{16} & = & 1\frac{3}{16} & = & 1\frac{3}{16} & = & 1\frac{3}{16} \\ +\,1\frac{1}{2} & = & +\,1\frac{1}{2}\cdot\frac{8}{8} & = & +\,1\frac{8}{16} & = & +\,1\frac{8}{16} \\ \hline & & & & \frac{15}{16} & & 3\frac{15}{16} \end{array}$$

State The combined length of the three races of the Triple Crown is $3\frac{15}{16}$ miles.

Check We can estimate to check the result. If we round $1\frac{1}{4}$ down to 1, round $1\frac{3}{16}$ down to 1, and round $1\frac{1}{2}$ up to 2, the approximate combined length of the three races is $1 + 1 + 2 = 4$ miles. Since $3\frac{15}{16}$ is close to 4, the result seems reasonable. ■

THINK IT THROUGH

"Americans are not getting the sleep they need which may affect their ability to perform well during the workday."

National Sleep Foundation Report, 2008

The 1,000 people who took part in the 2008 *Sleep in America* poll were asked when they typically wake up, when they go to bed, and how long they sleep on both workdays and non-workdays. The results are shown on the right. Write the average hours slept on a workday and on a non-workday as mixed numbers. How much longer does the average person sleep on a non-workday?

workday: $6\frac{2}{3}$ hr; non-workday: $7\frac{5}{12}$ hr; $\frac{3}{4}$ hr

Typical Workday and Non-workday Sleep Schedules

Average workday bedtime 10:53 PM

Average hours slept on workdays 6 hours 40 minutes

5:35 AM Average workday wake time

Average non-workday bedtime 11:24 PM

Average hours slept on non-workdays 7 hours 25 minutes

7:12 AM Average non-workday wake time

(Source: National Sleep Foundation, 2008)

EXAMPLE 11 *Baking* How much butter is left in a 10-pound tub if $2\frac{2}{3}$ pounds are used for a wedding cake?

Analyze

- The tub contained 10 pounds of butter.
- $2\frac{2}{3}$ pounds of butter are used for a cake.
- How much butter is left in the tub?

Form The key phrase *how much butter is left* indicates subtraction. We translate the words of the problem to numbers and symbols.

The amount of butter left in the tub	is equal to	the amount of butter in one tub	minus	the amount of butter used for the cake.
The amount of butter left in the tub	=	10	−	$2\frac{2}{3}$

Solve To find the difference, we will write the numbers in vertical form and borrow 1 (in the form of $\frac{3}{3}$) from 10.

In the fraction column, we need to have a fraction from which to subtract $\frac{2}{3}$.
Subtract the fractions separately.
Subtract the whole numbers separately.

$$\begin{array}{r} 10 \\ -\ 2\frac{2}{3} \\ \hline \end{array} = \begin{array}{r} \overset{9}{\cancel{10}}\frac{3}{3} \\ -\ 2\frac{2}{3} \\ \hline \frac{1}{3} \end{array} = \begin{array}{r} \overset{9}{\cancel{10}}\frac{3}{3} \\ -\ 2\frac{2}{3} \\ \hline 7\frac{1}{3} \end{array}$$

State There are $7\frac{1}{3}$ pounds of butter left in the tub.

Check We can check using addition. If $2\frac{2}{3}$ pounds of butter were used and $7\frac{1}{3}$ pounds of butter are left in the tub, then the tub originally contained $2\frac{2}{3} + 7\frac{1}{3} = 9\frac{3}{3} = 10$ pounds of butter. The result checks.

Self Check 11

TRUCKING The mixing barrel of a cement truck holds 9 cubic yards of concrete. How much concrete is left in the barrel if $6\frac{3}{4}$ cubic yards have already been unloaded? $2\frac{1}{4}$ yd^3

Now Try **Problem 95**

Teaching Example 11
REFRESHMENTS How much punch is left in a 20-gallon container if $9\frac{1}{2}$ gallons have been used?
Answer:
$10\frac{1}{2}$ gal

ANSWER TO SELF CHECKS

1. $4\frac{13}{15}$ **2.** $-1\frac{5}{6}$ **3.** $356\frac{23}{30}$ **4.** $94\frac{23}{24}$ **5.** $157\frac{5}{9}$ **6.** $126\frac{13}{24}$ **7.** $4\frac{5}{12}$ **8.** $82\frac{13}{16}$ **9.** $2{,}170\frac{1}{32}$ **10.** $41\frac{1}{8}$ oz **11.** $2\frac{1}{4}$ yd^3

SECTION 2.6 STUDY SET

VOCABULARY

Fill in the blanks.

1. A __mixed__ number, such as $1\frac{7}{8}$, contains a whole-number part and a fractional part.
2. We can add (or subtract) mixed numbers quickly when they are written in __vertical__ form by working in columns.
3. To add (or subtract) mixed numbers written in vertical form, we add (or subtract) the __fractions__ separately and the __whole__ numbers separately.
4. Fractions such as $\frac{11}{8}$, that are greater than or equal to 1, are called __improper__ fractions.

Selected exercises available online at **www.webassign.net/brookscole**

5. Consider the following problem:

$$\begin{array}{r} 36\frac{5}{7} \\ +\ 42\frac{4}{7} \\ \hline 78\frac{9}{7} = 78 + 1\frac{2}{7} = 79\frac{2}{7} \end{array}$$

Since we don't want an improper fraction in the answer, we write $\frac{9}{7}$ as $1\frac{2}{7}$, carry the 1, and add it to 78 to get 79.

6. Consider the following problem:

$$\begin{array}{rl} 86\frac{1}{3} = & \overset{5}{8}6\frac{1}{3} + \frac{3}{3} \\ -\ 24\frac{2}{3} = & -24\frac{2}{3} \\ \hline \end{array}$$

To subtract in the fraction column, we borrow 1 from 86 in the form of $\frac{3}{3}$.

CONCEPTS

7. a. For $76\frac{3}{4}$, list the whole-number part and the fractional part. $76, \frac{3}{4}$

b. Write $76\frac{3}{4}$ as a sum. $76 + \frac{3}{4}$

8. Use the commutative property of addition to rewrite the following expression with the whole numbers together and the fractions together. *You do not have to find the answer.*

$$14 + \frac{5}{8} + 53 + \frac{1}{6} \quad 14 + 53 + \frac{5}{8} + \frac{1}{6}$$

9. The *denominators* of two fractions are given. Find the least common denominator.

a. 3 and 4 12
b. 5 and 6 30
c. 6 and 9 18
d. 8 and 12 24

10. Simplify.

a. $9\frac{17}{16}$ $10\frac{1}{16}$
b. $1{,}288\frac{7}{3}$ $1{,}290\frac{1}{3}$
c. $16\frac{12}{8}$ $17\frac{1}{2}$
d. $45\frac{24}{20}$ $46\frac{1}{5}$

NOTATION

Fill in the blanks to complete each solution.

11.
$$\begin{array}{rcrcr} 6\frac{3}{5} & = & 6\frac{3}{5}\cdot\frac{7}{7} & = & 6\frac{21}{35} \\ +\ 3\frac{2}{7} & = & +\ 3\frac{2}{7}\cdot\frac{5}{5} & = & +\ 3\frac{10}{35} \\ \hline & & & & 9\frac{31}{35} \end{array}$$

12.
$$\begin{array}{rcrcrcrcr} 67\frac{3}{8} & = & 67\frac{3}{8}\cdot\frac{3}{3} & = & 67\frac{9}{24} & = & \overset{66}{67}\frac{9}{24} + \frac{24}{24} & = & 66\frac{33}{24} \\ -\ 23\frac{2}{3} & = & -\ 23\frac{2}{3}\cdot\frac{8}{8} & = & -\ 23\frac{16}{24} & = & -\ 23\frac{16}{24} & = & -\ 23\frac{16}{24} \\ \hline & & & & & & & & 43\frac{17}{24} \end{array}$$

GUIDED PRACTICE

Add. See Example 1.

13. $1\frac{1}{4} + 2\frac{1}{3}$ $3\frac{7}{12}$

▶ 14. $2\frac{2}{5} + 3\frac{1}{4}$ $5\frac{13}{20}$

15. $2\frac{1}{3} + 4\frac{2}{5}$ $6\frac{11}{15}$

16. $4\frac{1}{3} + 1\frac{1}{7}$ $5\frac{10}{21}$

Add. See Example 2.

17. $-4\frac{1}{8} + 1\frac{3}{4}$ $-2\frac{3}{8}$

18. $-3\frac{11}{15} + 2\frac{1}{5}$ $-1\frac{8}{15}$

19. $-6\frac{5}{6} + 3\frac{2}{3}$ $-3\frac{1}{6}$

▶ 20. $-6\frac{3}{14} + 1\frac{2}{7}$ $-4\frac{13}{14}$

Add. See Example 3.

21. $334\frac{1}{7} + 42\frac{2}{3}$ $376\frac{17}{21}$

22. $259\frac{3}{8} + 40\frac{1}{3}$ $299\frac{17}{24}$

23. $667\frac{1}{5} + 47\frac{3}{4}$ $714\frac{19}{20}$

▶ 24. $568\frac{1}{6} + 52\frac{3}{4}$ $620\frac{11}{12}$

Add. See Example 4.

25. $41\frac{2}{9} + 18\frac{2}{5}$ $59\frac{28}{45}$

▶ 26. $60\frac{3}{11} + 24\frac{2}{3}$ $84\frac{31}{33}$

27. $89\frac{6}{11} + 43\frac{1}{3}$ $132\frac{29}{33}$

28. $77\frac{5}{8} + 55\frac{1}{7}$ $132\frac{43}{56}$

Add and simplify, if possible. See Example 5.

29. $14\frac{1}{4} + 29\frac{1}{20} + 78\frac{3}{5}$ $121\frac{9}{10}$

▶ 30. $11\frac{1}{12} + 59\frac{1}{4} + 82\frac{1}{6}$ $152\frac{1}{2}$

31. $106\frac{5}{18} + 22\frac{1}{2} + 19\frac{1}{9}$ $147\frac{8}{9}$

32. $75\frac{2}{5} + 43\frac{7}{30} + 54\frac{1}{3}$ $172\frac{29}{30}$

Add and simplify, if possible. See Example 6.

33. $39\frac{5}{8} + 62\frac{11}{12}$ $102\frac{13}{24}$

34. $53\frac{5}{6} + 47\frac{3}{8}$ $101\frac{5}{24}$

35. $82\frac{8}{9} + 46\frac{11}{15}$ $129\frac{28}{45}$

▶ 36. $44\frac{2}{9} + 76\frac{20}{21}$ $121\frac{11}{63}$

Subtract and simplify, if possible. See Example 7.

37. $19\frac{11}{12} - 9\frac{2}{3}$ $10\frac{1}{4}$

38. $32\frac{2}{3} - 7\frac{1}{6}$ $25\frac{1}{2}$

39. $21\frac{5}{6} - 8\frac{3}{10}$ $13\frac{8}{15}$

▶ **40.** $41\frac{2}{5} - 6\frac{3}{20}$ $35\frac{1}{4}$

Subtract. See Example 8.

41. $47\frac{1}{11} - 15\frac{2}{3}$ $31\frac{14}{33}$

42. $58\frac{4}{11} - 15\frac{1}{2}$ $42\frac{19}{22}$

43. $84\frac{5}{8} - 12\frac{6}{7}$ $71\frac{43}{56}$

▶ **44.** $95\frac{4}{7} - 23\frac{5}{6}$ $71\frac{31}{42}$

Subtract. See Example 9.

45. $674 - 94\frac{11}{15}$ $579\frac{4}{15}$

46. $437 - 63\frac{6}{23}$ $373\frac{17}{23}$

47. $112 - 49\frac{9}{32}$ $62\frac{23}{32}$

▶ **48.** $221 - 88\frac{35}{64}$ $132\frac{29}{64}$

TRY IT YOURSELF

Add or subtract and simplify, if possible.

49. $140\frac{5}{6} - 129\frac{4}{5}$ $11\frac{1}{30}$

50. $291\frac{1}{4} - 289\frac{1}{12}$ $2\frac{1}{6}$

51. $4\frac{1}{6} + 1\frac{1}{5}$ $5\frac{11}{30}$

52. $2\frac{2}{5} + 3\frac{1}{4}$ $5\frac{13}{20}$

53. $5\frac{1}{2} + 3\frac{4}{5}$ $9\frac{3}{10}$

▶ **54.** $6\frac{1}{2} + 2\frac{2}{3}$ $9\frac{1}{6}$

55. $2 + 1\frac{7}{8}$ $3\frac{7}{8}$

56. $3\frac{3}{4} + 5$ $8\frac{3}{4}$

57. $8\frac{7}{9} - 3\frac{1}{9}$ $5\frac{2}{3}$

58. $9\frac{9}{10} - 6\frac{3}{10}$ $3\frac{3}{5}$

59. $140\frac{3}{16} - 129\frac{3}{4}$ $10\frac{7}{16}$

▶ **60.** $442\frac{1}{8} - 429\frac{2}{3}$ $12\frac{11}{24}$

61. $380\frac{1}{6} + 17\frac{1}{4}$ $397\frac{5}{12}$

▶ **62.** $103\frac{1}{2} + 210\frac{2}{5}$ $313\frac{9}{10}$

63. $-2\frac{5}{6} + 1\frac{3}{8}$ $-1\frac{11}{24}$

64. $-4\frac{5}{9} + 2\frac{1}{6}$ $-2\frac{7}{18}$

65. $3\frac{1}{4} + 4\frac{1}{4}$ $7\frac{1}{2}$

66. $2\frac{1}{8} + 3\frac{3}{8}$ $5\frac{1}{2}$

67. $-3\frac{3}{4} + \left(-1\frac{1}{2}\right)$ $-5\frac{1}{4}$

68. $-3\frac{2}{3} + \left(-1\frac{4}{5}\right)$ $-5\frac{7}{15}$

69. $7 - \frac{2}{3}$ $6\frac{1}{3}$

70. $6 - \frac{1}{8}$ $5\frac{7}{8}$

71. $12\frac{1}{2} + 5\frac{3}{4} + 35\frac{1}{6}$ $53\frac{5}{12}$

▶ **72.** $31\frac{1}{3} + 20\frac{2}{5} + 10\frac{1}{15}$ $61\frac{4}{5}$

73. $16\frac{1}{4} - 13\frac{3}{4}$ $2\frac{1}{2}$

▶ **74.** $40\frac{1}{7} - 19\frac{6}{7}$ $20\frac{2}{7}$

75. $-4\frac{5}{8} - 1\frac{1}{4}$ $-5\frac{7}{8}$

▶ **76.** $-2\frac{1}{16} - 3\frac{7}{8}$ $-5\frac{15}{16}$

77. $6\frac{5}{8} - 3$ $3\frac{5}{8}$

78. $10\frac{1}{2} - 6$ $4\frac{1}{2}$

79. $\frac{7}{3} + 2$ $4\frac{1}{3}$

▶ **80.** $\frac{9}{7} + 3$ $4\frac{2}{7}$

81. $58\frac{7}{8} + 340\frac{1}{2} + 61\frac{3}{4}$ $461\frac{1}{8}$

82. $191\frac{1}{2} + 233\frac{1}{16} + 16\frac{5}{8}$ $441\frac{3}{16}$

83. $9 - 8\frac{3}{4}$ $\frac{1}{4}$

84. $11 - 10\frac{4}{5}$ $\frac{1}{5}$

APPLICATIONS

▶ **85.** AIR TRAVEL A businesswoman's flight left Los Angeles and in $3\frac{3}{4}$ hours she landed in Minneapolis. She then boarded a commuter plane in Minneapolis and arrived at her final destination in $1\frac{1}{2}$ hours. Find the total time she spent on the flights. $5\frac{1}{4}$ hr

86. SHIPPING A passenger ship and a cargo ship left San Diego harbor at midnight. During the first hour, the passenger ship traveled south at $16\frac{1}{2}$ miles per hour, while the cargo ship traveled north at a rate of $5\frac{1}{5}$ miles per hour. How far apart were they at 1:00 A.M.? $21\frac{7}{10}$ mi

87. TRAIL MIX How many cups of trail mix will the recipe shown below make? $7\frac{1}{6}$ cups

Trail Mix

A healthy snack–great for camping trips

$2\frac{3}{4}$ cups peanuts	$\frac{1}{3}$ cup coconut
$\frac{1}{2}$ cup sunflower seeds	$2\frac{2}{3}$ cups oat flakes
$\frac{2}{3}$ cup raisins	$\frac{1}{4}$ cup pretzels

88. HARDWARE Refer to the illustration below. How long should the threaded part of the bolt be? $7\frac{9}{16}$ in.

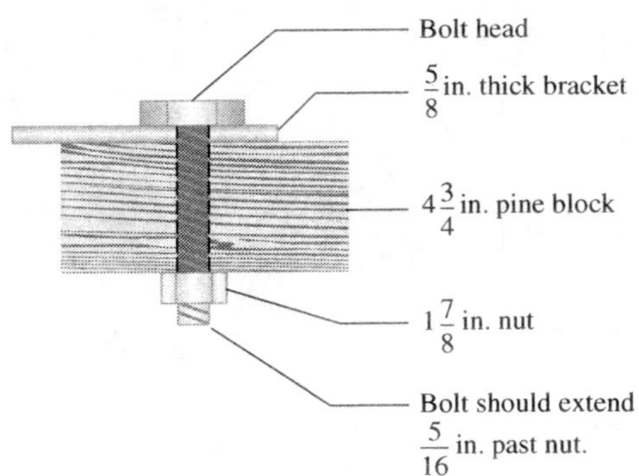

89. OCTUPLETS On January 26, 2009, at Kaiser Permanente Bellflower Medical Center in California, Nadya Suleman gave birth to eight babies. (The United States' first live octuplets were born in Houston in 1998 to Nkem Chukwu and Iyke Louis Udobi). Find the combined birthweights of the babies from the information shown below. (Source: The Nadya Suleman family website) $20\frac{1}{16}$ lb

No. 1: Noah, male, $2\frac{11}{16}$ pounds
No. 2: Maliah, female, $2\frac{3}{4}$ pounds
No. 3: Isaiah, male, $3\frac{1}{4}$ pounds
No. 4: Nariah, female, $2\frac{1}{2}$ pounds
No. 5: Makai, male, $1\frac{1}{2}$ pounds
No. 6: Josiah, male, $2\frac{3}{4}$ pounds
No. 7: Jeremiah, male, $1\frac{15}{16}$ pounds
No. 8: Jonah, male, $2\frac{11}{16}$ pounds

90. SEPTUPLETS On November 19, 1997, at Iowa Methodist Medical Center, Bobbie McCaughey gave birth to seven babies. Find the combined birthweights of the babies from the following information. (Source: *Los Angeles Times*, Nov. 20, 1997) $19\frac{7}{8}$ lb

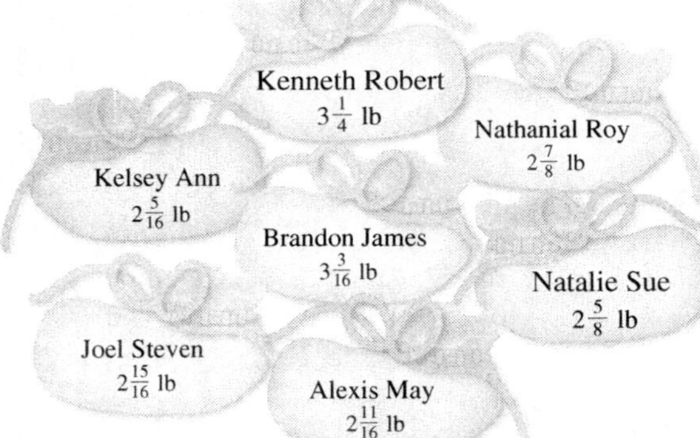

91. HISTORICAL DOCUMENTS The Declaration of Independence on display at the National Archives in Washington, D.C., is $24\frac{1}{2}$ inches wide by $29\frac{3}{4}$ inches high. How many inches of molding would be needed to frame it? $108\frac{1}{2}$ in.

92. STAMP COLLECTING The Pony Express Stamp, shown below, was issued in 1940. It is a favorite of collectors all over the world. A Postal Service document describes its size in an unusual way:

"The dimensions of the stamp are $\frac{84}{100}$ by $1\frac{44}{100}$ inches, arranged horizontally."

To display the stamp, a collector wants to frame it with gold braid. How many inches of braid are needed? $4\frac{14}{25}$ in.

Smithsonian National Postal Museum

93. FREEWAY SIGNS A freeway exit sign is shown. How far apart are the Citrus Ave. and Grand Ave. exits? $2\frac{3}{4}$ mi

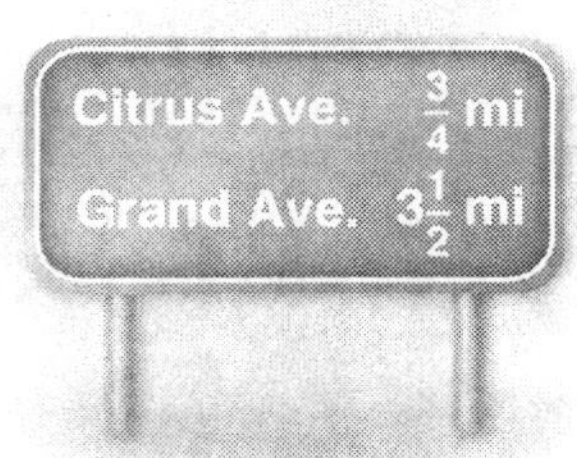

94. BASKETBALL See the graph below. What is the difference in height between the tallest and the shortest of the starting players? $9\frac{3}{8}$ in.

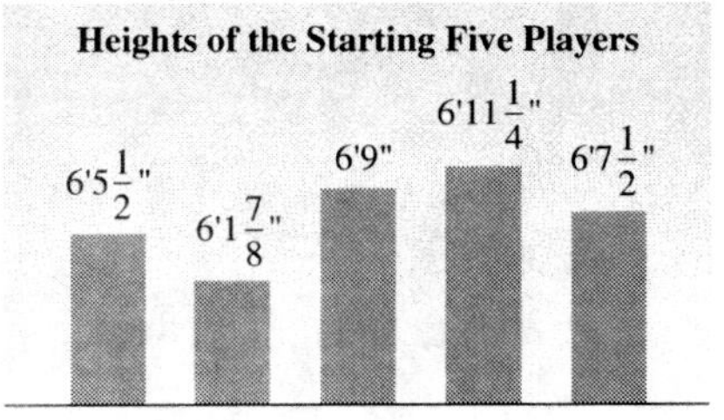

95. HOSE REPAIRS To repair a bad connector, a gardener removes $1\frac{1}{2}$ feet from the end of a 50-foot hose. How long is the hose after the repair? $48\frac{1}{2}$ ft

96. HAIRCUTS A mother makes her child get a haircut when his hair measures 3 inches in length. His barber uses clippers with attachment #2 that leaves $\frac{3}{8}$-inch of hair. How many inches does the child's hair grow between haircuts? $2\frac{5}{8}$ in.

97. SERVICE STATIONS Use the service station sign below to answer the following questions.

a. What is the difference in price between the least and most expensive types of gasoline at the self-service pump? 20¢

b. For each type of gasoline, how much more is the cost per gallon for full service compared to self service? 20¢

98. WATER SLIDES An amusement park added a new section to a water slide to create a slide $311\frac{5}{12}$ feet long. How long was the slide before the addition? $191\frac{2}{3}$ ft

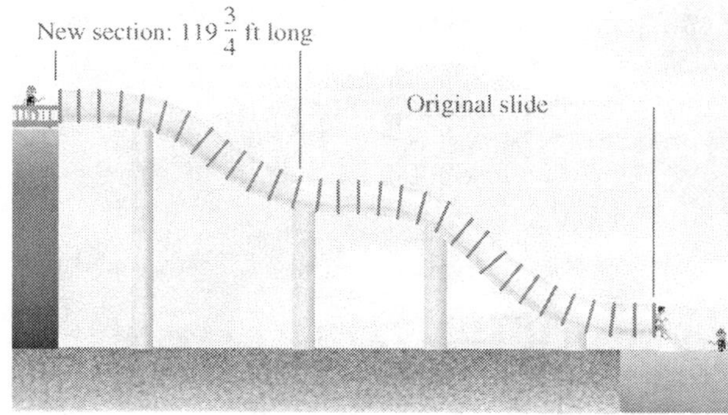

99. JEWELRY A jeweler cut a 7-inch-long silver wire into three pieces. To do this, he aligned a 6-inch-long ruler directly below the wire and made the proper cuts. Find the length of piece 2 of the wire. $3\frac{1}{4}$ in.

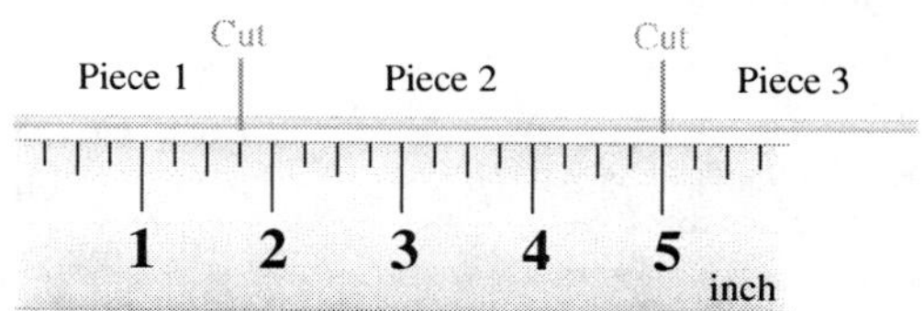

100. SEWING To make some draperies, an interior decorator needs $12\frac{1}{4}$ yards of material for the den and $8\frac{1}{2}$ yards for the living room. If the material comes only in 21-yard bolts, how much will be left over after completing both sets of draperies? $\frac{1}{4}$ yd

WRITING

101. Of the methods studied to add mixed numbers, which do you like better, and why?

102. LEAP YEAR It actually takes Earth $365\frac{1}{4}$ days, give or take a few minutes, to make one revolution around the sun. Explain why every four years we add a day to the calendar to account for this fact.

103. Explain the process of simplifying $12\frac{7}{5}$.

104. Consider the following problem:

$$\begin{array}{r} 108\frac{1}{3} \\ -\ 99\frac{2}{3} \\ \hline \end{array}$$

a. Explain why borrowing is necessary.

b. Explain how the borrowing is done.

REVIEW

Perform each operation and simplify, if possible.

105. a. $3\frac{1}{2} + 1\frac{1}{4}$ $4\frac{3}{4}$ **b.** $3\frac{1}{2} - 1\frac{1}{4}$ $2\frac{1}{4}$

c. $3\frac{1}{2} \cdot 1\frac{1}{4}$ $4\frac{3}{8}$ **d.** $3\frac{1}{2} \div 1\frac{1}{4}$ $2\frac{4}{5}$

106. a. $5\frac{1}{10} + \frac{4}{5}$ $5\frac{9}{10}$ **b.** $5\frac{1}{10} - \frac{4}{5}$ $4\frac{3}{10}$

c. $5\frac{1}{10} \cdot \frac{4}{5}$ $4\frac{2}{25}$ **d.** $5\frac{1}{10} \div \frac{4}{5}$ $6\frac{3}{8}$

Objectives

1. Identify the place value of a digit in a decimal number.
2. Write decimals in expanded form.
3. Read decimals and write them in standard form.
4. Compare decimals using inequality symbols.
5. Graph decimals on a number line.
6. Round decimals.
7. Read tables and graphs involving decimals.

SECTION 2.7
An Introduction to Decimals

The place value system for whole numbers can be extended to create the **decimal numeration system.** Numbers written using **decimal notation** are often simply called **decimals.** They are used in measurement, because it is easy to put them in order and compare them. And as you probably know, our money system is based on decimals.

The decimal 1,537.6 on the odometer represents the distance, in miles, that the car has traveled.

David Hoyt
612 Lelani
Haiku, HI 67512

Feb. 21, 20 10

PAY TO THE ORDER OF Nordstrom $ 82.94

Eighty-two and $\frac{94}{100}$ DOLLARS

BA Garden Branch
P.O. Box 57
Mango City, HI 32145

MEMO Shoes

45-828-02-33-4660

The decimal 82.94 repesents the amount of the check, in dollars.

1 Identify the place value of a digit in a decimal number.

Like fraction notation, decimal notation is used to represent part of a whole. However, when writing a number in decimal notation, we don't use a fraction bar, nor is a denominator shown. For example, consider the rectangular region below that has 1 of 10 equal parts colored red. We can use the fraction $\frac{1}{10}$ or the decimal 0.1 to describe the amount of the figure that is shaded. Both are read as "one-tenth," and we can write:

$$\frac{1}{10} = 0.1$$

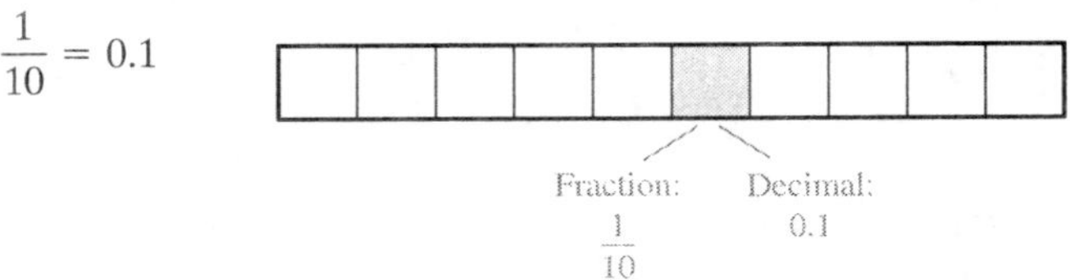

The square region on the right has 1 of 100 equal parts colored red. We can use the fraction $\frac{1}{100}$ or the decimal 0.01 to describe the amount of the figure that is shaded. Both are read as "one one-hundredth," and we can write:

$$\frac{1}{100} = 0.01$$

Fraction: $\frac{1}{100}$
Decimal: 0.01

Decimals are written by entering the digits 0, 1, 2, 3, 4, 5, 6, 7, 8, and 9 into place-value columns that are separated by a **decimal point.** The following **place-value chart** shows the names of the place-value columns. Those to the left of the decimal point form the **whole-number part** of the decimal number, and they have the familiar names ones, tens, hundreds, and so on. The columns to the right of the decimal point form the **fractional part.** Their place value names are similar to those in the whole-number part, but they end in "*ths*." Notice that there is no one*ths* place in the chart.

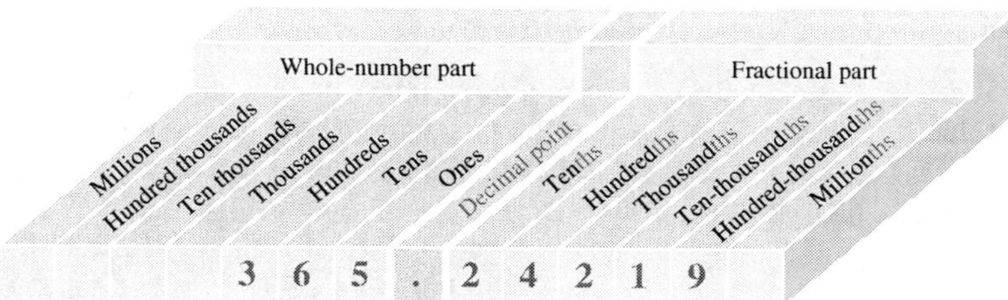

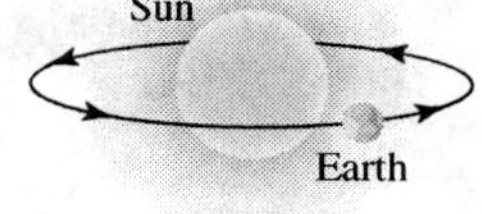

The decimal 365.24219, entered in the place-value chart above, represents the number of days it takes Earth to make one full orbit around the sun. We say that the decimal is written in **standard form** (also called **standard notation**). Each of the 2's in 365.24219 has a different place value because of its position. The place value of the red 2 is two tenths. The place value of the blue 2 is two thousandths.

EXAMPLE 1 Consider the decimal number: 2,864.709531

a. What is the place value of the digit 5?

b. Which digit tells the number of millionths?

Strategy We will locate the decimal point in 2,864.709531. Then, moving to the right, we will name each column (tenths, hundredths, and so on) until we reach 5.

WHY It's easier to remember the names of the columns if you begin at the decimal point and move to the right.

Solution

a. 2,864.709531 Say "Tenths, hundredths, thousandths, ten-thousandths" as you move from column to column.

5 ten-thousandths is the place value of the digit 5.

b. 2,864.709531 Say "Tenths, hundredths, thousandths, ten-thousandths, hundred thousandths, millionths" as you move from column to column.

The digit 1 is in the millionths column.

Caution! We *do not* separate groups of three digits on the right side of the decimal point with commas as we do on the left side. For example, it would be incorrect to write:

2,864.709,531

Self Check 1

Consider the decimal number: 56,081.639724

a. What is the place value of the digit 9? 9 thousandths

b. Which digit tells the number of hundred-thousandths? 2

Now Try **Problem 17**

Teaching Example 1 Consider the decimal number: 8,420.167953

a. What is the place value of the digit 5?

b. Which digit tells the number of hundredths?

Answers:

a. 5 hundred-thousandths

b. 6

We can write a whole number in decimal notation by placing a decimal point immediately to its right and then entering a zero, or zeros, to the right of the decimal point. For example,

99 = 99.0 = 99.00 Because $99 = 99\frac{0}{10} = 99\frac{00}{100}$.

A whole number (99); Place a decimal point here and enter a zero, or zeros, to the right of it.

When there is no whole-number part of a decimal, we can show that by entering a zero directly to the left of the decimal point. For example,

.83 = 0.83 Because $\frac{83}{100} = 0\frac{83}{100}$.

No whole-number part (.83); Enter a zero here, if desired.

Negative decimals are used to describe many situations that arise in everyday life, such as temperatures below zero and the balance in a checking account that is overdrawn. For example, the coldest natural temperature ever recorded on Earth was −128.6°F at the Russian Vostok Station in Antarctica on July 21, 1983.

© Les Welch/Icon SMI/Corbis

2 Write decimals in expanded form.

The decimal 4.458, entered in the place-value chart below, represents the time (in seconds) that it took women's record holder Melanie Troxel to cover a quarter mile in her top-fuel dragster. Notice that the place values of the columns for the whole-number part are 1, 10, 100, 1,000, and so on.

Whole-number part							Fractional part				
Hundred thousands	Ten thousands	Thousands	Hundreds	Tens	Ones	Decimal point	Tenths	Hundredths	Thousandths	Ten-thousandths	Hundred-thousandths
					4	.	4	5	8		
100,000	10,000	1,000	100	10	1		$\frac{1}{10}$	$\frac{1}{100}$	$\frac{1}{1,000}$	$\frac{1}{10,000}$	$\frac{1}{100,000}$

The place values of the columns for the fractional part of a decimal are $\frac{1}{10}$, $\frac{1}{100}$, $\frac{1}{1,000}$, and so on. Each of those columns has a value that is $\frac{1}{10}$ of the value of the place directly to its left. For example,

- The value of the tenths column is $\frac{1}{10}$ of the value of the ones column: $1 \cdot \frac{1}{10} = \frac{1}{10}$.
- The value of the hundredths column is $\frac{1}{10}$ of the value of the tenths column: $\frac{1}{10} \cdot \frac{1}{10} = \frac{1}{100}$.
- The value of the thousandths column is $\frac{1}{10}$ of the value of the hundredths column: $\frac{1}{100} \cdot \frac{1}{10} = \frac{1}{1,000}$.

The meaning of the decimal 4.458 becomes clear when we write it in **expanded form** (also called **expanded notation**).

4.458 = 4 ones + 4 tenths + 5 hundredths + 8 thousandths

which can be written as:

$$4.458 = 4 + \frac{4}{10} + \frac{5}{100} + \frac{8}{1,000}$$

> ***The Language of Mathematics*** The word *decimal* comes from the Latin word *decima,* meaning a tenth part.

Self Check 2

Write the decimal number 1,277.9465 in expanded form.

Now Try **Problems 23 and 27**

Self Check 2 Answer
$1,000 + 200 + 70 + 7 + \frac{9}{10} + \frac{4}{100} + \frac{6}{1,000} + \frac{5}{10,000}$

Teaching Example 2 Write the decimal number 549.2136 in expanded form.

Answer:
$500 + 40 + 9 + \frac{2}{10} + \frac{1}{100} + \frac{3}{1,000} + \frac{6}{10,000}$

EXAMPLE 2 Write the decimal number 592.8674 in expanded form.

Strategy Working from left to right, we will give the place value of each digit and combine them with + symbols.

WHY The term *expanded form* means to write the number as an addition of the place values of each of its digits.

Solution The expanded form of 592.8674 is:

5 hundreds + 9 tens + 2 ones + 8 tenths + 6 hundredths + 7 thousandths + 4 ten-thousandths

which can be written as

$$500 + 90 + 2 + \frac{8}{10} + \frac{6}{100} + \frac{7}{1,000} + \frac{4}{10,000}$$

3 Read decimals and write them in standard form.

To understand how to read a decimal, we will examine the expanded form of 4.458 in more detail. Recall that

$$4.458 = 4 + \frac{4}{10} + \frac{5}{100} + \frac{8}{1{,}000}$$

To add the fractions, we need to build $\frac{4}{10}$ and $\frac{5}{100}$ so that each has a denominator that is the LCD, 1,000.

$$\begin{aligned} 4.458 &= 4 + \frac{4}{10} \cdot \frac{100}{100} + \frac{5}{100} \cdot \frac{10}{10} + \frac{8}{1{,}000} \\ &= 4 + \frac{400}{1{,}000} + \frac{50}{1{,}000} + \frac{8}{1{,}000} \\ &= 4 + \frac{458}{1{,}000} \\ &= 4\frac{458}{1{,}000} \end{aligned}$$

We have found that $4.458 = 4\frac{458}{1{,}000}$ (Whole-number part: 4; Fractional part: .458 → $\frac{458}{1{,}000}$)

We read 4.458 as "four and four hundred fifty-eight thousandths" because 4.458 is the same as $4\frac{458}{1{,}000}$. Notice that the last digit in 4.458 is in the thousandths place. This observation suggests the following method for reading decimals.

Reading a Decimal

To read a decimal:

1. Look to the left of the decimal point and say the name of the whole number.
2. The decimal point is read as "and."
3. Say the fractional part of the decimal as a whole number followed by the name of the last place-value column of the digit that is the farthest to the right.

We can use the steps for reading a decimal to write it in words.

EXAMPLE 3 Write each decimal in words and then as a fraction or mixed number. **You do not have to simplify the fraction.**

a. Sputnik, the first satellite launched into space, weighed 184.3 pounds.

b. Usain Bolt of Jamaica holds the men's world record in the 100-meter dash: 9.69 seconds.

c. A one-dollar bill is 0.0043 inch thick.

d. Liquid mercury freezes solid at −37.7°F.

Strategy We will identify the whole number to the left of the decimal point, the fractional part to its right, and the name of the place-value column of the digit the farthest to the right.

WHY We need to know those three pieces of information to read a decimal or write it in words.

Self Check 3

Write each decimal in words and then as a fraction or mixed number. **You do not have to simplify the fraction.**

a. The average normal body temperature is 98.6ºF.

b. The planet Venus makes one full orbit around the sun every 224.7007 Earth days.

c. One gram is about 0.035274 ounce.

d. Liquid nitrogen freezes solid at −345.748°F.

Now Try Problems 31, 35, and 39

Self Check 3 Answers

a. ninety-eight and six tenths, $98\frac{6}{10}$

b. two hundred twenty-four and seven thousand seven ten-thousandths, $224\frac{7,007}{10,000}$

c. thirty-five thousand, two hundred seventy-four millionths, $\frac{35,274}{1,000,000}$

d. negative three hundred forty-five and seven hundred forty-eight thousandths, $-345\frac{748}{1,000}$

Teaching Example 3 Write each decimal in words and then as a fraction or mixed number. **You do not have to simplify the fraction.**

a. One gallon of milk weighs 8.6 pounds.

b. One meter is about 39.3701 inches.

c. The smallest freshwater fish is the dwarf pygmy goby. Adult males weigh 0.00014 ounce.

d. Ocean salt water freezes at −1.94° Celsius.

Answers:

a. eight and six tenths, $8\frac{6}{10}$

b. thirty-nine and three thousand, seven hundred one ten-thousandths, $39\frac{3,701}{10,000}$

c. fourteen hundred-thousandths, $\frac{14}{100,000}$

d. negative one and ninety-four hundredths, $-1\frac{94}{100}$

Self Check 4

Write each number in standard form:

a. *Eight hundred six and ninety-two hundredths* 806.92

b. *Twelve and sixty-seven ten-thousandths* 12.0067

Now Try Problems 41, 45, and 47

Teaching Example 4 Write each number in standard form:

a. *Sixty-seven and thirty-eight hundredths*

b. *Nineteen and twenty-five thousandths*

Answers:

a. 67.38

b. 19.025

Solution

a. **184 . 3** The whole-number part is 184. The fractional part is 3. The digit the farthest to the right, 3, is in the tenths place.

One hundred eighty-four and three tenths

Written as a mixed number, 184.3 is $184\frac{3}{10}$.

b. **9 . 69** The whole-number part is 9. The fractional part is 69. The digit the farthest to the right, 9, is in the hundredths place.

Nine and sixty-nine hundredths

Written as a mixed number, 9.69 is $9\frac{69}{100}$.

c. **0 . 0043** The whole-number part is 0. The fractional part is 43. The digit the farthest to the right, 4, is in the ten-thousandths place.

Forty-three ten-thousandths Since the whole-number part is 0, we need not write it nor the word and.

Written as a fraction, 0.0043 is $\frac{43}{10,000}$.

d. **−37 . 7** This is a negative decimal.

Negative *thirty-seven and seven tenths.*

Written as a negative mixed number, −37.7 is $-37\frac{7}{10}$.

The Language of Mathematics Decimals are often read in an informal way. For example, we can read 184.3 as "one hundred eighty-four point three" and 9.69 as "nine point six nine."

The procedure for reading a decimal can be applied in reverse to convert from written-word form to standard form.

EXAMPLE 4 Write each number in standard form:

a. *One hundred seventy-two and forty-three hundredths*

b. *Eleven and fifty-one thousandths*

Strategy We will locate the word *and* in the written-word form and translate the phrase that appears before it and the phrase that appears after it separately.

WHY The whole-number part of the decimal is described by the phrase that appears before the word *and.* The fractional part of the decimal is described by the phrase that follows the word *and.*

Solution

a. ***One hundred seventy-two and forty-three hundredths***

172.43

This is the hundredths place-value column.

b. Sometimes, when changing from written-word form to standard form, we must insert placeholder 0's in the fractional part of a decimal so that that the last digit appears in the proper place-value column.

Eleven and fifty-one thousandths

11.051

This is the thousandths place-value column.

A place holder 0 must be inserted here so that the last digit in 51 is in the thousandths column.

Caution! If a placeholder 0 is not written in 11.051, an incorrect answer of 11.51 (eleven and fifty-one *hundredths,* not *thousandths*) results.

4 Compare decimals using inequality symbols.

To develop a way to compare decimals, let's consider 0.3 and 0.271. Since 0.271 contains more digits, it may appear that 0.271 is greater than 0.3. However, the opposite is true. To show this, we write 0.3 and 0.271 in fraction form:

$$0.3 = \frac{3}{10} \qquad 0.271 = \frac{271}{1{,}000}$$

Now we build $\frac{3}{10}$ into an equivalent fraction so that it has a denominator of 1,000, like that of $\frac{271}{1{,}000}$.

$$0.3 = \frac{3}{10} \cdot \frac{100}{100} = \frac{300}{1{,}000}$$

Since $\frac{300}{1{,}000} > \frac{271}{1{,}000}$, it follows that $0.3 > 0.271$. This observation suggests a quicker method for comparing decimals.

Comparing Decimals

To compare two decimals:

1. Make sure both numbers have the same number of decimal places to the right of the decimal point. Write any additional zeros necessary to achieve this.
2. Compare the digits of each decimal, column by column, working from left to right.
3. *If the decimals are positive:* When two digits differ, the decimal with the greater digit is the greater number. *If the decimals are negative:* When two digits differ, the decimal with the smaller digit is the greater number.

EXAMPLE 5 Place an $<$ or $>$ symbol in the box to make a true statement:

a. 1.2679 ☐ 1.2658 **b.** 54.9 ☐ 54.929 **c.** −10.419 ☐ −10.45

Strategy We will stack the decimals and then, working from left to right, we will scan their place-value columns looking for a difference in their digits.

WHY We need only look in that column to determine which digit is the greater.

Solution

a. Since both decimals have the same number of places to the right of the decimal point, we can immediately compare the digits, column by column.

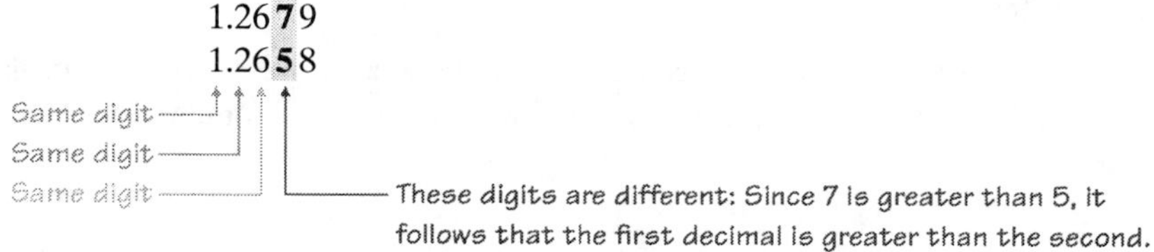

Thus, 1.2679 is greater than 1.2658 and we can write $1.2679 > 1.2658$.

b. We can write two zeros after the 9 in 54.9 so that the decimals have the same number of digits to the right of the decimal point. This makes the comparison easier.

54.9**0**0
54.9**2**9

As we work from left to right, this is the first column in which the digits differ. Since $2 > 0$, it follows that 54.929 is greater than 54.9 (or 54.9 is less than 54.929) and we can write $54.9 < 54.929$.

Self Check 5

Place an $<$ or $>$ symbol in the box to make a true statement:

a. 3.4308 < 3.4312

b. 678.3409 > 678.34

c. −703.8 < −703.78

Now Try **Problems 49, 55, and 59**

Teaching Example 5 Place an < or > symbol in the box to make a true statement:

a. 2.7446 ☐ 2.7439

b. 39.2 ☐ 39.203

c. −10.45 ☐ −10.419

Answers:

a. >

b. <

c. <

Success Tip Writing additional zeros *after the last digit to the right of the decimal point does not change the value of the decimal.* Also, deleting additional zeros after the last digit to the right of the decimal point does not change the value of the decimal. For example,

$$54.9 = 54.90 = 54.900$$

Because $54\frac{90}{100}$ and $54\frac{900}{1,000}$ in simplest form are equal to $54\frac{9}{10}$.

These additional zeros do not change the value of the decimal.

c. We are comparing two negative decimals. In this case, when two digits differ, the decimal with the smaller digit is the greater number.

$-10.4\mathbf{1}9$

$-10.4\mathbf{5}0$ Write a zero after 5 to help in the comparison.

As we work from left to right, this is the first column in which the digits differ. Since $1 < 5$, it follows that -10.419 is greater than -10.45 and we can write $-10.419 > -10.45$.

5 Graph decimals on a number line.

Decimals can be shown by drawing points on a number line.

Self Check 6

Graph -1.1, -1.64, -0.8, and 1.9 on a number line.

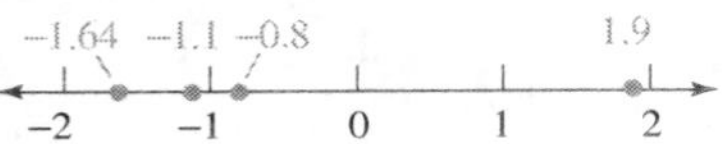

Now Try **Problem 61**

Teaching Example 6 Graph -1.37, 0.9, -1.7, and -0.2 on a number line.

Answer:

−1.37 −1.7 −0.2 0.9

−2 −1 0 1 2

EXAMPLE 6 Graph -1.8, -1.23, -0.3, and 1.89 on a number line.

Strategy We will locate the position of each decimal on the number line and draw a bold dot.

WHY To *graph a number* means to make a drawing that represents the number.

Solution The graph of each negative decimal is to the left of 0 and the graph of each positive decimal is to the right of 0. Since $-1.8 < -1.23$, the graph of -1.8 is to the left of -1.23.

−1.8 −1.23 −0.3 1.89

−2 −1 0 1 2

6 Round decimals.

When we don't need exact results, we can approximate decimal numbers by **rounding.** To round the decimal part of a decimal number, we use a method similar to that used to round whole numbers.

Rounding a Decimal

1. To round a decimal to a certain decimal place value, locate the **rounding digit** in that place.
2. Look at the **test digit** directly to the right of the rounding digit.
3. If the test digit is 5 or greater, round up by adding 1 to the rounding digit and dropping all the digits to its right. If the test digit is less than 5, round down by keeping the rounding digit and dropping all the digits to its right.

EXAMPLE 7 *Chemistry* A student in a chemistry class uses a digital balance to weigh a compound in grams. Round the reading shown on the balance to the nearest thousandth of a gram.

Strategy We will identify the digit in the thousandths column and the digit in the ten-thousandths column.

WHY To round to the nearest thousandth, the digit in the thousandths column is the rounding digit and the digit in the ten-thousandths column is the test digit.

Solution The rounding digit in the thousandths column is 8. Since the test digit 7 is 5 or greater, we round up.

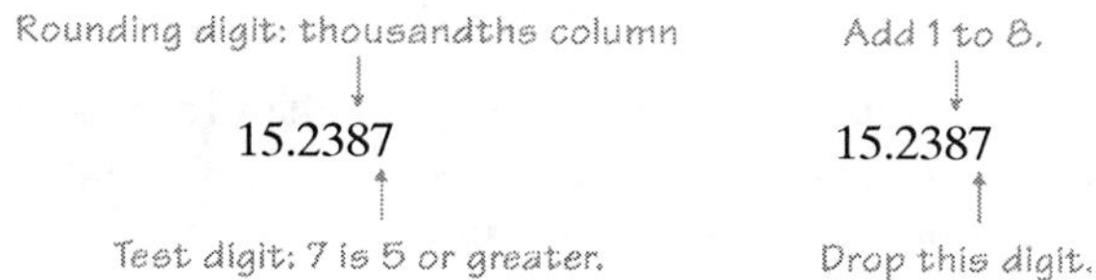

The reading on the balance is approximately 15.239 grams.

Self Check 7

Round 24.41658 to the nearest ten-thousandth. 24.4166

Now Try **Problems 65 and 69**

Teaching Example 7 Round 47.0676 to the nearest thousandth.
Answer:
47.068

EXAMPLE 8 Round each decimal to the indicated place value:

a. −645.1358 to the nearest tenth **b.** 33.096 to the nearest hundredth

Strategy In each case, we will first identify the rounding digit. Then we will identify the test digit and determine whether it is less than 5 or greater than or equal to 5.

WHY If the test digit is less than 5, we round down; if it is greater than or equal to 5, we round up.

Solution

a. Negative decimals are rounded in the same ways as positive decimals. The rounding digit in the tenths column is 1. Since the test digit 3 is less than 5, we round down.

Thus, −645.1358 rounded to the nearest tenth is −645.1.

b. The rounding digit in the hundredths column is 9. Since the test digit 6 is 5 or greater, we round up.

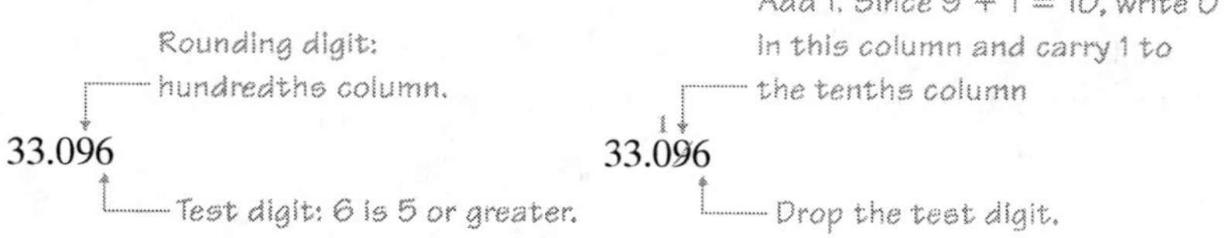

Thus, 33.096 rounded to the nearest hundredth is 33.10.

Caution! It would be incorrect to drop the 0 in the answer 33.10. If asked to round to a certain place value (in this case, thousandths), that place must have a digit, even if the digit is 0.

Self Check 8

Round each decimal to the indicated place value:

a. −708.522 to the nearest tenth

b. 9.1198 to the nearest thousandth

Now Try **Problems 73 and 77**

Self Check 8 Answers
a. −708.5
b. 9.120

Teaching Example 8 Round each decimal to the indicated place value:
a. −420.139 to the nearest tenth
b. 56.095 to the nearest hundredth
Answers:
a. −420.1
b. 56.10

There are many situations in our daily lives that call for rounding amounts of money. For example, a grocery shopper might round the unit cost of an item to the nearest cent or a taxpayer might round his or her income to the nearest dollar when filling out an income tax return.

Self Check 9

a. Round \$0.076601 to the nearest cent \$0.08

b. Round \$24,908.53 to the nearest dollar. \$24,909

Now Try **Problems 85 and 87**

Teaching Example 9
a. UTILITY BILLS A utility company calculates a homeowner's monthly natural gas bill by multiplying the unit cost of \$0.96412 by the number of therms used that month. Round the unit cost to the nearest cent.
b. ANNUAL INCOME A plumber earned \$76,350.87 dollars in one year. Round his income to the nearest dollar.
Answers:
a. \$0.96
b. \$76,351

EXAMPLE 9

a. *Utility Bills* A utility company calculates a homeowner's monthly electric bill by multiplying the unit cost of \$0.06421 by the number of kilowatt hours used that month. Round the unit cost to the nearest cent.

b. *Annual Income* A secretary earned \$36,500.91 dollars in one year. Round her income to the nearest dollar.

Strategy In part a, we will round the decimal to the nearest hundredth. In part b, we will round the decimal to the ones column.

WHY Since there are 100 cents in a dollar, each cent is $\frac{1}{100}$ of a dollar. To round to the *nearest cent* is the same as rounding to the *nearest hundredth* of a dollar. To round to the *nearest dollar* is the same as rounding to the *ones place.*

Solution

a. The rounding digit in the hundredths column is 6. Since the test digit 4 is less than 5, we round down.

Thus, \$0.06421 rounded to the nearest cent is \$0.06.

b. The rounding digit in the ones column is 0. Since the test digit 9 is 5 or greater, we round up.

Thus, \$36,500.91 rounded to the nearest dollar is \$36,501.

7 Read tables and graphs involving decimals.

Year	Pounds
1960	2.68
1970	3.25
1980	3.66
1990	4.50
2000	4.64
2007	4.62

(Source: U.S. Environmental Protection Agency)

The table on the left is an example of the use of decimals. It shows the number of pounds of trash generated daily per person in the United States for selected years from 1960 through 2007.

When the data in the table is presented in the form of a **bar graph,** a trend is apparent. The amount of trash generated daily per person increased steadily until the year 2000. Since then, it appears to have remained about the same.

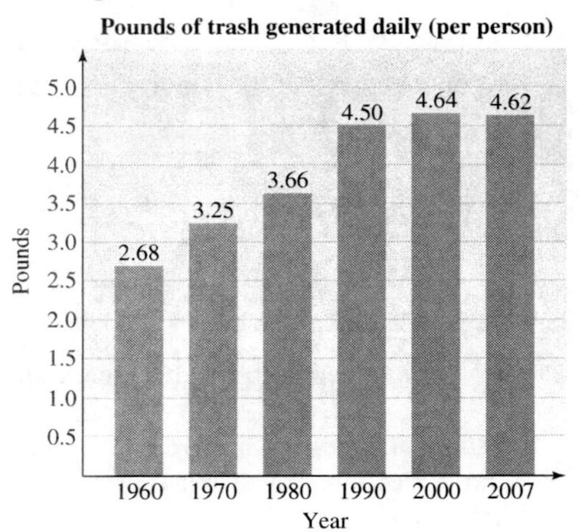

ANSWERS TO SELF CHECKS

1. a. 9 thousandths **b.** 2 **2.** $1{,}000 + 200 + 70 + 7 + \frac{9}{10} + \frac{4}{100} + \frac{6}{1{,}000} + \frac{5}{10{,}000}$ **3. a.** ninety-eight and six tenths, $98\frac{6}{10}$ **b.** two hundred twenty-four and seven thousand seven ten-thousandths, $224\frac{7{,}007}{10{,}000}$ **c.** thirty-five thousand, two hundred seventy-four millionths, $\frac{35{,}274}{1{,}000{,}000}$ **d.** negative three hundred forty-five and seven hundred forty-eight thousandths, $-345\frac{748}{1{,}000}$ **4. a.** 806.92 **b.** 12.0067 **5. a.** < **b.** > **c.** <
6. −1.64 −1.1 −0.8 1.9 (number line from −2 to 2) **7.** 24.4166 **8. a.** −708.5 **b.** 9.120
9. a. \$0.08 **b.** \$24,909

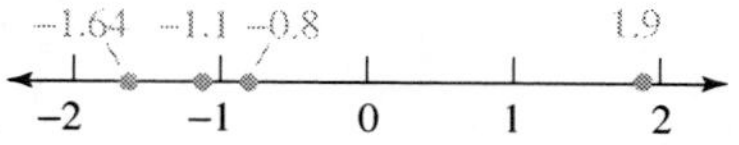

SECTION 2.7 STUDY SET

VOCABULARY

Fill in the blanks.

1. Decimals are written by entering the digits 0, 1, 2, 3, 4, 5, 6, 7, 8, and 9 into place-value columns that are separated by a decimal point.

2. The place-value columns to the left of the decimal point form the whole-number part of a decimal number and the place-value columns to the right of the decimal point form the fractional part.

3. We can show the value represented by each digit of the decimal 98.6213 by using expanded form:

$$98.6213 = 90 + 8 + \frac{6}{10} + \frac{2}{100} + \frac{1}{1{,}000} + \frac{3}{10{,}000}$$

4. When we don't need exact results, we can approximate decimal numbers by rounding.

CONCEPTS

5. Write the name of each column in the following place-value chart.

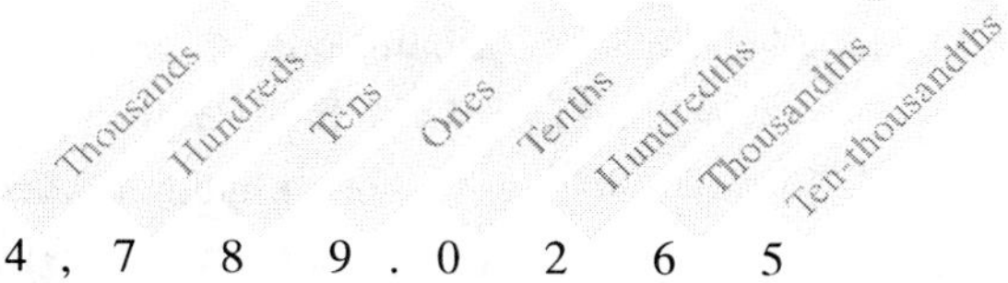

6. Write the value of each column in the following place-value chart.

7	2	.	3	1	9	5	8
10	1		$\frac{1}{10}$	$\frac{1}{100}$	$\frac{1}{1{,}000}$	$\frac{1}{10{,}000}$	$\frac{1}{100{,}000}$

7. Fill in the blanks.

   a. The value of each place in the whole-number part of a decimal number is 10 times greater than the column directly to its right.

   b. The value of each place in the fractional part of a decimal number is $\frac{1}{10}$ of the value of the place directly to its left.

8. Represent each situation using a signed number.

   a. A checking account overdrawn by \$33.45 −33.45

   b. A river 6.25 feet above flood stage 6.25

   c. 3.9 degrees below zero −3.9

   d. 17.5 seconds after liftoff 17.5

9. **a.** Represent the shaded part of the rectangular region as a fraction and a decimal. $\frac{7}{10}$, 0.7

   b. Represent the shaded part of the square region as a fraction and a decimal. $\frac{47}{100}$, 0.47

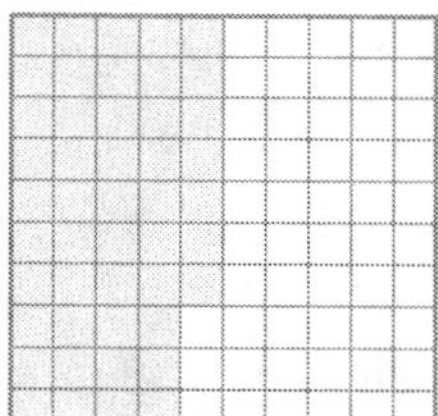

10. Write $400 + 20 + 8 + \frac{9}{10} + \frac{1}{100}$ as a decimal. 428.91

11. Fill in the blanks in the following illustration to label the *whole-number part* and the *fractional part.*

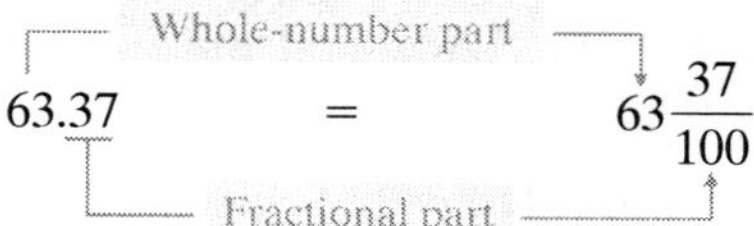

12. Fill in the blanks.

   a. To round \$0.13506 to the *nearest cent,* the rounding digit is 3 and the test digit is 5.

   b. To round \$1,906.47 to the *nearest dollar,* the rounding digit is 6 and the test digit is 4.

NOTATION

Fill in the blanks.

13. The columns to the right of the decimal point in a decimal number form its fractional part. Their place value names are similar to those in the whole-number part, but they end in the letters "ths."

14. When reading a decimal, such as 2.37, we can read the decimal point as "and" or as "point."

15. Write a decimal number that has . . .
6 in the ones column,
1 in the tens column,
0 in the tenths column,
8 in the hundreds column,
2 in the hundredths column,
9 in the thousands column,
4 in the thousandths column,
7 in the ten thousands column, and
5 in the ten-thousandths column. 79,816.0245

16. Determine whether each statement is true or false.
a. 0.9 = 0.90 true
b. 1.260 = 1.206 false
c. −1.2800 = −1.280 true
d. 0.001 = .0010 true

GUIDED PRACTICE

Answer the following questions about place value. See Example 1.

17. Consider the decimal number: 145.926
a. What is the place value of the digit 9? 9 tenths
b. Which digit tells the number of thousandths? 6
c. Which digit tells the number of tens? 4
d. What is the place value of the digit 5? 5 ones

18. Consider the decimal number: 304.817
a. What is the place value of the digit 1? 1 hundredth
b. Which digit tells the number of thousandths? 7
c. Which digit tells the number of hundreds? 3
d. What is the place value of the digit 7? 7 thousandths

19. Consider the decimal number: 6.204538
a. What is the place value of the digit 8? 8 millionths
b. Which digit tells the number of hundredths? 0
c. Which digit tells the number of ten-thousandths? 5
d. What is the place value of the digit 6? 6 ones

▶ **20.** Consider the decimal number: 4.390762
a. What is the place value of the digit 6? 6 hundred-thousandths
b. Which digit tells the number of thousandths? 0
c. Which digit tells the number of ten-thousandths? 7
d. What is the place value of the digit 4? 4 ones

Write each decimal number in expanded form. See Example 2.

21. 37.89 $30 + 7 + \frac{8}{10} + \frac{9}{100}$

22. 26.93 $20 + 6 + \frac{9}{10} + \frac{3}{100}$

23. 124.575 $100 + 20 + 4 + \frac{5}{10} + \frac{7}{100} + \frac{5}{1,000}$

▶ **24.** 231.973 $200 + 30 + 1 + \frac{9}{10} + \frac{7}{100} + \frac{3}{1,000}$

25. 7,498.6468 $7,000 + 400 + 90 + 8 + \frac{6}{10} + \frac{4}{100} + \frac{6}{1,000} + \frac{8}{10,000}$

26. 1,946.7221 $1,000 + 900 + 40 + 6 + \frac{7}{10} + \frac{2}{100} + \frac{2}{1,000} + \frac{1}{10,000}$

27. 6.40941 $6 + \frac{4}{10} + \frac{9}{1,000} + \frac{4}{10,000} + \frac{1}{100,000}$

28. 8.70214 $8 + \frac{7}{10} + \frac{2}{1,000} + \frac{1}{10,000} + \frac{4}{100,000}$

Write each decimal in words and then as a fraction or mixed number. See Example 3.

29. 0.3 three tenths, $\frac{3}{10}$

30. 0.9 nine tenths, $\frac{9}{10}$

31. 50.41 fifty and forty-one hundredths, $50\frac{41}{100}$

▶ **32.** 60.61 sixty and sixty-one hundredths, $60\frac{61}{100}$

33. 19.529 nineteen and five hundred twenty-nine thousandths, $19\frac{529}{1,000}$

34. 12.841 twelve and eight hundred forty-one thousandths, $12\frac{841}{1,000}$

35. 304.0003 three hundred four and three ten-thousandths, $304\frac{3}{10,000}$

36. 405.0007 four hundred five and seven ten-thousandths, $405\frac{7}{10,000}$

37. −0.00137 negative one hundred thirty-seven hundred-thousandths, $-\frac{137}{100,000}$

38. −0.00613 negative six hundred thirteen hundred-thousandths, $-\frac{613}{100,000}$

39. −1,072.499 negative one thousand seventy-two and four hundred ninety-nine thousandths, $-1,072\frac{499}{1,000}$

40. −3,076.177 negative three thousand seventy-six and one hundred seventy-seven thousandths, $-3,076\frac{177}{1,000}$

Write each number in standard form. See Example 4.

41. Six and one hundred eighty-seven thousandths 6.187

42. Four and three hundred ninety-two thousandths 4.392

43. Ten and fifty-six ten-thousandths 10.0056

44. Eleven and eighty-six ten-thousandths 11.0086

45. Negative sixteen and thirty-nine hundredths −16.39

▶ **46.** Negative twenty-seven and forty-four hundredths −27.44

47. One hundred four and four millionths 104.000004

48. Two hundred three and three millionths 203.000003

Place an < or an > symbol in the box to make a true statement. See Example 5.

49. 2.59 > 2.55

50. 5.17 > 5.14

51. 45.103 < 45.108

52. 13.874 < 13.879

53. 3.28724 > 3.2871

54. 8.91335 > 8.9132

55. 379.67 > 379.6088

56. 446.166 < 446.2

57. −23.45 < −23.1

58. −301.98 > −302.45

59. −0.065 > −0.066

▶ **60.** −3.99 < −3.9888

Graph each number on a number line. See Example 6.

61. 0.8, −0.7, −3.1, 4.5, −3.9

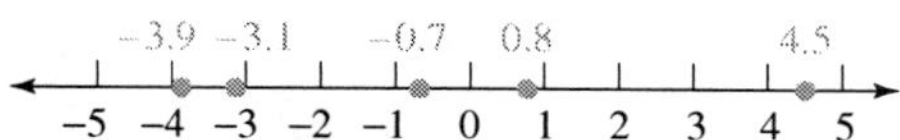

62. 0.6, −0.3, −2.7, 3.5, −2.2

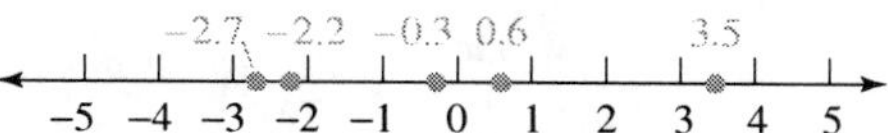

63. −1.21, −3.29, −4.25, 2.75, −1.84

−4.25 −3.29 −1.84 −1.21 2.75
−5 −4 −3 −2 −1 0 1 2 3 4 5

64. −3.19, −0.27, −3.95, 4.15, −1.66

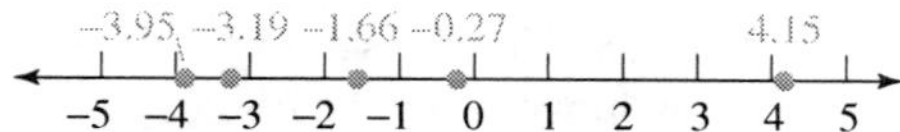

Round each decimal number to the indicated place value. See Example 7.

65. 506.198 nearest tenth 506.2

66. 51.451 nearest tenth 51.5

67. 33.0832 nearest hundredth 33.08

68. 64.0059 nearest hundredth 64.01

69. 4.2341 nearest thousandth 4.234

70. 8.9114 nearest thousandth 8.911

71. 0.36563 nearest ten-thousandth 0.3656

72. 0.77623 nearest ten-thousandth 0.7762

Round each decimal number to the indicated place value. See Example 8.

73. −0.137 nearest hundredth −0.14

74. −808.0897 nearest hundredth −808.09

75. −2.718218 nearest tenth −2.7

76. −3,987.8911 nearest tenth −3,987.9

77. 3.14959 nearest thousandth 3.150

78. 9.50966 nearest thousandth 9.510

79. 1.4142134 nearest millionth 1.414213

80. 3.9998472 nearest millionth 3.999847

81. 16.0995 nearest thousandth 16.100

82. 67.0998 nearest thousandth 67.100

83. 290.303496 nearest hundred-thousandth 290.30350

84. 970.457297 nearest hundred-thousandth 970.45730

Round each given dollar amount. See Example 9.

85. $0.284521 nearest cent $0.28

86. $0.312906 nearest cent $0.31

87. $27,841.52 nearest dollar $27,842

88. $44,633.78 nearest dollar $44,634

APPLICATIONS

89. READING METERS To what decimal is the arrow pointing? −0.7

90. MEASUREMENT Estimate a length of 0.3 inch on the 1-inch-long line segment below.

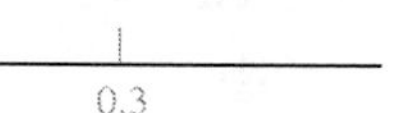

91. CHECKING ACCOUNTS Complete the check shown by writing in the amount, using a decimal. $1,025.78

Ellen Russell
455 Santa Clara Ave.
Parker, CO 25413
April 14, 20 10
PAY TO THE ORDER OF Citicorp $
One thousand twenty-five and 78/100 DOLLARS
BA Downtown Branch
P.O. Box 2456
Colorado Springs,CO 23712
MEMO Mortgage
Ellen Russell
45-828-02-33-4660

92. MONEY We use a decimal point when working with dollars, but the decimal point is not necessary when working with cents. For each dollar amount in the table, give the equivalent amount expressed as cents.

Dollars	Cents
$0.50	50
$0.05	5
$0.55	55
$5.00	500
$0.01	1

93. INJECTIONS A syringe is shown below. Use an arrow to show to what point the syringe should be filled if a 0.38-cc dose of medication is to be given. ("cc" stands for "cubic centimeters.")

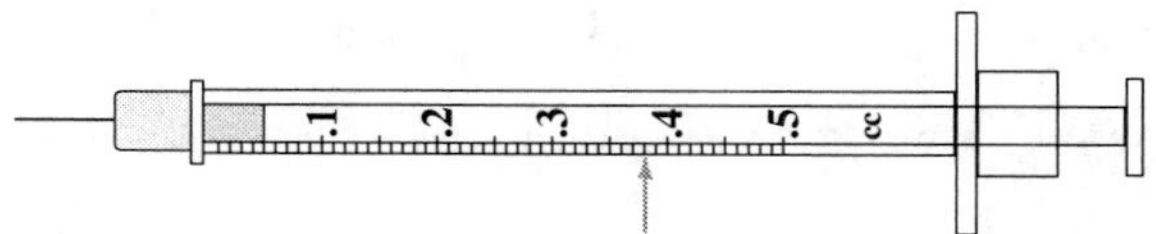

94. LASERS The laser used in laser vision correction is so precise that each pulse can remove 39 millionths of an inch of tissue in 12 billionths of a second. Write each of these numbers as a decimal.
0.000039 in., 0.000000012 sec

95. NASCAR The closest finish in NASCAR history took place at the Darlington Raceway on March 16, 2003, when Ricky Craven beat Kurt Busch by a mere 0.002 seconds. Write the decimal in words and then as a fraction in simplest form. (Source: NASCAR)
two-thousandths, $\frac{2}{1{,}000} = \frac{1}{500}$

96. THE METRIC SYSTEM The metric system is widely used in science to measure length (meters), weight (grams), and capacity (liters). Round each decimal to the nearest hundredth.

a. 1 ft is 0.3048 meter. 0.30

b. 1 mi is 1,609.344 meters. 1,609.34

c. 1 lb is 453.59237 grams. 453.59

d. 1 gal is 3.785306 liters. 3.79

97. UTILITY BILLS A portion of a homeowner's electric bill is shown below. Round each decimal dollar amount to the nearest cent. \$0.16, \$1.02, \$1.20, \$0.00, \$0.10

Billing Period

From	To	Meter Number	The Gas Company
06/05/10	07/05/10	10694435	

Next Meter Reading Date on or about Aug 03 2010

Summary of Charges

Customer Charge	30 Days	× \$0.16438
Baseline	14 Therms	× \$1.01857
Over Baseline	11 Therms	× \$1.20091
State Regulatory Fee	25 Therms	× \$0.00074
Public Purpose Surcharge	25 Therms	× \$0.09910

98. INCOME TAX A portion of a W-2 tax form is shown below. Round each dollar amount to the nearest dollar. \$35,674, \$7,134, \$38,204, \$2,369, \$38,204, \$550

Form W-2 Wage and Tax Statement 2010

1 Wages, tips, other comp *\$35,673.79*	2 Fed inc tax withheld *\$7,134.28*	3 Social security wages *\$38,204.16*
4 SS tax withheld *\$2,368.65*	5 Medicare wages & tips *\$38,204.16*	6 Medicare tax withheld *\$550.13*
7 Social security tips	8 Allocated tips	9 Advance EIC payment
10 Depdnt care benefits	11 Nonqualified plans	12a

▶ **99.** THE DEWEY DECIMAL SYSTEM When stacked on the shelves, the library books shown in the next column are to be in numerical order, least to greatest, *from left to right.* How should the titles be rearranged to be in the proper order?
candlemaking, crafts, hobbies, folk dolls, modern art

100. 2008 OLYMPICS The top six finishers in the women's individual all-around gymnastic competition in the Beijing Olympic Games are shown below in alphabetical order. If the highest score wins, which gymnasts won the gold (1st place), silver (2nd place), and bronze (3rd place) medals?
gold: Liukin, silver: Johnson, bronze: Yang

	Name	Nation	Score
	Yuyuan Jiang	China	60.900
	Shawn Johnson	U.S.A.	62.725
	Nastia Liukin	U.S.A.	63.325
	Steliana Nistor	Romania	61.050
	Ksenia Semenova	Russia	61.925
	Yilin Yang	China	62.650

(Source: SportsIllustrated.cnn.com)

▶ **101.** TUNE-UPS The six spark plugs from the engine of a Nissan Quest were removed, and the spark plug gap was checked. If vehicle specifications call for the gap to be from 0.031 to 0.035 inch, which of the plugs should be replaced? Cylinder 2, Cylinder 4

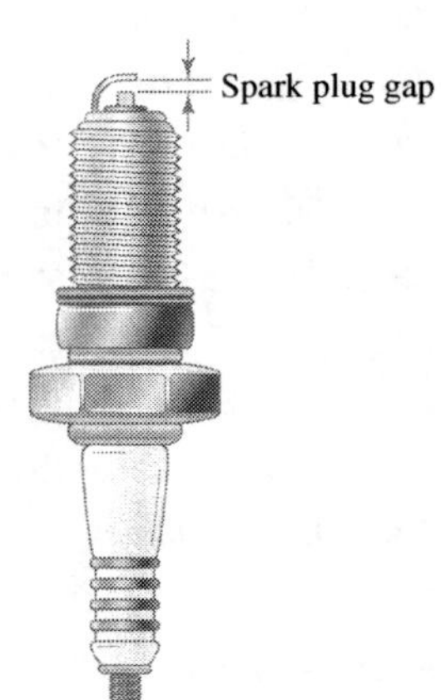

Cylinder 1: 0.035 in.
Cylinder 2: 0.029 in.
Cylinder 3: 0.033 in.
Cylinder 4: 0.039 in.
Cylinder 5: 0.031 in.
Cylinder 6: 0.032 in.

102. GEOLOGY Geologists classify types of soil according to the grain size of the particles that make up the soil. The four major classifications of soil are shown below. Classify each of the samples (A, B, C, and D) in the table as clay, silt, sand, or granule.

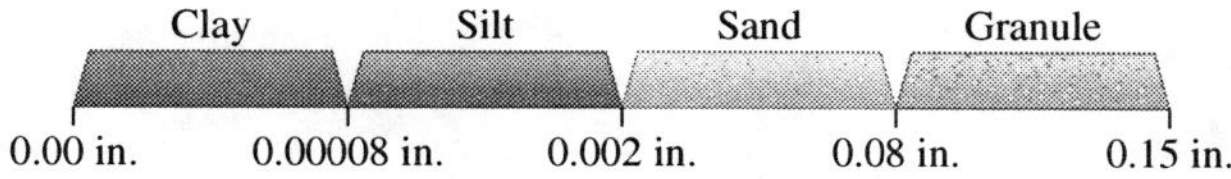

Sample	Location found	Grain size (in.)	Classification
A	Riverbank	0.009	sand
B	Pond	0.0007	silt
C	NE corner	0.095	granule
D	Dry lake	0.00003	clay

103. MICROSCOPES A microscope used in a lab is capable of viewing structures that range in size from 0.1 to as small as 0.0001 centimeter. Which of the structures listed in the table would be visible through this microscope? bacterium, plant cell, animal cell, asbestos fiber

Structure	Size (cm)
Bacterium	0.00011
Plant cell	0.015
Virus	0.000017
Animal cell	0.00093
Asbestos fiber	0.0002

104. FASTEST CARS The graph below shows AutoWeek's list of fastest cars for 2009. Find the time it takes each car to accelerate from 0 to 60 mph.

LIONEL VADAM/Maxppp/Landov

Bugatti: 2.6 sec, Lamborghini: 3.1 sec, Koenigsegg: 3.1 sec, Nissan: 3.4 sec, Corvette: 3.4 sec, Ferrari: 3.5 sec

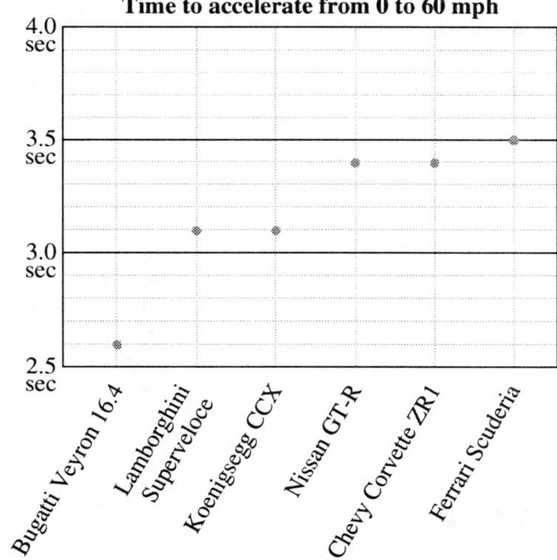

105. THE STOCK MARKET Refer to the graph below, which shows the earnings (and losses) in the value of one share of Goodyear Tire and Rubber Company stock over twelve quarters. (For accounting purposes, a year is divided into four quarters, each three months long.)

a. In what quarter, of what year, were the earnings per share the greatest? Estimate the gain. Q3, 2007; \$2.75

b. In what quarter, of what year, was the loss per share the greatest? Estimate the loss. Q4, 2006; −\$2.05

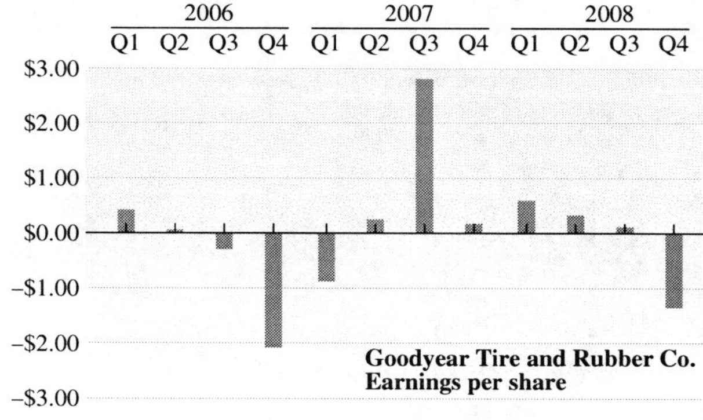

(Source: Wall Street Journal)

106. GASOLINE PRICES Refer to the graph below.

a. In what month, of what year, was the retail price of a gallon of gasoline the lowest? Estimate the price. Dec., 2008; \$1.70

b. In what month(s), of what year, was the retail price of a gallon of gasoline the highest? Estimate the price. June and July, 2008; \$4.10

c. In what month of 2007 was the price of a gallon of gasoline the greatest? Estimate the price. May, \$3.10

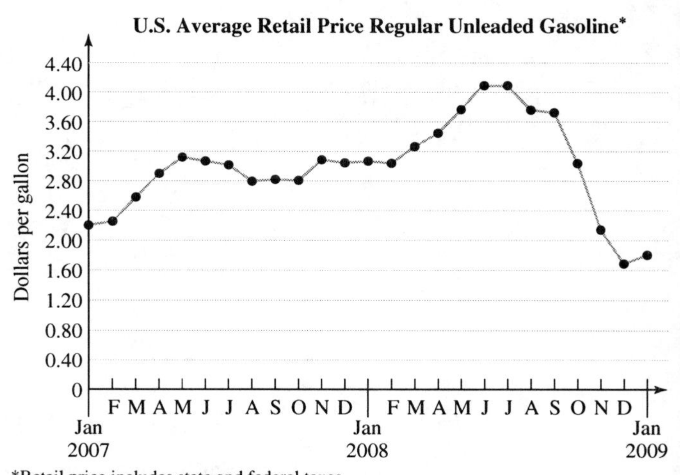

*Retail price includes state and federal taxes
(Source: EPA Short-Term Energy Outlook, March 2009)

WRITING

107. Explain the difference between ten and one-tenth.

108. "The more digits a number contains, the larger it is." Is this statement true? Explain.

109. Explain why is it wrong to read 2.103 as *"two and one hundred and three thousandths."*

110. SIGNS

a. A sign in front of a fast food restaurant had the cost of a hamburger listed as .99¢. Explain the error.

b. The illustration below shows the unusual notation that some service stations use to express the price of a gallon of gasoline. Explain the error.

REGULAR	UNLEADED	UNLEADED +
$2.79\frac{9}{10}$	$2.89\frac{9}{10}$	$2.99\frac{9}{10}$

111. Write a definition for each of these words.

decade *decathlon* *decimal*

112. Show that in the decimal numeration system, each place-value column for the fractional part of a decimal is $\frac{1}{10}$ of the value of the place directly to its left.

REVIEW

113. a. Find the perimeter of the rectangle shown below. $12\frac{1}{2}$ in.

b. Find the area of the rectangle. $9\frac{5}{8}$ ft^2

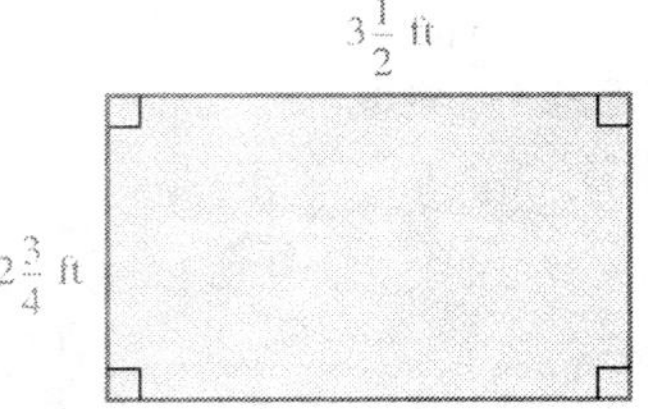

114. a. Find the perimeter of the triangle shown below. $3\frac{3}{5}$ in.

b. Find the area of the triangle. $\frac{27}{50}$ in.^{2}

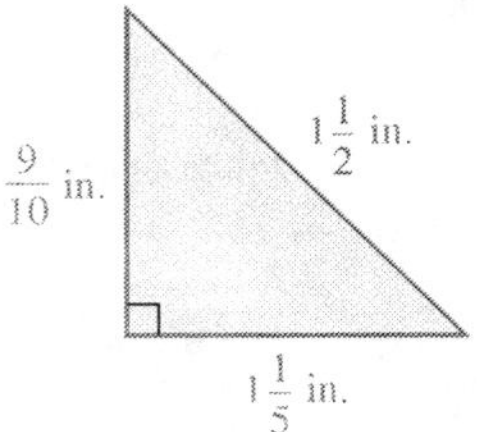

Objectives

1. Add decimals.
2. Subtract decimals.
3. Add and subtract signed decimals.
4. Estimate sums and differences of decimals.
5. Solve application problems by adding and subtracting decimals.

SECTION 2.8 Adding and Subtracting Decimals

To add or subtract objects, they must be similar. The federal income tax form shown below has a vertical line to make sure that dollars are added to dollars and cents added to cents. In this section, we show how decimal numbers are added and subtracted using this type of vertical form.

Form 1040EZ	Department of the Treasury—Internal Revenue Service **Income Tax Return for Single and Joint Filers With No Dependents 2010**			
Income **Attach Form(s) W-2 here.** Enclose, but do not attach, any payment.	1 Wages, salaries, and tips. This should be shown in box 1 of your Form(s) W-2. Attach your Form(s) W-2.	1	21,056	89
	2 Taxable interest. If the total is over $1,500, you cannot use Form 1040EZ.	2	42	06
	3 Unemployment compensation and Alaska Permanent Fund dividends (see page 11).	3	200	00
	4 Add lines 1, 2, and 3. This is your **adjusted gross income.**	4	21,298	95

1 Add decimals.

Adding decimals is similar to adding whole numbers. We use **vertical form** and stack the decimals with their corresponding place values and decimal points lined up. Then we add the digits in each column, working from right to left, making sure that hundredths are added to hundredths, tenths are added to tenths, ones are added to ones, and so on. We write the decimal point in the **sum** so that it lines up with the decimal points in the **addends.** For example, to find 4.21 + 1.23 + 2.45, we proceed as follows:

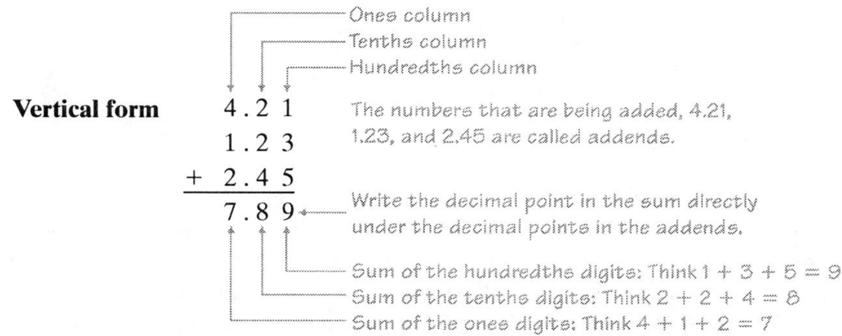

The sum is 7.89.

In this example, each addend had two decimal places, tenths and hundredths. If the number of decimal places in the addends are different, we can insert additional zeros so that the number of decimal places match.

Adding Decimals

To add decimal numbers:

1. Write the numbers in vertical form with the decimal points lined up.
2. Add the numbers as you would add whole numbers, from right to left.
3. Write the decimal point in the result from Step 2 directly below the decimal points in the addends.

Like whole number addition, if the sum of the digits in any place-value column is greater than 9, we must **carry.**

EXAMPLE 1 Add: 31.913 + 5.6 + 68 + 16.78

Strategy We will write the addition in vertical form so that the corresponding place values and decimal points of the addends are lined up. Then we will add the digits, column by column, working from right to left.

WHY We can only add digits with the same place value.

Solution To make the column additions easier, we will write two zeros after the 6 in the addend 5.6 and one zero after the 8 in the addend 16.78. Since whole numbers have an "understood" decimal point immediately to the right of their ones digit, we can write the addend 68 as 68.000 to help line up the columns.

```
   31.913
    5.600     Insert two zeros after the 6.
   68.000     Insert a decimal point and three zeros: 68 = 68.000.
 + 16.780     Insert a zero after the 8.
     ↑
     Line up the decimal points.
```

Now we add, right to left, as we would whole numbers, writing the sum from each column below the horizontal bar.

Self Check 1

Add: 41.07 + 35 + 67.888 + 4.1

Now Try **Problem 19**

Self Check 1 Answer
148.058

Teaching Example 1 Add:
36.824 + 8.5 + 79 + 12.65

Answer:
136.974

```
  2 2
 31.913    Carry a 2 (shown in blue) to the ones column.
  5.600    Carry a 2 (shown in green) to the tens column.
 68.000
+ 16.780
 122.293
    ↑ Write the decimal point in the result directly
      below the decimal points in the addends.
```

The sum is 122.293.

Success Tip In Example 1, the digits in each place-value column were added from *top to bottom.* To check the answer, we can instead add from *bottom to top.* Adding down or adding up should give the same result. If it does not, an error has been made and you should re-add.

```
             122.293
First add     31.913    To check,
top to         5.600    add
bottom        68.000    bottom
            + 16.780    to top
             122.293
```

Using Your CALCULATOR **Adding Decimals**

The bar graph on the right shows the number of grams of fiber in a standard serving of each of several foods. It is believed that men can significantly cut their risk of heart attack by eating at least 25 grams of fiber a day. Does this diet meet or exceed the 25-gram requirement?

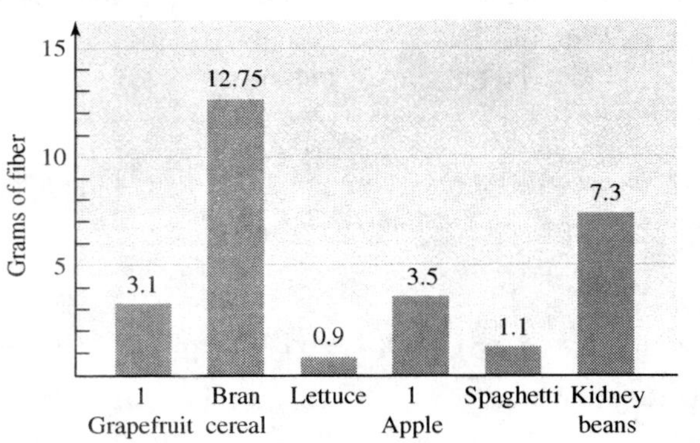

To find the total fiber intake, we add the fiber content of each of the foods. We can use a calculator to add the decimals.

3.1 [+] 12.75 [+] .9 [+] 3.5 [+] 1.1 [+] 7.3 [=]   28.65

On some calculators, the [ENTER] key is pressed to find the sum.

Since 28.65 > 25, this diet exceeds the daily fiber requirement of 25 grams.

2 Subtract decimals.

Subtracting decimals is similar to subtracting whole numbers. We use **vertical form** and stack the decimals with their corresponding place values and decimal points lined up so that we subtract similar objects—hundredths from hundredths, tenths from tenths, ones from ones, and so on. We write the decimal point in the **difference** so that it lines up with the decimal points in the **minuend** and **subtrahend.** For example, to find 8.59 − 1.27, we proceed as follows:

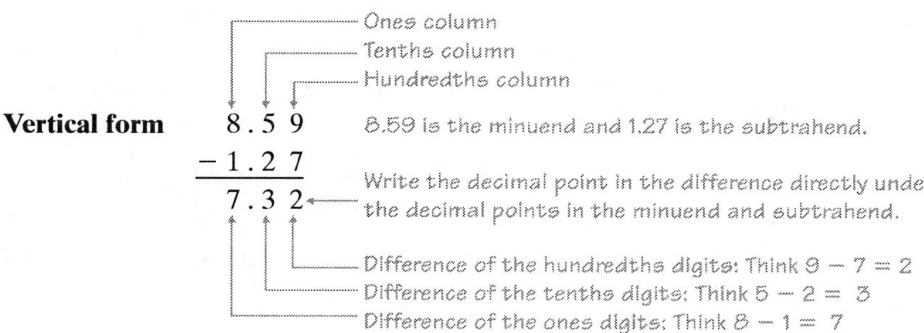

The difference is 7.32.

Subtracting Decimals

To subtract decimal numbers:

1. Write the numbers in vertical form with the decimal points lined up.
2. Subtract the numbers as you would subtract whole numbers from right to left.
3. Write the decimal point in the result from Step 2 directly below the decimal points in the minued and the subtrahend.

As with whole numbers, if the subtraction of the digits in any place-value column requires that we subtract a larger digit from a smaller digit, we must **borrow** or **regroup.**

EXAMPLE 2 Subtract: 279.6 − 138.7

Strategy As we prepare to subtract in each column, we will compare the digit in the subtrahend (bottom number) to the digit directly above it in the minuend (top number).

WHY If a digit in the subtrahend is greater than the digit directly above it in the minuend, we must borrow (regroup) to subtract in that column.

Solution Since 7 in the tenths column of 138.7 is greater than 6 in the tenths column of 279.6, we cannot immediately subtract in that column because 6 − 7 is *not* a whole number. To subtract in the tenths column, we must regroup by borrowing as shown below.

```
   8 16
  279.6    To subtract in the tenths column, borrow 1 one in the form of 10 tenths
− 138.7    from the ones column. Add 10 to the 6 in the tenths column to get 16
  140.9    (shown in blue).
```

Subtraction can be checked by addition. If a subtraction is done correctly, the sum of the difference and the subtrahend will equal the minuend: **Difference + subtrahend = minuend.**

Check:

```
    1
  140.9    Difference
+ 138.7    Subtrahend
  279.6    Minuend
```

Since the sum of the difference and the subtrahend is the minuend, the subtraction is correct.

Self Check 2

Subtract: 382.5 − 227.1 155.4

Now Try **Problem 27**

Teaching Example 2
Subtract: 356.4 − 123.6

Answer:
232.8

Some subtractions require borrowing from two (or more) place-value columns.

Self Check 3

Subtract 27.122 from 29.7. 2.578

Now Try **Problem 31**

Teaching Example 3 Subtract 42.318 from 45.6.

Answer:
3.282

EXAMPLE 3 Subtract 13.059 from 15.4.

Strategy We will translate the sentence to mathematical symbols and then perform the subtraction. As we prepare to subtract in each column, we will compare the digit in the subtrahend (bottom number) to the digit directly above it in the minuend (top number).

WHY If a digit in the subtrahend is greater than the digit directly above it in the minuend, we must borrow (regroup) to subtract in that column.

Solution Since 13.059 is the number to be subtracted, it is the subtrahend.

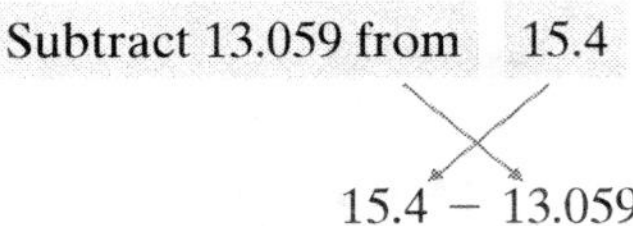

To find the difference, we write the subtraction in vertical form. To help with the column subtractions, we write two zeros to the right of 15.4 so that both numbers have three decimal places.

$$\begin{array}{r} 15.400 \\ -\,13.059 \\ \hline \end{array}$$

Insert two zeros after the 4 so that the decimal places match.

Line up the decimal points.

Since 9 in the thousandths column of 13.059 is greater than 0 in the thousandths column of 15.400, we cannot immediately subtract. It is not possible to borrow from the digit 0 in the hundredths column of 15.400. We can, however, borrow from the digit 4 in the tenths column of 15.400.

$$\begin{array}{r} \scriptstyle 3\,10 \\ 15.\not{4}00 \\ -\,13.059 \\ \hline \end{array}$$

Borrow 1 tenth in the form of 10 hundredths from 4 in the tenths column. Add 10 to 0 in the hundredths column to get 10 (shown in blue).

Now we complete the two-column borrowing process by borrowing from the 10 in the hundredths column. Then we subtract, column-by-column, from the right to the left to find the difference.

$$\begin{array}{r} \scriptstyle 9 \\ \scriptstyle 3\,\not{10}\,10 \\ 15.\not{4}\,\not{0}\,\not{0} \\ -\,13.0\,5\,9 \\ \hline 2.3\,4\,1 \end{array}$$

Borrow 1 hundredth in the form of 10 thousandths from 10 in the hundredths column. Add 10 to 0 in the thousandths column to get 10 (shown in green).

When 13.059 is subtracted from 15.4, the difference is 2.341.

Check:

$$\begin{array}{r} \scriptstyle 1\,1 \\ 2.341 \\ +\,13.059 \\ \hline 15.400 \end{array}$$

Since the sum of the difference and the subtrahend is the minuend, the subtraction is correct.

Using Your CALCULATOR **Subtracting Decimals**

A giant weather balloon is made of a flexible rubberized material that has an uninflated thickness of 0.011 inch. When the balloon is inflated with helium, the thickness becomes 0.0018 inch. To find the change in thickness, we need to subtract. We can use a calculator to subtract the decimals.

.011 [−] .0018 [=] 0.0092

On some calculators, the [ENTER] key is pressed to find the difference.

After the balloon is inflated, the rubberized material loses 0.0092 inch in thickness.

3 Add and subtract signed decimals.

To add signed decimals, we use the same rules that we used for adding integers.

Adding Two Decimals That Have the Same (Like) Signs

1. To add two positive decimals, add them as usual. The final answer is positive.
2. To add two negative decimals, add their absolute values and make the final answer negative.

Adding Two Decimals That Have Different (Unlike) Signs

To add a positive decimal and a negative decimal, subtract the smaller absolute value from the larger.

1. If the positive decimal has the larger absolute value, the final answer is positive.
2. If the negative decimal has the larger absolute value, make the final answer negative.

EXAMPLE 4 Add: $-6.1 + (-4.7)$

Strategy We will use the rule for adding two decimals that have the same sign.

WHY Both addends, -6.1 and -4.7, are negative.

Solution Find the absolute values: $|-6.1| = 6.1$ and $|-4.7| = 4.7$.

$-6.1 + (-4.7) = -10.8$ — Add the absolute values, 6.1 and 4.7, to get 10.8. Then make the final answer negative.

$$\begin{array}{r} 6.1 \\ +\ 4.7 \\ \hline 10.8 \end{array}$$

Self Check 4

Add: $-5.04 + (-2.32)$ -7.36

Now Try **Problem 35**

Teaching Example 4
Add: $-3.4 + (-8.3)$
Answer:
-11.7

EXAMPLE 5 Add: $5.35 + (-12.9)$

Strategy We will use the rule for adding two integers that have different signs.

WHY One addend is positive and the other is negative.

Solution Find the absolute values: $|5.35| = 5.35$ and $|-12.9| = 12.9$.

$5.35 + (-12.9) = -7.55$ — Subtract the smaller absolute value from the larger: $12.9 - 5.35 = 7.55$. Since the negative number, -12.9, has the larger absolute value, make the final answer negative.

$$\begin{array}{r} \scriptstyle 8\ 10 \\ 12.\not{9}\not{0} \\ -\ 5.35 \\ \hline 7.55 \end{array}$$

Self Check 5

Add: $-21.4 + 16.75$ -4.65

Now Try **Problem 39**

Teaching Example 5
Add: $15.21 + (-29.8)$
Answer:
-14.59

The rule for subtraction can be used with signed decimals: *To subtract two decimals, add the first decimal to the opposite of the decimal to be subtracted.*

EXAMPLE 6 Subtract: $-35.6 - 5.9$

Strategy We will apply the rule for subtraction: Add the first decimal to the opposite of the decimal to be subtracted.

WHY It is easy to make an error when subtracting signed decimals. We will probably be more accurate if we write the subtraction as addition of the opposite.

Self Check 6

Subtract: $-1.18 - 2.88$ -4.06

Now Try **Problem 43**

Teaching Example 6
Subtract: $-46.8 - 7.6$
Answer:
-54.4

Solution The number to be subtracted is 5.9. Subtracting 5.9 is the same as adding its opposite, −5.9.

Change the subtraction to addition.

$$-35.6 - 5.9 = -35.6 + (-5.9) = -41.5$$

Change the number being subtracted to its opposite.

Use the rule for adding two decimals with the same sign. Make the final answer negative.

$$\begin{array}{r} \overset{1\,1}{35.6} \\ +\ 5.9 \\ \hline 41.5 \end{array}$$

Self Check 7

Subtract: $-2.56 - (-4.4)$ 1.84

Now Try **Problem 47**

Teaching Example 7
Subtract: $-2.98 - (-27.3)$
Answer:
24.32

EXAMPLE 7 Subtract: $-8.37 - (-16.2)$

Strategy We will apply the rule for subtraction: Add the first decimal to the opposite of the decimal to be subtracted.

WHY It is easy to make an error when subtracting signed decimals. We will probably be more accurate if we write the subtraction as addition of the opposite.

Solution The number to be subtracted is −16.2. Subtracting −16.2 is the same as adding its opposite, 16.2.

Add . . .

$$-8.37 - (-16.2) = -8.37 + 16.2 = 7.83$$

. . . the opposite

Use the rule for adding two decimals with different signs. Since 16.2 has the larger absolute value, the final answer is positive.

$$\begin{array}{r} 16.20 \\ -\ 8.37 \\ \hline 7.83 \end{array}$$

Self Check 8

Evaluate: $-4.9 - (-1.2 + 5.6)$

Now Try **Problem 51**

Self Check 8 Answer
−9.3

Teaching Example 8
Evaluate: $-33.5 - (-16.3 + 7.9)$
Answer:
−25.1

EXAMPLE 8 Evaluate: $-12.2 - (-14.5 + 3.8)$

Strategy We will perform the operation within the parentheses first.

WHY This is the first step of the order of operations rule.

Solution We perform the addition within the grouping symbols first.

$$\begin{aligned} -12.2 - (-14.5 + 3.8) &= -12.2 - (-10.7) && \text{Perform the addition.} \\ &= -12.2 + 10.7 && \text{Add the opposite of } -10.7. \\ &= -1.5 && \text{Perform the addition.} \end{aligned}$$

$$\begin{array}{r} 14.5 \\ -\ 3.8 \\ \hline 10.7 \end{array} \qquad \begin{array}{r} 12.2 \\ -10.7 \\ \hline 1.5 \end{array}$$

4 Estimate sums and differences of decimals.

Estimation can be used to check the reasonableness of an answer to a decimal addition or subtraction. There are several ways to estimate, but the objective is the same: Simplify the numbers in the problem so that the calculations can be made easily and quickly.

Self Check 9

a. Estimate by rounding the addends to the nearest ten: 526.93 + 284.03 810

b. Estimate using front-end rounding: 512.33 − 36.47 460

Now Try **Problems 55 and 57**

EXAMPLE 9

a. Estimate by rounding the addends to the nearest ten: 261.76 + 432.94

b. Estimate using front-end rounding: 381.77 − 57.01

Strategy We will use rounding to approximate each addend, minuend, and subtrahend. Then we will find the sum or difference of the approximations.

WHY Rounding produces numbers that contain many 0's. Such numbers are easier to add or subtract.

Solution

a.

$$\begin{array}{rcr} 261.76 & \rightarrow & 260 \\ +\ 432.94 & \rightarrow & +\ 430 \\ \hline & & 690 \end{array}$$

Round to the nearest ten.
Round to the nearest ten.

The estimate is 690. If we compute 261.76 + 432.94, the sum is 694.7. We can see that the estimate is close; it's just 4.7 less than 694.7.

b. We use front-end rounding. Each number is rounded to its largest place value.

$$\begin{array}{rcr} 381.77 & \rightarrow & 400 \\ -\ 57.01 & \rightarrow & -\ 60 \\ \hline & & 340 \end{array}$$

Round to the nearest hundred.
Round to the nearest ten.

The estimate is 340. If we compute 381.77 − 57.01, the difference is 324.76. We can see that the estimate is close; it's 15.24 more than 324.76.

Teaching Example 9
a. Estimate by rounding the addends to the nearest ten: 659.59 + 223.75
b. Estimate using front-end rounding: 734.01 − 48.22

Answers:
a. 880
b. 650

5 Solve application problems by adding and subtracting decimals.

To make a profit, a merchant must sell an item for more than she paid for it. The price at which the merchant sells the product, called the **retail price,** is the *sum* of what the item **cost** the merchant plus the **markup.**

Retail price = cost + markup

EXAMPLE 10 *Pricing* Find the retail price of a Rubik's Cube if a game store owner buys them for $8.95 each and then marks them up $4.25 to sell in her store.

Analyze

- Rubik's Cubes cost the store owner $8.95 each. *Given*
- She marks up the price $4.25. *Given*
- What is the retail price of a Rubik's Cube? *Find*

Andrea Presazzi/Dreamstime.com

Form We translate the words of the problem to numbers and symbols.

The retail price	is equal to	the cost	plus	the markup.
The retail price	=	8.95	+	4.25

Solve Use vertical form to perform decimal addition:

$$\begin{array}{r} \overset{1\,1}{8.95} \\ +\ 4.25 \\ \hline 13.20 \end{array}$$

State The retail price of a Rubik's Cube is $13.20.

Check We can estimate to check the result. If we use $9 to approximate the cost of a Rubik's Cube to the store owner and $4 to be the approximate markup, then the retail price is about $9 + $4 = $13. The result, $13.20, seems reasonable.

Self Check 10
PRICING Find the retail price of a wool coat if a clothing outlet buys them for $109.95 each and then marks them up $99.95 to sell in its stores. $209.90

Now Try **Problem 91**

Teaching Example 10
PRICING Find the retail price of an electric stapler if an office supply company buys them for $29.50 each and then marks them up $12.95 to sell in its stores.

Answer:
$42.45

EXAMPLE 11 *Kitchen Sinks* One model of kitchen sink is made of 18-gauge stainless steel that is 0.0500 inch thick. Another, less expensive, model is made from 20-gauge stainless steel that is 0.0375 inch thick. How much thicker is the 18-gauge?

Self Check 11

ALUMINUM How much thicker is 16-gauge aluminum that is 0.0508 inch thick than 22-gauge aluminum that is 0.0253 inch thick? 0.0255 in.

Now Try **Problem 97**

Teaching Example 11
TABLES A kitchen table has a 20-gauge stainless steel top that is 0.0375 inch thick and legs made of 16-gauge stainless steel that is 0.0625 inch thick. How much thicker is 16-gauge stainless steel?
Answer:
0.025 inch

Analyze

- The18-gauge stainless steel is 0.0500 inch thick. *Given*
- The 20-gauge stainless steel is 0.0375 inch thick. *Given*
- How much thicker is the 18-gauge stainless steel? *Find*

Form Phrases such as *how much older, how much longer,* and, in this case, *how much thicker,* indicate subtraction. We translate the words of the problem to numbers and symbols.

How much thicker	is equal to	the thickness of the 18-gauge stainless steel	minus	the thickness of the 20-gauge stainless steel.
How much thicker	=	0.0500	−	0.0375

Solve Use vertical form to perform subtraction:

$$\begin{array}{r} \overset{4}{0.0\cancel{5}}\overset{\overset{9}{\cancel{10}}}{\cancel{0}}\overset{10}{\cancel{0}} \\ -\ 0.0375 \\ \hline 0.0125 \end{array}$$

State The 18-gauge stainless steel is 0.0125 inch thicker than the 20-gauge.

Check We can add to check the subtraction:

$$\begin{array}{rl} \overset{1\,1}{0.0125} & \text{Difference} \\ +\ 0.0375 & \text{Subtrahend} \\ \hline 0.0500 & \text{Minuend} \end{array}$$

The result checks. ■

Sometimes more than one operation is needed to solve a problem involving decimals.

Self Check 12

WRESTLING A 195.5-pound wrestler had to lose 6.5 pounds to make his weight class. After the weigh-in, he gained back 3.7 pounds. What did he weigh then? 192.7 lb

Now Try **Problem 103**

EXAMPLE 12 *Conditioning Programs* A 350-pound football player lost 15.7 pounds during the first week of practice. During the second week, he gained 4.9 pounds. Find his weight after the first two weeks of practice.

Analyze

- The football player's beginning weight was 350 pounds. *Given*
- The first week he lost 15.7 pounds. *Given*
- The second week he gained 4.9 pounds. *Given*
- What was his weight after two weeks of practice? *Find*

Form The word *lost* indicates subtraction. The word *gained* indicates addition. We translate the words of the problem to numbers and symbols.

The player's weight after two weeks of practice	is equal to	his beginning weight	minus	the first-week weight loss	plus	the second-week weight gain.
The player's weight after two weeks of practice	=	350	−	15.7	+	4.9

Solve To evaluate $350 - 15.7 + 4.9$, we work from left to right and perform the subtraction first, then the addition.

$$\begin{array}{r} \overset{4\ \overset{9}{\cancel{10}}\ 10}{3\,5\,\cancel{0}.\cancel{0}} \\ -\quad 1\,5.7 \\ \hline 3\,3\,4.3 \end{array}$$

Write the whole number 350 as 350.0 and use a two-column borrowing process to subtract in the tenths column.

This is the player's weight after one week of practice.

Next, we add the 4.9-pound gain to the previous result to find the player's weight after two weeks of practice.

$$\begin{array}{r} \overset{1}{334.3} \\ +\quad 4.9 \\ \hline 339.2 \end{array}$$

State The player's weight was 339.2 pounds after two weeks of practice.

Check We can estimate to check the result. The player lost about 16 pounds the first week and then gained back about 5 pounds the second week, for a net loss of 11 pounds. If we subtract the approximate 11 pound loss from his beginning weight, we get $350 - 11 = 339$ pounds. The result, 339.2 pounds, seems reasonable.

Teaching Example 12
CONDITIONING PROGRAMS A 180-pound baseball player lost 4.2 pounds during the first week of spring training. He gained back 1.9 pounds the second week. Find his weight after two weeks of spring training.
Answer:
177.7 lb

ANSWERS TO SELF CHECKS

1. 148.058 **2.** 155.4 **3.** 2.578 **4.** −7.36 **5.** −4.65 **6.** −4.06 **7.** 1.84 **8.** −9.3 **9. a.** 810 **b.** 460 **10.** \$209.90 **11.** 0.0255 in. **12.** 192.7 lb

SECTION 2.8 STUDY SET

VOCABULARY

Fill in the blanks.

1. In the addition problem shown below, label each *addend* and the *sum.*

1.72 ← addend
4.68 ← addend
+ 2.02 ← addend
8.42 ← sum

2. When using the vertical form to add decimals, if the addition of the digits in any one column produces a sum greater than 9, we must carry.

3. In the subtraction problem shown below, label the *minuend, subtrahend,* and the *difference.*

12.9 ← minuend
− 4.3 ← subtrahend
8.6 ← difference

4. If the subtraction of the digits in any place-value column requires that we subtract a larger digit from a smaller digit, we must borrow or *regroup.*

5. To see whether the result of an addition is reasonable, we can round the addends and estimate the sum.

6. In application problems, phrases such as *how much older, how much longer,* and *how much thicker* indicate the operation of subtraction.

CONCEPTS

7. Check the following result. Use addition to determine if 15.2 is the correct difference. It is not correct: $15.2 + 12.5 \neq 28.7$

$$\begin{array}{r} 28.7 \\ -\ 12.5 \\ \hline 15.2 \end{array}$$

8. Determine whether the *sign* of each result is positive or negative. *You do not have to find the sum.*

a. $-7.6 + (-1.8)$ negative

b. $-24.99 + 29.08$ positive

c. $133.2 + (-400.43)$ negative

▶ **9.** Fill in the blank: To subtract signed decimals, add the opposite of the decimal that is being subtracted.

10. Apply the rule for subtraction and fill in the three blanks.

$3.6 - (-2.1) = 3.6 + 2.1 = 5.7$

11. Fill in the blanks to rewrite each subtraction as addition of the opposite of the number being subtracted.
 a. 6.8 − 1.2 = 6.8 + (−1.2)
 b. 29.03 − (−13.55) = 29.03 + 13.55
 c. −5.1 − 7.4 = −5.1 + (−7.4)

12. Fill in the blanks to complete the estimation.

 567.7 → 570 Round to the nearest ten.
 + 214.3 → + 210 Round to the nearest ten.
 782.0 780

NOTATION

13. Copy the following addition problem. Insert a decimal point and additional zeros so that the number of decimal places in the addends match.

 46.600
 11.000
 + 15.702

14. Refer to the subtraction problem below. Fill in the blanks: To subtract in the hundredths column, we borrow 1 tenth in the form of 10 hundredths from the 3 in the tenths column.

 $\overset{2\,11}{29.\cancel{3}\cancel{1}}$
 − 25.16

GUIDED PRACTICE

Add. See Objective 1.

15. 32.5 + 7.4 = 39.9
▶ 16. 16.3 + 3.5 = 19.8
17. 3.04 + 4.12 + 1.43 = 8.59
18. 2.11 + 5.04 + 2.72 = 9.87

Add. See Example 1.

19. 36.821 + 7.3 + 42 + 15.44 101.561
20. 46.228 + 5.6 + 39 + 19.37 110.198
▶ 21. 27.471 + 6.4 + 157 + 12.12 202.991
22. 52.763 + 9.1 + 128 + 11.84 201.703

Subtract. See Objective 2.

23. 6.83 − 3.52 = 3.31
24. 9.47 − 5.06 = 4.41
25. 8.97 − 6.22 = 2.75
▶ 26. 7.56 − 2.33 = 5.23

Subtract. See Example 2.

27. 495.4 − 153.7 = 341.7
▶ 28. 977.6 − 345.8 = 631.8
29. 878.1 − 174.6 = 703.5
30. 767.2 − 614.7 = 152.5

Perform the indicated operation. See Example 3.

31. Subtract 11.065 from 18.3. 7.235
32. Subtract 15.041 from 17.8. 2.759
▶ 33. Subtract 23.037 from 66.9. 43.863
34. Subtract 31.089 from 75.6. 44.511

Add. See Example 4.

35. −6.3 + (−8.4) −14.7
36. −9.2 + (−6.7) −15.9
37. −9.5 + (−9.3) −18.8
▶ 38. −7.3 + (−5.4) −12.7

Add. See Example 5.

39. 4.12 + (−18.8) −14.68
40. 7.24 + (−19.7) −12.46
41. 6.45 + (−12.6) −6.15
▶ 42. 8.81 + (−14.9) −6.09

Subtract. See Example 6.

43. −62.8 − 3.9 −66.7
▶ 44. −56.1 − 8.6 −64.7
45. −42.5 − 2.8 −45.3
46. −93.2 − 3.9 −97.1

Subtract. See Example 7.

47. −4.49 − (−11.3) 6.81
48. −5.76 − (−13.6) 7.84
▶ 49. −6.78 − (−24.6) 17.82
50. −8.51 − (−27.4) 18.89

Evaluate each expression. See Example 8.

51. −11.1 − (−14.4 + 7.8) −4.5
▶ 52. −12.3 − (−13.6 + 7.9) −6.6
53. −16.4 − (−18.9 + 5.9) −3.4
54. −15.5 − (−19.8 + 5.7) −1.4

Estimate each sum by rounding the addends to the nearest ten. See Example 9.

55. 510.65 + 279.19 790
▶ 56. 424.08 + 169.04 590

Estimate each difference by using front-end rounding. See Example 9.

57. 671.01 − 88.35 610
▶ 58. 447.23 − 36.16 360

TRY IT YOURSELF

Perform the indicated operations.

59. −45.6 + 34.7 −10.9
60. −19.04 + 2.4 −16.64
61. −9.5 − 7.1 −16.6
62. −7.08 − 14.3 −21.38
63. 46.09 + (−7.8) 38.29
▶ 64. 34.7 + (−30.1) 4.6
65. 21.88 + 33.12 = 55.00
66. 19.05 + 31.95 = 51.00
67. 30.03 − (−17.88) 47.91
▶ 68. 143.3 − (−64.01) 207.31
69. 645 + 9.90005 + 0.12 + 3.02002 658.04007
70. 505.0103 + 23 + 0.989 + 12.0704 541.0697
71. Subtract 23.81 from 24. 0.19

72. Subtract 5.9 from 7.001. 1.101

73. $(3.4 - 6.6) + 7.3$ 4.1 **74.** $3.4 - (6.6 + 7.3)$ −10.5

75. $247.9 + 40 + 0.56$ 288.46

76. $0.0053 + 1.78 + 6$ 7.7853

77. $\begin{array}{r} 78.1 \\ -\ 7.81 \\ \hline \end{array}$ 70.29 **78.** $\begin{array}{r} 202.234 \\ -\ 19.34 \\ \hline \end{array}$ 182.894

79. $-7.8 + (-6.5)$ −14.3 **80.** $-5.78 + (-33.1)$ −38.88

81. $16 - (67.2 + 6.27)$ −57.47

82. $-43 - (0.032 - 0.045)$ −42.987

83. Find the sum of *two and forty-three hundredths* and *five and six tenths.* 8.03

84. Find the difference of *nineteen hundredths* and *six thousandths.* 0.184

85. $|-14.1 + 6.9| + 8$ 15.2 **86.** $15 - |-2.3 + (-2.4)|$ 10.3

87. $5 - 0.023$ 4.977 **88.** $30 - 11.98$ 18.02

89. $-2.002 - (-4.6)$ 2.598 **90.** $-0.005 - (-8)$ 7.995

APPLICATIONS

91. RETAILING Find the retail price of each appliance listed in the following table if a department store purchases them for the given costs and then marks them up as shown.

Appliance	Cost	Markup	Retail price
Refrigerator	$610.80	$205.00	$815.80
Washing machine	$389.50	$155.50	$545.00
Dryer	$363.99	$167.50	$531.49

92. PRICING Find the retail price of a Kenneth Cole two-button suit if a men's clothing outlet buys them for $210.95 each and then marks them up $144.95 to sell in its stores. $355.90

93. OFFSHORE DRILLING A company needs to construct a pipeline from an offshore oil well to a refinery located on the coast. Company engineers have come up with two plans for consideration, as shown. Use the information in the illustration to complete the table that is shown in the next column.

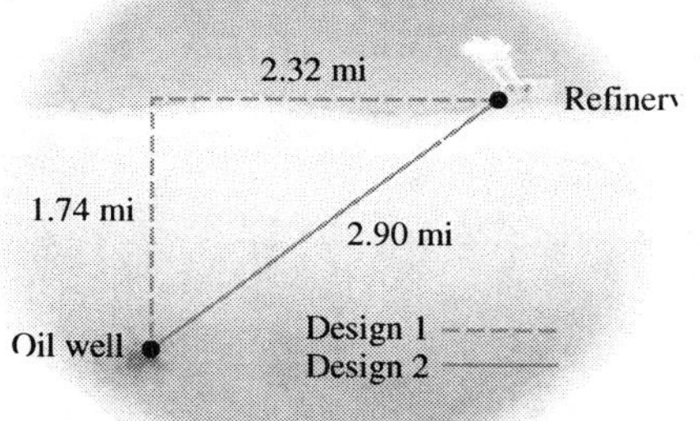

	Pipe underwater (mi)	Pipe underground (mi)	Total pipe (mi)
Design 1	1.74	2.32	4.06
Design 2	2.90	0	2.90

94. DRIVING DIRECTIONS Find the total distance of the trip using the information in the MapQuest printout shown below. 28.8 mi

START	1: Start out going EAST on SUNKIST AVE.	**0.0 mi**
	2: Turn LEFT onto MERCED AVE.	**0.4 mi**
	3: Turn Right onto PUENTE AVE.	**0.3 mi**
10	4: Merge onto I-10 W toward LOS ANGELES.	**2.2 mi**
605	5: Merge onto I-605 S.	**10.6 mi**
5	6: Merge onto I-5 S toward SANTA ANA.	**14.9 mi**
110 A EXIT	7: Take the HARBOR BLVD exit, EXIT 110A.	**0.3 mi**
	8: Turn RIGHT onto S HARBOR BLVD.	**0.1 mi**
END	9: End at 1313 S Harbor Blvd Anaheim, CA.	

Total Distance: ___?___ **miles** MAPQUEST®

95. PIPE (PVC) Find the *outside* diameter of the plastic sprinkler pipe shown below if the thickness of the pipe wall is 0.218 inch and the inside diameter is 1.939 inches. 2.375 in.

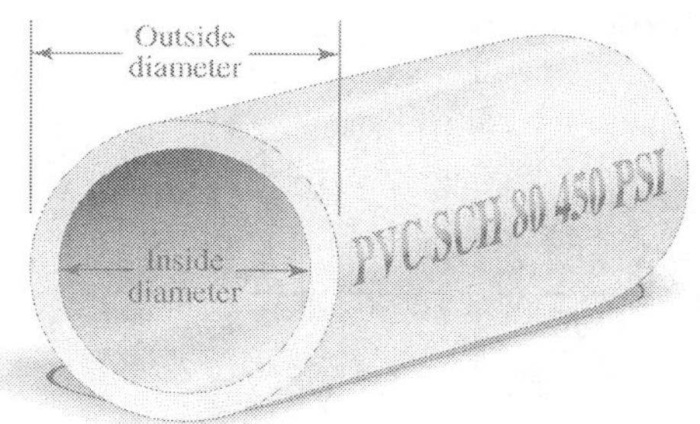

96. pH SCALE The pH scale shown below is used to measure the strength of acids and bases in chemistry. Find the difference in pH readings between

a. bleach and stomach acid. 10.95

b. ammonia and coffee. 7.02

c. blood and coffee. 2.37

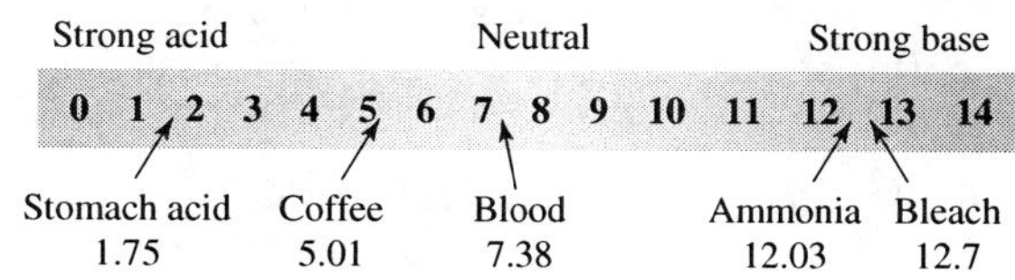

97. RECORD HOLDERS The late Florence Griffith-Joyner of the United States holds the women's world record in the 100-meter sprint: 10.49 seconds. Libby Trickett of Australia holds the women's world record in the 100-meter freestyle swim: 52.88 seconds. How much faster did Griffith-Joyner run the 100 meters than Trickett swam it? (Source: *The World Almanac and Book of Facts,* 2009) 42.39 sec

98. WEATHER REPORTS Barometric pressure readings are recorded on the weather map below. In a low-pressure area (L on the map), the weather is often stormy. The weather is usually fair in a high-pressure area (H). What is the difference in readings between the areas of highest and lowest pressure? 1.8

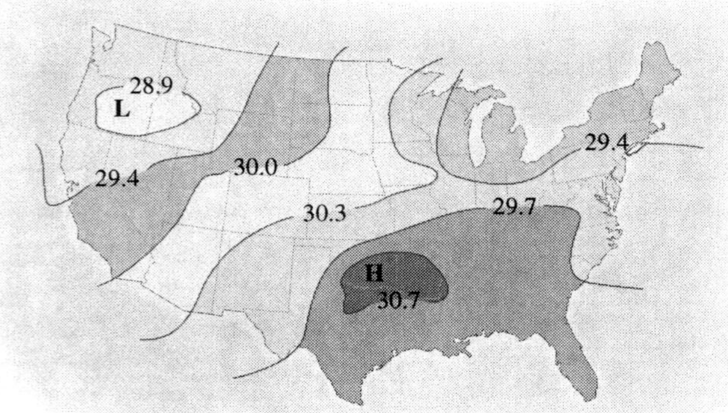

99. BANKING A businesswoman deposited several checks in her company's bank account, as shown on the deposit slip below. Find the *Subtotal* line on the slip by adding the amounts of the checks and total from the reverse side. If the woman wanted to get \$25 in cash back from the teller, what should she write as the *Total deposit* on the slip? \$523.19, \$498.19

Deposit slip

Cash		
Checks (properly endorsed)	116	10
	47	93
Total from reverse side	359	16
Subtotal		
Less cash	25	00
Total deposit		

100. SPORTS PAGES Decimals are often used in the sports pages of newspapers. Two examples are given below.

a. "German bobsledders set a world record today with a final run of 53.03 seconds, finishing ahead of the Italian team by only fourteen thousandths of a second." What was the time for the Italian bobsled team? 53.044 sec

b. "The women's figure skating title was decided by only thirty-three hundredths of a point." If the winner's point total was 102.71, what was the second-place finisher's total? (*Hint:* The highest score wins in a figure skating contest.) 102.38

▶ **101.** Suppose certain portions of a patient's morning (A.M.) temperature chart were not filled in. Use the given information to complete the chart below. (*Hint:* 98.6°F is considered normal.)

from Campus to Careers
Home Health Aide

Tetra Images/Getty Images

Day of week	Patient's A.M. temperature	Amount above normal
Monday	99.7°	1.1°
Tuesday	101.1°	2.5°
Wednesday	98.6°	0°
Thursday	100.0°	1.4°
Friday	99.5°	0.9°

▶ **102.** QUALITY CONTROL An electronics company has strict specifications for the silicon chips it uses in its computers. The company only installs chips that are within 0.05 centimeter of the indicated thickness. The table below gives that specifications for two types of chips. Fill in the blanks to complete the chart.

Chip type	Thickness specification	Acceptable range	
		Low	High
A	0.78 cm	0.73 cm	0.83 cm
B	0.643 cm	0.593 cm	0.693 cm

▶ **103.** FLIGHT PATHS Find the added distance a plane must travel to avoid flying through the storm. 20.01 mi

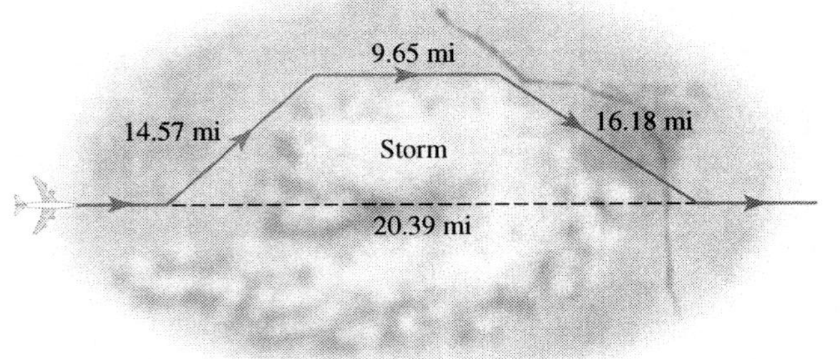

104. TELEVISION The following illustration shows the six most-watched television shows of all time (excluding Super Bowl games and the Olympics).

a. What was the combined total audience of all six shows? 500.5 million

b. How many more people watched the last episode of "MASH" than watched the last episode of "Seinfeld"? 29.7 million

c. How many more people would have had to watch the last "Seinfeld" to move it into a tie for fifth place? 0.4 million

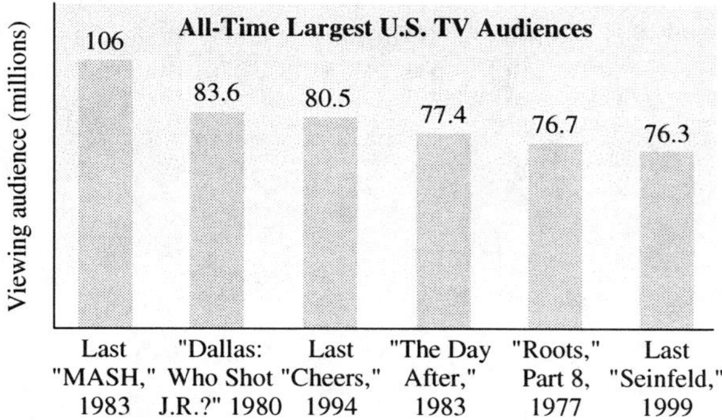

Source: Nielsen Media Research

105. THE HOME SHOPPING NETWORK The illustration shows a description of a cookware set that was sold on television.

a. Find the difference between the manufacturer's suggested retail price (MSRP) and the sale price. $101.94

b. Including shipping and handling (S & H), how much will the cookware set cost? $55.80

Item 229-442	
Continental 9-piece Cookware Set	
Stainless steel	
MSRP	$149.79
HSN Price	$59.85
On Sale	$47.85
S & H	$7.95

106. VEHICLE SPECIFICATIONS Certain dimensions of a compact car are shown. Find the wheelbase of the car. 103.4 in.

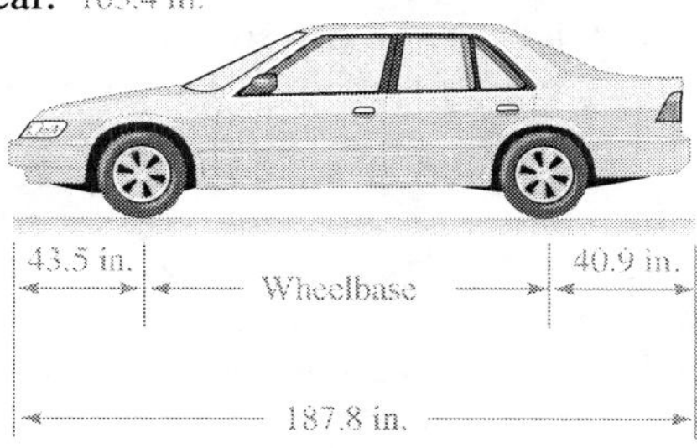

WRITING

107. Explain why we line up the decimal points and corresponding place-value columns when adding decimals.

108. Explain why we can write additional zeros to the right of a decimal such as 7.89 without affecting its value.

109. Explain what is wrong with the work shown below.

$$\begin{array}{r} 203.56 \\ 37 \\ + \quad 0.43 \\ \hline 204.36 \end{array}$$

110. Consider the following addition:

$$\begin{array}{r} \overset{2}{2}3.7 \\ 41.9 \\ +\ 12.8 \\ \hline 78.4 \end{array}$$

Explain the meaning of the small red 2 written above the ones column.

111. Write a set of instructions that explains the two-column borrowing process shown below.

$$\begin{array}{r} \scriptsize 4\ \overset{9}{\cancel{10}}\ 10 \\ 2.6\cancel{5}\cancel{0}\cancel{0} \\ -\ 1.3246 \\ \hline 1.3254 \end{array}$$

112. Explain why it is easier to add the decimals 0.3 and 0.17 than the fractions $\frac{3}{10}$ and $\frac{17}{100}$.

REVIEW

Perform the indicated operations.

113. a. $\frac{4}{5} + \frac{5}{12}$ $\frac{73}{60} = 1\frac{13}{60}$

b. $\frac{4}{5} - \frac{5}{12}$ $\frac{23}{60}$

c. $\frac{4}{5} \cdot \frac{5}{12}$ $\frac{1}{3}$

d. $\frac{4}{5} \div \frac{5}{12}$ $\frac{48}{25} = 1\frac{23}{25}$

114. a. $\frac{3}{8} + \frac{1}{6}$ $\frac{13}{24}$

b. $\frac{3}{8} - \frac{1}{6}$ $\frac{5}{24}$

c. $\frac{3}{8} \cdot \frac{1}{6}$ $\frac{1}{16}$

d. $\frac{3}{8} \div \frac{1}{6}$ $\frac{9}{4} = 2\frac{1}{4}$

Objectives

1. Multiply decimals.
2. Multiply decimals by powers of 10.
3. Multiply signed decimals.
4. Evaluate exponential expressions that have decimal bases.
5. Use the order of operations rule.
6. Evaluate formulas.
7. Estimate products of decimals.
8. Solve application problems by multiplying decimals.

SECTION 2.9 Multiplying Decimals

Since decimal numbers are *base-ten* numbers, multiplication of decimals is similar to multiplication of whole numbers. However, when multiplying decimals, there is one additional step—we must determine where to write the decimal point in the product.

1 Multiply decimals.

To develop a rule for multiplying decimals, we will consider the multiplication $0.3 \cdot 0.17$ and find the product in a roundabout way. First, we write 0.3 and 0.17 as fractions and multiply them in that form. Then we express the resulting fraction as a decimal.

$$0.3 \cdot 0.17 = \frac{3}{10} \cdot \frac{17}{100}$$ Express the decimals 0.3 and 0.17 as fractions.

$$= \frac{3 \cdot 17}{10 \cdot 100}$$ Multiply the numerators. Multiply the denominators.

$$= \frac{51}{1{,}000}$$

$$= 0.051$$ Write the resulting fraction $\frac{51}{1{,}000}$ as a decimal.

From this example, we can make observations about multiplying decimals.

- The digits in the answer are found by multiplying 3 and 17.

  $0.3 \cdot 0.17 = 0.051$

  $3 \cdot 17 = 51$

- The answer has 3 decimal places. The *sum* of the number of decimal places in the factors 0.3 and 0.17 is also 3.

  $0.3 \cdot 0.17 = 0.051$

  1 decimal place; 2 decimal places; 3 decimal places

These observations illustrate the following rule for multiplying decimals.

Multiplying Decimals

To multiply two decimals:

1. Multiply the decimals as if they were whole numbers.
2. Find the total number of decimal places in both factors.
3. Insert a decimal point in the result from step 1 so that the answer has the same number of decimal places as the total found in step 2.

Self Check 1

Multiply: $2.7 \cdot 4.3$ 11.61

Now Try **Problem 9**

EXAMPLE 1 Multiply: $5.9 \cdot 3.4$

Strategy We will ignore the decimal points and multiply 5.9 and 3.4 as if they were whole numbers. Then we will write a decimal point in that result so that the final answer has two decimal places.

WHY Since the factor 5.9 has 1 decimal place, and the factor 3.4 has 1 decimal place, the product should have $1 + 1 = 2$ decimal places.

Solution We write the multiplication in vertical form and proceed as follows:

Vertical form

```
     5.9  ← 1 decimal place  } The answer will have
×    3.4  ← 1 decimal place  } 1 + 1 = 2 decimal places.
     236
    1770
   20.06
```

Move 2 places from the right to the left and insert a decimal point in the answer.

Thus, $5.9 \cdot 3.4 = 20.06$.

> ***The Language of Mathematics*** Recall the vocabulary of multiplication.
>
> ```
>      5.9  ← Factor
> ×    3.4  ← Factor
>      236  }
>     1770  } Partial products
>    20.06  ← Product
> ```

> ***Success Tip*** When multiplying decimals, we do not need to line up the decimal points, as the next example illustrates.

Teaching Example 1
Multiply: $6.4 \cdot 3.7$
Answer:
23.68

EXAMPLE 2 Multiply: 1.3(0.005)

Strategy We will ignore the decimal points and multiply 1.3 and 0.005 as if they were whole numbers. Then we will write a decimal point in that result so that the final answer has four decimal places.

WHY Since the factor 1.3 has 1 decimal place, and the factor 0.005 has 3 decimal places, the product should have $1 + 3 = 4$ decimal places.

Solution Since many students find vertical form multiplication of decimals easier if the decimal with the smaller number of nonzero digits is written on the bottom, we will write 0.005 under 1.3.

```
     1.3  ← 1 decimal place   } The answer will have
× 0.005   ← 3 decimal places  } 1 + 3 = 4 decimal places.
  0.0065
```

Write 2 placeholder zeros in front of 6. Then move 4 places from the right to the left and insert a decimal point in the answer.

Thus, $1.3(0.005) = 0.0065$.

Self Check 2
Multiply: (0.0002)7.2 0.00144
Now Try **Problem 13**

Teaching Example 2
Multiply: 0.004(2.3)
Answer:
0.0092

EXAMPLE 3 Multiply: 234(5.1)

Strategy We will ignore the decimal point and multiply 234 and 5.1 as if they were whole numbers. Then we will write a decimal point in that result so that the final answer has one decimal place.

WHY Since the factor 234 has 0 decimal places, and the factor 5.1 has 1 decimal place, the product should have $0 + 1 = 1$ decimal place.

Self Check 3
Multiply: 178(4.7) 836.6
Now Try **Problem 17**

Teaching Example 3 Multiply: 286(3.9)
Answer:
1,115.4

Solution We write the multiplication in vertical form, with 5.1 under 234.

```
   234  ← No decimal places  } The answer will have
 × 5.1  ← 1 decimal place    } 0 + 1 = 1 decimal place.
  23 4
 1170 0
 1193.4    Move 1 place from the right to the left and
           insert a decimal point in the answer.
```

Thus, $234(5.1) = 1{,}193.4$.

Using Your CALCULATOR Multiplying Decimals

When billing a household, a gas company converts the amount of natural gas used to units of heat energy called *therms*. The number of therms used by a household in one month and the cost per therm are shown below.

Customer charge .... 39 therms @ $0.72264

To find the total charges for the month, we multiply the number of therms by the cost per therm: $39 \cdot 0.72264$.

39 [×] .72264 [=] 28.18296   [28.18296]

On some calculator models, the [ENTER] key is pressed to display the product. Rounding to the nearest cent, we see that the total charge is $28.18.

THINK IT THROUGH *Overtime*

"Employees covered by the Fair Labor Standards Act must receive overtime pay for hours worked in excess of 40 in a workweek of at least 1.5 times their regular rates of pay."

United States Department of Labor

The map of the United States shown below is divided into nine regions. The average hourly wage for private industry workers in each region is also listed in the legend below the map. Find the average hourly wage for the region where you live. Then calculate the corresponding average hourly overtime wage for that region.

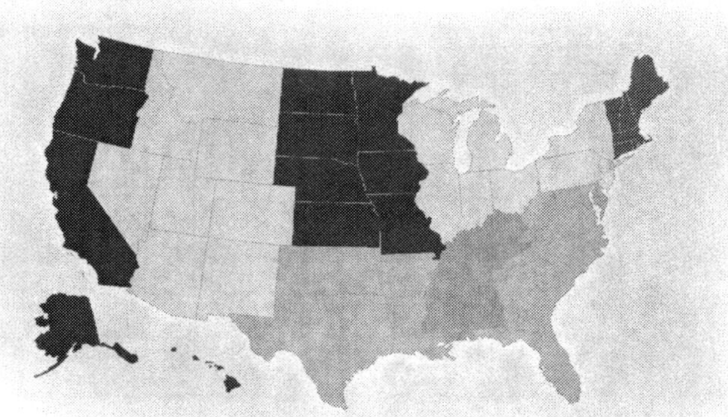

Legend

- West North Central: $17.42
- Mountain: $17.93
- Pacific: $21.68
- East South Central: $16.58
- East North Central: $18.82
- West South Central: $17.17
- New England: $22.38
- Middle Atlantic: $21.31
- South Atlantic: $18.34

(Source: Bureau of Labor Statistics, National Compensation Survey, 2008)

2 Multiply decimals by powers of 10.

The numbers 10, 100, and 1,000 are called **powers of 10,** because they are the results when we evaluate 10^1, 10^2, and 10^3. To develop a rule to find the product when multiplying a decimal by a power of 10, we multiply 8.675 by three different powers of 10.

Multiply: $8.675 \cdot 10$

$$\begin{array}{r} 8.675 \\ \times \quad 10 \\ \hline 0000 \\ 86750 \\ \hline 86.750 \end{array}$$

Multiply: $8.675 \cdot 100$

$$\begin{array}{r} 8.675 \\ \times \quad 100 \\ \hline 0000 \\ 00000 \\ 867500 \\ \hline 867.500 \end{array}$$

Multiply: $8.675 \cdot 1,000$

$$\begin{array}{r} 8.675 \\ \times \quad 1000 \\ \hline 0000 \\ 00000 \\ 000000 \\ 8675000 \\ \hline 8675.000 \end{array}$$

When we inspect the answers, the decimal point in the first factor 8.675 appears to be moved to the right by the multiplication process. The number of decimal places it moves depends on the power of 10 by which 8.675 is multiplied.

One zero in 10
$8.675 \cdot 10 = 86.75$
It moves 1 place to the right.

Two zeros in 100
$8.675 \cdot 100 = 867.5$
It moves 2 places to the right.

Three zeros in 1,000
$8.675 \cdot 1,000 = 8675$
It moves 3 places to the right.

These observations illustrate the following rule.

Multiplying a Decimal by 10, 100, 1,000, and So On

To find the product of a decimal and 10, 100, 1,000, and so on, move the decimal point to the right the same number of places as there are zeros in the power of 10.

EXAMPLE 4 Multiply: **a.** $2.81 \cdot 10$ **b.** $0.076(10,000)$

Strategy For each multiplication, we will identify the factor that is a power of 10, and count the number of zeros that it has.

WHY To find the product of a decimal and a power of 10 that is greater than 1, we move the decimal point to the right the same number of places as there are zeros in the power of 10.

Solution

a. $2.81 \cdot 10 = 28.1$ Since 10 has 1 zero, move the decimal point 1 place to the right.

b. $0.076(10,000) = 0760.$ Since 10,000 has 4 zeros, move the decimal point 4 places to the right. Write a placeholder zero (shown in blue).

$= 760$

Self Check 4

Multiply:

a. $0.721 \cdot 100$ 72.1

b. $6.08(1,000)$ 6,080

Now Try **Problems 21 and 23**

Teaching Example 4
Multiply:
a. $3.725 \cdot 100$
b. $46.3(100,000)$

Answers:
a. 372.5
b. 4,630,000

Numbers such as 10, 100, and 1,000 are powers of 10 that are *greater than 1.* There are also powers of 10 that are *less than 1,* such as 0.1, 0.01, and 0.001. To develop a rule to find the product when multiplying a decimal by one tenth, one hundredth, one thousandth, and so on, we will consider three examples:

Multiply: $5.19 \cdot 0.1$

$$\begin{array}{r} 5.19 \\ \times \quad 0.1 \\ \hline 0.519 \end{array}$$

Multiply: $5.19 \cdot 0.01$

$$\begin{array}{r} 5.19 \\ \times \quad 0.01 \\ \hline 0.0519 \end{array}$$

Multiply: $5.19 \cdot 0.001$

$$\begin{array}{r} 5.19 \\ \times \quad 0.001 \\ \hline 0.00519 \end{array}$$

When we inspect the answers, the decimal point in the first factor 5.19 appears to be moved to the left by the multiplication process. The number of places that it moves depends on the power of ten by which it is multiplied.

These observations illustrate the following rule.

Multiplying a Decimal by 0.1, 0.01, 0.001, and So On

To find the product of a decimal and 0.1, 0.01, 0.001, and so on, move the decimal point to the left the same number of decimal places as there are in the power of 10.

Self Check 5

Multiply:

a. 0.1(129.9) 12.99

b. 0.002 · 0.00001 0.00000002

Now Try **Problems 25 and 27**

Teaching Example 5 Multiply:
a. 542.6 · 0.0001
b. 0.83(0.01)
Answers:
a. 0.05426
b. 0.0083

EXAMPLE 5 Multiply: **a.** 145.8 · 0.01 **b.** 9.76(0.0001)

Strategy For each multiplication, we will identify the factor of the form 0.1, 0.01, and 0.001, and count the number of decimal places that it has.

WHY To find the product of a decimal and a power of 10 that is less than 1, we move the decimal point to the left the same number of decimal places as there are in the power of 10.

Solution

a. 145.8 · 0.01 = 1.458 — Since 0.01 has two decimal places, move the decimal point in 145.8 two places to the left.

b. 9.76(0.0001) = 0.000976 — Since 0.0001 has four decimal places, move the decimal point in 9.76 four places to the left. This requires that three placeholder zeros (shown in blue) be inserted in front of the 9.

Quite often, newspapers, websites, and television programs present large numbers in a shorthand notation that involves a decimal in combination with a place-value column name. For example,

- As of December 31, 2008, Sony had sold *21.3 million* Playstation 3 units worldwide. (Source: Sony Computer Entertainment)
- Boston's Big Dig was the most expensive single highway project in U.S. history. It cost about *$14.63 billion.* (Source: Roadtraffic-technology.com)
- The distance that light travels in one year is about *5.878 trillion* miles. (Source: Encyclopaedia Britannica)

We can use the rule for multiplying a decimal by a power of ten to write these large numbers in standard form.

Self Check 6

Write each number in standard notation:

a. 567.1 million 567,100,000

b. 50.82 billion 50,820,000,000

c. 4.133 trillion 4,133,000,000,000

Now Try **Now Try Problems 29, 31, and 33**

EXAMPLE 6 Write each number in standard notation:

a. 21.3 million **b.** 14.63 billion **c.** 5.9 trillion

Strategy We will express each of the large numbers as the product of a decimal and a power of 10.

WHY Then we can use the rule for multiplying a decimal by a power of 10 to find their product. The result will be in the required standard form.

Solution

a. 21.3 million = 21.3 · **1 million**

= 21.3 · **1,000,000** — Write 1 million in standard form.

= 21,300,000 — Since 1,000,000 has six zeros, move the decimal point in 21.3 six places to the right.

b. 14.63 billion $= 14.63 \cdot 1$ billion

$= 14.63 \cdot 1{,}000{,}000{,}000$ — Write 1 billion in standard form.

$= 14{,}630{,}000{,}000$ — Since 1,000,000,000 has *nine* zeros, move the decimal point in 14.63 *nine* places to the right.

c. 5.9 trillion $= 5.9 \cdot 1$ trillion

$= 5.9 \cdot 1{,}000{,}000{,}000{,}000$ — Write 1 trillion in standard form.

$= 5{,}900{,}000{,}000{,}000$ — Since 1,000,000,000,000 has *twelve* zeros, move the decimal point in 5.9 *twelve* places to the right.

Teaching Example 6 Write each number in standard notation:
a. In 2007, the U.S had *930.9 million* acres of farmland (Source: *The World Almanac and Book of Facts*, 2009)
b. Americans took *10.7 billion* trips on public transportation in 2008. (Source: American Public Transit Association)
c. It would take about *1.818 trillion* pennies to fill the Empire State Building. (Source: The Mega Penny Project)

Answers:
a. 930,900,000
b. 10,700,000,000
c. 1,818,000,000,000

3 Multiply signed decimals.

The rules for multiplying integers also hold for multiplying signed decimals. The product of two decimals with like signs is positive, and the product of two decimals with unlike signs is negative.

EXAMPLE 7 Multiply: **a.** $-1.8(4.5)$ **b.** $(-1{,}000)(-59.08)$

Strategy In part a, we will use the rule for multiplying signed decimals that have different (unlike) signs. In part b, we will use the rule for multiplying signed decimals that have the same (like) signs.

WHY In part a, one factor is negative and one is positive. In part b, both factors are negative.

Solution

a. Find the absolute values: $|-1.8| = 1.8$ and $|4.5| = 4.5$. Since the decimals have unlike signs, their product is negative.

$-1.8(4.5) = -8.1$ — Multiply the absolute values, 1.8 and 4.5, to get 8.1. Then make the final answer negative.

$$\begin{array}{r} 1.8 \\ \times\ 4.5 \\ \hline 90 \\ 720 \\ \hline 8.10 \end{array}$$

b. Find the absolute values: $|-1{,}000| = 1{,}000$ and $|-59.08| = 59.08$. Since the decimals have like signs, their product is positive.

$(-1{,}000)(-59.08) = 1{,}000(59.08)$

$= 59{,}080$ — Multiply the absolute values, 1,000 and 59.08. Since 1,000 has 3 zeros, move the decimal point in 59.08 3 places to the right. Write a placeholder zero. The answer is positive.

Self Check 7
Multiply:
a. $6.6(-5.5)$ −36.3
b. $-44.968(-100)$ 4,496.8

Now Try **Problems 37 and 41**

Teaching Example 7 Multiply:
a. $-3.6(2.8)$
b. $(-10{,}000)(-63.11)$

Answers:
a. −10.08
b. 631,100

4 Evaluate exponential expressions that have decimal bases.

We have evaluated exponential expressions that have whole number bases, integer bases, and fractional bases. The base of an exponential expression can also be a positive or a negative decimal.

EXAMPLE 8 Evaluate: **a.** $(2.4)^2$ **b.** $(-0.05)^2$

Strategy We will write each exponential expression as a product of repeated factors, and then perform the multiplication. This requires that we identify the base and the exponent.

WHY The exponent tells the number of times the base is to be written as a factor.

Self Check 8
Evaluate:
a. $(-1.3)^2$ 1.69
b. $(0.09)^2$ 0.0081

Now Try **Problems 45 and 47**

Teaching Example 8 Evaluate:
a. $(4.2)^2$
b. $(-0.07)^2$
Answers:
a. 17.64
b. 0.0049

Solution

a. $(2.4)^2 = 2.4 \cdot 2.4$ — The base is 2.4 and the exponent is 2. Write the base as a factor 2 times.

$= 5.76$ — Multiply the decimals.

$$\begin{array}{r} 2.4 \\ \times\ 2.4 \\ \hline 96 \\ 480 \\ \hline 5.76 \end{array}$$

b. $(-0.05)^2 = (-0.05)(-0.05)$ — The base is −0.05 and the exponent is 2. Write the base as a factor 2 times.

$= 0.0025$ — Multiply the decimals. The product of two decimals with like signs is positive.

$$\begin{array}{r} 0.05 \\ \times\ 0.05 \\ \hline 0.0025 \end{array}$$

5 Use the order of operations rule.

Recall that the order of operations rule is used to evaluate expressions that involve more than one operation.

Self Check 9
Evaluate:
$-2|-4.4 + 5.6| + (-0.8)^2$ −1.76
Now Try **Problem 49**

Teaching Example 9
Evaluate: $(-0.9)^2 + 4|-7.1 + 6.8|$
Answer:
2.01

EXAMPLE 9 Evaluate: $-(0.6)^2 + 5|-3.6 + 1.9|$

Strategy The absolute value bars are grouping symbols. We will perform the addition within them first.

WHY By the order of operations rule, we must perform all calculations within parentheses and other grouping symbols (such as absolute value bars) first.

Solution

$-(0.6)^2 + 5|-3.6 + 1.9|$

$= -(0.6)^2 + 5|-1.7|$ — Do the addition within the absolute value symbols. Use the rule for adding two decimals with different signs.

$= -(0.6)^2 + 5(1.7)$ — Simplify: $|-1.7| = 1.7$.

$= -0.36 + 5(1.7)$ — Evaluate: $(0.6)^2 = 0.36$.

$= -0.36 + 8.5$ — Do the multiplication: $5(1.7) = 8.5$.

$= 8.14$ — Use the rule for adding two decimals with different signs.

$$\begin{array}{r} \overset{2\ 16}{\cancel{3}.\cancel{6}} \\ -\ 1.9 \\ \hline 1.7 \end{array} \qquad \begin{array}{r} \overset{3}{1}.7 \\ \times\ \ 5 \\ \hline 8.5 \end{array} \qquad \begin{array}{r} \overset{4\,10}{8.\cancel{5}\cancel{0}} \\ -0.36 \\ \hline 8.14 \end{array}$$

6 Evaluate formulas.

Recall that to evaluate a formula, we replace the letters (called **variables**) with specific numbers and then use the order of operations rule.

Self Check 10
Evaluate $V = 1.3\pi r^3$ for $\pi = 3.14$ and $r = 3$. 110.214
Now Try **Problem 53**

Teaching Example 10
Evaluate $A = P + Prt$ for $P = 75.50$, $r = 0.12$, and $t = 2$.
Answer:
93.62

EXAMPLE 10 Evaluate the formula $S = 6.28r(h + r)$ for $h = 3.1$ and $r = 6$.

Strategy In the given formula, we will replace the letter r with 6 and h with 3.1.

WHY Then we can use the order of operations rule to find the value of the expression on the right side of the = symbol.

Solution

$S = 6.28r(h + r)$ — $6.28r(h + r)$ means $6.28 \cdot r \cdot (h + r)$.

$= 6.28(6)(3.1 + 6)$ — Replace r with 6 and h with 3.1.

$= 6.28(6)(9.1)$ — Do the addition within the parentheses.

$= 37.68(9.1)$ — Do the multiplication: $6.28(6) = 37.68$.

$= 342.888$ — Do the multiplication.

$$\begin{array}{r} 37.68 \\ \times\ \ 9.1 \\ \hline 3768 \\ 339120 \\ \hline 342.888 \end{array}$$

7 Estimate products of decimals.

Estimation can be used to check the reasonableness of an answer to a decimal multiplication. There are several ways to estimate, but the objective is the same: Simplify the numbers in the problem so that the calculations can be made easily and quickly.

EXAMPLE 11

a. Estimate using front-end rounding: $27 \cdot 6.41$

b. Estimate by rounding each factor to the nearest tenth: $13.91 \cdot 5.27$

c. Estimate by rounding: $0.1245(101.4)$

Strategy We will use rounding to approximate the factors. Then we will find the product of the approximations.

WHY Rounding produces factors that contain fewer digits. Such numbers are easier to multiply.

Solution

a. To estimate $27 \cdot 6.41$ by front-end rounding, we begin by rounding both factors to their *largest* place value.

$$\begin{array}{rcrl} 27 & \longrightarrow & 30 & \text{Round to the nearest ten.} \\ \times\ 6.41 & \longrightarrow & \times\ \ 6 & \text{Round to the nearest one.} \\ & & 180 & \end{array}$$

The estimate is 180. If we calculate $27 \cdot 6.41$, the product is exactly 173.07. The estimate is close: It's about 7 more than 173.07.

b. To estimate $13.91 \cdot 5.27$, we will round both decimals to the nearest tenth.

$$\begin{array}{rcrl} 13.91 & \longrightarrow & 13.9 & \text{Round to the nearest tenth.} \\ \times\ 5.27 & \longrightarrow & \times\ \ 5.3 & \text{Round to the nearest tenth.} \\ & & 417 & \\ & & 6950 & \\ & & 73.67 & \end{array}$$

The estimate is 73.67. If we calculate $13.91 \cdot 5.27$, the product is exactly 73.3057. The estimate is close: It's just slightly more than 73.3057.

c. Since 101.4 is approximately 100, we can estimate 0.1245(**101.4**) using 0.1245(**100**).

$$0.1245(100) = 12.45$$ Since 100 has two zeros, move the decimal point in 0.1245 two places to the right.

The estimate is 12.45. If we calculate 0.1245(101.4), the product is exactly 12.6243. Note that the estimate is close: It's slightly less than 12.6243.

Self Check 11

a. Estimate using front-end rounding: $4.337 \cdot 65$ 280

b. Estimate by rounding the factors to the nearest tenth: $3.092 \cdot 11.642$ 35.96

c. Estimate by rounding: 0.7899(985.34) 789.9

Now Try **Problems 61 and 63**

Teaching Example 11

a. Estimate using front-end rounding: $2.371 \cdot 76$

b. Estimate by rounding the factors to the nearest tenth: $9.1682 \cdot 7.344$

c. Estimate by rounding: 0.5301(97.89)

Answers:

a. 160

b. 67.16

c. 53.01

8 Solve application problems by multiplying decimals.

Application problems that involve repeated addition are often more easily solved using multiplication.

EXAMPLE 12

Coins Banks wrap pennies in rolls of 50 coins. If a penny is 1.55 millimeters thick, how tall is a stack of 50 pennies?

Analyze

- There are 50 pennies in a stack. *Given*
- A penny is 1.55 millimeters thick. *Given*
- How tall is a stack of 50 pennies? *Find*

Cookey/Dreamstime.com

Self Check 12

COINS Banks wrap nickels in rolls of 40 coins. If a nickel is 1.95 millimeters thick, how tall is a stack of 40 nickels? 78 mm

Now Try **Problem 97**

Teaching Example 12
COINS Banks wrap dimes in rolls of 50 coins. If a dime is 1.35 millimeters thick, how tall is a stack of 50 dimes?

Answer:
67.5 mm

Form The height (in millimeters) of a stack of 50 pennies, each of which is 1.55 thick, is the sum of fifty 1.55's. This repeated addition can be calculated more simply by multiplication.

The height of a stack of pennies	is equal to	the thickness of one penny	times	the number of pennies in the stack.
The height of stack of pennies	=	1.55	·	50

Solve Use vertical form to perform the multiplication:

$$\begin{array}{r} 1.55 \\ \times\quad 50 \\ \hline 000 \\ 7750 \\ \hline 77.50 \end{array}$$

State A stack of 50 pennies is 77.5 millimeters tall.

Check We can estimate to check the result. If we use 2 millimeters to approximate the thickness of one penny, then the height of a stack of 50 pennies is about $2 \cdot 50$ millimeters $= 100$ millimeters. The result, 77.5 mm, seems reasonable. ■

Sometimes more than one operation is needed to solve a problem involving decimals.

Self Check 13

WEEKLY EARNINGS A pharmacy assistant's basic workweek is 40 hours. After her daily shift is over, she can work overtime at a rate of 1.5 times her regular rate of $15.90 per hour. How much money will she earn in a week if she works 4 hours of overtime? $731.40

Now Try **Problem 113**

Teaching Example 13
WEEKLY EARNINGS An iron worker's basic workweek is 40 hours. After his daily shift is over, he can work overtime at a rate of 1.5 times his regular rate of $18.08 per hour. How much money will he earn in a week if he works 2 hours of overtime?

Answer:
$777.44

EXAMPLE 13 *Weekly Earnings* A cashier's basic workweek is 40 hours. After his daily shift is over, he can work overtime at a rate 1.5 times his regular rate of $13.10 per hour. How much money will he earn in a week if he works 6 hours of overtime?

Analyze

- A cashier's basic workweek is 40 hours. *Given*
- His overtime pay rate is 1.5 times his regular rate of $13.10 per hour. *Given*
- How much money will he earn in a week if he works his regular shift and 6 hours overtime? *Find*

Form To find the cashier's overtime pay rate, we multiply 1.5 times his regular pay rate, $13.10.

$$\begin{array}{r} 13.10 \\ \times\quad 1.5 \\ \hline 6550 \\ 13100 \\ \hline 19.650 \end{array}$$

The cashier's overtime pay rate is $19.65 per hour.

We now translate the words of the problem to numbers and symbols.

The total amount the cashier earns in a week	is equal to	40 hours	times	his regular pay rate	plus	the number of overtime hours	times	his overtime rate.
The total amount the cashier earns in a week	=	40	·	$13.10	+	6	·	$19.65

Solve We will use the rule for the order of operations to evaluate the expression:

$$40 \cdot 13.10 + 6 \cdot 19.65 = 524.00 + 117.90 \quad \text{Do the multiplication first.}$$
$$= 641.90 \quad \text{Do the addition.}$$

```
   13.10
 ×    40
    0000
    5240
  524.00

  5 3 3
   19.65
 ×     6
  117.90

   1
  524.00
 +117.90
  641.90
```

State The cashier will earn a total of $641.90 for the week.

Check We can use estimation to check. The cashier works 40 hours per week for approximately $13 per hour to earn about 40 · $13 = $520. His 6 hours of overtime at approximately $20 per hour earns him about 6 · $20 = $120. His total earnings that week are about $520 + $120 = $640. The result, $641.90, seems reasonable. ■

ANSWERS TO SELF CHECKS

1. 11.61 **2.** 0.00144 **3.** 836.6 **4. a.** 72.1 **b.** 6,080 **5. a.** 12.99 **b.** 0.00000002 **6. a.** 567,100,000 **b.** 50,820,000,000 **c.** 4,133,000,000,000 **7. a.** −36.3 **b.** 4,496.8 **8. a.** 1.69 **b.** 0.0081 **9.** −1.76 **10.** 110.214 **11. a.** 280 **b.** 35.96 **c.** 789.9 **12.** 78 mm **13.** $731.40

SECTION 2.9 STUDY SET

VOCABULARY

Fill in the blanks.

1. In the multiplication problem shown below, label each *factor*, the *partial products*, and the *product*.

```
  3.4  ← factor
× 2.6  ← factor
  204  ← partial product
  680  ← partial product
 8.84  ← product
```

▶ **2.** Numbers such as 10, 100, and 1,000 are called __powers__ of 10.

CONCEPTS

Fill in the blanks.

3. Insert a decimal point in the correct place for each product shown below. Write placeholder zeros, if necessary.

a.
```
  3.8   2.28
× 0.6
  228
```

b.
```
   1.79   14.499
×   8.1
    179
  14320
  14499
```

c.
```
 2.0   14.0
×  7
 140
```

d.
```
 0.013   0.00026
× 0.02
  0026
```

4. Fill in the blanks.

▶ **a.** To find the product of a decimal and 10, 100, 1,000, and so on, move the decimal point to the __right__ the same number of places as there are zeros in the power of 10.

b. To find the product of a decimal and 0.1, 0.01, 0.001, and so on, move the decimal point to the __left__ the same number of places as there are in the power of 10.

5. Determine whether the *sign* of each result is positive or negative. ***You do not have to find the product.***

a. −7.6(−1.8) positive

b. −4.09 · 2.274 negative

6. ▶ **a.** When we move its decimal point to the right, does a decimal number get larger or smaller? larger

b. When we move its decimal point to the left, does a decimal number get larger or smaller? smaller

NOTATION

7. a. List the first five powers of 10 that are greater than 1. 10, 100, 1,000, 10,000, 100,000

b. List the first five powers of 10 that are less than 1. 0.1, 0.01, 0.001, 0.0001, 0.00001

8. Write each number in standard notation.

a. one million 1,000,000

b. one billion 1,000,000,000

c. one trillion 1,000,000,000,000

GUIDED PRACTICE

Multiply. See Example 1.

9. $4.8 \cdot 6.2$ 29.76

▶ **10.** $3.5 \cdot 9.3$ 32.55

11. $5.6(8.9)$ 49.84

12. $7.2(8.4)$ 60.48

Multiply. See Example 2.

13. $0.003(2.7)$ 0.0081

14. $0.002(2.6)$ 0.0052

15. $\begin{array}{r} 5.8 \\ \times\ 0.009 \\ \hline \end{array}$ 0.0522

▶ **16.** $\begin{array}{r} 8.7 \\ \times\ 0.004 \\ \hline \end{array}$ 0.0348

Multiply. See Example 3.

17. $179(6.3)$ 1,127.7

▶ **18.** $225(4.9)$ 1,102.5

19. $\begin{array}{r} 316 \\ \times\ 7.4 \\ \hline \end{array}$ 2,338.4

20. $\begin{array}{r} 527 \\ \times\ 3.7 \\ \hline \end{array}$ 1,949.9

Multiply. See Example 4.

21. $6.84 \cdot 100$ 684

▶ **22.** $2.09 \cdot 100$ 209

23. $0.041(10,000)$ 410

24. $0.034(10,000)$ 340

Multiply. See Example 5.

25. $647.59 \cdot 0.01$ 6.4759

26. $317.09 \cdot 0.01$ 3.1709

27. $1.15(0.001)$ 0.00115

▶ **28.** $2.83(0.001)$ 0.00283

Write each number in standard notation. See Example 6.

29. 14.2 million 14,200,000

30. 33.9 million 33,900,000

31. 98.2 billion 98,200,000,000

▶ **32.** 80.4 billion 80,400,000,000

33. 1.421 trillion 1,421,000,000,000

34. 3.056 trillion 3,056,000,000,000

35. 657.1 billion 657,100,000,000

36. 422.7 billion 422,700,000,000

Multiply. See Example 7.

37. $-1.9(7.2)$ −13.68

38. $-5.8(3.9)$ −22.62

39. $-3.3(-1.6)$ 5.28

▶ **40.** $-4.7(-2.2)$ 10.34

41. $(-10,000)(-44.83)$ 448,300

42. $(-10,000)(-13.19)$ 131,900

43. $678.231(-1,000)$ −678,231

44. $491.565(-1,000)$ −491,565

Evaluate each expression. See Example 8.

45. $(3.4)^2$ 11.56

▶ **46.** $(5.1)^2$ 26.01

47. $(-0.03)^2$ 0.0009

48. $(-0.06)^2$ 0.0036

Evaluate each expression. See Example 9.

49. $-(-0.2)^2 + 4|-2.3 + 1.5|$ 3.16

▶ **50.** $-(-0.3)^2 + 6|-6.4 + 1.7|$ 28.11

51. $-(-0.8)^2 + 7|-5.1 - 4.8|$ 68.66

52. $-(-0.4)^2 + 6|-6.2 - 3.5|$ 58.04

Evaluate each formula. See Example 10.

53. $A = P + Prt$ for $P = 85.50, r = 0.08$, and $t = 5$ 119.70

54. $A = P + Prt$ for $P = 99.95, r = 0.05$, and $t = 10$ 149.925

55. $A = lw$ for $l = 5.3$ and $w = 7.2$ 38.16

▶ **56.** $A = 0.5bh$ for $b = 7.5$ and $h = 6.8$ 25.5

57. $P = 2l + 2w$ for $l = 3.7$ and $w = 3.6$ 14.6

58. $P = a + b + c$ for $a = 12.91, b = 19$, and $c = 23.6$ 55.51

59. $C = 2\pi r$ for $\pi = 3.14$ and $r = 2.5$ 15.7

60. $A = \pi r^2$ for $\pi = 3.14$ and $r = 4.2$ 55.3896

Estimate each product using front-end rounding. See Example 11.

61. $46 \cdot 5.3$ 250

▶ **62.** $37 \cdot 4.29$ 160

Estimate each product by rounding the factors to the nearest tenth. See Example 11.

63. $17.11 \cdot 3.85$ 66.69

▶ **64.** $18.33 \cdot 6.46$ 118.95

TRY IT YOURSELF

Perform the indicated operations.

65. $-0.56 \cdot 0.33$ −0.1848

66. $-0.64 \cdot 0.79$ −0.5056

67. $(-1.3)^2$ 1.69

68. $(-2.5)^2$ 6.25

69. $(-0.7 - 0.5)(2.4 - 3.1)$ 0.84

▶ **70.** $(-8.1 - 7.8)(0.3 + 0.7)$ −15.9

71. $\begin{array}{r} 0.008 \\ \times\ 0.09 \\ \hline \end{array}$ 0.00072

72. $\begin{array}{r} 0.003 \\ \times\ 0.09 \\ \hline \end{array}$ 0.00027

73. $-0.2 \cdot 1,000,000$ −200,000

74. $-1,000,000 \cdot 1.9$ −1,900,000

75. $(-5.6)(-2.2)$ 12.32

▶ **76.** $(-7.1)(-4.1)$ 29.11

77. $-4.6(23.4 - 19.6)$ −17.48

78. $6.9(9.8 - 8.9)$ 6.21

79. $(-4.9)(-0.001)$ 0.0049

80. $(-0.001)(-7.09)$ 0.00709

81. $(-0.2)^2 + 2(7.1)$ 14.24

82. $(-6.3)(3) - (1.2)^2$ −20.34

83. $\begin{array}{r} 2.13 \\ \times\ 4.05 \\ \hline \end{array}$ 8.6265

▶ **84.** $\begin{array}{r} 3.06 \\ \times\ 1.82 \\ \hline \end{array}$ 5.5692

85. $-7(8.1781)$ −57.2467

▶ **86.** $-5(4.7199)$ −23.5995

87. $-1,000(0.02239)$ −22.39

▶ **88.** $-100(0.0897)$ −8.97

89. $(0.5 + 0.6)^2(-3.2)$ −3.872

90. $(-5.1)(4.9 - 3.4)^2$ −11.475

91. $-0.2(306)(-0.4)$ 24.48

92. $-0.3(417)(-0.5)$ 62.55

93. $-0.01(|-2.6 - 6.7|)^2$ −0.8649

94. $-0.01(|-8.16 + 9.9|)^2$ −0.030276

Complete each table.

95.

Decimal	Its square
0.1	0.01
0.2	0.04
0.3	0.09
0.4	0.16
0.5	0.25
0.6	0.36
0.7	0.49
0.8	0.64
0.9	0.81

96.

Decimal	Its cube
0.1	0.001
0.2	0.008
0.3	0.027
0.4	0.064
0.5	0.125
0.6	0.216
0.7	0.343
0.8	0.512
0.9	0.729

APPLICATIONS

97. REAMS OF PAPER Find the thickness of a 500-sheet ream of copier paper if each sheet is 0.0038 inch thick. 1.9 in.

98. MILEAGE CLAIMS Each month, a salesman is reimbursed by his company for any work-related travel that he does in his own car at the rate of $0.445 per mile. How much will the salesman receive if he traveled a total of 120 miles in his car on business in the month of June? $53.40

99. SALARIES Use the following formula to determine the annual salary of a recording engineer who works 38 hours per week at a rate of $37.35 per hour. Round the result to the nearest hundred dollars. $74,100

$$\text{Annual salary} = \text{hourly rate} \cdot \text{hours per week} \cdot 52.2 \text{ weeks}$$

100. PAYCHECKS If you are paid every other week, your monthly gross income is your gross income from one paycheck times 2.17. Find the monthly gross income of a supermarket clerk who earns $1,095.70 every two weeks. Round the result to the nearest cent. $2377.67

101. BAKERY SUPPLIES A bakery buys various types of nuts as ingredients for cookies. Complete the table by filling in the cost of each purchase.

Type of nut	Price per pound	Pounds	Cost
Almonds	$5.95	16	$95.20
Walnuts	$4.95	25	$123.75

102. NEW HOMES Find the cost to build the home shown below if construction costs are $92.55 per square foot. $212,032.05

House Plan #DP-2203

Square Feet:	**2,291 Sq Ft.**	Width:	**70'70"**	Bedrooms:	**3**
Stories:	**Single Story**	Depth:	**64'0"**	Bathrooms:	**3**
				Garage Bays:	**2**

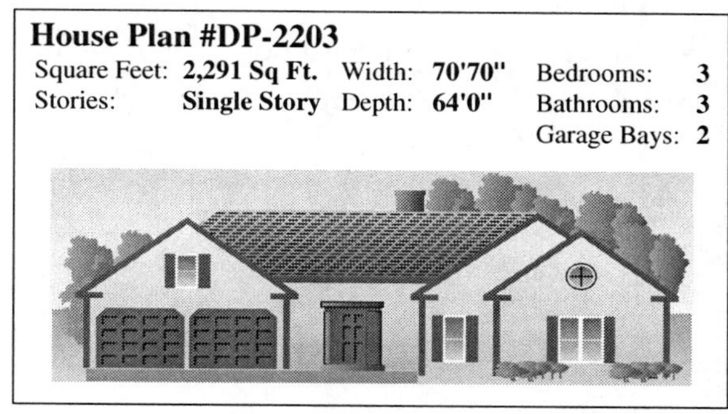

103. BIOLOGY Cells contain DNA. In humans, it determines such traits as eye color, hair color, and height. A model of DNA appears below. If 1 Å (angstrom) = 0.000000004 inch, find the dimensions of 34 Å, 3.4 Å, and 10 Å, shown in the illustration. 0.000000136 in., 0.0000000136 in., 0.00000004 in.

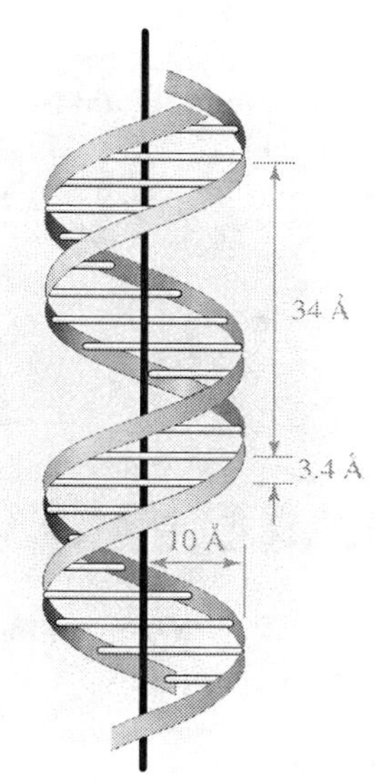

104. TACHOMETERS

a. Estimate the decimal number to which the tachometer needle points in the illustration below. 4.5

b. What engine speed (in rpm) does the tachometer indicate? 4,500 rpm

105. CITY PLANNING The streets shown in blue on the city map below are 0.35 mile apart. Find the distance of each trip between the two given locations.

a. The airport to the Convention Center 2.1 mi

b. City Hall to the Convention Center 3.5 mi

c. The airport to City Hall 5.6 mi

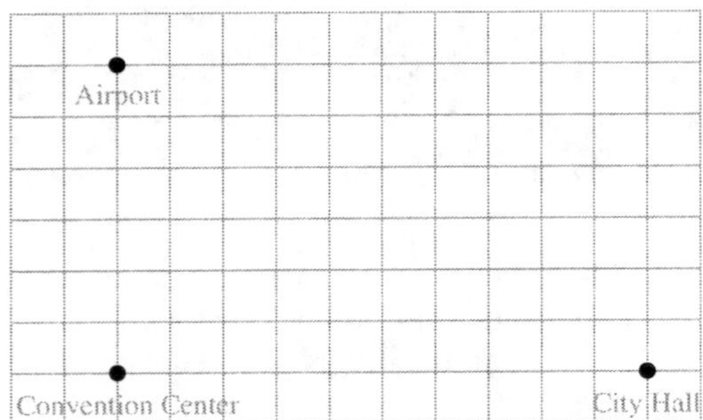

106. RETROFITS The illustration below shows the current widths of the three columns of a freeway overpass. A computer analysis indicated that the width of each column should actually be 1.4 times what it currently is to withstand the stresses of an earthquake. According to the analysis, how wide should each of the columns be? 6.3 ft, 4.9 ft, 3.5 ft

107. ELECTRIC BILLS When billing a household, a utility company charges for the number of kilowatt-hours used. A kilowatt-hour (kwh) is a standard measure of electricity. If the cost of 1 kwh is \$0.14277, what is the electric bill for a household that uses 719 kwh in a month? Round the answer to the nearest cent. \$102.65

108. UTILITY TAXES Some gas companies are required to tax the number of therms used each month by the customer. What are the taxes collected on a monthly usage of 31 therms if the tax rate is \$0.00566 per therm? Round the answer to the nearest cent. 18¢

109. Write each highlighted number in standard form.

a. CONSERVATION The ***19.6-million acre*** Arctic National Wildlife Refuge is located in the northeast corner of Alaska. (Source: National Wildlife Federation) 19,600,000 acres

b. POPULATION According to projections by the International Programs Center at the U.S. Census Bureau, at 7:16 P.M. eastern time on Saturday, February 25, 2006, the population of the Earth hit ***6.5 billion*** people. 6,500,000,000

c. DRIVING The U.S. Department of Transportation estimated that Americans drove a total of ***3.026 trillion miles*** in 2008. (Source: Federal Highway Administration) 3,026,000,000,000 miles

110. Write each highlighted number in standard form.

a. MILEAGE Irv Gordon, of Long Island, New York, has driven a record ***2.6 million miles*** in his 1966 Volvo P-1800. (Source: autoblog.com) 2,600,000 miles

b. E-COMMERCE Online spending during the 2008 holiday season (November 1 through December 23) was about ***\$25.5 billion.*** (Source: pcmag.com) \$25,500,000,000

c. FEDERAL DEBT On March 27, 2009, the U.S. national debt was ***\$11.073 trillion.*** (Source: National Debt Clock) \$11,073,000,000,000

111. SOCCER A soccer goal is rectangular and measures 24 feet wide by 8 feet high. Major league soccer officials are proposing to increase its width by 1.5 feet and increase its height by 0.75 foot.

a. What is the area of the goal opening now? 192 ft^2

b. What would the area be if the proposal is adopted? 223.125 ft^2

c. How much area would be added? 31.125 ft^2

112. SALT INTAKE Studies done by the Centers for Disease Control and Prevention found that the average American eats 3.436 grams of salt each day. The recommended amount is 1.5 grams per day. How many more grams of salt does the average American eat in one week compared with what the Center recommends? 13.552 g

113. CONCERT SEATING Two types of tickets were sold for a concert. Floor seating costs \$12.50 a ticket, and balcony seats cost \$15.75.

a. Complete the following table and find the receipts from each type of ticket.

b. Find the total receipts from the sale of both types of tickets. \$14,075

Ticket type	Price	Number sold	Receipts
Floor	\$12.50	1,000	\$12,500
Balcony	\$15.75	100	\$1,575

114. PLUMBING BILLS A corner of the invoice for plumbing work is torn. What is the labor charge for the 4 hours of work? What is the total charge (standard service charge, parts, labor)? $162.20, $226.70

Carter Plumbing 100 W. Dalton Ave.		Invoice #210
Standard service charge	$	25.75
Parts	$	38.75
Labor: 4 hr @ $40.55/hr	$	
Total charges	$	

115. WEIGHTLIFTING The barbell is evenly loaded with iron plates. How much plate weight is loaded on the barbell? 136.4 lb

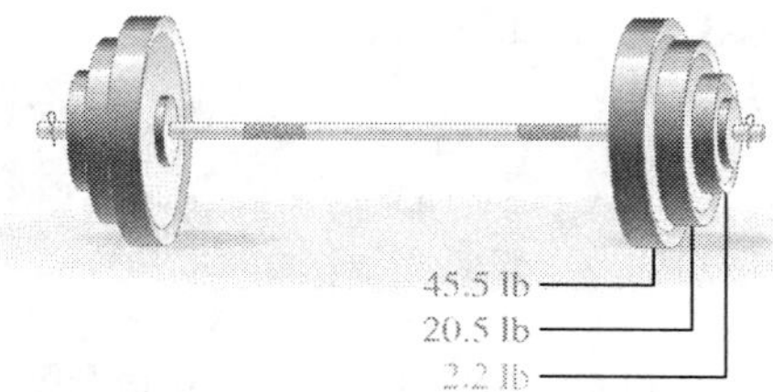

116. SWIMMING POOLS Long bricks, called *coping*, can be used to outline the edge of a swimming pool. How many meters of coping will be needed in the construction of the swimming pool shown? 160.6 m

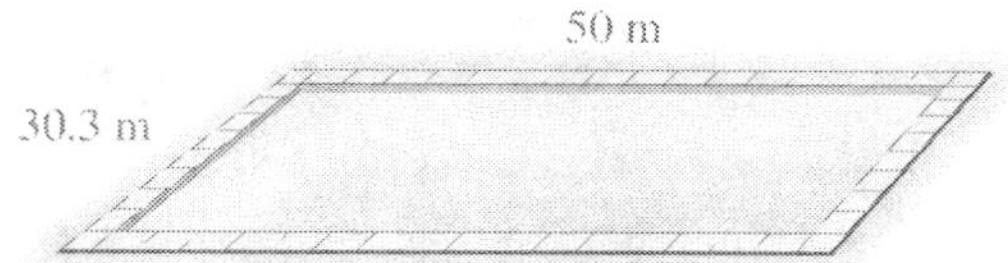

117. STORM DAMAGE After a rainstorm, the saturated ground under a hilltop house began to give way. A survey team noted that the house dropped 0.57 inch initially. In the next three weeks, the house fell 0.09 inch per week. How far did the house fall during this three-week period? 0.84 in.

118. WATER USAGE In May, the water level of a reservoir reached its high mark for the year. During the summer months, as water usage increased, the level dropped. In the months of May and June, it fell 4.3 feet each month. In August, and September, because of high temperatures, it fell another 8.7 feet each month. By the beginning of October, how far below the year's high mark had the water level fallen? 26 ft

WRITING

119. Explain how to determine where to place the decimal point in the answer when multiplying two decimals.

120. List the similarities and differences between whole-number multiplication and decimal multiplication.

121. Explain how to multiply a decimal by a power of 10 that is greater than 1, and by a power of ten that is less than 1.

122. Is it easier to multiply the decimals 0.4 and 0.16 or the fractions $\frac{4}{10}$ and $\frac{16}{100}$? Explain why.

123. Why do we have to line up the decimal points when adding, but we do not have to when multiplying?

124. Which vertical form for the following multiplication do you like better? Explain why.

$$\begin{array}{r} 0.000003 \\ \times \quad 2.7 \\ \hline \end{array} \qquad \begin{array}{r} 2.8 \\ \times\ 0.000003 \\ \hline \end{array}$$

REVIEW

Find the prime factorization of each number. Use exponents in your answer, when helpful.

125. 220 $2^2 \cdot 5 \cdot 11$

126. 400 $2^4 \cdot 5^2$

127. 162 $2 \cdot 3^4$

128. 735 $3 \cdot 5 \cdot 7^2$

Objectives

1 Divide a decimal by a whole number.
2 Divide a decimal by a decimal.
3 Round a decimal quotient.
4 Estimate quotients of decimals.
5 Divide decimals by powers of 10.
6 Divide signed decimals.
7 Use the order of operations rule.
8 Evaluate formulas.
9 Solve application problems by dividing decimals.

SECTION 2.10
Dividing Decimals

In Chapter 1, we used a process called long division to divide whole numbers.

Long division form

$$\begin{array}{r} 2 \\ 5\overline{)10} \\ \underline{10} \\ 0 \end{array}$$

2 ← Quotient; Divisor → 5; 10 ← Dividend; 0 ← Remainder

In this section, we consider division problems in which the divisor, the dividend, or both are decimals.

1 Divide a decimal by a whole number.

To develop a rule for decimal division, let's consider the problem $47 \div 10$. If we rewrite the division as $\frac{47}{10}$, we can use the long division method from Chapter 3 for changing an improper fraction to a mixed number to find the answer:

$$\begin{array}{r} 4\frac{7}{10} \\ 10\overline{)47} \\ \underline{-40} \\ 7 \end{array}$$

Here the result is written in quotient + $\frac{\text{remainder}}{\text{divisor}}$ form.

To perform this same division using decimals, we write 47 as 47.0 and divide as we would divide whole numbers.

$$\begin{array}{r} 4.7 \\ 10\overline{)47.0} \\ \underline{-40} \\ 7\,0 \\ \underline{-7\,0} \\ 0 \end{array}$$

Note that the decimal point in the quotient (answer) is placed directly above the decimal point in the dividend.

After subtracting 40 from 47, bring down the 0 and continue to divide.

The remainder is 0.

Since $4\frac{7}{10} = 4.7$, either method gives the same answer. This result suggests the following method for dividing a decimal by a whole number.

Dividing a Decimal by a Whole Number

To divide a decimal by a whole number:

1. Write the problem in long division form and place a decimal point in the quotient (answer) directly above the decimal point in the dividend.
2. Divide as if working with whole numbers.
3. If necessary, additional zeros can be written to the right of the last digit of the dividend to continue the division.

Self Check 1

Divide: $20.8 \div 4$. Check the result. 5.2

Now Try **Problem 15**

EXAMPLE 1 Divide: $42.6 \div 6$. Check the result.

Strategy Since the divisor, 6, is a whole number, we will write the problem in long division form and place a decimal point directly above the decimal point in 42.6. Then we will divide as if the problem was $426 \div 6$.

WHY To divide a decimal by a whole number, we divide as if working with whole numbers.

Solution

Step 1

Place a decimal point in the quotient that lines up with the decimal point in the dividend.

$$6\overline{)42.6}$$

Step 2 Now divide using the four-step division process: **estimate, multiply, subtract,** and **bring down.**

```
   7.1
 6)42.6     Ignore the decimal points and divide as if working with whole numbers.
 - 42
    0 6     After subtracting 42 from 42, bring down the 6 and continue to divide.
  -   6
      0     The remainder is 0.
```

Decimal division is checked in the same way: *The product of the quotient and the divisor should be the dividend.*

```
   7.1 ← Quotient          7.1
 ×   6 ← Divisor         6)42.6
  42.6 ← Dividend
```

The check confirms that $42.6 \div 6 = 7.1$.

Teaching Example 1 Divide: $21.9 \div 3$. Check the result.

Answer:
7.3

EXAMPLE 2 Divide: $71.68 \div 28$

Strategy Since the divisor is a whole number, 28, we will write the problem in long division form and place a decimal point directly above the decimal point in 71.68. Then we will divide as if the problem was $7{,}168 \div 28$.

WHY To divide a decimal by a whole number, we divide as if working with whole numbers.

Solution

Write the decimal point in the quotient (answer) directly above the decimal point in the dividend.

```
     2.56    Ignore the decimal points and divide as if working
 28)71.68    with whole numbers.
  - 56
    15 6     After subtracting 56 from 71, bring down the 6
  - 14 0     and continue to divide.
     1 68    After subtracting 140 from 156, bring down the 8
   - 1 68    and continue to divide.
        0    The remainder is 0.
```

We can use multiplication to check this result.

```
   2.56
 ×   28          2.56
   2048      28)71.68
   5120
  71.68
```

The check confirms that $71.68 \div 28 = 2.56$.

Self Check 2

Divide: $101.44 \div 32$ 3.17

Now Try **Problem 19**

Teaching Example 2 Divide: $88.32 \div 24$. Check the result.

Answer:
3.68

Self Check 3

Divide: 42.8 ÷ 8 5.35

Now Try **Problem 23**

Teaching Example 3
Divide: 37.4 ÷ 4. Check the result.

Answer:
9.35

EXAMPLE 3 Divide: 19.2 ÷ 5

Strategy We will write the problem in long division form, place a decimal point directly above the decimal point in 19.2, and divide. If necessary, we will write additional zeros to the right of the 2 in 19.2.

WHY Writing additional zeros to the right of the 2 allows us to continue the division process until we obtain a remainder of 0 or the digits in the quotient repeat in a pattern.

Solution

```
   3.8
5)19.2
 - 15↓
    4 2    After subtracting 15 from 19, bring down the 2 and continue to divide.
  - 4 0
      2    All the digits in the dividend have been used, but the remainder is not 0.
```

We can write a zero to the right of 2 in the dividend and continue the division process. Recall that writing additional zeros to the right of the decimal point does not change the value of the decimal. That is, 19.2 = 19.20.

```
   3.84
5)19.20    Write a zero to the right of the 2 and bring it down.
 - 15
    4 2
  - 4 0↓
      20   Continue to divide.
    - 20
       0   The remainder is 0.
```

Check:

```
   3.84
 ×    5
  19.20 ← Since this is the dividend, the result checks.
```

2 Divide a decimal by a decimal.

To develop a rule for division involving a decimal divisor, let's consider the problem $0.36\overline{)0.2592}$, where the divisor is the decimal 0.36. First, we express the division in fraction form.

$0.36\overline{)0.2592}$ can be represented by $\frac{0.2592}{0.36}$

(Divisor: 0.36 in both)

To be able to use the rule for dividing decimals by a *whole number* discussed earlier, we need to move the decimal point in the divisor 0.36 two places to the right. This can be accomplished by multiplying it by 100. However, if the denominator of the fraction is multiplied by 100, the numerator must also be multiplied by 100 so that the fraction maintains the same value. It follows that $\frac{100}{100}$ is the form of 1 that we should use to build $\frac{0.2592}{0.36}$.

$$\frac{0.2592}{0.36} = \frac{0.2592}{0.36} \cdot \frac{100}{100}$$ Multiply by a form of 1.

$$= \frac{0.2592 \cdot 100}{0.36 \cdot 100}$$ Multiply the numerators. Multiply the denominators.

$$= \frac{25.92}{36}$$ Multiplying both decimals by 100 moves their decimal points two places to the right.

This fraction represents the division problem $36\overline{)25.92}$. From this result, we have the following observations.

- The division problem $0.36\overline{)0.2592}$ is equivalent to $36\overline{)25.92}$; that is, they have the same answer.
- The decimal points in *both* the divisor and the dividend of the first division problem have been moved two decimal places to the right to create the second division problem.

$0.36\overline{)0.2592}$ becomes $36\overline{)25.92}$

These observations illustrate the following rule for division with a decimal divisor.

Division with a Decimal Divisor

To divide with a decimal divisor:

1. Write the problem in long division form.
2. Move the decimal point of the divisor so that it becomes a whole number.
3. Move the decimal point of the dividend the same number of places to the right.
4. Write the decimal point in the quotient (answer) directly above the decimal point in the dividend. Divide as if working with whole numbers.
5. If necessary, additional zeros can be written to the right of the last digit of the dividend to continue the division.

EXAMPLE 4 Divide: $\dfrac{0.2592}{0.36}$

Strategy We will move the decimal point of the divisor, 0.36, two places to the right and we will move the decimal point of the dividend, 0.2592, the same number of places to the right.

WHY We can then use the rule for dividing a decimal by a *whole number.*

Solution We begin by writing the problem in long division form.

$0\,36\overline{)0\,25.92}$ Move the decimal point two places to the right in the divisor and the dividend. Write the decimal point in the quotient (answer) directly above the decimal point in the dividend.

Since the divisor is now a whole number, we can use the rule for dividing a decimal by a whole number to find the quotient.

$$\begin{array}{r} 0.72 \\ 36\overline{)25.92} \\ -\,25\,2 \\ \hline 72 \\ -\,72 \\ \hline 0 \end{array}$$ Now divide as with whole numbers.

Check:

$$\begin{array}{r} 0.72 \\ \times\quad 36 \\ \hline 432 \\ 2160 \\ \hline 25.92 \end{array}$$ Since this is the dividend, the result checks.

Self Check 4

Divide: $\dfrac{0.6045}{0.65}$ 0.93

Now Try **Problem 27**

Teaching Example 4 Divide: $0.1596 \div 0.38$. Check the result.

Answer:
0.42

> ***Success Tip*** When dividing decimals, moving the decimal points the same number of places to the right in *both* the divisor and the dividend does not change the answer.

3 Round a decimal quotient.

In Example 4, the division process stopped after we obtained a 0 from the second subtraction. Sometimes when we divide, the subtractions never give a zero remainder, and the division process continues forever. In such cases, we can round the result.

Self Check 5

Divide: 12.82 ÷ 0.9. Round the quotient to the nearest hundredth. 14.24

Now Try **Problem 33**

Teaching Example 5 Divide: 11.07 ÷ 0.7. Round the quotient to the nearest hundredth.

Answer:
15.81

EXAMPLE 5 Divide: $\frac{9.35}{0.7}$. Round the quotient to the nearest hundredth.

Strategy We will use the methods of this section to divide to the thousandths column.

WHY To round to the hundredths column, we need to continue the division process for one more decimal place, which is the thousandths column.

Solution We begin by writing the problem in long division form.

$0.7\overline{)9.3.5}$ To write the divisor as a whole number, move the decimal point one place to the right. Do the same for the dividend. Place the decimal point in the quotient (answer) directly above the decimal point in the dividend.

We need to write two zeros to the right of the last digit of the dividend so that we can divide to the thousandths column.

$7\overline{)93.500}$

After dividing to the thousandths column, we round to the hundredths column.

The rounding digit in the hundredths column is 5.
The test digit in the thousandths column is 7.

```
   13.357
7)93.500
 - 7
   23
 - 21
    2 5
  - 2 1
      40
    - 35
       50
     - 49
        1
```

The division process can stop. We have divided to the thousandths column.

Since the test digit 7 is 5 or greater, we will round 13.357 up to approximate the quotient to the nearest hundredth.

$\frac{9.35}{0.7} \approx 13.36$ Read ≈ as "is approximately equal to."

Check:

```
  13.36  ← The approximation of the quotient
×   0.7  ← The original divisor
  9.352  ← Since this is close to the original dividend, 9.35, the result seems reasonable.
```

Success Tip To round a quotient to a certain decimal place value, continue the division process one more column to its right to find the *test digit.*

Using Your CALCULATOR Dividing Decimals

The nucleus of a cell contains vital information about the cell in the form of DNA. The nucleus is very small: A typical animal cell has a nucleus that is only 0.00023622 inch across. How many nuclei (plural of *nucleus*) would have to be laid end to end to extend to a length of 1 inch?

To find how many 0.00023622-inch lengths there are in 1 inch, we must use division: 1 ÷ 0.00023622.

1 [÷] .00023622 [=]   4233.3418

On some calculators, we press the [ENTER] key to display the quotient.

It would take approximately 4,233 nuclei laid end to end to extend to a length of 1 inch.

4 Estimate quotients of decimals.

There are many ways to make an error when dividing decimals. Estimation is a helpful tool that can be used to determine whether or not an answer seems reasonable.

To estimate quotients, we use a method that approximates both the dividend and the divisor so that they divide easily. There is one rule of thumb for this method: If possible, round both numbers up or both numbers down.

EXAMPLE 6 Estimate the quotient: 248.687 ÷ 43.1

Strategy We will round the dividend and the divisor down and find 240 ÷ 40.

WHY The division can be made easier if the dividend and the divisor end with zeros. Also, 40 divides 240 exactly.

Solution

The dividend is approximately

248.687 ÷ 43.1   240 ÷ 40 = 6   To divide, drop one zero from 240 and from 40, and find 24 ÷ 4.

The divisor is approximately

The estimate is 6.

If we calculate 248.687 ÷ 43.1, the quotient is exactly 5.77. Note that the estimate is close: It's just 0.23 more than 5.77.

Self Check 6

Estimate the quotient: 6,229.249 ÷ 68.9

Now Try **Problems 35 and 39**

Self Check 6 Answer
6,300 ÷ 70 = 630 ÷ 7 = 90

Teaching Example 6 Estimate the quotient: 481.797 ÷ 62.98
Answer:
480 ÷ 60 = 48 ÷ 6 = 8

5 Divide decimals by powers of 10.

To develop a set of rules for division of decimals by a power of 10, we consider the problems 8.13 ÷ 10 and 8.13 ÷ 0.1.

```
     0.813
 10)8.130     Write a zero to the
   - 8 0      right of the 3.
       13
     - 10
       30
     - 30
        0
```

```
      81.3
 0 1)81 3     Move the decimal points in the divisor
   - 8        and dividend one place to the right.
       1
     - 1
       3
     - 3
       0
```

Note that the quotients, 0.813 and 81.3, and the dividend, 8.13, are the same except for the location of the decimal points. The first quotient, 0.813, can be easily obtained by moving the decimal point of the dividend one place to the left. The second quotient, 81.3, is easily obtained by moving the decimal point of the dividend one place to the right. These observations illustrate the following rules for dividing a decimal by a power of 10.

Dividing a Decimal by 10, 100, 1,000, and So On

To find the quotient of a decimal and 10, 100, 1,000, and so on, move the decimal point to the left the same number of places as there are zeros in the power of 10.

Dividing a Decimal by 0.1, 0.01, 0.001, and So On

To find the quotient of a decimal and 0.1, 0.01, 0.001, and so on, move the decimal point to the right the same number of decimal places as there are in the power of 10.

Self Check 7

Find each quotient:

a. $721.3 \div 100$ 7.213

b. $\frac{1.07}{1,000}$ 0.00107

c. $19.4407 \div 0.0001$ 194,407

Now Try **Problems 43 and 49**

Teaching Example 7 Find each quotient:
a. $624.87 \div 100$
b. $\frac{1.67}{1,000}$
c. $49.87513 \div 0.0001$
Answers:
a. 6.2487
b. 0.00167
c. 498,751.3

EXAMPLE 7 Find each quotient:

a. $16.74 \div 10$ **b.** $8.6 \div 10,000$ **c.** $\frac{290.623}{0.01}$

Strategy We will identify the divisor in each division. If it is a power of 10 greater than 1, we will count the number of zeros that it has. If it is a power of 10 less than 1, we will count the number of decimal places that it has.

WHY Then we will know how many places to the right or left to move the decimal point in the dividend to find the quotient.

Solution

a. $16.74 \div 10 = 1.674$ Since the divisor 10 has one zero, move the decimal point one place to the left.

b. $8.6 \div 10,000 = .00086$ Since the divisor 10,000 has four zeros, move the decimal point four places to the left. Write three placeholder zeros (shown in blue).

$= 0.00086$

c. $\frac{290.623}{0.01} = 29062.3$ Since the divisor 0.01 has two decimal places, move the decimal point in 290.623 two places to the right.

6 Divide signed decimals.

The rules for dividing integers also hold for dividing signed decimals. The quotient of two decimals with *like signs* is positive, and the quotient of two decimals with *unlike signs* is negative.

Self Check 8

Divide:

a. $-100.624 \div 15.2$ −6.62

b. $\frac{-23.9}{-0.1}$ 239

EXAMPLE 8 Divide: **a.** $-104.483 \div 16.3$ **b.** $\frac{-38.677}{-0.1}$

Strategy In part a, we will use the rule for dividing signed decimals that have different (unlike) signs. In part b, we will use the rule for dividing signed decimals that have the same (like) signs.

WHY In part a, the divisor is positive and the dividend is negative. In part b, both the dividend and divisor are negative.

Solution

a. First, we find the absolute values: $|-104.483| = 104.483$ and $|16.3| = 16.3$. Then we divide the absolute values, 104.483 by 16.3, using the methods of this section.

$$\begin{array}{r} 6.41 \\ 163\overline{)1044.83} \\ -978 \\ \hline 66\ 8 \\ -65\ 20 \\ \hline 1\ 63 \\ -1\ 63 \\ \hline 0 \end{array}$$

Move the decimal point in the divisor and the dividend one place to the right.

Write the decimal point in the quotient (answer) directly above the decimal point in the dividend.

Divide as if working with whole numbers.

Since the signs of the original dividend and divisor are unlike, we make the final answer negative. Thus,

$$-104.483 \div 16.3 = -6.41$$

Check the result using multiplication.

b. We can use the rule for dividing a decimal by a power of 10 to find the quotient.

$$\frac{-38.677}{-0.1} = 386.77$$

Since the divisor 0.1 has *one* decimal place, move the decimal point in 38.677 *one* place to the right. Since the dividend and divisor have like signs, the quotient is positive.

Now Try **Problems 51 and 55**

Teaching Example 8 Divide:
a. $-113.016 \div 13.6$
b. $\frac{-31.93}{-0.1}$
Answers:
a. -8.31
b. 319.3

7 Use the order of operations rule.

Recall that the order of operations rule is used to evaluate expressions that involve more than one operation.

EXAMPLE 9 Evaluate: $\dfrac{2(0.351) + 0.5592}{0.2 - 0.6}$

Strategy We will evaluate the expression above and the expression below the fraction bar separately. Then we will do the indicated division, if possible.

WHY Fraction bars are grouping symbols. They group the numerator and denominator.

Solution

$$\frac{2(0.351) + 0.5592}{0.2 - 0.6}$$

$$= \frac{0.702 + 0.5592}{-0.4}$$ In the numerator, do the multiplication. In the denominator, do the subtraction.

$$= \frac{1.2612}{-0.4}$$ In the numerator, do the addition.

$$= -3.153$$ Do the division indicated by the fraction bar. The quotient of two numbers with unlike signs is negative.

$$\begin{array}{r} \overset{1}{0}.351 \\ \times\quad 2 \\ \hline 0.702 \end{array} \qquad \begin{array}{r} \overset{1\ 1}{0.7020} \\ +\ 0.5592 \\ \hline 1.2612 \end{array}$$

$$\begin{array}{r} 3.153 \\ 4\overline{)12.612} \\ -\ 12 \\ \hline 6 \\ -4 \\ \hline 21 \\ -20 \\ \hline 12 \\ -12 \\ \hline 0 \end{array}$$

Self Check 9

Evaluate: $\dfrac{2.7756 + 3(-0.63)}{0.4 - 1.2}$ −1.1

Now Try **Problem 59**

Teaching Example 9
Evaluate: $\dfrac{2(0.932) + 0.6764}{0.3 - 0.9}$
Answer:
-4.234

8 Evaluate formulas.

Self Check 10

Evaluate the formula $l = \frac{A}{w}$ for $A = 5.511$ and $w = 1.002$. 5.5

Now Try **Problem 63**

Teaching Example 10 Evaluate the formula $h = \frac{3V}{B}$ for $V = 3.144$ and $B = 2.4$.

Answer:
3.93

EXAMPLE 10 Evaluate the formula $b = \dfrac{2A}{h}$ for $A = 15.36$ and $h = 6.4$.

Strategy In the given formula, we will replace the letter A with 15.36 and h with 6.4.

WHY Then we can use the order of operations rule to find the value of the expression on the right side of the = symbol.

Solution

$$B = \frac{2A}{h}$$ This is the given formula.

$$= \frac{2(15.36)}{6.4}$$ Replace A with 15.36 and h with 6.4.

$$= \frac{30.72}{6.4}$$ In the numerator, do the multiplication.

$$= 4.8$$ Do the division indicated by the fraction bar.

$$\begin{array}{r} \overset{1\,1}{15.36} \\ \times \quad 2 \\ \hline 30.72 \end{array}$$

$$\begin{array}{r} 4.8 \\ 64\overline{)307.2} \\ -256 \\ \hline 51\,2 \\ -51\,2 \\ \hline 0 \end{array}$$

9 Solve application problems by dividing decimals.

Recall that application problems that involve forming equal-sized groups can be solved by division.

Self Check 11

FRUIT CAKES A 9-inch-long fruitcake loaf is cut into 0.25-inch-thick slices. How many slices are there in one fruitcake? 36 slices

Now Try **Problem 95**

Teaching Example 11
PEPPERONI A meat slicing machine cuts 12-inch-long pepperoni sausages into 0.125-inch-thick slices. How many slices are there in one sausage?

Answer:
96 slices

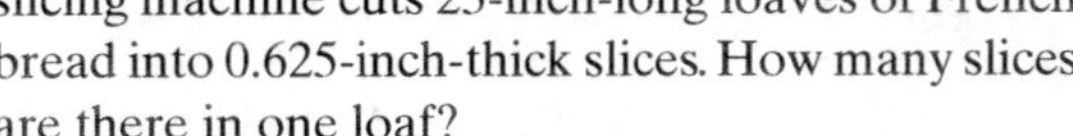

EXAMPLE 11 *French Bread* A bread slicing machine cuts 25-inch-long loaves of French bread into 0.625-inch-thick slices. How many slices are there in one loaf?

Analyze

- 25-inch-long loaves of French bread are cut into slices. *Given*
- Each slice is 0.625-inch thick. *Given*
- How many slices are there in one loaf? *Find*

Form Cutting a loaf of French bread into equally thick slices indicates division. We translate the words of the problem to numbers and symbols.

The number of slices in a loaf of French bread	is equal to	the length of the loaf of French bread	divided by	the thickness of one slice.
The number of slices in a loaf of French bread	=	25	÷	0.625

Solve When we write $25 \div 0.625$ in long division form, we see that the divisor is a decimal.

$0.625\overline{)25.000}$ To write the divisor as a whole number, move the decimal point three places to the right. To move the decimal point three places to the right in the dividend, three placeholder zeros must be inserted (shown in blue).

Now that the divisor is a whole number, we can perform the division.

$$\begin{array}{r} 40 \\ 625\overline{)25000} \\ -\,2500\downarrow \\ \hline 00 \\ -\,0 \\ \hline 0 \end{array}$$

State There are 40 slices in one loaf of French bread.

Check The multiplication below verifies that 40 slices, each 0.625-inch thick, makes a 25-inch-long loaf. The result checks.

$$\begin{array}{r} 0.625 \\ \times\quad 40 \\ \hline 0000 \\ 25000 \\ \hline 25.000 \end{array}$$

0.625 ← The thickness of one slice of bread (in inches)

40 ← The number of slices in one loaf

25.000 ← The length of one loaf of bread (in inches)

Recall that the **arithmetic mean,** or **average,** of several numbers is a value around which the numbers are grouped. We use addition and division to find the mean (average).

EXAMPLE 12 *Comparison Shopping* An online shopping website, Shopping.com, listed the four best prices for an automobile GPS receiver as shown below. What is the mean (average) price of the GPS?

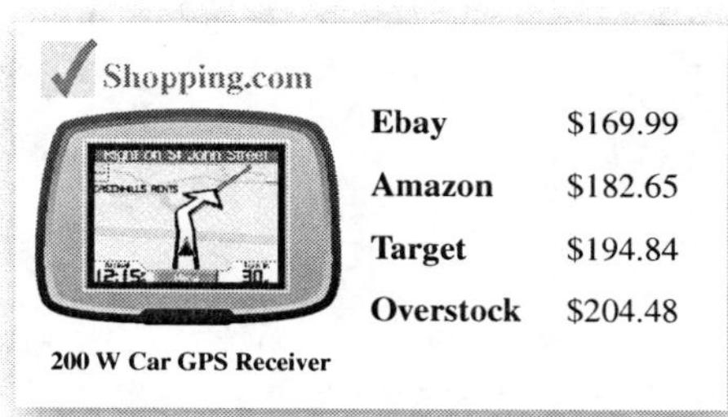

Strategy We will add 169.99, 182.65, 194.84, and 204.48 and divide the sum by 4.

WHY To find the mean (average) of a set of values, we divide the sum of the values by the number of values.

Solution

$$\text{Mean} = \frac{169.99 + 182.65 + 194.84 + 204.48}{4}$$ Since there are 4 prices, divide the sum by 4.

$$= \frac{751.96}{4}$$ In the numerator, do the addition.

$$= 187.99$$ Do the indicated division.

$$\begin{array}{r} \scriptstyle 222\ 2 \\ 169.99 \\ 182.65 \\ 194.84 \\ +204.48 \\ \hline 751.96 \end{array} \qquad \begin{array}{r} 187.99 \\ 4\overline{)751.96} \\ -4 \\ \hline 35 \\ -32 \\ \hline 31 \\ -28 \\ \hline 39 \\ -36 \\ \hline 36 \\ -36 \\ \hline 0 \end{array}$$

The mean (average) price of the GPS receiver is $187.99.

Self Check 12

U.S. NATIONAL PARKS Use the following data to determine the average number of visitors per year to the national parks for the years 2004 through 2008. (Source: National Park Service)

2.747 million visitors

Year	Visitors (millions)
2008	2.749
2007	2.756
2006	2.726
2005	2.735
2004	2.769

Now Try **Problem 103**

Teaching Example 12
BROADWAY SHOWS Use the following data to determine the average number of tickets that were sold per year to Broadway shows in New York City for the years 2004 through 2008. (Source: The Broadway League)

Season	Tickets sold (millions)
2008	12.32
2007	12.29
2006	12.00
2005	11.53
2004	11.61

Answer:
11.95 million tickets sold

THINK IT THROUGH *GPA*

"In considering all of the factors that are important to employers as they recruit students in colleges and universities nationwide, college major, grade point average, and work-related experience usually rise to the top of the list."

Mary D. Feduccia, Ph.D., Career Services Director, Louisiana State University

A grade point average (GPA) is a weighted average based on the grades received and the number of units (credit hours) taken. A GPA for one semester (or term) is defined as

the quotient of the sum of the grade points earned for each class and the sum of the number of units taken. The number of grade points earned for a class is the product of the number of units assigned to the class and the value of the grade received in the class.

1. Use the table of grade values below to compute the GPA for the student whose semester grade report is shown. Round to the nearest hundredth.
2.86

Grade	Value
A	4
B	3
C	2
D	1
F	0

Class	Units	Grade
Geology	4	C
Algebra	5	A
Psychology	3	C
Spanish	2	B

2. If you were enrolled in school last semester (or term), list the classes taken, units assigned, and grades received like those shown in the grade report above. Then calculate your GPA.

ANSWERS TO SELF CHECKS

1. 5.2 **2.** 3.17 **3.** 5.35 **4.** 0.93 **5.** 14.24 **6.** $6{,}300 \div 70 = 630 \div 7 = 90$ **7. a.** 7.213 **b.** 0.00107 **c.** 194,407 **8. a.** −6.62 **b.** 239 **9.** −1.107 **10.** 5.5 **11.** 36 slices **12.** 2.747 million visitors

SECTION 2.10 STUDY SET

VOCABULARY

Fill in the blanks.

1. In the division problem shown below, label the *dividend,* the *divisor,* and the *quotient.*

$$\text{divisor} \rightarrow 5\overline{)15.85} \quad 3.17 \leftarrow \text{quotient}; \quad 15.85 \leftarrow \text{dividend}$$

2. To perform the division $2.7\overline{)9.45}$, we move the decimal point of the divisor so that it becomes the <u>whole</u> number 27.

CONCEPTS

3. A decimal point is missing in each of the following quotients. Write a decimal point in the proper position.

a. $\begin{array}{r} 526 \\ 4\overline{)21.04} \end{array}$ 5.26

b. $\begin{array}{r} 0008 \\ 3\overline{)0.024} \end{array}$ 0.008

4. a. How many places to the right must we move the decimal point in 6.14 so that it becomes a whole number? two places

b. When the decimal point in 49.8 is moved three places to the right, what is the resulting number? 49,800

5. Move the decimal point in the divisor and the dividend the same number of places so that the divisor becomes a whole number. ***You do not have to find the quotient.***

a. $1.3\overline{)10.66}$ $13\overline{)106.6}$

b. $3.71\overline{)16.695}$ $371\overline{)1669.5}$

6. Fill in the blanks: To divide with a decimal divisor, write the problem in long division form. Move the decimal point of the divisor so that it becomes a whole number. Then move the decimal point of the dividend the same number of places to the right. Write the decimal point in the quotient directly above the decimal point in the dividend and divide as working with whole numbers.

7. To perform the division $7.8\overline{)14.562}$, the decimal points in the divisor and dividend are moved 1 place to the right. This is equivalent to multiplying $\frac{14.562}{7.8}$ by what form of 1? $\frac{10}{10}$

8. Use multiplication to check the following division. Is the result correct?

$$\frac{1.917}{0.9} = 2.13$$ yes, $2.13 \cdot 0.9 = 1.917$

9. When rounding a decimal to the hundredths column, to what other column must we look at first? thousandths

10. a. When 9.545 is divided by 10, is the answer smaller or larger than 9.545? smaller

b. When 9.545 is divided by 0.1, is the answer smaller or larger than 9.545? larger

11. Fill in the blanks.

▶ a. To find the quotient of a decimal and 10, 100, 1,000, and so on, move the decimal point to the left the same number of places as there are zeros in the power of 10.

b. To find the quotient of a decimal and 0.1, 0.01, 0.001, and so on, move the decimal point to the right the same number of decimal places as there are in the power of 10.

▶ 12. Determine whether the *sign* of each result is positive or negative. ***You do not have to find the quotient.***

a. $-15.25 \div (-0.5)$ positive

b. $\frac{-25.92}{3.2}$ negative

NOTATION

13. Explain what the red arrows are illustrating in the division problem below.

$467\overline{)3208.7}$ moving the decimal points in the divisor and dividend 2 places to the right

14. The division shown below is not finished. Why was the red 0 written after the 7 in the dividend?

$$\begin{array}{r} 2.3 \\ 2\overline{)4.70} \\ -4 \\ \hline 0\,7 \\ -6 \\ \hline 1 \end{array}$$

The red 0 was written after the 7 so that the division process could continue.

GUIDED PRACTICE

Divide. Check the result. See Example 1.

15. $12.6 \div 6$ 2.1

▶ 16. $40.8 \div 8$ 5.1

17. $3\overline{)27.6}$ 9.2

18. $4\overline{)28.8}$ 7.2

Divide. Check the result. See Example 2.

19. $98.21 \div 23$ 4.27

▶ 20. $190.96 \div 28$ 6.82

21. $37\overline{)320.05}$ 8.65

22. $32\overline{)125.12}$ 3.91

Divide. Check the result. See Example 3.

23. $13.4 \div 4$ 3.35

24. $38.3 \div 5$ 7.66

25. $5\overline{)22.8}$ 4.56

▶ 26. $6\overline{)28.5}$ 4.75

Divide. Check the result. See Example 4.

27. $\frac{0.1932}{0.42}$ 0.46

▶ 28. $\frac{0.2436}{0.29}$ 0.84

29. $0.29\overline{)0.1131}$ 0.39

30. $0.58\overline{)0.1566}$ 0.27

Divide. Round the quotient to the nearest hundredth. Check the result. See Example 5.

31. $\frac{11.83}{0.6}$ 19.72

▶ 32. $\frac{16.43}{0.9}$ 18.26

33. $\frac{17.09}{0.7}$ 24.41

34. $\frac{13.07}{0.6}$ 21.78

Estimate each quotient. See Example 6.

35. $289.842 \div 72.1$ $280 \div 70 = 28 \div 7 = 4$

▶ 36. $284.254 \div 91.4$ $270 \div 90 = 27 \div 9 = 3$

37. $383.76 \div 7.8$ $400 \div 8 = 50$

38. $348.84 \div 5.7$ $360 \div 6 = 60$

39. $3,883.284 \div 48.12$ $4,000 \div 50 = 400 \div 5 = 80$

40. $5,556.521 \div 67.89$ $5,600 \div 70 = 560 \div 7 = 80$

41. $6.1\overline{)15,819.74}$ $15,000 \div 5 = 3,000$

42. $9.2\overline{)19,460.76}$ $18,000 \div 9 = 2,000$

Find each quotient. See Example 7.

43. $451.78 \div 100$ 4.5178

▶ 44. $991.02 \div 100$ 9.9102

45. $\frac{30.09}{10,000}$ 0.003009

46. $\frac{27.07}{10,000}$ 0.002707

47. $1.25 \div 0.1$ 12.5

48. $8.62 \div 0.01$ 862

49. $\frac{545.2}{0.001}$ 545,200

50. $\frac{67.4}{0.001}$ 67,400

Divide. See Example 8.

51. $-110.336 \div 12.8$ −8.62

52. $-121.584 \div 14.9$ −8.16

53. $-91.304 \div (-22.6)$ 4.04

54. $-66.126 \div (-32.1)$ 2.06

55. $\dfrac{-20.3257}{-0.001}$ 20,325.7

56. $\dfrac{-48.8933}{-0.001}$ 48,893.3

57. $0.003 \div (-100)$ −0.00003

58. $0.008 \div (-100)$ −0.00008

Evaluate each expression. See Example 9.

59. $\dfrac{2(0.614) + 2.3854}{0.2 - 0.9}$ −5.162

60. $\dfrac{2(1.242) + 0.8932}{0.4 - 0.8}$ −8.443

61. $\dfrac{5.409 - 3(1.8)}{(0.3)^2}$ 0.1

62. $\dfrac{1.674 - 5(0.222)}{(0.1)^2}$ 56.4

Evaluate each formula. See Example 10.

63. $t = \dfrac{d}{r}$ for $d = 211.75$ and $r = 60.5$ 3.5

64. $h = \dfrac{2A}{b}$ for $A = 9.62$ and $b = 3.7$ 5.2

65. $r = \dfrac{d}{t}$ for $d = 219.375$ and $t = 3.75$ 58.5

66. $\pi = \dfrac{C}{d}$ for $C = 14.4513$ and $d = 4.6$ (Round to the nearest hundredth.) 3.14

TRY IT YOURSELF

Perform the indicated operations. Round the result to the specified decimal place, when indicated.

67. $4.5\overline{)11.97}$ 2.66

68. $4.1\overline{)14.637}$ 3.57

69. $\dfrac{75.04}{10}$ 7.504

70. $\dfrac{22.32}{100}$ 0.2232

71. $8\overline{)0.036}$ 0.0045

72. $4\overline{)0.073}$ 0.01825

73. $9\overline{)2.889}$ 0.321

74. $6\overline{)3.378}$ 0.563

75. $\dfrac{-3(0.2) - 2(3.3)}{30(0.4)^2}$ −1.5

76. $\dfrac{(-1.3)^2 + 9.2}{-2(0.2) - 0.5}$ −12.1

77. Divide 1.2202 by -0.01. −122.02

78. Divide -0.4531 by -0.001. 453.1

79. $-5.714 \div 2.4$ (nearest tenth) −2.4

80. $-21.21 \div 3.8$ (nearest tenth) −5.6

81. $-39 \div (-4)$ 9.75

82. $-26 \div (-8)$ 3.25

83. $7.8915 \div .00001$ 789,150

84. $23.025 \div 0.0001$ 230,250

85. $\dfrac{0.0102}{0.017}$ 0.6

86. $\dfrac{0.0092}{0.023}$ 0.4

87. $12.243 \div 0.9$ (nearest hundredth) 13.60

88. $13.441 \div 0.6$ (nearest hundredth) 22.40

89. $1{,}000\overline{)34.8}$ 0.0348

90. $10{,}000\overline{)678.9}$ 0.06789

91. $\dfrac{40.7(3 - 8.3)}{0.4 - 0.61}$ (nearest hundredth) 1,027.19

92. $\dfrac{(0.5)^2 - (0.3)^2}{0.005 + 0.1}$ (nearest hundredth) 1.52

93. Divide 0.25 by 1.6 0.15625

94. Divide 1.2 by 0.64 1.875

APPLICATIONS

95. BUTCHER SHOPS A meat slicer trims 0.05-inch-thick pieces from a sausage. If the sausage is 14 inches long, how many slices are there in one sausage? 280

96. ELECTRONICS The volume control on a computer is shown to the right. If the distance between the Low and High settings is 21 cm, how far apart are the equally spaced volume settings? 1.75 cm

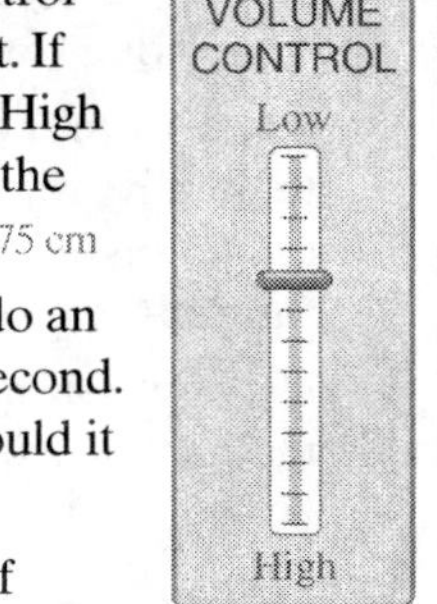

97. COMPUTERS A computer can do an arithmetic calculation in 0.00003 second. How many of these calculations could it do in 60 seconds? 2,000,000

98. THE LOTTERY In December of 2008, fifteen city employees of Piqua, Ohio, who had played the Mega Millions Lottery as a group, won the jackpot. They were awarded a total of \$94.5 million. If the money was split equally, how much did each person receive? (Source: pal-item.com) \$6.3 million

99. SPRAY BOTTLES Each squeeze of the trigger of a spray bottle emits 0.017 ounce of liquid. How many squeezes are there in an 8.5-ounce bottle? 500 squeezes

100. CAR LOANS See the loan statement below. How many more monthly payments must be made to pay off the loan? 15 payments

American Finance Company	June
Monthly payment: \$42.10	Paid to date: \$547.30
	Loan balance: \$631.50

101. HIKING Refer to the illustration below to determine how long it will take the person shown to complete the hike. Then determine at what time of the day she will complete the hike. 11 hr, 6 P.M.

102. HOURLY PAY The graph below shows the average hours worked and the average weekly earnings of U.S. production workers in manufacturing for the years 1998 and 2008. What did the average production worker in manufacturing earn per hour

a. in 1998? $13.45 **b.** in 2008? $17.25

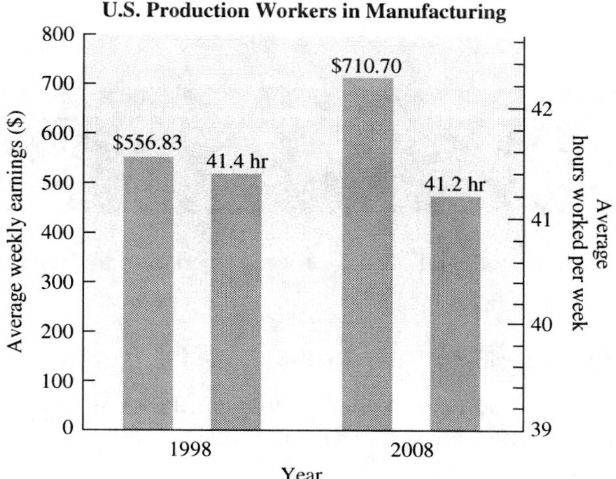

Source: *U.S. Department of Labor Statistic*

103. TRAVEL The illustration shows the annual number of person-trips of 50 miles or more (one way) for the years 2002–2007, as estimated by the Travel Industry Association of America. Find the average number of trips per year for this period of time. 1,453.4 million

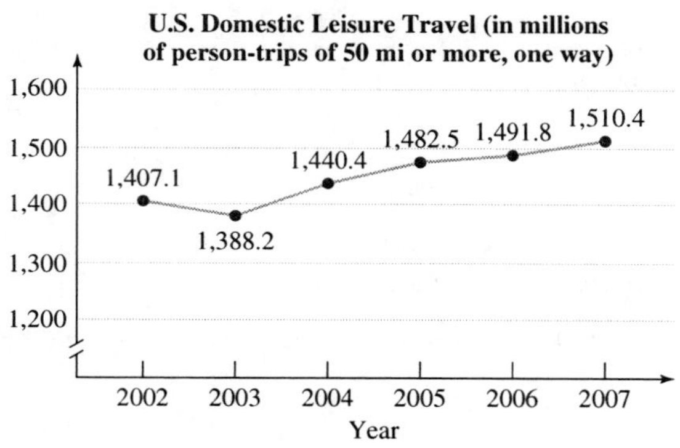

Source: *U.S. Travel Association*

104. OIL WELLS Geologists have mapped out the types of soil through which engineers must drill to reach an oil deposit. See the illustration below.

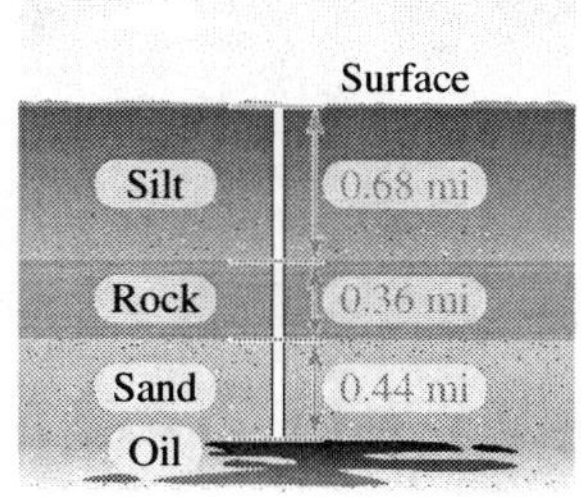

a. How far below the surface is the oil deposit? 1.48 mi

b. What is the average depth that must be drilled each week if the drilling is to be a four-week project? 0.37 mi

105. REFLEXES An online reaction time test is shown below. When the stop light changes from red to green, the participant is to immediately click on the large green button. The program then displays the participant's reaction time in the table. After the participant takes the test five times, the *average* reaction time is found. Determine the average reaction time for the results shown below. 0.231 sec

Test Number	Reaction Time (in seconds)	The stoplight to watch.	The button to click.
1	0.219		
2	0.233		Click here on green light
3	0.204		
4	0.297		
5	0.202		
AVG.	?		

106. INDY 500 Driver Scott Dixon, of New Zealand, had the fastest average qualifying speed for the 2008 Indianapolis 500-mile race. This earned him the *pole position* to begin the race. The speeds for each of his four qualifying laps are shown below. What was his average qualifying speed? 226.366 mph

Lap 1: 226.598 mph
Lap 2: 226.505 mph
Lap 3: 226.303 mph
Lap 4: 226.058 mph

(Source: indianapolismotorspeedway.com)

WRITING

107. Explain the process used to divide two numbers when both the divisor and the dividend are decimals. Give an example.

108. Explain why we must sometimes use rounding when we write the answer to a division problem.

109. The division $0.5\overline{)2.005}$ is equivalent to $5\overline{)20.05}$. Explain what equivalent means in this case.

110. In $3\overline{)0.7}$, why can additional zeros be placed to the right of 0.7 without affecting the result?

111. Explain how to estimate the following quotient: $0.75\overline{)2.415}$

112. Explain why multiplying $\frac{4.86}{0.2}$ by the form of 1 shown below moves the decimal points in the dividend, 4.86, and the divisor, 0.2, one place to the right.

$$\frac{4.86}{0.2} = \frac{4.86}{0.2} \cdot \frac{10}{10}$$

REVIEW

113. **a.** Find the GCF of 10 and 25. 5

b. Find the LCM of 10 and 25. 50

114. **a.** Find the GCF of 8, 12, and 16. 4

b. Find the LCM of 8, 12, and 16. 48

SECTION 2.11
Fractions and Decimals

Objectives

1. Write fractions as equivalent terminating decimals.
2. Write fractions as equivalent repeating decimals.
3. Round repeating decimals.
4. Graph fractions and decimals on a number line.
5. Compare fractions and decimals.
6. Evaluate expressions containing fractions and decimals.
7. Solve application problems involving fractions and decimals.

In this section, we continue to explore the relationship between fractions and decimals.

1 Write fractions as equivalent terminating decimals.

A fraction and a decimal are said to be **equivalent** if they name the same number. Every fraction can be written in an equivalent decimal form by dividing the numerator by the denominator, as indicated by the fraction bar.

Writing a Fraction as a Decimal

To write a fraction as a decimal, divide the numerator of the fraction by its denominator.

EXAMPLE 1 Write each fraction as a decimal.

a. $\frac{3}{4}$ **b.** $\frac{5}{8}$ **c.** $\frac{7}{2}$

Strategy We will divide the numerator of each fraction by its denominator. We will continue the division process until we obtain a zero remainder.

WHY We divide the numerator by the denominator because a fraction bar indicates division.

Solution

a. $\frac{3}{4}$ means $3 \div 4$. To find $3 \div 4$, we begin by writing it in long division form as $4\overline{)3}$. To proceed with the division, we must write the dividend 3 with a decimal point and some additional zeros. Then we use the procedure for dividing a decimal by a whole number.

$$\begin{array}{r} 0.75 \\ 4\overline{)3.00} \\ -2\,8\downarrow \\ 20 \\ -20 \\ \hline 0 \end{array}$$

Write a decimal point and two additional zeros to the right of 3.

← The remainder is 0.

Thus, $\frac{3}{4} = 0.75$. We say that the **decimal equivalent** of $\frac{3}{4}$ is 0.75.

Self Check 1

Write each fraction as a decimal.

a. $\frac{1}{2}$ 0.5

b. $\frac{3}{16}$ 0.1875

c. $\frac{9}{2}$ 4.5

Now Try **Problems 15, 17, and 21**

Teaching Example 1 Write each fraction as a decimal:

a. $\frac{1}{4}$ b. $\frac{7}{8}$ c. $\frac{11}{2}$

Answers:
a. 0.25
b. 0.875
c. 5.5

We can check the result by writing 0.75 as a fraction in simplest form:

$$0.75 = \frac{75}{100}$$ 0.75 is seventy-five hundredths.

$$= \frac{3 \cdot \overset{1}{\cancel{25}}}{4 \cdot \underset{1}{\cancel{25}}}$$ To simplify the fraction, factor 75 as 3 · 25 and 100 as 4 · 25 and remove the common factor of 25.

$$= \frac{3}{4}$$ This is the original fraction.

b. $\frac{5}{8}$ means 5 ÷ 8.

$$\begin{array}{r} 0.625 \\ 8\overline{)5.000} \\ -4\,8 \\ \hline 20 \\ -16 \\ \hline 40 \\ -40 \\ \hline 0 \end{array}$$

Write a decimal point and three additional zeros to the right of 5.

0 ← The remainder is 0.

Thus, $\frac{5}{8} = 0.625$.

c. $\frac{7}{2}$ means 7 ÷ 2.

$$\begin{array}{r} 3.5 \\ 2\overline{)7.0} \\ -6 \\ \hline 1\,0 \\ -1\,0 \\ \hline 0 \end{array}$$

Write a decimal point and one additional zero to the right of 7.

0 ← The remainder is 0.

Thus, $\frac{7}{2} = 3.5$.

Caution! A common error when finding a decimal equivalent for a fraction is to *incorrectly divide the denominator by the numerator.* An example of this is shown on the right, where the decimal equivalent of $\frac{5}{8}$ (a number less than 1) is incorrectly found to be 1.6 (a number greater than 1).

$$\begin{array}{r} 1.6 \\ 5\overline{)8.0} \\ -5 \\ \hline 3\,0 \\ -3\,0 \\ \hline 0 \end{array}$$

In parts a, b, and c of Example 1, the division process ended because a remainder of 0 was obtained. When such a division *terminates* with a remainder of 0, we call the resulting decimal a **terminating decimal.** Thus, 0.75, 0.625, and 3.5 are three examples of terminating decimals.

The Language of Mathematics To *terminate* means to bring to an end. In the movie *The Terminator,* actor Arnold Schwarzenegger plays a heartless machine sent to Earth to bring an end to his enemies.

2 Write fractions as equivalent repeating decimals.

Sometimes, when we are finding a decimal equivalent of a fraction, the division process never gives a remainder of 0. In this case, the result is a **repeating decimal.** Examples of repeating decimals are 0.4444 . . . and 1.373737 . . . . The three dots tell us that a block of digits repeats in the pattern shown. Repeating decimals can also be written using a bar over the repeating block of digits. For example, 0.4444 . . . can be written as $0.\overline{4}$, and 1.373737 . . . can be written as $1.\overline{37}$.

> ***Caution!*** When using an **overbar** to write a repeating decimal, use the least number of digits necessary to show the repeating block of digits.
>
> ~~$0.333\ldots = 0.\overline{333}$~~ ~~$6.7454545\ldots = 6.7\overline{454}$~~
>
> $0.333\ldots = 0.\overline{3}$ $6.7454545\ldots = 6.7\overline{45}$

Some fractions can be written as decimals using an alternate approach. If the denominator of a fraction in simplified form has factors of only 2's or 5's, or a combination of both, it can be written as a decimal by multiplying it by a form of 1. The objective is to write the fraction in an equivalent form with a denominator that is a power of 10, such as 10, 100, 1,000, and so on.

Self Check 2

Write each fraction as a decimal using multiplication by a form of 1:

a. $\frac{2}{5}$ 0.4

b. $\frac{8}{25}$ 0.32

Now Try **Problems 27 and 29**

Teaching Example 2 Write each fraction as a decimal using multiplication by a form of 1:

a. $\frac{1}{5}$ b. $\frac{9}{20}$

Answers:

a. 0.2

b. 0.45

EXAMPLE 2 Write each fraction as a decimal using multiplication by a form of 1: **a.** $\frac{4}{5}$ **b.** $\frac{11}{40}$

Strategy We will multiply $\frac{4}{5}$ by $\frac{2}{2}$ and we will multiply $\frac{11}{40}$ by $\frac{25}{25}$.

WHY The result of each multiplication will be an equivalent fraction with a denominator that is a power of 10. Such fractions are then easy to write in decimal form.

Solution

a. Since we need to multiply the denominator of $\frac{4}{5}$ by 2 to obtain a denominator of 10, it follows that $\frac{2}{2}$ should be the form of 1 that is used to build $\frac{4}{5}$.

$\frac{4}{5} = \frac{4}{5} \cdot \frac{2}{2}$ Multiply $\frac{4}{5}$ by 1 in the form of $\frac{2}{2}$.

$= \frac{8}{10}$ Multiply the numerators. Multiply the denominators.

$= 0.8$ Write the fraction as a decimal.

b. Since we need to multiply the denominator of $\frac{11}{40}$ by 25 to obtain a denominator of 1,000, it follows that $\frac{25}{25}$ should be the form of 1 that is used to build $\frac{11}{40}$.

$\frac{11}{40} = \frac{11}{40} \cdot \frac{25}{25}$ Multiply $\frac{11}{40}$ by 1 in the form of $\frac{25}{25}$.

$= \frac{275}{1{,}000}$ Multiply the numerators. Multiply the denominators.

$= 0.275$ Write the fraction as a decimal.

Mixed numbers can also be written in decimal form.

Self Check 3

Write the mixed number $3\frac{17}{20}$ in decimal form. 3.85

Now Try **Problem 37**

EXAMPLE 3 Write the mixed number $5\frac{7}{16}$ in decimal form.

Strategy We need only find the decimal equivalent for the fractional part of the mixed number.

WHY The whole-number part in the decimal form is the same as the whole-number part in the mixed number form.

Solution To write $\frac{7}{16}$ as a fraction, we find $7 \div 16$.

$$\begin{array}{r} 0.4375 \\ 16\overline{)7.0000} \\ -6\,4 \\ \hline 60 \\ -48 \\ \hline 120 \\ -112 \\ \hline 80 \\ -80 \\ \hline 0 \end{array}$$

Write a decimal point and four additionl zeros to the right of 7.

The remainder is 0.

Since the whole-number part of the decimal must be the same as the whole-number part of the mixed number, we have:

$$5\frac{7}{16} = 5.4375$$

We would have obtained the same result if we changed $5\frac{7}{16}$ to the improper fraction $\frac{87}{16}$ and divided 87 by 16.

Teaching Example 3 Write the mixed number $1\frac{15}{16}$ in decimal form.

Answer:
1.9375

EXAMPLE 4 Write $\frac{5}{12}$ as a decimal.

Strategy We will divide the numerator of the fraction by its denominator and watch for a repeating pattern of nonzero remainders.

WHY Once we detect a repeating pattern of remainders, the division process can stop.

Solution $\frac{5}{12}$ means $5 \div 12$.

$$\begin{array}{r} 0.4166 \\ 12\overline{)5.0000} \\ -4\,8 \\ \hline 20 \\ -12 \\ \hline 80 \\ -72 \\ \hline 80 \\ -72 \\ \hline 8 \end{array}$$

Write a decimal point and four additional zeros to the right of 5.

It is apparent that 8 will continue to reappear as the remainder. Therefore, 6 will continue to reappear in the quotient. Since the repeating pattern is now clear, we can stop the division.

We can use three dots to show that a repeating pattern of 6's appears in the quotient:

$$\frac{5}{12} = 0.416666\ldots$$

Or, we can use an overbar to indicate the repeating part (in this case, only the 6), and write the decimal equivalent in more compact form:

$$\frac{5}{12} = 0.41\overline{6}$$

Self Check 4

Write $\frac{1}{12}$ as a decimal. $0.08\overline{3}$

Now Try **Problem 41**

Teaching Example 4 Write $\frac{11}{12}$ as a decimal.

Answer:
$0.91\overline{6}$

EXAMPLE 5 Write $-\frac{6}{11}$ as a decimal.

Strategy To find the decimal equivalent for $-\frac{6}{11}$, we will first find the decimal equivalent for $\frac{6}{11}$. To do this, we will divide the numerator of $\frac{6}{11}$ by its denominator and watch for a repeating pattern of nonzero remainders.

Self Check 5

Write $-\frac{13}{33}$ as a decimal. $-0.\overline{39}$

Now Try **Problem 47**

Teaching Example 5 Write $-\frac{9}{11}$ as a decimal.
Answer:
$-0.\overline{81}$

WHY Once we detect a repeating pattern of remainders, the division process can stop.

Solution $\frac{6}{11}$ means $6 \div 11$.

$$\begin{array}{r} 0.54545 \\ 11\overline{)6.00000} \\ -5\,5 \\ \hline 50 \\ -44 \\ \hline 60 \\ -55 \\ \hline 50 \\ -44 \\ \hline 60 \\ -55 \\ \hline 5 \end{array}$$

Write a decimal point and five additional zeros to the right of 6.

It is apparent that 6 and 5 will continue to reappear as remainders. Therefore, 5 and 4 will continue to reappear in the quotient. Since the repeating pattern is now clear, we can stop the division process.

We can use three dots to show that a repeating pattern of 5 and 4 appears in the quotient:

$$\frac{6}{11} = 0.545454\ldots \text{ and therefore, } -\frac{6}{11} = -0.545454\ldots$$

Or, we can use an overbar to indicate the repeating part (in this case, 54), and write the decimal equivalent in more compact form:

$$\frac{6}{11} = 0.\overline{54} \text{ and therefore, } -\frac{6}{11} = -0.\overline{54}$$

The repeating part of the decimal equivalent of some fractions is quite long. Here are some examples:

$$\frac{9}{37} = 0.\overline{243}$$ A block of three digits repeats.

$$\frac{13}{101} = 0.\overline{1287}$$ A block of four digits repeats.

$$\frac{6}{7} = 0.\overline{857142}$$ A block of six digits repeats.

Every fraction can be written as either a terminating decimal or a repeating decimal. For this reason, the set of fractions (**rational numbers**) form a subset of the set of decimals called the set of **real numbers.** The set of real numbers corresponds to all points on a number line.

Not all decimals are terminating or repeating decimals. For example,

$$0.2020020002\ldots$$

does not terminate, and it has no repeating block of digits. This decimal cannot be written as a fraction with an integer numerator and a nonzero integer denominator. Thus, it is not a rational number. It is an example from the set of **irrational numbers.**

3 Round repeating decimals.

When a fraction is written in decimal form, the result is either a terminating or a repeating decimal. Repeating decimals are often rounded to a specified place value.

EXAMPLE 6 Write $\frac{1}{3}$ as a decimal and round to the nearest hundredth.

Strategy We will use the methods of this section to divide to the thousandths column.

WHY To round to the hundredths column, we need to continue the division process for one more decimal place, which is the thousandths column.

Solution $\frac{1}{3}$ means $1 \div 3$.

```
  0.333
3)1.000    Write a decimal point and three additional zeros to the right of 1.
 - 9
   10
  - 9
   10
  - 9
    1      The division process can stop. We have divided to the thousandths column.
```

After dividing to the thousandths column, we round to the hundredths column.

The rounding digit in the hundredths column is 3.
The test digit in the thousandths column is 3.

0.333 . . .

Since 3 is less than 5, we round down, and we have

$$\frac{1}{3} \approx 0.33$$ Read ≈ as "is approximately equal to."

Self Check 6

Write $\frac{4}{9}$ as a decimal and round to the nearest hundredth. 0.44

Now Try **Problem 51**

Teaching Example 6 Write $\frac{1}{9}$ as a decimal and round to the nearest hundredth.

Answer:
0.11

EXAMPLE 7 Write $\frac{2}{7}$ as a decimal and round to the nearest thousandth.

Strategy We will use the methods of this section to divide to the ten-thousandths column.

WHY To round to the thousandths column, we need to continue the division process for one more decimal place, which is the ten-thousandths column.

Solution $\frac{2}{7}$ means $2 \div 7$.

```
  0.2857
7)2.0000    Write a decimal point and four additional zeros to the right of 2.
- 1 4
    60
  - 56
     40
   - 35
      50
    - 49
       1    The division process can stop.
            We have divided to the ten-thousandths column.
```

After dividing to the ten-thousandths column, we round to the thousandths column.

The rounding digit in the thousandths column is 5.
The test digit in the ten-thousandths column is 7.

0.2857

Since 7 is greater than 5, we round up, and $\frac{2}{7} \approx 0.286$.

Self Check 7

Write $\frac{7}{24}$ as a decimal and round to the nearest thousandth. 0.292

Now Try **Problem 61**

Teaching Example 7 Write $\frac{11}{12}$ as a decimal and round to the nearest thousandth.

Answer:
0.917

Using Your CALCULATOR The Fixed-Point Key

After performing a calculation, a scientific calculator can round the result to a given decimal place. This is done using the *fixed-point key.* As we did in Example 7, let's find the decimal equivalent of $\frac{2}{7}$ and round to the nearest thousandth. This time, we will use a calculator.

First, we set the calculator to round to the third decimal place (thousandths) by pressing [2nd] [FIX] 3. Then we press 2 [÷] 7 [=] [0.286]

Thus, $\frac{2}{7} \approx 0.286$. To round to the nearest tenth, we would fix 1; to round to the nearest hundredth, we would fix 2; and so on. After using the FIX feature, don't forget to remove it and return the calculator to the normal mode.

Graphing calculators can also round to a given decimal place. See the owner's manual for the required keystrokes.

4 Graph fractions and decimals on a number line.

A number line can be used to show the relationship between fractions and their decimal equivalents. On the number line below, sixteen equally spaced marks are used to scale from 0 to 1. Some commonly used fractions that have terminating decimal equivalents are shown. For example, we see that $\frac{1}{8} = 0.125$ and $\frac{13}{16} = 0.8125$.

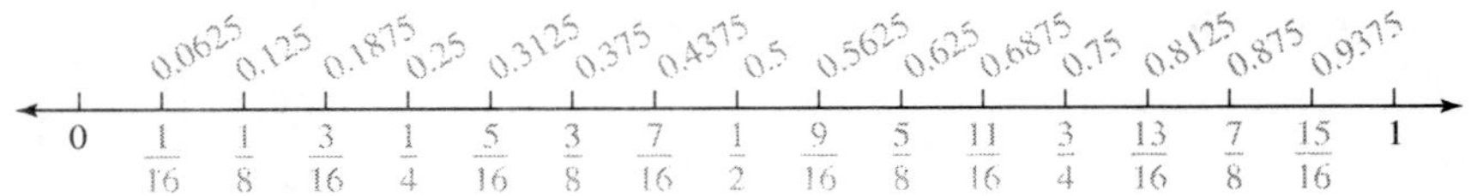

On the next number line, six equally spaced marks are used to scale from 0 to 1. Some commonly used fractions and their repeating decimal equivalents are shown.

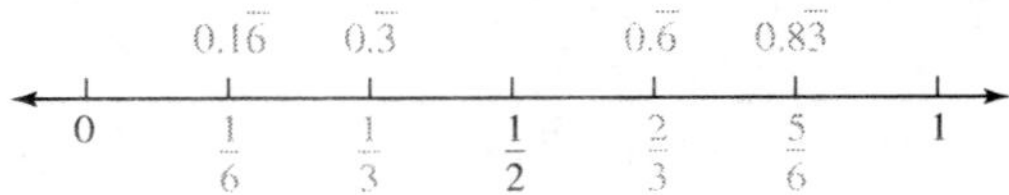

5 Compare fractions and decimals.

To compare the size of a fraction and a decimal, it is helpful to write the fraction in its equivalent decimal form.

Self Check 8

Place an <, >, or an = symbol in the box to make a true statement:

a. $\frac{3}{8} > 0.305$

b. $0.7\overline{6} < \frac{7}{9}$

c. $\frac{11}{4} = 2.75$

Now Try **Problems 67, 69, and 71**

EXAMPLE 8 Place an <, >, or an = symbol in the box to make a true statement: **a.** $\frac{4}{5}$ ☐ 0.91 **b.** $0.3\overline{5}$ ☐ $\frac{1}{3}$ **c.** $\frac{9}{4}$ ☐ 2.25

Strategy In each case, we will write the given fraction as a decimal.

WHY Then we can use the procedure for comparing two decimals to determine which number is the larger and which is the smaller.

Solution

a. To write $\frac{4}{5}$ as a decimal, we divide 4 by 5.

$$\begin{array}{r} 0.8 \\ 5\overline{)4.0} \\ -\,4\,0 \\ \hline 0 \end{array}$$

Write a decimal point and one additional zero to the right of 4.

Thus, $\frac{4}{5} = 0.8$.

To make the comparison of the decimals easier, we can write one zero after 8 so that they have the same number of digits to the right of the decimal point.

0.8 0 This is the decimal equivalent for $\frac{4}{5}$.
0.9 1

As we work from left to right, this is the first column in which the digits differ. Since $8 < 9$, it follows that $0.80 = \frac{4}{5}$ is less than 0.91, and we can write $\frac{4}{5} < 0.91$.

b. In Example 6, we saw that $\frac{1}{3} = 0.3333\ldots$. To make the comparison of these repeating decimals easier, we write them so that they have the same number of digits to the right of the decimal point.

0.3 5 55 . . . This is $0.3\overline{5}$.
0.3 3 33 . . . This is $\frac{1}{3}$.

As we work from left to right, this is the first column in which the digits differ. Since $5 > 3$, it follows that $0.3555\ldots = 0.3\overline{5}$ is greater than $0.3333\ldots = \frac{1}{3}$, and we can write $0.3\overline{5} > \frac{1}{3}$.

c. To write $\frac{9}{4}$ as a decimal, we divide 9 by 4.

```
   2.25
 4)9.00   Write a decimal point and two additional zeros to the right of 9.
  -8
   1 0
  -8
    20
   -20
     0
```

From the division, we see that $\frac{9}{4} = 2.25$.

Teaching Example 8 Place an <, >, or an = symbol in the box to make a true statement:

a. $\frac{3}{5}$ ☐ 0.66

b. $0.6\overline{7}$ ☐ $\frac{2}{3}$

c. $\frac{9}{8}$ ☐ 1.125

Answers:
a. <
b. >
c. =

EXAMPLE 9

Write the numbers in order from smallest to largest: 2.168, $2\frac{1}{6}$, $\frac{20}{9}$

Strategy We will write $2\frac{1}{6}$ and $\frac{20}{9}$ in decimal form.

WHY Then we can do a column-by-column comparison of the numbers to determine the largest and smallest.

Solution From the number line on page 378, we see that $\frac{1}{6} = 0.1\overline{6}$. Thus, $2\frac{1}{6} = 2.1\overline{6}$. To write $\frac{20}{9}$ as a decimal, we divide 20 by 9.

```
    2.222
 9)20.000   Write a decimal point and three additional zeros to the right of 20.
  -18
    20
   -18
     20
    -18
      20
     -18
       2
```

Thus, $\frac{20}{9} = 2.222\ldots$.

Self Check 9

Write the numbers in order from smallest to largest: 1.832, $\frac{9}{5}$, $1\frac{5}{6}$

Now Try **Problem 75**

Self Check 9 Answers
$\frac{9}{5}$, 1.832, $1\frac{5}{6}$

Teaching Example 9 Write the numbers in order from smallest to largest: 3.584, $3\frac{7}{12}$, $\frac{18}{5}$

Answer:
$3\frac{7}{12}$, 3.584, $\frac{18}{5}$

To make the comparison of the three decimals easier, we stack them as shown below.

2.1680	This is 2.168 with an additional 0.
2.1666...	This is $2\frac{1}{6} = 2.1\overline{6}$.
2.2222...	This is $\frac{20}{9}$.

Working from left to right, this is the first column in which the digits differ. Since 2 > 1, it follows that $2.222\ldots = \frac{20}{9}$ is the largest of the three numbers.

Working from left to right, this is the first column in which the top two numbers differ. Since 8 > 6, it follows that 2.168 is the next largest number and that $2.1\overline{6} = 2\frac{1}{6}$ is the smallest.

Written in order from smallest to largest, we have :

$$2\frac{1}{6},\ 2.168,\ \frac{20}{9}$$

6 Evaluate expressions containing fractions and decimals.

Expressions can contain both fractions and decimals. In the following examples, we show two methods that can be used to evaluate expressions of this type. With the first method we find the answer by working in terms of fractions.

Self Check 10

Evaluate by working in terms of fractions: $0.53 + \frac{1}{6}$ $\frac{209}{300}$

***Now Try* Problem 79**

Teaching Example 10 Evaluate $\frac{2}{3} + 0.11$ by working in terms of fractions.

Answer: $\frac{233}{300}$

EXAMPLE 10 Evaluate $\frac{1}{3} + 0.27$ by working in terms of fractions.

Strategy We will begin by writing 0.27 as a fraction.

WHY Then we can use the methods of Chapter 3 for adding fractions with unlike denominators to find the sum.

Solution To write 0.27 as a fraction, it is helpful to read it aloud as "twenty-seven hundredths."

$$\frac{1}{3} + 0.27 = \frac{1}{3} + \frac{27}{100}$$ Replace 0.27 with $\frac{27}{100}$.

$$= \frac{1}{3} \cdot \frac{100}{100} + \frac{27}{100} \cdot \frac{3}{3}$$ The LCD for $\frac{1}{3}$ and $\frac{27}{100}$ is 300. To build each fraction so that its denominator is 300, multiply by a form of 1.

$$= \frac{100}{300} + \frac{81}{300}$$ Multiply the numerators. Multiply the denominators.

$$= \frac{181}{300}$$ Add the numerators and write the sum over the common denominator 300.

Now we will evaluate the expression from Example 10 by working in terms of decimals.

Self Check 11

Estimate the result by working in terms of decimals: $0.53 - \frac{1}{6}$

***Now Try* Problem 87**

Self Check 11 Answer approximately 0.36

EXAMPLE 11 Estimate $\frac{1}{3} + 0.27$ by working in terms of decimals.

Strategy Since 0.27 has two decimal places, we will begin by finding a decimal approximation for $\frac{1}{3}$ to two decimal places.

WHY Then we can use the methods of this chapter for adding decimals to find the sum.

Solution We have seen that the decimal equivalent of $\frac{1}{3}$ is the repeating decimal 0.333 . . . . Rounded to the nearest hundredth: $\frac{1}{3} \approx 0.33$.

$$\frac{1}{3} + 0.27 \approx 0.33 + 0.27 \quad \text{Approximate } \tfrac{1}{3} \text{ with the decimal 0.33.}$$

$$\approx 0.60 \quad \text{Do the addition.}$$

$$\begin{array}{r} \overset{1}{0.33} \\ +0.27 \\ \hline 0.60 \end{array}$$

Teaching Example 11 Evaluate $\frac{2}{3} + 0.11$ by working in terms of decimals.
Answer: approximately 0.78

In Examples 10 and 11, we evaluated $\frac{1}{3} + 0.27$ in different ways. In Example 10, we obtained the exact answer, $\frac{181}{300}$. In Example 11, we obtained an approximation, 0.6. The results seem reasonable when we write $\frac{181}{300}$ in decimal form: $\frac{181}{300} = 0.60333\ldots$.

EXAMPLE 12

Evaluate: $\left(\frac{4}{5}\right)(1.35) + (0.5)^2$

Strategy We will find the decimal equivalent of $\frac{4}{5}$ and then evaluate the expression in terms of decimals.

WHY Its easier to perform multiplication and addition with the given decimals than it would be converting them to fractions.

Solution We use division to find the decimal equivalent of $\frac{4}{5}$.

$$\begin{array}{r} 0.8 \\ 5\overline{)4.0} \\ -\,4\,0 \\ \hline 0 \end{array} \quad \text{Write a decimal point and one additional zero to the right of the 4.}$$

Now we use the order of operation rule to evaluate the expression.

$$\left(\frac{4}{5}\right)(1.35) + (0.5)^2$$

$$= (0.8)(1.35) + (0.5)^2 \quad \text{Replace } \tfrac{4}{5} \text{ with its decimal equivalent, 0.8.}$$

$$= (0.8)(1.35) + 0.25 \quad \text{Evaluate: } (0.5)^2 = 0.25.$$

$$= 1.08 + 0.25 \quad \text{Do the multiplication: } (0.8)(1.35) = 1.08.$$

$$= 1.33 \quad \text{Do the addition.}$$

$$\begin{array}{r} \overset{2}{0.5} \\ \times\ 0.5 \\ \hline 0.25 \end{array} \qquad \begin{array}{r} \overset{2\,4}{1.35} \\ \times\ \ 0.8 \\ \hline 1.080 \end{array} \qquad \begin{array}{r} \overset{1}{1.08} \\ +0.25 \\ \hline 1.33 \end{array}$$

Self Check 12

Evaluate: $(-0.6)^2 + (2.3)\left(\frac{1}{8}\right)$
0.6475

Now Try **Problem 99**

Teaching Example 12
Evaluate: $\frac{3}{5}(1.75) + (0.6)^2$
Answer: 1.41

7 Solve application problems involving fractions and decimals.

EXAMPLE 13

Shopping A shopper purchased $\frac{3}{4}$ pound of fruit, priced at \$0.88 a pound, and $\frac{1}{3}$ pound of fresh-ground coffee, selling for \$6.60 a pound. Find the total cost of these items.

Analyze

- $\frac{3}{4}$ pound of fruit was purchased at \$0.88 per pound. *Given*
- $\frac{1}{3}$ pound of coffee was purchased at \$6.60 per pound. *Given*
- What was the total cost of the items? *Find*

Form To find the total cost of each item, multiply the number of pounds purchased by the price per pound.

Self Check 13

DELICATESSENS A shopper purchased $\frac{2}{3}$ pound of Swiss cheese, priced at \$2.19 per pound, and $\frac{3}{4}$ pound of sliced turkey, selling for \$6.40 per pound. Find the total cost of these items. \$6.26

Now Try **Problem 111**

The total cost of the items	is equal to	the number of pounds of fruit	times	the price per pound	plus	the number of pounds of coffee	times	the price per pound
The total cost of the items	=	$\frac{3}{4}$	·	\$0.88	+	$\frac{1}{3}$	·	\$6.60

Teaching Example 13
SHOPPING A shopper purchased $\frac{2}{3}$ pound of fruit, priced at \$0.99 per pound, and $\frac{1}{2}$ pound of fresh-ground coffee, selling for \$7.60 per pound. Find the total cost of these items.
Answer:
\$4.46

Solve Because 0.88 is divisible by 4 and 6.60 is divisible by 3, we can work with the decimals and fractions in this form; no conversion is necessary.

$$\frac{3}{4} \cdot 0.88 + \frac{1}{3} \cdot 6.60$$

$$= \frac{3}{4} \cdot \frac{0.88}{1} + \frac{1}{3} \cdot \frac{6.60}{1}$$ Express 0.88 as $\frac{0.88}{1}$ and 6.60 as $\frac{6.60}{1}$.

$$= \frac{2.64}{4} + \frac{6.60}{3}$$ Multiply the numerators. Multiply the denominators.

$$= 0.66 + 2.20$$ Do each division.

$$= 2.86$$ Do the addition.

$$\begin{array}{r} \overset{2}{0.88} \\ \times \quad 3 \\ \hline 2.64 \end{array}$$

$$\begin{array}{r} 0.66 \\ 4\overline{)2.64} \\ -2\,4 \\ \hline 24 \\ -24 \\ \hline 0 \end{array} \qquad \begin{array}{r} 2.20 \\ 3\overline{)6.60} \\ -6 \\ \hline 06 \\ -6 \\ \hline 00 \\ -0 \\ \hline 0 \end{array}$$

$$\begin{array}{r} 0.66 \\ +2.20 \\ \hline 2.86 \end{array}$$

State The total cost of the items is \$2.86.

Check If approximately 1 pound of fruit, priced at approximately \$1 per pound, was purchased, then about \$1 was spent on fruit. If exactly $\frac{1}{3}$ of a pound of coffee, priced at approximately \$6 per pound, was purchased, then about $\frac{1}{3} \cdot \$6$, or \$2, was spent on coffee. Since the approximate cost of the items \$1 + \$2 = \$3, is close to the result, \$2.86, the result seems reasonable.

ANSWERS TO SELF CHECKS

1. a. 0.5 **b.** 0.1875 **c.** 4.5 **2. a.** 0.4 **b.** 0.32 **3.** 3.85 **4.** $0.08\overline{3}$ **5.** $-0.\overline{39}$ **6.** 0.44 **7.** 0.292 **8. a.** > **b.** < **c.** = **9.** $\frac{9}{5}$, 1.832, $1\frac{5}{6}$ **10.** $\frac{209}{300}$ **11.** approximately 0.36 **12.** 0.6475 **13.** \$6.26

SECTION 2.11 STUDY SET

VOCABULARY

Fill in the blanks.

1. A fraction and a decimal are said to be equivalent if they name the same number.
2. The decimal equivalent of $\frac{3}{4}$ is 0.75.
3. 0.75, 0.625, and 3.5 are examples of terminating decimals.
4. 0.3333 . . . and 1.666 . . . are examples of repeating decimals.

CONCEPTS

Fill in the blanks.

5. $\frac{7}{8}$ means 7 ÷ 8.
6. To write a fraction as a decimal, divide the numerator of the fraction by its denominator.
7. To perform the division shown below, a decimal point and two additional zeros were written to the right of 3.

$$4\overline{)3.00}$$

8. Sometimes, when finding the decimal equivalent of a fraction, the division process ends because a remainder of 0 is obtained. We call the resulting decimal a terminating decimal.

9. Sometimes, when we are finding the decimal equivalent of a fraction, the division process never gives a remainder of 0. We call the resulting decimal a repeating decimal.

10. If the denominator of a fraction in simplified form has factors of only 2's or 5's, or a combination of both, it can be written as a decimal by multiplying it by a form of 1.

11. a. Round 0.3777 . . . to the nearest hundredth. 0.38

b. Round 0.212121 . . . to the nearest thousandth. 0.212

12. a. When evaluating the expression $0.25 + \left(2.3 + \frac{2}{5}\right)^2$, would it be easier to work in terms of fractions or decimals? decimals

b. What is the first step that should be performed to evaluate the expression? write $\frac{2}{5}$ as a decimal

NOTATION

▶ **13.** Write each decimal in fraction form.

a. 0.7 $\frac{7}{10}$ **b.** 0.77 $\frac{77}{100}$

14. Write each repeating decimal in simplest form using an overbar.

a. 0.888 . . . $0.\overline{8}$ **b.** 0.323232 . . . $0.\overline{32}$

c. 0.56333 . . . $0.56\overline{3}$ **d.** 0.8898989 . . . $0.8\overline{89}$

GUIDED PRACTICE

Write each fraction as a decimal. See Example 1.

15. $\frac{1}{2}$ 0.5 **16.** $\frac{1}{4}$ 0.25

17. $\frac{7}{8}$ 0.875 ▶ **18.** $\frac{3}{8}$ 0.375

19. $\frac{11}{20}$ 0.55 **20.** $\frac{17}{20}$ 0.85

21. $\frac{13}{5}$ 2.6 **22.** $\frac{15}{2}$ 7.5

23. $\frac{9}{16}$ 0.5625 ▶ **24.** $\frac{3}{32}$ 0.09375

25. $-\frac{17}{32}$ −0.53125 **26.** $-\frac{15}{16}$ −0.9375

Write each fraction as a decimal using multiplication by a form of 1. See Example 2.

27. $\frac{3}{5}$ 0.6 **28.** $\frac{13}{25}$ 0.52

29. $\frac{9}{40}$ 0.225 **30.** $\frac{7}{40}$ 0.175

31. $\frac{19}{25}$ 0.76 ▶ **32.** $\frac{21}{50}$ 0.42

33. $\frac{1}{500}$ 0.002 **34.** $\frac{1}{250}$ 0.004

Write each mixed number in decimal form. See Example 3.

35. $3\frac{3}{4}$ 3.75 **36.** $5\frac{4}{5}$ 5.8

37. $12\frac{11}{16}$ 12.6875 ▶ **38.** $32\frac{9}{16}$ 32.5625

Write each fraction as a decimal. Use an overbar in your answer. See Example 4.

39. $\frac{1}{9}$ $0.\overline{1}$ ▶ **40.** $\frac{8}{9}$ $0.\overline{8}$

41. $\frac{7}{12}$ $0.58\overline{3}$ **42.** $\frac{11}{12}$ $0.91\overline{6}$

43. $\frac{7}{90}$ $0.0\overline{7}$ **44.** $\frac{1}{99}$ $0.\overline{01}$

45. $\frac{1}{60}$ $0.01\overline{6}$ **46.** $\frac{1}{66}$ $0.0\overline{15}$

Write each fraction as a decimal. Use an overbar in your answer. See Example 5.

47. $-\frac{5}{11}$ $-0.\overline{45}$ **48.** $-\frac{7}{11}$ $-0.\overline{63}$

49. $-\frac{20}{33}$ $-0.\overline{60}$ ▶ **50.** $-\frac{16}{33}$ $-0.\overline{48}$

Write each fraction in decimal form. Round to the nearest hundredth. See Example 6.

51. $\frac{7}{30}$ 0.23 ▶ **52.** $\frac{8}{9}$ 0.89

53. $\frac{22}{45}$ 0.49 **54.** $\frac{17}{45}$ 0.38

55. $\frac{24}{13}$ 1.85 **56.** $\frac{34}{11}$ 3.09

57. $-\frac{13}{12}$ −1.08 **58.** $-\frac{25}{12}$ −2.08

Write each fraction in decimal form. Round to the nearest thousandth. See Example 7.

59. $\frac{5}{33}$ 0.152 **60.** $\frac{5}{24}$ 0.208

61. $\frac{10}{27}$ 0.370 ▶ **62.** $\frac{17}{21}$ 0.810

Graph the given numbers on a number line. See Objective 4.

63. $1\frac{3}{4}$, −0.75, $0.\overline{6}$, $-3.8\overline{3}$

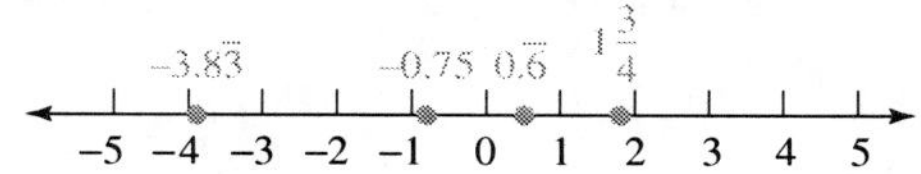

64. $2\frac{7}{8}$, -2.375, $0.\overline{3}$, $4.1\overline{6}$

-2.375 $0.\overline{3}$ $2\frac{7}{8}$ $4.1\overline{6}$

-5 -4 -3 -2 -1 0 1 2 3 4 5

65. 3.875, $-3.\overline{5}$, $0.\overline{2}$, $-1\frac{4}{5}$

$-3.\overline{5}$ $-1\frac{4}{5}$ $0.\overline{2}$ 3.875

-5 -4 -3 -2 -1 0 1 2 3 4 5

66. 1.375, $-4\frac{1}{7}$, $0.\overline{1}$, $-2.\overline{7}$

$-4\frac{1}{7}$ $-2.\overline{7}$ $0.\overline{1}$ 1.375

-5 -4 -3 -2 -1 0 1 2 3 4 5

Place an $<$, $>$, or an $=$ symbol in the box to make a true statement. See Example 8.

67. $\frac{7}{8}$ $<$ 0.895

68. $\frac{3}{8}$ $<$ 0.381

69. $0.\overline{7}$ $>$ $\frac{17}{22}$

70. $0.\overline{45}$ $>$ $\frac{7}{16}$

71. $\frac{52}{25}$ $=$ 2.08

72. 4.4 $=$ $\frac{22}{5}$

73. $-\frac{11}{20}$ $<$ $-0.\overline{48}$

74. $-0.0\overline{9}$ $<$ $-\frac{1}{11}$

Write the numbers in order from smallest to largest. See Example 9.

75. $6\frac{1}{2}$, 6.25, $\frac{19}{3}$ $6.25, \frac{19}{3}, 6\frac{1}{2}$

76. $7\frac{3}{8}$, 7.08, $\frac{43}{6}$ $7.08, \frac{43}{6}, 7\frac{3}{8}$

77. $-0.\overline{81}$, $-\frac{8}{9}$, $-\frac{6}{7}$ $-\frac{8}{9}, -\frac{6}{7}, -0.\overline{81}$

78. $-0.\overline{19}$, $-\frac{1}{11}$, -0.1 $-0.\overline{19}, -0.1, -\frac{1}{11}$

Evaluate each expression. Work in terms of fractions. See Example 10.

79. $\frac{1}{9} + 0.3$ $\frac{37}{90}$

80. $\frac{2}{3} + 0.1$ $\frac{23}{30}$

81. $0.9 - \frac{7}{12}$ $\frac{19}{60}$

82. $0.99 - \frac{5}{6}$ $\frac{47}{300}$

83. $\frac{5}{11}(0.3)$ $\frac{3}{22}$

84. $(0.9)\left(\frac{1}{27}\right)$ $\frac{1}{30}$

85. $\frac{1}{4}(0.25) + \frac{15}{16}$ 1

86. $\frac{2}{5}(0.02) - (0.04)$ $-\frac{4}{125}$

Estimate the value of each expression. Work in terms of decimals. See Example 11.

87. $0.24 + \frac{1}{3}$ 0.57

88. $0.02 + \frac{5}{6}$ 0.85

89. $5.69 - \frac{5}{12}$ 5.27

90. $3.19 - \frac{2}{3}$ 2.52

91. $0.43 - \frac{1}{12}$ 0.35

92. $0.27 + \frac{5}{12}$ 0.69

93. $\frac{1}{15} - 0.55$ -0.48

94. $\frac{7}{30} - 0.84$ -0.61

Evaluate each expression. Work in terms of decimals. See Example 12.

95. $(3.5 + 6.7)\left(-\frac{1}{4}\right)$ -2.55

96. $\left(-\frac{5}{8}\right)\left(5.3 - 3\frac{9}{10}\right)$ -0.875

97. $\left(\frac{1}{5}\right)^2(1.7)$ 0.068

98. $(2.35)\left(\frac{2}{5}\right)^2$ 0.376

99. $7.5 - (0.78)\left(\frac{1}{2}\right)^2$ 7.305

100. $8.1 - \left(\frac{3}{4}\right)^2(0.12)$ 8.0325

101. $\frac{3}{8}(3.2) + \left(4\frac{1}{2}\right)\left(-\frac{1}{4}\right)$ 0.075

102. $(-0.8)\left(\frac{1}{4}\right) + \left(\frac{1}{5}\right)(0.39)$ -0.122

APPLICATIONS

103. DRAFTING The architect's scale shown below has several measuring edges. The edge marked 16 divides each inch into 16 equal parts. Find the decimal form for each fractional part of 1 inch that is highlighted with a red arrow. 0.0625, 0.375, 0.5625, 0.9375

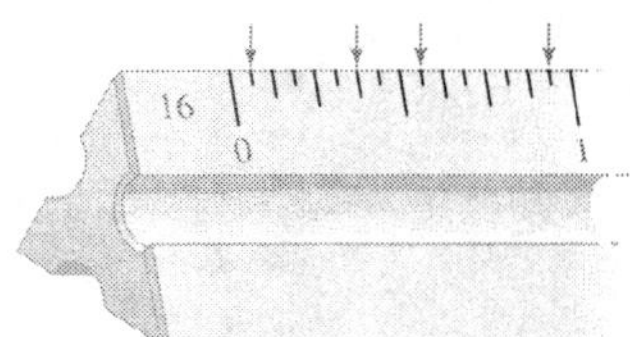

104. MILEAGE SIGNS The freeway sign shown below gives the number of miles to the next three exits. Convert the mileages to decimal notation. 0.75 mi, 2.25 mi, 3.5 mi

Barranca Ave. $\frac{3}{4}$ mi
210 Freeway $2\frac{1}{4}$ mi
Ada St. $3\frac{1}{2}$ mi

105. GARDENING Two brands of replacement line for a lawn trimmer shown below are labeled in different ways. On one package, the line's thickness is expressed as a decimal; on the other, as a fraction. Which line is thicker? $\frac{3}{40}$ in.

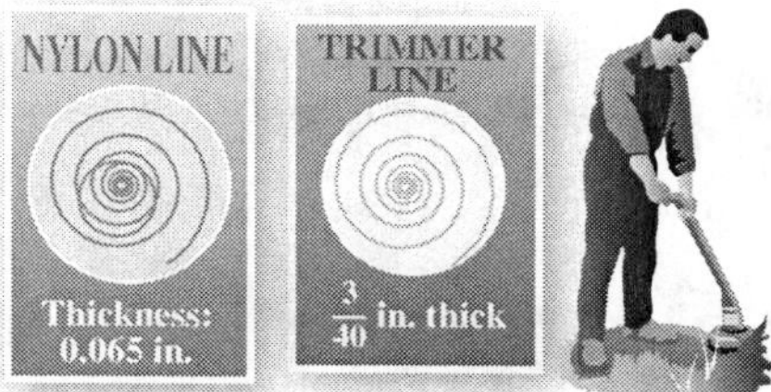

106. AUTO MECHANICS While doing a tune-up, a mechanic checks the gap on one of the spark plugs of a car to be sure it is firing correctly. The owner's manual states that the gap should be $\frac{2}{125}$ inch. The gauge the mechanic uses to check the gap is in decimal notation; it registers 0.025 inch. Is the spark plug gap too large or too small? too large

107. HORSE RACING In thoroughbred racing, the time a horse takes to run a given distance is measured using fifths of a second. For example, $:23^2$ (read "twenty-three and two") means $23\frac{2}{5}$ seconds. The illustration below lists four split times for a horse named *Speedy Flight* in a $1\frac{1}{16}$-mile race. Express each split time in decimal form. 23.4 sec, 23.8 sec, 24.2 sec, 32.6 sec

Speedy Flight	Turfway Park, Ky		3-year-old	
	17 May 2010		$1\frac{1}{16}$ mile	
	Splits	$:23^2$	$:23^4$	$:24^1$	$:32^3$

108. GEOLOGY A geologist weighed a rock sample at the site where it was discovered and found it to weigh $17\frac{7}{8}$ lb. Later, a more accurate digital scale in the laboratory gave the weight as 17.671 lb. What is the difference in the two measurements? 0.204 lb.

109. WINDOW REPLACEMENTS The amount of sunlight that comes into a room depends on the area of the windows in the room. What is the area of the window shown below? (*Hint:* Use the formula $A = \frac{1}{2}bh$.) 93.6 in.^{2}

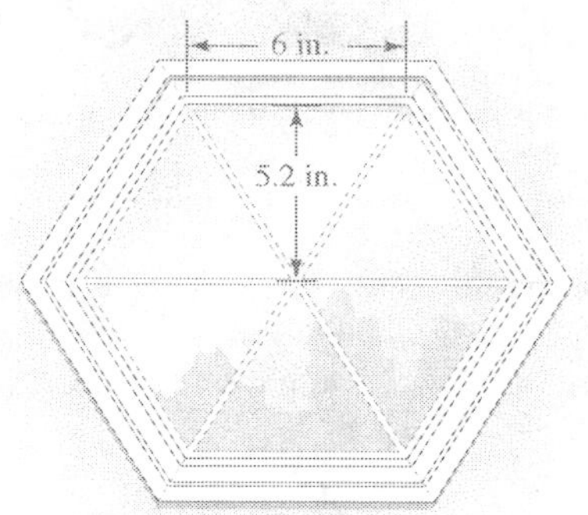

110. FORESTRY A command post asked each of three fire crews to estimate the length of the fire line they were fighting. Their reports came back in different forms, as shown. Find the perimeter of the fire. Round to the nearest tenth. 4.7 mi

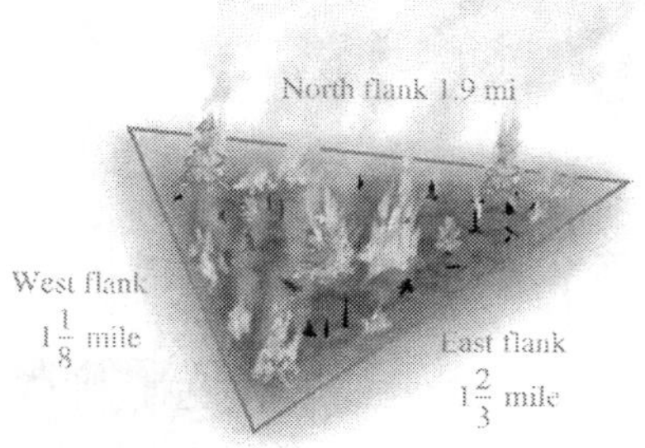

111. DELICATESSENS A shopper purchased $\frac{2}{3}$ pound of green olives, priced at \$4.14 per pound, and $\frac{3}{4}$ pound of smoked ham, selling for \$5.68 per pound. Find the total cost of these items. \$7.02

112. CHOCOLATE A shopper purchased $\frac{3}{4}$ pound of dark chocolate, priced at \$8.60 per pound, and $\frac{1}{3}$ pound of milk chocolate, selling for \$5.25 per pound. Find the total cost of these items. \$8.20

WRITING

113. Explain the procedure used to write a fraction in decimal form.

114. How does the terminating decimal 0.5 differ from the repeating decimal $0.\overline{5}$?

115. A student represented the repeating decimal 0.1333 . . . as $0.\overline{1333}$. Is this the best form? Explain why or why not.

116. Is 0.10100100010000 . . . a repeating decimal? Explain why or why not.

117. A student divided 19 by 25 to find the decimal equivalent of $\frac{19}{25}$ to be 0.76. Explain how she can check this result.

118. Explain the error in the following work to find the decimal equivalent for $\frac{5}{6}$.

$$\begin{array}{r} 1.2 \\ 5\overline{)\,6.0} \\ \underline{-5} \\ 10 \\ \underline{-10} \\ 0 \end{array} \qquad \text{Thus, } \frac{5}{6} = 1.2.$$

REVIEW

119. Write each set of numbers.

a. the first ten whole numbers {0, 1, 2, 3, 4, 5, 6, 7, 8, 9}

b. the first ten prime numbers {2, 3, 5, 7, 11, 13, 17, 19, 23, 29}

c. the integers {. . . , −3, −2, −1, 0, 1, 2, 3, . . .}

120. Give an example of each property.

a. the commutative property of addition

b. the associative property of multiplication

c. the multiplication property of 1

a. $2 + 3 = 3 + 2$ b. $2 + (3 + 5) = (2 + 3) + 5$ c. $2 \cdot 1 = 2$

Objectives

1. Define circle, radius, chord, diameter, and arc.
2. Find the circumference of a circle.
3. Find the area of a circle.

SECTION 2.12
Circles

In this section, we will discuss the circle, one of the most useful geometric figures of all. In fact, the discoveries of fire and the circular wheel are two of the most important events in the history of the human race. We will begin our study by introducing some basic vocabulary associated with circles.

1 Define circle, radius, chord, diameter, and arc.

Circle

A **circle** is the set of all points in a plane that lie a fixed distance from a point called its **center.**

A segment drawn from the center of a circle to a point on the circle is called a **radius.** (The plural of *radius* is *radii.*) From the definition, it follows that all radii of the same circle are the same length.

A **chord** of a circle is a line segment that connects two points on the circle. A **diameter** is a chord that passes through the center of the circle. Since a diameter D of a circle is twice as long as a radius r, we have

$$D = 2r$$

Each of the previous definitions is illustrated in figure (a) below, in which O is the center of the circle.

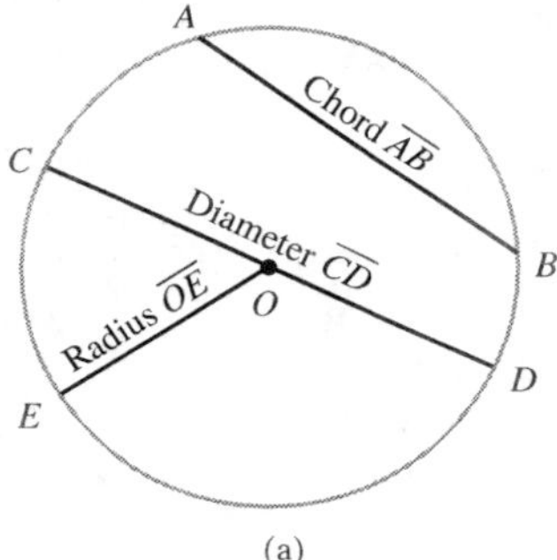

(a)

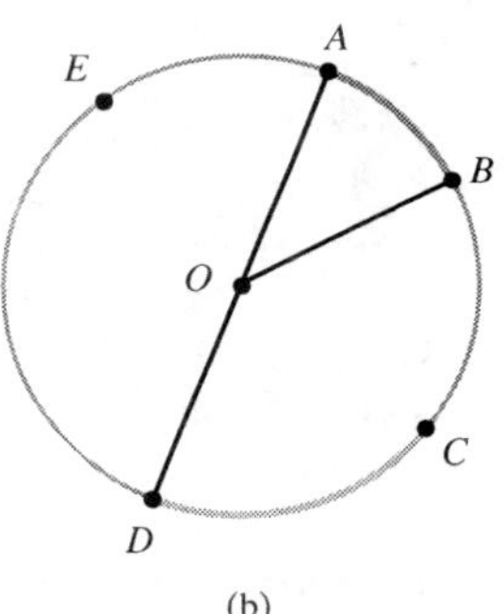

(b)

Any part of a circle is called an **arc.** In figure (b) above, the part of the circle from point A to point B that is highlighted in blue is $\overset{\frown}{AB}$, read as "arc AB." $\overset{\frown}{CD}$ is the part of the circle from point C to point D that is highlighted in green. An arc that is half of a circle is a **semicircle.**

Semicircle

A **semicircle** is an arc of a circle whose endpoints are the endpoints of a diameter.

If point O is the center of the circle in figure (b), $\overline{AD}$ is a diameter and $\overset{\frown}{AED}$ is a semicircle. The middle letter E distinguishes semicircle $\overset{\frown}{AED}$ (the part of the circle from point A to point D that includes point E) from semicircle $\overset{\frown}{ABD}$ (the part of the circle from point A to point D that includes point B).

An arc that is shorter than a semicircle is a **minor arc.** An arc that is longer than a semicircle is a **major arc.** In figure (b),

$\overset{\frown}{AE}$ is a minor arc and $\overset{\frown}{ABE}$ is a major arc.

Success Tip It is often possible to name a major arc in more than one way. For example, in figure (b), major arc $\overset{\frown}{ABE}$ is the part of the circle from point A to point E that includes point B. Two other names for the same major arc are $\overset{\frown}{ACE}$ and $\overset{\frown}{ADE}$.

2 Find the circumference of a circle.

Since early history, mathematicians have known that the ratio of the distance around a circle (the circumference) divided by the length of its diameter is approximately 3. First Kings, Chapter 7, of the Bible describes a round bronze tank that was 15 feet from brim to brim and 45 feet in circumference, and $\frac{45}{15} = 3$. Today, we use a more precise value for this ratio, known as π (pi). If C is the circumference of a circle and D is the length of its diameter, then

$$\pi = \frac{C}{D} \quad \text{where } \pi = 3.141592653589\ldots$$ $\frac{22}{7}$ and 3.14 are often used as estimates of π.

If we multiply both sides of $\pi = \frac{C}{D}$ by D, we have the following formula.

Circumference of a Circle

The circumference of a circle is given by the formula

$C = \pi D$ where C is the circumference and D is the length of the diameter

Since a diameter of a circle is twice as long as a radius r, we can substitute $2r$ for D in the formula $C = \pi D$ to obtain another formula for the circumference C:

$C = 2\pi r$ The notation $2\pi r$ means $2 \cdot \pi \cdot r$.

EXAMPLE 1 Find the circumference of the circle shown on the right. Give the exact answer and an approximation.

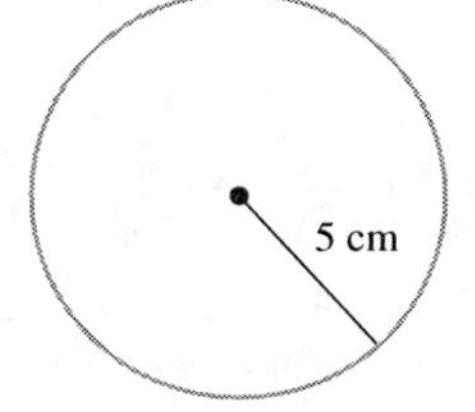

Strategy We will substitute 5 for r in the formula $C = 2\pi r$ and evaluate the right side.

WHY The variable C represents the unknown circumference of the circle.

Solution

$C = 2\pi r$ This is the formula for the circumference of a circle.

$C = 2\pi(5)$ Substitute 5 for r, the radius.

$C = 2(5)\pi$ When a product involves π, we usually rewrite it so that π is the last factor.

$C = 10\pi$ Do the first multiplication: $2(5) = 10$. This is the exact answer.

The circumference of the circle is exactly 10π cm. If we replace π with 3.14, we get an approximation of the circumference.

Self Check 1

Find the circumference of the circle shown below. Give the exact answer and an approximation. 24π m ≈ 75.4 m

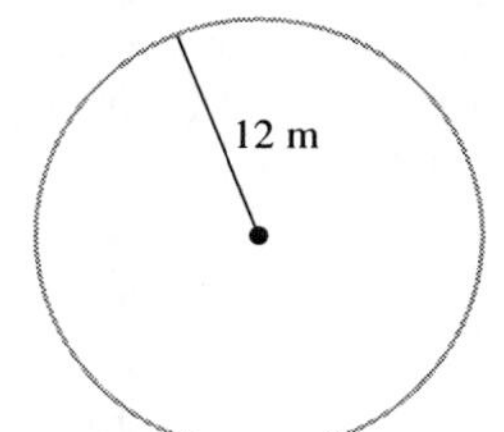

Now Try **Problem 25**

Teaching Example 1 Find the circumference of a circle with radius 9 meters. Give the exact answer and an approximation.

Answer:
18π m ≈ 56.5 m

$C = 10\pi$

$C \approx 10(3.14)$

$C \approx 31.4$ To multiply by 10, move the decimal point in 3.14 one place to the right.

The circumference of the circle is approximately 31.4 cm.

Using Your CALCULATOR **Calculating Revolutions of a Tire**

When the [π] key on a scientific calculator is pressed (on some models, the [2nd] key must be pressed first), an approximation of π is displayed. To illustrate how to use this key, consider the following problem. How many times does the tire shown to the right revolve when a car makes a 25-mile trip?

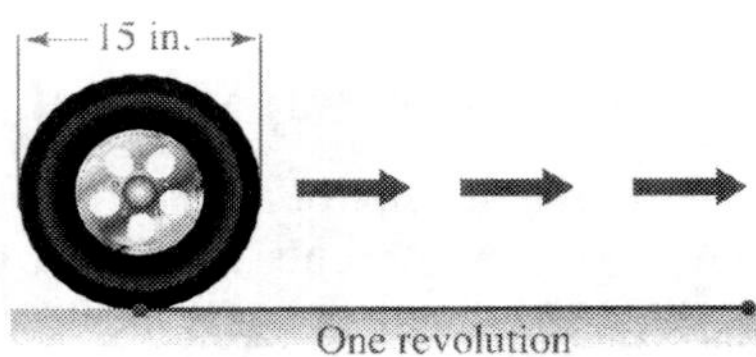

We first find the circumference of the tire. From the figure, we see that the diameter of the tire is 15 inches. Since the circumference of a circle is the product of π and the length of its diameter, the tire's circumference is $\pi \cdot 15$ inches, or 15π inches. (Normally, we rewrite a product such as $\pi \cdot 15$ so that π is the second factor.)

We then change the 25 miles to inches using two unit conversion factors.

$$\frac{25 \text{ miles}}{1} \cdot \frac{5{,}280 \text{ feet}}{1 \text{ mile}} \cdot \frac{12 \text{ inches}}{1 \text{ foot}} = 25 \cdot 5{,}280 \cdot 12 \text{ inches}$$

The units of miles and feet can be removed.

The length of the trip is $25 \cdot 5{,}280 \cdot 12$ inches.

Finally, we divide the length of the trip by the circumference of the tire to get

$$\text{The number of revolutions of the tire} = \frac{25 \cdot 5{,}280 \cdot 12}{15\pi}$$

We can use a scientific calculator to make this calculation.

[( ] 25 [×] 5280 [×] 12 [ )] [÷] [( ] 15 [×] [π] [ )] [=] **33613.52398**

The tire makes about 33,614 revolutions.

Self Check 2

Find the perimeter of the figure shown below. Round to the nearest hundredth. (Assume the arc is a semicircle.) 39.42 m

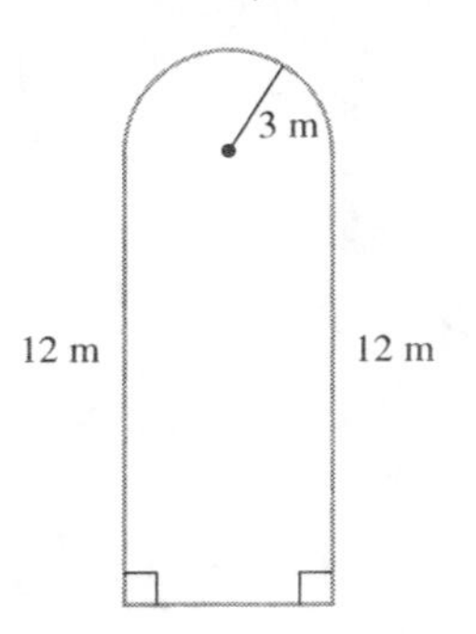

EXAMPLE 2 *Architecture* A Norman window is constructed by adding a semicircular window to the top of a rectangular window. Find the perimeter of the Norman window shown here.

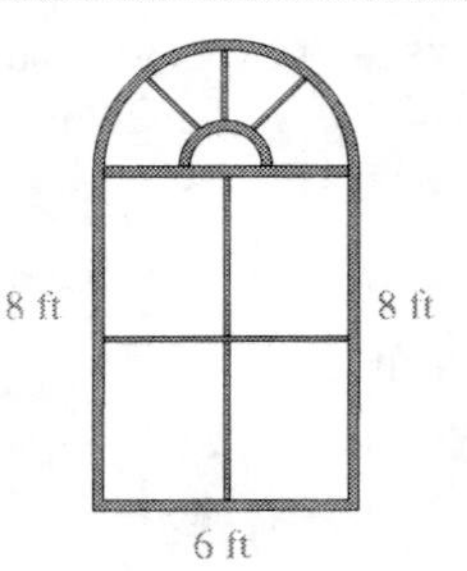

Strategy We will find the perimeter of the rectangular part and the circumference of the circular part of the window and add the results.

WHY The window is a combination of a rectangle and a semicircle.

Solution The perimeter of the rectangular part is

$P_{\text{rectangular part}} = 8 + 6 + 8 = 22$ Add only 3 sides of the rectangle.

The perimeter of the semicircle is one-half of the circumference of a circle that has a 6-foot diameter.

$P_{\text{semicircle}} = \frac{1}{2}C$ This is the formula for the circumference of a semicircle.

$P_{\text{semicircle}} = \frac{1}{2}\pi D$ Since we know the diameter, replace C with πD. We could also have replaced C with $2\pi r$.

$= \frac{1}{2}\pi(6)$ Substitute 6 for D, the diameter.

≈ 9.424777961 Use a calculator to do the multiplication.

The total perimeter is the sum of the two parts.

$$P_{\text{total}} = P_{\text{rectangular part}} + P_{\text{semicircle}}$$
$$P_{\text{total}} \approx 22 + 9.424777961$$
$$\approx 31.424777961$$

To the nearest hundredth, the perimeter of the window is 31.42 feet.

Now Try **Problem 29**

Teaching Example 2 Find the perimeter of the figure shown below. Round to the nearest hundredth. (Assume the arc is a semicircle.)

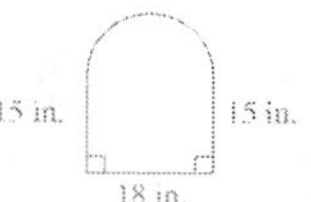

Answer:
76.27 in.

3 Find the area of a circle.

If we divide the circle shown in figure (a) on the following page into an even number of pie-shaped pieces and then rearrange them as shown in figure (b), we have a figure that looks like a parallelogram. The figure has a base b that is one-half the circumference of the circle, and its height h is about the same length as a radius of the circle.

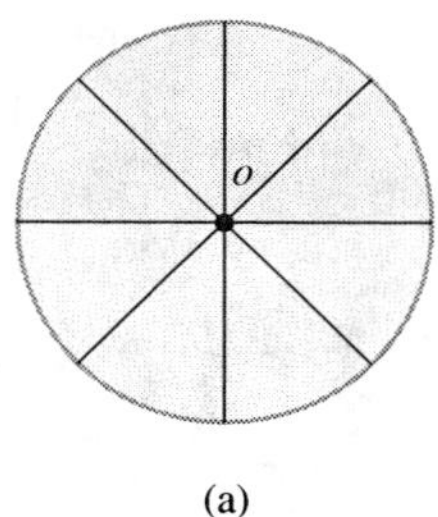

(a)

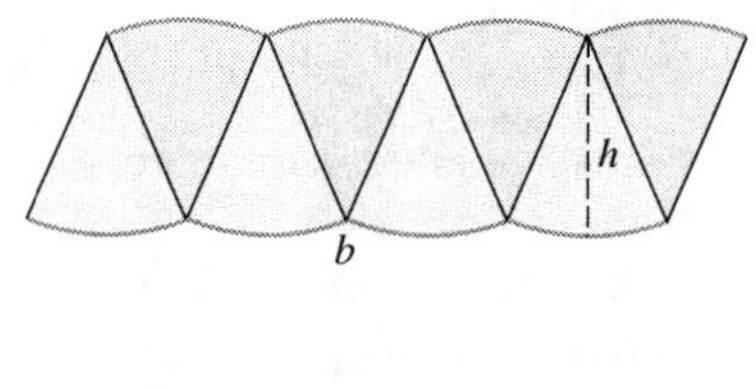

(b)

If we divide the circle into more and more pie-shaped pieces, the figure will look more and more like a parallelogram, and we can find its area by using the formula for the area of a parallelogram.

$A = bh$

$A = \frac{1}{2}Cr$ Substitute $\frac{1}{2}$ of the circumference for b, the length of the base of the "parallelogram." Substitute r for the height of the "parallelogram."

$= \frac{1}{2}(2\pi r)r$ Substitute $2\pi r$ for C.

$= \pi r^2$ Simplify: $\frac{1}{2} \cdot 2 = 1$ and $r \cdot r = r^2$.

This result gives the following formula.

Area of a Circle

The area of a circle with radius r is given by the formula

$$A = \pi r^2$$

Self Check 3

Find the area of a circle with a diameter of 12 feet. Give the exact answer and an approximation to the nearest tenth. 36π ft^2 ≈ 113.1 ft^2

Now Try **Problem 33**

Teaching Example 3 Find the area of a circle with a diameter of 16 feet. Give the exact answer and an approximation to the nearest tenth.

Answer:
64π ft^2 ≈ 201.1 ft^2

EXAMPLE 3 Find the area of the circle shown on the right. Give the exact answer and an approximation to the nearest tenth.

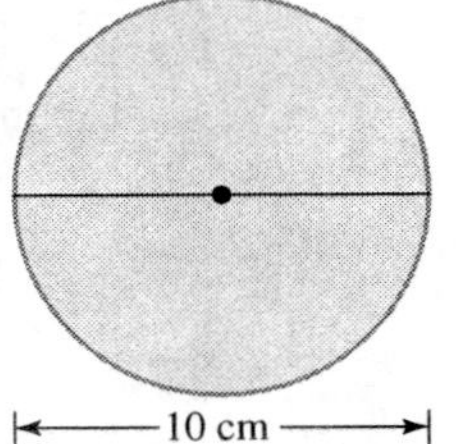

Strategy We will find the radius of the circle, substitute that value for r in the formula $A = \pi r^2$, and evaluate the right side.

WHY The variable A represents the unknown area of the circle.

Solution Since the length of the diameter is 10 centimeters and the length of a diameter is twice the length of a radius, the length of the radius is 5 centimeters.

$A = \pi r^2$ This is the formula for the area of a circle.

$A = \pi(5)^2$ Substitute 5 for r, the radius of the circle. The notation πr^2 means $\pi \cdot r^2$.

$= \pi(25)$ Evaluate the exponential expression.

$= 25\pi$ Write the product so that π is the last factor.

The exact area of the circle is 25π cm^2. We can use a calculator to approximate the area.

$A \approx 78.53981634$ Use a calculator to do the multiplication: $25 \cdot \pi$.

To the nearest tenth, the area is 78.5 cm^2.

Using Your CALCULATOR **Painting a Helicopter Landing Pad**

Orange paint is available in gallon containers at \$19 each, and each gallon will cover 375 ft^2. To calculate how much the paint will cost to cover a circular helicopter landing pad 60 feet in diameter, we first calculate the area of the helicopter pad.

$A = \pi r^2$ This is the formula for the area of a circle.

$A = \pi(30)^2$ Substitute one-half of 60 for r, the radius of the circular pad.

$= 30^2\pi$ Write the product so that π is the last factor.

The area of the pad is exactly $30^2\pi$ ft^2. Since each gallon of paint will cover 375 ft^2, we can find the number of gallons of paint needed by dividing $30^2\pi$ by 375.

$$\text{Number of gallons needed} = \frac{30^2\pi}{375}$$

We can use a scientific calculator to make this calculation.

30 [x^2] [×] [π] [=] [÷] 375 [=] **7.539822369**

Because paint comes only in full gallons, the painter will need to purchase 8 gallons. The cost of the paint will be 8(\$19), or \$152.

EXAMPLE 4 Find the area of the shaded figure on the right. Round to the nearest hundredth.

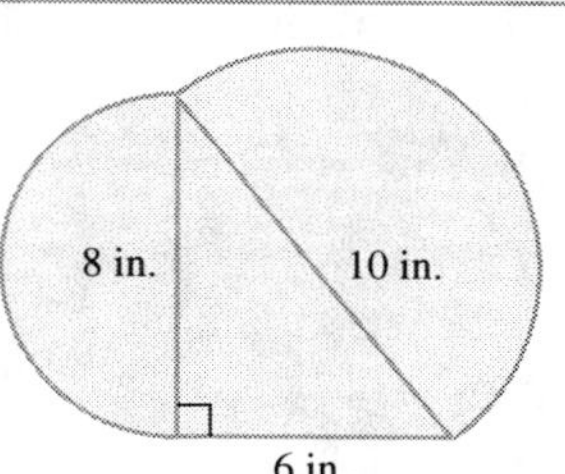

Strategy We will find the area of the entire shaded figure using the following approach:

$$A_{\text{total}} = A_{\text{triangle}} + A_{\text{smaller semicircle}} + A_{\text{larger semicircle}}$$

WHY The shaded figure is a combination of a triangular region and two semicircular regions.

Solution The area of the triangle is

$$A_{\text{triangle}} = \frac{1}{2}bh = \frac{1}{2}(6)(8) = \frac{1}{2}(48) = 24$$

Since the formula for the area of a circle is $A = \pi r^2$, the formula for the area of a semicircle is $A = \frac{1}{2}\pi r^2$. Thus, the area enclosed by the smaller semicircle is

$$A_{\text{smaller semicircle}} = \frac{1}{2}\pi r^2 = \frac{1}{2}\pi(4)^2 = \frac{1}{2}\pi(16) = 8\pi$$

The area enclosed by the larger semicircle is

$$A_{\text{larger semicircle}} = \frac{1}{2}\pi r^2 = \frac{1}{2}\pi(5)^2 = \frac{1}{2}\pi(25) = 12.5\pi$$

$$\begin{array}{r} 12.5 \\ 2\overline{)25.0} \\ \underline{-2} \\ 05 \\ \underline{-4} \\ 1\,0 \\ \underline{-1\,0} \\ 0 \end{array}$$

The total area is the sum of the three results:

$$A_{\text{total}} = 24 + 8\pi + 12.5\pi \approx 88.4026494$$ Use a calculator to perform the operations.

To the nearest hundredth, the area of the shaded figure is 88.40 in.^{2}.

Self Check 4

Find the area of the shaded figure below. Round to the nearest hundredth. 424.73 yd^2

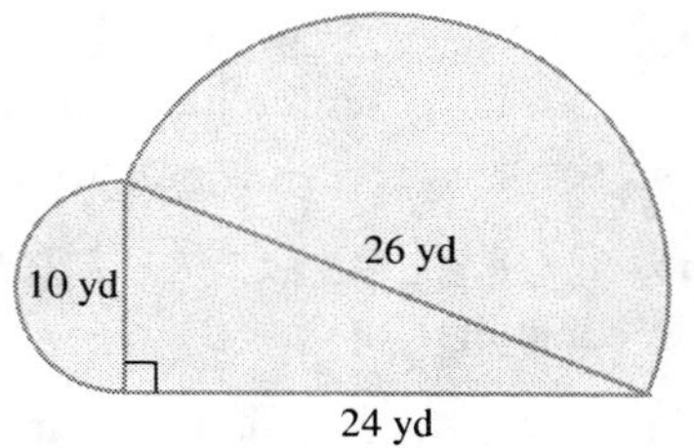

Now Try **Problem 37**

Teaching Example 4 Find the area of the shaded figure. Round to the nearest hundredth.

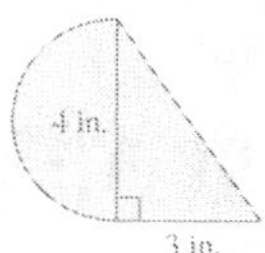

Answer: 12.28 in.^{2}

ANSWERS TO SELF CHECKS

1. 24π m ≈ 75.4 m **2.** 39.42 m **3.** 36π ft^2 ≈ 113.1 ft^2 **4.** 424.73 yd^2

SECTION 2.12 STUDY SET

VOCABULARY

Fill in the blanks.

1. A segment drawn from the center of a circle to a point on the circle is called a radius.

2. A segment joining two points on a circle is called a chord.

3. A diameter is a chord that passes through the center of a circle.

4. An arc that is one-half of a complete circle is a semicircle.

5. The distance around a circle is called its circumference.

6. The surface enclosed by a circle is called its area.

7. A diameter of a circle is twice as long as a radius.

8. Suppose the exact circumference of a circle is 3π feet. When we write $C \approx 9.42$ feet, we are giving an approximation of the circumference.

CONCEPTS

Refer to the figure below, where point O is the center of the circle.

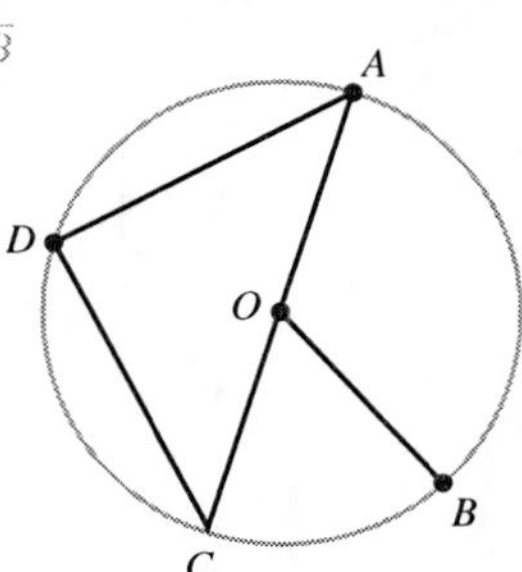

9. Name each radius. $\overline{OA}, \overline{OC}, \overline{OB}$

10. Name a diameter. $\overline{AC}$

11. Name each chord. $\overline{DA}, \overline{DC}, \overline{AC}$

12. Name each minor arc. $\overset{\frown}{AD}, \overset{\frown}{AB}, \overset{\frown}{BC}, \overset{\frown}{CD}, \overset{\frown}{BCD}$

13. Name each semicircle. $\overset{\frown}{ABC}, \overset{\frown}{ADC}$

14. Name major arc $\overset{\frown}{ABD}$ in another way. $\overset{\frown}{ACD}$

15. a. If you know the radius of a circle, how can you find its diameter? Multiply the radius by 2.
 b. If you know the diameter of a circle, how can you find its radius? Divide the diameter by 2.

16. a. What are the two formulas that can be used to find the circumference of a circle? $C = \pi D$, $C = 2\pi r$
 b. What is the formula for the area of a circle? $A = \pi r^2$

17. If C is the circumference of a circle and D is its diameter, then $\frac{C}{D}$ = π .

18. If D is the diameter of a circle and r is its radius, then D = 2 r.

19. When evaluating $\pi(6)^2$, what operation should be performed first? square 6

20. Round $\pi = 3.141592653589\ldots$ to the nearest hundredth. 3.14

NOTATION

Fill in the blanks.

21. The symbol $\widehat{AB}$ is read as "arc AB."

22. To the nearest hundredth, the value of π is 3.14.

23. a. In the expression $2\pi r$, what operations are indicated? multiplication: $2 \cdot \pi \cdot r$
 b. In the expression πr^2, what operations are indicated? raising to a power and multiplication: $\pi \cdot r^2$

24. Write each expression in better form. Leave π in your answer.
 a. $\pi(8)$ 8π b. $2\pi(7)$ 14π c. $\pi \cdot \frac{25}{3}$ $\frac{25\pi}{3}$

GUIDED PRACTICE

The answers to the problems in this Study Set may vary slightly, depending on which approximation of π is used.

Find the circumference of the circle shown below. Give the exact answer and an approximation to the nearest tenth. See Example 1.

25.
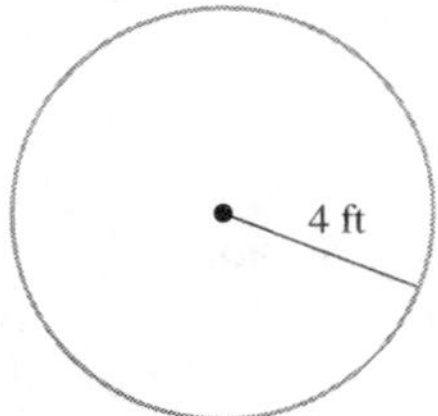

8π ft ≈ 25.1 ft

26.
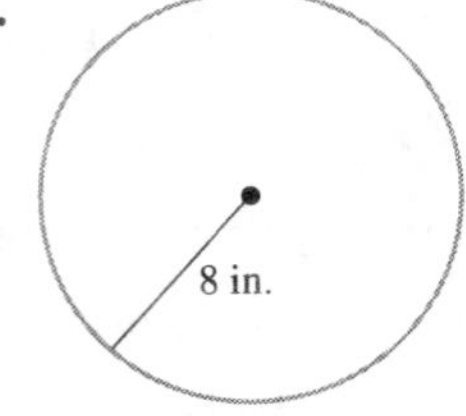

16π in. ≈ 50.3 in.

27.
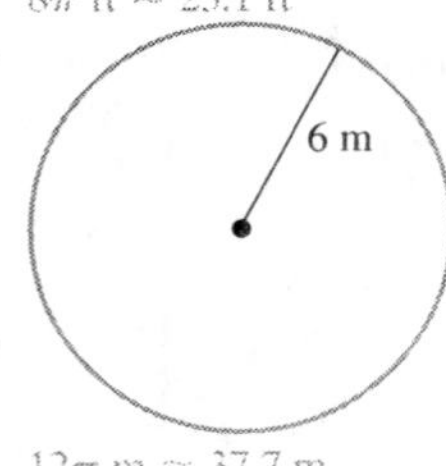

12π m ≈ 37.7 m

28.
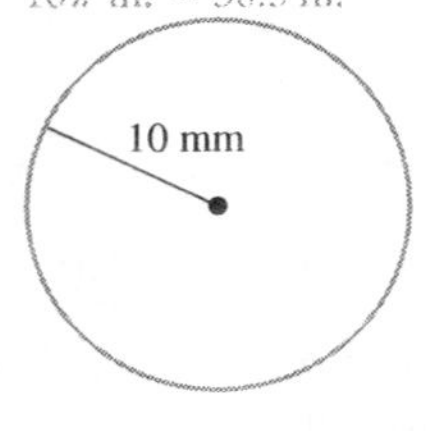

20π mm ≈ 62.8 mm

Find the perimeter of each figure. Assume each arc is a semicircle. Round to the nearest hundredth. See Example 2.

29. 30.
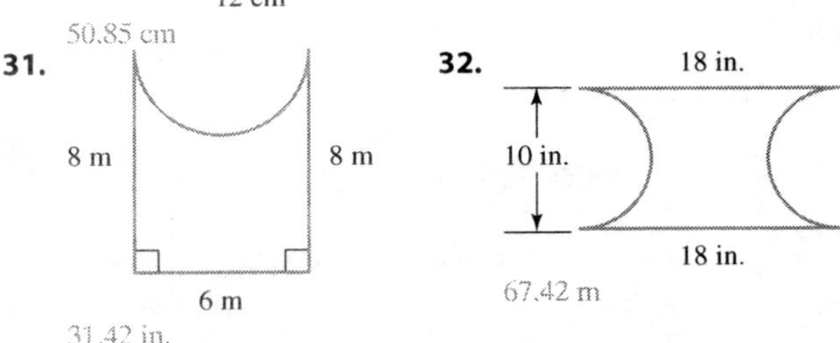

29. 50.85 cm 30. 25.42 ft

31. 32.
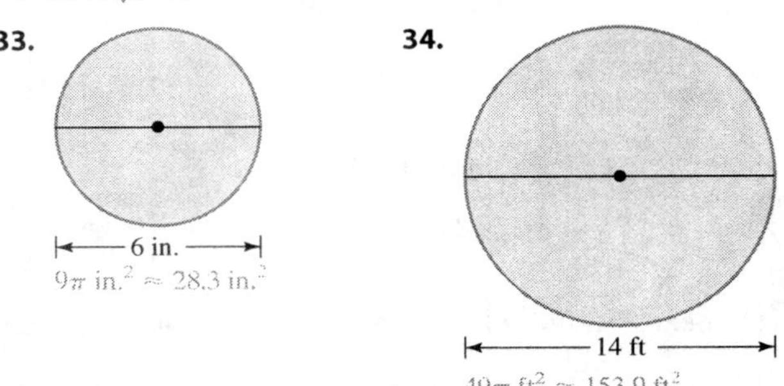

31. 31.42 in. 32. 67.42 m

Find the area of each circle given the following information. Give the exact answer and an approximation to the nearest tenth. See Example 3.

33. 6 in. 9π in.^{2} ≈ 28.3 in.^{2}

34. 14 ft 49π ft^2 ≈ 153.9 ft^2

35. Find the area of a circle with diameter 18 inches. 81π in.^{2} ≈ 254.5 in.^{2}

36. Find the area of a circle with diameter 20 meters. 100π m^2 ≈ 314.2 m^2

Find the total area of each figure. Assume each arc is a semicircle. Round to the nearest tenth. See Example 4.

37. 38.
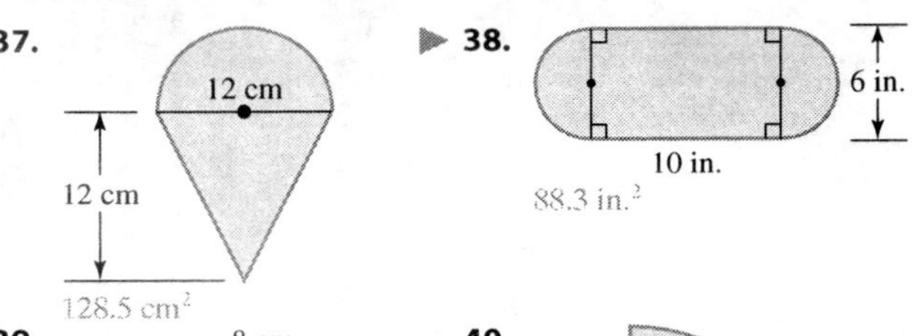

37. 128.5 cm^2 38. 88.3 in.^{2}

39. 40.
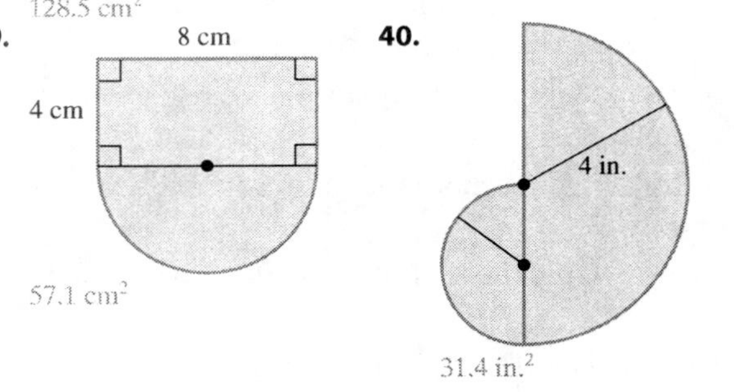

39. 57.1 cm^2 40. 31.4 in.^{2}

TRY IT YOURSELF

Find the area of each shaded region. Round to the nearest tenth.

41. 
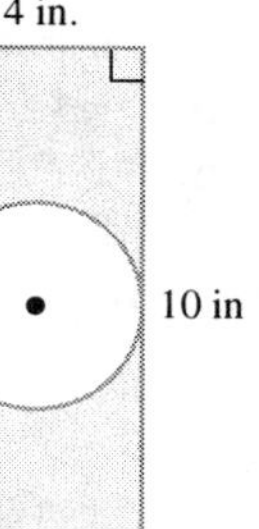

27.4 in.^{2}

42. 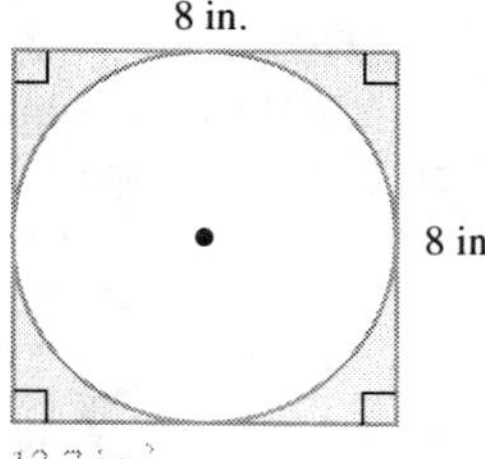

13.7 in.^{2}

43. 
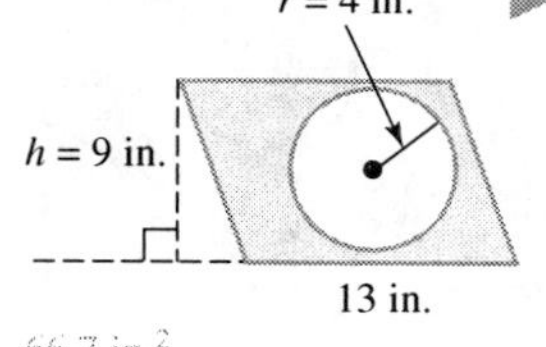

66.7 in.^{2}

44. 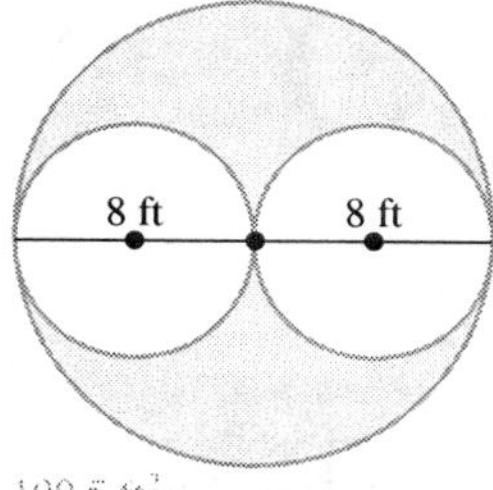

100.5 ft^2

45. Find the circumference of the circle shown below. Give the exact answer and an approximation to the nearest hundredth. 50π yd $\approx$ 157.08 yd

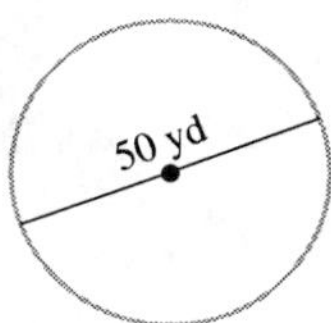

46. Find the circumference of the semicircle shown below. Give the exact answer and an approximation to the nearest hundredth. $\frac{25\pi}{2}$ cm $\approx$ 39.27 cm

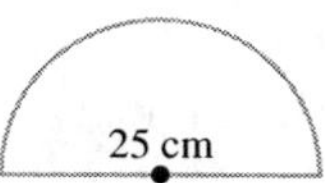

47. Find the circumference of the circle shown below if the square has sides of length 6 inches. Give the exact answer and an approximation to the nearest tenth. 6π in. $\approx$ 18.8 in.

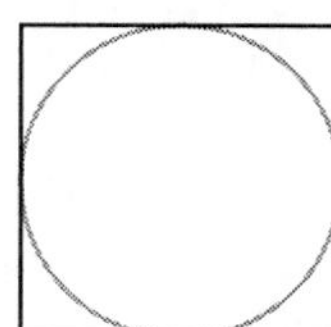

48. Find the circumference of the semicircle shown below if the length of the rectangle in which it is enclosed is 8 feet. Give the exact answer and an approximation to the nearest tenth. 4π ft $\approx$ 12.6 ft

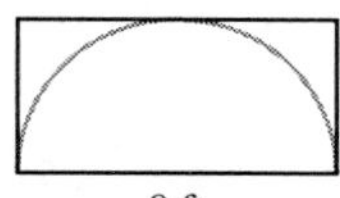

49. Find the area of the circle shown below if the square has sides of length 9 millimeters. Give the exact answer and an approximation to the nearest tenth. 20.25π mm^2 $\approx$ 63.6 mm^2

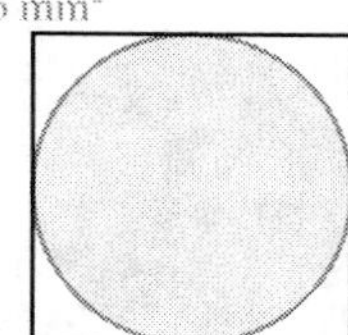

50. Find the area of the shaded semicircular region shown below. Give the exact answer and an approximation to the nearest tenth. 10.5625π mi^2 $\approx$ 33.2 mi^2

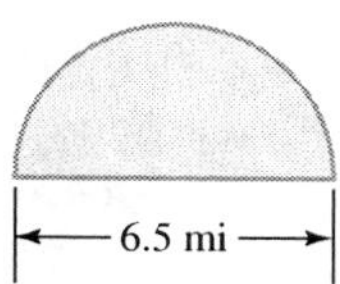

APPLICATIONS

51. Suppose the two "legs" of the compass shown below are adjusted so that the distance between the pointed ends is 1 inch. Then a circle is drawn.

a. What will the radius of the circle be? 1 in.

b. What will the diameter of the circle be? 2 in.

c. What will the circumference of the circle be? Give an exact answer and an approximation to the nearest hundredth. 2π in. $\approx$ 6.28 in.

d. What will the area of the circle be? Give an exact answer and an approximation to the nearest hundredth. π in.^{2} $\approx$ 3.14 in.^{2}

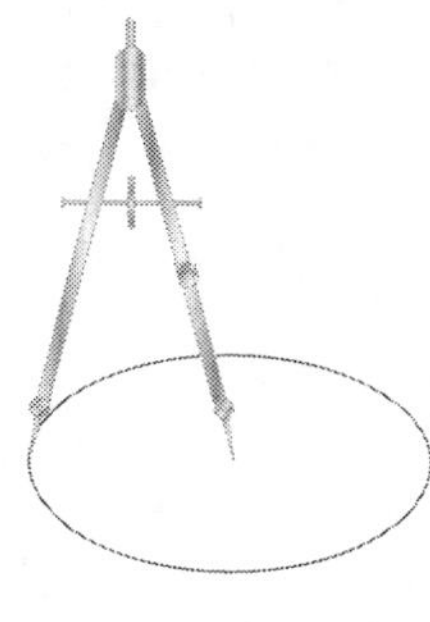

52. Suppose we find the distance around a can and the distance across the can using a measuring tape, as shown to the right. Then we make a comparison, in the form of a ratio:

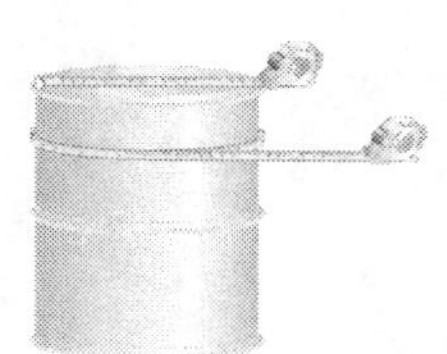

$$\frac{\text{The distance around the can}}{\text{The distance across the top of the can}}$$

After we do the indicated division, the result will be close to what number? π

When appropriate, give the exact answer and an approximation to the nearest hundredth. Answers may vary slightly, depending on which approximation of π is used.

53. LAKES Round Lake has a circular shoreline that is 2 miles in diameter. Find the area of the lake. π mi^2 $\approx$ 3.14 mi^2

54. HELICOPTERS Refer to the figure below. How far does a point on the tip of a rotor blade travel when it makes one complete revolution? 36π ft ≈ 113.10 ft

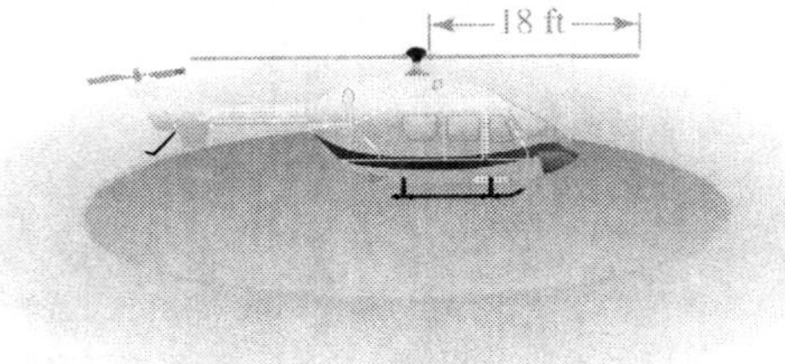

55. GIANT SEQUOIA The largest sequoia tree is the General Sherman Tree in Sequoia National Park in California. In fact, it is considered to be the largest living thing in the world. According to the *Guinness Book of World Records,* it has a diameter of 32.66 feet, measured $4\frac{1}{2}$ feet above the ground. What is the circumference of the tree at that height? 32.66π ft ≈ 102.60 ft

56. TRAMPOLINE See the figure below. The distance from the center of the trampoline to the edge of its steel frame is 7 feet. The protective padding covering the springs is 18 inches wide. Find the area of the circular jumping surface of the trampoline, in square feet. 30.25π ft^2 ≈ 95.03 ft^2

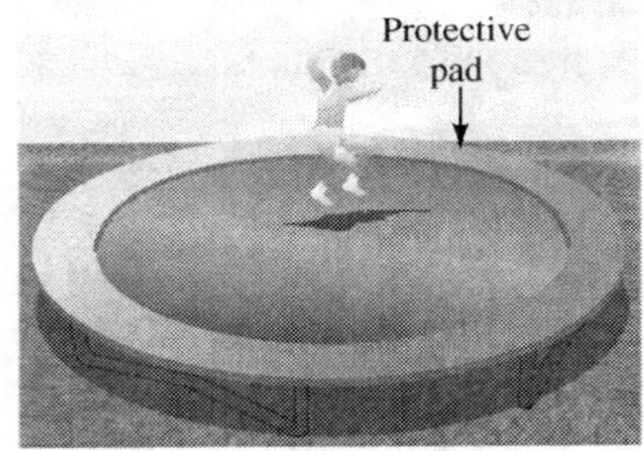

57. JOGGING Joan wants to jog 10 miles on a circular track $\frac{1}{4}$ mile in diameter. How many times must she circle the track? Round to the nearest lap. 13 times

58. CARPETING A state capitol building has a circular floor 100 feet in diameter. The legislature wishes to have the floor carpeted. The lowest bid is \$83 per square yard, including installation. How much must the legislature spend for the carpeting project? Round to the nearest dollar. \$72,431

59. ARCHERY See the figure on the right. Find the area of the entire target and the area of the bull's eye. What percent of the area of the target is the bull's eye? 4π ft^2 ≈ 12.57 ft^2; 0.25π ft^2 ≈ 0.79 ft^2; 6.25%

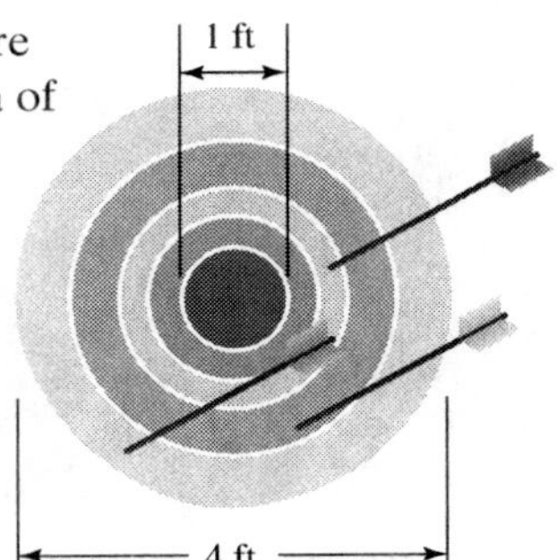

60. LANDSCAPE DESIGN See the figure on the right. How many square feet of lawn does not get watered by the four sprinklers at the center of each circle? 193.14 ft^2

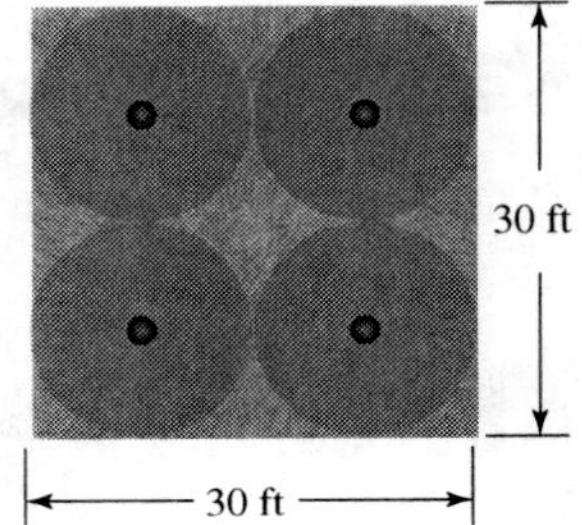

WRITING

61. Explain what is meant by the circumference of a circle.

62. Explain what is meant by the area of a circle.

63. Explain the meaning of π.

64. Explain what it means for a car to have a small *turning radius.*

Note: Scientific notation appears as a Student Learning Outcome in both Module 1 and 2. Let us know if you would like it to appear in only these modules.

SECTION 2.13

Scientific Notation

Objectives

1. Define scientific notation.
2. Write numbers in scientific notation.
3. Convert from scientific notation to standard notation.
4. Perform computations with scientific notation.

Scientists often deal with extremely large and extremely small numbers. Two examples are shown below.

The distance from Earth to the sun is approximately 150,000,000 kilometers.

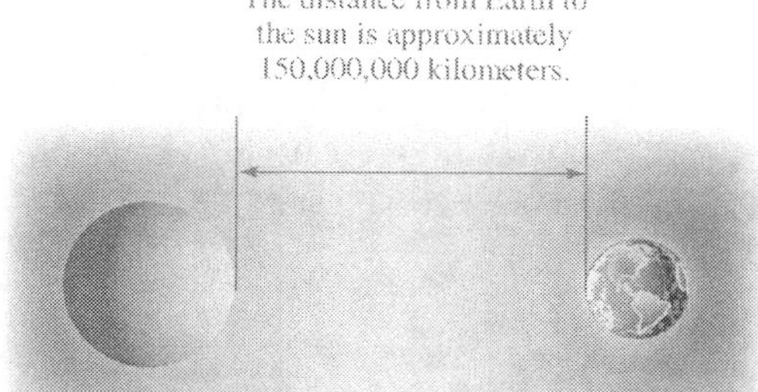

The influenza virus, which causes "flu" symptoms of cough, sore throat, headache, and congestion, has a diameter of 0.00000256 inch.

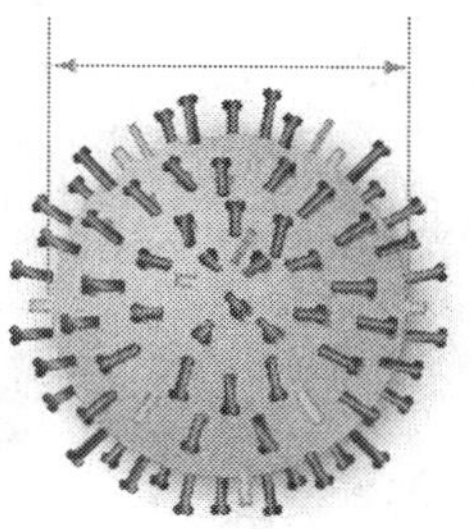

The large number of zeros in 150,000,000 and 0.00000256 makes them difficult to read and hard to remember. In this section, we will discuss a notation that will make such numbers easier to use.

1 Define scientific notation.

Scientific notation provides a compact way of writing large numbers, such as 5,213,000,000,000, and small numbers, such as 0.000000000000914.

Scientific Notation

A number is written in **scientific notation** when it is written as the product of a number between 1 (including 1) and 10, denoted N, and an integer power of 10, denoted n. In symbols, scientific notation has the form $N \times 10^n$.

These numbers are written in scientific notation:

$$3.9 \times 10^6, \quad 2.24 \times 10^{-4}, \quad \text{and} \quad 9.875 \times 10^{22}$$

Every number written in scientific notation has the following form:

An integer exponent

$$\_.\_ \times 10^{\_}$$

A decimal between 1 and 10

2 Write numbers in scientific notation.

To write a number in scientific notation ($N \times 10^n$), we first determine N then n.

Self Check 1

The distance from Earth to the sun is approximately 93,000,000 miles. Write this number in scientific notation. 9.3×10^7

Now Try **Problem 20**

Teaching Example 1 Change to scientific notation: 2,340,000,000
Answer:
2.34×10^9

EXAMPLE 1 Change to scientific notation: 150,000,000

Strategy We will write the number as a product of a number between 1 and 10 and a power of 10.

WHY Numbers written in scientific notation have the form $N \times 10^n$.

Solution
We note that 1.5 lies between 1 and 10. To obtain 150,000,000, the decimal point in 1.5 must be moved eight places to the right.

1.50000000
8 places to the right

Because multiplying a number by 10 moves the decimal point one place to the right, we can accomplish this by multiplying 1.5 by 10 eight times. We can show the multiplication of 1.5 by 10 eight times using the notation 10^8. Thus, 150,000,000 written in scientific notation is 1.5×10^8.

Self Check 2

The *Salmonella* bacterium, which causes food poisoning, is 0.00009055 inch long. Write this number in scientific notation. 9.055×10^{-5}

Now Try **Problem 26**

Teaching Example 2 Change 0.000000057 to scientific notation.
Answer:
5.7×10^{-8}

EXAMPLE 2 Change to scientific notation: 0.00000256

Strategy We will write the number as a product of a number between 1 and 10 and a power of 10.

WHY Numbers written in scientific notation have the form $N \times 10^n$.

Solution
We note that 2.56 is between 1 and 10. To obtain 0.00000256, the decimal point in 2.56 must be moved six places to the left.

000002.56
6 places to the left

We can accomplish this by dividing 2.56 by 10^6, which is equivalent to multiplying 2.56 by $\frac{1}{10^6}$ (or by 10^{-6}). Thus, 0.00000256 written in scientific notation is 2.56×10^{-6}.

Self Check 3

Write in scientific notation:
a. 17,500 1.75×10^4
b. 0.657 6.57×10^{-1}

Now Try **Problems 27 and 29**

Teaching Example 3 Write in scientific notation
a. 0.000042 **b.** 5,367,000,000
Answers:
a. 4.2×10^{-5} **b.** 5.367×10^9

EXAMPLE 3 Write in scientific notation: **a.** 235,000 **b.** 0.0000073

Strategy We will write each number as a product of a number between 1 and 10 and a power of 10.

WHY Numbers written in scientific notation have the form $N \times 10^n$.

Solution
a. $235{,}000 = 2.35 \times 10^5$ Because $2.35 \times 10^5 = 235{,}000$ and 2.35 is between 1 and 10

b. $0.0000073 = 7.3 \times 10^{-6}$ Because $7.3 \times 10^{-6} = 0.0000073$ and 7.3 is between 1 and 10

Sucess Tip From Examples 1, 2, and 3, we see that in scientific notation, a positive exponent is used when writing a number that is greater than 10. A negative exponent is used when writing a number that is between 0 and 1.

Using Your CALCULATOR **Calculators and Scientific Notation**

When displaying a very large or a very small number as an answer, most scientific calculators express it in scientific notation. To show this, we will find the values of $(453.46)^5$ and $(0.0005)^{12}$. We enter these numbers and press these keys.

453.46 [y^x] 5 [=] 1.917321395 13

.0005 [y^x] 12 [=] 2.44140625 −40

Since the answers in standard notation require more space than the calculator display has, the calculator gives each result in scientific notation. The first display represents $1.917321395 \times 10^{13}$, and the second represents $2.44140625 \times 10^{-40}$.

If we evaluate the same two expressions using a graphing or direct-entry calculator, we see that the letter E is used when displaying a number in scientific notation.

453.46 [∧] 5 [ENTER] 453.46^5
1.917321395E13

.0005 [∧] 12 [ENTER] .0005^12
2.44140625E − 40

Caution! When reading an answer such as [1.917321395 13] off the calculator, be careful to write $1.917321395 \times 10^{13}$, not 1.917321395^{13}.

EXAMPLE 4 Write in scientific notation: 432.0×10^5

Strategy We will write the number as a product of a number between 1 and 10 and a power of 10.

WHY Numbers written in scientific notation have the form $N \times 10^n$.

Solution

The number 432.0×10^5 is not written in scientific notation, because 432.0 is not a number between 1 and 10. To write this number in scientific notation, we proceed as follows:

$$432.0 \times 10^5 = 4.32 \times 10^2 \times 10^5$$ Write 432.0 in scientific notation.

$$= 4.32 \times 10^7$$ $10^2 \times 10^5 = 10^{2+5} = 10^7$.

Self Check 4

Write in scientific notation: 85×10^{-3} 8.5×10^{-2}

Now Try **Problem 40**

Teaching Example 4 Write 0.026×10^5 in scientific notation.
Answer:
2.6×10^3

3 Convert from scientific notation to standard notation.

We can change a number written in scientific notation to **standard notation.** For example, to write 9.3×10^7 in standard notation, we multiply 9.3 by 10^7.

$$9.3 \times 10^7 = 9.3 \times 10{,}000{,}000$$ 10^7 is equal to 1 followed by 7 zeros.

$$= 93{,}000{,}000$$

The following numbers are written in both scientific and standard notation. In each case, the exponent gives the number of places that the decimal point moves, and the sign of the exponent indicates the direction that it moves.

$5.32 \times 10^5 = 532000.$ The decimal point moves 5 places to the right.

$8.95 \times 10^{-4} = 0.000895$ The decimal point moves 4 places to the left.

$9.77 \times 10^0 = 9.77$ There is no movement of the decimal point.

The following summarizes our observations.

Converting from Scientific to Standard Notation

1. If the exponent on 10 is positive, move the decimal point the same number of places to the right as the exponent.
2. If the exponent on 10 is negative, move the decimal point the same number of places to the left as the absolute value of the exponent.

Self Check 5

Convert to standard notation:

a. 4.76×10^5 476,000

b. 9.8×10^{-3} 0.0098

Now Try **Problems 50 and 52**

Teaching Example 5 Convert to standard notation:
a. 2.47×10^{-5} b. 7.142×10^7
Answers:
a. 0.0000247
b. 71,420,000

EXAMPLE 5 Convert to standard notation: **a.** 3.4×10^5 **b.** 2.1×10^{-4}

Strategy We will identify the exponent on the 10 and consider its sign.

WHY The exponent gives the number of decimal places that we should move the decimal point. The sign of the exponent indicates whether it should be moved to the right or the left.

Solution

a. $3.4 \times 10^5 = 3.4 \times 100{,}000$
$= 340{,}000$

b. $2.1 \times 10^{-4} = 2.1 \times \frac{1}{10^4}$
$= 2.1 \times \frac{1}{10{,}000}$
$= 2.1 \times 0.0001$
$= 0.00021$

4 Perform computations with scientific notation.

Another advantage of scientific notation becomes apparent when we evaluate products or quotients that contain very large or very small numbers.

Self Check 6

Use scientific notation to evaluate:
(2,540,000,000,000) (0.00041)

Now Try **Problem 55**

Self Check 6 Answer
1.0414×10^9

Teaching Example 6 Use scientific notation to evaluate:
(0.0000024) (5,310,000,000,000)
Answer:
1.2744×10^7 or 12,744,000

EXAMPLE 6 *Astronomy* Except for the sun, the nearest star visible to the naked eye from most parts of the United States is Sirius. Light from Sirius reaches Earth in about 70,000 hours. If light travels at approximately 670,000,000 mph, how far from Earth is Sirius?

NASA

Strategy We will use the formula $d = rt$ to find the distance from Sirius to Earth.

WHY We know the *rate* at which light travels and the *time* it takes to travel from Sirius to Earth. We want to know the distance.

Solution

We are given the rate at which light travels (670,000,000 mph) and the time it takes the light to travel from Sirius to Earth (70,000 hr). We can find the distance the light travels using the formula $d = rt$.

$d = rt$

$d = 670{,}000{,}000(70{,}000)$ Substitute 670,000,000 for r and 70,000 for t.

$= (6.7 \times 10^8)(7.0 \times 10^4)$ Write each number in scientific notation.

$= (6.7 \cdot 7.0) \times (10^8 \cdot 10^4)$ Group the numbers together and the powers of 10 together.

$= (6.7 \cdot 7.0) \times 10^{8+4}$ Keep the base and add the exponents.

$= 46.9 \times 10^{12}$ Perform the multiplication. Perform the addition.

We note that 46.9 is not between 0 and 1, so 46.9×10^{12} is not written in scientific notation. To answer in scientific notation, we proceed as follows.

$= 4.69 \times 10^1 \times 10^{12}$ Write 46.9 in scientific notation as 4.69×10^1.

$= 4.69 \times 10^{13}$ Keep the base of 10 and add the exponents.

Sirius is approximately 4.69×10^{13} or 46,900,000,000,000 miles from Earth.

THINK IT THROUGH *Science Majors and Space Travel*

"The number of U.S. college students earning degrees in science, technology, engineering, and math has fallen over the last 15 years. What a better way to hook our children than with a new space exploration plan?"

Patricia Arnold, Space Foundation, 2004

It has been almost 40 years since a U.S. astronaut last walked on the moon. Many educators feel that manned flights to the moon and Mars would ignite a passion for space and science studies among young people. However, the minimum distance Mars is from Earth is 135 times further than the moon is from Earth. Traveling such a long way poses many problems. If the average distance from Earth to the moon is about 2.4×10^5 miles, what is the distance between Earth and Mars? Express the result in scientific notation. 3.24×10^7 mi.

EXAMPLE 7 *Atoms* Scientific notation is used in chemistry. As an example, we can approximate the weight (in grams) of one atom of the heaviest naturally occurring element, uranium, by evaluating the following expression.

$$\frac{2.4 \times 10^2}{6.0 \times 10^{23}}$$

Strategy We will divide the numbers and the powers of 10 separately.

WHY We can use the quotient rule for exponents to simplify the calculations.

Solution

$$\frac{2.4 \times 10^2}{6.0 \times 10^{23}} = \frac{2.4}{6.0} \times \frac{10^2}{10^{23}}$$ Divide the numbers and the powers of 10 separately.

$$= \frac{2.4}{6.0} \times 10^{2-23}$$ For the powers of 10, keep the base and subtract the exponents.

$= 0.4 \times 10^{-21}$ Perform the division. Then subtract the exponents.

$= 4.0 \times 10^{-1} \times 10^{-21}$ Write 0.4 in scientific notation as 4.0×10^{-1}.

$= 4.0 \times 10^{-22}$ Keep the base and add the exponents.

One atom of uranium weighs 4.0×10^{-22} gram. Written in standard notation, this is 0.00000000000000000000004 g.

Self Check 7

Find the approximate weight (in grams) of one atom of gold by evaluating: $\dfrac{1.98 \times 10^2}{6.0 \times 10^{23}}$

Now Try **Problem 58**

Self Check 7 Answer

3.3×10^{-22} g

Teaching Example 7 Evaluate: $\dfrac{5.2 \times 10^{15}}{4.0 \times 10^6}$

Answer:

1.3×10^9

Using Your CALCULATOR **Entering Numbers in Scientific Notation**

We can evaluate the expression from Example 7 by entering the numbers written in scientific notation, using the EE key on a scientific calculator.

2.4 EE 2 ÷ 6 EE 23 = 4.⁻22

The result shown in the display means 4.0×10^{-22}.

If we use a graphing calculator, the keystrokes are similar.

2.4 2nd EE 2 ÷ 6 2nd EE 23 ENTER

2.4E2/6E23
4 E − 22

ANSWERS TO SELF CHECKS

1. 9.3×10^7 **2.** 9.055×10^{-5} **3. a.** 1.75×10^4 **b.** 6.57×10^{-1} **4.** 8.5×10^{-2} **5. a.** 476,000 **b.** 0.0098 **6.** 1.0414×10^9 **7.** 3.3×10^{-22} g

SECTION 2.13 STUDY SET

VOCABULARY

Fill in the blanks.

1. A number is written in scientific notation when it is written as the product of a number between 1 (including 1) and 10 and an integer power of 10.

▶ **2.** The number 125,000 is written in standard notation.

CONCEPTS

Fill in the blanks by writing the number in standard notation.

3. $2.5 \times 10^2 = 250$ **4.** $2.5 \times 10^{-2} = 0.025$

5. $2.5 \times 10^{-5} = 0.000025$ **6.** $2.5 \times 10^5 = 250{,}000$

Fill in the blanks with a power of 10.

7. $387{,}000 = 3.87 \times 10^5$ **8.** $38.7 = 3.87 \times 10^1$

9. $0.00387 = 3.87 \times 10^{-3}$ **10.** $0.000387 = 3.87 \times 10^{-4}$

11. When we multiply a decimal by 10^5, the decimal point moves 5 places to the right.

12. When we multiply a decimal by 10^{-7}, the decimal point moves 7 places to the left.

13. Dividing a decimal by 10^4 is equivalent to multiplying it by 10^{-4}.

14. Multiplying a decimal by 10^0 does not move the decimal point, because $10^0 = 1$.

15. When a real number greater than 10 is written in scientific notation, the exponent on 10 is a positive number.

▶ **16.** When a real number between 0 and 1 is written in scientific notation, the exponent on 10 is a negative number.

NOTATION

Complete each solution.

17. Write in scientific notation: 63.7×10^5

$$63.7 \times 10^5 = 6.37 \times 10^1 \times 10^5$$
$$= 6.37 \times 10^{1+5}$$
$$= 6.37 \times 10^6$$

▶ **18.** Simplify: $\dfrac{64{,}000}{0.00004}$

$$\frac{64{,}000}{0.00004} = \frac{6.4 \times 10^4}{4 \times 10^{-5}}$$
$$= \frac{6.4}{4} \times \frac{10^4}{10^{-5}}$$
$$= 1.6 \times 10^{4-(-5)}$$
$$= 1.6 \times 10^9$$

GUIDED PRACTICE

Write each number in scientific notation. See Example 1.

19. 23,000 2.3×10^4 **20.** 4,750 4.75×10^3

21. 625,000 6.25×10^5 ▶ **22.** 320,000 3.2×10^5

Write each answer in scientific notation. See Example 2.

23. 0.062 6.2×10^{-2}
24. 0.75 7.5×10^{-1}
25. 0.00073 7.3×10^{-4}
26. 0.000057 5.7×10^{-5}

Write each number in scientific notation. See Example 3.

27. 543,000 5.43×10^{5}
28. 17,000,000 1.7×10^{7}
29. 0.00000875 8.75×10^{-6}
30. 0.000002 2×10^{-6}
31. 1,700,000 1.7×10^{6}
32. 290,000 2.9×10^{5}
33. 909,000,000 9.09×10^{8}
34. 7,007,000,000 7.007×10^{9}
35. 0.00502 5.02×10^{-3}
36. 0.0000081 8.1×10^{-6}
37. 0.0000051 5.1×10^{-6}
38. 0.04 4.0×10^{-2}

Write each number in scientific notation. See Example 4.

39. 42.5×10^2 4.25×10^{3}
40. 25.2×10^{-3} 2.52×10^{-2}
41. 0.25×10^{-2} 2.5×10^{-3}
42. 0.3×10^{3} 3.0×10^{2}
43. 201.8×10^{15} 2.018×10^{17}
44. 154.3×10^{17} 1.543×10^{19}
45. 0.073×10^{-3} 7.3×10^{-5}
46. 0.0017×10^{-4} 1.7×10^{-7}

Write each number in standard notation. See Example 5.

47. 2.3×10^2 230
48. 3.75×10^4 37,500
49. 8.12×10^5 812,000
50. 1.2×10^3 1,200
51. 1.15×10^{-3} 0.00115
52. 4.9×10^{-2} 0.049
53. 9.76×10^{-4} 0.000976
54. 7.63×10^{-5} 0.0000763

Use scientific notation and the rules for exponents to simplify each expression. Give all answers in standard notation. See Examples 6–7.

55. $(3.4 \times 10^2)(2.1 \times 10^3)$ 714,000
56. $(4.1 \times 10^{-3})(3.4 \times 10^4)$ 139.4
57. $\dfrac{9.3 \times 10^2}{3.1 \times 10^{-2}}$ 30,000
58. $\dfrac{7.2 \times 10^6}{1.2 \times 10^8}$ 0.06

TRY IT YOURSELF

Simplify if necessary, then write the answer in standard notation.

59. 25×10^6 25,000,000
60. 0.07×10^3 70
61. 0.51×10^{-3} 0.00051
62. 2.37×10^{-4} 0.000237
63. 617×10^{-2} 6.17
64. $5,280 \times 10^{-3}$ 5.280
65. 0.699×10^3 699
66. 0.012×10^4 120
67. $\dfrac{0.00000129}{0.0003}$ 0.0043
68. $\dfrac{169,000,000,000}{26,000,000}$ 6,500
69. $\dfrac{96,000}{(12,000)(0.00004)}$ 200,000
70. $\dfrac{(0.48)(14,400,000)}{96,000,000}$ 0.072
71. $(456.4)^6$ 9,038,030,748,000,000
72. $(0.053)^4$ 0.000007890481
73. $(0.009)^{-6}$ 1,881,676,423,000
74. 225^{-3} 0.0000000877914952
75. $\left(\frac{1}{3}\right)^{-25}$ 847,288,609,400
76. $\left(\frac{8}{5}\right)^{50}$ 16,069,380,440

APPLICATIONS

77. ASTRONOMY The distance from Earth to Alpha Centauri (the nearest star outside our solar system) is about 25,700,000,000,000 miles. Express this number in scientific notation. 2.57×10^{13} mi

78. SPEED OF SOUND The speed of sound in air is 33,100 centimeters per second. Express this number in scientific notation. 3.31×10^{4} cm/sec

79. GEOGRAPHY The largest ocean in the world is the Pacific Ocean, which covers 6.38×10^7 square miles. Express this number in standard notation. 63,800,000 mi^2

80. ATOMS The number of atoms in 1 gram of iron is approximately 1.08×10^{22}. Express this number in standard notation. 10,800,000,000,000,000,000,000

81. LENGTH OF A METER One meter is approximately 0.00622 mile. Use scientific notation to express this number. 6.22×10^{-3} mi

82. ANGSTROM One angstrom is 1.0×10^{-7} millimeter. Express this number in standard notation. 0.0000001 mm

83. WAVELENGTHS Transmitters, vacuum tubes, and lights emit energy that can be modeled as a wave, as shown. Examples of the most common types of electromagnetic waves are given in the table. List the wavelengths in order from shortest to longest. g, x, u, v, i, m, r

This distance between the two crests of the wave is called the wavelength.

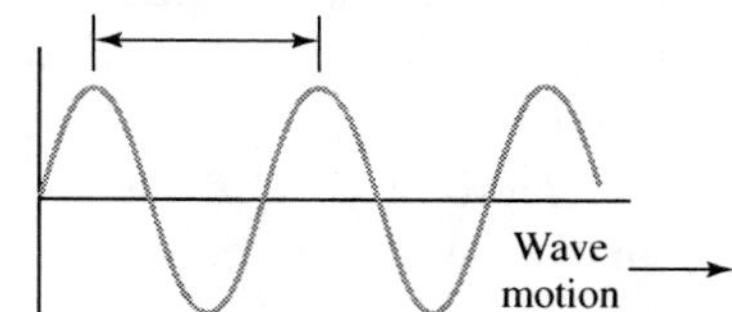

Type	Use	Wavelength (m)
visible light	lighting	9.3×10^{-6}
infrared	photography	3.7×10^{-5}
x-ray	medical	2.3×10^{-11}
radio wave	communication	3.0×10^{2}
gamma ray	treating cancer	8.9×10^{-14}
microwave	cooking	1.1×10^{-2}
ultraviolet	sun lamp	6.1×10^{-8}

84. SPACE EXPLORATION On July 4, 1997, the *Pathfinder,* carrying the rover vehicle called Sojourner, landed on Mars to perform a scientific investigation of the planet. The distance from Mars to Earth is approximately 3.5×10^7 miles. Use scientific notation to express this distance in feet. (*Hint:* 5,280 feet = 1 mile.) 1.848×10^{11} ft

Space Frontiers/Hulton Archive/Getty Images

85. PROTONS The mass of one proton is approximately 1.7×10^{-24} gram. Use scientific notation to express the mass of 1 million protons. 1.7×10^{-18} g

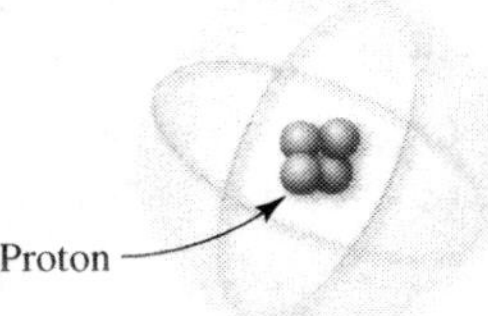

86. SPEED OF SOUND The speed of sound in air is approximately 3.3×10^4 centimeters per second. Use scientific notation to express this speed in kilometers per second. (*Hint:* 100 centimeters = 1 meter and 1,000 meters = 1 kilometer.) 3.3×10^{-1} km/sec

87. LIGHT YEARS One light year is about 5.87×10^{12} miles. Use scientific notation to express this distance in feet. (*Hint:* 5,280 feet = 1 mile.) 3.099363×10^{16} ft

88. OIL RESERVES In 2006, Saudi Arabia had crude oil reserves of about 2.643×10^{11} barrels. A barrel contains 42 gallons of oil. Use scientific notation to express Saudi Arabia oil reserves in gallons. (Source: infoplease) 1.11006×10^{13} gal

89. INSURED DEPOSITS In 2006, the total insured deposits in U.S. banks and savings and loans was approximately 6.4×10^{12} dollars. If this money was invested at 4% simple annual interest, how much would it earn in 1 year? Use scientific notation to express the answer. (Source: Federal Deposit Insurance Corporation.) 2.56×10^{11} dollars

90. CURRENCY In 2006, the number of \$20 bills in circulation was approximately 5.96×10^9. Find the total value of the currency. Use scientific notation to express the answer. (Source: The Federal Reserve.) 1.192×10^{11} dollars

91. THE MILITARY The graph shows the number of U.S. troops for several years. Estimate each of the following and express your answers in scientific and standard notation.

a. The number of troops in 1993 1.7×10^6, 1,700,000

b. The largest numbers of troops during these years 1986: 2.05×10^6, 2,050,000

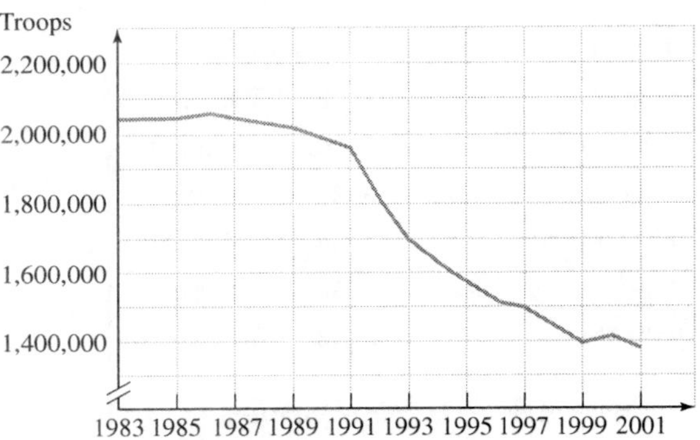

Based on data from the U.S. Department of Defense

92. SUPERCOMPUTERS In 2006, the world's fastest computer was IBM's BlueGene/L System. If it could make 2.81×10^{14} calculations in one second, how many could it make in one minute? Give the answer in scientific notation. 1.686×10^{16}

© Kimberly White/Reuters/Corbis

WRITING

93. In what situations would scientific notation be more convenient than standard notation?

94. To multiply a number by a power of 10, we move the decimal point. Which way, and how far? Explain.

95. 2.3×10^{-3} contains a negative sign but represents a positive number. Explain.

96. Is this a true statement? $2.0 \times 10^3 = 2 \times 10^3$ Explain.

REVIEW

97. If $y = -1$, find the value of $-5y^{55}$. 5

98. What is the y-intercept of the graph of $y = -3x - 5$? $(0, -5)$

Determine which property of real numbers justifies each statement.

99. $5 + z = z + 5$ commutative property of addition

100. $7(u + 3) = 7u + 7 \cdot 3$ distributive property

Solve each equation.

101. $3(x - 4) - 6 = 0$ 6

102. $8(3x - 5) - 4(2x + 3) = 12$ 4

Module 3: Proportion/ Ratios/Rates/Percents

DMA 030

Nick White/Getty Images

from Campus to Careers

Chef

Chefs prepare and cook a wide range of foods—from soups, snacks, and salads to main dishes, side dishes, and desserts. They work in a variety of restaurants and food service kitchens. They measure, mix, and cook ingredients according to recipes, using a variety of equipment and tools. They are also responsible for directing the tasks of other kitchen workers, estimating food requirements, and ordering food supplies.

In **Problem 90** of **Study Set 3.2,** you will see how a chef can use proportions to determine the correct amounts of each ingredient needed to make a large batch of brownies.

JOB TITLE:
Chef
EDUCATION: Training programs are available through culinary schools, 2- or 4-year college degree programs, and the armed forces.
JOB OUTLOOK: Job openings are expected to be plentiful through 2016.
ANNUAL EARNINGS: The average (median) salary in 2008 was $55,976.
FOR MORE INFORMATION:
www.searchbydegree.com/chef-cook-career.html

Objectives

1. Write ratios as fractions.
2. Simplify ratios involving decimals and mixed numbers.
3. Convert units to write ratios.
4. Write rates as fractions.
5. Find unit rates.
6. Find the best buy based on unit price.

SECTION 3.1

Ratios

Ratios are often used to describe important relationships between two quantities. Here are three examples:

To prepare fuel for an outboard marine engine, gasoline must be mixed with oil in the ratio of 50 to 1.

To make 14-karat jewelry, gold is combined with other metals in the ratio of 14 to 10.

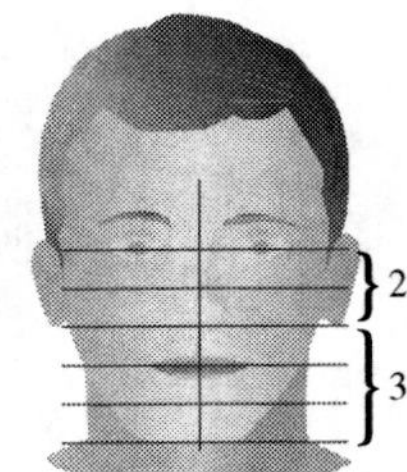

In this drawing, the eyes-to-nose distance and the nose-to-chin distance are drawn using a ratio of 2 to 3.

1 Write ratios as fractions.

Ratios give us a way to compare two numbers or two quantities measured in the same units.

Ratios

A **ratio** is the quotient of two numbers or the quotient of two quantities that have the same units.

There are three ways to write a ratio. The most comon way is as a fraction. Ratios can also be written as two numbers separated by the word *to,* or as two numbers separated by a colon. For example, the ratios described in the illustrations above can be expressed as:

$\frac{50}{1}$, 14 to 10, and 2:3

- The fraction $\frac{50}{1}$ is read as "the ratio of 50 to 1." — A fraction bar separates the numbers being compared.
- 14 to 10 is read as "the ratio of 14 to 10." — The word "to" separates the numbers being compared.
- 2:3 is read as "the ratio of 2 to 3." — A colon separates the numbers being compared.

Writing a Ratio as a Fraction

To **write a ratio as a fraction,** write the first number (or quantity) mentioned as the numerator and the second number (or quantity) mentioned as the denominator. Then simplify the fraction, if possible.

EXAMPLE 1 Write each ratio as a fraction: **a.** 3 to 7 **b.** 10:11

Strategy We will identify the numbers before and after the word *to* and the numbers before and after the colon.

WHY The word *to* and the colon separate the numbers to be compared in a ratio.

Solution

To write the ratio as a fraction, the first number mentioned is the numerator and the second number mentioned is the denominator.

a. The ratio 3 to 7 can be written as $\frac{3}{7}$. The fraction $\frac{3}{7}$ is in simplest form.

b. The ratio 10 : 11 can be written as $\frac{10}{11}$. The fraction $\frac{10}{11}$ is in simplest form.

Self Check 1

Write each ratio as a fraction:

a. 4 to 9 $\frac{4}{9}$ **b.** 8:15 $\frac{8}{15}$

Now Try **Problem 13**

Teaching Example 1
Write each ratio as a fraction:
a. 2 to 5 **b.** 8:27
Answers:
a. $\frac{2}{5}$ **b.** $\frac{8}{27}$

Caution! When a ratio is written as a fraction, the fraction should be in simplest form. (Recall from Chapter 3 that a fraction is in **simplest form,** or **lowest terms,** when the numerator and denominator have no common factors other than 1.)

EXAMPLE 2 Write the ratio 35 to 10 as a fraction in simplest form.

Strategy We will translate the ratio from its given form in words to fractional form. Then we will look for any factors common to the numerator and denominator and remove them.

WHY We need to make sure that the numerator and denominator have no common factors other than 1. If that is the case, the ratio will be in *simplest form.*

Solution

The ratio 35 to 10 can be written as $\frac{35}{10}$. The fraction $\frac{35}{10}$ is not in simplest form.

Now, we simplify the fraction.

$$\frac{35}{10} = \frac{\overset{1}{\cancel{5}} \cdot 7}{2 \cdot \underset{1}{\cancel{5}}}$$ Factor 35 as 5 · 7 and 10 as 2 · 5. Then remove the common factor of 5 in the numerator and denominator.

$$= \frac{7}{2}$$

The ratio 35 to 10 can be written as the fraction $\frac{35}{10}$, which simplifies to $\frac{7}{2}$ (read as "7 to 2"). Because the fractions $\frac{35}{10}$ and $\frac{7}{2}$ represent equal numbers, they are called **equal ratios.**

Self Check 2

Write the ratio 12 to 9 as a fraction in simplest form. $\frac{4}{3}$

Now Try **Problems 17 and 23**

Teaching Example 2 Write the ratio 30 to 18 as a fraction in simplest form.
Answer:
$\frac{5}{3}$

> **Caution!** Since ratios are comparisons of two numbers, it would be *incorrect* in Example 2 to write the ratio $\frac{7}{2}$ as the mixed number $3\frac{1}{2}$. Ratios written as improper fractions are perfectly acceptable—just make sure the numerator and denominator have no common factors other than 1.

To write a ratio in simplest form, we remove any common factors of the numerator and denominator as well as any common units.

Self Check 3

CARRY-ON LUGGAGE

a. Write the ratio of the height to the length of the carry-on space shown in the illustration in Example 3 as a fraction in simplest form. $\frac{2}{3}$

b. Write the ratio of the length of the carry-on space to its height in simplest form. $\frac{3}{2}$

Now Try **Problem 27**

Teaching Example 3
BASKETBALL NBA basketball courts are 50 feet wide and 94 feet long.

a. Write the ratio of the width of the court to the length as a fraction in simplest form.

b. Write the ratio of the length of the court to the width as a fraction in simplest form.

Answers:
a. $\frac{25}{47}$ b. $\frac{47}{25}$

EXAMPLE 3 *Carry-on Luggage* An airline allows its passengers to carry a piece of luggage onto an airplane only if it will fit in the space shown below.

a. Write the ratio of the width of the space to its length as a fraction in simplest form.

b. Write the ratio of the length of the space to its width as a fraction in simplest form.

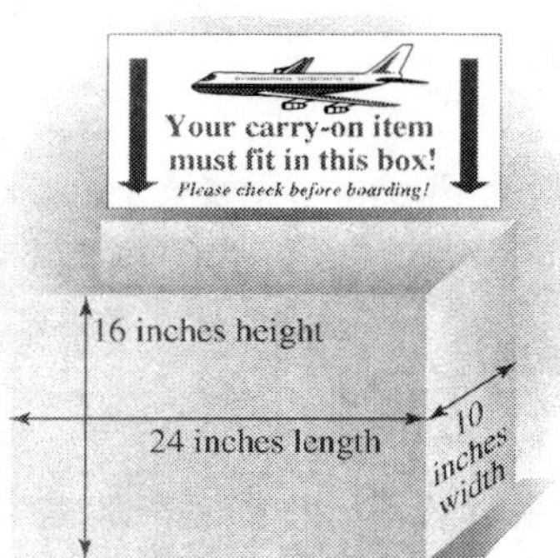

Strategy To write each ratio as a fraction, we will identify the quantity before the word *to* and the quantity after it.

WHY The first quantity mentioned is the numerator of the fraction and the second quantity mentioned is the denominator.

Solution

a. The ratio of the width of the space to its length is $\frac{10 \text{ inches}}{24 \text{ inches}}$.

To write a ratio in simplest form, we remove the common factors *and* the common units of the numerator and denominator.

$$\frac{10 \text{ inches}}{24 \text{ inches}} = \frac{\overset{1}{\cancel{2}} \cdot 5 \cancel{\text{ inches}}}{\underset{1}{\cancel{2}} \cdot 12 \cancel{\text{ inches}}}$$

Factor 10 as $2 \cdot 5$ and 24 as $2 \cdot 12$. Then remove the common factor of 2 and the common units of inches from the numerator and denominator.

$$= \frac{5}{12}$$

The width-to-length ratio of the carry-on space is $\frac{5}{12}$ (read as "5 to 12").

b. The ratio of the length of the space to its width is $\frac{24 \text{ inches}}{10 \text{ inches}}$.

$$\frac{24 \text{ inches}}{10 \text{ inches}} = \frac{\overset{1}{\cancel{2}} \cdot 12 \cancel{\text{ inches}}}{\underset{1}{\cancel{2}} \cdot 5 \cancel{\text{ inches}}}$$

Factor 24 and 10. Then remove the common factor of 2 and the common units of inches from the numerator and denominator.

$$= \frac{12}{5}$$

The length-to-width ratio of the carry-on space is $\frac{12}{5}$ (read as "12 to 5").

> ***Caution!*** Example 3 shows that order is important when writing a ratio. The width-to-length ratio is $\frac{5}{12}$ while the length-to-width ratio is $\frac{12}{5}$.

2 Simplify ratios involving decimals and mixed numbers.

EXAMPLE 4 Write the ratio 0.3 to 1.2 as a fraction in simplest form.

Strategy After writing the ratio as a fraction, we will multiply it by a form of 1 to obtain an equivalent ratio of whole numbers.

WHY A ratio of whole numbers is easier to understand than a ratio of decimals.

Solution

The ratio 0.3 to 1.2 can be written as $\frac{0.3}{1.2}$.

To write this as a ratio of *whole numbers,* we need to move the decimal points in the numerator and denominator one place to the right. Recall that to find the product of a decimal and 10, we simply move the decimal point one place to the right. Therefore, it follows that $\frac{10}{10}$ is the form of 1 that we should use to build $\frac{0.3}{1.2}$ into an equivalent ratio.

$\frac{0.3}{1.2} = \frac{0.3}{1.2} \cdot \frac{10}{10}$ Multiply the ratio by a form of 1.

$\frac{0.3}{1.2} = \frac{0.3 \cdot 10}{1.2 \cdot 10}$ Multiply the numerators. Multiply the denominators.

$= \frac{3}{12}$ Do the multiplications by moving each decimal point one place to the right. $0.3 \cdot 10 = 3$ and $1.2 \cdot 10 = 12$.

$= \frac{1}{4}$ Simplify the fraction: $\frac{3}{12} = \frac{\overset{1}{\cancel{3}}}{\underset{1}{\cancel{3}} \cdot 4} = \frac{1}{4}$.

Self Check 4

Write the ratio 0.8 to 2.4 as a fraction in simplest form. $\frac{1}{3}$

Now Try **Problems 29 and 33**

Teaching Example 4 Write the ratio 0.6 to 4.8 as a fraction in simplest form.
Answer:
$\frac{1}{8}$

THINK IT THROUGH ***Student-to-Instructor Ratio***

"A more personal classroom atmosphere can sometimes be an easier adjustment for college freshmen. They are less likely to feel like a number, a feeling that can sometimes impact students' first semester grades."

From *The Importance of Class Size* by Stephen Pemberton

The data below come from a nationwide study of mathematics programs at two-year colleges. Determine which course has the lowest student-to-instructor ratio. (Assume that there is one instructor per section.)

23:1, 24:1, 25:1; Basic Mathematics has the lowest student-to-instructor ratio.

	Basic Mathematics	Elementary Algebra	Intermediate Algebra
Students enrolled	101,200	367,920	318,750
Number of sections	4,400	15,330	12,750

Source: Conference Board of the Mathematical Science, 2005 CBMS Survey of Undergraduate Programs (The data has been rounded to yield ratios involving whole numbers.)

Self Check 5

Write the ratio $3\frac{1}{3}$ to $1\frac{1}{9}$ as a fraction in simplest form. $\frac{3}{1}$

Now Try **Problem 37**

Teaching Example 5 Write the ratio $6\frac{3}{4}$ to $1\frac{1}{8}$ as a fraction in simplest form.
Answer:
$\frac{6}{1}$

EXAMPLE 5 Write the ratio $4\frac{2}{3}$ to $1\frac{1}{6}$ as a fraction in simplest form.

Strategy After writing the ratio as a fraction, we will use the method for simplifying a complex fraction to obtain an equivalent ratio of whole numbers.

WHY A ratio of whole numbers is easier to understand than a ratio of mixed numbers.

Solution

The ratio of $4\frac{2}{3}$ to $1\frac{1}{6}$ can be written as $\frac{4\frac{2}{3}}{1\frac{1}{6}}$.

The resulting ratio is a complex fraction. To write the ratio in simplest form, we perform the division indicated by the main fraction bar (shown in red).

$$\frac{4\frac{2}{3}}{1\frac{1}{6}} = \frac{\frac{14}{3}}{\frac{7}{6}} \quad \text{Write } 4\tfrac{2}{3} \text{ and } 1\tfrac{1}{6} \text{ as improper fractions.}$$

$$= \frac{14}{3} \div \frac{7}{6} \quad \text{Write the division indicated by the main fraction bar using a } \div \text{ symbol.}$$

$$= \frac{14}{3} \cdot \frac{6}{7} \quad \text{Use the rule for dividing fractions: Multiply the first fraction by the reciprocal of } \tfrac{7}{6}\text{, which is } \tfrac{6}{7}.$$

$$= \frac{14 \cdot 6}{3 \cdot 7} \quad \text{Multiply the numerators. Multiply the denominators.}$$

$$= \frac{2 \cdot \overset{1}{\cancel{7}} \cdot 2 \cdot \overset{1}{\cancel{3}}}{\underset{1}{\cancel{3}} \cdot \underset{1}{\cancel{7}}} \quad \text{To simplify the fraction, factor 14 as } 2 \cdot 7 \text{ and 6 as } 2 \cdot 3. \text{ Then remove the common factors 3 and 7.}$$

$$= \frac{4}{1} \quad \text{Multiply the remaining factors in the numerator. Multiply the remaining factors in the denominator.}$$

We would normally simplify the result $\frac{4}{1}$ and write it as 4. But since a ratio compares two numbers, we leave the result in fractional form.

3 Convert units to write ratios.

When a ratio compares 2 quantities, both quantities must be measured in the same units. For example, inches must be compared to inches, pounds to pounds, and seconds to seconds.

Self Check 6

Write the ratio *6 feet to 3 yards* as a fraction in simplest form. (*Hint:* 3 feet = 1 yard.) $\frac{2}{3}$

Now Try **Problem 41**

EXAMPLE 6 Write the ratio *12 ounces to 2 pounds* as a fraction in simplest form.

Strategy We will convert 2 pounds to ounces and write a ratio that compares ounces to ounces. Then we will simplify the ratio.

WHY A ratio compares two quantities that have the *same* units. When the units are different, it's usually easier to write the ratio using the smaller unit of measurement. Since ounces are smaller than pounds, we will compare in ounces.

Solution

To express 2 pounds in ounces, we use the fact that there are 16 ounces in one pound.

$$2 \cdot 16 \text{ ounces} = 32 \text{ ounces}$$

We can now express the ratio *12 ounces to 2 pounds* using the same units:

12 ounces to 32 ounces

Next, we write the ratio in fraction form and simplify.

$$\frac{12 \text{ ounces}}{32 \text{ ounces}} = \frac{3 \cdot \overset{1}{\cancel{4}} \, \cancel{\text{ounces}}}{\underset{1}{\cancel{4}} \cdot 8 \, \cancel{\text{ounces}}}$$

To simplify, factor 12 as 3 · 4 and 32 as 4 · 8. Then remove the common factor of 4 and the common units of ounces from the numerator and denominator.

$$= \frac{3}{8}$$

The ratio in simplest form is $\frac{3}{8}$.

Teaching Example 6
Write the ratio *18 seconds to 2 minutes* as a fraction in simplest form.
Answer:
$\frac{3}{20}$

4 Write rates as fractions.

When we compare two quantities that have different units (and neither unit can be converted to the other), we call the comparison a **rate,** and we can write it as a fraction. For example, on the label of the can of paint shown on the right, we see that 1 quart of paint is needed for every 200 square feet to be painted. Writing this as a rate in fractional form, we have

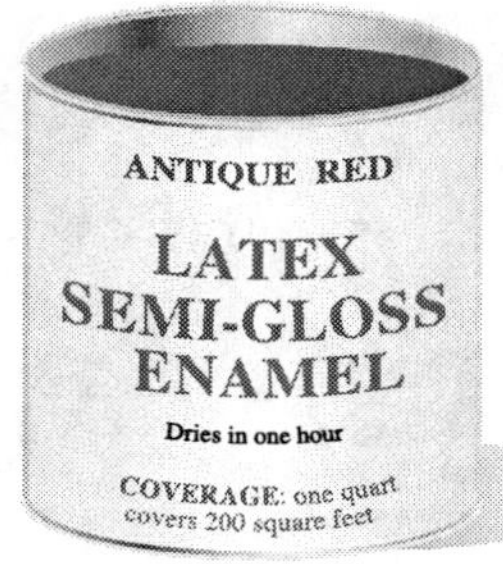

$$\frac{1 \text{ quart}}{200 \text{ square feet}}$$

Read as "1 quart per 200 square feet."

The Language of Mathematics The word *per* is associated with the operation of division, and it means "for each" or "for every." For example, when we say 1 quart of paint *per* 200 square feet, we mean 1 quart of paint *for every* 200 square feet.

Rates

A **rate** is a quotient of two quantities that have different units.

When writing a rate, always include the units. Some other examples of rates are:

- 16 computers for 75 students
- 1,550 feet in 4.5 seconds
- 88 tomatoes from 3 plants
- 250 miles on 2 gallons of gasoline

The Language of Mathematics As seen above, words such as *per, for, in, from,* and *on* are used to separate the two quantities that are compared in a rate.

Writing a Rate as a Fraction

To **write a rate as a fraction,** write the first quantity mentioned as the numerator and the second quantity mentioned as the denominator, and then simplify, if possible. Write the units as part of the fraction.

Self Check 7

GROWTH RATES The fastest-growing flowering plant on record grew 12 feet in 14 days. Write the rate of growth as a fraction in simplest form. $\frac{6 \text{ feet}}{7 \text{ days}}$

Now Try **Problems 49 and 53**

Teaching Example 7 HOSPITALS In a 6-hour span, 21 patients were treated in a hospital emergency room. Write the rate of patients treated in the emergency room as a fraction in simplest form.
Answer:
$\frac{7 \text{ patients}}{2 \text{ hours}}$

EXAMPLE 7 *Snowfall* According to the *Guinness Book of World Records,* a total of 78 inches of snow fell at Mile 47 Camp, Cooper River Division, Arkansas, in a 24-hour period in 1963. Write the rate of snowfall as a fraction in simplest form.

Strategy We will use a fraction to compare the amount of snow that fell (in inches) to the amount of time in which it fell (in hours). Then we will simplify it.

WHY A rate is a quotient of two quantities with different units.

Solution

78 inches **in** 24 hours can be written as $\frac{78 \text{ inches}}{24 \text{ hours}}$.

Now, we simplify the fraction.

$$\frac{78 \text{ inches}}{24 \text{ hours}} = \frac{\overset{1}{\cancel{6}} \cdot 13 \text{ inches}}{4 \cdot \underset{1}{\cancel{6}} \text{ hours}}$$

To simplify, factor 78 as 6 · 13 and 24 as 4 · 6. Then remove the common factor of 6 from the numerator and denominator.

$$= \frac{13 \text{ inches}}{4 \text{ hours}}$$

Since the units are different, they cannot be removed.

The snow fell at a rate of 13 inches per 4 hours.

5 Find unit rates.

Unit Rate

A **unit rate** is a rate in which the denominator is 1.

To illustrate the concept of a unit rate, suppose a driver makes the 354-mile trip from Pittsburgh to Indianapolis in 6 hours. Then the motorist's rate (or more specifically, rate of speed) is given by

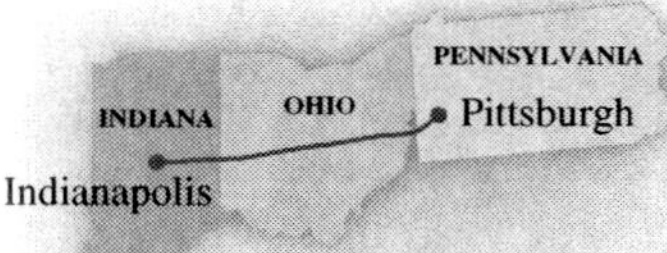

$$\frac{354 \text{ miles}}{6 \text{ hours}} = \frac{\overset{1}{\cancel{6}} \cdot 59 \text{ miles}}{\underset{1}{\cancel{6}} \cdot \text{hours}}$$

Factor 354 as 6 · 59 and remove the common factor of 6 from the numerator and denominator.

$$= \frac{59 \text{ miles}}{1 \text{ hour}}$$

Since the units are different, they cannot be removed. Note that the denominator is 1.

We can also find the unit rate by dividing 354 by 6.

Rate:

$$\frac{354 \text{ miles}}{6 \text{ hours}} \qquad \begin{array}{r} 59 \\ 6\overline{)354} \\ -\ 30 \\ \hline 54 \\ -\ 54 \\ \hline 0 \end{array}$$

This quotient is the numerical part of the unit rate, written as a fraction. The numerical part of the denominator is always 1.

Unit rate: $\frac{59 \text{ miles}}{1 \text{ hour}}$

The unit rate $\frac{59 \text{ miles}}{1 \text{ hour}}$ can be expressed in any of the following forms:

$59 \frac{\text{miles}}{\text{hour}}$, 59 miles per hour, 59 miles/hour, or 59 mph

> ***The Language of Mathematics*** A slash mark / is often used to write a unit rate. In such cases, we read the slash mark as "per." For example, 33 pounds/gallon is read as 33 pounds *per* gallon.

Writing a Rate as a Unit Rate

To **write a rate as a unit rate,** divide the numerator of the rate by the denominator.

EXAMPLE 8 *Coffee* There are 384 calories in a 16-ounce cup of caramel Frappuccino blended coffee with whip cream. Write this rate as a unit rate. (*Hint:* Find the number of calories in 1 ounce.)

Strategy We will translate the rate from its given form in words to fractional form. Then we will perform the indicated division.

WHY To write a rate as a unit rate, we divide the numerator of the rate by the denominator.

Solution

384 calories in 16 ounces can be written as $\frac{384 \text{ calories}}{16 \text{ ounces}}$.

To find the number of calories in 1 ounce of the coffee (the unit rate), we perform the division as indicated by the fraction bar:

$$\begin{array}{r} 24 \\ 16\overline{)384} \\ -32 \\ \hline 64 \\ -64 \\ \hline 0 \end{array}$$

Divide the numerator of the rate by the denominator.

For the caramel Frappuccino blended coffee with whip cream, the unit rate is $\frac{24 \text{ calories}}{1 \text{ ounce}}$, which can be written as 24 calories per ounce or 24 calories /ounce.

Self Check 8

NUTRITION There are 204 calories in a 12-ounce can of cranberry juice. Write this rate as a unit rate. (*Hint:* Find the number of calories in 1 ounce.) 17 calories/oz

Now Try **Problem 57**

Teaching Example 8 NUTRITION There are 180 calories in a 12-ounce serving of apple juice. Write this rate as a unit rate. (*Hint:* Find the number of calories in 1 ounce.)
Answer:
15 calories/oz

Self Check 9

FULL-TIME JOBS Joan earns $436 per 40-hour week managing a dress shop. Write this rate as a unit rate. (*Hint:* Find her hourly rate of pay.) $10.90 per hour

Now Try **Problem 61**

Teaching Example 9 PART-TIME JOBS A student earns $90 for working 8 hours in a school cafeteria. Write this rate as a unit rate. (*Hint:* Find her hourly rate of pay.)
Answer:
$11.25/hr

EXAMPLE 9 *Part-time Jobs* A student earns $74 for working 8 hours in a bookstore. Write this rate as a unit rate. (*Hint:* Find his hourly rate of pay.)

Strategy We will translate the rate from its given form in words to fractional form. Then we will perform the indicated division.

WHY To write a rate as a unit rate, we divide the numerator of the rate by the denominator.

Solution

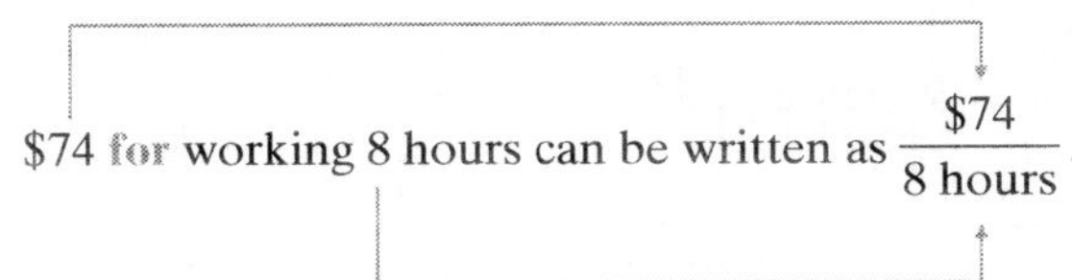

$74 **for** working 8 hours can be written as $\frac{\$74}{8 \text{ hours}}$.

To find the rate of pay for 1 hour of work (the unit rate), we divide 74 by 8.

$$\begin{array}{r} 9.25 \\ 8\overline{)74.00} \\ -72 \\ \hline 2\,0 \\ -1\,6 \\ \hline 40 \\ -40 \\ \hline 0 \end{array}$$

Write a decimal point and two additional zeros to the right of 4.

The unit rate of pay is $\frac{\$9.25}{1 \text{ hour}}$, which can be written as $9.25 per hour or $9.25/hr.

6 Find the best buy based on unit price.

If a grocery store sells a 5-pound package of hamburger for $18.75, a consumer might want to know what the hamburger costs per pound. When we find the cost of 1 pound of the hamburger, we are finding a **unit price.** To find the unit price of an item, we begin by comparing its price to the number of units.

$$\frac{\$18.75}{5 \text{ pounds}} \begin{array}{l} \leftarrow \text{Price} \\ \leftarrow \text{Number of units} \end{array}$$

Then we divide the price by the number of units.

$$\begin{array}{r} 3.75 \\ 5\overline{)18.75} \end{array}$$

The unit price of the hamburger is $3.75 per pound.

Other examples of unit prices are:

- $8.15 per ounce
- $200 per day
- $0.75 per foot

Unit Price

A **unit price** is a rate that tells how much is paid for *one* unit (or *one* item). It is the quotient of price to the number of units.

$$\text{Unit price} = \frac{\text{price}}{\text{number of units}}$$

When shopping, it is often difficult to determine the best buys because the items that we purchase come in so many different sizes and brands. Comparison shopping can be made easier by finding unit prices. *The best buy is the item that has the lowest unit price.*

EXAMPLE 10 *Comparison Shopping*

Olives come packaged in a 10-ounce jar, which sells for \$2.49, or in a 6-ounce jar, which sells for \$1.53. Which is the better buy?

Strategy We will find the unit price for each jar of olives. Then we will identify which jar has the lower unit price.

WHY The better buy is the jar of olives that has the lower unit price.

Solution

To find the unit price of each jar of olives, we write the quotient of its price and its weight, and then perform the indicated division. Before dividing, we convert each price from dollars to cents so that the unit price can be expressed in cents per ounce.

The 10-ounce jar:

$$\frac{\$2.49}{10 \text{ oz}} = \frac{249¢}{10 \text{ oz}}$$ Write the rate: $\frac{\text{price}}{\text{number of units}}$. Then change \$2.49 to 249 cents.

$$= 24.9¢ \text{ per oz}$$ Divide 249 by 10 by moving the decimal point 1 place to the left.

The 6-ounce jar:

$$\frac{\$1.53}{6 \text{ oz}} = \frac{153¢}{6 \text{ oz}}$$ Write the rate: $\frac{\text{price}}{\text{number of units}}$. Then change \$1.53 to 153 cents.

$$= 25.5¢ \text{ per oz}$$ Do the division.

$$\begin{array}{r} 25.5 \\ 6\overline{)153.0} \\ -12 \\ \hline 33 \\ -30 \\ \hline 3\,0 \\ -3\,0 \\ \hline 0 \end{array}$$

One ounce for 24.9¢ is a better buy than one ounce for 25.5¢. The unit price is less when olives are packaged in 10-ounce jars, so that is the better buy.

Self Check 10

COMPARISON SHOPPING A fast-food restaurant sells a 12-ounce cola for 72¢ and a 16-ounce cola for 99¢. Which is the better buy? the 12-oz cola

Now Try **Problems 65 and 101**

Teaching Example 10
GUITAR LESSONS A music store charges \$27 for a 30-minute guitar lesson and \$36 for a 45-minute lesson. Which is the better buy?
Answer:
The 45-min lesson

ANSWERS TO SELF CHECKS

1. a. $\frac{4}{9}$ **b.** $\frac{8}{15}$ **2.** $\frac{4}{3}$ **3. a.** $\frac{2}{3}$ **b.** $\frac{3}{2}$ **4.** $\frac{1}{3}$ **5.** $\frac{3}{1}$ **6.** $\frac{2}{3}$ **7.** $\frac{6 \text{ feet}}{7 \text{ days}}$
8. 17 calories/oz **9.** \$10.90 per hour **10.** the 12-oz cola

SECTION 3.1 STUDY SET

VOCABULARY

Fill in the blanks.

1. A ratio is the quotient of two numbers or the quotient of two quantities that have the same units.

2. A rate is the quotient of two quantities that have different units.

3. A unit rate is a rate in which the denominator is 1.

4. A unit price is a rate that tells how much is paid for one unit or one item.

CONCEPTS

5. To write the ratio $\frac{15}{24}$ in lowest terms, we remove any common factors of the numerator and denominator. What common factor do they have? 3

6. Complete the solution. Write the ratio $\frac{14}{21}$ in lowest terms.

$$\frac{14}{21} = \frac{2 \cdot 7}{3 \cdot 7} = \frac{2 \cdot \overset{1}{\cancel{7}}}{3 \cdot \underset{1}{\cancel{7}}} = \frac{2}{3}$$

7. Consider the ratio $\frac{0.5}{0.6}$. By what number should we multiply numerator and denominator to make this a ratio of whole numbers? 10

8. What should be done to write the ratio $\frac{15 \text{ inches}}{22 \text{ inches}}$ in simplest form? Remove the common units of inches in the numerator and denominator.

9. Write $\frac{11 \text{ minutes}}{1 \text{ hour}}$ so that it compares the same units and then simplify. $\frac{11 \text{ minutes}}{60 \text{ minutes}} = \frac{11}{60}$

10. a. Consider the rate $\frac{\$248}{16 \text{ hours}}$. What division should be performed to find the unit rate in dollars per hour? $248 \div 16$

b. Suppose 3 pairs of socks sell for $7.95: $\frac{\$7.95}{3 \text{ pairs}}$. What division should be performed to find the unit price of one pair of socks? $7.95 \div 3$

NOTATION

11. Write the ratio of the flag's length to its width using a fraction, using the word *to,* and using a colon. $\frac{13}{9}$, 13 to 9, 13:9

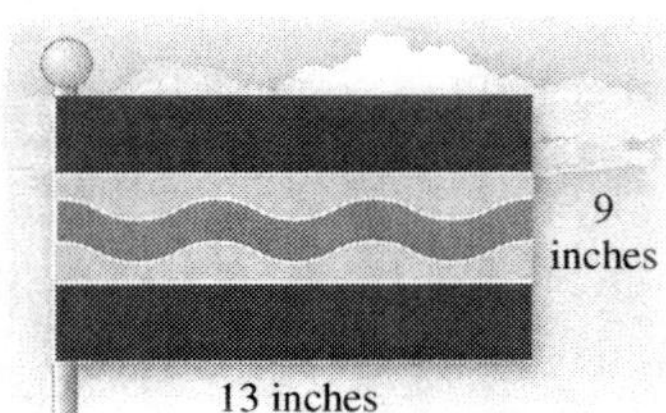

12. The rate $\frac{55 \text{ miles}}{1 \text{ hour}}$ can be expressed as

- 55 __miles__ __per__ __hour__ (in three words)
- 55 __miles__ / __hour__ (in two words with a slash)
- 55 __m__ __p__ __h__ (in three letters)

GUIDED PRACTICE

Write each ratio as a fraction. See Example 1.

13. 5 to 8 $\frac{5}{8}$

14. 3 to 23 $\frac{3}{23}$

15. 11:16 $\frac{11}{16}$

16. 9:25 $\frac{9}{25}$

Write each ratio as a fraction in simplest form. See Example 2.

17. 25 to 15 $\frac{5}{3}$

18. 45 to 35 $\frac{9}{7}$

19. 63:36 $\frac{7}{4}$

20. 54:24 $\frac{9}{4}$

21. 22:33 $\frac{2}{3}$

22. 14:21 $\frac{2}{3}$

23. 17 to 34 $\frac{1}{2}$

24. 19 to 38 $\frac{1}{2}$

Write each ratio as a fraction in simplest form. See Example 3.

25. 4 ounces to 12 ounces $\frac{1}{3}$

26. 3 inches to 15 inches $\frac{1}{5}$

27. 24 miles to 32 miles $\frac{3}{4}$

28. 56 yards to 64 yards $\frac{7}{8}$

Write each ratio as a fraction in simplest form. See Example 4.

29. 0.3 to 0.9 $\frac{1}{3}$

30. 0.2 to 0.6 $\frac{1}{3}$

31. 0.65 to 0.15 $\frac{13}{3}$

32. 2.4 to 1.5 $\frac{8}{5}$

33. 3.8:7.8 $\frac{19}{39}$

34. 4.2:8.2 $\frac{21}{41}$

35. 7:24.5 $\frac{2}{7}$

36. 5:22.5 $\frac{2}{9}$

Write each ratio as a fraction in simplest form. See Example 5.

37. $2\frac{1}{3}$ to $4\frac{2}{3}$ $\frac{1}{2}$

38. $1\frac{1}{4}$ to $1\frac{1}{2}$ $\frac{5}{6}$

39. $10\frac{1}{2}$ to $1\frac{3}{4}$ $\frac{6}{1}$

40. $12\frac{3}{4}$ to $2\frac{1}{8}$ $\frac{6}{1}$

Write each ratio as a fraction in simplest form. See Example 6.

41. 12 minutes to 1 hour $\frac{1}{5}$

42. 8 ounces to 1 pound $\frac{1}{2}$

43. 3 days to 1 week $\frac{3}{7}$

44. 4 inches to 1 yard $\frac{1}{9}$

45. 18 months to 2 years $\frac{3}{4}$

46. 8 feet to 4 yards $\frac{2}{3}$

47. 21 inches to 3 feet $\frac{7}{12}$

48. 32 seconds to 2 minutes $\frac{4}{15}$

Write each rate as a fraction in simplest form. See Example 7.

49. 64 feet in 6 seconds $\frac{32 \text{ ft}}{3 \text{ sec}}$

50. 45 applications for 18 openings $\frac{5 \text{ applications}}{2 \text{ openings}}$

51. 75 days on 20 gallons of water $\frac{15 \text{ days}}{4 \text{ gal}}$

52. 3,000 students over a 16-year career $\frac{375 \text{ students}}{2 \text{ yr}}$

53. 84 made out of 100 attempts $\frac{21 \text{ made}}{25 \text{ attempts}}$

54. 16 right compared to 34 wrong $\frac{8 \text{ right}}{17 \text{ wrong}}$

55. 18 beats every 12 measures $\frac{3 \text{ beats}}{2 \text{ measures}}$

56. 10 inches as a result of 30 turns $\frac{1 \text{ in.}}{3 \text{ turns}}$

Write each rate as a unit rate. See Example 8.

57. 60 revolutions in 5 minutes 12 revolutions per min

58. 14 trips every 2 months 7 trips per month

59. $50,000 paid over 10 years $5,000 per year

60. 245 presents for 35 children 7 presents per child

Write each rate as a unit rate. See Example 9.

61. 12 errors in 8 hours 1.5 errors per hr

62. 114 times in a 12-month period 9.5 times per month

63. 4,007,500 people living in 12,500 square miles 320.6 people per square mi

64. 117.6 pounds of pressure on 8 square inches 14.7 pounds per square in.

Find the unit price of each item. See Example 10.

65. They charged $48 for 12 minutes. $4 per min

66. 150 barrels cost $4,950. $33 per barrel

67. Four sold for $272. $68 per person

68. 7,020 pesos will buy six tickets. 1,170 pesos per ticket

69. 65 ounces sell for 78 cents. 1.2 cents per ounce

70. For 7 dozen, you will pay $10.15. $1.45 per dozen

71. $3.50 for 50 feet $0.07 per ft

72. $4 billion over a 5-month span $0.8 billion per month

APPLICATIONS

73. GEAR RATIOS Refer to the illustration below.

a. Write the ratio of the number of teeth of the smaller gear to the number of teeth of the larger gear in simplest form. $\frac{2}{3}$

b. Write the ratio of the number of teeth of the larger gear to the number of teeth of the smaller gear in simplest form. $\frac{3}{2}$

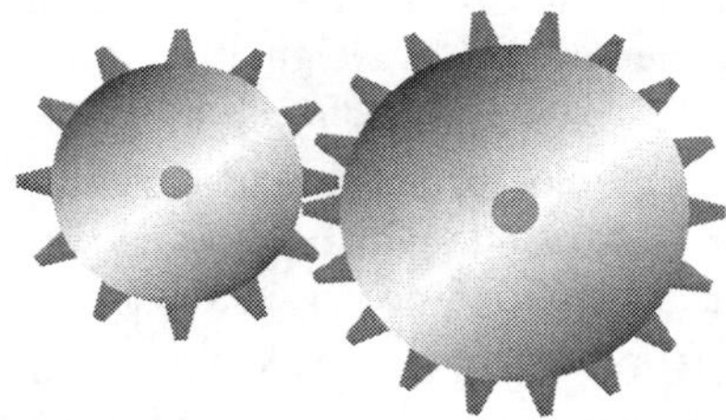

74. CARDS The suit of hearts from a deck of playing cards is shown below. What is the ratio of the number of face cards to the total number of cards in the suit? (*Hint:* A face card is a Jack, Queen, or King.) $\frac{3}{13}$

75. SKIN Refer to the cross-section of human skin shown below. Write the ratio of the thickness of the stratum corneum to the thickness of the dermis in simplest form. (*Source:* Philips Research Laboratories) $\frac{1}{55}$

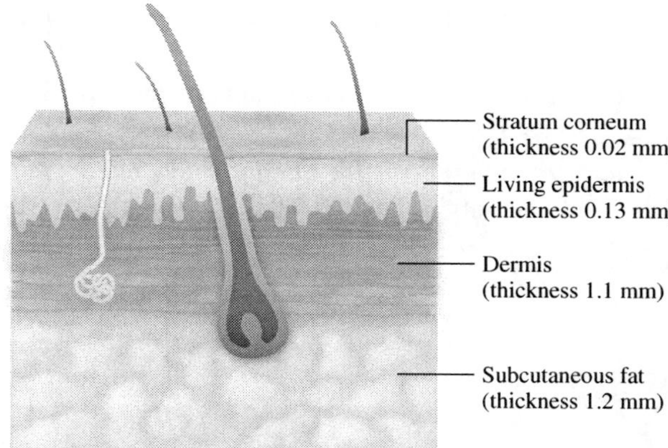

76. PAINTING A 9.5-mil thick coat of fireproof paint is applied with a roller to a wall. (A *mil* is a unit of measure equal to 1/1,000 of an inch.) The coating dries to a thickness of 5.7 mils. Write the ratio of the thickness of the coating when wet to the thickness when dry in simplest form. $\frac{5}{3}$

77. BAKING A recipe for sourdough bread calls for $5\frac{1}{4}$ cups of all-purpose flour and $1\frac{3}{4}$ cups of water. Write the ratio of flour to water in simplest form. $\frac{3}{1}$

78. DESSERTS Refer to the recipe card shown below. Write the ratio of milk to sugar in simplest form. $\frac{7}{3}$

Frozen Chocolate Slush
(Serves 8)

Once frozen, this chocolate can be cut into cubes and stored in sealed plastic bags for a spur-of-the-moment dessert.

$\frac{1}{2}$ cup Dutch cocoa powder, sifted

$1\frac{1}{2}$ cups sugar

$3\frac{1}{2}$ cups skim milk

79. BUDGETS Refer to the circle graph below that shows a monthly budget for a family. Write each ratio in simplest form.

a. Find the total amount for the monthly budget. $1,800

b. Write the ratio of the amount budgeted for rent to the total budget. $\frac{4}{9}$

c. Write the ratio of the amount budgeted for food to the total budget. $\frac{1}{3}$

d. Write the ratio of the amount budgeted for the phone to the total budget. $\frac{1}{18}$

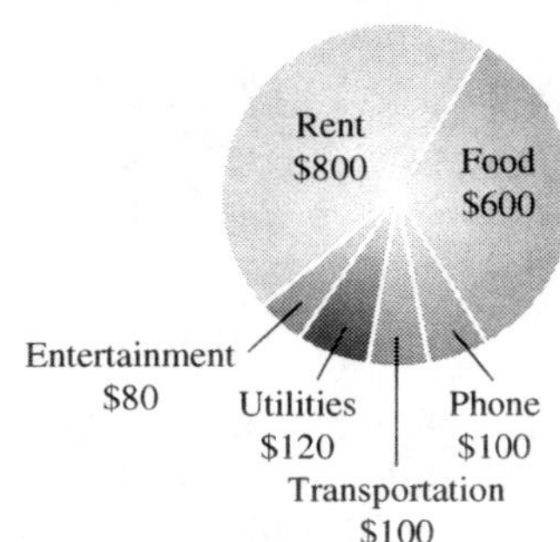

80. TAXES Refer to the list of tax deductions shown below. Write each ratio in simplest form.

a. Write the ratio of the real estate tax deduction to the total deductions. $\frac{1}{7}$

b. Write the ratio of the charitable contributions to the total deductions. $\frac{1}{5}$

c. Write the ratio of the mortgage interest deduction to the union dues deduction. $\frac{35}{4}$

Item	Amount
Medical expenses	$875
Real estate taxes	$1,250
Charitable contributions	$1,750
Mortgage interest	$4,375
Union dues	$500
Total deductions	$8,750

81. ART HISTORY Leonardo da Vinci drew the human figure shown within a square. Write the ratio of the length of the man's outstretched arms to his height. (*Hint:* All four sides of a square are the same length.) $\frac{1}{1}$

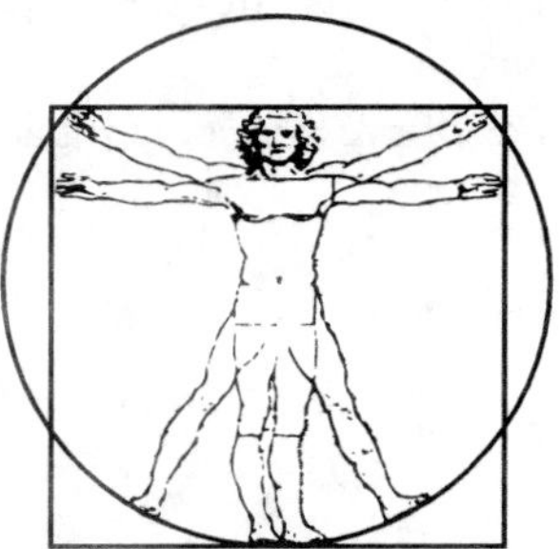

82. FLAGS The checkered flag is composed of 24 equal-sized squares. What is the ratio of the width of the flag to its length? (*Hint:* All four sides of a square are the same length.) $\frac{2}{3}$

83. BANKRUPTCY After declaring bankruptcy, a company could pay its creditors only 5¢ on the dollar. Write this as a ratio in simplest form. $\frac{1}{20}$

84. EGGS An average-sized ostrich egg weighs 3 pounds and an average-sized chicken egg weighs 2 ounces. Write the ratio of the weight of an ostrich egg to the weight of a chicken egg in simplest form. $\frac{24}{1}$

85. CPR A paramedic performed 125 compressions to 50 breaths on an adult with no pulse. What compressions-to-breaths rate did the paramedic use? $\frac{5 \text{ compressions}}{2 \text{ breaths}}$

86. FACULTY–STUDENT RATIOS At a college, there are 125 faculty members and 2,000 students. Find the rate of faculty to students. (This is often referred to as the faculty–student *ratio*, even though the units are different.) $\frac{1 \text{ faculty member}}{16 \text{ students}}$

87. AIRLINE COMPLAINTS An airline had 3.29 complaints for every 1,000 passengers. Write this as a rate of whole numbers. $\frac{329 \text{ complaints}}{100{,}000 \text{ passengers}}$

88. FINGERNAILS On average, fingernails grow 0.02 inch per week. Write this rate using whole numbers. $\frac{1 \text{ inch}}{50 \text{ weeks}}$

89. INTERNET SALES A website determined that it had 112,500 hits in one month. Of those visiting the site, 4,500 made purchases.

a. Those that visited the site, but did not make a purchase, are called *browsers*. How many browsers visited the website that month? 108,000

b. What was the browsers-to-buyers unit rate for the website that month? 24 browsers per buyer

90. TYPING A secretary typed a document containing 330 words in 5 minutes. Write this rate as a unit rate. 66 wpm

91. UNIT PRICES A 12-ounce can of cola sells for 84¢. Find the unit price in cents per ounce. 7¢ per oz

92. DAYCARE A daycare center charges $32 for 8 hours of supervised care. Find the unit price in dollars per hour for the daycare. $4 per hour

93. PARKING A parking meter requires 25¢ for 20 minutes of parking. Find the unit price to park. 1.25¢ per min

94. GASOLINE COST A driver pumped 17 gallons of gasoline into the tank of his pickup truck at a cost of $32.13. Find the unit price of the gasoline. $1.89 per gal

95. LANDSCAPING A 50-pound bag of grass seed sells for $222.50. Find the unit price of grass seed. $4.45 per lb

96. UNIT COSTS A 24-ounce package of green beans sells for $1.29. Find the unit price in cents per ounce. 5.375¢ per oz

97. DRAINING TANKS An 11,880-gallon tank of water can be emptied in 27 minutes. Find the unit rate of flow of water out of the tank. 440 gal per min

98. PAY RATE Ricardo worked for 27 hours to help insulate a hockey arena. For his work, he received $337.50. Find his hourly rate of pay. $12.50 per hr

99. AUTO TRAVEL A car's odometer reads 34,746 at the beginning of a trip. Five hours later, it reads 35,071.

a. How far did the car travel? 325 mi

b. What was its rate of speed? 65 mph

100. RATES OF SPEED An airplane travels from Chicago to San Francisco, a distance of 1,883 miles, in 3.5 hours. Find the rate of speed of the plane. 538 mph

101. COMPARISON SHOPPING A 6-ounce can of orange juice sells for 89¢, and an 8-ounce can sells for $1.19. Which is the better buy? the 6-oz can

102. COMPARISON SHOPPING A 30-pound bag of planting mix costs $12.25, and an 80-pound bag costs $30.25. Which is the better buy? the 80-lb bag

103. COMPARISON SHOPPING A certain brand of cold and sinus medication is sold in 20-tablet boxes for $4.29 and in 50-tablet boxes for $9.59. Which is the better buy? the 50-tablet boxes

104. COMPARISON SHOPPING Which tire shown is the better buy? the economy model

105. COMPARING SPEEDS A car travels 345 miles in 6 hours, and a truck travels 376 miles in 6.2 hours. Which vehicle is going faster? the truck

106. READING One seventh-grader read a 54-page book in 40 minutes. Another read an 80-page book in 62 minutes. If the books were equally difficult, which student read faster? the first student

107. GAS MILEAGE One car went 1,235 miles on 51.3 gallons of gasoline, and another went 1,456 miles on 55.78 gallons. Which car got the better gas mileage? the second car

108. ELECTRICITY RATES In one community, a bill for 575 kilowatt-hours of electricity is $38.81. In a second community, a bill for 831 kwh is $58.10. In which community is electricity cheaper? the first community

WRITING

109. Are the ratios 3 to 1 and 1 to 3 the same? Explain why or why not.

110. Give three examples of ratios (or rates) that you have encountered in the past week.

111. How will the topics studied in this section make you a better shopper?

112. What is a unit rate? Give some examples.

REVIEW

Use front-end rounding to estimate each result.

113. 12,897 + 29,431 + 2,595 43,000

114. 6,302 − 788 5,200

115. 410 · 21 8,000

116. 63,467 ÷ 3,103 20

Objectives

1. Write proportions.
2. Determine whether proportions are true or false.
3. Solve a proportion to find an unknown term.
4. Write proportions to solve application problems.

SECTION 3.2 Proportions

One of the most useful concepts in mathematics is the *equation.* An **equation** is a statement indicating that two expressions are equal. All equations contain an = symbol. Some examples of equations are:

$$4 + 4 = 8, \quad 15.6 - 4.3 = 11.3, \quad \frac{1}{2} \cdot 10 = 5, \quad \text{and} \quad -16 \div 8 = -2$$

Each of the equations shown above is true. Equations can also be false. For example,

$$3 + 2 = 6 \quad \text{and} \quad -40 \div (-5) = -8$$

are false equations.

In this section, we will work with equations that state that two ratios (or rates) are equal.

1 Write proportions.

Like any tool, a ladder can be dangerous if used improperly. When setting up an extension ladder, users should follow the *4-to-1 rule:* For every 4 feet of ladder height, position the legs of the ladder 1 foot away from the base of the wall. The 4-to-1 rule for ladders can be expressed using a ratio.

$$\frac{4 \text{ feet}}{1 \text{ foot}} = \frac{4 \cancel{\text{feet}}}{1 \cancel{\text{foot}}} = \frac{4}{1}$$ Remove the common units of feet.

The figure on the right shows how the 4-to-1 rule was used to properly position the legs of a ladder 3 feet from the base of a 12-foot-high wall. We can write a ratio comparing the ladder's height to its distance from the wall.

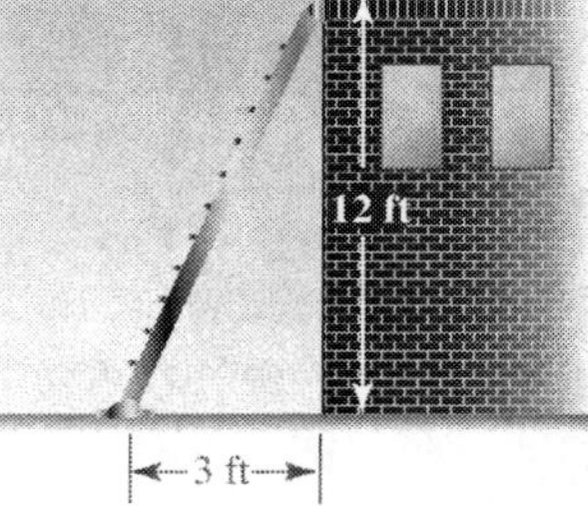

$$\frac{12 \text{ feet}}{3 \text{ feet}} = \frac{12 \cancel{\text{feet}}}{3 \cancel{\text{feet}}} = \frac{12}{3}$$ Remove the common units of feet.

Since this ratio satisfies the 4-to-1 rule, the two ratios $\frac{4}{1}$ and $\frac{12}{3}$ must be equal. Therefore, we have

$$\frac{4}{1} = \frac{12}{3}$$

Equations like this, which show that two ratios are equal, are called *proportions.*

> **Proportion**
>
> A **proportion** is a statement that two ratios (or rates) are equal.

Some examples of proportions are

- $\frac{1}{2} = \frac{3}{6}$ Read as "1 is to 2 as 3 is to 6."
- $\frac{3 \text{ waiters}}{7 \text{ tables}} = \frac{9 \text{ waiters}}{21 \text{ tables}}$ Read as "3 waiters are to 7 tables as 9 waiters are to 21 tables."

EXAMPLE 1 Write each statement as a proportion.

a. 22 is to 6 as 11 is to 3.

b. 1,000 administrators is to 8,000 teachers as 1 administrator is to 8 teachers.

Strategy We will locate the word *as* in each statement and identify the ratios (or rates) before and after it.

WHY The word *as* translates to the = symbol that is needed to write the statement as a proportion (equation).

Solution

a. This proportion states that two ratios are equal.

22 is to 6 as 11 is to 3. Recall that the word "to" is used to separate the numbers being compared.

$$\frac{22}{6} = \frac{11}{3}$$

b. This proportion states that two rates are equal.

1,000 administrators is to 8,000 teachers as 1 administrator is to 8 teachers

$$\frac{1{,}000 \text{ administrators}}{8{,}000 \text{ teachers}} = \frac{1 \text{ administrator}}{8 \text{ teachers}}$$

When proportions involve rates, the units are often written outside of the proportion, as shown below:

$$\text{Administrators} \rightarrow \frac{1{,}000}{8{,}000} = \frac{1}{8} \leftarrow \text{Administrators}$$
Teachers → ... ← Teachers

Self Check 1

Write each statement as a proportion.

a. 16 is to 28 as 4 is to 7. $\frac{16}{28} = \frac{4}{7}$

b. 300 children is to 500 adults as 3 children is to 5 adults. $\frac{300 \text{ children}}{500 \text{ adults}} = \frac{3 \text{ children}}{5 \text{ adults}}$

Now Try **Problems 17 and 19**

Teaching Example 1 Write each statement as a proportion.
a. 45 is to 50 as 9 is to 10.
b. 900 applicants is to 600 jobs as 3 applicants is to 2 jobs.
Answers:
a. $\frac{45}{50} = \frac{9}{10}$
b. $\frac{900 \text{ applicants}}{600 \text{ jobs}} = \frac{3 \text{ applicants}}{2 \text{ jobs}}$

2 Determine whether proportions are true or false.

Since a proportion is an equation, a proportion can be true or false. A proportion is true if its ratios (or rates) are equal and false if it its ratios (or rates) are not equal. One way to determine whether a proportion is true is to use the fraction simplifying skills of Chapter 3.

EXAMPLE 2 Determine whether each proportion is true or false by simplifying.

a. $\frac{3}{8} = \frac{21}{56}$ **b.** $\frac{30}{4} = \frac{45}{12}$

Strategy We will simplify any ratios in the proportion that are not in simplest form. Then we will compare them to determine whether they are equal.

WHY If the ratios are equal, the proportion is true. If they are not equal, the proportion is false.

Solution

a. On the left side of the proportion $\frac{3}{8} = \frac{21}{56}$, the ratio $\frac{3}{8}$ is in simplest form. On the right side, the ratio $\frac{21}{56}$ can be simplified.

$$\frac{21}{56} = \frac{3 \cdot \overset{1}{\cancel{7}}}{\underset{1}{\cancel{7}} \cdot 8} = \frac{3}{8}$$

Factor 21 and 56 and then remove the common factor of 7 in the numerator and denominator.

Since the ratios on the left and right sides of the proportion are equal, the proportion is true.

Self Check 2

Determine whether each proportion is true or false by simplifying.

a. $\frac{4}{5} = \frac{16}{20}$ true **b.** $\frac{30}{24} = \frac{28}{16}$ false

Now Try **Problem 23**

Teaching Example 2 Determine whether each proportion is true or false by simplifying.
a. $\frac{7}{9} = \frac{72}{81}$ b. $\frac{16}{12} = \frac{44}{33}$
Answers:
a. false b. true

b. Neither ratio in the proportion $\frac{30}{4} = \frac{45}{12}$ is in simplest form. To simplify each ratio, we proceed as follows:

$$\frac{30}{4} = \frac{\overset{1}{\not{2}} \cdot 15}{\underset{1}{\not{2}} \cdot 2} = \frac{15}{2} \qquad \frac{45}{12} = \frac{\overset{1}{\not{3}} \cdot 15}{\underset{1}{\not{3}} \cdot 4} = \frac{15}{4}$$

Since the ratios on the left and right sides of the proportion are not equal $\left(\frac{15}{2} \neq \frac{15}{4}\right)$, the proportion is false.

There is another way to determine whether a proportion is true or false. Before we can discuss it, we need to introduce some more vocabulary of proportions.

Each of the four numbers in a proportion is called a **term.** The first and fourth terms are called the **extremes,** and the second and third terms are called the **means.**

First term (extreme) → 1, Third term (mean) → 3, Second term (mean) → 2, Fourth term (extreme) → 6

$$\frac{1}{2} = \frac{3}{6}$$

In the proportion shown above, the *product of the extremes is equal to the product of the means.*

$$1 \cdot 6 = 6 \qquad \text{and} \qquad 2 \cdot 3 = 6$$

These products can be found by multiplying diagonally in the proportion. We call $1 \cdot 6$ and $2 \cdot 3$ **cross products.**

Cross products

$$1 \cdot 6 = 6 \qquad 2 \cdot 3 = 6$$

$$\frac{1}{2} = \frac{3}{6}$$

Note that the cross products are equal. This example illustrates the following property of proportions.

Cross-Products Property (Means-Extremes Property)

To determine whether a proportion is true or false, first multiply along one diagonal, and then multiply along the other diagonal.

- If the cross products are *equal,* the proportion is true.
- If the cross products are *not equal,* the proportion is false.

(If the product of the extremes is *equal* to the product of the means, the proportion is true. If the product of the extremes is *not equal* to the product of the means, the proportion is false.)

Self Check 3

Determine whether the proportion

$$\frac{6}{13} = \frac{18}{39}$$

is true or false. true

Now Try **Problem 25**

Teaching Example 3 Determine whether each proportion is true or false.

a. $\frac{7}{24} = \frac{2}{7}$ b. $\frac{12}{8} = \frac{9}{6}$

Answers:

a. false b. true

EXAMPLE 3 Determine whether each proportion is true or false.

a. $\frac{3}{7} = \frac{9}{21}$ **b.** $\frac{8}{3} = \frac{13}{5}$

Strategy We will check to see whether the cross products are equal (the product of the extremes is equal to the product of the means).

WHY If the cross products are equal, the proportion is true. If the cross products are not equal, the proportion is false.

Solution

a. $3 \cdot 21 = 63 \qquad 7 \cdot 9 = 63$

$$\frac{3}{7} = \frac{9}{21}$$

Each cross product is 63.

Since the cross products are equal, the proportion is true.

b. $8 \cdot 5 = 40$ $\quad\quad$ $3 \cdot 13 = 39$

$$\frac{8}{3} = \frac{13}{5}$$

One cross product is 40 and the other is 39.

Since the cross products are not equal, the proportion is false.

Caution! We cannot remove common factors "across" an = symbol. When this is done, the true proportion from Example 3 part a, $\frac{3}{7} = \frac{9}{21}$, is changed into the false proportion $\frac{1}{7} = \frac{9}{7}$.

$$\frac{\overset{1}{\cancel{3}}}{7} = \frac{9}{\underset{7}{\cancel{21}}}$$

EXAMPLE 4 Determine whether each proportion is true or false.

a. $\frac{0.9}{0.6} = \frac{2.4}{1.5}$ **b.** $\frac{2\frac{1}{3}}{3\frac{1}{2}} = \frac{4\frac{2}{3}}{7}$

Strategy We will check to see whether the cross products are equal (the product of the extremes is equal to the product of the means).

WHY If the cross products are equal, the proportion is true. If the cross products are not equal, the proportion is false.

Solution

a.

$$\begin{array}{r} 1.5 \\ \times\ 0.9 \\ \hline 1.35 \end{array} \qquad \begin{array}{r} 2.4 \\ \times\ 0.6 \\ \hline 1.44 \end{array}$$

$$\frac{0.9}{0.6} = \frac{2.4}{1.5}$$

One cross product is 1.35 and the other is 1.44.

Since the cross products are not equal, the proportion is not true.

b.

$$2\frac{1}{3} \cdot 7 = \frac{7}{3} \cdot \frac{7}{1} = \frac{49}{3}$$

$$3\frac{1}{2} \cdot 4\frac{2}{3} = \frac{7}{2} \cdot \frac{14}{3} = \frac{7 \cdot \overset{1}{\cancel{2}} \cdot 7}{\underset{1}{\cancel{2}} \cdot 3} = \frac{49}{3}$$

$$\frac{2\frac{1}{3}}{3\frac{1}{2}} = \frac{4\frac{2}{3}}{7}$$

Each cross product is $\frac{49}{3}$.

Since the cross products are equal, the proportion is true.

Self Check 4

Determine whether each proportion is true or false.

a. $\frac{9.9}{13.2} = \frac{1.125}{1.5}$ true

b. $\frac{3\frac{3}{16}}{2\frac{1}{2}} = \frac{4\frac{1}{4}}{3\frac{1}{3}}$ true

Now Try **Problems 31 and 35**

Teaching Example 4 Determine whether each proportion is true or false.

a. $\frac{0.7}{2.4} = \frac{0.9}{4.1}$ b. $\frac{3\frac{1}{3}}{2\frac{1}{12}} = \frac{1\frac{1}{5}}{\frac{3}{4}}$

Answers:
a. false b. true

When two pairs of numbers such as 2, 3 and 8, 12 form a true proportion, we say that they are **proportional.** To show that 2, 3 and 8, 12 are proportional, we check to see whether the equation

$$\frac{2}{3} = \frac{8}{12}$$

is a true proportion. To do so, we find the cross products.

$$2 \cdot 12 = 24 \qquad 3 \cdot 8 = 24$$

Since the cross products are equal, the proportion is true, and the numbers are proportional.

Self Check 5

Determine whether 6, 11 and 54, 99 are proportional. yes

Now Try **Problem 37**

Teaching Example 5 Determine whether 6, 8 and 81, 99 are proportional.
Answer:
The numbers are not proportional.

EXAMPLE 5 Determine whether 3, 7 and 36, 91 are proportional.

Strategy We will use the given pairs of numbers to write two ratios and form a proportion. Then we will find the cross products.

WHY If the cross products are equal, the proportion is true, and the numbers are proportional. If the cross products are not equal, the proportion is false, and the numbers are not proportional.

Solution

The pair of numbers 3 and 7 form one ratio and the pair of numbers 36 and 91 form a second ratio. To write a proportion, we set the ratios equal. Then we find the cross products.

$3 \cdot 91 = 273$ $\quad$ $7 \cdot 36 = 252$

$$\frac{3}{7} = \frac{36}{91}$$ One cross product is 273 and the other is 252.

Since the cross products are not equal, the numbers are not proportional.

3 Solve a proportion to find an unknown term.

Suppose that we know three of the four terms in the following proportion.

$$\frac{?}{5} = \frac{24}{20}$$

In mathematics, we often let a letter represent an unknown number. We call such a letter a **variable.** To find the unknown term, we let the variable x represent it in the proportion and we can write:

$$\frac{x}{5} = \frac{24}{20}$$

If the proportion is to be true, the cross products must be equal.

$x \cdot 20 = 5 \cdot 24$ Find the cross products for $\frac{x}{5} = \frac{24}{20}$ and set them equal.

$x \cdot 20 = 120$ To simplify the right side of the equation, do the multiplication: $5 \cdot 24 = 120$.

On the left side of the equation, the unknown number x is multiplied by 20. To undo the multiplication by 20 and isolate x, we divide both sides of the equation by 20.

$$\frac{x \cdot 20}{20} = \frac{120}{20}$$

We can simplify the fraction on the left side of the equation by removing the common factor of 20 from the numerator and denominator. On the right side, we perform the division indicated by the fraction bar.

$$\frac{x \cdot \overset{1}{\cancel{20}}}{\underset{1}{\cancel{20}}} = 6$$ To simplify the left side of the equation, remove the common factor of 20 in the numerator and denominator. To simplify the right side of the equation, do the division: $120 \div 20 = 6$.

Since the product of any number and 1 is that number, it follows that the numerator $x \cdot 1$ on the left side can be replaced by x.

$$\frac{x}{1} = 6$$

Since the quotient of any number and 1 is that number, it follows that $\frac{x}{1}$ on the left side of the equation can be replaced with x. Therefore,

$$x = 6$$

We have found that the unknown term in the proportion is 6 and we can write:

$$\frac{6}{5} = \frac{24}{20}$$

To check this result, we find the cross products.

Check:

$$\frac{6}{5} \stackrel{?}{=} \frac{24}{20} \qquad 20 \cdot 6 = 120 \qquad 5 \cdot 24 = 120$$

Since the cross products are equal, the result, 6, checks.

In the previous example, when we find the value of the variable x that makes the given proportion true, we say that we have *solved the proportion* to find the unknown term.

The Language of Mathematics We solve proportions by writing a series of steps that result in an equation of the form x = a number or a number = x. We say that the variable x is *isolated* on one side of the equation. *Isolated* means alone or by itself.

Solving a Proportion to Find an Unknown Term

1. Set the cross products equal to each other to form an equation.
2. Isolate the variable on one side of the equation by dividing both sides by the number that is multiplied by that variable.
3. Check by substituting the result into the original proportion and finding the cross products.

EXAMPLE 6

Solve the proportion: $\frac{12}{20} = \frac{3}{x}$

Strategy We will set the cross products equal to each other to form an equation.

WHY Then we can isolate the variable x on one side of the equation to find the unknown term that it represents.

Solution

$\frac{12}{20} = \frac{3}{x}$ This is the proportion to solve.

$12 \cdot x = 20 \cdot 3$ Set the cross products equal to each other to form an equation.

$12 \cdot x = 60$ To simplify the right side of the equation, multiply: $20 \cdot 3 = 60$.

$\frac{12 \cdot x}{12} = \frac{60}{12}$ To undo the multiplication by 12 and isolate x, divide both sides by 12.

$x = 5$ To simplify the left side, remove the common factor of 12. To simplify the right side of the equation, do the division: $60 \div 12 = 5$.

$$\begin{array}{r} 5 \\ 12\overline{)60} \\ -60 \\ \hline 0 \end{array}$$

Thus, x is 5. To check this result, we substitute 5 for x in the original proportion.

Check:

$$\frac{12}{20} \stackrel{?}{=} \frac{3}{5} \qquad 5 \cdot 12 = 60 \qquad 20 \cdot 3 = 60$$

Since the cross products are equal, the result, 5, checks.

Self Check 6

Solve the proportion: $\frac{15}{x} = \frac{20}{32}$ 24

Now Try **Problem 41**

Teaching Example 6

Solve the proportion: $\frac{8}{30} = \frac{4}{x}$

Answer:

15

Self Check 7

Solve the proportion:

$$\frac{6.7}{x} = \frac{33.5}{38} \quad 7.6$$

Now Try **Problem 45**

Teaching Example 7

Solve the proportion: $\frac{3.6}{8.1} = \frac{x}{12.15}$

Answer:

5.4

EXAMPLE 7 Solve the proportion: $\frac{3.5}{7.2} = \frac{x}{15.84}$

Strategy We will set the cross products equal to each other to form an equation.

WHY Then we can isolate the variable x on one side of the equation to find the unknown term that it represents.

Solution

$\frac{3.5}{7.2} = \frac{x}{15.84}$ This is the proportion to solve.

$3.5 \cdot 15.84 = 7.2 \cdot x$ Set the cross products equal to each other to form an equation.

$55.44 = 7.2 \cdot x$ To simplify the left side of the equation, multiply: $3.5 \cdot 15.84 = 55.44$.

$\frac{55.44}{7.2} = \frac{7.2 \cdot x}{7.2}$ To undo the multiplication by 7.2 and isolate x, divide both sides by 7.2.

$7.7 = x$ To simplify the left side of the equation, do the division: $55.44 \div 7.2 = 7.7$. To simplify the right side, remove the common factor of 7.2.

$$\begin{array}{r} 15.84 \\ \times\ 3.5 \\ \hline 7920 \\ 47520 \\ \hline 55.440 \end{array}$$

$$\begin{array}{r} 7.7 \\ 7.2\overline{)55.44} \\ -\ 50\ 4 \\ \hline 5\ 04 \\ -\ 5\ 04 \\ \hline 0 \end{array}$$

Thus, x is 7.7. Check the result in the original proportion.

Self Check 8

Solve the proportion:

$$\frac{x}{2\frac{1}{3}} = \frac{2\frac{1}{4}}{1\frac{1}{2}}$$

Write the result as a mixed number. $3\frac{1}{2}$

Now Try **Problem 49**

Teaching Example 8

Solve the proportion:

$$\frac{x}{1\frac{4}{7}} = \frac{3\frac{2}{5}}{4\frac{2}{5}}$$

Write the result as a mixed number.

Answer:

$1\frac{3}{14}$

EXAMPLE 8 Solve the proportion $\frac{x}{4\frac{1}{5}} = \frac{5\frac{1}{2}}{16\frac{1}{2}}$. Write the result as a mixed number.

Strategy We will set the cross products equal to each other to form an equation.

WHY Then we can isolate the variable x on one side of the equation to find the unknown term that it represents.

Solution

$\frac{x}{4\frac{1}{5}} = \frac{5\frac{1}{2}}{16\frac{1}{2}}$ This is the proportion to solve.

$x \cdot 16\frac{1}{2} = 4\frac{1}{5} \cdot 5\frac{1}{2}$ Set the cross products equal to each other to form an equation.

$x \cdot \frac{33}{2} = \frac{21}{5} \cdot \frac{11}{2}$ Write each mixed number as an improper fraction.

$\frac{x \cdot \frac{33}{2}}{\frac{33}{2}} = \frac{\frac{21}{5} \cdot \frac{11}{2}}{\frac{33}{2}}$ To undo the multiplication by $\frac{33}{2}$ and isolate x, divide both sides by $\frac{33}{2}$.

$x = \frac{21}{5} \cdot \frac{11}{2} \cdot \frac{2}{33}$ To simplify the left side, remove the common factor of $\frac{33}{2}$ in the numerator and denominator. Perform the division on the right side indicated by the complex fraction bar. Multiply the numerator of the complex fraction by the reciprocal of $\frac{33}{2}$, which is $\frac{2}{33}$.

$x = \frac{21 \cdot 11 \cdot 2}{5 \cdot 2 \cdot 33}$ Multiply the numerators. Multiply the denominators.

$$x = \frac{\overset{1}{\cancel{3}} \cdot 7 \cdot \overset{1}{\cancel{11}} \cdot \overset{1}{\cancel{2}}}{5 \cdot \underset{1}{\cancel{2}} \cdot \underset{1}{\cancel{3}} \cdot \underset{1}{\cancel{11}}}$$ To simplify the fraction, factor 21 and 33, and then remove the common factors 2, 3, and 11 in the numerator and denominator.

$$x = \frac{7}{5}$$ Multiply the remaining factors in the numerator. Multiply the remaining factors in the denominator.

$$x = 1\frac{2}{5}$$ Write the improper fraction as a mixed number.

Thus, x is $1\frac{2}{5}$. Check this result in the original proportion.

Using Your CALCULATOR Solving Proportions with a Calculator

To solve the proportion in Example 7, we set the cross products equal and divided both sides by 7.2 to isolate the variable x.

$$\frac{3.5 \cdot 15.84}{7.2} = x$$

We can find x by entering these numbers and pressing these keys on a calculator.

3.5 [×] 15.84 [÷] 7.2 [=] **7.7**

On some calculators, the [ENTER] key is pressed to find the result. Thus, x is 7.7.

4 Write proportions to solve application problems.

Proportions can be used to solve application problems from a wide variety of fields such as medicine, accounting, construction, and business. It is easy to spot problems that can be solved using a proportion. You will be given a ratio (or rate) and asked to find the missing part of another ratio (or rate). It is helpful to follow the five-step problem-solving strategy seen earlier in the text to solve proportion problems.

EXAMPLE 9 *Shopping* If 5 apples cost \$1.15, find the cost of 16 apples.

Analyze

- We can express the fact that 5 apples cost \$1.15 using the rate: $\frac{5 \text{ apples}}{\$1.15}$.
- What is the cost of 16 apples?

Form We will let the variable c represent the unknown cost of 16 apples. If we compare the number of apples to their cost, we know that the two rates must be equal and we can write a proportion.

5 apples is to \$1.15 as 16 apples is to \$$c$.

$$\frac{5}{1.15} = \frac{16}{c}$$

5 apples → 5; Cost of 5 apples → 1.15; 16 ← 16 apples; c ← Cost of 16 apples. The units can be written outside of the proportion.

Solve To find the cost of 16 apples, we solve the proportion for c.

$5 \cdot c = 1.15 \cdot 16$ Set the cross products equal to each other to form an equation.

$5 \cdot c = 18.4$ To simplify the right side of the equation, multiply: 1.15(16) = 18.4.

$\frac{5 \cdot c}{5} = \frac{18.4}{5}$ To undo the multiplication by 5 and isolate c, divide both sides by 5.

$c = 3.68$ To simplify the left side, remove the common factor of 5. On the right side, do the division: 18.4 ÷ 5 = 3.68.

```
   3.68
5)18.40
 -15
   3 4
  -3 0
     40
    -40
      0
```

Self Check 9

CONCERT TICKETS If 9 tickets to a concert cost \$112.50, find the cost of 15 tickets. \$187.50

Now Try **Problem 73**

Teaching Example 9 GROCERY SHOPPING If 3 avocados cost \$2.67, find the cost of 10 avocados.
Answer:
\$8.90

State Sixteen apples will cost \$3.68.

Check If 5 apples cost \$1.15, then 15 apples would cost 3 times as much: $3 \cdot \$1.15 = \$3.45$. It seems reasonable that 16 apples would cost \$3.68.

In Example 9, we could have compared the cost of the apples to the number of apples:

\$1.15 is to 5 apples as \$c is to 16 apples. This would have led to the proportion

$$\frac{1.15}{5} = \frac{c}{16}$$

Cost of 5 apples → 1.15; 5 apples → 5; c ← Cost of 16 apples; 16 ← 16 apples

If we solve this proportion for c, we obtain the same result: 3.68.

Caution! When solving problems using proportions, make sure that the units of the numerators are the same and the units of the denominators are the same. For Example 9, it would be incorrect to write

$$\frac{1.15}{5} = \frac{16}{c}$$

Cost of 5 apples → 1.15; 5 apples → 5; 16 ← 16 apples; c ← Cost of 16 apples

Self Check 10

SCALE MODELS In a scale model of a city, a 300-foot-tall building is 4 inches high. An observation tower in the model is 9 inches high. How tall is the actual tower? 675 ft

Now Try **Problem 83**

Teaching Example 10
SCALE DRAWINGS
The distance between the wheels in the scale drawing of the airplane is 1.25 inches. What is the actual distance between the wheels?
Answer:
7.5 ft

EXAMPLE 10 *Scale Drawings* A **scale** is a ratio (or rate) that compares the size of a model, drawing, or map to the size of an actual object. The airplane shown below is drawn using a scale of 1 inch: 6 feet. This means that 1 inch on the drawing is actually 6 feet on the plane. The distance from wing tip to wing tip (the wingspan) on the drawing is 4.5 inches. What is the actual wingspan of the plane?

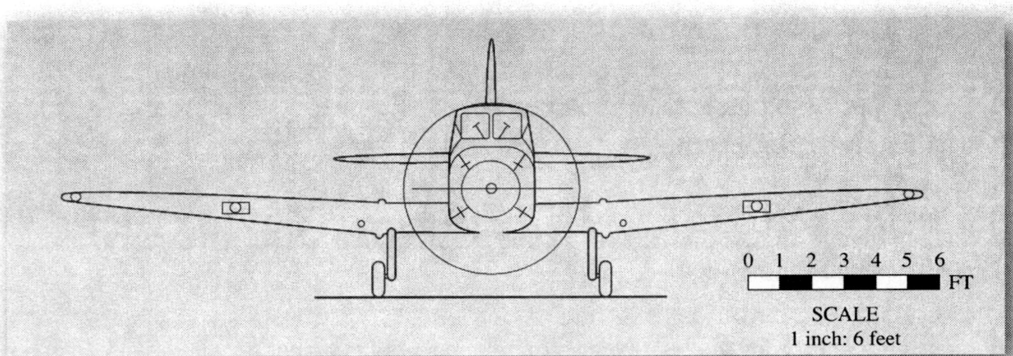

Analyze

- The airplane is drawn using a scale of 1 inch: 6 feet, which can be written as a rate in fraction form as: $\frac{1 \text{ inch}}{6 \text{ feet}}$.
- The wingspan of the airplane on the drawing is 4.5 inches.
- What is the actual wingspan of the plane?

Form We will let w represent the unknown actual wingspan of the plane. If we compare the measurements on the drawing to their actual measurement of the plane, we know that those two rates must be equal and we can write a proportion.

1 inch corresponds to 6 feet as 4.5 inches corresponds to w feet.

$$\frac{1}{6} = \frac{4.5}{w}$$

Measure on the drawing → 1, 4.5 ← Measure on the drawing
Measure on the plane → 6, w ← Measure on the plane

Solve To find the actual wingspan of the airplane, we solve the proportion for w.

$1 \cdot w = 6 \cdot 4.5$ Set the cross products equal to form an equation.

$w = 27$ To simplify each side of the equation, do the multiplication.

$$\begin{array}{r} \overset{3}{4}.5 \\ \times\ 6 \\ \hline 27.0 \end{array}$$

State The actual wingspan of the plane is 27 feet.

Check Every 1 inch on the scale drawing corresponds to an actual length of 6 feet on the plane. Therefore, a 5-inch measurement corresponds to an actual wingspan of $5 \cdot 6$ feet, or 30 feet. It seems reasonable that a 4.5-inch measurement corresponds to an actual wingspan of 27 feet.

EXAMPLE 11 *Baking* A recipe for chocolate cake calls for $1\frac{1}{2}$ cups of sugar for every $2\frac{1}{4}$ cups of flour. If a baker has only $\frac{1}{2}$ cup of sugar on hand, how much flour should he add to it to make chocolate cake batter?

Analyze

- The rate of $1\frac{1}{2}$ cups of sugar for every $2\frac{1}{4}$ cups of flour can be expressed as:

$$\frac{1\frac{1}{2} \text{ cups sugar}}{2\frac{1}{4} \text{ cups flour}}$$

- How much flour should be added to $\frac{3}{4}$ cups of sugar?

Form We will let the variable f represent the unknown cups of flour. If we compare the cups of sugar to the cups of flour, we know that the two rates must be equal and we can write a proportion.

$1\frac{1}{2}$ cups of sugar is to $2\frac{1}{4}$ cups of flour as $\frac{1}{2}$ cup of sugar is to f cups of flour

$$\frac{1\frac{1}{2}}{2\frac{1}{4}} = \frac{\frac{1}{2}}{f}$$

Cups of sugar → $1\frac{1}{2}$, $\frac{1}{2}$ ← Cup of sugar
Cups of flour → $2\frac{1}{4}$, f ← Cups of flour

Solve To find the amount of flour that is needed, we solve the proportion for f.

$$\frac{1\frac{1}{2}}{2\frac{1}{4}} = \frac{\frac{1}{2}}{f}$$ This is the proportion to solve.

$$1\frac{1}{2} \cdot f = 2\frac{1}{4} \cdot \frac{1}{2}$$ Set the cross products equal to each other to form an equation.

$$\frac{3}{2} \cdot f = \frac{9}{4} \cdot \frac{1}{2}$$ Write each mixed number as an improper fraction.

$$\frac{\frac{3}{2} \cdot f}{\frac{3}{2}} = \frac{\frac{9}{4} \cdot \frac{1}{2}}{\frac{3}{2}}$$ To undo the multiplication by $\frac{3}{2}$ and isolate f, divide both sides by $\frac{3}{2}$.

Self Check 11

BAKING See Example 11. How many cups of flour will be needed to make several chocolate cakes that will require a total of $12\frac{1}{2}$ cups of sugar? $18\frac{3}{4}$ cups

Now Try **Problem 89**

Teaching Example 11 BAKING A recipe for coffee cake calls for $1\frac{3}{4}$ cups of sugar for every $5\frac{1}{4}$ cups of flour. If a baker has only $\frac{7}{8}$ cup sugar, how much flour should she add to make the coffee cake batter?
Answer:
$2\frac{5}{8}$ cups

$f = \frac{9}{4} \cdot \frac{1}{2} \cdot \frac{2}{3}$ To simplify the left side, remove the common factor of $\frac{3}{2}$ in the numerator and denominator. Perform the division on the right side indicated by the complex fraction bar. Multiply the numerator of the complex fraction by the reciprocal of $\frac{3}{2}$, which is $\frac{2}{3}$.

$f = \frac{9 \cdot 1 \cdot 2}{4 \cdot 2 \cdot 3}$ Multiply the numerators. Multiply the denominators.

$f = \frac{\overset{1}{\cancel{3}} \cdot 3 \cdot 1 \cdot \overset{1}{\cancel{2}}}{4 \cdot \underset{1}{\cancel{2}} \cdot \underset{1}{\cancel{3}}}$ To simplify the fraction, factor 9 and then remove the common factors 2 and 3 in the numerator and denominator.

$f = \frac{3}{4}$ Multiply the remaining factors in the numerator. Multiply the remaining factors in the denominator.

State The baker should use $\frac{3}{4}$ cups of flour.

Check The rate of $1\frac{1}{2}$ cups of sugar for every $2\frac{1}{4}$ cups of flour is about 1 to 2. The rate of $\frac{1}{2}$ cup of sugar to $\frac{3}{4}$ cup flour is also about 1 to 2. The result, $\frac{3}{4}$, seems reasonable.

Success Tip In Example 11, an alternate approach would be to write each term of the proportion in its equivalent decimal form and then solve for *f*.

Fractions and mixed numbers		**Decimals**
$\frac{1\frac{1}{2}}{2\frac{1}{4}} = \frac{\frac{1}{2}}{f}$	→	$\frac{1.5}{2.25} = \frac{0.5}{f}$

ANSWERS TO SELF CHECKS

1. a. $\frac{16}{28} = \frac{4}{7}$ **b.** $\frac{300 \text{ children}}{500 \text{ adults}} = \frac{3 \text{ children}}{5 \text{ adults}}$ **2. a.** true **b.** false **3.** true **4. a.** true **b.** true **5.** yes **6.** 24 **7.** 7.6 **8.** $3\frac{1}{2}$ **9.** \$187.50 **10.** 675 ft **11.** $18\frac{3}{4}$

SECTION 3.2 STUDY SET

VOCABULARY

Fill in the blanks.

1. A proportion is a statement that two ratios (or rates) are equal.
2. In $\frac{1}{2} = \frac{5}{10}$, the terms 1 and 10 are called the extremes of the proportion and the terms 2 and 5 are called the means of the proportion.
3. ▶ The cross products for the proportion $\frac{4}{7} = \frac{36}{x}$ are $4 \cdot x$ and $7 \cdot 36$.
4. When two pairs of numbers form a proportion, we say that the numbers are proportional.
5. A letter that is used to represent an unknown number is called a variable.
6. When we find the value of *x* that makes the proportion $\frac{3}{8} = \frac{x}{16}$ true, we say that we have solved the proportion.
7. We solve proportions by writing a series of steps that result in an equation of the form x = a number or a number = x. We say that the variable x is isolated on one side of the equation.
8. A scale is a ratio (or rate) that compares the size of a model, drawing, or map to the size of an actual object.

CONCEPTS

Fill in the blanks.

9. If the cross products of a proportion are equal, the proportion is true. If the cross products are *not equal,* the proportion is false.

10. The proportion $\frac{2}{5} = \frac{4}{10}$ will be true if the product $2 \cdot 10$ is equal to the product $5 \cdot 4$.

11. Complete the cross products.

$$9 \cdot 10 = 90 \qquad 2 \cdot 45 = 90$$
$$\frac{9}{2} = \frac{45}{10}$$

12. In the equation $6 \cdot x = 2 \cdot 12$, to undo the multiplication by 6 and isolate x, divide both sides of the equation by 6.

13. Label the missing units in the proportion.

$$\begin{matrix}\text{Teacher's aides} \to \\ \text{Children} \to\end{matrix} \frac{12}{100} = \frac{3}{25} \begin{matrix}\leftarrow \text{Teacher's aides} \\ \leftarrow \text{Childre}\end{matrix}$$

14. Consider the following problem: *For every 15 feet of chain link fencing, 4 support posts are used. How many support posts will be needed for 300 feet of chain link fencing?* Which of the proportions below could be used to solve this problem? i, iv

i. $\frac{15}{4} = \frac{300}{x}$ **ii.** $\frac{15}{4} = \frac{x}{300}$

iii. $\frac{4}{15} = \frac{300}{x}$ **iv.** $\frac{4}{15} = \frac{x}{300}$

NOTATION

Complete each solution.

15. Solve the proportion: $\frac{2}{3} = \frac{x}{9}$

$$2 \cdot 9 = 3 \cdot x$$
$$18 = 3 \cdot x$$
$$\frac{18}{3} = \frac{3 \cdot x}{3}$$
$$6 = x$$

The solution is 6.

16. Solve the proportion: $\frac{14}{x} = \frac{49}{17.5}$

$$14 \cdot 17.5 = x \cdot 49$$
$$245 = x \cdot 49$$
$$\frac{245}{49} = \frac{x \cdot 49}{49}$$
$$5 = x$$

The solution is 5.

GUIDED PRACTICE

Write each statement as a proportion. See Example 1.

17. 20 is to 30 as 2 is to 3. $\frac{20}{30} = \frac{2}{3}$

18. 9 is to 36 as 1 is to 4. $\frac{9}{36} = \frac{1}{4}$

19. 400 sheets is to 100 beds as 4 sheets is to 1 bed. $\frac{400 \text{ sheets}}{100 \text{ beds}} = \frac{4 \text{ sheets}}{1 \text{ bed}}$

20. 50 shovels is to 125 laborers as 2 shovels is to 5 laborers. $\frac{50 \text{ shovels}}{125 \text{ laborers}} = \frac{2 \text{ shovels}}{5 \text{ laborers}}$

Determine whether each proportion is true or false by simplifying. See Example 2.

21. $\frac{7}{9} = \frac{70}{81}$ false

22. $\frac{2}{5} = \frac{8}{20}$ true

23. $\frac{21}{14} = \frac{18}{12}$ true

24. $\frac{42}{38} = \frac{95}{60}$ false

Determine whether each proportion is true or false by finding cross products. See Example 3.

25. $\frac{4}{32} = \frac{2}{16}$ true

26. $\frac{6}{27} = \frac{4}{18}$ true

27. $\frac{9}{19} = \frac{38}{80}$ false

28. $\frac{40}{29} = \frac{29}{22}$ false

Determine whether each proportion is true or false by finding cross products. See Example 4.

29. $\frac{0.5}{0.8} = \frac{1.1}{1.3}$ false

30. $\frac{0.6}{1.4} = \frac{0.9}{2.1}$ true

31. $\frac{1.2}{3.6} = \frac{1.8}{5.4}$ true

32. $\frac{3.2}{4.5} = \frac{1.6}{2.7}$ false

33. $\frac{1\frac{4}{5}}{3\frac{3}{7}} = \frac{2\frac{3}{16}}{4\frac{1}{6}}$ true

34. $\frac{2\frac{1}{2}}{1\frac{1}{5}} = \frac{3\frac{3}{4}}{2\frac{9}{10}}$ false

35. $\frac{\frac{1}{5}}{1\frac{1}{6}} = \frac{1\frac{1}{7}}{11\frac{2}{3}}$ false

36. $\frac{11\frac{1}{4}}{2\frac{1}{2}} = \frac{\frac{3}{4}}{\frac{1}{6}}$ true

Determine whether the numbers are proportional. See Example 5.

37. 18, 54 and 3, 9 yes

38. 4, 3 and 12, 9 yes

39. 8, 6 and 21, 16 no

40. 15, 7 and 13, 6 no

Solve each proportion. Check each result. See Example 6.

41. $\frac{5}{10} = \frac{3}{c}$ 6

42. $\frac{7}{14} = \frac{2}{x}$ 4

43. $\frac{2}{3} = \frac{x}{6}$ 4

▶ **44.** $\frac{3}{6} = \frac{x}{8}$ 4

Solve each proportion. Check each result. See Example 7.

45. $\frac{0.6}{9.6} = \frac{x}{4.8}$ 0.3

▶ **46.** $\frac{0.4}{3.4} = \frac{x}{13.6}$ 1.6

47. $\frac{2.75}{x} = \frac{1.5}{1.2}$ 2.2

48. $\frac{9.8}{x} = \frac{2.8}{5.4}$ 18.9

Solve each proportion. Check each result. Write each result as a fraction or mixed number. See Example 8.

49. $\frac{x}{1\frac{1}{2}} = \frac{10\frac{1}{2}}{4\frac{1}{2}}$ $3\frac{1}{2}$

▶ **50.** $\frac{x}{3\frac{1}{3}} = \frac{1\frac{1}{2}}{1\frac{9}{11}}$ $2\frac{3}{4}$

51. $\frac{x}{1\frac{1}{6}} = \frac{2\frac{5}{8}}{3\frac{1}{2}}$ $\frac{7}{8}$

52. $\frac{x}{2\frac{2}{3}} = \frac{1\frac{1}{20}}{3\frac{1}{2}}$ $\frac{4}{5}$

TRY IT YOURSELF

Solve each proportion.

53. $\frac{4{,}000}{x} = \frac{3.2}{2.8}$ 3,500

▶ **54.** $\frac{0.4}{1.6} = \frac{96.7}{x}$ 386.8

55. $\frac{12}{6} = \frac{x}{\frac{1}{4}}$ $\frac{1}{2}$

56. $\frac{15}{10} = \frac{x}{\frac{1}{3}}$ $\frac{1}{2}$

57. $\frac{x}{800} = \frac{900}{200}$ 36

58. $\frac{x}{200} = \frac{1{,}800}{600}$ 600

59. $\frac{x}{2.5} = \frac{3.7}{9.25}$ 1

▶ **60.** $\frac{8.5}{x} = \frac{4.25}{1.7}$ 3.4

61. $\frac{0.8}{2} = \frac{x}{5}$ 2

▶ **62.** $\frac{0.9}{0.3} = \frac{6}{x}$ 2

63. $\frac{x}{4\frac{1}{10}} = \frac{3\frac{3}{4}}{1\frac{7}{8}}$ $8\frac{1}{5}$

64. $\frac{x}{2\frac{1}{4}} = \frac{\frac{1}{2}}{\frac{1}{5}}$ $5\frac{5}{8}$

65. $\frac{340}{51} = \frac{x}{27}$ 180

66. $\frac{480}{36} = \frac{x}{15}$ 200

67. $\frac{0.4}{1.2} = \frac{6}{x}$ 18

▶ **68.** $\frac{5}{x} = \frac{2}{4.4}$ 11

69. $\frac{4.65}{7.8} = \frac{x}{5.2}$ 3.1

70. $\frac{8.6}{2.4} = \frac{x}{6}$ 21.5

71. $\frac{\frac{3}{4}}{\frac{1}{2}} = \frac{0.25}{x}$ $\frac{1}{6}$

72. $\frac{\frac{7}{8}}{\frac{1}{2}} = \frac{0.25}{x}$ $\frac{1}{7}$

APPLICATIONS

To solve each problem, write and then solve a proportion.

73. SCHOOL LUNCHES A manager of a school cafeteria orders 750 pudding cups. What will the order cost if she purchases them wholesale, 6 cups for \$1.75? \$218.75

▶ **74.** CLOTHES SHOPPING As part of a spring clearance, a men's store put dress shirts on sale, 2 for \$25.98. How much will a businessman pay if he buys five shirts? \$64.95

▶ **75.** ANNIVERSARY GIFTS A florist sells a dozen long-stemmed red roses for \$57.99. In honor of their 16th wedding anniversary, a man wants to buy 16 roses for his wife. What will the roses cost? (*Hint:* How many roses are in one dozen?) \$77.32

▶ **76.** COOKING A recipe for spaghetti sauce requires four 16-ounce bottles of ketchup to make 2 gallons of sauce. How many bottles of ketchup are needed to make 10 gallons of sauce? (*Hint:* Read the problem very carefully.) 20

77. BUSINESS PERFORMANCE The following bar graph shows the yearly costs and the revenue received by a business. Are the ratios of costs to revenue for 2009 and 2010 equal? yes

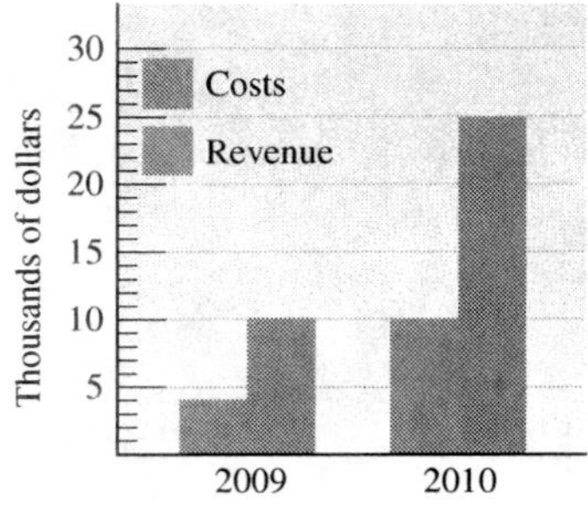

78. RAMPS Write a ratio of the rise to the run for each ramp shown. Set the ratios equal.

a. Is the resulting proportion true? $\frac{12}{20} = \frac{18}{30}$, yes

b. Is one ramp steeper than the other? no

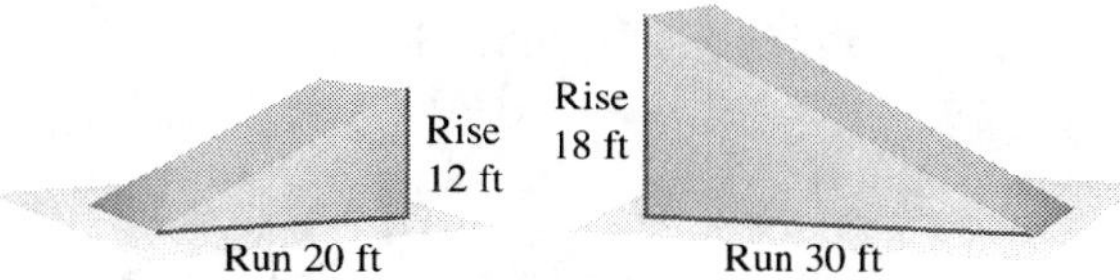

79. MIXING PERFUMES A perfume is to be mixed in the ratio of 3 drops of pure essence to 7 drops of alcohol. How many drops of pure essence should be mixed with 56 drops of alcohol? 24

80. MAKING COLOGNE A cologne can be made by mixing 2 drops of pure essence with 5 drops of distilled water. How much water should be used with 15 drops of pure essence? 37.5

81. LAB WORK In a red blood cell count, a drop of the patient's diluted blood is placed on a grid like that shown below. Instead of counting each and every red blood cell in the 25-square grid, a technician counts only the number of cells in the five highlighted squares. Then he or she uses a proportion to estimate the total red blood cell count. If there are 195 red blood cells in the blue squares, about how many red blood cells are in the entire grid? 975

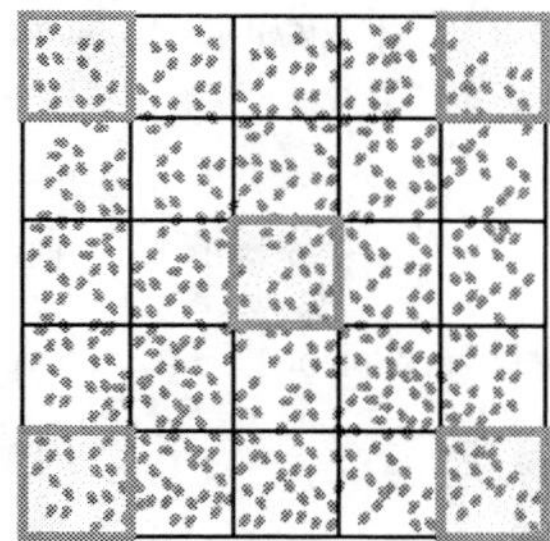

82. DOSAGES The proper dosage of a certain medication for a 30-pound child is shown. At this rate, what would be the dosage for a 45-pound child? $1\frac{1}{8}$ oz

83. DRAFTING In a scale drawing, a 280-foot antenna tower is drawn 7 inches high. The building next to it is drawn 2 inches high. How tall is the actual building? 80 ft

84. BLUEPRINTS The scale for the drawing in the blueprint tells the reader that a $\frac{1}{4}$-inch length $\left(\frac{1}{4}''\right)$ on the drawing corresponds to an actual size of 1 foot (1′0″). Suppose the length of the kitchen is $2\frac{1}{2}$ inches on the blueprint. How long is the actual kitchen? 10 ft

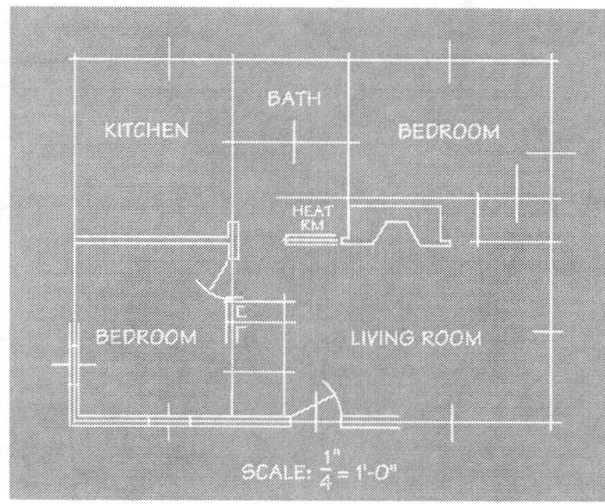

85. MODEL RAILROADS An HO-scale model railroad engine is 9 inches long. If HO scale is 87 feet to 1 foot, how long is a real engine? (*Hint:* Compare feet to inches. How many inches are in one foot?) 65.25 ft = 65 ft 3 in.

86. MODEL RAILROADS An N-scale model railroad caboose is 4 inches long. If N scale is 169 feet to 1 foot, how long is a real caboose? (*Hint:* Compare feet to inches. How many inches are in one foot?) $56\frac{1}{3}$ ft = 56 ft 4 in.

87. CAROUSELS The ratio in the illustration below indicates that 1 inch on the model carousel is equivalent to 160 inches on the actual carousel. How wide should the model be if the actual carousel is 35 feet wide? (*Hint:* Convert 35 feet to inches.) 2.625 in. = $2\frac{5}{8}$ in.

88. MIXING FUELS The instructions on a can of oil intended to be added to lawn mower gasoline read as shown. Are these instructions correct? (*Hint*: There are 128 ounces in 1 gallon.) not exactly, but close

Recommended	Gasoline	Oil
50 to 1	6 gal	16 oz

89. MAKING COOKIES A recipe for chocolate chip cookies calls for $1\frac{1}{4}$ cups of flour and 1 cup of sugar. The recipe will make $3\frac{1}{2}$ dozen cookies. How many cups of flour will be needed to make 12 dozen cookies? $4\frac{2}{7}$, which is about $4\frac{1}{4}$

90. MAKING BROWNIES A recipe for brownies calls for 4 eggs and $1\frac{1}{2}$ cups of flour. If the recipe makes 15 brownies, how many cups of flour will be needed to make 130 brownies? 13

from Campus to Careers
Chef

Nick White/Getty Images

91. COMPUTER SPEED Using the *Mathematica 3.0* program, a Dell Dimension XPS R350 (Pentium II) computer can perform a set of 15 calculations in 2.85 seconds. How long will it take the computer to perform 100 such calculations? 19 sec

92. QUALITY CONTROL Out of a sample of 500 men's shirts, 17 were rejected because of crooked collars. How many crooked collars would you expect to find in a run of 15,000 shirts? 510

93. DOGS Refer to the illustration below. A Saint Bernard website lists the "ideal proportions for the *height at the withers* to *body length* as 5:6." What is the ideal height at the withers for a Saint Bernard whose body length is $37\frac{1}{2}$ inches? 31.25 in. = $31\frac{1}{4}$ in.

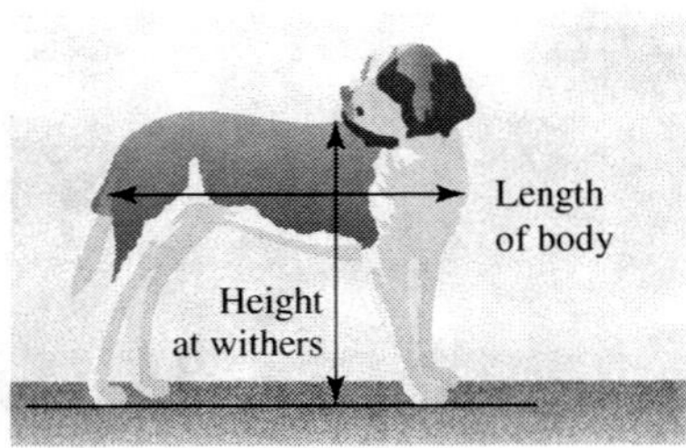

94. MILEAGE Under normal conditions, a Hummer can travel 325 miles on a full tank (25 gallons) of diesel. How far can it travel on its auxiliary tank, which holds 17 gallons of diesel? 221 mi

95. PAYCHECKS Billie earns $412 for a 40-hour week. If she missed 10 hours of work last week, how much did she get paid? $309

96. STAFFING A school board has determined that there should be 3 teachers for every 50 students. Complete the table by filling in the number of teachers needed at each school.

	Glenwood High	Goddard Junior High	Sellers Elementary
Enrollment	2,700	1,900	850
Teachers	162	114	51

WRITING

97. Explain the difference between a ratio and a proportion.

98. The following paragraph is from a book about dollhouses. What concept from this section is mentioned?

Today, the internationally recognized scale for dollhouses and miniatures is 1 in. = 1 ft. This is small enough to be defined as a miniature, yet not too small for all details of decoration and furniture to be seen clearly.

99. Write a problem that could be solved using the following proportion.

$$\frac{4}{639} = \frac{10}{x}$$

Ounces of cashews → 4; Calories → 639; 10 ← Ounces of cashews; x ← Calories

100. Write a problem about a situation you encounter in your daily life that could be solved by using a proportion.

REVIEW

Perform each operation.

101. $7.4 + 6.78 + 35 + 0.008$ 49.188

102. $29.5 + 34.4 + 12.8$ 76.7

103. $48.8 - 17.372$ 31.428

104. $78.47 - 53.3$ 25.17

105. $-3.8 - (-7.9)$ 4.1

106. $-17.1 + 8.4$ −8.7

107. $-35.1 - 13.99$ −49.09

108. $-5.55 + (-1.25)$ −6.8

SECTION 3.3
Similar Triangles

Objectives

1. Identify corresponding parts of congruent triangles.
2. Use congruence properties to prove that two triangles are congruent.
3. Determine whether two triangles are similar.
4. Use similar triangles to find unknown lengths in application problems.

In our everyday lives, we see many types of triangles. Triangular-shaped kites, sails, roofs, tortilla chips, and ramps are just a few examples. In this section, we will discuss how to compare the size and shape of two given triangles. From this comparison, we can make observations about their side lengths and angle measures.

© iStockphoto.com/Lucinda Deitman

1 Identify corresponding parts of congruent triangles.

Simply put, two geometric figures are congruent if they have the same shape and size. For example, if $\triangle ABC$ and $\triangle DEF$ shown below are congruent, we can write

$\triangle ABC \cong \triangle DEF$ Read as "Triangle ABC is congruent to triangle DEF."

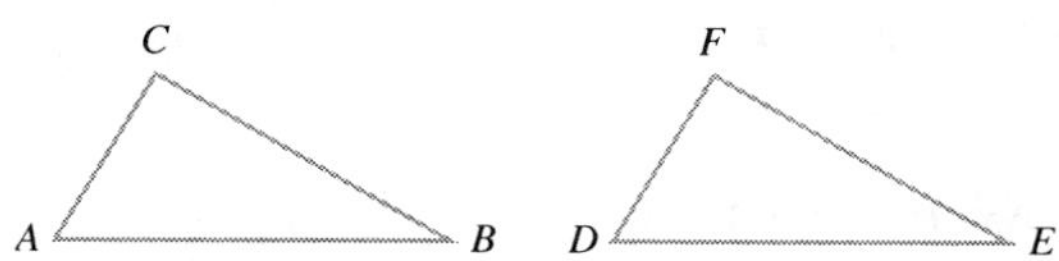

One way to determine whether two triangles are congruent is to see if one triangle can be moved onto the other triangle in such a way that it fits exactly. When we write $\triangle ABC \cong \triangle DEF$, we are showing how the vertices of one triangle are matched to the vertices of the other triangle to obtain a "perfect fit." We call this matching of points a **correspondence.**

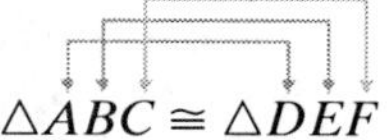

$\triangle ABC \cong \triangle DEF$

$A \leftrightarrow D$ Read as "Point A corresponds to point D."

$B \leftrightarrow E$ Read as "Point B corresponds to point E."

$C \leftrightarrow F$ Read as "Point C corresponds to point F."

When we establish a correspondence between the vertices of two congruent triangles, we also establish a correspondence between the angles and the sides of the triangles. Corresponding angles and corresponding sides of congruent triangles are called **corresponding parts.** *Corresponding parts of congruent triangles are always congruent.* That is, corresponding parts of congruent triangles always have the same measure. For the congruent triangles shown above, we have

$m(\angle A) = m(\angle D)$ $m(\angle B) = m(\angle E)$ $m(\angle C) = m(\angle F)$

$m(\overline{BC}) = m(\overline{EF})$ $m(\overline{AC}) = m(\overline{DF})$ $m(\overline{AB}) = m(\overline{DE})$

Congruent Triangles

Two triangles are congruent if and only if their vertices can be matched so that the corresponding sides and the corresponding angles are congruent.

EXAMPLE 1 Refer to the figure below, where $\triangle XYZ \cong \triangle PQR$.

a. Name the six congruent corresponding parts of the triangles.

b. Find $m(\angle P)$.

c. Find $m(\overline{XZ})$.

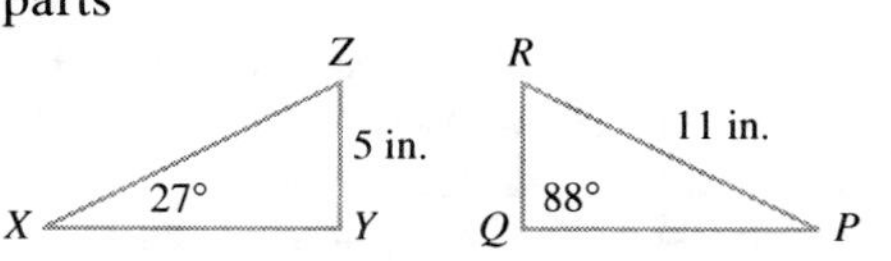

Self Check 1

Refer to the figure below, where $\triangle ABC \cong \triangle EDF$.

a. Name the six congruent corresponding parts of the triangles.

b. Find $m(\angle C)$.

c. Find $m(\overline{FE})$.

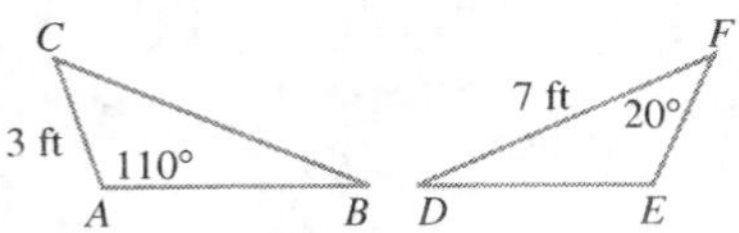

Now Try **Problem 33**

Self Check 1 Answers

a. $\angle A \cong \angle E, \angle B \cong \angle D, \angle C \cong \angle F,$ $\overline{AB} \cong \overline{ED}, \overline{BC} \cong \overline{DF}, \overline{CA} \cong \overline{FE}$

b. 20°

c. 3 ft

Teaching Example 1 Refer to the figure, where $\triangle RST \cong \triangle NMO$

a. Name the six congruent corresponding parts of the triangles.

b. Find $m(\angle T)$.

c. Find $m(\overline{MN})$.

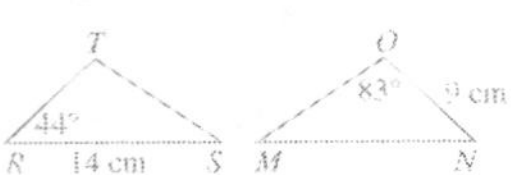

Answers:

a. $\angle R \cong \angle N, \angle S \cong \angle M, \angle T \cong \angle O,$ $\overline{RS} \cong \overline{NM}, \overline{ST} \cong \overline{MO}, \overline{TR} \cong \overline{ON}$

b. 83°

c. 14 cm

Strategy We will establish the correspondence between the vertices of $\triangle XYZ$ and the vertices of $\triangle PQR$.

WHY This will, in turn, establish a correspondence between the congruent corresponding angles and sides of the triangles.

Solution

a. The correspondence between the vertices is

$$\triangle XYZ \cong \triangle PQR$$

$$X \leftrightarrow P \qquad Y \leftrightarrow Q \qquad Z \leftrightarrow R$$

Corresponding parts of congruent triangles are congruent. Therefore, the congruent corresponding angles are

$$\angle X \cong \angle P \qquad \angle Y \cong \angle Q \qquad \angle Z \cong \angle R$$

The congruent corresponding sides are

$$\overline{YZ} \cong \overline{QR} \qquad \overline{XZ} \cong \overline{PR} \qquad \overline{XY} \cong \overline{PQ}$$

b. From the figure, we see that $m(\angle X) = 27°$. Since $\angle X \cong \angle P$, it follows that $m(\angle P) = 27°$.

c. From the figure, we see that $m(\overline{PR}) = 11$ inches. Since $\overline{XZ} \cong \overline{PR}$, it follows that $m(\overline{XZ}) = 11$ inches.

2 Use congruence properties to prove that two triangles are congruent.

Sometimes it is possible to conclude that two triangles are congruent without having to show that three pairs of corresponding angles are congruent and three pairs of corresponding sides are congruent. To do so, we apply one of the following properties.

SSS Property

If three sides of one triangle are congruent to three sides of a second triangle, the triangles are congruent.

We can show that the triangles shown below are congruent by the SSS property:

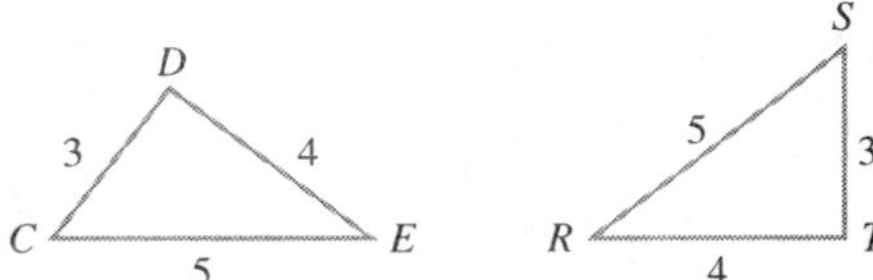

$\overline{CD} \cong \overline{ST}$ Since $m(\overline{CD}) = 3$ and $m(\overline{ST}) = 3$, the segments are congruent.

$\overline{DE} \cong \overline{TR}$ Since $m(\overline{DE}) = 4$ and $m(\overline{TR}) = 4$, the segments are congruent.

$\overline{EC} \cong \overline{RS}$ Since $m(\overline{EC}) = 5$ and $m(\overline{RS}) = 5$, the segments are congruent.

Therefore, $\triangle CDE \cong \triangle STR$.

SAS Property

If two sides and the angle between them in one triangle are congruent, respectively, to two sides and the angle between them in a second triangle, the triangles are congruent.

We can show that the triangles shown below are congruent by the SAS property:

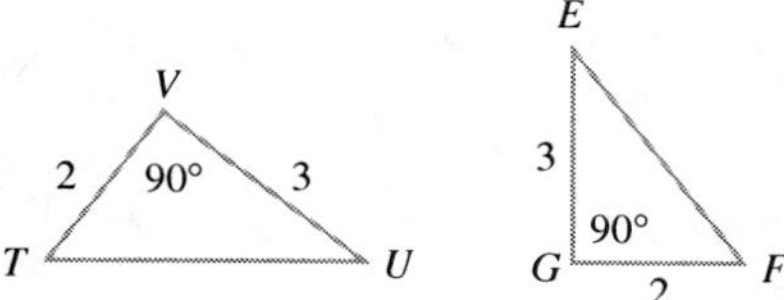

$\overline{TV} \cong \overline{FG}$ Since $m(\overline{TV}) = 2$ and $m(\overline{FG}) = 2$, the segments are congruent.

$\angle V \cong \angle G$ Since $m(\angle V) = 90°$ and $m(\angle G) = 90°$, the angles are congruent.

$\overline{UV} \cong \overline{EG}$ Since $m(\overline{UV}) = 3$ and $m(\overline{EG}) = 3$, the segments are congruent.

Therefore, $\triangle TVU \cong \triangle FGE$.

ASA Property

If two angles and the side between them in one triangle are congruent, respectively, to two angles and the side between them in a second triangle, the triangles are congruent.

We can show that the triangles shown below are congruent by the ASA property:

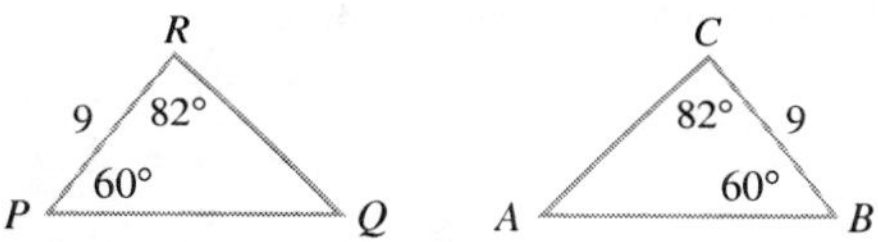

$\angle P \cong \angle B$ Since $m(\angle P) = 60°$ and $m(\angle B) = 60°$, the angles are congruent.

$\overline{PR} \cong \overline{BC}$ Since $m(\overline{PR}) = 9$ and $m(\overline{BC}) = 9$, the segments are congruent.

$\angle R \cong \angle C$ Since $m(\angle R) = 82°$ and $m(\angle C) = 82°$, the angles are congruent.

Therefore, $\triangle PQR \cong \triangle BAC$.

Caution! There is no SSA property. To illustrate this, consider the triangles shown below. Two sides and an angle of $\triangle ABC$ are congruent to two sides and an angle of $\triangle DEF$. But the congruent angle is not between the congruent sides.

We refer to this situation as SSA. Obviously, the triangles are not congruent because they are not the same shape and size.

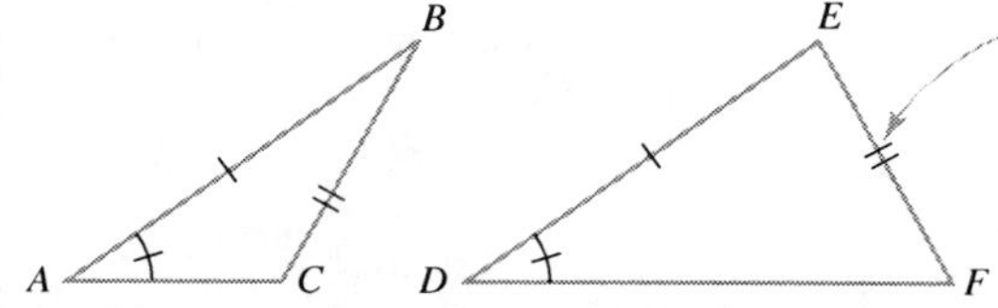

The tick marks indicate congruent parts. That is, the sides with one tick mark are the same length, the sides with two tick marks are the same length, and the angles with one tick mark have the same measure.

EXAMPLE 2 Explain why the triangles in the figure on the following page are congruent.

Strategy We will show that two sides and the angle between them in one triangle are congruent, respectively, to two sides and the angle between them in a second triangle.

Self Check 2

Are the triangles in the figure below congruent? Explain why or why not. yes, by the SAS property

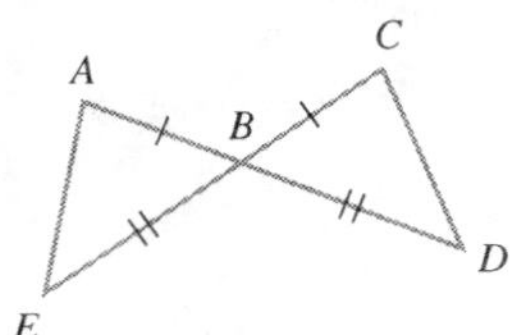

Now Try **Problem 35**

Self Check 3

Are the triangles in the following figure congruent? Explain why or why not. yes, by the SSS property

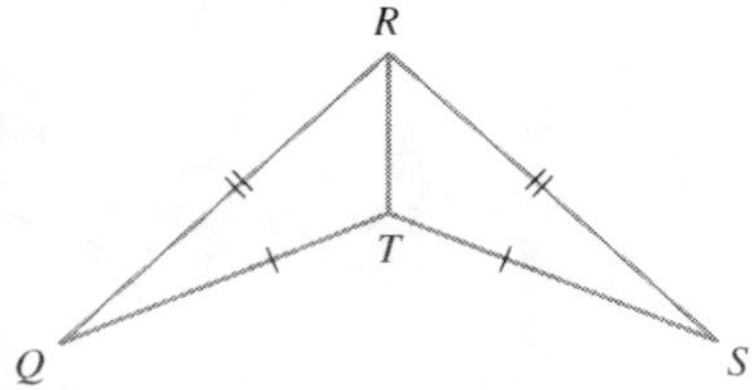

Now Try **Problem 37**

Teaching Example 2 Explain why the triangles in the figure are congruent.

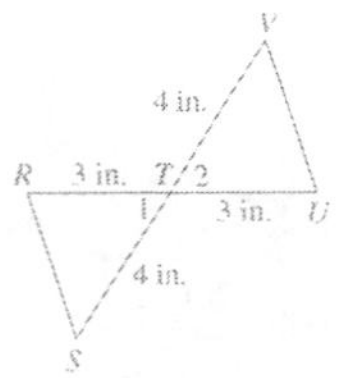

Answer:
$\triangle RST \cong \triangle UVT$ by the SAS property: $\overline{RT} \cong \overline{UT}$, $\angle 1 \cong \angle 2$, and $\overline{ST} \cong \overline{VT}$

Teaching Example 3 Are $\triangle ABC$ and $\triangle ADC$ congruent?

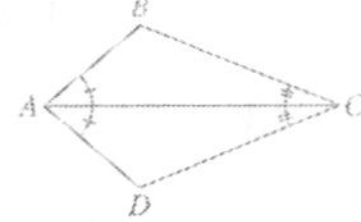

Answer:
yes, by the ASA property: $\angle BAC \cong \angle DAC$, $\overline{AC} \cong \overline{AC}$, and $\angle BCA \cong \angle DCA$

WHY Then we know that the two triangles are congruent by the SAS property.

Solution Since vertical angles are congruent,

$$\angle 1 \cong \angle 2$$

From the figure, we see that

$$\overline{AC} \cong \overline{EC} \quad \text{and} \quad \overline{BC} \cong \overline{DC}$$

Since two sides and the angle between them in one triangle are congruent, respectively, to two sides and the angle between them in a second triangle, $\triangle ABC \cong \triangle EDC$ by the SAS property.

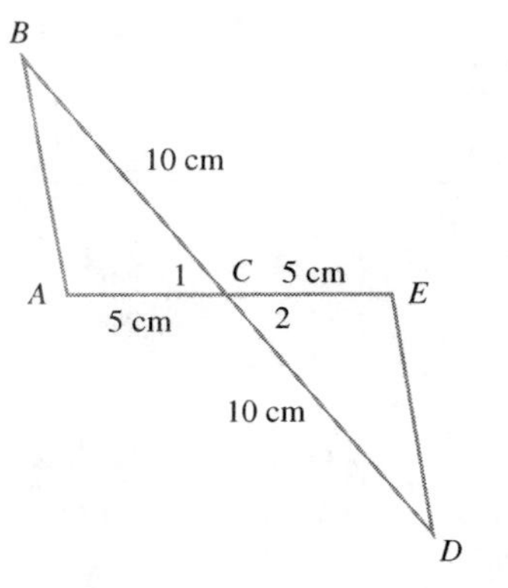

EXAMPLE 3

Are $\triangle RST$ and $\triangle RUT$ in the figure on the right congruent?

Strategy We will show that two angles and the side between them in one triangle are congruent, respectively, to two angles and the side between them in a second triangle.

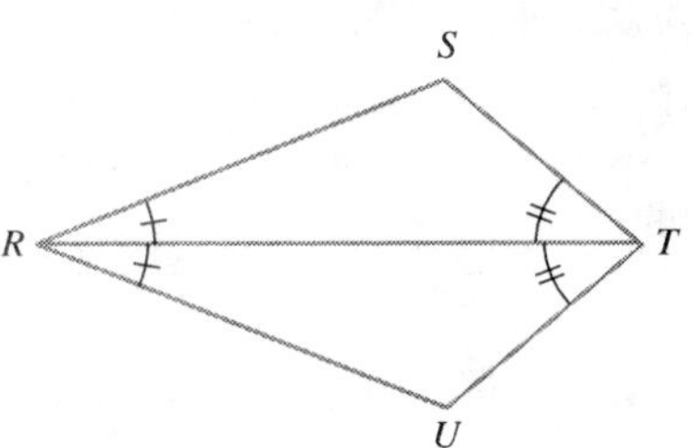

WHY Then we know that the two triangles are congruent by the ASA property.

Solution From the markings on the figure, we know that two pairs of angles are congruent.

$\angle SRT \cong \angle URT$ These angles are marked with 1 tick mark, which indicates that they have the same measure.

$\angle STR \cong \angle UTR$ These angles are marked with 2 tick marks, which indicates that they have the same measure.

From the figure, we see that the triangles have side $\overline{RT}$ in common. Furthermore, $\overline{RT}$ is between each pair of congruent angles listed above. Since every segment is congruent to itself, we also have

$$\overline{RT} \cong \overline{RT}$$

Knowing that two angles and the side between them in $\triangle RST$ are congruent, respectively, to two angles and the side between them in $\triangle RUT$, we can conclude that $\triangle RST \cong \triangle RUT$ by the ASA property.

3 Determine whether two triangles are similar.

We have seen that congruent triangles have the same shape and size. **Similar triangles** have the same shape, but not necessarily the same size. That is, one triangle is an exact scale model of the other triangle. If the triangles in the figure below are similar, we can write $\triangle ABC \sim \triangle DEF$ (read the symbol $\sim$ as "is similar to").

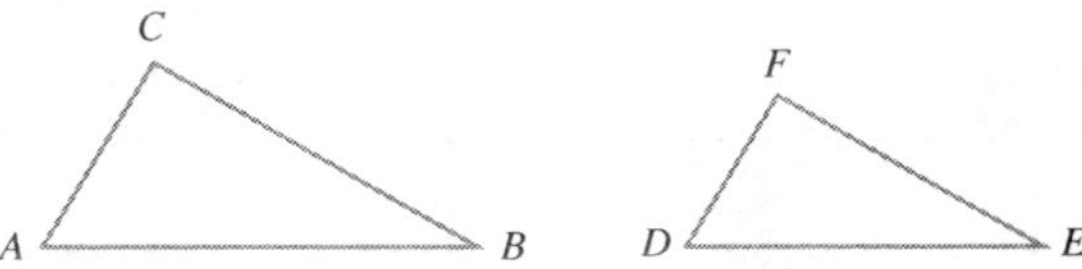

Success Tip Note that congruent triangles are always similar, but similar triangles are not always congruent.

The formal definition of similar triangles requires that we establish a correspondence between the vertices of the triangles. The definition also involves the word *proportional.*

Recall that a **proportion** is a mathematical statement that two ratios (fractions) are equal. An example of a proportion is

$$\frac{1}{2} = \frac{4}{8}$$

In this case, we say that $\frac{1}{2}$ and $\frac{4}{8}$ are *proportional.*

Similar Triangles

Two triangles are similar if and only if their vertices can be matched so that corresponding angles are congruent and the lengths of corresponding sides are proportional.

EXAMPLE 4 Refer to the figure below. If $\triangle PQR \sim \triangle CDE$, name the congruent angles and the sides that are proportional.

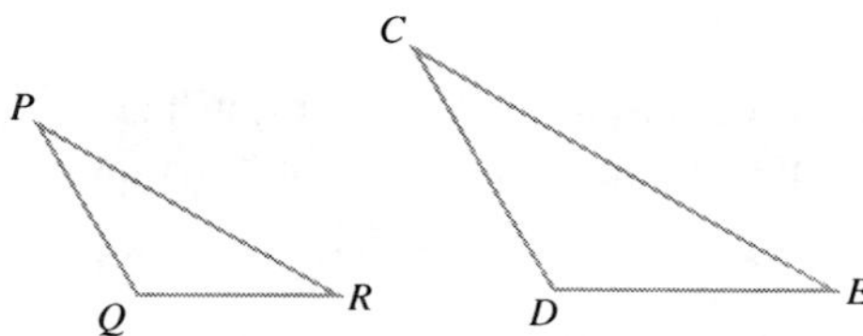

Strategy We will establish the correspondence between the vertices of $\triangle PQR$ and the vertices of $\triangle CDE$.

WHY This will, in turn, establish a correspondence between the congruent corresponding angles and proportional sides of the triangles.

Solution When we write $\triangle PQR \sim \triangle CDE$, a correspondence between the vertices of the triangles is established.

$$\triangle PQR \sim \triangle CDE$$

Since the triangles are similar, corresponding angles are congruent:

$$\angle P \cong \angle C \qquad \angle Q \cong \angle D \qquad \angle R \cong \angle E$$

The lengths of the corresponding sides are proportional. To simplify the notation, we will now let $PQ = m(\overline{PQ})$, $CD = m(\overline{CD})$, $QR = m(\overline{QR})$, and so on.

$$\frac{PQ}{CD} = \frac{QR}{DE} \qquad \frac{QR}{DE} = \frac{PR}{CE} \qquad \frac{PQ}{CD} = \frac{PR}{CE}$$

Written in a more compact way, we have

$$\frac{PQ}{CD} = \frac{QR}{DE} = \frac{PR}{CE}$$

Self Check 4

If $\triangle GEF \sim \triangle IJH$, name the congruent angles and the sides that are proportional.

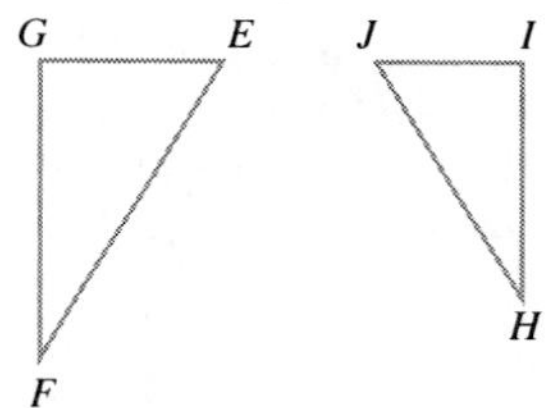

Now Try **Problem 39**

Self Check 4 Answer

$\angle G \cong \angle I$, $\angle E \cong \angle J$, $\angle F \cong \angle H$; $\frac{EG}{JI} = \frac{GF}{IH} = \frac{FE}{HJ}$

Teaching Example 4 If $\triangle RST \sim \triangle WYX$, name the congruent angles and the sides that are proportional.

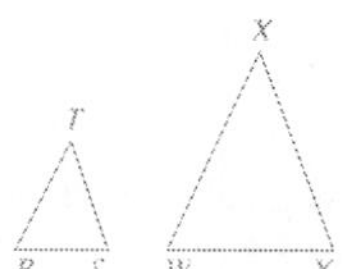

Answer:

$\angle R \cong \angle W$, $\angle S \cong \angle Y$, $\angle T \cong \angle X$; $\frac{RS}{WY} = \frac{RT}{WX} = \frac{TS}{XY}$

Property of Similar Triangles

If two triangles are similar, all pairs of corresponding sides are in proportion.

It is possible to conclude that two triangles are similar without having to show that all three pairs of corresponding angles are congruent and that the lengths of all three pairs of corresponding sides are proportional.

AAA Similarity Theorem

If the angles of one triangle are congruent to corresponding angles of another triangle, the triangles are similar.

Self Check 5

In the figure below, $\overline{YA} \parallel \overline{ZB}$. Are $\triangle XYA$ and $\triangle XZB$ similar triangles?

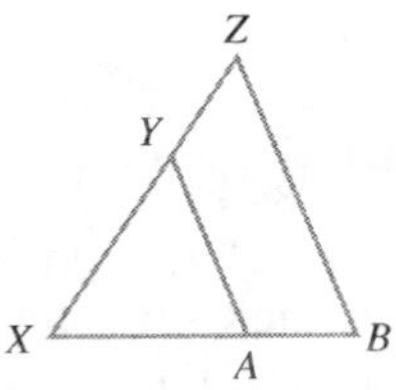

Now Try **Problems 41 and 43**

Self Check 5 Answer

yes, by the AAA similarity theorem: $\angle X \cong \angle X$, $\angle XYA \cong \angle XZB$, $\angle XAY \cong \angle XBZ$

Teaching Example 5 In the figure, $\overline{MN} \parallel \overline{QP}$. Are $\triangle MNO$ and $\triangle PQO$ similar triangles?

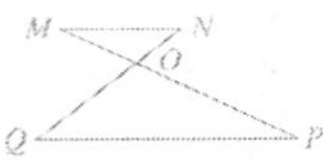

Answer:

yes, by the AAA similarity theorem: $\angle MON \cong \angle POQ$, $\angle M \cong \angle P$, $\angle N \cong \angle Q$

EXAMPLE 5 In the figure on the right, $\overline{PR} \parallel \overline{MN}$. Are $\triangle PQR$ and $\triangle NQM$ similar triangles?

Strategy We will show that the angles of one triangle are congruent to corresponding angles of another triangle.

WHY Then we know that the two triangles are similar by the AAA property.

Solution Since vertical angles are congruent,

$\angle PQR \cong \angle NQM$ This is one pair of congruent corresponding angles.

In the figure, we can view $\overleftrightarrow{PN}$ as a transversal cutting parallel line segments $\overline{PR}$ and $\overline{MN}$. Since alternate interior angles are then congruent, we have:

$\angle RPQ \cong \angle MNQ$ This is a second pair of congruent corresponding angles.

Furthermore, we can view $\overleftrightarrow{RM}$ as a transversal cutting parallel line segments $\overline{PR}$ and $\overline{MN}$. Since alternate interior angles are then congruent, we have:

$\angle QRP \cong \angle QMN$ This is a third pair of congruent corresponding angles.

These observations are summarized in the figure on the right. We see that corresponding angles of $\triangle PQR$ are congruent to corresponding angles of $\triangle NQM$. By the AAA similarity theorem, we can conclude that

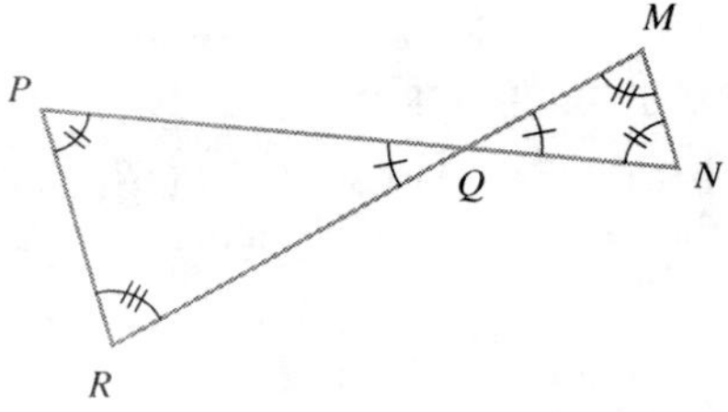

$\triangle PQR \sim \triangle NQM$

Self Check 6

In the figure below, $\triangle DEF \sim \triangle GHI$. Find:

a. x 6 **b.** y 11.25

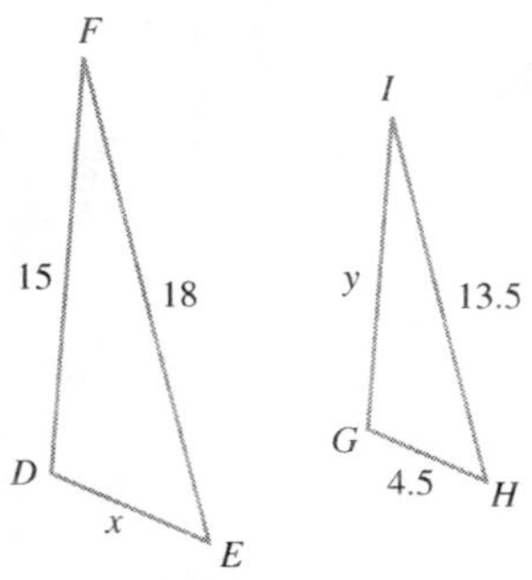

Now Try **Problem 53**

EXAMPLE 6 In the figure below, $\triangle RST \sim \triangle JKL$. Find: **a.** x **b.** y

Strategy To find x, we will write a proportion of corresponding sides so that x is the only unknown. Then we will solve the proportion for x. We will use a similar method to find y.

WHY Since $\triangle RST \sim \triangle JKL$, we know that the lengths of corresponding sides of $\triangle RST$ and $\triangle JKL$ are proportional.

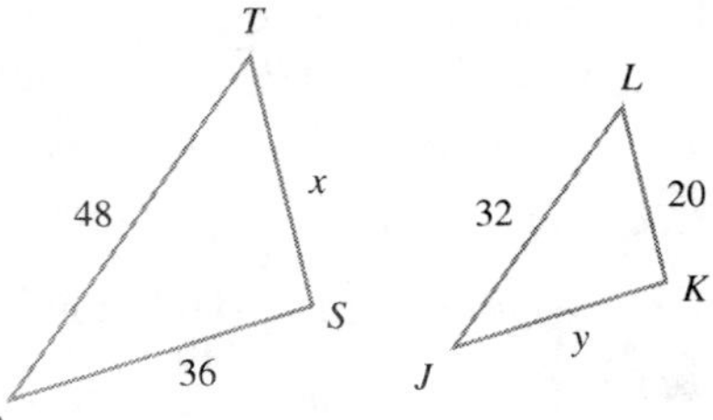

Solution

a. When we write $\triangle RST \sim \triangle JKL$, a correspondence between the vertices of the two triangles is established.

$\triangle RST \sim \triangle JKL$

The lengths of corresponding sides of these similar triangles are proportional.

$\frac{RT}{JL} = \frac{ST}{KL}$ Each fraction is a ratio of a side length of $\triangle RST$ to its corresponding side length of $\triangle JKL$.

$\frac{48}{32} = \frac{x}{20}$ Substitute: $RT = 48$, $JL = 32$, $ST = x$, and $KL = 20$.

$48(20) = 32x$ Find each cross product and set them equal.

$960 = 32x$ Do the multiplication.

$30 = x$ To isolate x, undo the multiplication by 32 by dividing both sides by 32.

$$\begin{array}{r} 48 \\ \times 20 \\ \hline 960 \end{array} \qquad \begin{array}{r} 30 \\ 32\overline{)960} \\ -96 \\ \hline 00 \\ -00 \\ \hline 0 \end{array}$$

Thus, x is 30.

b. To find y, we write a proportion of corresponding side lengths in such a way that y is the only unknown.

$\frac{RT}{JL} = \frac{RS}{JK}$

$\frac{48}{32} = \frac{36}{y}$ Substitute: $RT = 48$, $JL = 32$, $RS = 36$, and $JK = y$.

$48y = 32(36)$ Find each cross product and set them equal.

$48y = 1{,}152$ Do the multiplication.

$y = 24$ To isolate y, undo the multiplication by 48 by dividing both sides by 48.

$$\begin{array}{r} 36 \\ \times 32 \\ \hline 72 \\ 1080 \\ \hline 1152 \end{array} \qquad \begin{array}{r} 24 \\ 48\overline{)1{,}152} \\ -96 \\ \hline 192 \\ -192 \\ \hline 0 \end{array}$$

Thus, y is 24.

Teaching Example 6 In the figure below, $\triangle XYZ \sim \triangle ABC$. Find:
a. s b. t

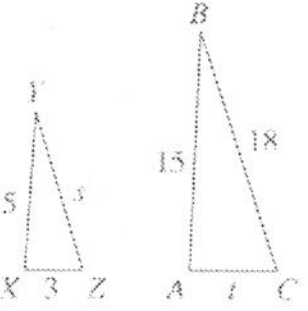

Answers:
a. 6
b. 9

4 Use similar triangles to find unknown lengths in application problems.

Similar triangles and proportions can be used to find lengths that would normally be difficult to measure. For example, we can use the reflective properties of a mirror to calculate the height of a flagpole while standing safely on the ground.

EXAMPLE 7 To determine the height of a flagpole, a woman walks to a point 20 feet from its base, as shown below. Then she takes a mirror from her purse, places it on the ground, and walks 2 feet farther away, where she can see the top of the pole reflected in the mirror. Find the height of the pole.

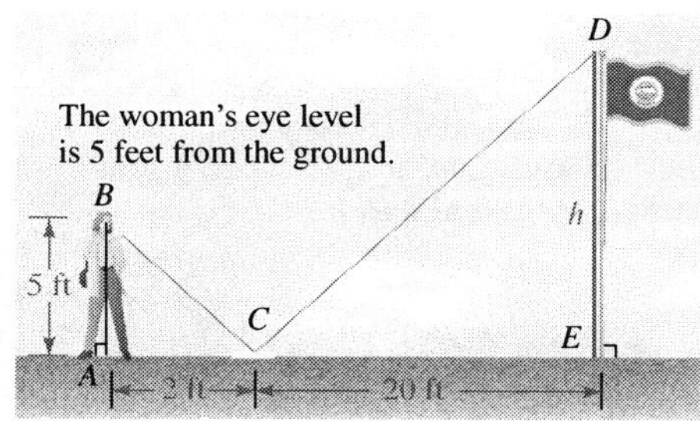

Strategy We will show that $\triangle ABC \sim \triangle EDC$.

WHY Then we can write a proportion of corresponding sides so that h is the only unknown and we can solve the proportion for h.

Solution To show that $\triangle ABC \sim \triangle EDC$, we begin by applying an important fact about mirrors. When a beam of light strikes a mirror, it is reflected at the same angle as it hits the mirror. Therefore, $\angle BCA \cong \angle DCE$. Furthermore, $\angle A \cong \angle E$ because the woman and the flagpole are perpendicular to the ground. Finally, if two pairs of

Self Check 7

In the figure below, $\triangle ABC \sim \triangle EDC$. Find h. 500 ft

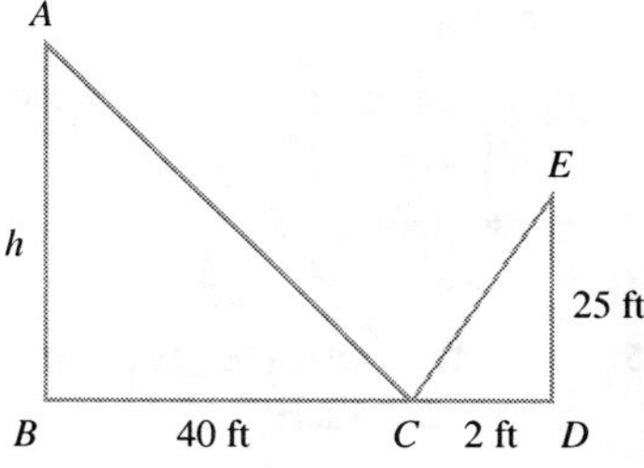

Now Try **Problem 85**

Teaching Example 7 In the figure, $\triangle SQR \sim \triangle STU$. Find h.

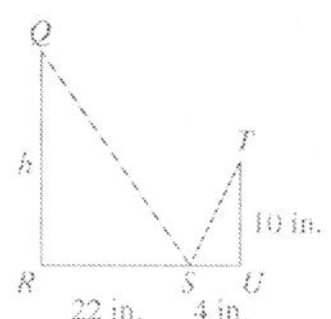

Answer:
55 in.

corresponding angles are congruent, it follows that the third pair of corresponding angles are also congruent: $\angle B \cong \angle D$. By the AAA similarity theorem, we conclude that $\triangle ABC \sim \triangle EDC$.

Since the triangles are similar, the lengths of their corresponding sides are in proportion. If we let h represent the height of the flagpole, we can find h by solving the following proportion.

$$\frac{h}{5} = \frac{20}{2}$$

Height of the flagpole → h; Height of the woman → 5; ← Distance from flagpole to mirror 20; ← Distance from woman to mirror 2

$2h = 5(20)$ Find each cross product and set them equal.

$2h = 100$ Do the multiplication.

$h = 50$ To isolate h, divide both sides by 2.

The flagpole is 50 feet tall.

ANSWERS TO SELF CHECKS

1. a. $\angle A \cong \angle E, \angle B \cong \angle D, \angle C \cong \angle F, \overline{AB} \cong \overline{ED}, \overline{BC} \cong \overline{DF}, \overline{CA} \cong \overline{FE}$ **b.** 20° **c.** 3 ft **2.** yes, by the SAS property **3.** yes, by the SSS property **4.** $\angle G \cong \angle I, \angle E \cong \angle J, \angle F \cong \angle H; \frac{EG}{JI} = \frac{GF}{IH}, \frac{GF}{IH} = \frac{FE}{HJ}, \frac{EG}{JI} = \frac{FE}{HJ}$ **5.** yes, by the AAA similarity theorem: $\angle X \cong \angle X, \angle XYA \cong \angle XZB, \angle XAY \cong \angle XBZ$ **6. a.** 6 **b.** 11.25 **7.** 500 ft

SECTION 3.3 STUDY SET

VOCABULARY

Fill in the blanks.

1. Congruent triangles are the same size and the same shape.
2. When we match the vertices of $\triangle ABC$ with the vertices of $\triangle DEF$, as shown below, we call this matching of points a correspondence.

   $A \leftrightarrow D \quad B \leftrightarrow E \quad C \leftrightarrow F$

3. Two angles or two line segments with the same measure are said to be congruent.
4. Corresponding parts of congruent triangles are congruent.
5. If two triangles are similar, they have the same shape but not necessarily the same size.
6. A mathematical statement that two ratios (fractions) are equal, such as $\frac{x}{18} = \frac{4}{9}$, is called a proportion.

CONCEPTS

7. Refer to the triangles below.

   a. Do these triangles appear to be congruent? Explain why or why not. No, they are different sizes.
   b. Do these triangles appear to be similar? Explain why or why not. Yes, they have the same shape.

8. a. Draw a triangle that is congruent to $\triangle CDE$ shown below. Label it $\triangle ABC$.

   b. Draw a triangle that is similar to, but not congruent to, $\triangle CDE$. Label it $\triangle MNO$.

Fill in the blanks.

9. $\triangle XYZ \cong \triangle$ PRQ

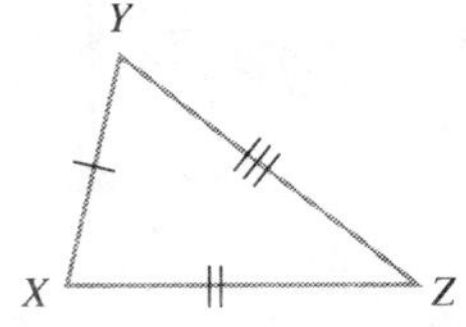

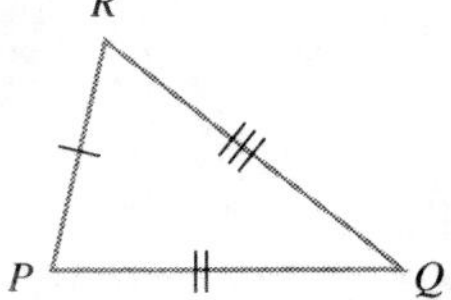

10. $\triangle$ ABC $\cong \triangle DEF$

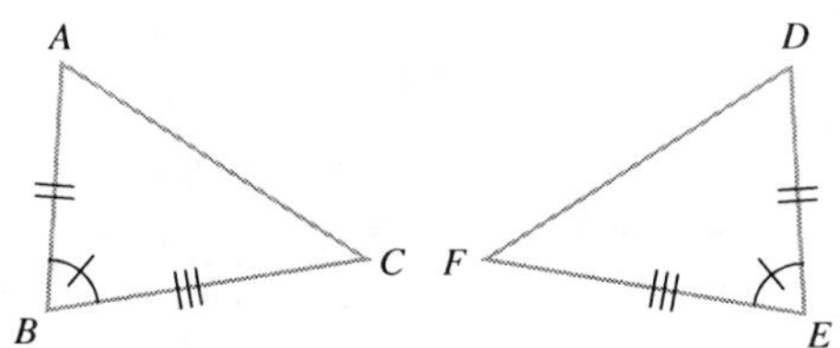

11. $\triangle RST \sim \triangle$ MNO

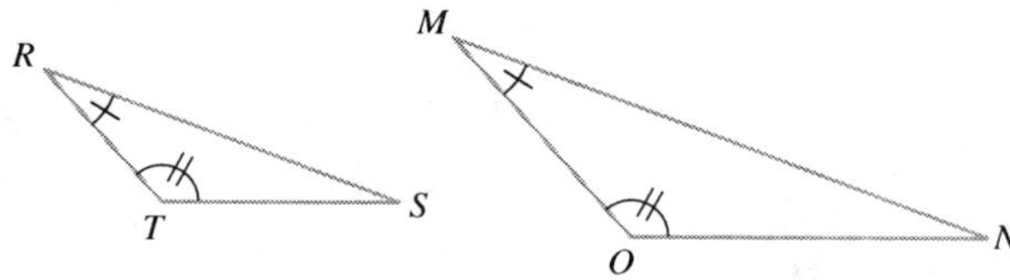

12. $\triangle$ BDE $\sim \triangle TAC$

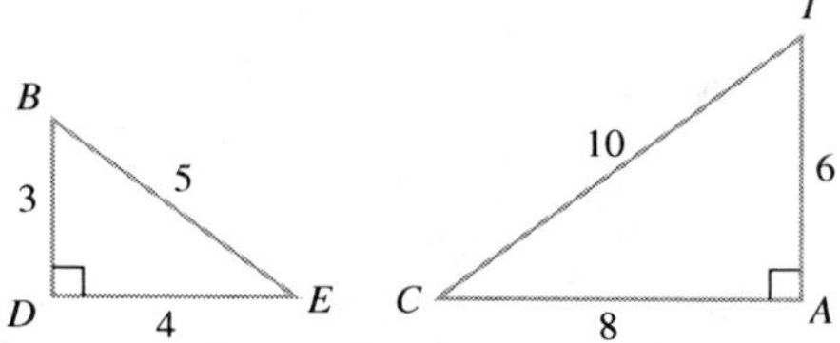

13. Name the six corresponding parts of the congruent triangles shown below. $\angle A \cong \angle B, \angle Y \cong \angle T, \angle Z \cong \angle R, \overline{YZ} \cong \overline{TR}, \overline{AZ} \cong \overline{BR}, \overline{AY} \cong \overline{BT}$

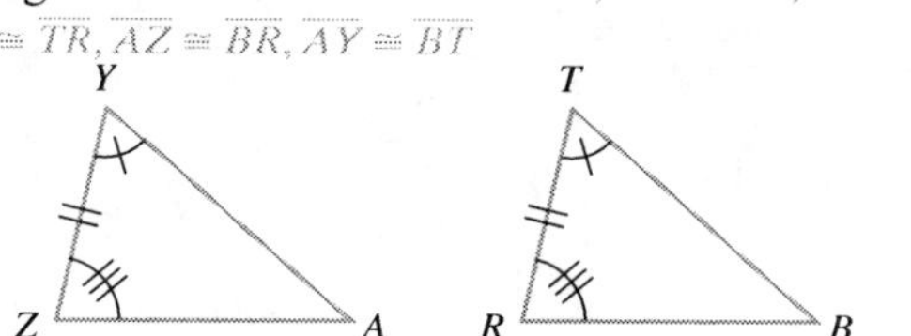

14. Name the six corresponding parts of the congruent triangles shown below. $\angle S \cong \angle F, \angle T \cong \angle G, \angle R \cong \angle E, \overline{TS} \cong \overline{GF}, \overline{TR} \cong \overline{GE}, \overline{RS} \cong \overline{EF}$

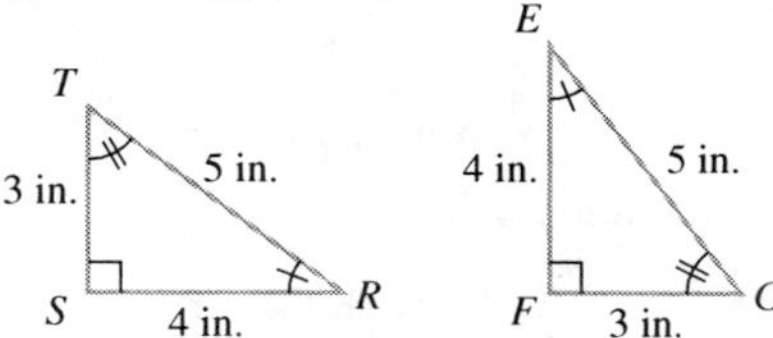

Fill in the blanks.

15. Two triangles are congruent if and only if their vertices can be matched so that the corresponding sides and the corresponding angles are congruent.

16. SSS property: If three sides of one triangle are congruent to three sides of a second triangle, the triangles are congruent.

17. SAS property: If two sides and the angle between them in one triangle are congruent, respectively, to two sides and the angle between them in a second triangle, the triangles are congruent.

18. ASA property: If two angles and the side between them in one triangle are congruent, respectively, to two angles and the side between them in a second triangle, the triangles are congruent.

Solve each proportion.

19. $\frac{x}{15} = \frac{20}{3}$ 100

20. $\frac{5}{8} = \frac{35}{x}$ 56

21. $\frac{h}{2.6} = \frac{27}{13}$ 5.4

22. $\frac{11.2}{4} = \frac{h}{6}$ 16.8

Fill in the blanks.

23. Two triangles are similar if and only if their vertices can be matched so that corresponding angles are congruent and the lengths of corresponding sides are proportional.

24. If the angles of one triangle are congruent to corresponding angles of another triangle, the triangles are similar.

25. Congruent triangles are always similar, but similar triangles are not always congruent.

26. For certain application problems, similar triangles and proportions can be used to find lengths that would normally be difficult to measure.

NOTATION

Fill in the blanks.

27. The symbol $\cong$ is read as "is congruent to."

28. The symbol $\sim$ is read as "is similar to."

29. Use tick marks to show the congruent parts of the triangles shown below.

$\angle K \cong \angle H \quad \overline{KR} \cong \overline{HJ} \quad \angle M \cong \angle E$

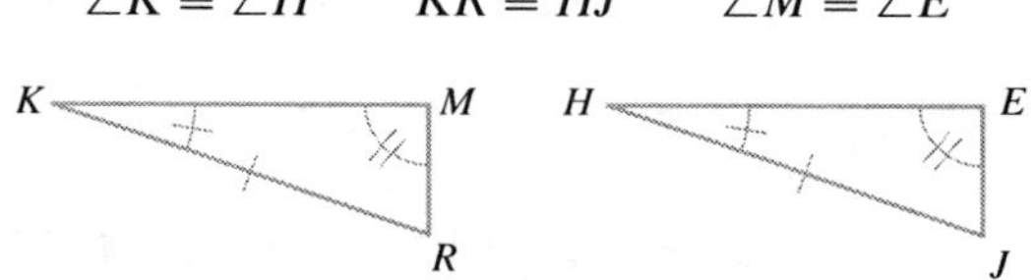

30. Use tick marks to show the congruent parts of the triangles shown below.

$\angle P \cong \angle T \quad \overline{LP} \cong \overline{RT} \quad \overline{FP} \cong \overline{ST}$

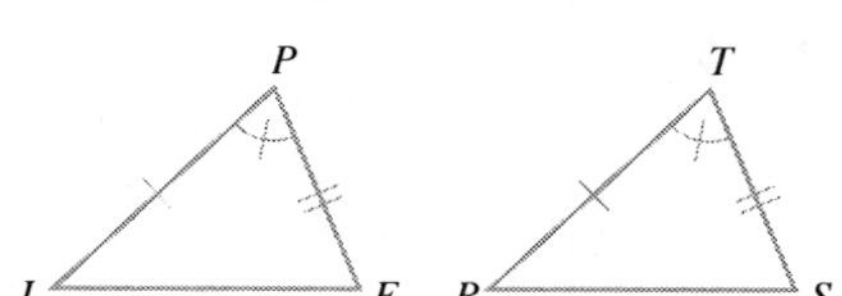

GUIDED PRACTICE

Name the six corresponding parts of the congruent triangles. See Objective 1.

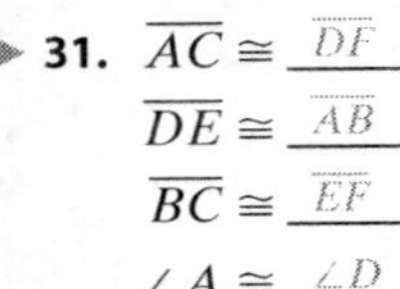

31. $\overline{AC} \cong$ $\overline{DF}$
$\overline{DE} \cong$ $\overline{AB}$
$\overline{BC} \cong$ $\overline{EF}$
$\angle A \cong$ $\angle D$
$\angle E \cong$ $\angle B$
$\angle F \cong$ $\angle C$

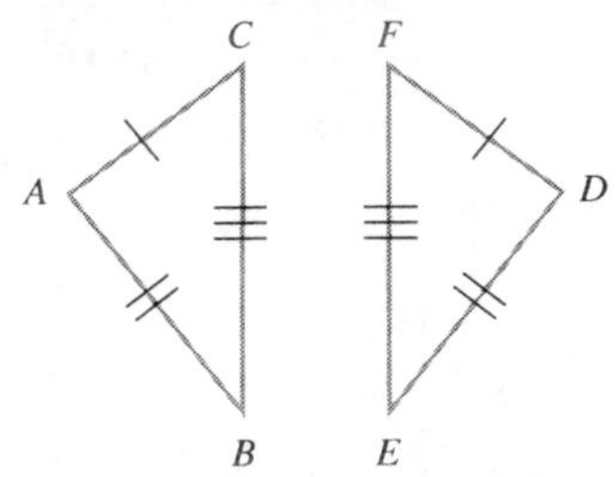

32. $\overline{AB} \cong$ $\overline{DE}$
$\overline{EC} \cong$ $\overline{BC}$
$\overline{AC} \cong$ $\overline{DC}$
$\angle D \cong$ $\angle A$
$\angle B \cong$ $\angle E$
$\angle 1 \cong$ $\angle 2$

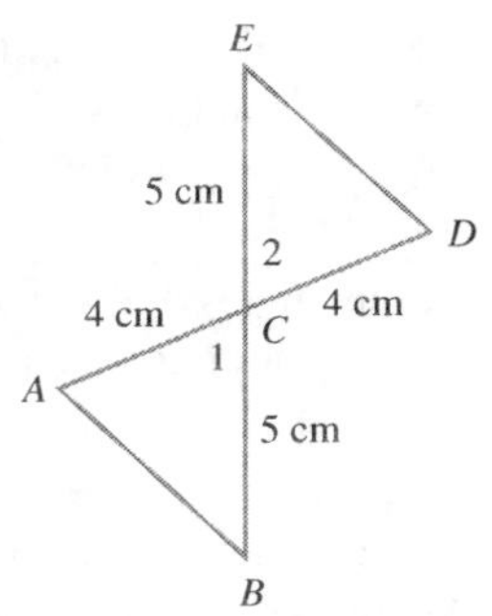

33. Refer to the figure below, where $\triangle BCD \cong \triangle MNO$.

a. Name the six congruent corresponding parts of the triangles. See Example 1. $\angle B \cong \angle M$, $\angle C \cong \angle N$, $\angle D \cong \angle O$, $\overline{BC} \cong \overline{MN}$, $\overline{CD} \cong \overline{NO}$, $\overline{BD} \cong \overline{MO}$

b. Find m($\angle N$). 72°

c. Find m($\overline{MO}$). 10 ft

d. Find m($\overline{CD}$). 9 ft

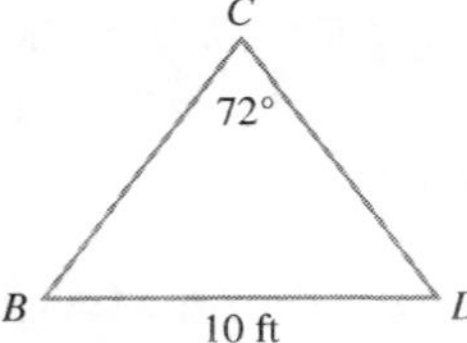

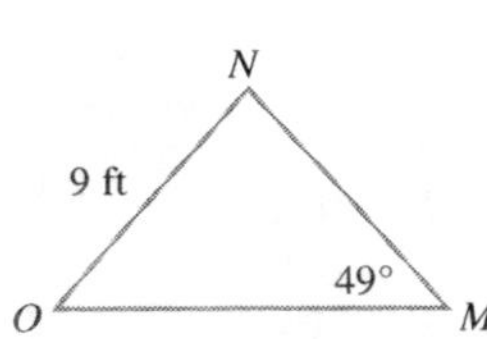

34. Refer to the figure below, where $\triangle DCG \cong \triangle RST$.

a. Name the six congruent corresponding parts of the triangles. See Example 1. $\angle D \cong \angle R$, $\angle C \cong \angle S$, $\angle G \cong \angle T$, $\overline{DC} \cong \overline{RS}$, $\overline{CG} \cong \overline{ST}$, $\overline{DG} \cong \overline{RT}$

b. Find m($\angle R$). 60°

c. Find m($\overline{DG}$). 2 in.

d. Find m($\overline{ST}$). 3 in.

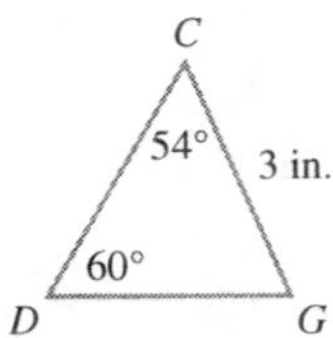

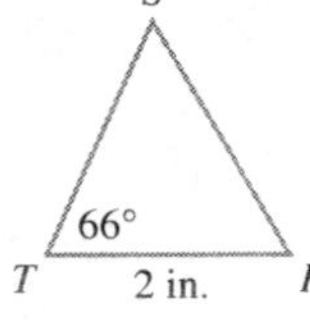

Determine whether each pair of triangles is congruent. If they are, tell why. See Examples 2 and 3.

35. **36.**

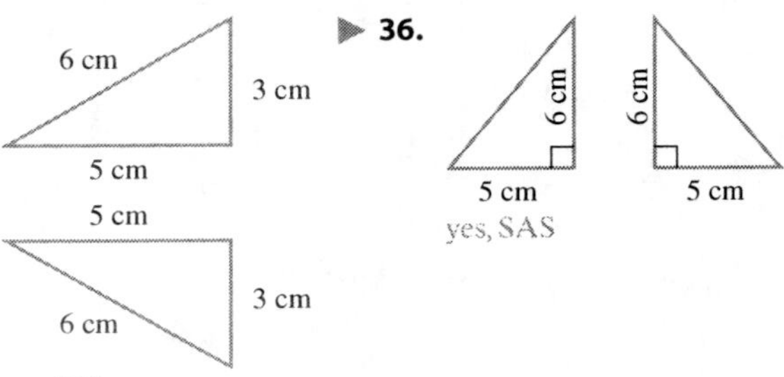

35. yes, SSS

36. yes, SAS

37.

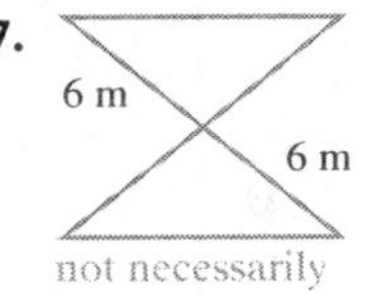

not necessarily

38.

yes, ASA

39. Refer to the similar triangles shown below. See Example 4.

a. Name 3 pairs of congruent angles. $\angle L \cong \angle H$, $\angle M \cong \angle J$, $\angle R \cong \angle E$

b. Complete each proportion.

$$\frac{LM}{HJ} = \frac{MR}{JE} \qquad \frac{MR}{JE} = \frac{LR}{HE} \qquad \frac{LM}{HJ} = \frac{LR}{HE}$$

c. We can write the answer to part b in a more compact form:

$$\frac{LM}{HJ} = \frac{MR}{JE} = \frac{LR}{HE}$$

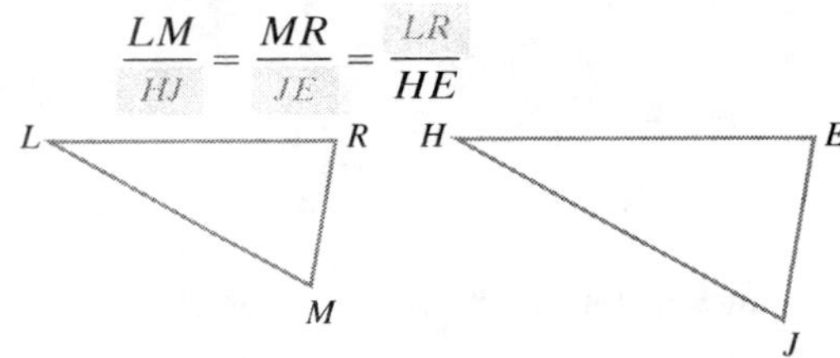

40. Refer to the similar triangles shown below. See Example 4.

a. Name 3 pairs of congruent angles. $\angle W \cong \angle D$, $\angle Y \cong \angle F$, $\angle X \cong \angle E$

b. Complete each proportion.

$$\frac{WY}{DF} = \frac{YX}{FE} \qquad \frac{WX}{DE} = \frac{YX}{FE} \qquad \frac{XY}{EF} = \frac{WY}{DF}$$

c. We can write the answer to part b in a more compact form:

$$\frac{WY}{DF} = \frac{YX}{FE} = \frac{WX}{DE}$$

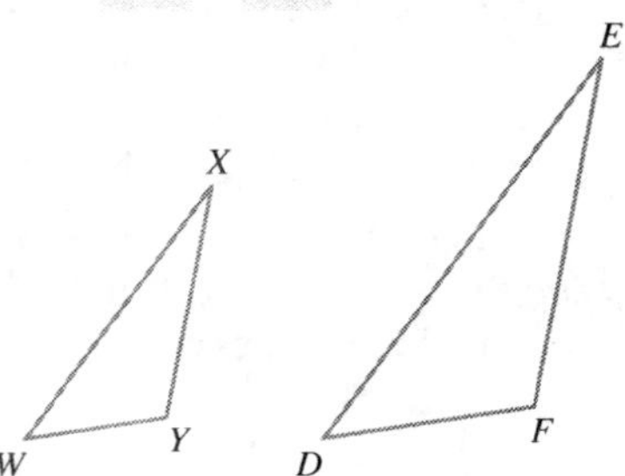

Tell whether the triangles are similar. See Example 5.

41. **42.**

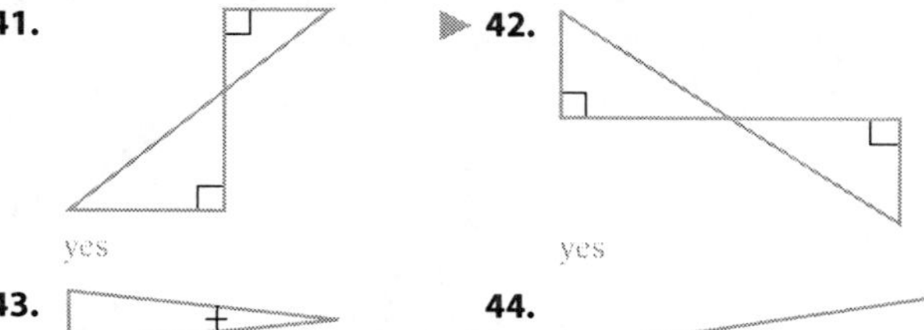

41. yes 42. yes

43. **44.**

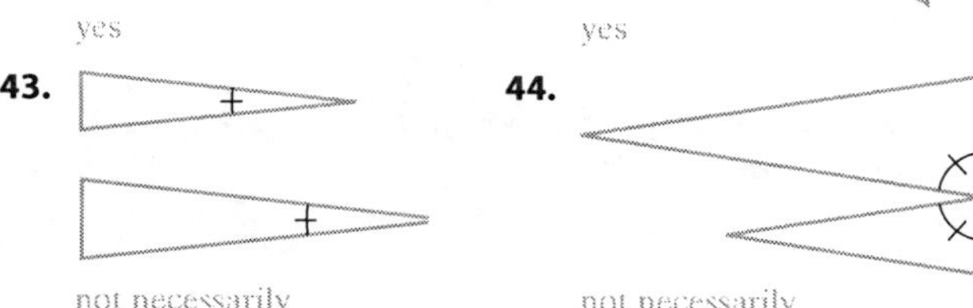

43. not necessarily 44. not necessarily

45. **46.**

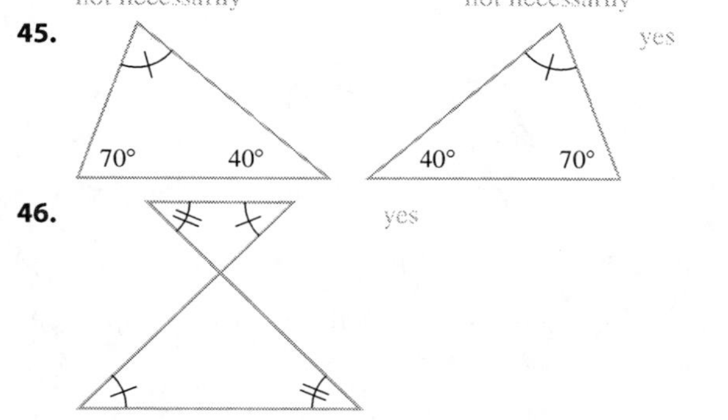

45. yes 46. yes

47. **48.**

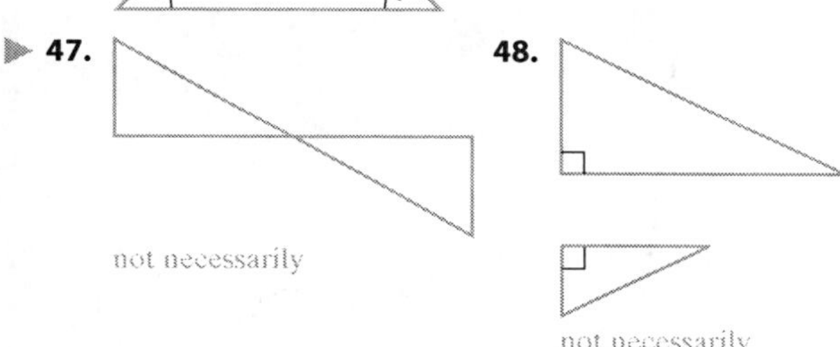

47. not necessarily 48. not necessarily

49. $\overline{XY} \parallel \overline{ZD}$ yes **50.** $\overline{QR} \parallel \overline{TU}$ yes

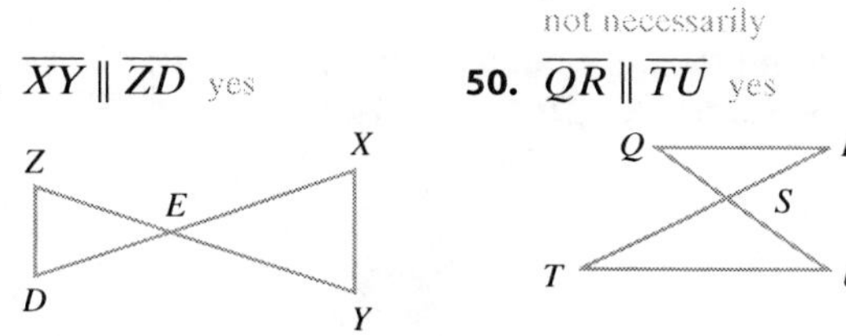

51. **52.**

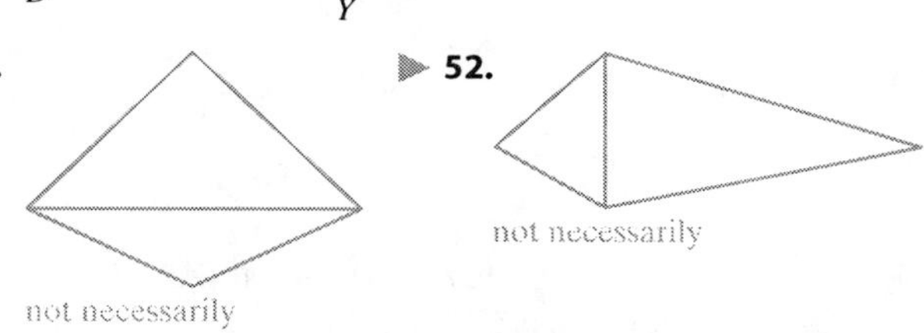

51. not necessarily 52. not necessarily

In Problems 53 and 54, $\triangle MSN \sim \triangle TPR$. Find x and y. See Example 6.

53. 8, 35

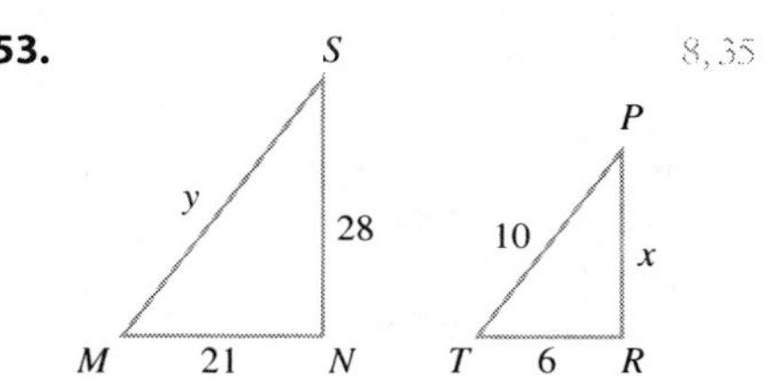

54. 8, 9

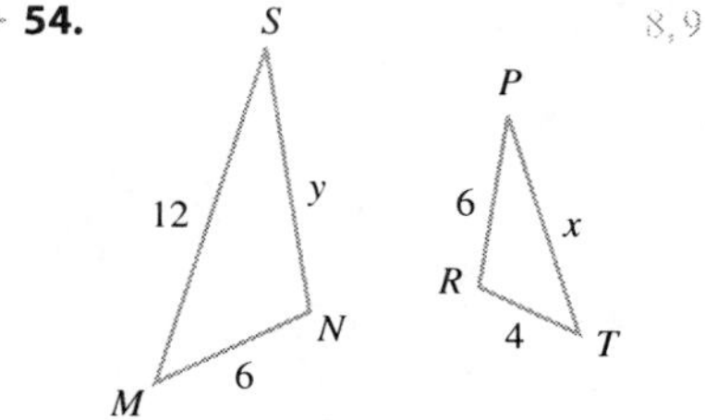

In Problems 55 and 56, $\triangle MSN \sim \triangle TPN$. Find x and y. See Example 6.

55. **56.**

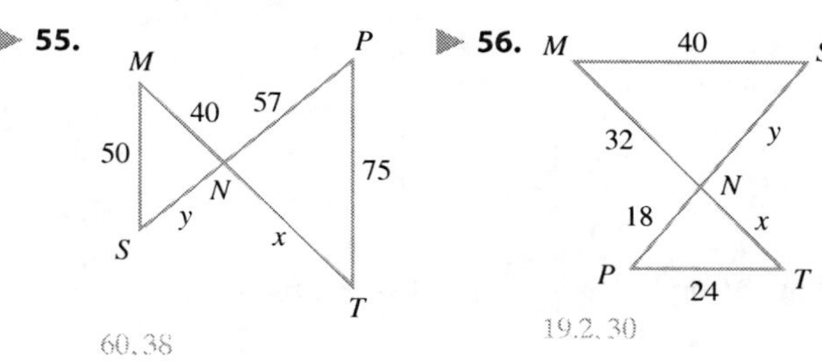

55. 60, 38 56. 19.2, 30

TRY IT YOURSELF

Tell whether each statement is true. If a statement is false, tell why.

57. If three sides of one triangle are the same length as the corresponding three sides of a second triangle, the triangles are congruent. true

58. If two sides of one triangle are the same length as two sides of a second triangle, the triangles are congruent. false: need SSS or SAS

59. If two sides and an angle of one triangle are congruent, respectively, to two sides and an angle of a second triangle, the triangles are congruent. false: the angles must be between congruent sides

60. If two angles and the side between them in one triangle are congruent, respectively, to two angles and the side between them in a second triangle, the triangles are congruent. true

Determine whether each pair of triangles are congruent. If they are, tell why.

61. **62.**

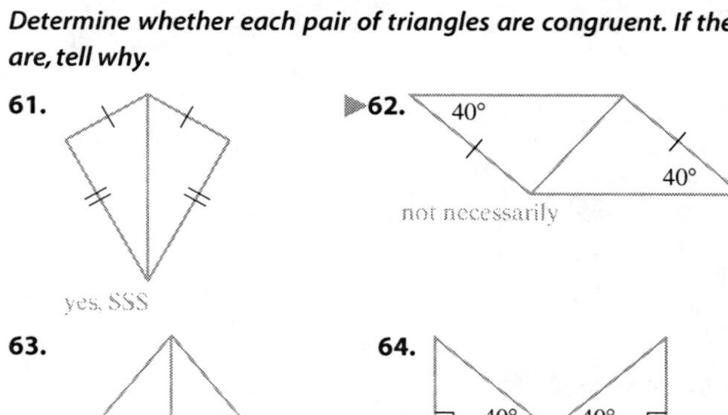

61. yes, SSS 62. not necessarily

63. **64.**

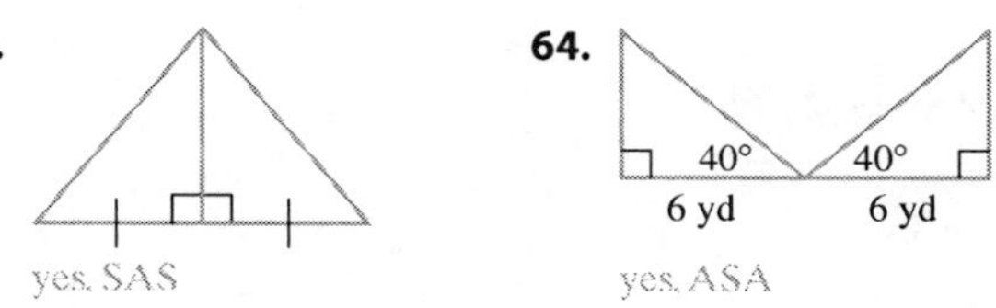

63. yes, SAS 64. yes, ASA

65. $\overline{AB} \parallel \overline{DE}$ yes, ASA

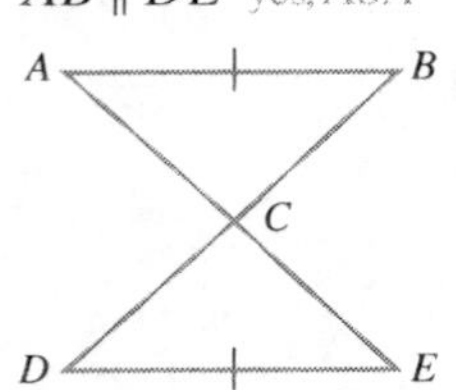

66. $\overline{XY} \parallel \overline{ZQ}$ yes, ASA

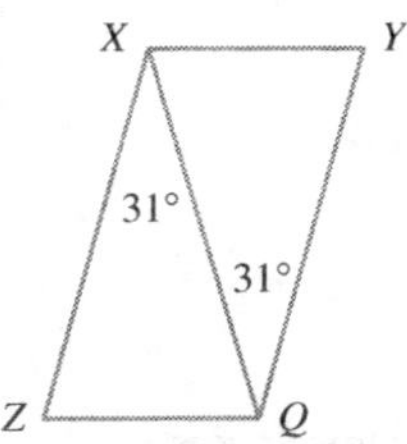

67.

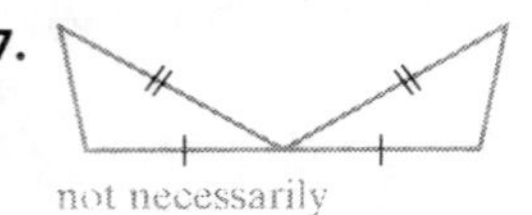

not necessarily

68.

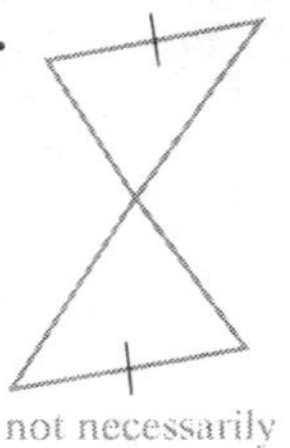

not necessarily

In Problems 69 and 70, $\triangle ABC \cong \triangle DEF$. Find x and y.

69. 80°, 2 yd

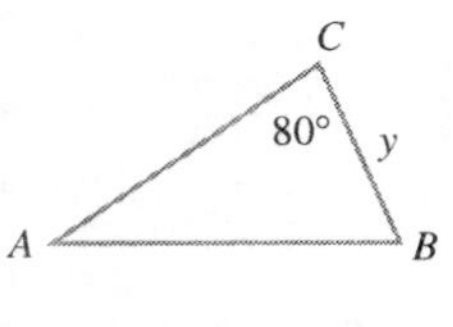

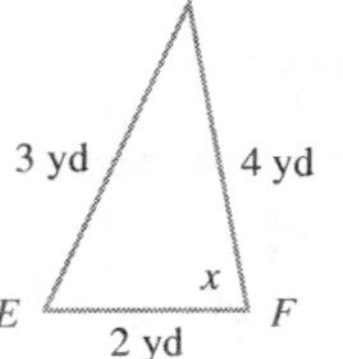

70.

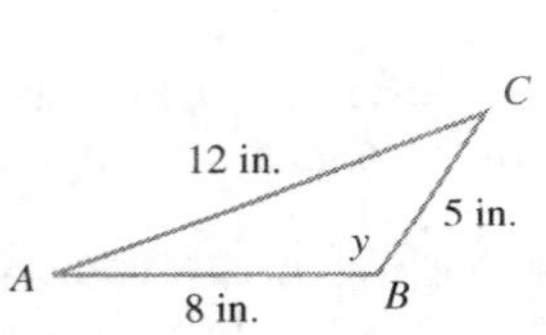

12 in., 135°

In Problems 71 and 72, find x and y.

71. $\triangle ABC \cong \triangle ABD$ 19°, 14 m

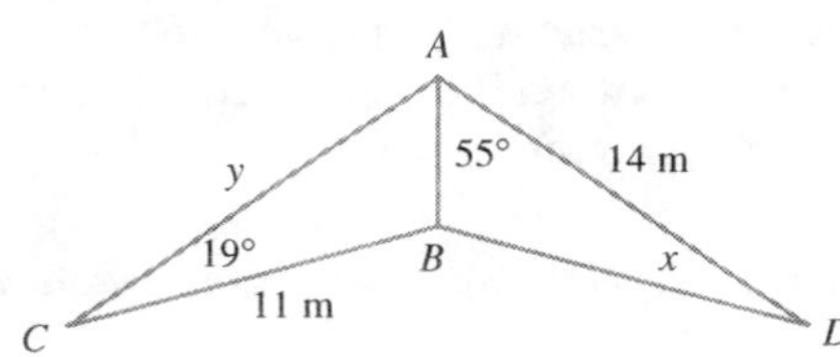

72. $\triangle ABC \cong \triangle DEC$ 8 mi, 37°

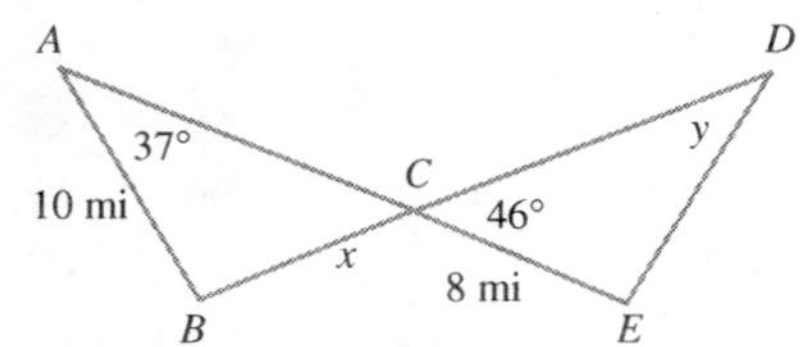

In Problems 73–76, find x.

73.

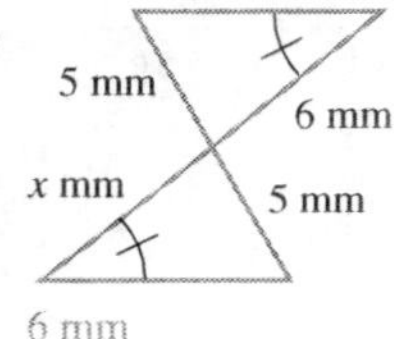

6 mm

74.

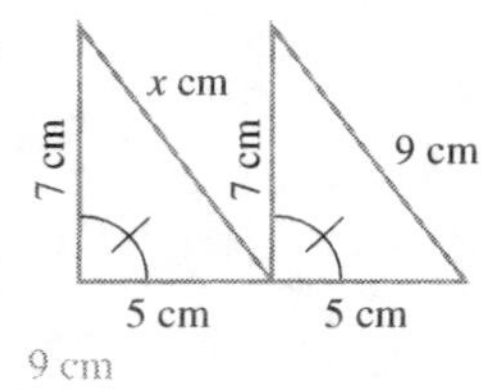

9 cm

75.

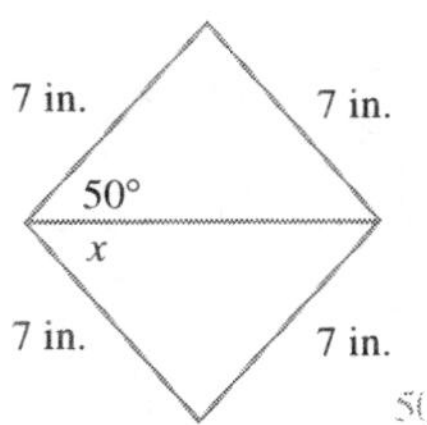

50°

76.

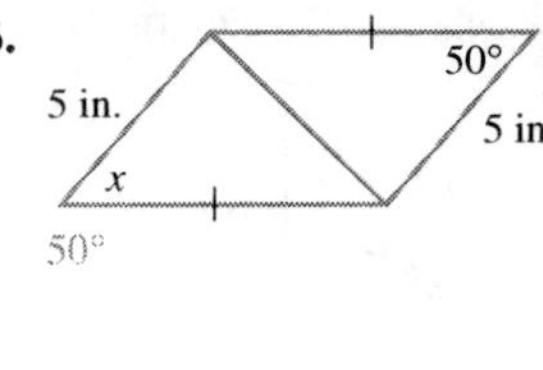

50°

77. If $\overline{DE}$ in the figure below is parallel to $\overline{AB}$, $\triangle ABC$ will be similar to $\triangle DEC$. Find x. $\frac{25}{6} = 4\frac{1}{6}$

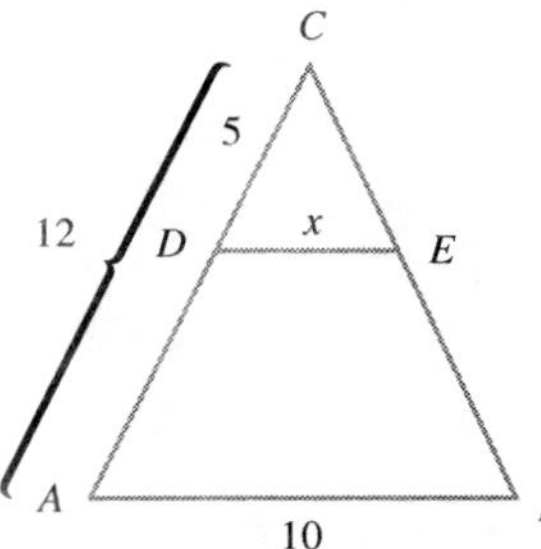

78. If $\overline{SU}$ in the figure below is parallel to $\overline{TV}$, $\triangle SRU$ will be similar to $\triangle TRV$. Find x. 18

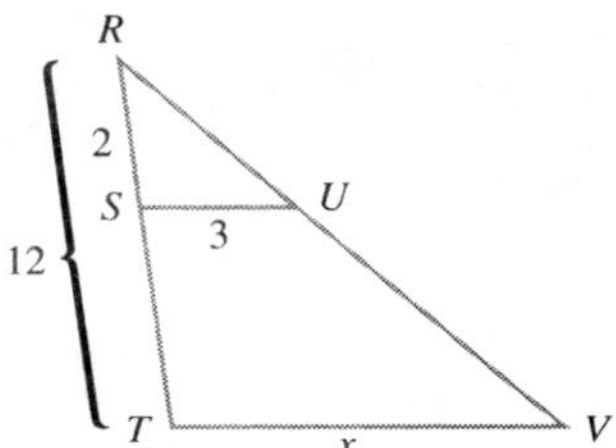

79. If $\overline{DE}$ in the figure below is parallel to $\overline{CB}$, $\triangle EAD$ will be similar to $\triangle BAC$. Find x. 16

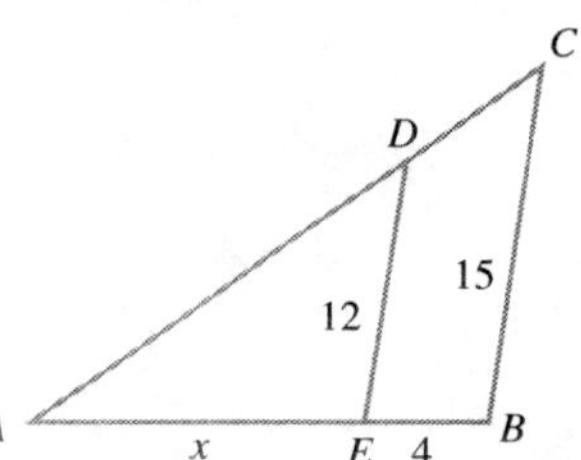

80. If $\overline{HK}$ in the figure below is parallel to $\overline{AB}$, $\triangle HCK$ will be similar to $\triangle ACB$. Find x. 4

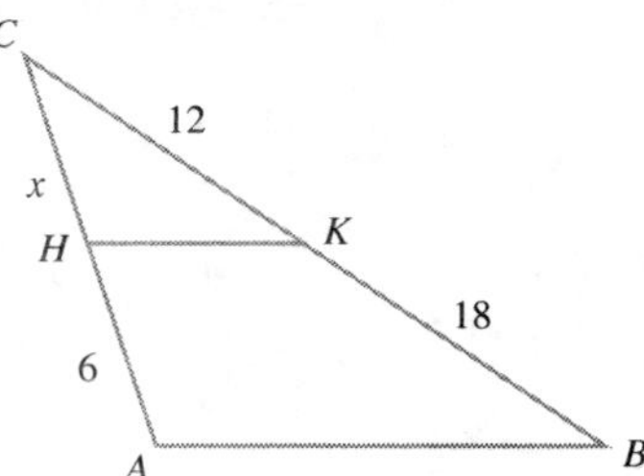

APPLICATIONS

81. SEWING The pattern that is sewn on the rear pocket of a pair of blue jeans is shown below. If $\triangle AOB \cong \triangle COD$, how long is the stitching from point A to point D? 17.5 cm

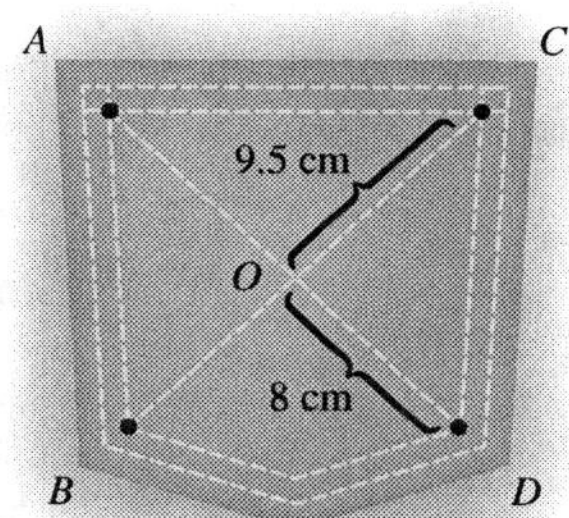

82. CAMPING The base of the tent pole is placed at the midpoint between the stake at point A and the stake at point B, and it is perpendicular to the ground, as shown below. Explain why $\triangle ACD \cong \triangle BCD$.
SAS property: $\overline{AD} \cong \overline{BD}$, $\angle ABC \cong \angle BDC$, $\overline{CD} \cong \overline{CD}$

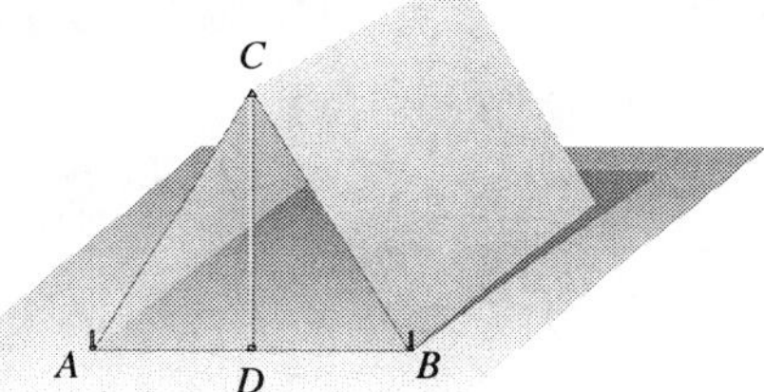

83. A surveying crew needs to find the width of the river shown in the illustration below. Because of a dangerous current, they decide to stay on the west side of the river and use geometry to find its width. Their approach is to create two similar right triangles on dry land. Then they write and solve a proportion to find w. What is the width of the river? 59.2 ft

from Campus to Careers
Surveyor

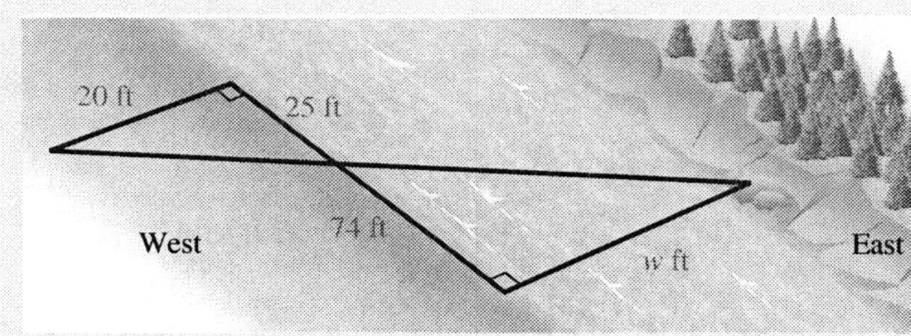

84. HEIGHT OF A BUILDING A man places a mirror on the ground and sees the reflection of the top of a building, as shown below. Find the height of the building. 36 ft

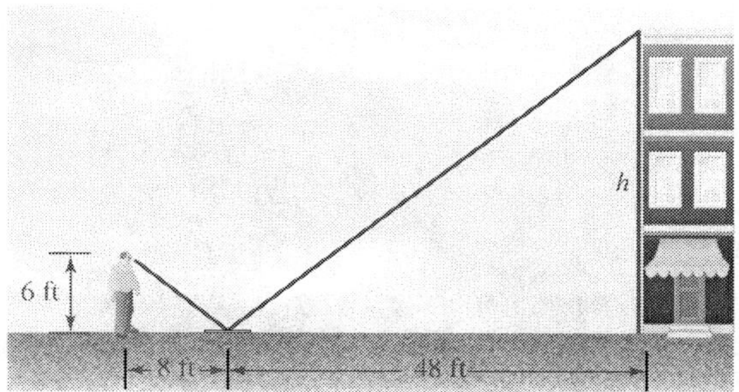

85. HEIGHT OF A TREE The tree shown below casts a shadow 24 feet long when a man 6 feet tall casts a shadow 4 feet long. Find the height of the tree. 36 ft

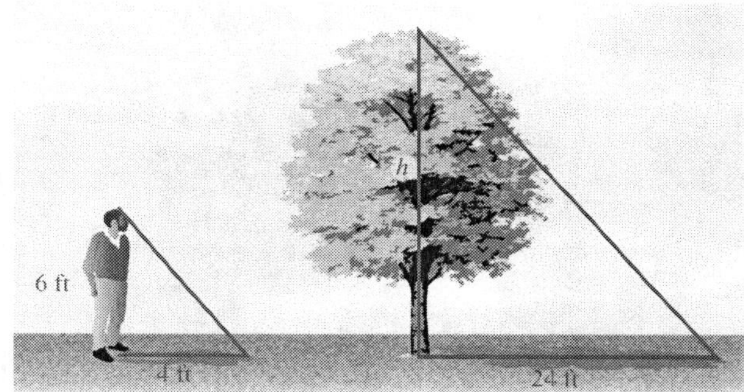

86. WASHINGTON, D.C. The Washington Monument casts a shadow of $166\frac{1}{2}$ feet at the same time as a 5-foot-tall tourist casts a shadow of $1\frac{1}{2}$ feet. Find the height of the monument. 555 ft

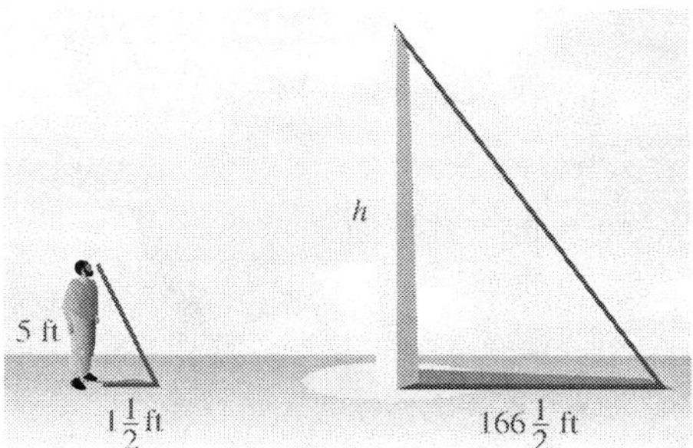

87. HEIGHT OF A TREE A tree casts a shadow of 29 feet at the same time as a vertical yardstick casts a shadow of 2.5 feet. Find the height of the tree. 34.8 ft

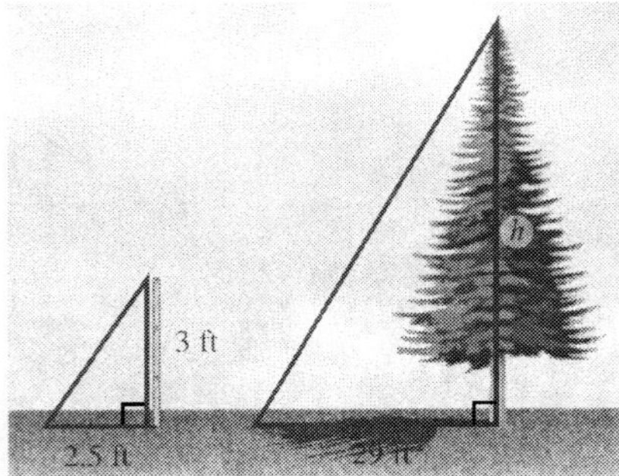

88. GEOGRAPHY The diagram below shows how a laser beam was pointed over the top of a pole to the top of a mountain to determine the elevation of the mountain. Find h. 1,204 ft + 5 ft = 1,209 ft

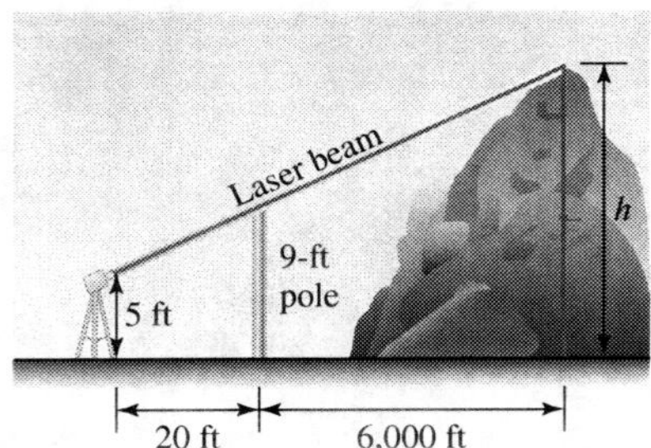

89. FLIGHT PATH An airplane ascends 200 feet as it flies a horizontal distance of 1,000 feet, as shown in the following figure. How much altitude is gained as it flies a horizontal distance of 1 mile? (*Hint:* 1 mile = 5,280 feet.) 1,056 ft

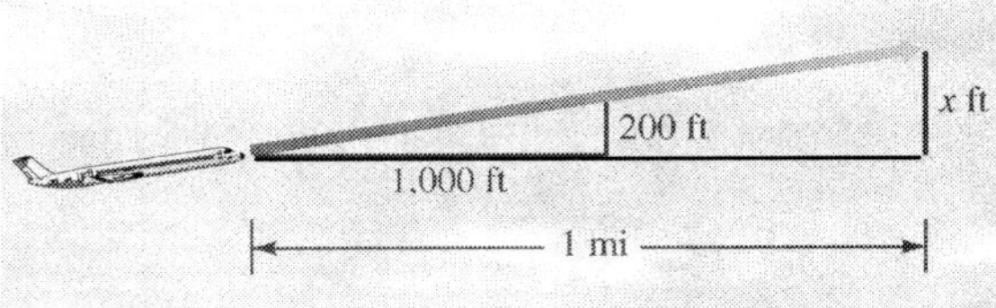

WRITING

90. Tell whether the statement is true or false. Explain your answer.

a. Congruent triangles are always similar.

b. Similar triangles are always congruent.

91. Explain why there is no SSA property for congruent triangles.

REVIEW

Find the LCM of the given numbers.

92. 16, 20 80

93. 21, 27 189

Find the GCF of the given numbers.

94. 18, 96 6

95. 63, 84 21

SECTION 3.3
Similar Triangles

Objectives

1. Write ratios and rates in simplest form.
2. Solve proportions.
3. Use proportions to solve problems.
4. Use proportions to solve problems that involve similar triangles.

Note: The two consecutive sections on similar triangles can be combined or edited so that they fit the North Carolina Student Learning Outcomes exactly.

In this section, we will discuss a problem-solving tool called a *proportion.* A proportion is a type of rational equation that involves two *ratios* or two *rates.*

1 Write ratios and rates in simplest form.

Ratios enable us to compare numerical quantities.

- To prepare fuel for a lawnmower, gasoline must be mixed with oil in the ratio of 50 to 1.
- To make 14-karat jewelry, gold is mixed with other metals in the ratio of 14 to 10.
- In the stock market, winning stocks might outnumber losing stocks in the ratio of 7 to 4.

Ratios

A **ratio** is the quotient of two numbers or the quotient of two quantities that have the same units.

There are three common ways to write a ratio: as a fraction, with the word *to,* or with a colon. For example, the ratio comparing the number of winning stocks to the number of losing stocks mentioned earlier can be written as

$$\frac{7}{4}, \qquad 7 \text{ to } 4, \qquad \text{or} \qquad 7{:}4$$

Each of these forms can be read as "the ratio of 7 to 4."

EXAMPLE 1 Translate each phrase into a ratio written in fractional form:

a. The ratio of 5 to 9 **b.** 12 ounces to 2 pounds

Strategy To translate, we need to identify the number (or quantity) before the word *to* and the number (or quantity) after it.

WHY The number before the word *to* is the numerator of the ratio and the number after it is the denominator.

Solution

a. The ratio of 5 to 9 is written $\frac{5}{9}$.

b. To write a ratio of two quantities with the same units, we must express 2 pounds in terms of ounces. Since 1 pound = 16 ounces, 2 pounds = 32 ounces. The ratio of 12 ounces to 32 ounces can be simplified so that no units appear in the final form.

$$\frac{12 \text{ ounces}}{32 \text{ ounces}} = \frac{3 \cdot \overset{1}{\cancel{4}}\ \overset{1}{\cancel{\text{ounces}}}}{\underset{1}{\cancel{4}} \cdot 8\ \underset{1}{\cancel{\text{ounces}}}} = \frac{3}{8}$$

Self Check 1

Translate each phrase into a ratio written in fractional form:

a. The ratio of 15 to 2 $\frac{15}{2}$

b. 12 hours to 2 days $\frac{1}{4}$

Now Try **Problems 19 and 25**

Teaching Example 1 Translate each phrase into a ratio written in fractional form:

a. The ratio of 12 to 27

b. 154 cm to 2 m

Answers:

a. $\frac{12}{27}$ b. $\frac{77}{100}$

The Language of Algebra A ratio that is the quotient of two quantities having the same units should be simplified so that no units appear in the final answer.

When quotients are used to compare quantities with different units, they are called *rates.* For example, if the 495-mile drive from New Orleans to Dallas takes 9 hours, the average rate of speed is the quotient of the miles driven to the length of time the trip takes.

$$\text{Average rate of speed} = \frac{495 \text{ miles}}{9 \text{ hours}} = \frac{55 \text{ miles}}{1 \text{ hour}} \qquad \frac{495}{9} = \frac{\overset{1}{\cancel{9}} \cdot 55}{\underset{1}{\cancel{9}} \cdot 1} = \frac{55}{1}.$$

Rates

A **rate** is a quotient of two quantities that have different units.

THINK IT THROUGH ***Student Loan Calculations***

"A consistent majority of students who borrow to pay for their higher education believe they could not have gone to college without student loans. Over 70% agree that student loans were very or extremely important in allowing them access to education after high school."

National Student Loan Survey, 2002

Many student loan programs calculate a *debt-to-income ratio* to assist them in determining whether the borrower has sufficient income to repay the loan. A debt-to-income ratio compares an applicant's monthly debt payments (mortgages, credit cards, auto loans, etc.) to their gross monthly income. Most education lenders require borrower debt-to-income ratios of $\frac{2}{5}$ or less, according to the Nellie Mae Debt Management Edvisor. Calculate the debt-to-income ratio for each loan applicant shown below. Then determine whether it makes them eligible for a student loan.

	Applicant #1	Applicant #2	Applicant #3
Monthly debt payments	\$250	\$1,000	\$1,200
Gross monthly income	\$1,000	\$2,000	\$3,000
Debt-to-income ratio	$\frac{1}{4}$	$\frac{1}{2}$	$\frac{2}{5}$
Is the ratio $\leq \frac{2}{5}$?	yes	no	yes

2 Solve proportions.

Consider the following table, in which we are given the costs of various numbers of gallons of gasoline.

Number of gallons	Cost
2	\$3.72
5	\$9.30
8	\$14.88
12	\$22.32
20	\$37.20

If we compare the costs to the numbers of gallons purchased, we see that they are equal. In this example, each quotient represents the cost of 1 gallon of gasoline, which is \$1.86.

$$\frac{\$3.72}{2} = \$1.86, \quad \frac{\$9.30}{5} = \$1.86, \quad \frac{\$14.88}{8} = \$1.86,$$

$$\frac{\$22.32}{12} = \$1.86, \quad \text{and} \quad \frac{\$37.20}{20} = \$1.86$$

When two ratios or rates $\left(\text{such as } \frac{\$3.72}{2} \text{ and } \frac{\$9.30}{5}\right)$ are equal, they form a *proportion.*

Proportions

A **proportion** is a mathematical statement that two ratios or two rates are equal.

Some examples of proportions are

$$\frac{1}{2} = \frac{3}{6}, \quad \frac{3 \text{ waiters}}{7 \text{ tables}} = \frac{9 \text{ waiters}}{21 \text{ tables}}, \quad \text{and} \quad \frac{a}{b} = \frac{c}{d}$$

- The proportion $\frac{1}{2} = \frac{3}{6}$ can be read as "1 is to 2 as 3 is to 6."
- The proportion $\frac{3 \text{ waiters}}{7 \text{ tables}} = \frac{9 \text{ waiters}}{21 \text{ tables}}$ can be read as "3 waiters is to 7 tables as 9 waiters is to 21 tables."
- The proportion $\frac{a}{b} = \frac{c}{d}$ can be read as "a is to b as c is to d."

In the proportion $\frac{a}{b} = \frac{c}{d}$, a and d are called the **extremes,** and b and c are called the **means.** We can show that the product of the extremes (ad) is equal to the product of the means (bc) by multiplying both sides of the proportion by bd and observing that $ad = bc$.

$$\frac{a}{b} = \frac{c}{d}$$

$$\overset{1}{\cancel{b}}d \cdot \frac{a}{\underset{1}{\cancel{b}}} = b\overset{1}{\cancel{d}} \cdot \frac{c}{\underset{1}{\cancel{d}}}$$ To clear the equation of fractions, multiply both sides by the LCD, which is bd.

$$ad = bc$$ Perform each multiplication and simplify.

Since $ad = bc$, the product of the extremes equals the product of the means.

The Fundamental Property of Proportions

In a proportion, the product of the extremes is equal to the product of the means. If $\frac{a}{b} = \frac{c}{d}$, then $ad = bc$, and if $ad = bc$, then $\frac{a}{b} = \frac{c}{d}$.

To determine whether an equation is a proportion, we can check to see whether the product of the extremes is equal to the product of the means.

EXAMPLE 2

Determine whether each equation is a proportion:

a. $\frac{3}{7} = \frac{9}{21}$ **b.** $\frac{8}{3} = \frac{13}{5}$

Strategy We will check to see whether the product of the extremes is equal to the product of the means.

WHY If the product of the extremes equals the product of the means, the equation is a proportion. If the cross products are not equal, the equation is not a proportion.

Solution

In each case, we check to see whether the product of the extremes is equal to the product of the means.

a. The product of the extremes is $3 \cdot 21 = 63$. The product of the means is $7 \cdot 9 = 63$. Since the products are equal, the equation is a proportion: $\frac{3}{7} = \frac{9}{21}$.

$3 \cdot 21 = 63 \qquad 7 \cdot 9 = 63$

$$\frac{3}{7} = \frac{9}{21}$$ The product of the extremes and the product of the means are also known as cross products.

b. The product of the extremes is $8 \cdot 5 = 40$. The product of the means is $3 \cdot 13 = 39$. Since the cross products are not equal, the equation is not a proportion: $\frac{8}{3} \neq \frac{13}{5}$.

Self Check 2

Determine whether the equation is a proportion: $\frac{6}{13} = \frac{24}{53}$ no

Now Try **Problems 34 and 35**

Teaching Example 2 Determine whether each equation is a proportion:
a. $\frac{7}{13} = \frac{5}{9}$ b. $\frac{5}{12} = \frac{20}{48}$

Answers:
a. no b. yes

$8 \cdot 5 = 40 \qquad 3 \cdot 13 = 39$

$$\frac{8}{3} = \frac{13}{5}$$ One cross product is 40 and the other is 39.

Suppose that we know three terms in the proportion

$$\frac{x}{5} = \frac{24}{20}$$

To find the unknown term, we can multiply both sides of the equation by 20 to clear it of fractions, and then solve for x. However, with proportions, it is often easier to simply compute the cross products, set them equal, and solve for the variable.

$$\frac{x}{5} = \frac{24}{20}$$

$20 \cdot x = 5 \cdot 24$ In a proportion, the product of the extremes equals the product of the means.

$20x = 120$ Perform the multiplication: $5 \cdot 24 = 120$.

$\frac{20x}{20} = \frac{120}{20}$ To undo the multiplication by 20, divide both sides by 20.

$x = 6$ Perform the divisions.

Thus, x is 6. To check this result, we substitute 6 for x in $\frac{x}{5} = \frac{24}{20}$ and find the cross products.

$$\frac{6}{5} \stackrel{?}{=} \frac{24}{20} \qquad 6 \cdot 20 = 120 \qquad 5 \cdot 24 = 120$$

Since the cross products are equal, this is a proportion. The result, 6, is correct.

Self Check 3

Solve: $\frac{15}{x} = \frac{25}{40}$ 24

Now Try **Problem 40**

Teaching Example 3 Solve: $\frac{15}{6} = \frac{10}{x}$

Answer:
4

EXAMPLE 3 Solve: $\frac{12}{18} = \frac{3}{x}$

Strategy To solve for x, we will set the cross products equal.

WHY Since the equation is a proportion, the product of the means equals the product of the extremes.

Solution

$$\frac{12}{18} = \frac{3}{x}$$

$12 \cdot x = 18 \cdot 3$ In a proportion, the product of the extremes equals the product of the means.

$12x = 54$ Multiply: $18 \cdot 3 = 54$.

$\frac{12x}{12} = \frac{54}{12}$ To undo the multiplication by 12, divide both sides by 12.

$x = \frac{9}{2}$ Simplify: $\frac{54}{12} = \frac{9 \cdot \overset{1}{\cancel{6}}}{\underset{1}{\cancel{6}} \cdot 2} = \frac{9}{2}$.

Thus, x is $\frac{9}{2}$. Check the result.

Success Tip Since proportions are rational equations, they can also be solved by multiplying both sides by the LCD. Here an alternate approach is to multiply both sides by $18x$.

Caution! Remember that a cross product is the product of the means or extremes of a *proportion.* For example, it would be incorrect to try to compute cross products to solve the rational equation $\frac{12}{18} = \frac{3}{x} + \frac{1}{2}$. The right-hand side is not a ratio, so the equation is *not* a proportion.

Using Your CALCULATOR **Solving Proportions with a Calculator**

To solve the proportion $\frac{3.5}{7.2} = \frac{x}{15.84}$ with a calculator, we can proceed as follows.

$$\frac{3.5}{7.2} = \frac{x}{15.84}$$

$$\frac{3.5(15.84)}{7.2} = x$$ To undo the division by 15.84 and isolate x, multiply both sides of the equation by 15.84.

We can find x by entering these numbers into a scientific calculator.

3.5 [×] 15.84 [÷] 7.2 [=]   7.7

Using a graphing calculator, we enter these numbers and press these keys.

3.5 [×] 15.84 [÷] 7.2 [ENTER]   3.5*15.84/7.2   7.7

Thus, x is 7.7.

EXAMPLE 4 Solve: $\frac{2a + 1}{4} = \frac{10}{8}$

Strategy To solve for a, we will set the cross products equal.

WHY Since the equation is a proportion, the product of the means equals the product of the extremes.

Solution

$$\frac{2a + 1}{4} = \frac{10}{8}$$

$8(2a + 1) = 40$ In a proportion, the product of the extremes equals the product of the means.

$16a + 8 = 40$ Distribute the multiplication by 8.

$16a + 8 - 8 = 40 - 8$ To undo the addition of 8, subtract 8 from both sides.

$16a = 32$ Combine like terms.

$\frac{16a}{16} = \frac{32}{16}$ To undo the multiplication by 16, divide both sides by 16.

$a = 2$ Perform the divisions.

Thus, a is 2. Check the result.

Self Check 4

Solve: $\frac{3x - 1}{2} = \frac{12.5}{5}$ 2

Now Try **Problem 49**

Teaching Example 4 Solve: $\frac{3a + 2}{5} = \frac{-1}{5}$

Answer: -1

EXAMPLE 5 Solve: $\frac{a}{2} = \frac{4}{a - 2}$

Strategy To solve for a, we will set the cross products equal.

WHY Since this equation is a proportion, the product of the means equals the product of the extremes.

Self Check 5

Solve: $\frac{6}{c} = \frac{c - 1}{5}$ $-5, 6$

Now Try **Problem 53**

Teaching Example 5 Solve: $\frac{x}{5} = \frac{3}{x + 14}$

Answer: $-15, 1$

Solution

$$\frac{a}{2} = \frac{4}{a-2}$$ This is the given proportion.

$$a(a-2) = 2 \cdot 4$$ Find each cross product and set them equal. Don't forget to write the parentheses.

$$a^2 - 2a = 8$$ On the left hand side, distribute the multiplication by a. This is a quadratic equation.

$$a^2 - 2a - 8 = 0$$ To get 0 on the right side of the equation, subtract 8 from both sides.

$$(a+2)(a-4) = 0$$ Factor $a^2 - 2a - 8$.

$$a + 2 = 0 \quad \text{or} \quad a - 4 = 0$$ Set each factor equal to 0.

$$a = -2 \quad | \quad a = 4$$ Solve each equation.

The solutions are -2 and 4. Verify this using a check.

3 Use proportions to solve problems.

We can use proportions to solve many real-world problems. If we are given a ratio (or rate) comparing two quantities, the words of the problem can be translated to a proportion, and we can solve it to find the unknown.

Self Check 6

If 9 tickets to a concert cost \$112.50, how much will 15 tickets cost? \$187.50

Now Try **Problem 77**

© iStockphoto.com/Alex Potemkin

Teaching Example 6 If 6 tickets to a Broadway show cost \$345, how much do 11 tickets cost?
Answer:
\$632.50

EXAMPLE 6 *Grocery Shopping* If 6 apples cost \$1.38, how much will 16 apples cost?

Analyze We know the cost of 6 apples; we are to find the cost of 16 apples.

Form Let c = the cost of 16 apples. If we compare the number of apples to their cost, we know that the two rates are equal.

6 apples is to \$1.38 as 16 apples is to \$c.

Number of apples → 6 / Cost of the apples → 1.38 = 16 ← Number of apples / c ← Cost of the apples

$$\frac{6}{1.38} = \frac{16}{c}$$

Solve

$$6 \cdot c = 1.38(16)$$ In a proportion, the product of the extremes equals the product of the means.

$$6c = 22.08$$ Perform the multiplication: $1.38(16) = 22.08$.

$$\frac{6c}{6} = \frac{22.08}{6}$$ To undo the multiplication by 6, divide both sides by 6.

$$c = 3.68$$ Divide: $\frac{22.08}{6} = 3.68$.

State Sixteen apples will cost \$3.68.

Check If 16 apples are bought, this is about 3 times as many as 6 apples, which cost \$1.38. If we multiply \$1.38 by 3, we get an estimate of the cost of 16 apples: $\$1.38 \cdot 3 = \$4.14$. The result, \$3.68, seems reasonable.

In Example 6, we could have compared the cost of the apples to the number of apples: \$1.38 is to 6 apples as \$$c$ is to 16 apples. This would have led to the proportion

Cost of the apples → 1.38 / Number of apples → 6 = c ← Cost of the apples / 16 ← Number of apples

$$\frac{1.38}{6} = \frac{c}{16}$$

If we solve this proportion for c, we will obtain the same result: $c = 3.68$.

> ***Caution!*** When solving problems using proportions, we must make sure that the units of both numerators are the same and the units of both denominators are the same. In Example 6, it would be incorrect to write
>
> $$\begin{array}{r} \text{Cost of the apples} \rightarrow \\ \text{Number of apples} \rightarrow \end{array} \frac{1.38}{6} = \frac{16}{c} \begin{array}{l} \leftarrow \text{Number of apples} \\ \leftarrow \text{Cost of the apples} \end{array}$$

EXAMPLE 7 *Scale Models* A **scale** is a ratio (or rate) that compares the size of a model, drawing, or map to the size of an actual object. The scale shown in the figure indicates that 1 inch on the model carousel is equivalent to 160 inches on the actual carousel. How wide should the model be if the actual carousel is 35 feet wide?

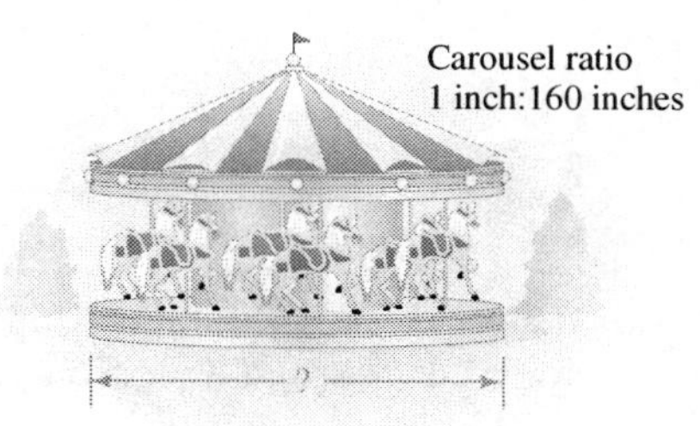

Analyze We are asked to determine the width of the miniature carousel, if a ratio of 1 inch to 160 inches is used. We would like the width of the model to be given in inches, not feet, so we will express the 35-foot width of the actual carousel as $35 \cdot 12 = 420$ inches.

Form Let $w =$ the width of the model. The ratios of the dimensions of the model to the corresponding dimensions of the actual carousel are equal.

1 inch is to 160 inches as w inches is to 420 inches.

$$\begin{array}{r} \text{model} \rightarrow \\ \text{actual} \rightarrow \end{array} \frac{1}{160} = \frac{w}{420} \begin{array}{l} \leftarrow \text{model} \\ \leftarrow \text{actual} \end{array}$$

Solve

$420 = 160w$ In a proportion, the product of the extremes is equal to the product of the means.

$\frac{420}{160} = \frac{160w}{160}$ To undo the multiplication by 160, divide both sides by 160.

$2.625 = w$ Do the division: $\frac{420}{160} = 2.625$.

State The width of the miniature carousel should be 2.625 in., or $2\frac{5}{8}$ in.

Check A width of $2\frac{5}{8}$ in. is approximately 3 in. When we write the ratio of the model's approximate width to the width of the actual carousel, we get $\frac{3}{420} = \frac{1}{140}$, which is about $\frac{1}{160}$. The answer seems reasonable.

Self Check 7

The scale for a blueprint indicates $\frac{1}{4}$ inch on the print is equivalent to 1 foot for the actual building. If the width of the building on the print is 7.5 inches, what is the width of the actual building? 30 ft

Now Try **Problem 90**

Teaching Example 7 An N scale model railroad car is 4.75 inches long. If the N scale is 1 to 160, how long is the real railroad car, in inches and in feet?
Answer:
760 in., $63\frac{1}{3}$ ft

EXAMPLE 8 *Baking* A recipe for rhubarb cake calls for $1\frac{1}{4}$ cups of sugar for every $2\frac{1}{2}$ cups of flour. How many cups of flour are needed if the baker intends to use 3 cups of sugar?

Analyze The baker needs to maintain the same ratio between the amounts of sugar and flour as is called for in the original recipe.

Form Let $f =$ the number of cups of flour to be mixed with the 3 cups of sugar. The ratios of the cups of sugar to the cups of flour are equal.

Self Check 8

How many cups of sugar will be needed to make several cakes that will require a total of 25 cups of flour? $12\frac{1}{2}$

Now Try **Problem 83**

Teaching Example 8 Refer to Example 8.
How many cups of sugar will be needed to make several cakes that require a total of 30 cups of flour?
Answer:
15

$1\frac{1}{4}$ cups sugar is to $2\frac{1}{2}$ cups flour as 3 cups sugar is to f cups flour.

$$\begin{array}{r} \text{Cups sugar} \rightarrow \\ \text{Cups flour} \rightarrow \end{array} \frac{1\frac{1}{4}}{2\frac{1}{2}} = \frac{3}{f} \begin{array}{l} \leftarrow \text{Cups sugar} \\ \leftarrow \text{Cups flour} \end{array}$$

Solve

$\frac{1.25}{2.5} = \frac{3}{f}$ Change the fractions to decimals.

$1.25f = 2.5 \cdot 3$ In a proportion, the product of the extremes equals the product of the means.

$1.25f = 7.5$ Perform the multiplication: $2.5 \cdot 3 = 7.5$.

$\frac{1.25f}{\mathbf{1.25}} = \frac{7.5}{\mathbf{1.25}}$ To undo the multiplication by 1.25, divide both sides by 1.25.

$f = 6$ Divide: $\frac{7.5}{1.25} = 6$.

State The baker should use 6 cups of flour.

Check The recipe calls for about 2 cups of flour for about 1 cup of sugar. If 3 cups of sugar are used, 6 cups of flour seems reasonable.

4 Use proportions to solve problems that involve similar triangles.

If two angles of one triangle have the same measures as two angles of a second triangle, the triangles have the same shape. Triangles with the same shape are called **similar triangles.** In the figure, $\triangle ABC \sim \triangle DEF$. (Read the symbol $\sim$ as "is similar to.")

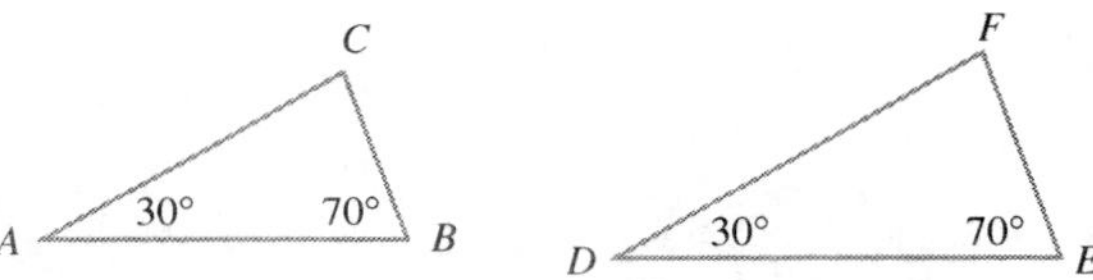

Property of Similar Triangles

If two triangles are **similar,** all pairs of corresponding sides are in proportion.

In the similar triangles shown in the figure above, the following proportions are true.

$$\frac{AB}{DE} = \frac{BC}{EF}, \quad \frac{BC}{EF} = \frac{CA}{FD}, \quad \text{and} \quad \frac{CA}{FD} = \frac{AB}{DE}$$ Read AB as "the length of segment AB."

Self Check 9

Find the height of the tree in Example 9 if the woman is 5 feet 6 inches tall and her shadow is 1.5 feet long. 66 ft

Now Try **Problem 97**

EXAMPLE 9 *Finding the Height of a Tree* A tree casts a shadow 18 feet long at the same time as a woman 5 feet tall casts a shadow 1.5 feet long. Find the height of the tree.

Analyze The figure shows the similar triangles determined by the tree and its shadow and the woman and her shadow. Since the triangles are similar, the lengths of their corresponding sides are in proportion. We can use this fact to find the height of the tree.

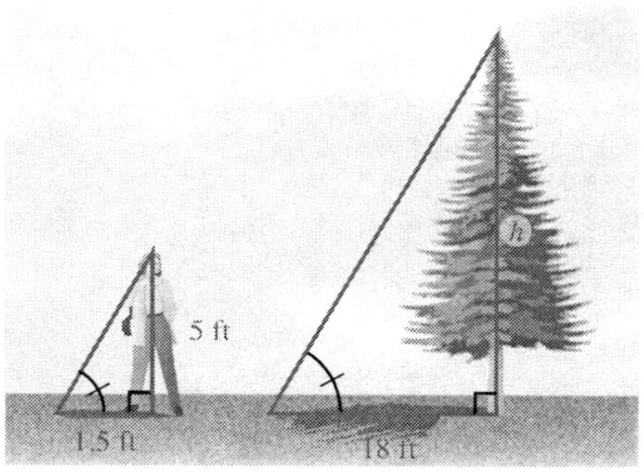

Each triangle has a right angle. Since the sun's rays strike the ground at the same angle, the angles highlighted with a tick mark have the same measure. Therefore, two angles of the smaller triangle have the same measures as two angles of the larger triangle; the triangles are similar.

Form If we let h = the height of the tree, we can find h by solving the following proportion.

$$\frac{h}{5} = \frac{18}{1.5} \qquad \frac{\text{Height of the tree}}{\text{Height of the woman}} = \frac{\text{Length of shadow of the tree}}{\text{Length of shadow of the woman}}$$

Solve

$1.5h = 5(18)$ In a proportion, the product of the extremes equals the product of the means.

$1.5h = 90$ Perform the multiplication.

$\frac{1.5h}{1.5} = \frac{90}{1.5}$ To undo the multiplication by 1.5, divide both sides by 1.5.

$h = 60$ Divide: $\frac{90}{1.5} = 60$.

State The tree is 60 feet tall.

Check $\frac{18}{1.5} = 12$ and $\frac{60}{5} = 12$. The ratios are the same. The result checks.

Teaching Example 9 A light pole casts a shadow of 15 feet at the same time a man 6 feet tall casts a shadow of 2.5 feet. Find the height of the light pole.
Answer:
36 ft

ANSWERS TO SELF CHECKS

1. a. $\frac{15}{2}$ **b.** $\frac{1}{4}$ **2.** no **3.** 24 **4.** 2 **5.** −5, 6 **6.** \$187.50 **7.** 30 ft **8.** $12\frac{1}{2}$ **9.** 66 ft

SECTION 3.3 STUDY SET

VOCABULARY

Fill in the blanks.

1. A ratio of two numbers is the quotient of two quantities with the same units.
2. A rate is a quotient of two quantities that have different units.
3. A proportion is a mathematical statement that two ratios or two rates are equal.
4. In the proportion $\frac{a}{b} = \frac{c}{d}$, a and d are called the extremes of the proportion.
5. In the proportion $\frac{a}{b} = \frac{c}{d}$, b and c are called the means of the proportion.
6. The product of the extremes and the product of the means of a proportion are also known as cross products.
7. If two triangles have the same shape, they are said to be *similar.*
8. If two triangles are similar, their corresponding sides are in proportion.

Selected exercises available online at **www.webassign.net/brookscole**

CONCEPTS

Fill in the blanks.

9. WEST AFRICA Write the ratio (in fractional form) of the number of red stripes to the number of white stripes on the flag of Liberia. $\frac{6}{5}$

▶ **10.** The equation $\frac{a}{b} = \frac{c}{d}$ is a proportion if the cross product _ad_ is equal to the cross product _bc_.

▶ **11.** Is 45 a solution of $\frac{5}{3} = \frac{75}{x}$? yes

12. Consider: $\frac{2}{3} = \frac{x}{15}$

a. Solve the proportion by multiplying both sides by the LCD. 10

b. Solve the proportion by setting the cross products equal. 10

13. MINIATURES A high-wheeler bicycle is shown below. A model of it is to be made using a scale of 2 inches to 15 inches. The following proportion was set up to determine the height of the front wheel of the model. Explain the error.

$$\frac{2}{15} = \frac{48}{h}$$ The ratio on the right side should be $\frac{h}{48}$.

▶ **14.** Two similar triangles are shown below. Fill in the blanks to make the proportions true.

$$\frac{AB}{DE} = \frac{BC}{EF} \qquad \frac{BC}{EF} = \frac{CA}{FD} \qquad \frac{CA}{FD} = \frac{AB}{DE}$$

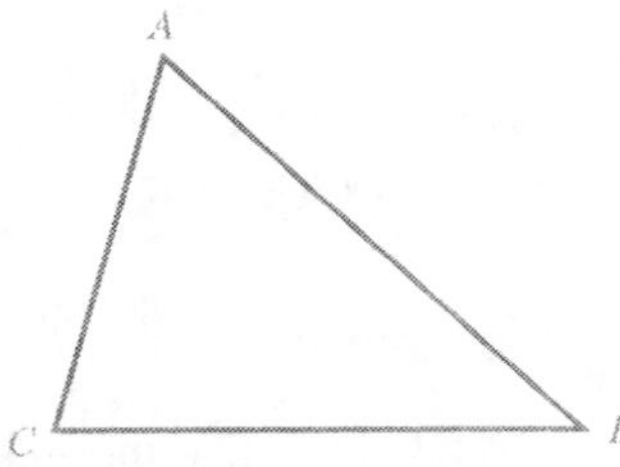

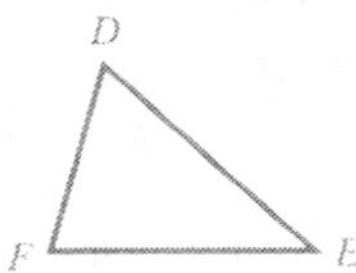

NOTATION

Complete each solution.

15. Solve for x: $\frac{12}{18} = \frac{x}{24}$

$$12 \cdot 24 = 18 \cdot x$$
$$288 = 18x$$
$$\frac{288}{18} = \frac{18x}{18}$$
$$16 = x$$

▶ **16.** Solve for x: $\frac{14}{x} = \frac{49}{17.5}$

$$14 \cdot 17.5 = 49x$$
$$245 = 49x$$
$$\frac{245}{49} = \frac{49x}{49}$$
$$5 = x$$

17. We read "$\triangle ABC$" as "_triangle_ ABC."

18. The symbol $\sim$ is read as "_is similar to_."

GUIDED PRACTICE

Translate each ratio into a ratio in simplest form. See Example 1.

19. 4 boxes to 15 boxes $\frac{4}{15}$

▶ **20.** 2 miles to 9 miles $\frac{2}{9}$

21. 18 watts to 24 watts $\frac{3}{4}$

22. 11 cans to 121 cans $\frac{1}{11}$

23. 30 days to 24 days $\frac{5}{4}$

24. 45 people to 30 people $\frac{3}{2}$

25. 90 minutes to 3 hours $\frac{1}{2}$

26. 20 inches to 2 feet $\frac{5}{6}$

27. 8 quarts to 4 gallons $\frac{1}{2}$

28. 6 feet to 12 yards $\frac{1}{6}$

29. 6,000 feet to 1 mile $\frac{25}{22}$ (*Hint:* 1 mi = 5,280 ft)

30. 5 tons to 4,000 pounds $\frac{5}{2}$ (*Hint:* 1 ton = 2,000 lb)

Determine whether each equation is a proportion. See Example 2.

31. $\frac{9}{7} = \frac{81}{70}$ no

32. $\frac{5}{2} = \frac{20}{8}$ yes

33. $\frac{7}{3} = \frac{14}{6}$ yes

▶ **34.** $\frac{13}{19} = \frac{65}{95}$ yes

35. $\frac{9}{19} = \frac{38}{80}$ no

36. $\frac{40}{29} = \frac{29}{22}$ no

37. $\frac{10.4}{3.6} = \frac{41.6}{14.4}$ yes

38. $\frac{13.23}{3.45} = \frac{39.96}{11.35}$ no

Solve each proportion. See Example 3.

39. $\frac{2}{3} = \frac{x}{6}$ 4

▶ **40.** $\frac{3}{6} = \frac{x}{8}$ 4

41. $\frac{5}{10} = \frac{3}{c}$ 6

▶ **42.** $\frac{7}{14} = \frac{2}{x}$ 4

Solve each proportion. See Example 4.

43. $\dfrac{x+1}{5} = \dfrac{3}{15}$ 0

44. $\dfrac{x-1}{7} = \dfrac{2}{21}$ $\frac{5}{3}$

45. $\dfrac{x+3}{12} = \dfrac{-7}{6}$ -17

▶ 46. $\dfrac{x+7}{-4} = \dfrac{1}{4}$ -8

47. $\dfrac{13}{4-x} = \dfrac{26}{11}$ $-\frac{3}{2}$

48. $\dfrac{17}{5-x} = \dfrac{34}{13}$ $-\frac{3}{2}$

49. $\dfrac{14}{3} = \dfrac{2x+1}{18}$ $\frac{83}{2}$

▶ 50. $\dfrac{9}{54} = \dfrac{2x-1}{18}$ 2

Solve each proportion. See Example 5.

▶ 51. $\dfrac{y}{4} = \dfrac{4}{y}$ $4, -4$

▶ 52. $\dfrac{2}{3x} = \dfrac{6x}{36}$ $2, -2$

53. $\dfrac{2}{c} = \dfrac{c-3}{2}$ $4, -1$

54. $\dfrac{b-5}{3} = \dfrac{2}{b}$ $6, -1$

55. $\dfrac{a-4}{a} = \dfrac{15}{a+4}$ $-1, 16$

56. $\dfrac{s}{s-5} = \dfrac{s+5}{24}$ $-1, 25$

57. $\dfrac{t+3}{t+5} = \dfrac{-1}{2t}$ $-\frac{5}{2}, -1$

▶ 58. $\dfrac{5h}{14h+3} = \dfrac{1}{h}$ $-\frac{1}{5}, 3$

TRY IT YOURSELF

Solve each proportion.

59. $\dfrac{6}{x} = \dfrac{8}{4}$ 3

▶ 60. $\dfrac{4}{x} = \dfrac{2}{8}$ 16

61. $\dfrac{x}{3} = \dfrac{9}{3}$ 9

▶ 62. $\dfrac{x}{2} = \dfrac{18}{6}$ 6

▶ 63. $\dfrac{2}{x+6} = \dfrac{-2x}{5}$ $-5, -1$

▶ 64. $\dfrac{x-1}{x+1} = \dfrac{2}{3x}$ $-\frac{1}{3}, 2$

▶ 65. $\dfrac{x+1}{4} = \dfrac{3x}{8}$ 2

66. $\dfrac{x-1}{9} = \dfrac{2x}{3}$ $-\frac{1}{5}$

67. $\dfrac{3}{4x} = \dfrac{x-4}{x+\frac{5}{3}}$ $-\frac{1}{4}, 5$

68. $\dfrac{3}{x-1} = \dfrac{x}{4}$ $4, -3$

69. $\dfrac{y-4}{y+1} = \dfrac{y+3}{y+6}$ $-\frac{27}{2}$

70. $\dfrac{r-6}{r-8} = \dfrac{r+1}{r-4}$ $\frac{32}{3}$

71. $\dfrac{c}{10} = \dfrac{10}{c}$ $-10, 10$

72. $\dfrac{-6}{r} = \dfrac{r}{-6}$ $-6, 6$

73. $\dfrac{m}{3} = \dfrac{4}{m+1}$ $-4, 3$

74. $\dfrac{n}{2} = \dfrac{5}{n+3}$ $-5, 2$

75. $\dfrac{3}{3b+4} = \dfrac{2}{5b-6}$ $\frac{26}{9}$

76. $\dfrac{2}{4d-1} = \dfrac{3}{2d+1}$ $\frac{5}{8}$

APPLICATIONS

Set up and solve a proportion. Use a calculator if it is helpful. See Examples 6–8.

77. GROCERY SHOPPING If 3 pints of yogurt cost \$1, how much will 51 pints cost? \$17

78. SHOPPING FOR CLOTHES If shirts are on sale at two for \$25, how much will five shirts cost? \$62.50

79. ADVERTISING In 2008, a 30-second TV ad during the Super Bowl telecast cost \$2.2 million. At this rate, what was the cost of a 45-second ad? \$3.3 million

▶ 80. COOKING A recipe for spaghetti sauce requires four 16-ounce bottles of ketchup to make 2 gallons of sauce. How many bottles of ketchup are needed to make 10 gallons of sauce? 20

▶ 81. MIXING PERFUME A perfume is to be mixed in the ratio of 3 drops of pure essence to 7 drops of alcohol. How many drops of pure essence should be mixed with 56 drops of alcohol? 24

82. CPR A first aid handbook states that when performing cardiopulmonary resuscitation on an adult, the ratio of chest compressions to breaths should be 30:2. If 210 compressions were administered to an adult patient, how many breaths should have been given? 14

83. COOKING A recipe for wild rice soup is shown. Find the amounts of chicken broth, rice, and flour needed to make 15 servings. $7\frac{1}{2}, 1\frac{2}{3}, 5$

Wild Rice Soup

A sumptuous side dish with a nutty flavor

3 cups chicken broth	1 cup light cream
$\frac{2}{3}$ cup uncooked rice	2 tablespoons flour
$\frac{1}{4}$ cup sliced onions	$\frac{1}{8}$ teaspoon pepper
$\frac{1}{2}$ cup shredded carrots	Serves: 6

84. QUALITY CONTROL In a manufacturing process, 95% of the parts made are to be within specifications. How many defective parts would be expected in a run of 940 pieces? 47

85. QUALITY CONTROL Out of a sample of 500 men's shirts, 17 were rejected because of crooked collars. How many crooked collars would you expect to find in a run of 15,000 shirts? 510

▶ 86. GAS CONSUMPTION If a car can travel 42 miles on 1 gallon of gas, how much gas is needed to travel 315 miles? $7\frac{1}{2}$ gal

87. HIP-HOP According to the *Guinness Book of World Records,* Rebel X.D. of Chicago rapped 674 syllables in 54.9 seconds. At this rate, how many syllables could he rap in 1 minute? Round to the nearest syllable. 737

▶ 88. BANKRUPTCY After filing for bankruptcy, a company was able to pay its creditors only 15 cents on the dollar. If the company owed a lumberyard \$9,712, how much could the lumberyard expect to be paid? \$1,456.80

▶ 89. COMPUTING A PAYCHECK Billie earns \$412 for a 40-hour week. If she missed 10 hours of work last week, how much did she get paid? \$309

90. MODEL RAILROADS A model railroad engine is 9 inches long. If the scale is 87 feet to 1 foot, how long is a real engine? 65 ft, 3 in.

91. MODEL RAILROADS A model railroad caboose is 3.5 inches long. If the scale is 169 feet to 1 foot, how long is a real caboose? 49 ft, $3\frac{1}{2}$ in.

92. NUTRITION The following table shows the nutritional facts about a 10-oz chocolate milkshake sold by a fast-food restaurant. Use the information to complete the table for the 16-oz shake. Round to the nearest unit when an answer is not exact.

	Calories	Fat (gm)	Protein (gm)
10-oz chocolate milkshake	355	8	9
16-oz chocolate milkshake	568	13	14

93. DRIVER'S LICENSES Of the 50 states, Alabama has one of the largest ratios of licensed drivers to residents. If the ratio is 800:1,000 and Alabama's population is 4,500, 000, how many residents of that state have a driver's license? 3,600,000

94. MIXING FUEL The instructions on a can of oil intended to be added to lawnmower gasoline read as follows:

Recommended	Gasoline	Oil
50 to 1	6 gal	16 oz

Are the instructions correct? (*Hint:* There are 128 ounces in 1 gallon.) not exactly, but close

95. PHOTO ENLARGEMENT In the illustration, the 3-by-5 photograph is to be blown up to the larger size. Find x. $3\frac{3}{4}$ in.

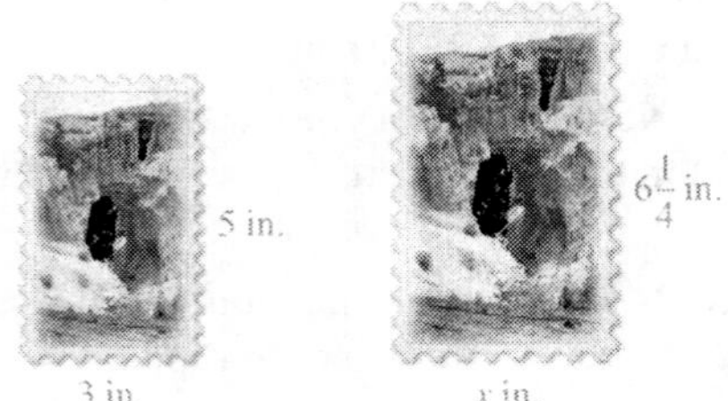

96. BLUEPRINTS The scale for the blueprint shown in the next column tells the reader that a $\frac{1}{4}$-inch length $\left(\frac{1}{4}''\right)$ on the drawing corresponds to an actual size of 1 foot (1′0″). Suppose the length of the kitchen is $2\frac{1}{2}$ inches on the drawing. How long is the actual kitchen? 10 ft

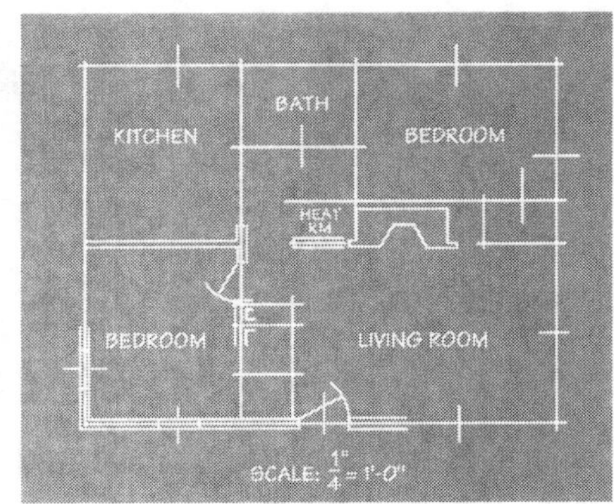

Use similar triangles to solve each problem. See Example 9.

97. HEIGHT OF A TREE A tree casts a shadow of 26 feet at the same time as a 6-foot man casts a shadow of 4 feet. Find the height of the tree. 39 ft

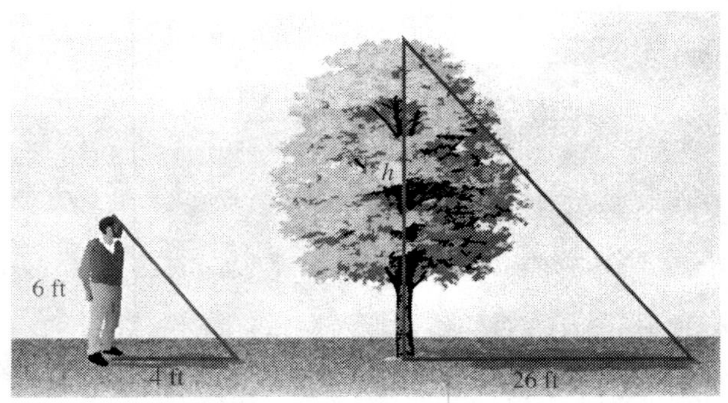

98. HEIGHT OF A BUILDING A man places a mirror on the ground and sees the reflection of the top of a building, as shown. The two triangles in the illustration are similar. Find the height, h, of the building. 25 ft

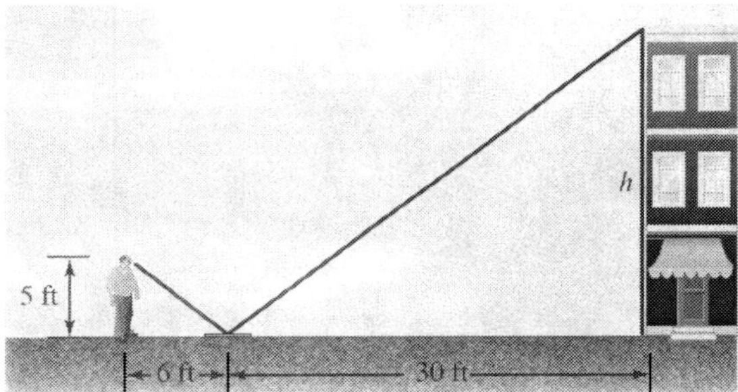

99. WIDTH OF A RIVER Use the dimensions in the illustration to find w, the width of the river. (The two triangles in the illustration are similar.) $46\frac{7}{8}$ ft

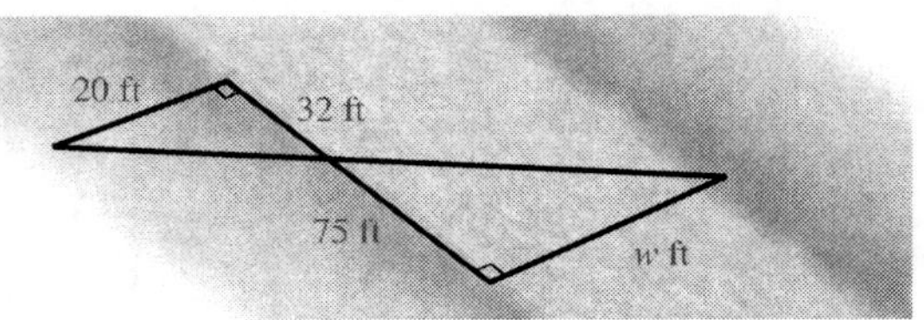

100. FLIGHT PATHS The airplane shown below ascends 100 feet as it flies a horizontal distance of 1,000 feet. How much altitude will it gain as it flies a horizontal distance of 1 mile? (*Hint:* 5,280 feet = 1 mile.) 528 ft

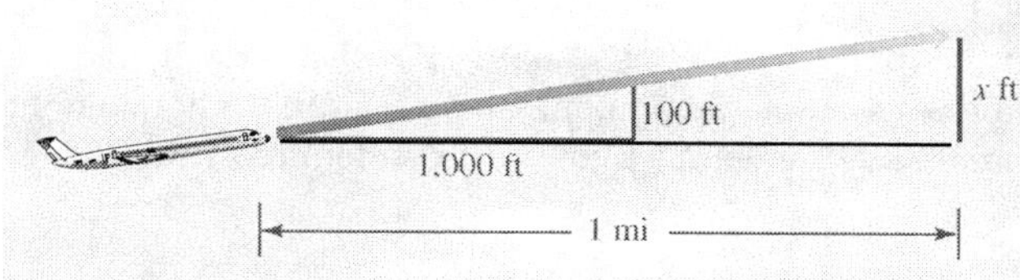

101. FLIGHT PATHS An airplane descends 1,350 feet as it flies a horizontal distance of 1 mile. How much altitude is lost as it flies a horizontal distance of 5 miles? 6,750 ft

102. SKI RUNS A ski course falls 100 feet in every 300 feet of horizontal run. If the total horizontal run is $\frac{1}{2}$ mile, find the height of the hill. 880 ft

WRITING

103. Explain the difference between a ratio and a proportion.

104. Explain how to tell whether $\frac{3.2}{3.7} = \frac{5.44}{6.29}$ is a proportion.

105. Explain why the concept of cross products cannot be used to solve the equation

$$\frac{x}{3} - \frac{3x}{4} = \frac{1}{12}$$

106. Write a problem about a situation you encounter in your daily life that could be solved by using a proportion.

REVIEW

107. Change $\frac{9}{10}$ to a percent. 90%

108. Change $33\frac{1}{3}\%$ to a fraction. $\frac{1}{3}$

109. Find 30% of 1,600. 480

110. SHOPPING Maria bought a dress for 25% off the original price of \$98. How much did the dress cost? \$73.50

111. Find the slope of the line passing through $(-2, -2)$ and $(-12, -8)$. $\frac{3}{5}$

112. What are the slope and the y-intercept of the graph of $y = 2x - 3$? 2, (0, −3)

SECTION 3.4
American Units of Measurement

Objectives

1. Use a ruler to measure lengths in inches.
2. Define American units of length.
3. Convert from one American unit of length to another.
4. Define American units of weight.
5. Convert from one American unit of weight to another.
6. Define American units of capacity.
7. Convert from one American unit of capacity to another.
8. Define units of time.
9. Convert from one unit of time to another.

Two common systems of measurement are the **American** (or **English**) **system** and the **metric system.** We will discuss American units of measurement in this section and metric units in the next. Some common American units are *inches, feet, miles, ounces, pounds, tons, cups, pints, quarts,* and *gallons.* These units are used when measuring length, weight, and capacity.

A newborn baby is 20 inches long.

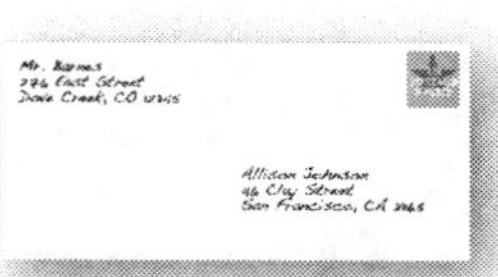

First-class postage for a letter that weighs less than 1 ounce is 44¢.

Milk is sold in gallon containers.

1 Use a ruler to measure lengths in inches.

A ruler is one of the most common tools used for measuring distances or lengths. The figure below shows part of a ruler. Most rulers are 12 inches (1 foot) long. Since 12 inches = 1 foot, a ruler is divided into 12 equal lengths of 1 inch. Each inch is divided into halves of an inch, quarters of an inch, eighths of an inch, and sixteenths of an inch.

The left end of a ruler can be (but sometimes isn't) labeled with a 0. Each point on a ruler, like each point on a number line, has a number associated with it. That number is the distance between the point and 0. Several lengths on the ruler are shown below.

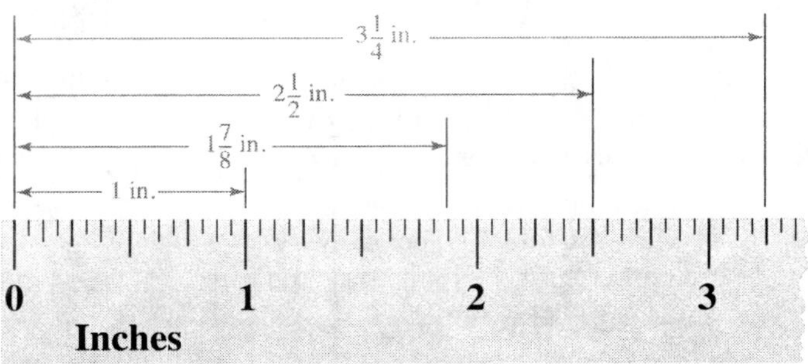

Actual size

Self Check 1

Find the length of the jumbo paper clip. $1\frac{7}{8}$ in.

Now Try **Problem 27**

EXAMPLE 1 Find the length of the paper clip shown here.

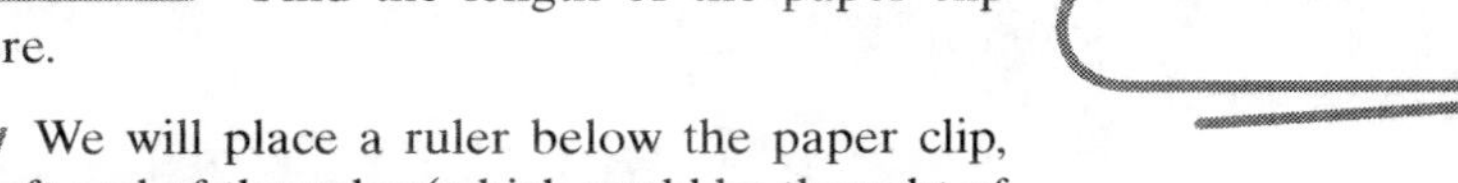

Strategy We will place a ruler below the paper clip, with the left end of the ruler (which could be thought of as 0) directly underneath one end of the paper clip.

WHY Then we can find the length of the paper clip by identifying where its other end lines up on the tick marks printed in black on the ruler.

Solution

Since the tick marks between 0 and 1 on the ruler create eight equal spaces, the ruler is scaled in eighths of an inch. The paper clip is $1\frac{3}{8}$ inches long.

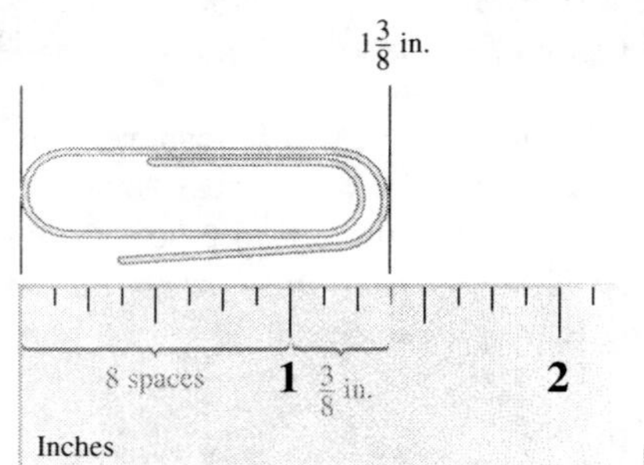

EXAMPLE 2 Find the length of the nail shown below.

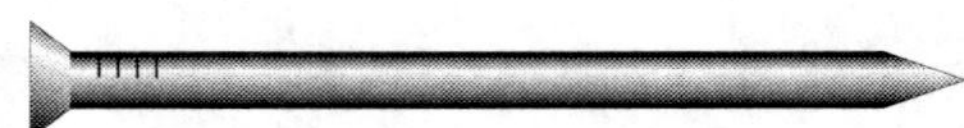

Strategy We will place a ruler below the nail, with the left end of the ruler (which could be thought of as 0) directly underneath the head of the nail.

WHY Then we can find the length of the nail by identifying where its pointed end lines up on the tick marks printed in black on the ruler.

Solution

Since the tick marks between 0 and 1 on the ruler create sixteen equal spaces, the ruler is scaled in sixteenths of an inch.

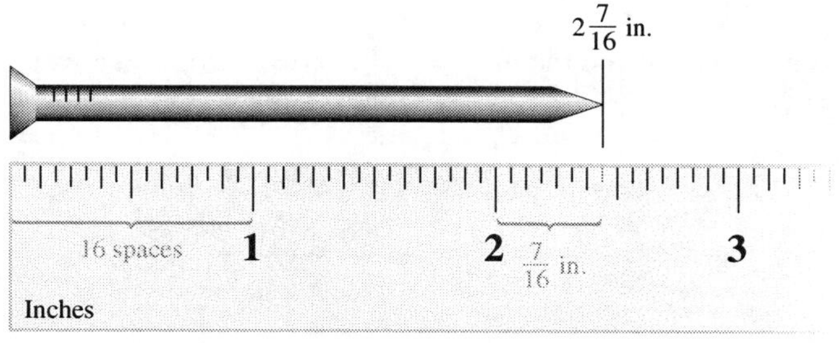

The nail is $2\frac{7}{16}$ inches long.

Self Check 2

Find the width of the circle. $1\frac{1}{4}$ in.

Now Try **Problem 29**

2 Define American units of length.

The American system of measurement uses the units of **inch, foot, yard,** and **mile** to measure length. These units are related in the following ways.

American Units of Length

1 foot (ft) = 12 inches (in.)	1 yard (yd) = 36 inches
1 yard = 3 feet	1 mile (mi) = 5,280 feet

The abbreviation for each unit is written within parentheses.

The Language of Mathematics According to some sources, the inch was originally defined as the length from the tip of the thumb to the first knuckle. In some languages the word for *inch* is similar to or the same as *thumb*. For example, in Spanish, *pulgada* is inch and *pulgar* is thumb. In Swedish, *tum* is inch and *tumme* is thumb. In Italian, *pollice* is both inch and thumb.

3 Convert from one American unit of length to another.

To convert from one unit of length to another, we use *unit conversion factors.* To find the unit conversion factor between yards and feet, we begin with this fact:

$$3 \text{ ft} = 1 \text{ yd}$$

If we divide both sides of this equation by 1 yard, we get

$$\frac{3 \text{ ft}}{1 \text{ yd}} = \frac{1 \text{ yd}}{1 \text{ yd}}$$

$$\frac{3 \text{ ft}}{1 \text{ yd}} = 1$$ Simplify the right side of the equation. A number divided by itself is 1: $\frac{1 \text{ yd}}{1 \text{ yd}} = 1$.

The fraction $\frac{3\text{ ft}}{1\text{ yd}}$ is called a **unit conversion factor,** because its value is 1. It can be read as "3 feet per yard." Since this fraction is equal to 1, multiplying a length by this fraction does not change its measure; it changes only the *units* of measure.

To convert units of length in the American system of measurement, we use the following unit conversion factors. Each conversion factor shown below is a form of 1.

To convert from	Use the unit conversion factor	To convert from	Use the unit conversion factor
feet to inches	$\frac{12\text{ in.}}{1\text{ ft}}$	inches to feet	$\frac{1\text{ ft}}{12\text{ in.}}$
yards to feet	$\frac{3\text{ ft}}{1\text{ yd}}$	feet to yards	$\frac{1\text{ yd}}{3\text{ ft}}$
yards to inches	$\frac{36\text{ in.}}{1\text{ yd}}$	inches to yards	$\frac{1\text{ yd}}{36\text{ in.}}$
miles to feet	$\frac{5{,}280\text{ ft}}{1\text{ mi}}$	feet to miles	$\frac{1\text{ mi}}{5{,}280\text{ ft}}$

Self Check 3

Convert 9 yards to feet. 27 ft

Now Try **Problem 35**

Teaching Example 3
Convert 5 yards to feet.
Answer:
15 ft

EXAMPLE 3 Convert 8 yards to feet.

Strategy We will multiply 8 yards by a carefully chosen unit conversion factor.

WHY If we multiply by the proper unit conversion factor, we can eliminate the unwanted units of yards and convert to feet.

Solution

To convert from yards to feet, we must use a unit conversion factor that relates feet to yards. Since there are 3 feet per yard, we multiply 8 yards by the unit conversion factor $\frac{3\text{ ft}}{1\text{ yd}}$.

$$8\text{ yd} = \frac{8\text{ yd}}{1} \cdot \frac{3\text{ ft}}{1\text{ yd}}$$ Write 8 yd as a fraction: $8\text{ yd} = \frac{8\text{ yd}}{1}$. Then multiply by a form of 1: $\frac{3\text{ ft}}{1\text{ yd}}$.

$$= \frac{8\text{ }\cancel{\text{yd}}}{1} \cdot \frac{3\text{ ft}}{1\text{ }\cancel{\text{yd}}}$$ Remove the common units of yards from the numerator and denominator. Notice that the units of feet remain.

$$= 8 \cdot 3\text{ ft}$$ Simplify.

$$= 24\text{ ft}$$ Multiply: $8 \cdot 3 = 24$.

8 yards is equal to 24 feet.

Success Tip Notice that in Example 3, we eliminated the units of yards and introduced the units of feet by multiplying by the appropriate unit conversion factor. In general, a unit conversion factor is a fraction with the following form:

$$\frac{\text{Unit we want to introduce}}{\text{Unit we want to eliminate}}$$ ← Numerator, ← Denominator

EXAMPLE 4 Convert $1\frac{3}{4}$ feet to inches.

Strategy We will multiply $1\frac{3}{4}$ feet by a carefully chosen unit conversion factor.

WHY If we multiply by the proper unit conversion factor, we can eliminate the unwanted units of feet and convert to inches.

Solution

To convert from feet to inches, we must choose a unit conversion factor whose numerator contains the units we want to introduce (inches), and whose denominator contains the units we want to eliminate (feet). Since there are 12 inches per foot, we will use

$$\frac{12 \text{ in.}}{1 \text{ ft}}$$ ← This is the unit we want to introduce. / ← This is the unit we want to eliminate (the original unit).

To perform the conversion, we multiply.

$$1\frac{3}{4} \text{ ft} = \frac{7}{4} \text{ ft} \cdot \frac{12 \text{ in.}}{1 \text{ ft}}$$ Write $1\frac{3}{4}$ as an improper fraction: $1\frac{3}{4} = \frac{7}{4}$. Then multiply by a form of 1: $\frac{12 \text{ in.}}{1 \text{ ft}}$.

$$= \frac{7}{4} \text{ ft} \cdot \frac{12 \text{ in.}}{1 \text{ ft}}$$ Remove the common units of feet from the numerator and denominator. Notice that the units of inches remain.

$$= \frac{7 \cdot 12}{4 \cdot 1} \text{ in.}$$ Multiply the fractions.

$$= \frac{7 \cdot 3 \cdot \overset{1}{\cancel{4}}}{\underset{1}{\cancel{4}} \cdot 1} \text{ in.}$$ To simplify the fraction, factor 12. Then remove the common factor of 4 from the numerator and denominator.

$$= 21 \text{ in.}$$ Simplify.

$1\frac{3}{4}$ feet is equal to 21 inches.

Self Check 4

Convert $1\frac{1}{2}$ feet to inches. 18 in.

Now Try **Problem 39**

Teaching Example 4

Convert $2\frac{1}{4}$ feet to inches.

Answer:
27 in.

> ***Caution!*** When converting lengths, if no common units appear in the numerator and denominator to remove, you have chosen the wrong conversion factor.

Sometimes we must use two (or more) unit conversion factors to eliminate the given units while introducing the desired units. The following example illustrates this concept.

EXAMPLE 5 ***Football*** A football field (including both end zones) is 120 yards long. Convert this length to miles. Give the exact answer and a decimal approximation, rounded to the nearest hundredth of a mile.

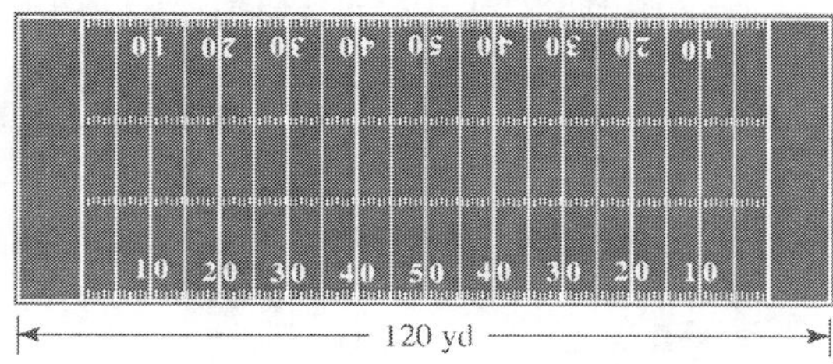

Strategy We will use a two-part multiplication process that converts 120 yards to feet and then converts that result to miles.

Self Check 5

MARATHONS The *marathon* is a long-distance race with an official distance of 26 miles 385 yards. Convert 385 yards to miles. Give the exact answer and a decimal approximation, rounded to the nearest hundredth of a mile. $\frac{7}{32}$ mi ≈ 0.22 mi

Now Try **Problem 43**

Teaching Example 5 THE MASTERS GOLF TOURNAMENT Hole number 8 of the Augusta National course is 570 yards long. Convert the length of the hole to miles. Give the exact answer and a decimal approximation, rounded to the nearest hundredth of a mile.
Answer:
$\frac{57}{176}$ mi ≈ 0.32 mi

WHY We must use a two-part process because the table on page 445 does not contain a single unit conversion factor that converts from yards to miles.

Solution

Since there are 3 feet per yard, we can convert 120 yards to feet by multiplying by the unit conversion factor $\frac{3\text{ft}}{1\text{yd}}$. Since there is 1 mile for every 5,280 feet, we can convert that result to miles by multiplying by the unit conversion factor $\frac{1\text{ mi}}{5{,}280\text{ ft}}$.

$$120\text{ yd} = \frac{120\text{ yd}}{1} \cdot \frac{3\text{ ft}}{1\text{ yd}} \cdot \frac{1\text{ mi}}{5{,}280\text{ ft}}$$

Write 120 yd as a fraction: 120 yd $= \frac{120\text{ yd}}{1}$. Then multiply by two unit conversion factors: $\frac{3\text{ ft}}{1\text{ yd}} = 1$ and $\frac{1\text{ mi}}{5{,}280\text{ ft}} = 1$.

$$= \frac{120\text{ }\cancel{\text{yd}}}{1} \cdot \frac{3\text{ }\cancel{\text{ft}}}{1\text{ }\cancel{\text{yd}}} \cdot \frac{1\text{ mi}}{5{,}280\text{ }\cancel{\text{ft}}}$$

Remove the common units of yards and feet in the numerator and denominator. Notice that all the units are removed except for miles.

$$= \frac{120 \cdot 3}{5{,}280}\text{ mi}$$

Multiply the fractions.

$$= \frac{\overset{1}{\cancel{2}} \cdot \overset{1}{\cancel{2}} \cdot \overset{1}{\cancel{2}} \cdot \overset{1}{\cancel{3}} \cdot \overset{1}{\cancel{5}} \cdot 3}{\underset{1}{\cancel{2}} \cdot \underset{1}{\cancel{2}} \cdot \underset{1}{\cancel{2}} \cdot 2 \cdot 2 \cdot \underset{1}{\cancel{3}} \cdot \underset{1}{\cancel{5}} \cdot 11}\text{ mi}$$

To simplify the fraction, prime factor 120 and 5,280, and remove the common factors 2, 3, and 5.

$$= \frac{3}{44}\text{ mi}$$

Multiply the remaining factors in the numerator. Multiply the remaining factors in the

A football field (including the end zones) is *exactly* $\frac{3}{44}$ miles long.

We can also present this conversion as a decimal. If we divide 3 by 44 (as shown on the right), and round the result to the nearest hundredth, we see that a football field (including the end zones) is *approximately* 0.07 mile long.

$$\begin{array}{r} 0.068 \\ 44\overline{)3.000} \\ -\ 0 \\ \hline 3\ 00 \\ -\ 2\ 64 \\ \hline 360 \\ -\ 352 \\ \hline 8 \end{array}$$

4 Define American units of weight.

The American system of measurement uses the units of **ounce, pound,** and **ton** to measure weight. These units are related in the following ways.

American Units of Weight

1 pound (lb) = 16 ounces (oz)   1 ton (T) = 2,000 pounds

The abbreviation for each unit is written within parentheses.

5 Convert from one American unit of weight to another.

To convert units of weight in the American system of measurement, we use the following unit conversion factors. Each conversion factor shown below is a form of 1.

To convert from	Use the unit conversion factor	To convert from	Use the unit conversion factor
pounds to ounces	$\frac{16\text{ oz}}{1\text{ lb}}$	ounces to pounds	$\frac{1\text{ lb}}{16\text{ oz}}$
tons to pounds	$\frac{2{,}000\text{ lb}}{1\text{ ton}}$	pounds to tons	$\frac{1\text{ ton}}{2{,}000\text{ lb}}$

EXAMPLE 6 Convert 40 ounces to pounds.

Strategy We will multiply 40 ounces by a carefully chosen unit conversion factor.

WHY If we multiply by the proper unit conversion factor, we can eliminate the unwanted units of ounces and convert to pounds.

Solution

To convert from ounces to pounds, we must chose a unit conversion factor whose numerator contains the units we want to introduce (pounds), and whose denominator contains the units we want to eliminate (ounces). Since there is 1 pound for every 16 ounces, we will use

$$\frac{1 \text{ lb}}{16 \text{ oz}}$$

1 lb ← This is the unit we want to introduce.
16 oz ← This is the unit we want to eliminate (the original unit).

To perform the conversion, we multiply.

$$40 \text{ oz} = \frac{40 \text{ oz}}{1} \cdot \frac{1 \text{ lb}}{16 \text{ oz}}$$ Write 40 oz as a fraction: 40 oz $= \frac{40 \text{ oz}}{1}$. Then multiply by a form of 1: $\frac{1 \text{ lb}}{16 \text{ oz}}$.

$$= \frac{40 \not{\text{oz}}}{1} \cdot \frac{1 \text{ lb}}{16 \not{\text{oz}}}$$ Remove the common units of ounces from the numerator and denominator. Notice that the units of pounds remain.

$$= \frac{40}{16} \text{ lb}$$ Multiply the fractions.

There are two ways to complete the solution. First, we can remove any common factors of the numerator and denominator to simplify the fraction. Then we can write the result as a mixed number.

$$\frac{40}{16} \text{ lb} = \frac{5 \cdot \overset{1}{\not{8}}}{2 \cdot \underset{1}{\not{8}}} \text{ lb} = \frac{5}{2} \text{ lb} = 2\frac{1}{2} \text{ lb}$$

A second approach is to divide the numerator by the denominator and express the result as a decimal.

$$\frac{40}{16} \text{ lb} = 2.5 \text{ lb}$$ Perform the division: 40 ÷ 16.

```
   2.5
16)40.0
  -32
    8 0
   -8 0
      0
```

40 ounces is equal to $2\frac{1}{2}$ lb (or 2.5 lb).

Self Check 6

Convert 60 ounces to pounds. $3\frac{3}{4}$ lb = 3.75 lb

Now Try **Problem 47**

Teaching Example 6 Convert 20 ounces to pounds.
Answer:
$1\frac{1}{4}$ lb = 1.25 lb

EXAMPLE 7 Convert 25 pounds to ounces.

Strategy We will multiply 25 pounds by a carefully chosen unit conversion factor.

WHY If we multiply by the proper unit conversion factor, we can eliminate the unwanted units of pounds and convert to ounces.

Solution

To convert from pounds to ounces, we must chose a unit conversion factor whose numerator contains the units we want to introduce (ounces), and whose denominator contains the units we want to eliminate (pounds). Since there are 16 ounces per pound, we will use

$$\frac{16 \text{ oz}}{1 \text{ lb}}$$

16 oz ← This is the unit we want to introduce.
1 lb ← This is the unit we want to eliminate (the original unit).

Self Check 7

Convert 60 pounds to ounces. 960 oz

Now Try **Problem 51**

Teaching Example 7
Convert 90 pounds to ounces.
Answer:
1,440 oz

To perform the conversion, we multiply.

$$25 \text{ lb} = \frac{25 \text{ lb}}{1} \cdot \frac{16 \text{ oz}}{1 \text{ lb}}$$ Write 25 lb as a fraction: 25 lb $= \frac{25 \text{ lb}}{1}$. Then multiply by a form of 1: $\frac{16 \text{ oz}}{1 \text{ lb}}$.

$$= \frac{25 \not{\text{lb}}}{1} \cdot \frac{16 \text{ oz}}{1 \not{\text{lb}}}$$ Remove the common units of pounds from the numerator and denominator. Notice that the units of ounces remain.

$$= 25 \cdot 16 \text{ oz}$$ Simplify.

$$= 400 \text{ oz}$$ Multiply: $25 \cdot 16 = 400$.

$$\begin{array}{r} 25 \\ \times 16 \\ \hline 150 \\ 250 \\ \hline 400 \end{array}$$

25 pounds is equal to 400 ounces.

6 Define American units of capacity.

The American system of measurement uses the units of **ounce, cup, pint, quart,** and **gallon** to measure capacity. These units are related as follows.

The Language of Mathematics The word *capacity* means the amount that can be contained. For example, a gas tank might have a *capacity* of 12 gallons.

American Units of Capacity

1 cup (c) = 8 fluid ounces (fl oz) 1 pint (pt) = 2 cups
1 quart (qt) = 2 pints 1 gallon (gal) = 4 quarts

The abbreviation for each unit is written within parentheses.

7 Convert from one American unit of capacity to another.

To convert units of capacity in the American system of measurement, we use the following unit conversion factors. Each conversion factor shown below is a form of 1.

To convert from	Use the unit conversion factor	To convert from	Use the unit conversion factor
cups to ounces	$\frac{8 \text{ fl oz}}{1 \text{ c}}$	ounces to cups	$\frac{1 \text{ c}}{8 \text{ fl oz}}$
pints to cups	$\frac{2 \text{ c}}{1 \text{ pt}}$	cups to pints	$\frac{1 \text{ pt}}{2 \text{ c}}$
quarts to pints	$\frac{2 \text{ pt}}{1 \text{ qt}}$	pints to quarts	$\frac{1 \text{ qt}}{2 \text{ pt}}$
gallons to quarts	$\frac{4 \text{ qt}}{1 \text{ gal}}$	quarts to gallons	$\frac{1 \text{ gal}}{4 \text{ qt}}$

EXAMPLE 8 *Cooking* If a recipe calls for 3 pints of milk, how many fluid ounces of milk should be used?

Strategy We will use a two-part multiplication process that converts 3 pints to cups and then converts that result to fluid ounces.

WHY We must use a two-part process because the table on page 449 does not contain a single unit conversion factor that converts from pints to fluid ounces.

Solution

Since there are 2 cups per pint, we can convert 3 pints to cups by multiplying by the unit conversion factor $\frac{2\text{ c}}{1\text{ pt}}$. Since there are 8 fluid ounces per cup, we can convert that result to fluid ounces by multiplying by the unit conversion factor $\frac{8\text{ fl oz}}{1\text{ c}}$.

$$3\text{ pt} = \frac{3\text{ pt}}{1} \cdot \frac{2\text{ c}}{1\text{ pt}} \cdot \frac{8\text{ fl oz}}{1\text{ c}}$$

Write 3 pt as a fraction: $3\text{ pt} = \frac{3\text{ pt}}{1}$. Multiply by two unit conversion factors: $\frac{2\text{ c}}{1\text{ pt}} = 1$ and $\frac{8\text{ fl oz}}{1\text{ c}} = 1$.

$$= \frac{3\not{\text{pt}}}{1} \cdot \frac{2\not{\text{c}}}{1\not{\text{pt}}} \cdot \frac{8\text{ fl oz}}{1\not{\text{c}}}$$

Remove the common units of pints and cups in the numerator and denominator. Notice that all the units are removed except for fluid ounces.

$$= 3 \cdot 2 \cdot 8\text{ fl oz}$$

Simplify.

$$= 48\text{ fl oz}$$

Multiply.

Since 3 pints is equal to 48 fluid ounces, 48 fluid ounces of milk should be used.

Self Check 8

Convert 2.5 pints to fluid ounces. 40 fl oz

Now Try **Problem 55**

© Felix Wirth/Corbis

Teaching Example 8 DESSERTS If a recipe for homemade ice cream calls for 4 pints of cream, how many fluid ounces of cream should be used?

Answer:

64 fl oz

8 Define units of time.

The American system of measurement (and the metric system) use the units of **second, minute, hour,** and **day** to measure time. These units are related as follows.

Units of Time

1 minute (min) = 60 seconds (sec)   1 hour (hr) = 60 minutes

1 day = 24 hours

The abbreviation for each unit is written within parentheses.

To convert units of time, we use the following unit conversion factors. Each conversion factor shown below is a form of 1.

To convert from	Use the unit conversion factor	To convert from	Use the unit conversion factor
minutes to seconds	$\frac{60\text{ sec}}{1\text{ min}}$	seconds to minutes	$\frac{1\text{ min}}{60\text{ sec}}$
hours to minutes	$\frac{60\text{ min}}{1\text{ hr}}$	minutes to hours	$\frac{1\text{ hr}}{60\text{ min}}$
days to hours	$\frac{24\text{ hr}}{1\text{ day}}$	hours to days	$\frac{1\text{ day}}{24\text{ hr}}$

9 Convert from one unit of time to another.

Self Check 9

THE SUN A solar eclipse (eclipse of the sun) can last as long as 450 seconds. Express this time in minutes. $7\frac{1}{2}$ min

Now Try **Problem 59**

Teaching Example 9 SPACE FLIGHT On February 20, 1962, John Glenn was the first American astronaut to orbit the Earth. The Mercury–Atlas 6 mission in the spacecraft *Friendship 7* lasted a total of 295 minutes. Express this time in hours.
Answer:
$4\frac{11}{12}$ hr

EXAMPLE 9 *Astronomy* A lunar eclipse occurs when the Earth is between the sun and the moon in such a way that Earth's shadow darkens the moon. (See the figure below, which is not to scale.) A total lunar eclipse can last as long as 105 minutes. Express this time in hours.

Strategy We will multiply 105 minutes by a carefully chosen unit conversion factor.

WHY If we multiply by the proper unit conversion factor, we can eliminate the unwanted units of minutes and convert to hours.

Solution

To convert from minutes to hours, we must chose a unit conversion factor whose numerator contains the units we want to introduce (hours), and whose denominator contains the units we want to eliminate (minutes). Since there is 1 hour for every 60 minutes, we will use

$$\frac{1 \text{ hr}}{60 \text{ min}}$$

← This is the unit we want to introduce. (numerator)
← This is the unit we want to eliminate (the original unit). (denominator)

To perform the conversion, we multiply.

$105 \text{ min} = \frac{105 \text{ min}}{1} \cdot \frac{1 \text{ hr}}{60 \text{ min}}$ Write 105 min as a fraction: $105 = \frac{105 \text{ min}}{1}$. Then multiply by a form of 1: $\frac{1 \text{ hr}}{60 \text{ min}}$.

$= \frac{105 \cancel{\text{min}}}{1} \cdot \frac{1 \text{ hr}}{60 \cancel{\text{min}}}$ Remove the common units of minutes in the numerator and denominator. Notice that the units of hours remain.

$= \frac{105}{60} \text{ hr}$ Multiply the fractions.

$= \frac{\overset{1}{\cancel{3}} \cdot \overset{1}{\cancel{5}} \cdot 7}{2 \cdot 2 \cdot \underset{1}{\cancel{3}} \cdot \underset{1}{\cancel{5}}} \text{ hr}$ To simplify the fraction, prime factor 105 and 60. Then remove the common factors 3 and 5 in the numerator and denominator.

$= \frac{7}{4} \text{ hr}$ Multiply the remaining factors in the numerator. Multiply the remaining factors in the denominator.

$= 1\frac{3}{4} \text{ hr}$ Write $\frac{7}{4}$ as a mixed number.

A total lunar eclipse can last as long as $1\frac{3}{4}$ hours.

ANSWERS TO SELF CHECKS

1. $1\frac{7}{8}$ in. **2.** $1\frac{1}{4}$ in. **3.** 27 ft **4.** 18 in. **5.** $\frac{7}{32}$ mi ≈ 0.22 mi **6.** $3\frac{3}{4}$ lb = 3.75 lb **7.** 960 oz **8.** 40 fl oz **9.** $7\frac{1}{2}$ min

SECTION 3.4 STUDY SET

VOCABULARY

Fill in the blanks.

1. A ruler is used for measuring length.
2. Inches, feet, and miles are examples of American units of length.
3. $\frac{3\text{ ft}}{1\text{ yd}}$, $\frac{1\text{ ton}}{2{,}000\text{ lb}}$, and $\frac{4\text{ qt}}{1\text{ gal}}$ are examples of unit conversion factors.
4. Ounces, pounds, and tons are examples of American units of weight.
5. Some examples of American units of capacity are cups, pints, quarts, and gallons.
6. ▶ Some units of time are seconds, minutes, hours, and days.

CONCEPTS

Fill in the blanks.

7. a. 12 inches = 1 foot
   b. 3 feet = 1 yard
   c. 1 yard = 36 inches
   d. 1 mile = 5,280 feet
8. a. 16 ounces = 1 pound
   b. 2,000 pounds = 1 ton
9. a. 1 cup = 8 fluid ounces
   b. 1 pint = 2 cups
   c. 2 pints = 1 quart
   d. 4 quarts = 1 gallon
10. a. 1 day = 24 hours
    ▶ b. 2 hours = 120 minutes
11. The value of any unit conversion factor is 1.
12. In general, a unit conversion factor is a fraction with the following form:

    Unit that we want to introduce ← Numerator
    Unit that we want to eliminate ← Denominator

13. Consider the work shown below.

$$\frac{48\text{ oz}}{1} \cdot \frac{1\text{ lb}}{16\text{ oz}}$$

    a. What units can be removed? oz
    b. What units remain? lb

14. Consider the work shown below.

$$\frac{600\text{ yd}}{1} \cdot \frac{3\text{ ft}}{1\text{ yd}} \cdot \frac{1\text{ mi}}{5{,}280\text{ ft}}$$

    a. What units can be removed? yd, ft
    b. What units remain? mi

15. Write a unit conversion factor to convert
    a. pounds to tons $\frac{1\text{ ton}}{2{,}000\text{ lb}}$
    b. quarts to pints $\frac{2\text{ pt}}{1\text{ qt}}$
16. Write the two unit conversion factors used to convert
    a. inches to yards $\frac{1\text{ ft}}{12\text{ in.}}$, $\frac{1\text{ yd}}{3\text{ ft}}$
    b. days to minutes $\frac{24\text{ hr}}{1\text{ day}}$, $\frac{60\text{ min}}{1\text{ hr}}$
17. Match each item with its proper measurement.
    a. Length of the U.S. coastline iv
    b. Height of a Barbie doll i
    c. Span of the Golden Gate Bridge ii
    d. Width of a football field iii

    i. $11\frac{1}{2}$ in.
    ii. 4,200 ft
    iii. 53.5 yd
    iv. 12,383 mi
18. Match each item with its proper measurement.
    a. Weight of the men's shot put used in track and field ii
    b. Weight of an African elephant iii
    c. Amount of gold that is worth $500 i

    i. $1\frac{1}{2}$ oz
    ii. 16 lb
    iii. 7.2 tons
19. Match each item with its proper measurement.
    a. Amount of blood in an adult iii
    b. Size of the Exxon Valdez oil spill in 1989 iv
    c. Amount of nail polish in a bottle i
    d. Amount of flour to make 3 dozen cookies ii

    i. $\frac{1}{2}$ fluid oz
    ii. 2 cups
    iii. 5 qt
    iv. 10,080,000 gal
20. Match each item with its proper measurement.
    a. Length of first U.S. manned space flight ii
    b. A leap year iv
    c. Time difference between New York and Fairbanks, Alaska iii
    d. Length of Wright Brothers' first flight i

    i. 12 sec
    ii. 15 min
    iii. 4 hr
    iv. 366 days

NOTATION

21. What unit does each abbreviation represent?

a. lb pound **b.** oz ounce

c. fl oz fluid ounce

22. What unit does each abbreviation represent?

a. qt quart **b.** c cup

c. pt pint

Complete each solution.

23. Convert 2 yards to inches.

$$2 \text{ yd} = \frac{2 \text{ yd}}{1} \cdot \frac{36 \text{ in.}}{1 \text{ yd}}$$
$$= 2 \cdot 36 \text{ in.}$$
$$= 72 \text{ in.}$$

24. Convert 24 pints to quarts.

$$24 \text{ pt} = \frac{24 \text{ pt}}{1} \cdot \frac{1 \text{ qt}}{2 \text{ pt}}$$
$$= \frac{24}{1} \cdot \frac{1}{2} \text{ qt}$$
$$= 12 \text{ qt}$$

▶ **25.** Convert 1 ton to ounces.

$$1 \text{ ton} = \frac{1 \text{ ton}}{1} \cdot \frac{2{,}000 \text{ lb}}{1 \text{ ton}} \cdot \frac{16 \text{ oz}}{1 \text{ lb}}$$
$$= 1 \cdot 2{,}000 \cdot 16 \text{ oz}$$
$$= 32{,}000 \text{ oz}$$

26. Convert 37,440 minutes to days.

$$37{,}440 \text{ min} = 37{,}440 \text{ min} \cdot \frac{1 \text{ hr}}{60 \text{ min}} \cdot \frac{1 \text{ day}}{24 \text{ hr}}$$
$$= \frac{37{,}440}{60 \cdot 24} \text{ days}$$
$$= 26 \text{ days}$$

GUIDED PRACTICE

Refer to the given ruler to answer each question. See Example 1.

27. a. Each inch is divided into how many equal parts? 8

b. Determine which measurements the arrows point to on the ruler. $\frac{5}{8}$ in., $1\frac{1}{4}$ in., $2\frac{7}{8}$ in.

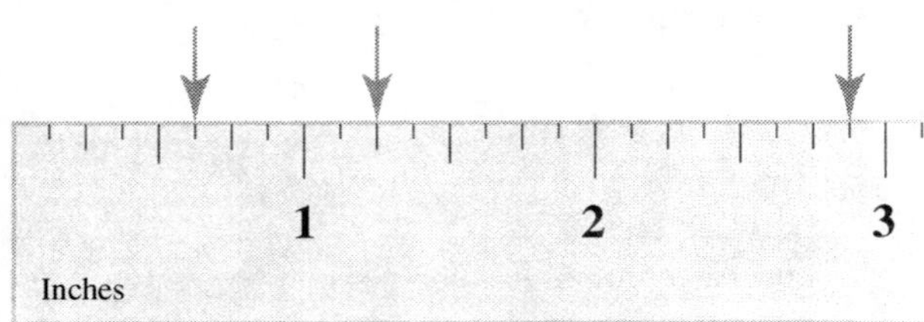

▶ **28.** Find the length of the needle. $1\frac{3}{8}$ in.

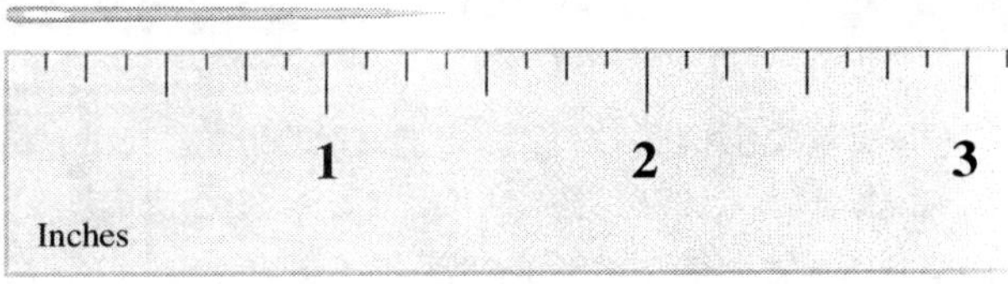

Refer to the given ruler to answer each question. See Example 2.

29. a. Each inch is divided into how many equal parts? 16

b. Determine which measurements the arrows point to on the ruler. $\frac{9}{16}$ in., $1\frac{3}{4}$ in., $2\frac{3}{16}$ in.

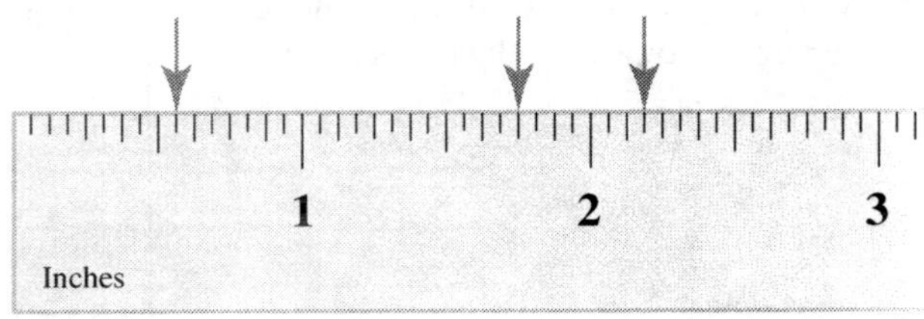

▶ **30.** Find the length of the bolt. $2\frac{15}{16}$ in.

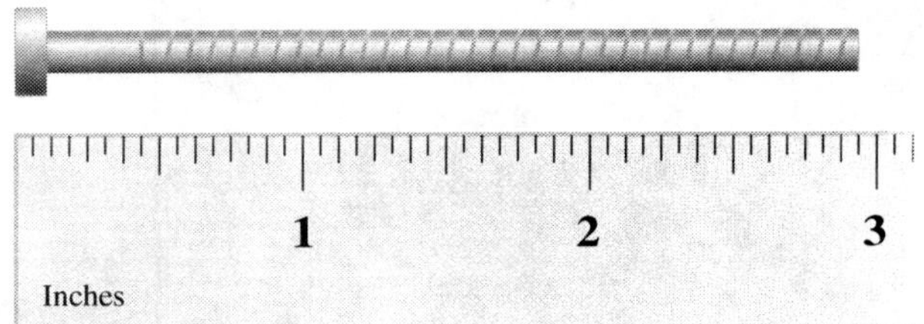

Use a ruler scaled in sixteenths of an inch to measure each object. See Example 2.

31. The width of a dollar bill $2\frac{9}{16}$ in.

32. The length of a dollar bill $6\frac{1}{8}$ in.

33. The length (top to bottom) of this page $10\frac{7}{8}$ in.

34. The length of the word as printed here: supercalifragilisticexpialidocious $1\frac{7}{8}$ in.

Perform each conversion. See Example 3.

35. 4 yards to feet 12 ft ▶ **36.** 6 yards to feet 18 ft

37. 35 yards to feet 105 ft **38.** 33 yards to feet 99 ft

Perform each conversion. See Example 4.

39. $3\frac{1}{2}$ feet to inches 42 in. ▶ **40.** $2\frac{2}{3}$ feet to inches 32 in.

41. $5\frac{1}{4}$ feet to inches 63 in. **42.** $6\frac{1}{2}$ feet to inches 78 in.

Use two unit conversion factors to perform each conversion. Give the exact answer and a decimal approximation, rounded to the nearest hundredth, when necessary. See Example 5.

43. 105 yards to miles $\frac{21}{352}$ mi ≈ 0.06 mi

44. 198 yards to miles $\frac{9}{80}$ mi = 0.1125 mi

45. 1,540 yards to miles $\frac{7}{8}$ mi = 0.875 mi

46. 1,512 yards to miles $\frac{189}{220}$ mi ≈ 0.86 mi

Perform each conversion. See Example 6.

47. Convert 44 ounces to pounds. $2\frac{3}{4}$ lb = 2.75 lb

48. Convert 24 ounces to pounds. $1\frac{1}{2}$ lb = 1.5 lb

49. Convert 72 ounces to pounds. $4\frac{1}{2}$ lb = 4.5 lb

50. Convert 76 ounces to pounds. $4\frac{3}{4}$ lb = 4.75 lb

Perform each conversion. See Example 7.

51. 50 pounds to ounces 800 oz

52. 30 pounds to ounces 480 oz

53. 87 pounds to ounces 1,392 oz

54. 79 pounds to ounces 1,264 oz

Perform each conversion. See Example 8.

55. 8 pints to fluid ounces 128 fl oz

56. 5 pints to fluid ounces 80 fl oz

57. 21 pints to fluid ounces 336 fl oz

58. 30 pints to fluid ounces 480 fl oz

Perform each conversion. See Example 9.

59. 165 minutes to hours $2\frac{3}{4}$ hr

60. 195 minutes to hours $3\frac{1}{4}$ hr

61. 330 minutes to hours $5\frac{1}{2}$ hr

62. 80 minutes to hours $1\frac{1}{3}$ hr

TRY IT YOURSELF

Perform each conversion.

63. 3 quarts to pints 6 pt

64. 20 quarts to gallons 5 gal

65. 7,200 minutes to days 5 days

66. 691,200 seconds to days 8 days

67. 56 inches to feet $4\frac{2}{3}$ ft

68. 44 inches to feet $3\frac{2}{3}$ ft

69. 4 feet to inches 48 in.

70. 7 feet to inches 84 in.

71. 16 pints to gallons 2 gal

72. 3 gallons to fluid ounces 384 fl oz

73. 80 ounces to pounds 5 lb

74. 8 pounds to ounces 128 oz

75. 240 minutes to hours 4 hr

76. 2,400 seconds to hours $\frac{2}{3}$ hr

77. 8 yards to inches 288 in.

78. 324 inches to yards 9 yd

79. 90 inches to yards $2\frac{1}{2}$ yd = 2.5 yd

80. 12 yards to inches 432 in.

81. 5 yards to feet 15 ft

82. 21 feet to yards 7 yd

83. 12.4 tons to pounds 24,800 lb

84. 48,000 ounces to tons $1\frac{1}{2}$ tons = 1.5 tons

85. 7 feet to yards $2\frac{1}{3}$ yd

86. $4\frac{2}{3}$ yards to feet 14 ft

87. 15,840 feet to miles 3 mi

88. 2 miles to feet 10,560 ft

89. $\frac{1}{2}$ mile to feet 2,640 ft

90. 1,320 feet to miles $\frac{1}{4}$ mi = 0.25 mi

91. 7,000 pounds to tons $3\frac{1}{2}$ tons = 3.5 tons

92. 2.5 tons to ounces 80,000 oz

93. 32 fluid ounces to pints 2 pt

94. 2 quarts to fluid ounces 64 fl oz

APPLICATIONS

95. THE GREAT PYRAMID The Great Pyramid in Egypt is about 450 feet high. Express this distance in yards. 150 yd

96. THE WRIGHT BROTHERS In 1903, Orville Wright made the world's first sustained flight. It lasted 12 seconds, and the plane traveled 120 feet. Express the length of the flight in yards. 40 yd

Hulton Archive/Getty Images

97. THE GREAT SPHINX The Great Sphinx of Egypt is 240 feet long. Express this in inches. 2,880 in.

98. HOOVER DAM The Hoover Dam in Nevada is 726 feet high. Express this distance in inches. 8,712 in.

99. THE SEARS TOWER The Sears Tower in Chicago has 110 stories and is 1,454 feet tall. To the nearest hundredth, express this height in miles. 0.28 mi

100. NFL RECORDS Emmit Smith, the former Dallas Cowboys and Arizona Cardinals running back, holds the National Football League record for yards rushing in a career: 18,355. How many miles is this? Round to the nearest tenth of a mile. 10.4 mi

101. NFL RECORDS When Dan Marino of the Miami Dolphins retired, it was noted that Marino's career passing total was nearly 35 miles! How many yards is this? 61,600 yd

102. LEWIS AND CLARK The trail traveled by the Lewis and Clark expedition is shown below. When the expedition reached the Pacific Ocean, Clark estimated that they had traveled 4,162 miles. (It was later determined that his guess was within 40 miles of the actual distance.) Express Clark's estimate of the distance in feet. 21,975,360 ft

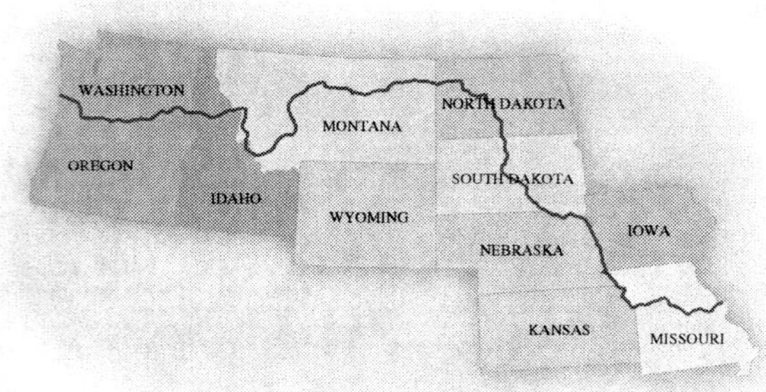

103. WEIGHT OF WATER One gallon of water weighs about 8 pounds. Express this weight in ounces. 128 oz

104. WEIGHT OF A BABY A newborn baby boy weighed 136 ounces. Express this weight in pounds. $8\frac{1}{2}$ lb = 8.5 lb

105. HIPPOS An adult hippopotamus can weigh as much as 9,900 pounds. Express this weight in tons. $4\frac{19}{20}$ tons = 4.95 tons

106. ELEPHANTS An adult elephant can consume as much as 495 pounds of grass and leaves in one day. How many ounces is this? 7,920 oz

107. BUYING PAINT A painter estimates that he will need 17 gallons of paint for a job. To take advantage of a closeout sale on quart cans, he decides to buy the paint in quarts. How many cans will he need to buy? 68 quart cans

108. CATERING How many cups of apple cider are there in a 10-gallon container of cider? 160 cups

109. SCHOOL LUNCHES Each student attending Eagle River Elementary School receives 1 pint of milk for lunch each day. If 575 students attend the school, how many gallons of milk are used each day? $71\frac{7}{8}$ gal = 71.875 gal

110. RADIATORS The radiator capacity of a piece of earth-moving equipment is 39 quarts. If the radiator is drained and new coolant put in, how many gallons of new coolant will be used? $9\frac{3}{4}$ gal = 9.75 gal

111. CAMPING How many ounces of camping stove fuel will fit in the container shown? 320 oz

112. HIKING A college student walks 11 miles in 155 minutes. To the nearest tenth, how many hours does he walk? $2\frac{7}{12}$ hr ≈ 2.6 hr

113. SPACE TRAVEL The astronauts of the Apollo 8 mission, which was launched on December 21, 1968, were in space for 147 hours. How many days did the mission take? $6\frac{1}{8}$ days = 6.125 days

114. AMELIA EARHART In 1935, Amelia Earhart became the first woman to fly across the Atlantic Ocean alone, establishing a new record for the crossing: 13 hours and 30 minutes. How many minutes is this? 810 min

WRITING

115. **a.** Explain how to find the unit conversion factor that will convert feet to inches.

b. Explain how to find the unit conversion factor that will convert pints to gallons.

116. Explain why the unit conversion factor $\frac{1\text{ lb}}{16\text{ oz}}$ is a form of 1.

REVIEW

117. Round 3,673.263 to the

a. nearest hundred 3,700

b. nearest ten 3,670

c. nearest hundredth 3,673.26

d. nearest tenth 3,673.3

118. Round 0.100602 to the

a. nearest thousandth 0.101

b. nearest hundredth 0.10

c. nearest tenth 0.1

d. nearest one 0

SECTION 3.5
Metric Units of Measurement

Objectives

1. Define metric units of length.
2. Use a metric ruler to measure lengths.
3. Use unit conversion factors to convert metric units of length.
4. Use a conversion chart to convert metric units of length.
5. Define metric units of mass.
6. Convert from one metric unit of mass to another.
7. Define metric units of capacity.
8. Convert from one metric unit of capacity to another.
9. Define a cubic centimeter.

The metric system is the system of measurement used by most countries in the world. All countries, including the United States, use it for scientific purposes. The metric system, like our decimal numeration system, is based on the number 10. For this reason, converting from one metric unit to another is easier than with the American system.

1 Define metric units of length.

The basic metric unit of length is the **meter** (m). One meter is approximately 39 inches, which is slightly more than 1 yard. The figure below compares the length of a yardstick to a meterstick.

1 yard: 36 inches
1 2 3 4 5 6 7 8 9 10 11 12 13 14 15 16 17 18 19 20 21 22 23 24 25 26 27 28 29 30 31 32 33 34 35 36

1 meter: about 39 inches
10 20 30 40 50 60 70 80 90 100

Longer and shorter metric units of length are created by adding **prefixes** to the front of the basic unit, *meter*.

kilo means thousands
hecto means hundreds
deka means tens
deci means tenths
centi means hundredths
milli means thousandths

Metric Units of Length

Prefix	kilo-**meter**	hecto-**meter**	deka-**meter**	**meter**	deci-**meter**	centi-**meter**	milli-**meter**
Meaning	1,000 meters	100 meters	10 meters	1 meter	$\frac{1}{10}$ or 0.1 of a meter	$\frac{1}{100}$ or 0.01 of a meter	$\frac{1}{1,000}$ or 0.001 of a meter
Abbreviation	km	hm	dam	m	dm	cm	mm

The Language of Mathematics It is helpful to memorize the prefixes listed above because they are also used with metric units of weight and capacity.

The most often used metric units of length are kilometers, meters, centimeters, and millimeters. It is important that you gain a practical understanding of metric lengths just as you have for the length of an inch, a foot, and a mile. Some examples of metric lengths are shown below.

1 kilometer is about the length of 60 train cars.

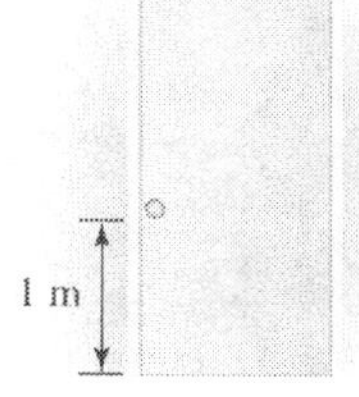

1 meter is about the distance from a doorknob to the floor.

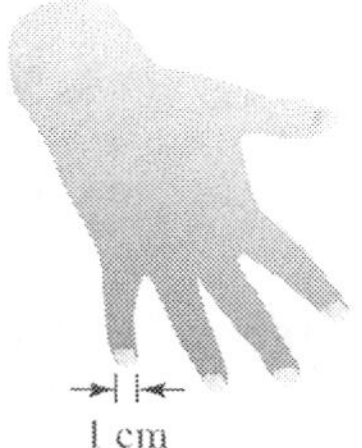

1 centimeter is about as wide as the nail on your little finger.

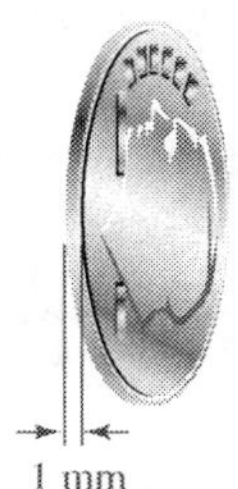

1 millimeter is about the thickness of a dime.

2 Use a metric ruler to measure lengths.

Parts of a metric ruler, scaled in centimeters, and a ruler scaled in inches are shown below. Several lengths on the metric ruler are highlighted.

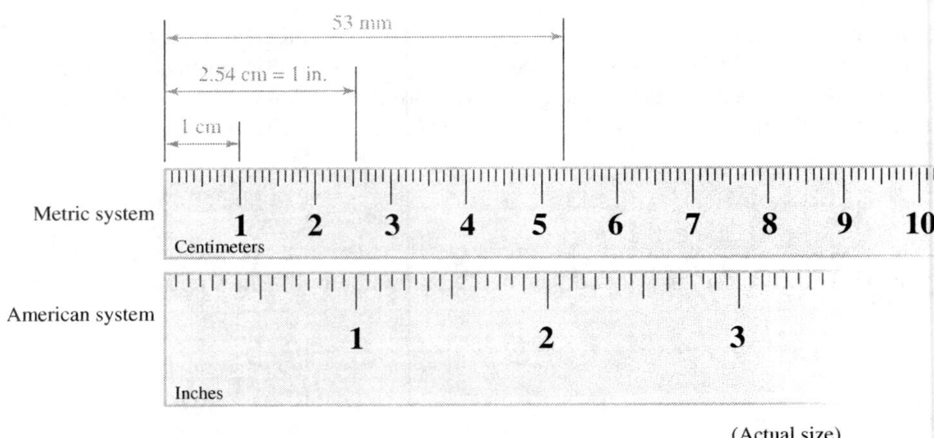

(Actual size)

Self Check 1

To the nearest centimeter, find the width of the circle. 3 cm

Now Try **Problem 23**

EXAMPLE 1 Find the length of the nail shown below.

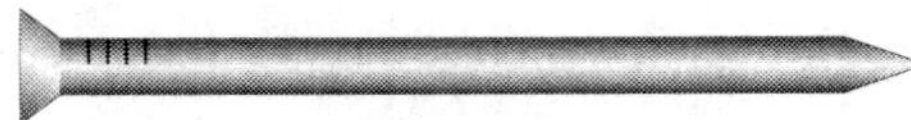

Strategy We will place a metric ruler below the nail, with the left end of the ruler (which could be thought of as 0) directly underneath the head of the nail.

WHY Then we can find the length of the nail by identifying where its pointed end lines up on the tick marks printed in black on the ruler.

Solution

The longest tick marks on the ruler (those labeled with numbers) mark lengths in centimeters. Since the pointed end of the nail lines up on 6, the nail is 6 centimeters long.

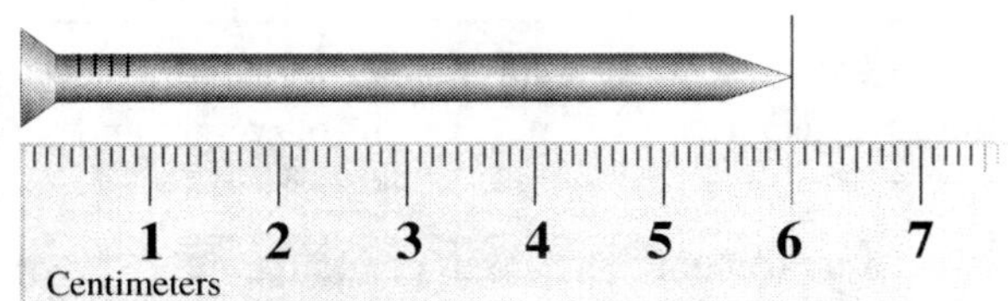

Self Check 2

Find the length of the jumbo paper clip. 47 mm

Now Try **Problem 25**

EXAMPLE 2 Find the length of the paper clip shown below.

Strategy We will place a metric ruler below the paper clip, with the left end of the ruler (which could be thought of as 0) directly underneath one end of the paper clip.

WHY Then we can find the length of the paper clip by identifying where its other end lines up on the tick marks printed in black on the ruler.

Solution
On the ruler, the shorter tick marks divide each centimeter into 10 millimeters, as shown. If we begin at the left end of the ruler and count by tens as we move right to 3, and then add an additional 6 millimeters to that result, we find that the length of the paper clip is 30 + 6 = 36 millimeters.

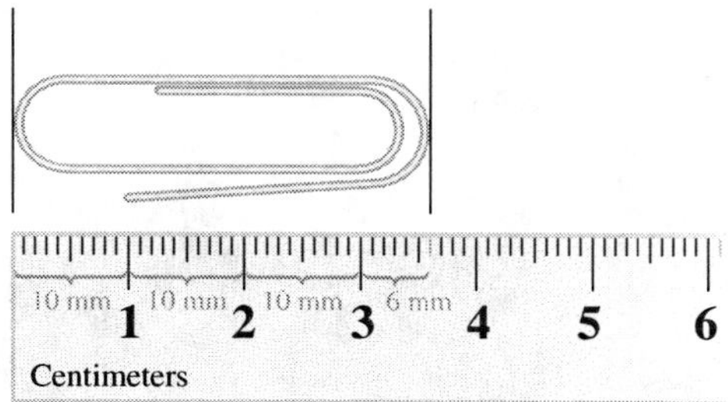

3 Use unit conversion factors to convert metric units of length.

Metric units of length are related as shown in the following table.

Metric Units of Length

1 kilometer (km) = 1,000 meters	1 meter = 10 decimeters (dm)
1 hectometer (hm) = 100 meters	1 meter = 100 centimeters (cm)
1 dekameter (dam) = 10 meters	1 meter = 1,000 millimeters (mm)

The abbreviation for each unit is written within parentheses.

We can use the information in the table to write unit conversion factors that can be used to convert metric units of length. For example, in the table we see that

1 meter = 100 centimeters

From this fact, we can write two unit conversion factors.

$$\frac{1 \text{ m}}{100 \text{ cm}} = 1 \quad \text{and} \quad \frac{100 \text{ cm}}{1 \text{ m}} = 1$$

To obtain the first unit conversion factor, divide both sides of the equation 1 m = 100 cm by 100 cm. To obtain the second unit conversion factor, divide both sides by 1 m.

One advantage of the metric system is that multiplying or dividing by a unit conversion factor involves multiplying or dividing by a power of 10.

EXAMPLE 3 Convert 350 centimeters to meters.

Strategy We will multiply 350 centimeters by a carefully chosen unit conversion factor.

WHY If we multiply by the proper unit conversion factor, we can eliminate the unwanted units of centimeters and convert to meters.

Solution
To convert from centimeters to meters, we must choose a unit conversion factor whose numerator contains the units we want to introduce (meters), and whose denominator contains the units we want to eliminate (centimeters). Since there is 1 meter for every 100 centimeters, we will use

$$\frac{1 \text{ m}}{100 \text{ cm}}$$

← This is the unit we want to introduce.
← This is the unit we want to eliminate (the original unit).

Self Check 3

Convert 860 centimeters to meters. 8.6 m

Now Try **Problem 31**

Teaching Example 3
Convert 410 centimeters to meters.
Answer:
4.1 m

To perform the conversion, we multiply 350 centimeters by the unit conversion factor $\frac{1\text{ m}}{100\text{ cm}}$.

$$350\text{ cm} = \frac{350\text{ cm}}{1} \cdot \frac{1\text{ m}}{100\text{ cm}}$$ Write 350 cm as a fraction: $350\text{ cm} = \frac{350\text{ cm}}{1}$. Multiply by a form of 1: $\frac{1\text{ m}}{100\text{ cm}}$.

$$= \frac{350\text{ cm}}{1} \cdot \frac{1\text{ m}}{100\text{ cm}}$$ Remove the common units of centimeters from the numerator and denominator. Notice that the units of meter remain.

$$= \frac{350}{100}\text{ m}$$ Multiply the fractions.

$$= \frac{350.0}{100}\text{ m}$$ Write the whole number 350 as a decimal by placing a decimal point immediately to its right and entering a zero: 350 = 350.0

$$= 3.5\text{ m}$$ Divide 350.0 by 100 by moving the decimal point 2 places to the left: 3.500.

Thus, 350 centimeters = 3.5 meters.

4 Use a conversion chart to convert metric units of length.

In Example 3, we converted 350 centimeters to meters using a unit conversion factor. We can also make this conversion by recognizing that all units of length in the metric system are powers of 10 of a meter.

To see this, review the table of metric units of length on page 456. Note that each unit has a value that is $\frac{1}{10}$ of the value of the unit immediately to its left and 10 times the value of the unit immediately to its right. Converting from one unit to another is as easy as multiplying (or dividing) by the correct power of 10 or, simply moving a decimal point the correct number of places to the right (or left). For example, in the **conversion chart** below, we see that to convert from centimeters to meters, we move 2 places to the left.

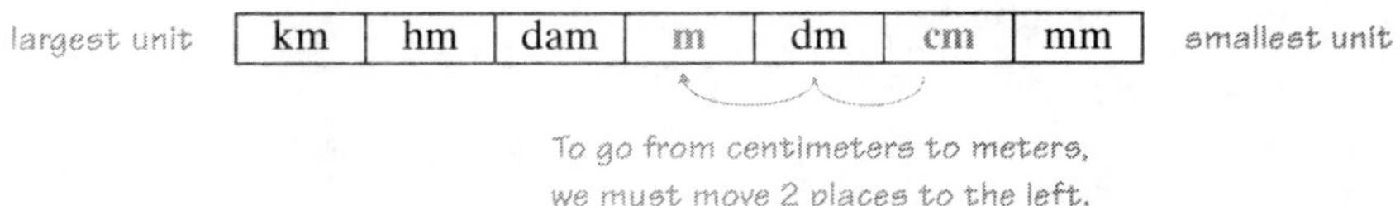

If we write 350 centimeters as 350.0 centimeters, we can convert to meters by moving the decimal point 2 places to the left.

350.0 centimeters = 3.500 meters = 3.5 meters

Move 2 places to the left.

With the unit conversion factor method or the conversion chart method, we get 350 cm = 3.5 m.

Caution! When using a chart to help make a metric conversion, be sure to list the units from *largest to smallest* when reading from left to right.

Self Check 4

Convert 5.3 meters to millimeters. 5,300 mm

Now Try **Problem 35**

EXAMPLE 4 Convert 2.4 meters to millimeters.

Strategy On a conversion chart, we will count the places and note the direction as we move from the original units of meters to the conversion units of millimeters.

WHY The decimal point in 2.4 must be moved the same number of places and in that same direction to find the conversion to millimeters.

Solution
To construct a conversion chart, we list the metric units of length from largest (kilometers) to smallest (millimeters), working from left to right. Then we locate the original units of meters and move to the conversion units of millimeters, as shown below.

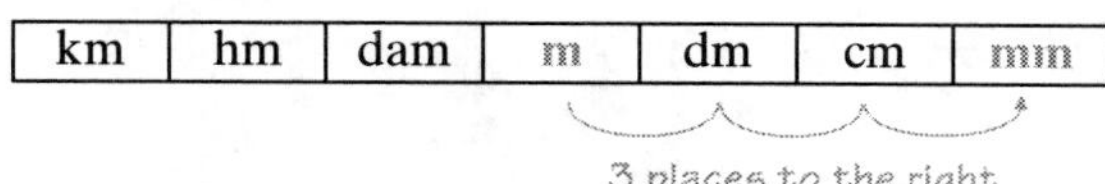

We see that the decimal point in 2.4 should be moved 3 places to the right to convert from meters to millimeters.

2.4 meters = 2 400. millimeters = 2,400 millimeters

Move 3 places to the right.

We can use the unit conversion factor method to confirm this result. Since there are 1,000 millimeters per meter, we multiply 2.4 meters by the unit conversion factor $\frac{1{,}000 \text{ mm}}{1 \text{ m}}$.

$2.4 \text{ m} = \frac{2.4 \text{ m}}{1} \cdot \frac{1{,}000 \text{ mm}}{1 \text{ m}}$ Write 2.4 m as a fraction: $2.4 \text{ m} = \frac{2.4 \text{ m}}{1}$. Multiply by a form 1: $\frac{1{,}000 \text{ mm}}{1 \text{ m}}$.

$= \frac{2.4 \text{ m}}{1} \cdot \frac{1{,}000 \text{ mm}}{1 \text{ m}}$ Remove the common units of meters from the numerator and denominator. Notice that the units of millimeters remain.

$= 2.4 \cdot 1{,}000 \text{ mm}$ Multiply the fractions and simplify.

$= 2{,}400 \text{ mm}$ Multiply 2.4 by 1,000 by moving the decimal point 3 places to the right: 2 400.

Teaching Example 4
Convert 1.9 meters to millimeters.
Answer:
1,900 mm

EXAMPLE 5 Convert 3.2 centimeters to kilometers.

Strategy On a conversion chart, we will count the places and note the direction as we move from the original units of centimeters to the conversion units of kilometers.

WHY The decimal point in 3.2 must be moved the same number of places and in that same direction to find the conversion to kilometers.

Solution
We locate the original units of centimeters on a conversion chart, and then move to the conversion units of kilometers, as shown below.

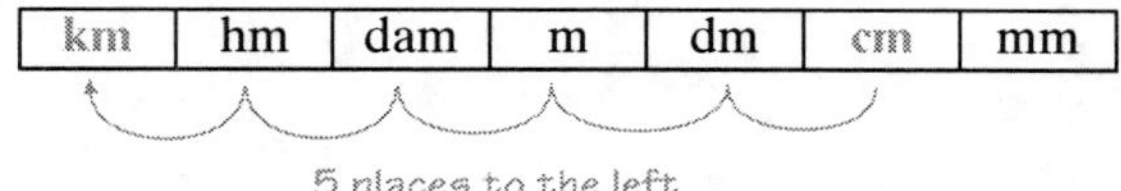

We see that the decimal point in 3.2 should be moved 5 places to the left to convert centimeters to kilometers.

3.2 centimeters = 0.000032 kilometers = 0.000032 kilometers

Move 5 places to the left.

We can use the unit conversion factor method to confirm this result. To convert to kilometers, we must use two unit conversion factors so that the units of centimeters drop out and the units of kilometers remain. Since there is 1 meter for

Self Check 5
Convert 5.15 centimeters to kilometers. 0.0000515 km

Now Try **Problem 39**

Teaching Example 5
Convert 9.1 centimeters to kilometers.
Answer:
0.000091 km

every 100 centimeters and 1 kilometer for every 1,000 meters, we multiply by $\frac{1\text{ m}}{100\text{ cm}}$ and $\frac{1\text{ km}}{1{,}000\text{ m}}$.

$$3.2\text{ cm} = \frac{3.2\text{ cm}}{1} \cdot \frac{1\text{ m}}{100\text{ cm}} \cdot \frac{1\text{ km}}{1{,}000\text{ m}}$$ Remove the common units of centimeters and meters. The units of km remain.

$$= \frac{3.2}{100 \cdot 1{,}000}\text{ km}$$ Multiply the fractions.

$$= 0.000032\text{ km}$$ Divide 3.2 by 1,000 and 100 by moving the decimal point 5 places to the left.

5 Define metric units of mass.

The **mass** of an object is a measure of the amount of material in the object. When an object is moved about in space, its mass does not change. One basic unit of mass in the metric system is the **gram** (g). A gram is defined to be the mass of water contained in a cube having sides 1 centimeter long. (See the figure below.)

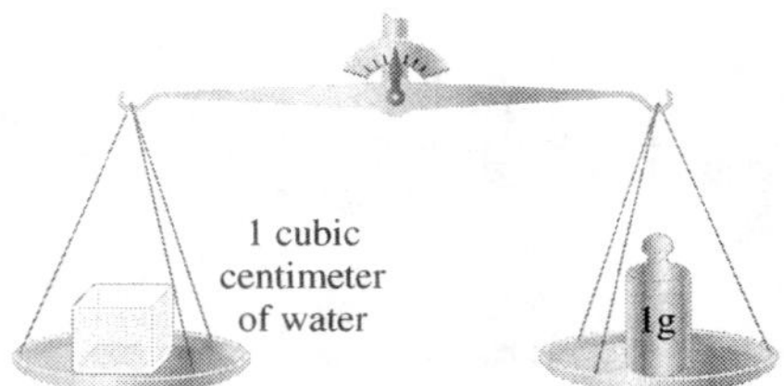

Other units of mass are created by adding prefixes to the front of the basic unit, *gram*.

Metric Units of Mass

Prefix	kilo- **gram**	hecto- **gram**	deka- **gram**	**gram**	deci- **gram**	centi- **gram**	milli- **gram**
Meaning	1,000 grams	100 grams	10 grams	1 gram	$\frac{1}{10}$ or 0.1 of a gram	$\frac{1}{100}$ or 0.01 of a gram	$\frac{1}{1{,}000}$ or 0.001 of a gram
Abbreviation	kg	hg	dag	g	dg	cg	mg

The most often used metric units of mass are kilograms, grams, and milligrams. Some examples are shown below.

An average bowling ball weighs about 6 kilograms.

A raisin weighs about 1 gram.

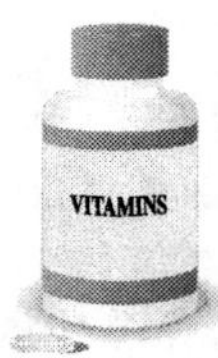

A certain vitamin tablet contains 450 milligrams of calcium.

The **weight** of an object is determined by the Earth's gravitational pull on the object. Since gravitational pull on an object decreases as the object gets farther from Earth, the object weighs less as it gets farther from Earth's surface. This is why astronauts experience weightlessness in space. However, since most of us remain near Earth's surface, we will use the words *mass* and *weight* interchangeably. Thus, a mass of 30 grams is said to weigh 30 grams.

Metric units of mass are related as shown in the following table.

Metric Units of Mass

1 kilogram (kg) = 1,000 grams	1 gram = 10 decigrams (dg)
1 hectogram (hg) = 100 grams	1 gram = 100 centigrams (cg)
1 dekagram (dag) = 10 grams	1 gram = 1,000 milligrams (mg)

The abbreviation for each unit is written within parentheses.

We can use the information in the table to write unit conversion factors that can be used to convert metric units of mass. For example, in the table we see that

1 kilogram = 1,000 grams

From this fact, we can write two unit conversion factors.

$$\frac{1\text{ kg}}{1{,}000\text{ g}} = 1 \quad \text{and} \quad \frac{1{,}000\text{ g}}{1\text{ kg}} = 1$$

To obtain the first unit conversion factor, divide both sides of the equation 1 kg = 1,000 g by 1,000 g. To obtain the second unit conversion factor, divide both sides by 1 kg.

6 Convert from one metric unit of mass to another.

EXAMPLE 6 Convert 7.86 kilograms to grams.

Strategy On a conversion chart, we will count the places and note the direction as we move from the original units of kilograms to the conversion units of grams.

WHY The decimal point in 7.86 must be moved the same number of places and in that same direction to find the conversion to grams.

Solution

To construct a conversion chart, we list the metric units of mass from largest (kilograms) to smallest (milligrams), working from left to right. Then we locate the original units of kilograms and move to the conversion units of grams, as shown below.

largest unit

kg	hg	dag	g	dg	cg	mg

smallest unit

3 places to the right

We see that the decimal point in 7.86 should be moved 3 places to the right to change kilograms to grams.

7.86 kilograms = 7 860. grams = 7,860 grams

Move 3 places to the right.

Self Check 6

Convert 5.83 kilograms to grams. 5,830 g

Now Try **Problem 43**

Teaching Example 6

Convert 1.21 kilograms to grams.

Answer:

1,210 g

We can use the unit conversion factor method to confirm this result. To convert to grams, we must chose a unit conversion factor such that the units of kilograms drop out and the units of grams remain. Since there are 1,000 grams per 1 kilogram, we multiply 7.86 kilograms by $\frac{1,000 \text{ g}}{1 \text{ kg}}$.

$$7.86 \text{ kg} = \frac{7.86 \text{ kg}}{1} \cdot \frac{1,000 \text{ g}}{1 \text{ kg}}$$ Remove the common units of kilograms in the numerator and denominator. The units of g remain.

$$= 7.86 \cdot 1,000 \text{ g}$$ Simplify.

$$= 7,860 \text{ g}$$ Multiply 7.86 by 1,000 by moving the decimal point 3 places to the right.

Self Check 7

MEDICATIONS A bottle of Isoptin (a drug taken for high blood pressure) contains 90 tablets, and each has 200 mg of active ingredient, how many grams of active ingredient are in the bottle? 1.8 g

Now Try **Problems 47 and 95**

Teaching Example 7 MEDICATIONS A drug taken for high cholesterol contains 65 tablets. If each tablet contains 120 mg of active ingredient, how many grams of active ingredient are there in the bottle?
Answer:
7.8 g

EXAMPLE 7 *Medications* A bottle of Verapamil, a drug taken for high blood pressure, contains 30 tablets. If each tablet has 180 mg of active ingredient, how many grams of active ingredient are in the bottle?

Strategy We will multiply the number of tablets in one bottle by the number of milligrams of active ingredient in each tablet.

WHY We need to know the total number of milligrams of active ingredient in one bottle before we can convert that number to grams.

Solution

Since there are 30 tablets, and each one contains 180 mg of active ingredient, there are

$$30 \cdot 180 \text{ mg} = 5,400 \text{ mg} = 5400.0 \text{ mg}$$

$$\begin{array}{r} 180 \\ \times 30 \\ \hline 000 \\ 5400 \\ \hline 5,400 \end{array}$$

of active ingredient in the bottle. To use a conversion chart to solve this problem, we locate the original units of milligrams and then move to the conversion units of grams, as shown below.

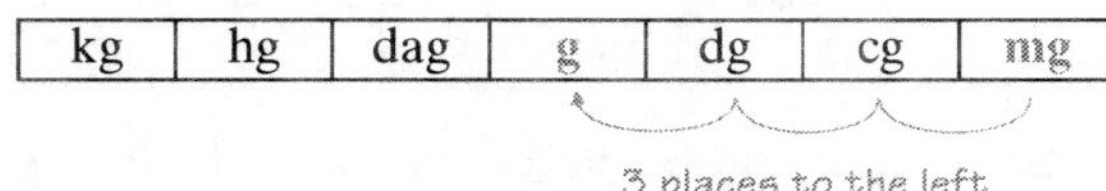

3 places to the left

We see that the decimal point in 5,400.0 should be moved 3 places to the left to convert from milligrams to grams.

$$5,400 \text{ milligrams} = 5.400 \text{ grams}$$

Move 3 places to the left.

There are 5.4 grams of active ingredient in the bottle.

We can use the unit conversion factor method to confirm this result. To convert milligrams to grams, we multiply 5,400 milligrams by $\frac{1 \text{ g}}{1,000 \text{ mg}}$.

$$5,400 \text{ mg} = \frac{5,400 \text{ mg}}{1} \cdot \frac{1 \text{ g}}{1,000 \text{ mg}}$$ Remove the common units of milligrams from the numerator and denominator. The units of g remain.

$$= \frac{5,400}{1,000} \text{ g}$$ Multiply the fractions.

$$= 5.4 \text{ g}$$ Divide 5,400 by 1,000 by moving the understood decimal point in 5,400 three places to the left.

7 Define metric units of capacity.

In the metric system, one basic unit of capacity is the **liter** (L), which is defined to be the capacity of a cube with sides 10 centimeters long. Other units of capacity are created by adding prefixes to the front of the basic unit, liter.

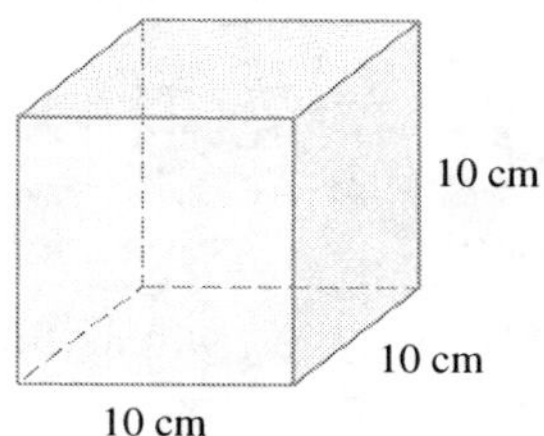

Metric Units of Capacity

Prefix	kilo- **liter**	hecto- **liter**	deka- **liter**	**liter**	deci- **liter**	centi- **liter**	milli- **liter**
Meaning	1,000 liters	100 liters	10 liters	1 liter	$\frac{1}{10}$ or 0.1 of a liter	$\frac{1}{100}$ or 0.01 of a liter	$\frac{1}{1,000}$ or 0.001 of a liter
Abbreviation	kL	hL	daL	L	dL	cL	mL

The most often used metric units of capacity are liters and milliliters. Here are some examples.

Soft drinks are sold in 2-liter plastic bottles.

The fuel tank of a minivan can hold about 75 liters of gasoline.

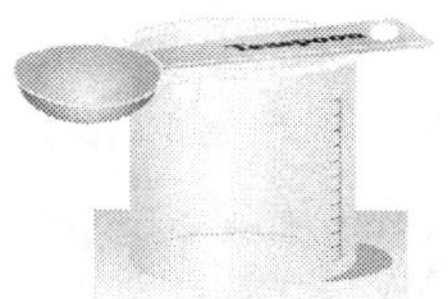

A teaspoon holds about 5 milliliters.

Metric units of capacity are related as shown in the following table.

Metric Units of Capacity

1 kiloliter (kL) = 1,000 liters	1 liter = 10 deciliters (dL)
1 hectoliter (hL) = 100 liters	1 liter = 100 centiliters (cL)
1 dekaliter (daL) = 10 liters	1 liter = 1,000 milliliters (mL)

The abbreviation for each unit is written within parentheses.

We can use the information in the table to write unit conversion factors that can be used to convert metric units of capacity. For example, in the table we see that

1 liter = 1,000 milliliters

From this fact, we can write two unit conversion factors.

$$\frac{1\text{ L}}{1{,}000\text{ mL}} = 1 \quad \text{and} \quad \frac{1{,}000\text{ mL}}{1\text{ L}} = 1$$

8 Convert from one metric unit of capacity to another.

Self Check 8

SOFT DRINKS How many milliliters are in a case of *twelve* 2-liter bottles of cola? 24,000 mL

Now Try **Problems 51 and 97**

Teaching Example 8 ORANGE JUICE How many milliliters are in *six* 2-liter cartons of orange juice?
Answer:
12,000 mL

EXAMPLE 8 *Soft Drinks* How many milliliters are in *three* 2-liter bottles of cola?

Strategy We will multiply the number of bottles of cola by the number of liters of cola in each bottle.

WHY We need to know the total number of liters of cola before we can convert that number to milliliters.

Solution

Since there are three bottles, and each contains 2 liters of cola, there are

$$3 \cdot 2\text{ L} = 6\text{ L} = 6.0\text{ L}$$

of cola in the bottles. To construct a conversion chart, we list the metric units of capacity from largest (kiloliters) to smallest (milliliters), working from left to right. Then we locate the original units of liters and move to the conversion units of milliliters, as shown below.

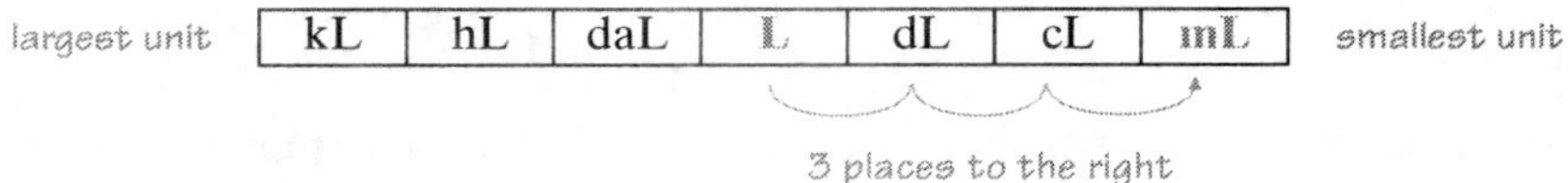

We see that the decimal point in 6.0 should be moved 3 places to the right to convert from liters to milliliters.

6 liters = 6 000. milliliters = 6,000 milliliters

Move 3 places to the right.

Thus, there are 6,000 milliliters in *three* 2-liter bottles of cola.

We can use the unit conversion factor method to confirm this result. To convert to milliliters, we must chose a unit conversion factor such that liters drop out and the units of milliliters remain. Since there are 1,000 milliliters per 1 liter, we multiply 6 liters by the unit conversion factor $\frac{1{,}000\text{ mL}}{1\text{ L}}$.

$6\text{ L} = \frac{6\text{ L}}{1} \cdot \frac{1{,}000\text{ mL}}{1\text{ L}}$ Remove the common units of liters in the numerator and denominator. The units of mL remain.

$= 6 \cdot 1{,}000\text{ mL}$ Simplify.

$= 6{,}000\text{ mL}$ Multiply 6 by 1,000 by moving the understood decimal point in 6 three places to the right.

9 Define a cubic centimeter.

Another metric unit of capacity is the **cubic centimeter,** which is represented by the notation cm^3 or, more simply, cc. One milliliter and one cubic centimeter represent the same capacity.

$$1\text{ mL} = 1\text{ cm}^3 = 1\text{ cc}$$

The units of cubic centimeters are used frequently in medicine. For example, when a nurse administers an injection containing 5 cc of medication, the dosage can also be expressed using milliliters.

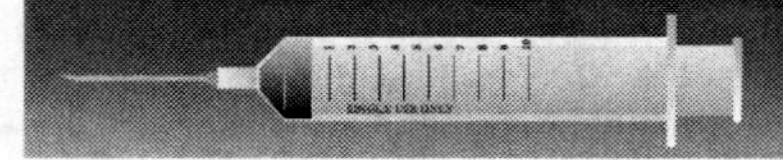

$$5\text{ cc} = 5\text{ mL}$$

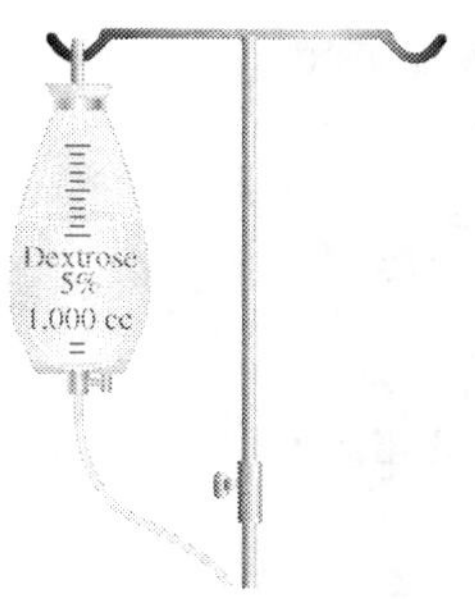

When a doctor orders that a patient be put on 1,000 cc of dextrose solution, the request can be expressed in different ways.

1,000 cc = 1,000 mL = 1 liter

ANSWERS TO SELF CHECKS

1. 3 cm **2.** 47 mm **3.** 8.6 m **4.** 5,300 mm **5.** 0.0000515 km **6.** 5,830 g **7.** 1.8 g **8.** 24,000 mL

SECTION 5.4 STUDY SET

VOCABULARY

Fill in the blanks.

1. The meter, the gram, and the liter are basic units of measurement in the metric system.
2. **a.** The basic unit of length in the metric system is the meter.
   b. The basic unit of mass in the metric system is the gram.
   c. The basic unit of capacity in the metric system is the liter.
3. **a.** *Deka* means tens.
   b. *Hecto* means hundreds.
   c. *Kilo* means thousands.
4. **a.** *Deci* means tenths.
   b. *Centi* means hundredths.
   c. *Milli* means thousandths.
5. We can convert from one unit to another in the metric system using unit conversion factors or a conversion chart like that shown below.

km	hm	dam	m	dm	cm	mm

6. The mass of an object is a measure of the amount of material in the object.
7. ▶ The weight of an object is determined by the Earth's gravitational pull on the object.
8. Another metric unit of capacity is the cubic centimeter, which is represented by the notation cm^3, or, more simply, cc.

CONCEPTS

Fill in the blanks.

9. **a.** 1 kilometer = 1,000 meters
   b. 100 centimeters = 1 meter
   c. 1,000 millimeters = 1 meter
10. **a.** 1 gram = 1,000 milligrams
    b. 1 kilogram = 1,000 grams
11. **a.** 1,000 milliliters = 1 liter
    b. 1 dekaliter = 10 liters
12. **a.** 1 milliliter = 1 cubic centimeter
    b. 1 liter = 1,000 cubic centimeters
13. Write a unit conversion factor to convert
    a. meters to kilometers $\frac{1\text{ km}}{1{,}000\text{ m}}$
    b. grams to centigrams $\frac{100\text{ cg}}{1\text{ g}}$
    c. liters to milliliters $\frac{1{,}000\text{ milliliters}}{1\text{ liter}}$
14. Use the chart to determine how many decimal places and in which direction to move the decimal point when converting the following.
    a. Kilometers to centimeters 5 places to the right

km	hm	dam	m	dm	cm	mm

    b. Milligrams to grams 3 places to the left

kg	hg	dag	g	dg	cg	mg

    c. Hectoliters to centiliters 4 places to the right

kL	hL	daL	L	dL	cL	mL

15. Match each item with its proper measurement.
    a. Thickness of a phone book iii — **i.** 6,275 km
    b. Length of the Amazon River i — **ii.** 2 m
    c. Height of a soccer goal ii — **iii.** 6 cm
16. Match each item with its proper measurement.
    a. Weight of a giraffe i — **i.** 800 kg
    b. Weight of a paper clip ii — **ii.** 1 g
    c. Active ingredient in an aspirin tablet iii — **iii.** 325 mg

17. Match each item with its proper measurement.

a. Amount of blood in an adult ii — **i.** 290,000 kL

b. Cola in an aluminum can iii — **ii.** 6 L

c. Kuwait's daily production of crude oil i — **iii.** 355 mL

18. Of the objects shown below, which can be used to measure the following?

a. Millimeters micrometer

b. Milligrams balance

c. Milliliters beaker

Balance

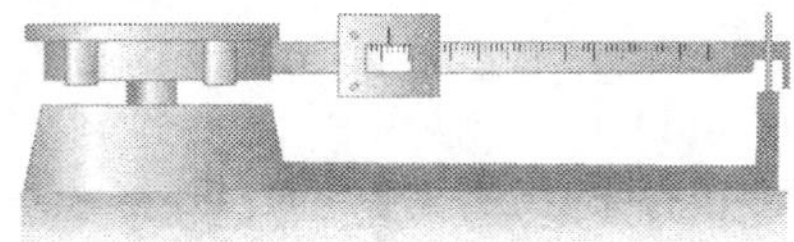

Beaker

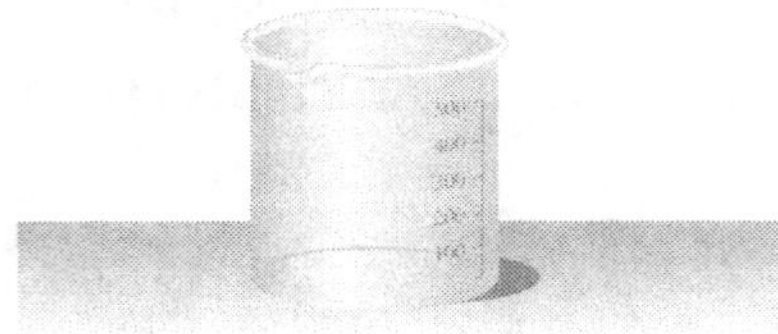

Micrometer

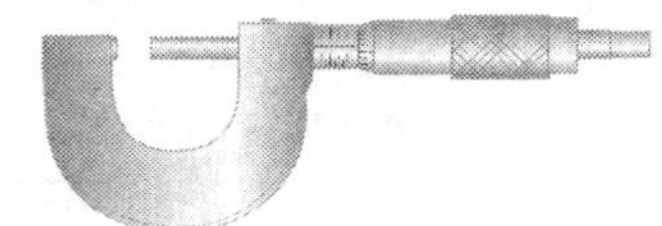

NOTATION

Complete each solution.

19. Convert 20 centimeters to meters.

$$20 \text{ cm} = \frac{20 \text{ cm}}{1} \cdot \frac{1 \text{ m}}{100 \text{ cm}}$$
$$= \frac{20}{100} \text{ m}$$
$$= 0.2 \text{ m}$$

20. Convert 3,000 milligrams to grams.

$$3{,}000 \text{ mg} = \frac{3{,}000 \text{ mg}}{1} \cdot \frac{1 \text{ g}}{1{,}000 \text{ mg}}$$
$$= \frac{3{,}000}{1{,}000} \text{ g}$$
$$= 3 \text{ g}$$

21. Convert 0.2 kilograms to milligrams.

$$0.2 \text{ kg} = \frac{0.2 \text{ kg}}{1} \cdot \frac{1{,}000 \text{ g}}{1 \text{ kg}} \cdot \frac{1{,}000 \text{ mg}}{1 \text{ g}}$$
$$= 0.2 \cdot 1{,}000 \cdot 1{,}000 \text{ mg}$$
$$= 200{,}000 \text{ mg}$$

22. Convert 400 milliliters to kiloliters.

$$400 \text{ mL} = \frac{400 \text{ mL}}{1} \cdot \frac{1 \text{ L}}{1{,}000 \text{ mL}} \cdot \frac{1 \text{ kL}}{1{,}000 \text{ L}}$$
$$= \frac{400}{1{,}000 \cdot 1{,}000} \text{ kL}$$
$$= 0.0004 \text{ kL}$$

GUIDED PRACTICE

Refer to the given ruler to answer each question. See Example 1.

23. Determine which measurements the arrows point to on the metric ruler. 1 cm, 3 cm, 5 cm

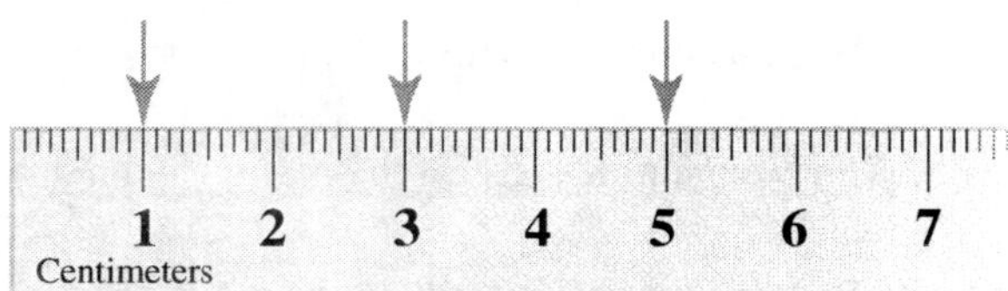

24. Find the length of the birthday candle (including the wick). 6 cm

Refer to the given ruler to answer each question. See Example 2.

25. a. Refer to the metric ruler below. Each centimeter is divided into how many equal parts? What is the length of one of those parts? 10, 1 millimeter

b. Determine which measurements the arrows point to on the ruler. 27 mm, 41 mm, 55 mm

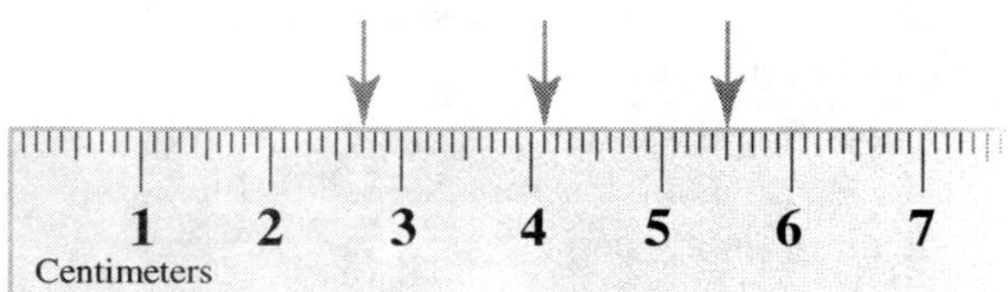

26. Find the length of the stick of gum. 74 mm

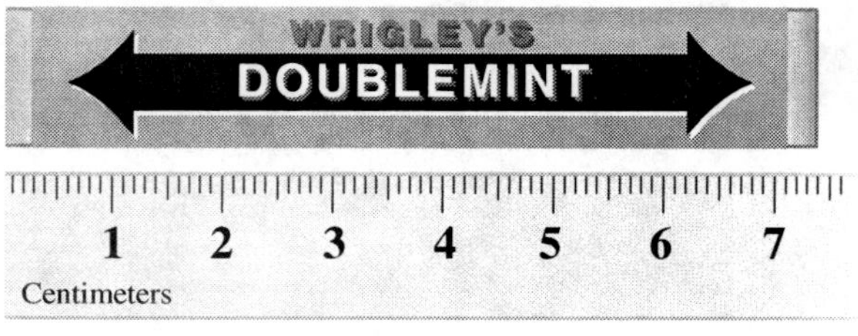

Use a metric ruler scaled in millimeters to measure each object. See Example 2.

27. The length of a dollar bill 156 mm

28. The width of a dollar bill 66 mm

29. The length (top to bottom) of this page 280 mm

30. The length of the word antidisestablishmentarianism as printed here. 40 mm

Perform each conversion. See Example 3.

31. 380 centimeters to meters 3.8 m

32. 590 centimeters to meters 5.9 m

33. 120 centimeters to meters 1.2 m

34. 640 centimeters to meters 6.4 m

Perform each conversion. See Example 4.

35. 8.7 meters to millimeters 8,700 mm

36. 1.3 meters to millimeters 1,300 mm

37. 2.89 meters to millimeters 2,890 mm

38. 4.06 meters to millimeters 4,060 mm

Perform each conversion. See Example 5.

39. 4.5 centimeters to kilometers 0.000045 km

40. 6.2 centimeters to kilometers 0.000062 km

41. 0.3 centimeters to kilometers 0.000003 km

42. 0.4 centimeters to kilometers 0.000004 km

Perform each conversion. See Example 6.

43. 1.93 kilograms to grams 1,930 g

44. 8.99 kilograms to grams 8,990 g

45. 4.531 kilograms to grams 4,531 g

46. 6.077 kilograms to grams 6,077 g

Perform each conversion. See Example 7.

47. 6,000 milligrams to grams 6 g

48. 9,000 milligrams to grams 9 g

49. 3,500 milligrams to grams 3.5 g

50. 7,500 milligrams to grams 7.5 g

Perform each conversion. See Example 8.

51. 3 liters to milliliters 3,000 mL

52. 4 liters to milliliters 4,000 mL

53. 26.3 liters to milliliters 26,300 mL

54. 35.2 liters to milliliters 35,200 mL

TRY IT YOURSELF

Perform each conversion.

55. 0.31 decimeters to centimeters 3.1 cm

56. 73.2 meters to decimeters 732 dm

57. 500 milliliters to liters 0.5 L

58. 500 centiliters to milliliters 5,000 mL

59. 2 kilograms to grams 2,000 g

60. 4,000 grams to kilograms 4 kg

61. 0.074 centimeters to millimeters 0.74 mm

62. 0.125 meters to millimeters 125 mm

63. 1,000 kilograms to grams 1,000,000 g

64. 2 kilograms to centigrams 200,000 cg

65. 658.23 liters to kiloliters 0.65823 kL

66. 0.0068 hectoliters to kiloliters 0.00068 kL

67. 4.72 cm to dm 0.472 dm

68. 0.593 cm to dam 0.000593 dam

69. 10 mL = 10 cc

70. 2,000 cc = 2 L

71. 500 mg to g 0.5 g

72. 500 mg to cg 50 cg

73. 5,689 g to kg 5.689 kg

74. 0.0579 km to mm 57,900 mm

75. 453.2 cm to m 4.532 m

76. 675.3 cm to m 6.753 m

77. 0.325 dL to L 0.0325 L

78. 0.0034 mL to L 0.0000034 L

79. 675 dam = 675,000 cm

80. 76.8 hm = 7,680,000 mm

81. 0.00777 cm = 0.0000077 dam

82. 400 liters to hL 4 hL

83. 134 m to hm 1.34 hm

84. 6.77 mm to cm 0.677 cm

85. 65.78 km to dam 6,578 dam

86. 5 g to cg 500 cg

APPLICATIONS

87. SPEED SKATING American Eric Heiden won an unprecedented five gold medals by capturing the men's 500-m, 1,000-m, 1,500-m, 5,000-m, and 10,000-m races at the 1980 Winter Olympic Games in Lake Placid, New York. Convert each race length to kilometers. 0.5 km, 1 km, 1.5 km, 5 km, 10 km

88. THE SUEZ CANAL The 163-km-long Suez Canal connects the Mediterranean Sea with the Red Sea. It provides a shortcut for ships operating between European and American ports. Convert the length of the Suez Canal to meters. 163,000 m

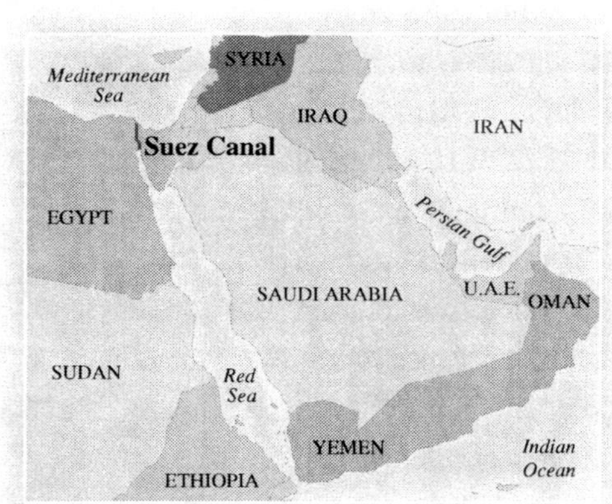

89. SKYSCRAPERS The John Hancock Center in Chicago has 100 stories and is 343 meters high. Give this height in hectometers. 3.43 hm

90. WEIGHT OF A BABY A baby weighs 4 kilograms. Give this weight in centigrams. 400,000 cg

91. HEALTH CARE Blood pressure is measured by a sphygmomanometer *(see at right)*. The measurement is read at two points and is expressed, for example, as 120/80. This indicates a *systolic* pressure of 120 millimeters of mercury and a *diastolic* pressure of 80 millimeters of mercury. Convert each measurement to centimeters of mercury. 12 cm, 8 cm

92. JEWELRY A gold chain weighs 1,500 milligrams. Give this weight in grams. 1.5 g

93. EYE DROPPERS One drop from an eye dropper is 0.05 mL. Convert the capacity of one drop to liters. 0.00005 L

94. BOTTLING How many liters of wine are in a 750-mL bottle? $\frac{3}{4}$ L or 0.75 L

95. MEDICINE A bottle of hydrochlorothiazine contains 60 tablets. If each tablet contains 50 milligrams of active ingredient, how many grams of active ingredient are in the bottle? 3 g

96. IBUPROFEN What is the total weight, in grams, of all the tablets in the box shown at right? 33 g

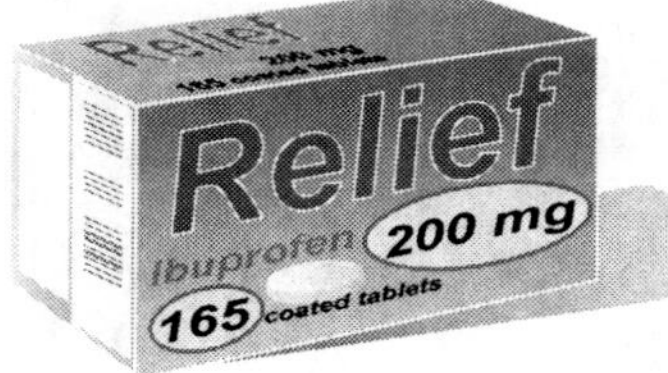

97. SIX PACKS Some stores sell Fanta orange soda in 0.5 liter bottles. How many milliliters are there in a six pack of this size bottle? 3,000 mL

98. CONTAINERS How many deciliters of root beer are in *two* 2-liter bottles? 40 dL

99. OLIVES The net weight of a bottle of olives is 284 grams. Find the smallest number of bottles that must be purchased to have at least 1 kilogram of olives. 4

100. COFFEE A can of Cafe Vienna has a net weight of 133 grams. Find the smallest number of cans that must be packaged to have at least 1 metric ton of coffee. (*Hint:* 1 metric ton = 1,000 kg.) 7,519

101. INJECTIONS The illustration below shows a 3cc syringe. Express its capacity using units of milliliters. 3 mL

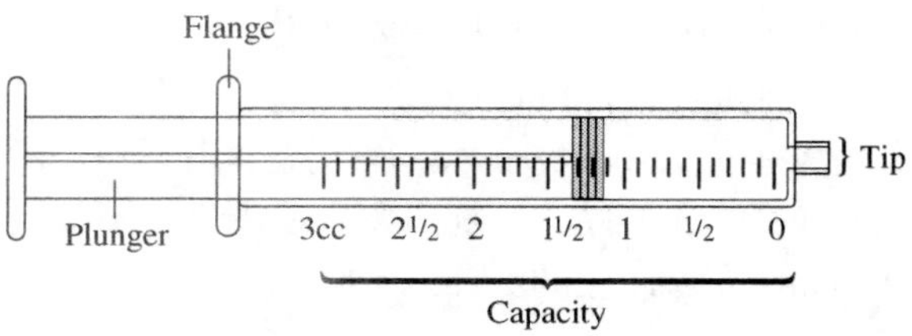

102. MEDICAL SUPPLIES A doctor ordered 2,000 cc of a saline (salt) solution from a pharmacy. How many liters of saline solution is this? 2 liters

WRITING

103. To change 3.452 kilometers to meters, we can move the decimal point in 3.452 three places to the right to get 3,452 meters. Explain why.

104. To change 7,532 grams to kilograms, we can move the decimal point in 7,532 three places to the left to get 7.532 kilograms. Explain why.

105. A *centimeter* is one hundredth of a meter. Make a list of five other words that begin with the prefix *centi* or *cent* and write a definition for each.

106. List the advantages of the metric system of measurement as compared to the American system. There have been several attempts to bring the metric system into general use in the United States. Why do you think these efforts have been unsuccessful?

REVIEW

Write each fraction as a decimal. Use an overbar in your answer.

107. $\frac{8}{9}$ $0.\overline{8}$

108. $\frac{11}{12}$ $0.91\overline{6}$

109. $\frac{7}{90}$ $0.0\overline{7}$

110. $\frac{1}{66}$ $0.0\overline{15}$

SECTION 3.6

Converting between American and Metric Units

Objectives

1. Use unit conversion factors to convert between American and metric units.
2. Convert between Fahrenheit and Celsius temperatures.

It is often necessary to convert between American units and metric units. For example, we must convert units to answer the following questions.

- Which is higher: Pikes Peak (elevation 14,110 feet) or the Matterhorn (elevation 4,478 meters)?
- Does a 2-pound tub of butter weigh more than a 1-kilogram tub?
- Is a quart of soda pop more or less than a liter of soda pop?

In this section, we discuss how to answer such questions.

1 Use unit conversion factors to convert between American and metric units.

The following table shows some conversions between American and metric units of length. In all but one case, the conversions are rounded approximations. An ≈ symbol is used to show this. The one exact conversion in the table is 1 inch = 2.54 centimeters.

Equivalent Lengths

American to metric	Metric to American
1 in. = 2.54 cm	1 cm ≈ 0.39 in.
1 ft ≈ 0.30 m	1 m ≈ 3.28 ft
1 yd ≈ 0.91 m	1 m ≈ 1.09 yd
1 mi ≈ 1.61 km	1 km ≈ 0.62 mi

1 foot

1 yard

1 meter

Unit conversion factors can be formed from the facts in the table to make specific conversions between American and metric units of length.

EXAMPLE 1 *Clothing Labels* The figure shows a label sewn into some pants made in Mexico that are for sale in the United States. Express the waist size to the nearest inch.

WAIST: 82 cm
INSEAM: 76 cm
RN-80811
SEE REVERSE FOR CARE
MADE IN MEXICO

Strategy We will multiply 82 centimeters by a carefully chosen unit conversion factor.

WHY If we multiply by the proper unit conversion factor, we can eliminate the unwanted units of centimeters and convert to inches.

Solution

To convert from centimeters to inches, we must choose a unit conversion factor whose numerator contains the units we want to introduce (inches), and whose denominator contains the units we want to eliminate (centimeters). From the first row of the *Metric to American* column of the table, we see that there is approximately 0.39 inch per centimeter. Thus, we will use the unit conversion factor:

$$\frac{0.39 \text{ in.}}{1 \text{ cm}}$$

← This is the unit we want to introduce.
← This is the unit we want to eliminate (the original unit).

Self Check 1

CLOTHING LABELS Refer to the figure in Example 1. What is the inseam length, to the nearest inch? 30 in.

Now Try **Problem 13**

Teaching Example 1 CLOTHING LABELS The length of a sleeve of a dress shirt made in Italy is 92 centimeters. Express the length of the sleeve to the nearest inch.
Answer:
36 in.

To perform the conversion, we multiply.

$$82 \text{ cm} \approx \frac{82 \text{ cm}}{1} \cdot \frac{0.39 \text{ in.}}{1 \text{ cm}}$$ Write 82 cm as a fraction: $82 \text{ cm} = \frac{82 \text{ cm}}{1}$. Multiply by a form of 1: $\frac{0.39 \text{ in.}}{1 \text{ cm}}$.

$$\approx \frac{82 \text{ cm}}{1} \cdot \frac{0.39 \text{ in.}}{1 \text{ cm}}$$ Remove the common units of centimeters from the numerator and denominator. The units of inches remain.

$\approx 82 \cdot 0.39$ in. Simplify.

≈ 31.98 in. Do the multiplication.

≈ 32 in. Round to the nearest inch (ones column).

```
  0.39
 × 82
    78
  3120
 31.98
```

To the nearest inch, the waist size is 32 inches.

Self Check 2

TRACK AND FIELD Which is longer: a 500-meter race or a 550-yard race? the 550-yard race

Now Try **Problem 17**

Teaching Example 2 VOLCANOS The elevation of the Lassen Peak volcano in California is 10,456 feet. The elevation of the Fuego volcano in Guatemala is 3,763 meters. Which volcano is higher?
Answer:
the Fuego volcano

EXAMPLE 2 ***Mountain Elevations*** Pikes Peak, one of the most famous peaks in the Rocky Mountains, has an elevation of 14,110 feet. The Matterhorn, in the Swiss Alps, rises to an elevation of 4,478 meters. Which mountain is higher?

Strategy We will convert the elevation of Pikes Peak, which given in feet, to meters.

WHY Then we can compare the mountain's elevations in the same units, meters.

Solution

To convert Pikes Peak elevation from feet to meters we must choose a unit conversion factor whose numerator contains the units we want to introduce (meters) and whose denominator contains the units we want to eliminate (feet). From the second row of the *American to metric* column of the table, we see that there is approximately 0.30 meter per foot. Thus, we will use the unit conversion factor:

$$\frac{0.30 \text{ m}}{1 \text{ ft}}$$ ← This is the unit we want to introduce. ← This is the unit we want to eliminate (the original unit).

To perform the conversion, we multiply.

$$14{,}110 \text{ ft} \approx \frac{14{,}110 \text{ ft}}{1} \cdot \frac{0.30 \text{ m}}{1 \text{ ft}}$$ Write 14,110 ft as a fraction: $14{,}110 \text{ ft} = \frac{14{,}110 \text{ ft}}{1}$. Multiply by a form of 1: $\frac{0.30 \text{ m}}{1 \text{ ft}}$.

$$\approx \frac{14{,}110 \text{ ft}}{1} \cdot \frac{0.30 \text{ m}}{1 \text{ ft}}$$ Remove the common units of feet from the numerator and denominator. The units of meters remain.

$\approx 14{,}110 \cdot 0.30$ m Simplify.

$\approx 4{,}233$ m Do the multiplication.

```
     1
 14,110
 × 0.30
 000 00
4233 00
4233.00
```

Since the elevation of Pikes Peak is about 4,233 meters, we can conclude that the Matterhorn, with an elevation of 4,478 meters, is higher.

We can convert between American units of weight and metric units of mass using the rounded approximations in the following table.

1 pound

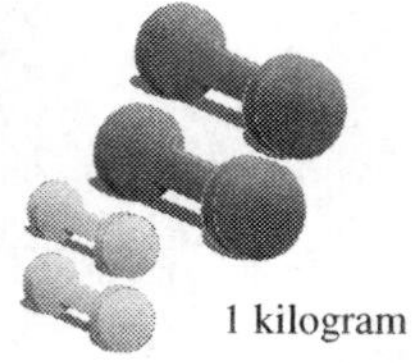
1 kilogram

Equivalent Weights and Masses	
American to metric	**Metric to American**
1 oz ≈ 28.35 g	1 g ≈ 0.035 oz
1 lb ≈ 0.45 kg	1 kg ≈ 2.20 lb

EXAMPLE 3 Convert 50 pounds to grams.

Strategy We will use a two-part multiplication process that converts 50 pounds to ounces, and then converts that result to grams.

WHY We must use a two-part process because the conversion table on page 471 does not contain a single unit conversion factor that converts from pounds to grams.

Solution

Since there are 16 ounces per pound, we can convert 50 pounds to ounces by multiplying by the unit conversion factor $\frac{16\text{ oz}}{1\text{ lb}}$. Since there are approximately 28.35 g per ounce, we can convert that result to grams by multiplying by the unit conversion factor $\frac{28.35\text{ g}}{1\text{ oz}}$.

$$50\text{ lb} \approx \frac{50\text{ lb}}{1} \cdot \frac{16\text{ oz}}{1\text{ lb}} \cdot \frac{28.35\text{ g}}{1\text{ oz}}$$

Write 50 lb as a fraction: 50 lb = $\frac{50\text{ lb}}{1}$. Multiply by two forms of 1: $\frac{16\text{ oz}}{1\text{ lb}}$ and $\frac{28.35\text{ g}}{1\text{ oz}}$.

$$\approx \frac{50\,\cancel{\text{lb}}}{1} \cdot \frac{16\,\cancel{\text{oz}}}{1\,\cancel{\text{lb}}} \cdot \frac{28.35\text{ g}}{1\,\cancel{\text{oz}}}$$

Remove the common units of pounds and ounces from the numerator and denominator. The units of grams remain.

$$\approx 50 \cdot 16 \cdot 28.35\text{ g}$$ Simplify.

$$\approx 800 \cdot 28.35\text{ g}$$ Multiply: $50 \cdot 16 = 800$.

$$\approx 22{,}680\text{ g}$$ Do the multiplication.

$\overset{3}{16}$	$\overset{6\,2\,4}{28.35}$
$\times\ 50$	$\times\ 800$
800	22680.00

Thus, 50 pounds ≈ 22,680 grams.

Self Check 3

Convert 68 pounds to grams. Round to the nearest gram. 30,845 g

Now Try **Problem 21**

Teaching Example 3
Convert 40 pounds to grams.
Answer:
18,144 g

EXAMPLE 4 *Packaging* Does a 2.5 pound tub of butter weigh more than a 1.5-kilogram tub?

Strategy We will convert the weight of the 1.5-kilogram tub of butter to pounds.

WHY Then we can compare the weights of the tubs of butter in the same units, pounds.

Solution

To convert 1.5 kilograms to pounds we must choose a unit conversion factor whose numerator contains the units we want to introduce (pounds), and whose denominator contains the units we want to eliminate (kilograms). From the second row of the *Metric to American* column of the table, we see that there are approximately 2.20 pounds per kilogram. Thus, we will use the unit conversion factor:

$$\frac{2.20\text{ lb}}{1\text{ kg}}$$

2.20 lb ← This is the unit we want to introduce.
1 kg ← This is the unit we want to eliminate (the original unit).

To perform the conversion, we multiply.

$$1.5\text{ kg} \approx \frac{1.5\text{ kg}}{1} \cdot \frac{2.20\text{ lb}}{1\text{ kg}}$$

Write 1.5 kg as a fraction: 1.5 kg = $\frac{1.5\text{ kg}}{1}$. Multiply by a form of 1: $\frac{2.20\text{ lb}}{1\text{ kg}}$.

$$\approx \frac{1.5\,\cancel{\text{kg}}}{1} \cdot \frac{2.20\text{ lb}}{1\,\cancel{\text{kg}}}$$

Remove the common units of kilograms from the numerator and denominator. The units of pounds remain.

$$\approx 1.5 \cdot 2.20\text{ lb}$$ Simplify.

$$\approx 3.3\text{ lb}$$ Do the multiplication.

2.20
$\times\ 1.5$
1100
2200
3.300

Since a 1.5-kilogram tub of butter weighs about 3.3 pounds, the 1.5-kilogram tub weighs more.

Self Check 4

BODY WEIGHT Who weighs more, a person who weighs 165 pounds or one who weighs 76 kilograms? the person who weighs 76 kg

Now Try **Problem 25**

Teaching Example 4
WEIGHTLIFTING Which weighs more, a 45-pound iron plate or a 15-kilogram dumbell?
Answer:
the 45-pound plate

We can convert between American and metric units of capacity using the rounded approximations in the following table.

1 liter 1 quart

Equivalent Capacities	
American to metric	**Metric to American**
1 fl oz ≈ 29.57 mL	1 L ≈ 33.81 fl oz
1 pt ≈ 0.47 L	1 L ≈ 2.11 pt
1 qt ≈ 0.95 L	1 L ≈ 1.06 qt
1 gal ≈ 3.79 L	1 L ≈ 0.264 gal

THINK IT THROUGH *Studying in Other Countries*

"Over the past decade, the number of U.S. students studying abroad has more than doubled."

From The Open Doors 2008 Report

In 2006/2007, a record number of 241,791 college students received credit for study abroad. Since students traveling to other countries are almost certain to come into contact with the metric system of measurement, they need to have a basic understanding of metric units.

Suppose a student studying overseas needs to purchase the following school supplies. For each item in red, choose the appropriate metric units.

1. $8\frac{1}{2}$ in. × 11 in. notebook paper: 216 mm × 279 mm

216 meters × 279 meters 216 centimeters × 279 centimeters 216 millimeters × 279 millimeters

2. A backpack that can hold 20 pounds of books: 9 kilograms

9 kilograms 9 grams 9 milligrams

3. $\frac{3}{4}$ fluid ounce bottle of Liquid Paper correction fluid: 22.2 milliliters

22.5 hectoliters 2.5 liters 22.2 milliliters

Self Check 5

DRINKING WATER A student bought a 360-mL bottle of water. Convert this measure to quarts. Round to the nearest tenth. 0.4 qt

***Now Try* Problem 29**

Teaching Example 5 MOTOR OIL A can contains 850 milliliters of motor oil. Convert this measure to quarts. Round to the nearest tenth.
Answer:
0.9 qt

EXAMPLE 5 *Cleaning Supplies* A bottle of window cleaner contains 750 milliliters of solution. Convert this measure to quarts. Round to the nearest tenth.

Strategy We will use a two-part multiplication process that converts 750 milliliters to liters, and then converts that result to quarts.

WHY We must use a two-part process because the conversion table at the top of this page does not contain a single unit conversion factor that converts from milliliters to quarts.

Solution

Since there is 1 liter for every 1,000 mL, we can convert 750 milliliters to liters by multiplying by the unit conversion factor $\frac{1\text{ L}}{1{,}000\text{ mL}}$. Since there are approximately

1.06 qt per liter, we can convert that result to quarts by multiplying by the unit conversion factor $\frac{1.06\text{ qt}}{1\text{ L}}$.

$$750\text{ mL} \approx \frac{750\text{ mL}}{1} \cdot \frac{1\text{ L}}{1{,}000\text{ mL}} \cdot \frac{1.06\text{ qt}}{1\text{ L}}$$

Write 750 mL as a fraction: 750 mL $= \frac{750\text{ mL}}{1}$. Multiply by two forms of 1: $\frac{1\text{ L}}{1{,}000\text{ mL}}$ and $\frac{1.06\text{ qt}}{1\text{ L}}$.

$$\approx \frac{750\,\cancel{\text{mL}}}{1} \cdot \frac{1\,\cancel{\text{L}}}{1{,}000\,\cancel{\text{mL}}} \cdot \frac{1.06\text{ qt}}{1\,\cancel{\text{L}}}$$

Remove the common units of milliliters and liters from the numerator and denominator. The units of quarts remain.

$$\approx \frac{750 \cdot 1.06}{1{,}000}\text{ qt}$$

Multiply the fractions.

$$\approx \frac{795}{1{,}000}\text{ qt}$$

Multiply: $750 \cdot 1.06 = 795$.

$$\begin{array}{r} 750 \\ \times\ 1.06 \\ \hline 4500 \\ 0000 \\ 75000 \\ \hline 795.00 \end{array}$$

$$\approx 0.795\text{ qt}$$

Divide 795 by 1,000 by moving the decimal point 3 places to the left.

$$\approx 0.8\text{ qt}$$

Round to the nearest tenth.

The bottle contains approximately 0.8 qt of cleaning solution.

2 Convert between Fahrenheit and Celsius temperatures.

In the American system, we measure temperature using **degrees Fahrenheit** (°F). In the metric system, we measure temperature using **degrees Celsius** (°C). These two scales are shown on the thermometers on the right. From the figures, we can see that

- 212°F ≈ 100°C Water boils
- 32°F ≈ 0°C Water freezes
- 5°F ≈ −15°C A cold winter day
- 95°F ≈ 35°C A hot summer day

There are formulas that enable us to convert from degrees Fahrenheit to degrees Celsius and from degrees Celsius to degrees Fahrenheit.

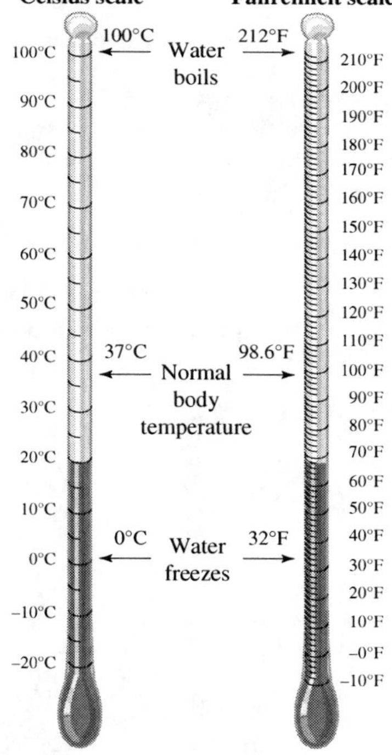

Conversion Formulas for Temperature

If F is the temperature in degrees Fahrenheit and C is the corresponding temperature in degrees Celsius, then

$$C = \frac{5}{9}(F - 32) \qquad \text{and} \qquad F = \frac{9}{5}C + 32$$

Self Check 6

COFFEE Hot coffee is 110°F. Express this temperature in degrees Celsius. Round to the nearest tenth of a degree. 43.3°C

Now Try **Problem 33**

Teaching Example 6 HAMBURGERS The recommended safe minimal internal temperature when cooking ground beef is 160°F. Express this temperature in degrees Celsius. Round to the nearest tenth of a degree.
Answer:
71.1°C

EXAMPLE 6 *Bathing* Warm bath water is 90°F. Express this temperature in degrees Celsius. Round to the nearest tenth of a degree.

Strategy We will substitute 90 for F in the formula $C = \frac{5}{9}(F - 32)$.

WHY Then we can use the rule for the order of operations to evaluate the right side of the equation and find the value of C, the temperature in degrees Celsius of the bath water.

Solution

$C = \frac{5}{9}(F - 32)$ This is the formula to find degrees Celsius.

$= \frac{5}{9}(90 - 32)$ Substitute 90 for F.

$= \frac{5}{9}(58)$ Do the subtraction within the parentheses first: $90 - 32 = 58$.

$= \frac{5}{9}\left(\frac{58}{1}\right)$ Write 58 as a fraction: $58 = \frac{58}{1}$.

$= \frac{290}{9}$ Multiply the numerators. Multiply the denominators.

$= 32.222\ldots$ Do the division.

≈ 32.2 Round to the nearest tenth.

$$\begin{array}{r} \overset{4}{58} \\ \times\, 5 \\ \hline 290 \end{array}$$

$$\begin{array}{r} 32.22 \\ 9\overline{)290.00} \\ -\,27 \\ \hline 20 \\ -\,18 \\ \hline 20 \\ -\,18 \\ \hline 20 \\ -\,18 \\ \hline 2 \end{array}$$

To the nearest tenth of a degree, the temperature of the bath water is 32.2°C.

Self Check 7

FEVERS To determine whether a baby has a fever, her mother takes her temperature with a Celsius thermometer. If the reading is 38.8°C, does the baby have a fever? (*Hint:* Normal body temperature is 98.6°F.) yes

Now Try **Problem 37**

Teaching Example 7 OLD FAITHFUL Just before it erupts, the temperature of the water in the Old Faithful geyser in Yellowstone National Park reaches 95.6°C. Express this temperature in degrees Fahrenheit. Round to the nearest degree.
Answer:
204°F

EXAMPLE 7 *Dishwashers* A dishwasher manufacturer recommends that dishes be rinsed in hot water with a temperature of 60°C. Express this temperature in degrees Fahrenheit.

Strategy We will substitute 60 for C in the formula $F = \frac{9}{5}C + 32$.

WHY Then we can use the rule for the order of operations to evaluate the right side of the equation and find the value of F, the temperature in degrees Fahrenheit of the water.

Solution

$F = \frac{9}{5}C + 32$ This is the formula to find degrees Fahrenheit.

$= \frac{9}{5}(60) + 32$ Substitute 60 for C.

$= \frac{540}{5} + 32$ Multiply: $\frac{9}{5}(60) = \frac{9}{5}\left(\frac{60}{1}\right) = \frac{540}{5}$.

$= 108 + 32$ Do the division.

$= 140$ Do the addition.

$$\begin{array}{r} 60 \\ \times\, 9 \\ \hline 540 \end{array}$$

$$\begin{array}{r} 108 \\ 5\overline{)540} \\ -\,5 \\ \hline 4 \\ -\,0 \\ \hline 40 \\ -\,40 \\ \hline 0 \end{array}$$

The manufacturer recommends that dishes be rinsed in 140°F water.

ANSWERS TO SELF CHECKS

1. 30 in. **2.** the 550-yard race **3.** 30,845 g **4.** the person who weighs 76 kg **5.** 0.4 qt **6.** 43.3°C **7.** yes

SECTION 3.6 STUDY SET

VOCABULARY

Fill in the blanks.

1. In the American system, temperatures are measured in degrees Fahrenheit. In the metric system, temperatures are measured in degrees Celsius.
2. a. Inches and centimeters are units used to measure length.
   b. Pounds and grams are used to measure mass (weight).
   c. Gallons and liters are units used to measure capacity.

CONCEPTS

3. Which is longer:
   a. A yard or a meter? meter
   b. A foot or a meter? meter
   c. An inch or a centimeter? inch
   d. A mile or a kilometer? mile
4. Which is heavier:
   a. An ounce or a gram? ounce
   b. A pound or a kilogram? kilogram
5. Which is the greater unit of capacity:
   a. A pint or a liter? liter
   b. A quart or a liter? liter
   c. A gallon or a liter? gallon
6. a. What formula is used for changing degrees Celsius to degrees Fahrenheit? $F = \frac{9}{5}C + 32$
   b. What formula is used for changing degrees Fahrenheit to degrees Celsius? $C = \frac{5}{9}(F - 32)$
7. Write a unit conversion factor to convert
   a. feet to meters $\frac{0.03 \text{ m}}{1 \text{ ft}}$
   b. pounds to kilograms $\frac{0.45 \text{ kg}}{1 \text{ lb}}$
   c. gallons to liters $\frac{3.79 \text{ L}}{1 \text{ gal}}$
8. Write a unit conversion factor to convert
   a. centimeters to inches $\frac{0.39 \text{ in.}}{1 \text{ cm}}$
   b. grams to ounces $\frac{0.035 \text{ oz}}{1 \text{ g}}$
   c. liters to fluid ounces $\frac{33.81 \text{ fl oz}}{1 \text{ L}}$

NOTATION

Complete each solution.

9. Convert 4,500 feet to meters.

$$4{,}500 \text{ ft} \approx \frac{4{,}500\text{ft}}{1} \cdot \frac{0.30 \text{ m}}{1\text{ft}}$$
$$\approx 1{,}350 \text{ m}$$

10. Convert 8 liters to gallons.

$$8 \text{ L} \approx \frac{8 \text{ L}}{1} \cdot \frac{0.264 \text{ gal}}{1 \text{ L}}$$
$$\approx 2.112 \text{ gal}$$

11. Convert 3 kilograms to ounces.

$$3 \text{ kg} \approx \frac{3 \text{ kg}}{1} \cdot \frac{1{,}000 \text{ g}}{1 \text{ kg}} \cdot \frac{0.035 \text{ oz}}{1 \text{ g}}$$
$$\approx 3 \cdot 1{,}000 \cdot 0.035 \text{ oz}$$
$$\approx 105 \text{ oz}$$

12. Convert 70°C to degrees Fahrenheit.

$$F = \frac{9}{5}C + 32$$
$$= \frac{9}{5}(70) + 32$$
$$= 126 + 32$$
$$= 158$$

Thus, 70°C = 158 °F

GUIDED PRACTICE

Perform each conversion. Round to the nearest inch. See Example 1.

13. 25 centimeters to inches 10 in.
14. 35 centimeters to inches 14 in.
15. 88 centimeters to inches 34 in.
16. 91 centimeters to inches 35 in.

Perform each conversion. See Example 2.

17. 8,400 feet to meters 2,520 m
18. 7,300 feet to meters 2,190 m
19. 25,115 feet to meters 7,534.5 m
20. 36,242 feet to meters 10,872.6 m

Perform each conversion. See Example 3.

21. 20 pounds to grams 9,072 g
22. 30 pounds to grams 13,608 g
23. 75 pounds to grams 34,020 g
24. 95 pounds to grams 43,092 g

Perform each conversion. See Example 4.

25. 6.5 kilograms to pounds 14.3 lb
26. 7.5 kilograms to pounds 16.5 lb
27. 300 kilograms to pounds 660 lb
28. 800 kilograms to pounds 1,760 lb

Perform each conversion. Round to the nearest tenth. See Example 5.

29. 650 milliliters to quarts 0.7 qt

▶ **30.** 450 milliliters to quarts 0.5 qt

31. 1,200 milliliters to quarts 1.3 qt

32. 1,500 milliliters to quarts 1.6 qt

Express each temperature in degrees Celsius. Round to the nearest tenth of a degree. See Example 6.

33. 120°F 48.9°C

▶ **34.** 110°F 43.3°C

35. 35°F 1.7°C

36. 45°F 7.2°C

Express each temperature in degrees Fahrenheit. See Example 7.

37. 75°C 167°F

▶ **38.** 85°C 185°F

39. 10°C 50°F

40. 20°C 68°F

TRY IT YOURSELF

Perform each conversion. If necessary, round answers to the nearest tenth. Since most conversions are approximate, answers will vary slightly depending on the method used.

41. 25 pounds to grams 11,340 g

▶ **42.** 7.5 ounces to grams 212.6 g

43. 50°C to degrees Fahrenheit 122°F

44. 36.2°C to degrees Fahrenheit 97.2°F

45. 0.75 quarts to milliliters 712.5 mL

46. 3 pints to milliliters 1,410 mL

47. 0.5 kilograms to ounces 17.6 oz

48. 35 grams to pounds 0.1 lb

49. 3.75 meters to inches 147.6 in.

▶ **50.** 2.4 kilometers to miles 1.5 mi

51. 3 fluid ounces to liters 0.1 L

▶ **52.** 2.5 pints to liters 1.2 L

53. 12 kilometers to feet 39,283 ft

54. 3,212 centimeters to feet 104.4 ft

55. 37 ounces to kilograms 1.0 kg

▶ **56.** 10 pounds to kilograms 4.5 kg

57. −10°C to degrees Fahrenheit 14°F

▶ **58.** −22.5°C to degrees Fahrenheit −8.5°F

59. 17 grams to ounces 0.6 oz

60. 100 kilograms to pounds 220 lb

61. 7.2 liters to fluid ounces 243.4 fl oz

62. 5 liters to quarts 5.3 qt

63. 3 feet to centimeters 91.4 cm

▶ **64.** 7.5 yards to meters 6.8 m

65. 500 milliliters to quarts 0.5 qt

▶ **66.** 2,000 milliliters to gallons 0.5 gal

67. 50°F to degrees Celsius 10°C

68. 67.7°F to degrees Celsius 19.8°C

69. 5,000 inches to meters 127 m

▶ **70.** 25 miles to kilometers 40.3 km

71. − 5°F to degrees Celsius −20.6°C

72. − 10°F to degrees Celsius −23.3°C

APPLICATIONS

Since most conversions are approximate, answers will vary slightly depending on the method used.

73. THE MIDDLE EAST The distance between Jerusalem and Bethlehem is 8 kilometers. To the nearest mile, give this distance in miles. 5 mi

▶ **74.** THE DEAD SEA The Dead Sea is 80 kilometers long. To the nearest mile, give this distance in miles. 50 mi

75. CHEETAHS A cheetah can run 112 kilometers per hour. Express this speed in mph. Round to the nearest mile. 70 mph

▶ **76.** LIONS A lion can run 50 mph. Express this speed in kilometers per hour. 80.5 kph

77. MOUNT WASHINGTON The highest peak of the White Mountains of New Hampshire is Mount Washington, at 6,288 feet. Give this height in kilometers. Round to the nearest tenth. 1.9 km

▶ **78.** TRACK AND FIELD Track meets are held on an oval track. One lap around the track is usually 400 meters. However, some older tracks in the United States are 440-yard ovals. Are these two types of tracks the same length? If not, which is longer? The 440-yard track is longer.

79. HAIR GROWTH When hair is short, its rate of growth averages about $\frac{3}{4}$ inch per month. How many centimeters is this a month? Round to the nearest tenth of a centimeter. 1.9 cm

80. WHALES An adult male killer whale can weigh as much as 12,000 pounds and be as long as 25 feet. Change these measurements to kilograms and meters. 5,400 kg, 7.5 m

81. WEIGHTLIFTING The table lists the personal best bench press records for two of the world's best powerlifters. Change each metric weight to pounds. Round to the nearest pound. 411 lb, 770 lb

Name	Hometown	Bench press
Liz Willet	Ferndale, Washington	187 kg
Brian Siders	Charleston, W. Virginia	350 kg

82. WORDS OF WISDOM Refer to the wall hanging. Convert the first metric weight to ounces and the second to pounds. What famous saying results? An ounce of prevention is worth a pound of cure.

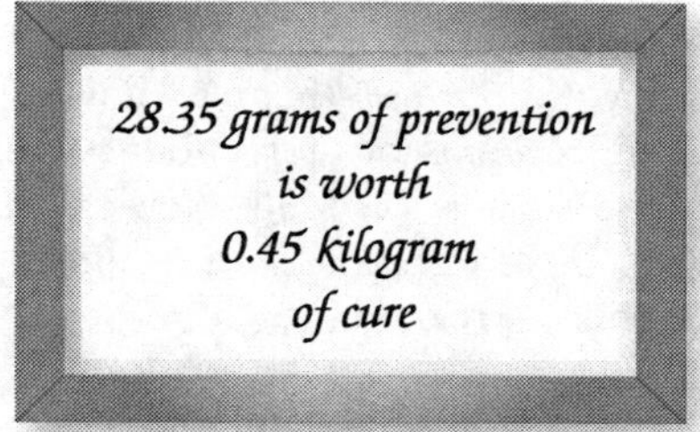

83. OUNCES AND FLUID OUNCES

a. There are 310 calories in 8 ounces of broiled chicken. Convert 8 ounces to grams. 226.8 g

b. There are 112 calories in a glass of fresh Valencia orange juice that holds 8 fluid ounces. Convert 8 fluid ounces to liters. Round to the nearest hundredth. 0.24 L

84. TRACK AND FIELD A shot-put weighs 7.264 kilograms. Convert this weight to pounds. Round to the nearest pound. 16 lb

85. POSTAL REGULATIONS You can mail a package weighing up to 70 pounds via priority mail. Can you mail a package that weighs 32 kilograms by priority mail? no

86. NUTRITION Refer to the nutrition label shown below for a packet of oatmeal. Change each circled weight to ounces. 1.61 oz, 0.0175 oz, 0.00875 oz, 0.14 oz

Nutrition Facts
Serving Size: 1 Packet (46g)
Servings Per Container: 10

Amount Per Serving	
Calories 170	Calories from Fat 20
	% Daily Value
Total fat 2g	3%
Saturated fat (0.5g)	2%
Polyunsaturated Fat 0.5g	
Monounsaturated Fat 1g	
Cholesterol 0mg	0%
Sodium (250mg)	10%
Total carbohydrate 35g	12%
Dietary fiber 3g	12%
Soluble Fiber 1g	
Sugars 16g	
Protein (4g)	

87. HOT SPRINGS The thermal springs in Hot Springs National Park in central Arkansas emit water as warm as 143°F. Change this temperature to degrees Celsius. about 62°C

88. COOKING MEAT Meats must be cooked at temperatures high enough to kill harmful bacteria. According to the USDA and the FDA, the internal temperature for cooked roasts and steaks should be at least 145°F, and whole poultry should be 180°F. Convert these temperatures to degrees Celsius. Round up to the next degree. 63°C, 83°C

89. TAKING A SHOWER When you take a shower, which water temperature would you choose: 15°C, 28°C, or 50°C? 28°C

90. DRINKING WATER To get a cold drink of water, which temperature would you choose: −2°C, 10°C, or 25°C? 10°C

91. SNOWY WEATHER At which temperatures might it snow: −5°C, 0°C, or 10°C? −5°C and 0°C

92. AIR CONDITIONING At which outside temperature would you be likely to run the air conditioner: 15°, 20°C, or 30°C? 30°C

93. COMPARISON SHOPPING Which is the better buy: 3 quarts of root beer for \$4.50 or 2 liters of root beer for \$3.60? the 3 quarts

94. COMPARISON SHOPPING Which is the better buy: 3 gallons of antifreeze for \$10.35 or 12 liters of antifreeze for \$10.50? the 12 liters

WRITING

95. Explain how to change kilometers to miles.

96. Explain how to change 50°C to degrees Fahrenheit.

97. The United States is the only industrialized country in the world that does not officially use the metric system. Some people claim this is costing American businesses money. Do you think so? Why?

98. What is meant by the phrase *a table of equivalent measures*?

REVIEW

Perform each operation.

99. $\frac{3}{5} + \frac{4}{3}$ $\frac{29}{15}$

100. $\frac{3}{5} - \frac{4}{3}$ $-\frac{11}{15}$

101. $\frac{3}{5} \cdot \frac{4}{3}$ $\frac{4}{5}$

102. $\frac{3}{5} \div \frac{4}{3}$ $\frac{9}{20}$

103. $3.25 + 4.8$ 8.05

104. $3.25 - 4.8$ −1.55

105. $3.25 \cdot 4.8$ 15.6

106. $4.8\overline{)15.6}$ 3.25

Objectives

1. Explain the meaning of percent.
2. Write percents as fractions.
3. Write percents as decimals.
4. Write decimals as percents.
5. Write fractions as percents.

SECTION 3.7
Percents, Decimals, and Fractions

We see percents everywhere, everyday. Stores use them to advertise discounts, manufacturers use them to describe the contents of their products, and banks use them to list interest rates for loans and savings accounts. Newspapers are full of information presented in percent form. In this section, we introduce percents and show how fractions, decimals, and percents are related.

1 Explain the meaning of percent.

A percent tells us the number of parts per one hundred. You can think of a percent as the *numerator* of a fraction (or ratio) that has a denominator of 100.

Percent

Percent means parts per one hundred.

The Language of Mathematics The word *percent* is formed from the prefix *per,* which means ratio, and the suffix *cent,* which comes from the Latin word *centum,* meaning 100.

per • cent

ratio → per; cent ← 100

In the figure below, there are 100 equal-sized square regions, and 93 of them are shaded. Thus, $\frac{93}{100}$ or 93 percent of the figure is shaded. The word *percent* can be written using the symbol %, so we say that 93% of the figure is shaded.

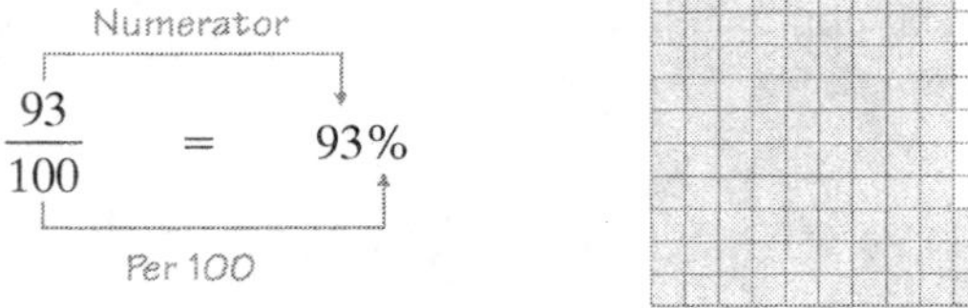

If the entire figure had been shaded, we would say that 100 out of the 100 square regions, or 100%, was shaded. Using this fact, we can determine what percent of the figure is *not* shaded by subtracting the percent of the figure that is shaded from 100%.

$$100\% - 93\% = 7\%$$

So 7% of the figure is *not* shaded.

To illustrate a percent greater than 100%, say 121%, we would shade one entire figure and 21 of the 100 square regions in a second, equal-sized grid.

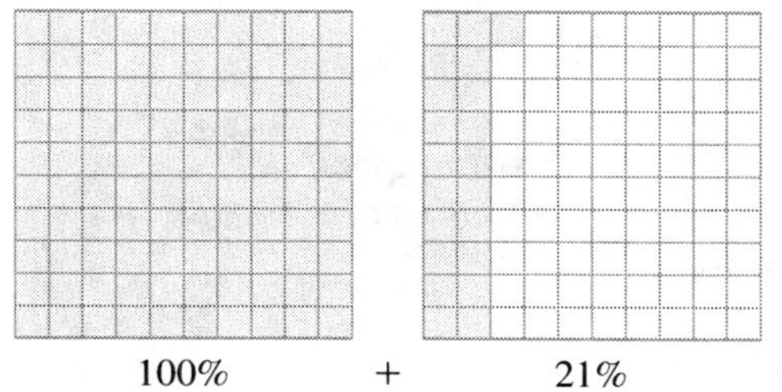

100% + 21% = 121%

EXAMPLE 1 *Tossing a Coin* A coin was tossed 100 times and it landed heads up 51 times.

a. What percent of the time did the coin land heads up?

b. What percent of the time did it land tails up?

Strategy We will write a fraction that compares the number of times that the coin landed heads up (or tails up) to the total number of tosses.

WHY Since the denominator in each case will be 100, the numerator of the fraction will give the percent.

Solution

a. If a coin landed heads up 51 times after being tossed 100 times, then

$$\frac{51}{100} = 51\%$$

of the time it landed heads up.

b. The number of times the coin landed tails up is $100 - 51 = 49$ times. If a coin landed tails up 49 times after being tossed 100 times, then

$$\frac{49}{100} = 49\%$$

of the time it landed tails up.

Self Check 1

BOARD GAMES A standard Scrabble game contains 100 tiles. There are 42 vowel tiles, 2 blank tiles, and the rest are consonant tiles.

a. What percent of the tiles are vowels? 42%

b. What percent of the letter tiles are consonants? 56%

Now Try **Problem 13**

Teaching Example 1
GOVERNMENT In 2009, 17 of the 100 U.S. Senators were women.
a. What percent of the Senators were women?
b. What percent of the Senators were men?
Answers:
a. 17% **b.** 83%

2 Write percents as fractions.

We can use the definition of percent to write any percent in an equivalent fraction form.

Writing Percents as Fractions

To write a percent as a fraction, drop the % symbol and write the given number over 100. Then simplify the fraction, if possible.

EXAMPLE 2 *Earth* The chemical makeup of Earth's atmosphere is 78% nitrogen, 21% oxygen, and 1% other gases. Write each percent as a fraction in simplest form.

Strategy We will drop the % symbol and write the given number over 100. Then we will simplify the resulting fraction, if possible.

WHY *Percent* means parts per one hundred, and the word *per* indicates a ratio (fraction).

Self Check 2

WATERMELONS An average watermelon is 92% water. Write this percent as a fraction in simplest form. $\frac{23}{25}$

Now Try **Problems 17 and 23**

Teaching Example 2
ANATOMY The human body is 65% water. Write this percent as a fraction in simplest form. (Source: Microsoft Encarta Online Encyclopedia, 2009)
Answer:
$\frac{13}{20}$

Solution We begin with nitrogen.

$$78\% = \frac{78}{100}$$ Drop the % symbol and write 78 over 100.

$$= \frac{\overset{1}{\cancel{2}} \cdot 39}{\underset{1}{\cancel{2}} \cdot 50}$$ To simplify the fraction, factor 78 as $2 \cdot 39$ and 100 as $2 \cdot 50$. Then remove the common factor of 2 from the numerator and denominator.

$$= \frac{39}{50}$$

Nitrogen makes up $\frac{78}{100}$, or $\frac{39}{50}$, of Earth's atmosphere.

Oxygen makes up 21%, or $\frac{21}{100}$, of Earth's atmosphere. Other gases make up 1%, or $\frac{1}{100}$, of the atmosphere.

Self Check 3
UNIONS In 2002, 13.3% of the U.S. labor force belonged to a union. Write this percent as a fraction in simplest form. $\frac{133}{1{,}000}$
Now Try **Problems 27 and 31**

Teaching Example 3
UNIONS In 1983, 20.1% of the U.S. labor force belonged to a union. Write this percent as a fraction in simplest form.
Answer:
$\frac{201}{1{,}000}$

EXAMPLE 3 *Unions*

In 2007, 12.1% of the U.S. labor force belonged to a union. Write this percent as a fraction in simplest form. (*Source:* Bureau of Labor Statistics)

Strategy We will drop the % symbol and write the given number over 100. Then we will multiply the resulting fraction by a form of 1 and simplify, if possible.

WHY When writing a percent as a fraction, the numerator and denominator of the fraction should be whole numbers that have no common factors (other than 1).

Solution

$$12.1\% = \frac{12.1}{100}$$ Drop the % symbol and write 12.1 over 100.

To write this as an equivalent fraction of *whole numbers,* we need to move the decimal point in the numerator one place to the right. (Recall that to find the product of a decimal and 10, we simply move the decimal point one place to the right.) Therefore, it follows that $\frac{10}{10}$ is the form of 1 that we should use to build $\frac{12.1}{100}$.

$$\frac{12.1}{100} = \frac{12.1}{100} \cdot \frac{10}{10}$$ Multiply the fraction by a form of 1.

$$= \frac{12.1 \cdot 10}{100 \cdot 10}$$ Multiply the numerators. Multiply the denominators.

$$= \frac{121}{1{,}000}$$ Since 121 and 1,000 do not have any common factors (other than 1), the fraction is in simplest form.

Thus, $12.1\% = \frac{121}{1{,}000}$. This means that 121 out of every 1,000 workers in the U.S. labor force belonged to a union in 2007.

Self Check 4
Write $83\frac{1}{3}\%$ as a fraction in simplest form. $\frac{5}{6}$
Now Try **Problem 35**

Teaching Example 4 Write $16\frac{2}{3}\%$ as a fraction in simplest form.
Answer:
$\frac{1}{6}$

EXAMPLE 4

Write $66\frac{2}{3}\%$ as a fraction in simplest form.

Strategy We will drop the % symbol and write the given number over 100. Then we will perform the division indicated by the fraction bar and simplify, if possible.

WHY When writing a percent as a fraction, the numerator and denominator of the fraction should be whole numbers that have no common factors (other than 1).

Solution

$$66\frac{2}{3}\% = \frac{66\frac{2}{3}}{100}$$ Drop the % symbol and write $66\frac{2}{3}$ over 100.

To write this as a fraction of whole numbers, we will perform the division indicated by the fraction bar.

$$\frac{66\frac{2}{3}}{100} = 66\frac{2}{3} \div 100$$ The fraction bar indicates division.

$$= \frac{200}{3} \cdot \frac{1}{100}$$ Write $66\frac{2}{3}$ as a mixed number and then multiply by the reciprocal of 100.

$$= \frac{200 \cdot 1}{3 \cdot 100}$$ Multiply the numerators. Multiply the denominators.

$$= \frac{2 \cdot \overset{1}{\cancel{100}} \cdot 1}{3 \cdot \underset{1}{\cancel{100}}}$$ To simplify the fraction, factor 200 as 2 · 100. Then remove the common factor of 100 from the numerator and denominator.

$$= \frac{2}{3}$$

EXAMPLE 5 **a.** Write 175% as a fraction in simplest form.
b. Write 0.22% as a fraction in simplest form.

Strategy We will drop the % symbol and write each given number over 100. Then we will simplify the resulting fraction, if possible.

WHY *Percent* means parts per one hundred and the word *per* indicates a ratio (fraction).

Solution

a. $175\% = \frac{175}{100}$ Drop the % symbol and write 175 over 100.

$$= \frac{\overset{1}{\cancel{5}} \cdot \overset{1}{\cancel{5}} \cdot 7}{2 \cdot 2 \cdot \underset{1}{\cancel{5}} \cdot \underset{1}{\cancel{5}}}$$ To simplify the fraction, prime factor 175 and 100. Remove the common factors of 5 from the numerator and denominator.

$$= \frac{7}{4}$$

5 | 175	2 | 100
5 | 35	2 | 50
7	5 | 25
	5

Thus, $175\% = \frac{7}{4}$.

b. $0.22\% = \frac{0.22}{100}$ Drop the % symbol and write 175 over 100.

To write this as an equivalent fraction of *whole numbers,* we need to move the decimal point in the numerator two places to the right. (Recall that to find the product of a decimal and 100, we simply move the decimal point two places to the right.) Therefore, it follows that $\frac{100}{100}$ is the form of 1 that we should use to build $\frac{0.22}{100}$.

$$\frac{0.22}{100} = \frac{0.22}{100} \cdot \frac{100}{100}$$ Multiply the fraction by a form of 1.

$$= \frac{0.22 \cdot 100}{100 \cdot 100}$$ Multiply the numerators. Multiply the denominators.

$$= \frac{22}{10{,}000}$$

$$= \frac{\overset{1}{\cancel{2}} \cdot 11}{\underset{1}{\cancel{2}} \cdot 5{,}000}$$ To simplify the fraction, factor 22 and 10,000. Remove the common factor of 2 from the numerator and denominator.

$$= \frac{11}{5{,}000}$$

Thus, $0.22\% = \frac{11}{5{,}000}$.

Self Check 5

a. Write 210% as a fraction in simplest form. $\frac{21}{10}$

b. Write 0.54% as a fraction in simplest form. $\frac{27}{5{,}000}$

Now Try **Problems 39 and 43**

Teaching Example 5
a. Write 150% as a fraction in simplest form.
b. Write 0.42% as a fraction in simplest form.
Answers:
a. $\frac{3}{2}$
b. $\frac{21}{5{,}000}$

Success Tip When percents that are greater than 100% are written as fractions, the fractions are greater than 1. When percents that are less than 1% are written as fractions, the fractions are less than $\frac{1}{100}$.

3 Write percents as decimals.

To write a percent as a decimal, recall that a percent can be written as a fraction with denominator 100 and that a denominator of 100 indicates division by 100.

For example, consider 14%, which means 14 parts per 100.

$14\% = \frac{14}{100}$ Use the definition of percent: write 14 over 100.

$= 14 \div 100$ The fraction bar indicates division.

$= 14.0 \div 100$ Write the whole number 14 in decimal notation by placing a decimal point immediately to its right and entering a zero to the right of the decimal point.

$= .14\,0$ Since the divisor 100 has two zeros, move the decimal point 2 places to the left.

$= 0.14$ Write a zero to the left of the decimal point.

We have found that 14% = 0.14. This example suggests the following procedure.

Writing Percents as Decimals

To write a percent as a decimal, drop the % symbol and divide the given number by 100 by moving the decimal point 2 places to the left.

Self Check 6

a. Write 16.43% as a decimal.

b. Write 2.06% as a decimal.

Now Try **Problems 51 and 57**

Self Check 6 Answers
a. 0.1643
b. 0.0206

Teaching Example 6
TV WEBSITES The graph on the right shows the percent of market share for the top 5 network TV show websites.
a. Write the percent of market share for the *Dancing with the Stars* website as a decimal.
b. Write the percent of market share for the *America's Most Wanted* website as a decimal.

Answers:
a. 0.1042 b. 0.0349

EXAMPLE 6 *TV Websites* The graph below shows the percent of market share for the top 5 network TV show websites.

a. Write the percent of market share for the *American Idol* website as a decimal.

b. Write the percent of market share for the *Deal or No Deal* website as a decimal.

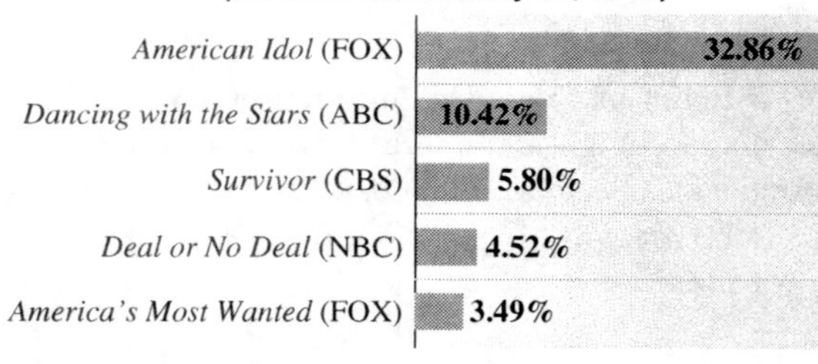

(*Source:* marketingcharts.com)

Strategy We will drop the % symbol and divide each given number by 100 by moving the decimal point 2 places to the left.

WHY To find the quotient of a decimal and 10, 100, 1,000, and so on, move the decimal point to the left the same number of places as there are zeros in the power of 10.

Solution

a. From the graph, we see that the percent market share for the *American Idol* website is 32.86%. To write this percent as a decimal, we proceed as follows.

$32.86\% = .32\,86$ Drop the % symbol and divide 32.86 by 100 by moving the decimal point 2 places to the left.

$= 0.3286$ Write a zero to the left of the decimal point.

32.86%, written as a decimal, is 0.3286.

b. From the graph, we see that the percent market share for the *Deal or No Deal* website is 4.52%. To write this percent as a decimal, we proceed as follows.

$4.52\% = .04\,52$ Drop the % symbol and divide 4.52 by 100 by moving the decimal point 2 places to the left. This requires that a placeholder zero (shown in blue) be inserted in front of the 4.

$= 0.0452$ Write a zero to the left of the decimal point.

4.52%, written as a decimal, is 0.0452.

EXAMPLE 7 *Population*

The population of the state of Oregon is approximately $1\frac{1}{4}\%$ of the population of the United States. Write this percent as a decimal. (*Source:* U.S. Census Bureau)

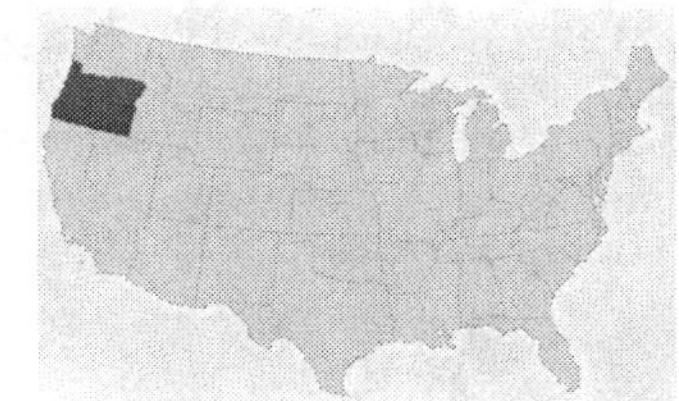

Strategy We will write the mixed number $1\frac{1}{4}$ in decimal notation.

WHY With $1\frac{1}{4}$ in mixed-number form, we cannot apply the rule for writing a percent as a decimal; there is no decimal point to move 2 places to the left.

Solution To change a percent to a decimal, we drop the percent symbol and divide by 100 by moving the decimal point 2 places to the left. In this case, however, there is no decimal point to move in $1\frac{1}{4}\%$. Since $1\frac{1}{4} = 1 + \frac{1}{4}$, and since the decimal equivalent of $\frac{1}{4}$ is 0.25, we can write $1\frac{1}{4}\%$ in an equivalent form as 1.25%.

$1\frac{1}{4}\% = 1.25\%$ Write $1\frac{1}{4}$ as 1.25.

$= .01\,25$ Drop the % symbol and divide 1.25 by 100 by moving the decimal point 2 places to the left. This requires that a placeholder zero (shown in blue) be inserted in front of the 1.

$= 0.0125$ Write a zero to the left of the decimal point.

$1\frac{1}{4}\%$, written as a decimal, is 0.0125.

Self Check 7

POPULATION The population of the state of Ohio is approximately $3\frac{3}{4}\%$ of the population of the United States. Write this percent as a decimal. (*Source:* U.S. Census Bureau) 0.0375

Now Try **Problem 59**

Teaching Example 7
POPULATION The population of the state of Virginia is approximately $2\frac{1}{2}\%$ of the population of the United States. Write this percent as a decimal. (*Source:* U.S. Census Bureau)
Answer:
0.025

EXAMPLE 8

a. Write 310% as a decimal. **b.** Write 0.9% as a decimal.

Strategy We will drop the % symbol and divide each given number by 100 by moving the decimal point two places to the left.

WHY Recall that to find the quotient of a decimal and 100, we move the decimal point to the left the same number of places as there are zeros in 100.

Solution

a. $310\% = 310.0\%$ Write the whole number 310 in decimal notation: 310 = 310.0.

$= 3.10\,0$ Drop the % symbol and divide 310 by 100 by moving the decimal point 2 places to the left.

$= 3.1$ Drop the unnecessary zeros to the right of the 1.

310%, written as a decimal, is 3.1.

b. $0.9\% = .00\,9$ Drop the % symbol and divide 0.9 by 100 by moving the decimal point 2 places to the left. This requires that a placeholder zero (shown in blue) be inserted in front of the 0.

$= 0.009$ Write a zero to the left of the decimal point.

0.9%, written as a decimal, is 0.009.

Self Check 8

a. Write 600% as a decimal. 6

b. Write 0.8% as a decimal. 0.008

Now Try **Problems 63 and 67**

Teaching Example 8
a. Write 540% as a decimal.
b. Write 0.1% as a decimal.
Answers:
a. 5.4 b. 0.001

Success Tip When percents that are greater than 100% are written as decimals, the decimals are greater than 1.0. When percents that are less than 1% are written as decimals, the decimals are less than 0.01.

4 Write decimals as percents.

To write a percent as a decimal, we drop the % symbol and move the decimal point 2 places to the left. To write a decimal as a percent, we do the opposite: we move the decimal point 2 places to the right and insert a % symbol.

Writing Decimals as Percents

To write a decimal as a percent, multiply the decimal by 100 by moving the decimal point 2 places to the right, and then insert a % symbol.

Self Check 9

Write 0.5343 as a percent. 53.43%

Now Try **Problems 71 and 75**

Teaching Example 9 Write 0.457 as a percent.

Answer:
45.7%

EXAMPLE 9 ***Geography*** Land areas make up 0.291 of Earth's surface. Write this decimal as a percent.

Strategy We will multiply the decimal by 100 by moving the decimal point 2 places to the right, and then insert a % symbol.

WHY To write a *decimal as a percent,* we reverse the steps used to write a *percent as a decimal.*

Solution

$0.291 = 029.1\%$ Multiply 0.291 by 100 by moving the decimal point 2 places to the right, and then insert a % symbol.

$= 29.1\%$

0.291, written as a percent, is 29.1%

5 Write fractions as percents.

We use a two-step process to write a fraction as a percent. First, we write the fraction as a decimal. Then we write that decimal as a percent.

Fraction ⟶ decimal ⟶ percent

Writing Fractions as Percents

To write a fraction as a percent:

1. Write the fraction as a decimal by dividing its numerator by its denominator.
2. Multiply the decimal by 100 by moving the decimal point 2 places to the right, and then insert a % symbol.

Self Check 10

Write 7 out of 8 as a percent.

Now Try **Problem 79**

Self Check 10 Answer
87.5%

EXAMPLE 10 ***Television*** The highest-rated television show of all time was a special episode of *M*A*S*H* that aired February 28, 1983. Surveys found that three out of every five American households watched this show. Express the rating as a percent.

Strategy First, we will translate the phrase *three out of every five* to fraction form and write that fraction as a decimal. Then we will write that decimal as a percent.

WHY A fraction-to-decimal-to-percent approach must be used to write a fraction as a percent.

Solution

Step 1 The phrase *three out of every five* can be expressed as $\frac{3}{5}$. To write this fraction as a decimal, we divide the numerator, 3, by the denominator, 5.

$$\begin{array}{r} 0.6 \\ 5\overline{)3.0} \\ -3\,0 \\ \hline 0 \end{array}$$

Write a decimal point and one additional zero to the right of 3.

The remainder is 0.

The result is a terminating decimal.

Step 2 To write 0.6 as a percent, we proceed as follows.

$$\frac{3}{5} = 0.6$$

$0.6 = 0\,60.\%$ Write a placeholder 0 to the right of the 6 (shown in blue). Multiply 0.60 by 100 by moving the decimal point 2 places to the right, and then insert a % symbol.

$= 60\%$

60% of American households watched the special episode of *M*A*S*H*.

Teaching Example 10
ADVERTISING There is a commercial that says, "Four out of five dentists recommend sugarless gum for their patients who chew gum." Express this recommendation as a percent.

Answer:
80%

EXAMPLE 11 Write $\frac{13}{4}$ as a percent.

Strategy We will write the fraction $\frac{13}{4}$ as a decimal. Then we will write that decimal as a percent.

WHY A fraction-to-decimal-to-percent approach must be used to write a fraction as a percent.

Solution

Step 1 To write $\frac{13}{4}$ as a decimal, we divide the numerator, 13, by the denominator, 4.

$$\begin{array}{r} 3.25 \\ 4\overline{)13.00} \\ -12 \\ \hline 1\,0 \\ -8 \\ \hline 20 \\ -20 \\ \hline 0 \end{array}$$

Write a decimal point and two additional zeros to the right of 3.

The remainder is 0.

The result is a terminating decimal.

Step 2 To write 3.25 as a percent, we proceed as follows.

$3.25 = 3\,25\,\%$ Multiply 3.25 by 100 by moving the decimal point 2 places to the right, and then insert a % symbol.

$= 325\%$

The fraction $\frac{13}{4}$, written as a percent, is 325%.

Self Check 11

Write $\frac{5}{2}$ as a percent. 250%

Now Try **Problem 85**

Teaching Example 11
Write $\frac{15}{4}$ as a percent.

Answer:
375%

> ***Success Tip*** When fractions that are greater than 1 are written as percents, the percents are greater than 100%.

In Examples 10 and 11, the result of the division was a terminating decimal. Sometimes when we write a fraction as a decimal, the result of the division is a repeating decimal.

Self Check 12

Write $\frac{2}{3}$ as a percent. Give the exact answer and an approximation to the nearest tenth of one percent. $66\frac{2}{3}\% \approx 66.7\%$

Now Try **Problem 91**

Teaching Example 12 Write $\frac{1}{3}$ as a percent. Give the exact answer and an approximation to the nearest tenth of one percent.

Answer:

$33\frac{1}{3}\% \approx 33.3\%$

EXAMPLE 12 Write $\frac{5}{6}$ as a percent. Give the exact answer and an approximation to the nearest tenth of one percent.

Strategy We will write the fraction $\frac{5}{6}$ as a decimal. Then we will write that decimal as a percent.

WHY A fraction-to-decimal-to-percent approach must be used to write a fraction as a percent.

Solution

Step 1 To write $\frac{5}{6}$ as a decimal, we divide the numerator, 5, by the denominator, 6.

$$\begin{array}{r} 0.8333 \\ 6\overline{)5.0000} \\ -4\,8 \\ \hline 20 \\ -18 \\ \hline 20 \\ -18 \\ \hline 20 \\ -18 \\ \hline 2 \end{array}$$

Write a decimal point and several zeros to the right of 5.

2 ← The repeating pattern is now clear. We can stop the division.

The result is a repeating decimal.

Step 2 To write the decimal as a percent, we proceed as follows.

$$\frac{5}{6} = 0.8333\ldots$$

$$0.833\ldots = 0\,83.33\ldots\%$$ Multiply 0.8333 . . . by 100 by moving the decimal point 2 places to the right, and then insert a % symbol.

$$= 83.33\ldots\%$$

We must now decide whether we want an exact answer or an approximation. For an exact answer, we can represent *the repeating part of the decimal using an equivalent fraction.* For an approximation, we can round 83.333 . . .% to a specific place value.

Exact answer:

$$\frac{5}{6} = 83.3333\ldots\%$$

$$= 83\frac{1}{3}\%$$ Use the fraction $\frac{1}{3}$ to represent .3333 . . . .

Thus,

$$\frac{5}{6} = 83\frac{1}{3}\%$$

Approximation:

$$\frac{5}{6} = 83.33\ldots\%$$

$$\approx 83.3\%$$ Round to the nearest tenth.

Thus,

$$\frac{5}{6} \approx 83.3\%$$

Some percents occur so frequently that it is useful to memorize their fractional and decimal equivalents.

Percent	Decimal	Fraction
1%	0.01	$\frac{1}{100}$
10%	0.1	$\frac{1}{10}$
$16\frac{2}{3}\%$	0.1666 . . .	$\frac{1}{6}$
20%	0.2	$\frac{1}{5}$
25%	0.25	$\frac{1}{4}$

Percent	Decimal	Fraction
$33\frac{1}{3}\%$	0.3333 . . .	$\frac{1}{3}$
50%	0.5	$\frac{1}{2}$
$66\frac{2}{3}\%$	0.6666 . . .	$\frac{2}{3}$
$83\frac{1}{3}\%$	0.8333 . . .	$\frac{5}{6}$
75%	0.75	$\frac{3}{4}$

ANSWERS TO SELF CHECKS

1. a. 42% **b.** 56% **2.** $\frac{23}{25}$ **3.** $\frac{133}{1,000}$ **4.** $\frac{5}{6}$ **5. a.** $\frac{21}{10}$ **b.** $\frac{27}{5,000}$ **6. a.** 0.1643 **b.** 0.0206 **7.** 0.0375 **8. a.** 6 **b.** 0.008 **9.** 53.43% **10.** 87.5% **11.** 250% **12.** $66\frac{2}{3}\% \approx 66.7\%$

SECTION 3.7 STUDY SET

VOCABULARY

Fill in the blanks.

1. _Percent_ means parts per one hundred.
2. The word *percent* is formed from the prefix *per,* which means _ratio_, and the suffix *cent,* which comes from the Latin word *centum,* meaning _100_.

CONCEPTS

Fill in the blanks.

3. To write a percent as a fraction, drop the % symbol and write the given number over _100_. Then _simplify_ the fraction, if possible.
4. To write a percent as a decimal, drop the % symbol and divide the given number by 100 by moving the decimal point 2 places to the _left_.
5. To write a decimal as a percent, multiply the decimal by 100 by moving the decimal point 2 places to the _right_, and then insert a % symbol.
6. To write a fraction as a percent, first write the fraction as a _decimal_. Then multiply the decimal by 100 by moving the decimal point 2 places to the right, and then insert a _%_ symbol.

NOTATION

7. What does the symbol % mean? percent
8. Write the whole number 45 as a decimal. 45.0

GUIDED PRACTICE

What percent of the figure is shaded? What percent of the figure is not shaded? See Objective 1.

9.

84%, 16%

10.

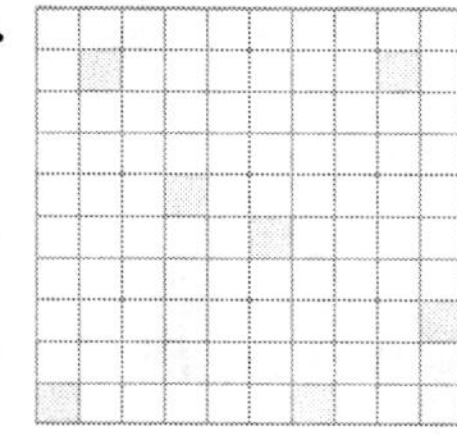

7%, 93%

In the following illustrations, each set of 100 square regions represents 100%. What percent is shaded?

11.

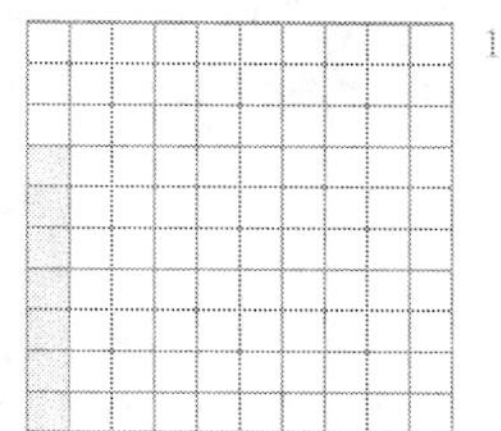

107%

12.

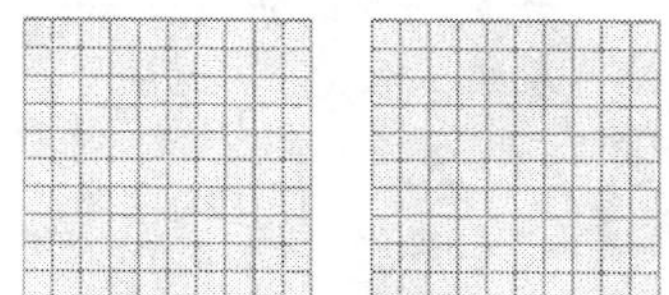

249%

For Problems 13–16, see Example 1.

13. THE INTERNET The following sentence appeared on a technology blog: "Ask Internet users what they want from their service and 99 times out of 100 the answer will be the same: more speed." According to the blog, what percent of the time do Internet users give that answer? 99%
14. BASKETBALL RECORDS In 1962, Wilt Chamberlain of the Philadelphia Warriors scored a total of 100 points in an NBA game. If twenty-eight of his points came from made free throws, what percent of his point total came from free throws? 28%
15. QUILTS A quilt is made from 100 squares of colored cloth.
    a. If fifteen of the squares are blue, what percent of the squares in the quilt are blue? 15%
    b. What percent of the squares are not blue? 85%
16. DIVISIBILITY Of the natural numbers from 1 through 100, only fourteen of them are divisible by 7.
    a. What percent of the numbers are divisible by 7? 14%
    b. What percent of the numbers are not divisible by 7? 86%

Write each percent as a fraction. Simplify, if possible. See Example 2.

17. 17% $\frac{17}{100}$ ▶ **18.** 31% $\frac{31}{100}$
19. 91% $\frac{91}{100}$ **20.** 89% $\frac{89}{100}$
21. 4% $\frac{1}{25}$ **22.** 5% $\frac{1}{20}$
23. 60% $\frac{3}{5}$ **24.** 40% $\frac{2}{5}$

Write each percent as a fraction. Simplify, if possible. See Example 3.

25. 1.9% $\frac{19}{1,000}$ ▶ **26.** 2.3% $\frac{23}{1,000}$
27. 54.7% $\frac{547}{1,000}$ **28.** 97.1% $\frac{971}{1,000}$
29. 12.5% $\frac{1}{8}$ **30.** 62.5% $\frac{5}{8}$
31. 6.8% $\frac{17}{250}$ **32.** 4.2% $\frac{21}{500}$

Write each percent as a fraction. Simplify, if possible. See Example 4.

33. $1\frac{1}{3}\%$ $\frac{1}{75}$ ▶ **34.** $3\frac{1}{3}\%$ $\frac{1}{30}$
35. $14\frac{1}{6}\%$ $\frac{17}{120}$ **36.** $10\frac{5}{6}\%$ $\frac{13}{120}$

Write each percent as a fraction. Simplify, if possible. See Example 5.

37. 130% $\frac{13}{10}$ ▶ **38.** 160% $\frac{8}{5}$
39. 220% $\frac{11}{5}$ **40.** 240% $\frac{12}{5}$
41. 0.35% $\frac{7}{2,000}$ ▶ **42.** 0.45% $\frac{9}{2,000}$
43. 0.25% $\frac{1}{400}$ **44.** 0.75% $\frac{3}{400}$

Write each percent as a decimal. See Objective 3.

45. 16% 0.16 **46.** 11% 0.11
47. 81% 0.81 ▶ **48.** 93% 0.93

Write each percent as a decimal. See Example 6.

49. 34.12% 0.3412 ▶ **50.** 27.21% 0.2721
51. 50.033% 0.50033 **52.** 40.083% 0.40083
53. 6.99% 0.0699 **54.** 4.77% 0.0477
55. 1.3% 0.013 **56.** 8.6% 0.086

Write each percent as a decimal. See Example 7.

57. $7\frac{1}{4}\%$ 0.0725 ▶ **58.** $9\frac{3}{4}\%$ 0.0975
59. $18\frac{1}{2}\%$ 0.185 **60.** $25\frac{1}{2}\%$ 0.255

Write each percent as a decimal. See Example 8.

61. 460% 4.6 ▶ **62.** 230% 2.3
63. 316% 3.16 **64.** 178% 1.78
65. 0.5% 0.005 **66.** 0.9% 0.009
67. 0.03% 0.0003 ▶ **68.** 0.06% 0.0006

Write each decimal or whole number as a percent. See Example 9.

69. 0.362 36.2% ▶ **70.** 0.245 24.5%
71. 0.98 98% **72.** 0.57 57%
73. 1.71 171% **74.** 4.33 433%
75. 4 400% ▶ **76.** 9 900%

Write each fraction as a percent. See Example 10.

77. $\frac{2}{5}$ 40% ▶ **78.** $\frac{1}{5}$ 20%
79. $\frac{4}{25}$ 16% **80.** $\frac{9}{25}$ 36%
81. $\frac{5}{8}$ 62.5% **82.** $\frac{3}{8}$ 37.5%
83. $\frac{7}{16}$ 43.75% **84.** $\frac{9}{16}$ 56.25%

Write each fraction as a percent. See Example 11.

85. $\frac{9}{4}$ 225% **86.** $\frac{11}{4}$ 275%
87. $\frac{21}{20}$ 105% ▶ **88.** $\frac{33}{20}$ 165%

Write each fraction as a percent. Give the exact answer and an approximation to the nearest tenth of one percent. See Example 12.

89. $\frac{1}{6}$ $16\frac{2}{3}\% \approx 16.7\%$ ▶ **90.** $\frac{2}{9}$ $22\frac{2}{9}\% \approx 22.2\%$
91. $\frac{5}{3}$ $166\frac{2}{3}\% \approx 166.7\%$ **92.** $\frac{4}{3}$ $133\frac{1}{3}\% \approx 133.3\%$

TRY IT YOURSELF

Complete the table. Give an exact answer and an approximation to the nearest tenth of one percent when necessary. Round decimals to the nearest hundredth when necessary.

	Fraction	Decimal	Percent
93.	$\frac{157}{5,000}$	0.0314	3.14%
94.	$\frac{21}{10,000}$	0.0021	0.21%
95.	$\frac{51}{125}$	0.408	40.8%
96.	$\frac{171}{500}$	0.342	34.2%
97.	$\frac{21}{400}$	0.0525	$5\frac{1}{4}\%$
98.	$\frac{27}{400}$	0.0675	$6\frac{3}{4}\%$
99.	$\frac{7}{3}$	2.33	$233\frac{1}{3}\% \approx 233.3\%$
100.	$\frac{7}{9}$	0.78	$77\frac{7}{9}\% \approx 77.8\%$

APPLICATIONS

101. THE RED CROSS A fact sheet released by the American Red Cross in 2008 stated, "An average of 91 cents of every dollar donated to the Red Cross is spent on services and programs." What percent of the money donated to the Red Cross went to services and programs? 91%

102. SAVING MONEY According to an article on the CNN website, in 1970 Americans saved 14 cents out of every dollar earned. (*Source:* CNN.com/living, May 21, 2009)

a. Express the amount saved for every dollar earned as a fraction in simplest form. $\frac{14}{100} = \frac{7}{50}$

b. Write your answer to part a as a percent. 14%

103. REGIONS OF THE COUNTRY The continental United States is divided into seven regions as shown below.

a. What percent of the 50 states are in the Rocky Mountain region? 12%

b. What percent of the 50 states are in the Midwestern region? 24%

c. What percent of the 50 states are not located in any of the seven regions shown here? 4% (Alaska, Hawaii)

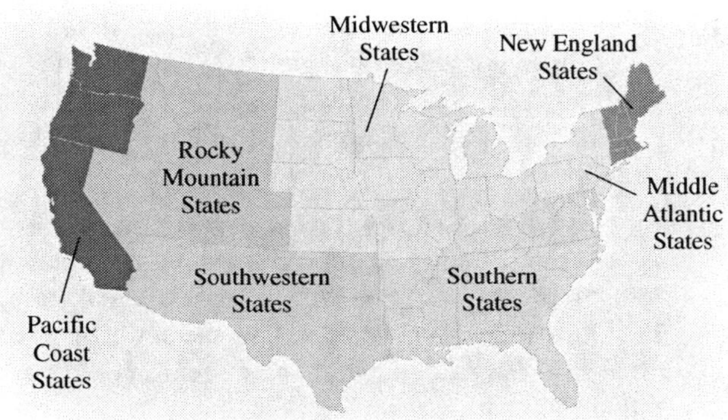

104. ROAD SIGNS Sometimes, signs like that shown below are posted to warn truckers when they are approaching a steep grade on the highway.

a. Write the grade shown on the sign as a fraction. $\frac{5}{100} = \frac{1}{20}$

b. Write the grade shown on the sign as a decimal. 0.05

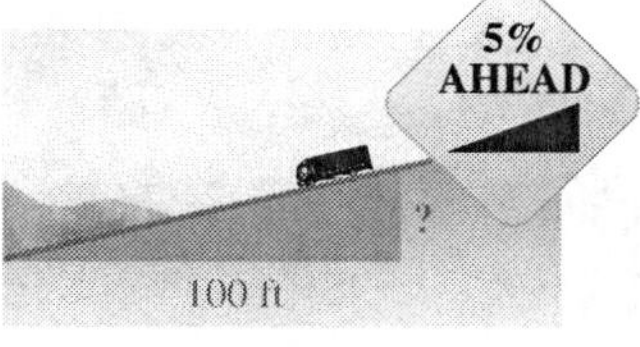

105. INTEREST RATES Write each interest rate for the following accounts as a decimal.

a. Home loan: 7.75% 0.0775

b. Savings account: 5% 0.05

c. Credit card: 14.25% 0.1425

106. DRUNK DRIVING In most states, it is illegal to drive with a blood alcohol concentration of 0.08% or higher.

a. Write this percent as a fraction. Do not simplify. $\frac{8}{10,000}$

b. Use your answer to part a to fill in the blanks: A blood alcohol concentration of 0.08% means 8 parts alcohol to 10,000 parts blood.

107. HUMAN SKIN The illustration below shows what percent of the total skin area that each section of the body covers. Find the missing percent for the torso, and then complete the bar graph. (*Source:* Burn Center at Sherman Oaks Hospital, American Medical Assn. Encyclopedia of Medicine) torso: 27.5%

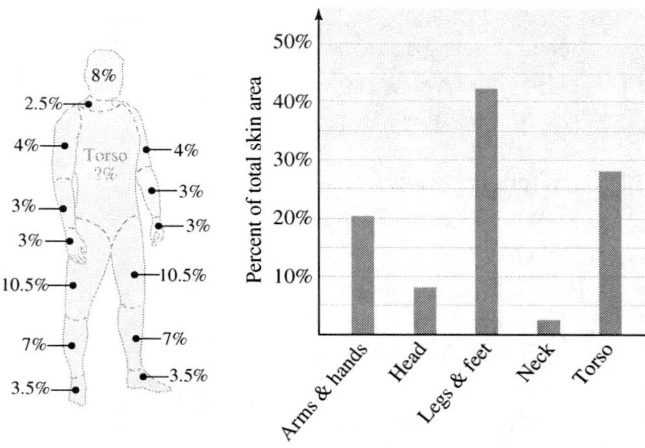

108. RAP MUSIC The table below shows what percent rap/hip-hop music sales were of total U.S. dollar sales of recorded music for the years 2001–2007. Use the data to construct a line graph.

2001	2002	2003	2004	2005	2006	2007
11.4%	13.8%	13.3%	12.1%	13.3%	11.4%	10.8%

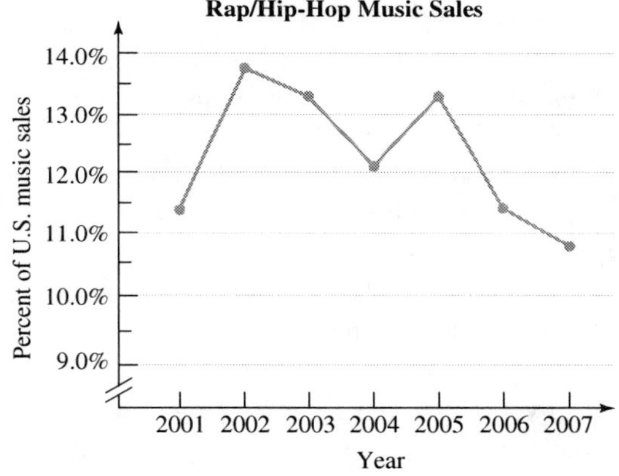

Source: Recording Industry Association of America

109. THE U.N. SECURITY COUNCIL The United Nations has 192 members. The United States, Russia, the United Kingdom, France, and China, along with ten other nations, make up the Security Council. (Source: *The World Almanac and Book of Facts,* 2009)

a. What fraction of the members of the United Nations belong to the Security Council? Write your answer in simplest form. $\frac{5}{64}$

b. Write your answer to part a as a decimal. (*Hint:* Divide to six decimal places. The result is a terminating decimal.) 0.078125

c. Write your answer to part b as a percent. 7.8125%

110. SOAP Ivory soap claims to be $99\frac{44}{100}\%$ pure. Write this percent as a decimal. 0.9944

▶ **111.** LOGOS In the illustration, what part of the company's logo is shaded red? Express your answer as a percent (exact), a fraction, and a decimal (using an overbar). $33\frac{1}{3}\%, \frac{1}{3}, 0.\overline{3}$

Recycling Industries Inc.

112. THE HUMAN SPINE The human spine consists of a group of bones (vertebrae) as shown.

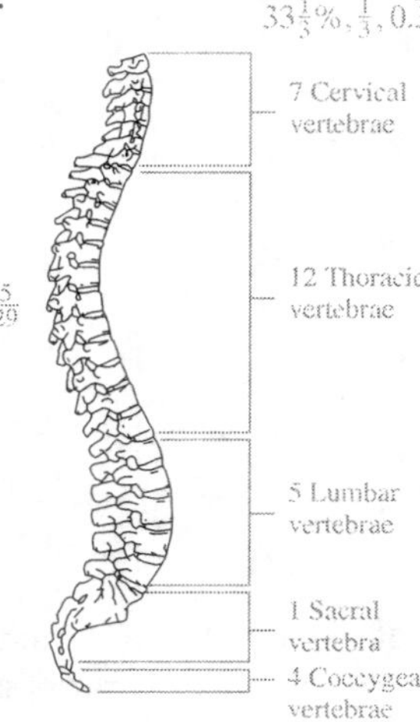

a. What fraction of the vertebrae are lumbar? $\frac{5}{29}$

b. What percent of the vertebrae are lumbar? (Round to the nearest one percent.) 17%

c. What percent of the vertebrae are cervical? (Round to the nearest one percent.) 24%

113. BOXING Oscar De La Hoya won 39 out of 45 professional fights.

a. What fraction of his fights did he win? $\frac{13}{15}$

b. What percent of his fights did he win? Give the exact answer and an approximation to the nearest tenth of one percent. $86\frac{2}{3}\% \approx 86.7\%$

114. MAJOR LEAGUE BASEBALL In 2008, the Milwaukee Brewers won 90 games and lost 72 during the regular season.

a. What was the total number of regular season games that the Brewers played in 2008? 162 games

b. What percent of the games played did the Brewers win in 2008? Give the exact answer and an approximation to the nearest tenth of one percent. $55\frac{5}{9}\% \approx 55.6\%$

▶ **115.** ECONOMIC FORECASTS One economic indicator of the national economy is the number of orders placed by manufacturers. One month, the number of orders rose *one-fourth of 1 percent.*

a. Write this using a % symbol. $\frac{1}{4}\%$

b. Express it as a fraction. $\frac{1}{400}$

c. Express it as a decimal. 0.0025

▶ **116.** TAXES In August of 2008, Springfield, Missouri, voters approved a *one-eighth of one percent* sales tax to fund transportation projects in the city.

a. Write the percent as a decimal. 0.00125

b. Write the percent as a fraction. $\frac{1}{800}$

117. BIRTHDAYS If the day of your birthday represents $\frac{1}{365}$ of a year, what percent of the year is it? Round to the nearest hundredth of a percent. 0.27%

▶ **118.** POPULATION As a fraction, each resident of the United States represents approximately $\frac{1}{305{,}000{,}000}$ of the U.S. population. Express this as a percent. Round to one nonzero digit. 0.0000003%

WRITING

119. If you were writing advertising, which form do you think would attract more customers: "25% off" or "$\frac{1}{4}$ off"? Explain your reasoning.

120. Many coaches ask their players to give a 110% effort during practices and games. What do you think this means? Is it possible?

▶ **121.** Explain how an amusement park could have an attendance that is 103% of capacity.

122. WON-LOST RECORDS In sports, when a team wins as many games as it loses, it is said to be playing "500 ball." Suppose in its first 40 games, a team wins 20 games and loses 20 games. Use the concepts in this section to explain why such a record could be called "500 ball."

REVIEW

123. The width of a rectangle is 6.5 centimeters and its length is 10.5 centimeters.

▶ **a.** Find its perimeter. 34 cm

b. Find its area. 68.25 cm^2

124. The length of a side of a square is 9.8 meters.

a. Find its perimeter. 39.2 m

b. Find its area. 96.04 m^2

SECTION 3.8

Solving Percent Problems Using Percent Equations and Proportions

Objectives

PERCENT EQUATIONS (begins below)

1. Translate percent sentences to percent equations.
2. Solve percent equations to find the amount.
3. Solve percent equations to find the percent.
4. Solve percent equations to find the base.

PERCENT PROPORTIONS (see p. 520)

1. Write percent proportions.
2. Solve percent proportions to find the amount.
3. Solve percent proportions to find the percent.
4. Solve percent proportions to find the base.
5. Read circle graphs.

The articles on the front page of the newspaper on the right illustrate three types of percent problems.

Type 1 In the labor article, if we want to know how many union members voted to accept the new offer, we would ask:

What number is 84% of 500?

Type 2 In the article on drinking water, if we want to know what percent of the wells are safe, we would ask:

38 is what percent of 40?

Type 3 In the article on new appointees, if we want to know how many members are on the State Board of Examiners, we would ask:

6 is 75% of what number?

DAILY NEWS

Circulation Monday, March 23 50 cents

Transit Strike Averted!

Labor: 84% of 500-member union votes to accept new offer

Drinking Water
38 of 40 Wells Declared Safe

New Appointees

These six area residents now make up 75% of the State Board of Examiners

To the instructor: Note that the two sets of objectives for this section are basically the same. Determine which method you want your students to use to solve percent problems: the percent equation method or the proportion method. You need not cover both. The Study Set problems for this section can be solved using either approach.

This section introduces two methods that can be used to solve the percent problems shown above. The first method involves writing and solving *percent equations.* The second method involves writing and solving *percent proportions.* If your instructor only requires you to learn the proportion method, then turn to page 520 and begin reading Objective 1.

METHOD 1: PERCENT EQUATIONS

1 Translate percent sentences to percent equations.

The **percent sentences** highlighted in blue in the introduction above have three things in common.

- Each contains the word *is.* Here, *is* can be translated as an = symbol.
- Each contains the word *of.* In this case, *of* means multiply.
- Each contains a phrase such as *what number* or *what percent.* In other words, there is an unknown number that can be represented by a variable.

These observations suggest that each percent sentence contains key words that can be translated to form an equation. The equation, called a **percent equation,** will contain three numbers (two known and one unknown represented by a variable), the operation of multiplication, and, of course, an = symbol.

The Language of Mathematics The key words in a percent sentence translate as follows:

- ***is*** translates to an equal symbol = .
- ***of*** translates to multiplication that is shown with a raised dot ·
- ***what number*** or ***what percent*** translates to an unknown number that is represented by a variable.

Self Check 1

Translate each percent sentence to a percent equation.

a. What number is 33% of 80?

b. What percent of 55 is 6?

c. 172% of what number is 4?

***Now Try* Problem 17**

Self Check 1 Answers

a. $x = 33\% \cdot 80$
b. $x \cdot 55 = 6$
c. $172\% \cdot x = 4$

Teaching Example 1 Translate each percent sentence to a percent equation.
a. What number is 25% of 37?
b. What percent of 300 is 12?
c. 110% of what number is 341?

Answers:
a. $x = 25\% \cdot 37$
b. $x \cdot 300 = 12$
c. $110\% \cdot x = 341$

EXAMPLE 1 Translate each percent sentence to a percent equation.

a. What number is 12% of 64?

b. What percent of 88 is 11?

c. 165% of what number is 366?

Strategy We will look for the key words *is, of,* and *what number* (or *what percent*) in each percent sentence.

WHY These key words translate to mathematical symbols that form the percent equation.

Solution In each case, we will let the variable x represent the unknown number. However, any letter can be used.

a. What number is 12% of 64? — *This is the given percent sentence.*

$x = 12\% \cdot 64$ — *This is the percent equation.*

b. What percent of 88 is 11? — *This is the given percent sentence.*

$x \cdot 88 = 11$ — *This is the percent equation.*

c. 165% of what number is 366? — *This is the given percent sentence.*

$165\% \cdot x = 366$ — *This is the percent equation.*

2 Solve percent equations to find the amount.

To solve the labor union percent problem (Type 1 from the newspaper), we translate the percent sentence into a percent equation and then find the unknown number.

Self Check 2

What number is 36% of 400? 144

***Now Try* Problems 19 and 71**

Teaching Example 2 What number is 28% of 300?

Answer:
84

EXAMPLE 2 What number is 84% of 500?

DAILY NEWS
Monday, March 23
Transit Strike Averted!
Labor: 84% of 500-member union votes to accept new offer
Drinking Water
38 of 40 Wells Declared Safe
New Appointees
These six area residents now make up 75% of the State Board of Examiners

Strategy We will look for the key words *is, of,* and *what number* in the percent sentence and translate them to mathematical symbols to form a percent equation.

WHY Then it will be clear what operation should be performed to find the unknown number.

Solution First, we translate.

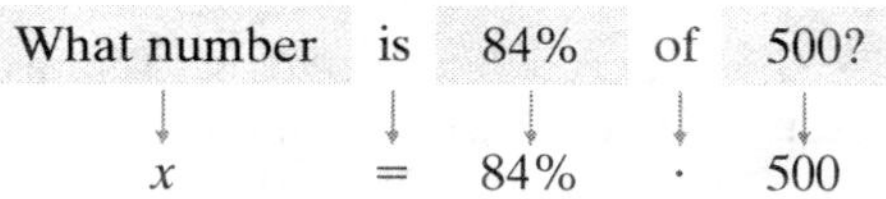

What number is 84% of 500?

$x = 84\% \cdot 500$ — *Translate to a percent equation.*

Now we perform the multiplication on the right side of the equation.

$x = 0.84 \cdot 500$ — *Write 84% as a decimal: 84% = 0.84.*

$x = 420$ — *Do the multiplication.*

We have found that 420 is 84% of 500. That is, 420 union members mentioned in the newspaper article voted to accept the new offer.

The Language of Mathematics When we find the value of the variable that makes a percent equation true, we say that we have **solved the equation.** In Example 2, we *solved* $x = 84\% \cdot 500$ to find that the variable x is 420.

> **Caution!** When solving percent equations, always write the percent as a decimal (or a fraction) before performing any calculations. In Example 2, we wrote 84% as 0.84 before multiplying by 500.

Percent sentences involve a comparison of numbers. In the statement "420 is 84% of 500," the number 420 is called the **amount,** 84% is the **percent,** and 500 is called the **base.** Think of the base as the standard of comparison—it represents the **whole** of some quantity. The amount is a **part** of the base, but it can exceed the base when the percent is more than 100%. The percent, of course, has the % symbol.

42	is	84%	of	500.
↓		↓		↓
Amount (part)		**percent**		**base** (whole)

In any percent problem, the relationship between the amount, the percent, and the base is as follows: *Amount is percent of base.* This relationship is shown below as the **percent equation** (also called the **percent formula**).

Percent Equation (Formula)

Any percent sentence can be translated to a percent equation that has the form:

Amount = percent · base or Part = percent · whole

EXAMPLE 3 What number is 160% of 15.8?

Strategy We will look for the key words *is, of,* and *what number* in the percent sentence and translate them to mathematical symbols to form a percent equation.

WHY Then it will be clear what operation needs to be performed to find the unknown number.

Solution First, we translate.

What number	is	160%	of	15.8?
↓	↓	↓	↓	↓
x	=	160%	·	15.8

x is the amount, 160% is the percent, and 15.8 is the base.

Now we solve the equation by performing the multiplication on the right side.

$x = 1.6 \cdot 15.8$ Write 160% as a decimal: 160% = 1.6.

$x = 25.28$ Do the multiplication.

$$\begin{array}{r} 15.8 \\ \times\ 1.6 \\ \hline 948 \\ 1580 \\ \hline 25.28 \end{array}$$

Thus, 25.28 is 160% of 15.8. In this case, the amount exceeds the base because the percent is more than 100%.

Self Check 3

What number is 240% of 80.3?

Now Try **Problem 23**

Self Check 3 Answer

192.72

Teaching Example 3 What number is 340% of 28.4?

Answer:

96.56

3 Solve percent equations to find the percent.

In the drinking water problem (Type 2 from the newspaper), we must find the percent. Once again, we translate the words of the problem into a percent equation and solve it.

The Language of Mathematics We solve percent equations by writing a series of steps that result in an equation of the form $x =$ **a number** or **a number** $= x$. We say that the variable x is *isolated* on one side of the equation. *Isolated* means alone or by itself.

Self Check 4

4 is what percent of 80? 5%

Now Try **Problems 27 and 79**

Teaching Example 4 34 is what percent of 40?

Answer:
85%

EXAMPLE 4 38 is what percent of 40?

Strategy We will look for the key words *is, of,* and *what percent* in the percent sentence and translate them to mathematical symbols to form a percent equation.

WHY Then we can solve the equation to find the unknown percent.

Solution First, we translate.

38	is	what percent	of	40?
↓	↓	↓	↓	↓
38	=	x	·	40

38 is the amount, x is the percent, and 40 is the base.

$38 = x \cdot 40$ This is the equation to solve.

On the right side of the equation, the unknown number x is multiplied by 40. To undo the multiplication by 40 and isolate x, we divide both sides by 40.

$$\frac{38}{40} = \frac{x \cdot 40}{40}$$

We can simplify the fraction on the right side of the equation by removing the common factor of 40 from the numerator and denominator. On the left side, we perform the division indicated by the fraction bar.

$$0.95 = \frac{x \cdot \overset{1}{\cancel{40}}}{\underset{1}{\cancel{40}}}$$ To simplify the left side, divide 38 by 40.

$$0.95 = x$$

$$\begin{array}{r} 0.95 \\ 40\overline{)38.00} \\ -36\ 0 \\ \hline 2\ 00 \\ -2\ 00 \\ \hline 0 \end{array}$$

Since we want to find the percent, we need to write the decimal 0.95 as a percent.

$0.95\% = x$ To write 0.95 as a percent, multiply it by 100 by moving the decimal point two places to the right, and then insert a % symbol.

$95\% = x$

We have found that 38 is 95% of 40. That is, 95% of the wells mentioned in the newspaper article were declared safe.

Self Check 5

9 is what percent of 16? 56.25%

Now Try **Problem 31**

Teaching Example 5 5 is what percent of 16?

Answer:
31.25%

EXAMPLE 5 14 is what percent of 32?

Strategy We will look for the key words *is, of,* and *what percent* in the percent sentence and translate them to mathematical symbols to form a percent equation.

WHY Then we can solve the equation to find the unknown percent.

Solution First, we translate.

14	is	what percent	of	32?
↓	↓	↓	↓	↓
14	=	x	·	32

14 is the amount, x is the percent, and 32 is the base.

$14 = x \cdot 32$ This is the equation to solve.

$\frac{14}{32} = \frac{x \cdot 32}{32}$ To undo the multiplication by 32 and isolate x on the right side of the equation, divide both sides by 32.

$0.4375 = \frac{x \cdot \overset{1}{\cancel{32}}}{\underset{1}{\cancel{32}}}$ To simplify the fraction on the right side of the equation, remove the common factor of 32 from the numerator and denominator. On the left side, divide 14 by 32.

$0.4375 = x$

$0\,43.75\% = x$ To write the decimal 0.4375 as a percent, multiply it by 100 by moving the decimal point two places to the right, and then insert a % symbol.

$43.75\% = x$

$$\begin{array}{r} 0.4375 \\ 32\overline{)14.0000} \\ -12\,8 \\ \hline 1\,20 \\ -96 \\ \hline 240 \\ -224 \\ \hline 160 \\ -160 \\ \hline 0 \end{array}$$

Thus, 14 is 43.75% of 32.

Using Your CALCULATOR Cost of an Air Bag

An air bag is estimated to add an additional $500 to the cost of a car. What percent of the $16,295 sticker price is the cost of the air bag?

First, we translate the words of the problem into a percent equation.

What percent	of	the $16,295 sticker price	is	the cost of the air bag?
↓	↓	↓	↓	↓
x	$\cdot$	16,295	=	500

500 is the amount, x is the percent, and 16,295 is the base.

Then we solve the equation.

$x \cdot 16{,}295 = 500$

$\frac{x \cdot 16{,}295}{16{,}295} = \frac{500}{16{,}295}$ To undo the multiplication by 16,295 and isolate x on the left side, divide both sides of the equation by 16,295.

$x = \frac{500}{16{,}295}$ To simplify the fraction on the left side, remove the common factor of 16,295 from the numerator and denominator.

To perform the division on the right side using a scientific calculator, enter the following:

500 [÷] 16295 [=]   `0.030684259`

This display gives the answer in decimal form. To change it to a percent, we multiply the result by 100. This moves the decimal point 2 places to the right. (See the display.) Then we insert a % symbol. If we round to the nearest tenth of a percent, the cost of the air bag is about 3.1% of the sticker price.

`3.068425898`

EXAMPLE 6 What percent of 6 is 7.5?

Strategy We will look for the key words *is, of,* and *what percent* in the percent sentence and translate them to mathematical symbols to form a percent equation.

WHY Then we can solve the equation to find the unknown percent.

Self Check 6

What percent of 5 is 8.5? 170%

Now Try **Problem 35**

Teaching Example 6 What percent of 7 is 9.1?
Answer:
130%

Solution First, we translate.

What percent of 6 is 7.5
$$x \cdot 6 = 7.5$$

$x \cdot 6 = 7.5$ This is the equation to solve.

$\frac{x \cdot 6}{6} = \frac{7.5}{6}$ To undo the multiplication by 6 and isolate x on the left side of the equation, divide both sides by 6.

$\frac{x \cdot \overset{1}{\cancel{6}}}{\underset{1}{\cancel{6}}} = 1.25$ To simplify the fraction on the left side of the equation, remove the common factor of 6 from the numerator and denominator. On the right side, divide 7.5 by 6.

$$\begin{array}{r} 1.25 \\ 6\overline{)7.50} \\ -6 \\ 1\,5 \\ -1\,2 \\ 30 \\ -30 \\ 0 \end{array}$$

$x = 1.25$

$x = 1.25\%$ To write the decimal 1.25 as a percent, multiply it by 100 by moving the decimal point two places to the right, and then insert a % symbol.

$x = 125\%$

Thus, 7.5 is 125% of 6.

4 Solve percent equations to find the base.

In the percent problem about the State Board of Examiners (Type 3 from the newspaper), we must find the base. As before, we translate the percent sentence into a percent equation and then find the unknown number.

Self Check 7
3 is 5% of what number? 60
Now Try **Problem 39**

Teaching Example 7 7 is 35% of what number?
Answer:
20

EXAMPLE 7 6 is 75% of what number?

Strategy We will look for the key words *is*, *of*, and *what number* in the percent sentence and translate them to mathematical symbols to form a percent equation.

WHY Then we can solve the equation to find the unknown number.

DAILY NEWS
Transit Strike Averted!
Labor: 84% of 500-member union votes to accept new offer
Drinking Water 38 of 40 Wells Declared Safe
New Appointees
These six area residents now make up 75% of the State Board of Examiners

Solution First, we translate.

6 is 75% of what number?
$$6 = 75\% \cdot x$$
6 is the amount, 75% is the percent, and x is the base.

Now we solve the equation.

$6 = 0.75 \cdot x$ Write 75% as a decimal: 75% = 0.75.

$\frac{6}{0.75} = \frac{0.75 \cdot x}{0.75}$ To undo the multiplication by 0.75 and isolate x on the right side, divide both sides of the equation by 0.75.

$8 = \frac{\overset{1}{\cancel{0.75}} \cdot x}{\underset{1}{\cancel{0.75}}}$ To simplify the fraction on the right side of the equation, remove the common factor of 0.75. On the left side, divide 6 by 0.75.

$$\begin{array}{r} 8 \\ 75\overline{)600} \\ -600 \\ 0 \end{array}$$

$8 = x$

Thus, 6 is 75% of 8. That is, there are 8 members on the State Board of Examiners mentioned in the newspaper article.

Success Tip Sometimes the calculations to solve a percent problem are made easier if we write the percent as a fraction instead of a decimal. This is the case with percents that have *repeating* decimal equivalents such as $33\frac{1}{3}\%$, $66\frac{2}{3}\%$, and $16\frac{2}{3}\%$. You may want to review the table of percents and their fractional equivalents on page 508.

EXAMPLE 8 31.5 is $33\frac{1}{3}\%$ of what number?

Strategy We will look for the key words *is, of,* and *what number* in the percent sentence and translate them to mathematical symbols to form a percent equation.

WHY Then we can solve the equation to find the unknown number.

Solution First, we translate.

31.5	is	$33\frac{1}{3}\%$	of	what number?
↓	↓	↓	↓	↓
31.5	=	$33\frac{1}{3}\%$	·	x

31.5 is the amount, $33\frac{1}{3}\%$ is the percent, and x is the base.

In this case, the calculations can be made easier by writing $33\frac{1}{3}\%$ as a fraction instead of as a repeating decimal.

$$31.5 = \frac{1}{3} \cdot x$$ Recall that $33\frac{1}{3}\% = \frac{1}{3}$.

$$\frac{31.5}{\frac{1}{3}} = \frac{\frac{1}{3} \cdot x}{\frac{1}{3}}$$ To undo the multiplication by $\frac{1}{3}$ and isolate x on the right side of the equation, divide both sides by $\frac{1}{3}$.

$$\frac{31.5}{\frac{1}{3}} = \frac{\frac{\overset{1}{\cancel{1}}}{\cancel{3}} \cdot x}{\frac{\cancel{1}}{\underset{1}{\cancel{3}}}}$$ To simplify the fraction on the right side of the equation, remove the common factor of $\frac{1}{3}$ from the numerator and denominator.

$$31.5 \div \frac{1}{3} = x$$ On the left side, the fraction bar indicates division.

$$\frac{31.5}{1} \cdot \frac{3}{1} = x$$ On the left side, write 31.5 as a fraction: $\frac{31.5}{1}$. Then use the rule for dividing fractions: Multiply by the reciprocal of $\frac{1}{3}$, which is $\frac{3}{1}$.

$$94.5 = x$$ Do the multiplication.

$$\begin{array}{r} \overset{1}{31.5} \\ \times\ 3 \\ \hline 94.5 \end{array}$$

Thus, 31.5 is $33\frac{1}{3}\%$ of 94.5.

Self Check 8

150 is $66\frac{2}{3}\%$ of what number? 225

Now Try **Problems 43 and 83**

Teaching Example 8 22.6 is $33\frac{1}{3}\%$ of what number?

Answer: 67.8

To solve percent application problems, we often have to rewrite the facts of the problem in percent sentence form before we can translate to an equation.

EXAMPLE 9 *Rentals* In an apartment complex, 198 of the units are currently occupied. If this represents an 88% occupancy rate, how many units are in the complex?

Strategy We will carefully read the problem and use the given facts to write them in the form of a percent sentence.

Self Check 9

CAPACITY OF A GYM A total of 784 people attended a graduation in a high school gymnasium. If this was 98% of capacity, what is the total capacity of the gym? 800 people

Now Try Problem 81

Teaching Example 9
CLOSED CLASSES On the first day of classes, 36 of the algebra sections offered by a college mathematics department were closed. If this represented 72% of all the sections of algebra, what is the total number of algebra sections offered that semester?
Answer:
50 classes

WHY Then we can translate the sentence into a percent equation and solve it to find the unknown number of units in the complex.

Solution An occupancy rate of 88% means that 88% of the units are occupied. Thus, the 198 units that are currently occupied are 88% of some unknown number of units in the complex, and we can write:

198 is 88% of what number?

$$198 = 88\% \cdot x$$

198 is the amount, 88% is the percent, and x is the base.

Now we solve the equation.

$198 = 88\% \cdot x$

$198 = 0.88 \cdot x$ Write 88% as a decimal: 88% = 0.88.

$\frac{198}{0.88} = \frac{0.88 \cdot x}{0.88}$ To undo the multiplication by 0.88 and isolate x on the right side, divide both sides of the equation by 0.88.

$\frac{198}{0.88} = \frac{\overset{1}{\cancel{0.88}} \cdot x}{\underset{1}{\cancel{0.88}}}$ To simplify the fraction on the right side of the equation, remove the common factor of 0.88 from the numerator and denominator. On the left side, divide 198 by 0.88.

$225 = x$

$$\begin{array}{r} 225 \\ 88\overline{)19800} \\ -176 \\ \hline 220 \\ -176 \\ \hline 440 \\ -440 \\ \hline 0 \end{array}$$

The apartment complex has 225 units, of which 198, or 88%, are occupied.

If you are only learning the percent equation method for solving percent problems, turn to page 527 and pick up your reading at Objective 5.

METHOD 2: PERCENT PROPORTIONS

1 Write percent proportions.

Another method to solve percent problems involves writing and then solving a proportion. To introduce this method, consider the figure on the right. The vertical line down its middle divides the figure into two equal-sized parts. Since 1 of the 2 parts is shaded red, the shaded portion of the figure can be described by the ratio $\frac{1}{2}$. We call this an **amount-to-base** (or **part-to-whole**) **ratio.**

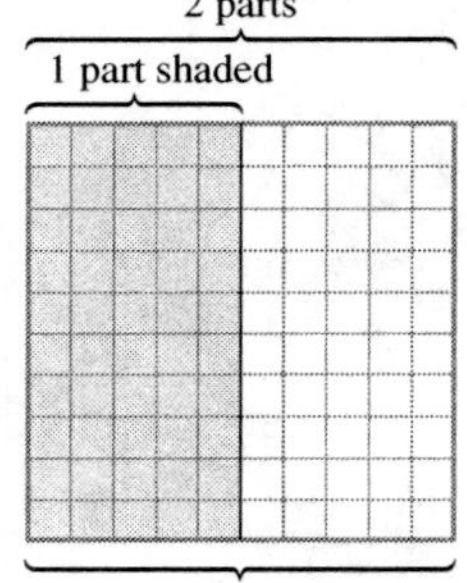

50 of the 100 parts shaded: 50% shaded

Now consider the 100 equal-sized square regions within the figure. Since 50 of them are shaded red, we say that $\frac{50}{100}$, or 50% of the figure is shaded. The ratio $\frac{50}{100}$ is called a **percent ratio.**

Since the amount-to-base ratio, $\frac{1}{2}$, and the percent ratio, $\frac{50}{100}$, represent the same shaded portion of the figure, they must be equal, and we can write

The amount-to-base ratio $\frac{1}{2} = \frac{50}{100}$ The percent ratio

Statements of this type stating that two ratios are equal are called *proportions.* We call $\frac{1}{2} = \frac{50}{100}$ a **percent proportion.** The four terms of a percent proportion are shown on the following page.

Percent Proportion

To translate a percent sentence to a **percent proportion,** use the following form:

Amount is to base as percent is to 100. *Part is to whole as percent is to 100.*

$$\frac{\text{amount}}{\text{base}} = \frac{\text{percent}}{100} \quad \text{or} \quad \frac{\text{part}}{\text{whole}} = \frac{\text{percent}}{100}$$

This is always 100 because percent means parts per one hundred.

To write a percent proportion, you must identify 3 of the terms as you read the problem. (Remember, the fourth term of the proportion is always 100.) Here are some ways to identify those terms.

- The **percent** is easy to find. Look for the % symbol or the words *what percent.*
- The **base** (or **whole**) usually follows the word *of.*
- The **amount** (or **part**) is compared to the base (or whole).

EXAMPLE 1 Translate each percent sentence to a percent proportion.

a. What number is 12% of 64?

b. What percent of 88 is 11?

c. 165% of what number is 366?

Strategy A percent proportion has the form $\frac{\text{amount}}{\text{base}} = \frac{\text{percent}}{100}$. Since one of the terms of the percent proportion is always 100, we only need to identify three terms to write the proportion. We will begin by identifying the percent and the base in the given sentence.

WHY The remaining number (or unknown) must be the amount.

Solution

a. We will identify the terms in this order:

- *First:* the percent (next to the % symbol)
- *Second:* the base (usually after the word *of*)
- *Last:* the amount (the number that remains)

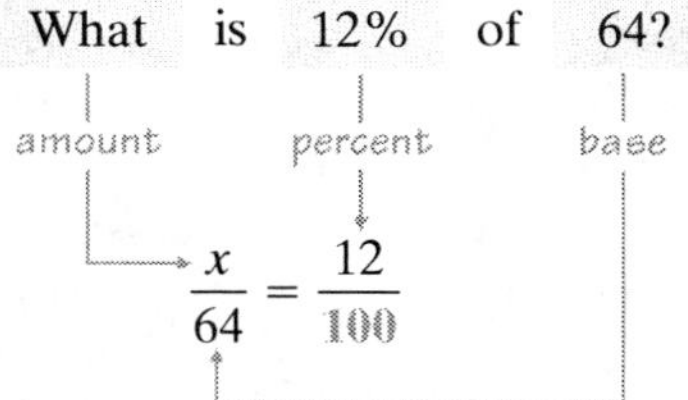

b. 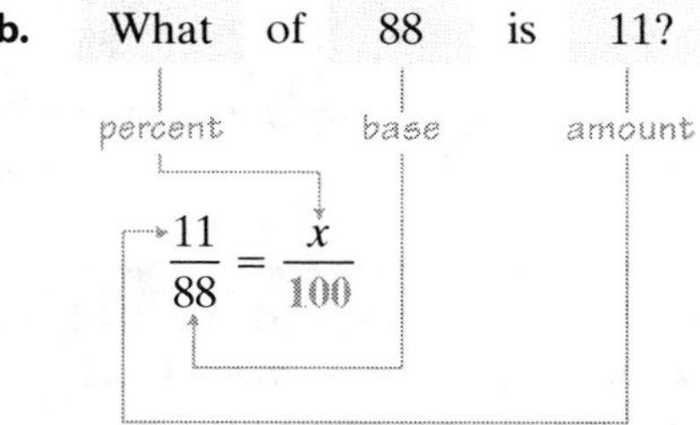

Self Check 1

Translate each percent sentence to a percent proportion.

a. What number is 33% of 80?

b. What percent of 55 is 6?

c. 172% of what number is 4?

Now Try **Problem 17**

Self Check 1 Answers

a. $\frac{x}{80} = \frac{33}{100}$

b. $\frac{6}{55} = \frac{x}{100}$

c. $\frac{4}{x} = \frac{172}{100}$

Teaching Example 1 Translate each percent sentence to a percent proportion.

a. What number is 25% of 37?

b. What percent of 300 is 12?

c. 110% of what number is 341?

Answers:

a. $\frac{x}{37} = \frac{25}{100}$

b. $\frac{12}{300} = \frac{x}{100}$

c. $\frac{341}{x} = \frac{110}{100}$

c. 165% of what number is 366?

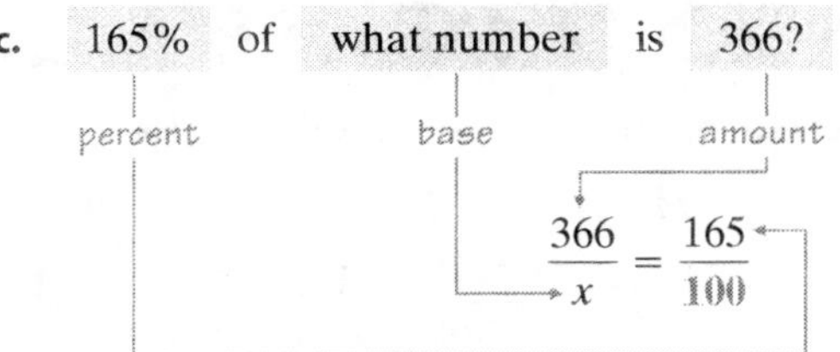

$$\frac{366}{x} = \frac{165}{100}$$

2 Solve percent proportions to find the amount.

Recall the labor union problem from the newspaper example in the introduction to this section. We can write and solve a percent proportion to find the unknown amount.

Self Check 2

What number is 36% of 400? 144

Now Try **Problems 19 and 71**

Teaching Example 2 What number is 28% of 300?

Answer:
84

EXAMPLE 2 What number is 84% of 500?

Strategy We will identify the percent, the base, and the amount and write a percent proportion of the form $\frac{\text{amount}}{\text{base}} = \frac{\text{percent}}{100}$.

WHY Then we can solve the proportion to find the unknown number.

Solution First, we write the percent proportion.

What number is 84% of 500?
(What number → amount; 84% → percent; 500 → base)

$$\frac{x}{500} = \frac{84}{100}$$ This is the proportion to solve.

To make the calculations easier, it is helpful to simplify the ratio $\frac{84}{100}$ at this time.

$$\frac{x}{500} = \frac{21}{25}$$ On the right side, simplify: $\frac{84}{100} = \frac{\overset{1}{\cancel{4}} \cdot 21}{\underset{1}{\cancel{4}} \cdot 25} = \frac{21}{25}$.

To solve a proportion we use the cross products.

$x \cdot 25 = 500 \cdot 21$ Find the cross products: $\frac{x}{500} = \frac{21}{25}$. Then set them equal.

$x \cdot 25 = 10{,}500$ To simplify the right side of the equation, do the multiplication: $500 \cdot 21 = 10{,}500$.

$\frac{x \cdot \overset{1}{\cancel{25}}}{\underset{1}{\cancel{25}}} = \frac{10{,}500}{25}$ To undo the multiplication by 25 and isolate x on the left side, divide both sides of the equation by 25. Then remove the common factor of 25 from the numerator and denominator.

$x = 420$ On the right side, divide 10,500 by 25.

$$\begin{array}{r} 500 \\ \times\ 21 \\ \hline 500 \\ 10\,000 \\ \hline 10{,}500 \end{array} \qquad \begin{array}{r} 420 \\ 25\overline{)10{,}500} \\ -10\,0 \\ \hline 50 \\ -50 \\ \hline 00 \\ -0 \\ \hline 0 \end{array}$$

We have found that 420 is 84% of 500. That is, 420 union members mentioned in the newspaper article voted to accept the new offer.

The Language of Mathematics When we find the value of the variable that makes a percent proportion true, we say that we have **solved the proportion.** In Example 2, we *solved* $\frac{x}{500} = \frac{84}{100}$ to find that the variable x is 420.

EXAMPLE 3 What number is 160% of 15.8?

Strategy We will identify the percent, the base, and the amount and write a percent proportion of the form $\frac{\text{amount}}{\text{base}} = \frac{\text{percent}}{100}$.

WHY Then we can solve the proportion to find the unknown number.

Solution First, we write the percent proportion.

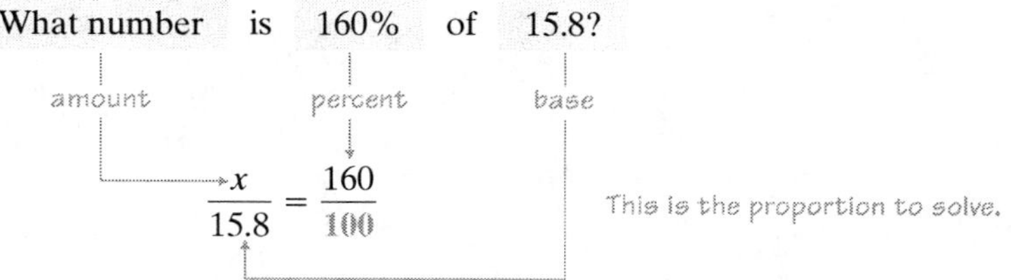

$$\frac{x}{15.8} = \frac{160}{100}$$

To make the calculations easier, it is helpful to simplify the ratio $\frac{160}{100}$ at this time.

$\frac{x}{15.8} = \frac{8}{5}$ On the right side, simplify: $\frac{160}{100} = \frac{8 \cdot \cancel{20}}{5 \cdot \cancel{20}} = \frac{8}{5}$.

$x \cdot 5 = 15.8 \cdot 8$ Find the cross products: $\frac{x}{15.8} = \frac{8}{5}$. Then set them equal.

$x \cdot 5 = 126.4$ To simplify the right side of the equation, do the multiplication: $15.8 \cdot 8 = 126.4$.

$\frac{x \cdot \cancel{5}}{\cancel{5}} = \frac{126.4}{5}$ To undo the multiplication by 5 and isolate x on the left side, divide both sides of the equation by 5. Then remove the common factor of 5 from the numerator and denominator.

$x = 25.28$ On the right side, divide 126.4 by 5.

$$\begin{array}{r} \overset{4\,6}{15.8} \\ \times\ 8 \\ \hline 126.4 \end{array} \qquad \begin{array}{r} 25.28 \\ 5\overline{)126.40} \\ -10 \\ \hline 26 \\ -25 \\ \hline 14 \\ -10 \\ \hline 40 \\ -40 \\ \hline 0 \end{array}$$

Thus, 25.28 is 160% of 15.8.

Self Check 3

What number is 240% of 80.3?

Now Try **Problem 23**

Self Check 3 Answer
192.72

Teaching Example 3 What number is 340% of 28.4?
Answer:
96.56

3 Solve percent proportions to find the percent.

Recall the drinking water problem from the newspaper example in the introduction to this section. We can write and solve a percent proportion to find the unknown percent.

EXAMPLE 4 38 is what percent of 40?

DAILY NEWS
Circulation Monday, March 23 50 cents
Transit Strike Averted!
Labor: 84% of 500-member union votes to accept new offer
Drinking Water 38 of 40 Wells Declared Safe
New Appointees
These six area residents now make up 75% of the State Board of Examiners

Strategy We will identify the percent, the base, and the amount and write a percent proportion of the form $\frac{\text{amount}}{\text{base}} = \frac{\text{percent}}{100}$.

WHY Then we can solve the proportion to find the unknown percent.

Solution First, we write the percent proportion.

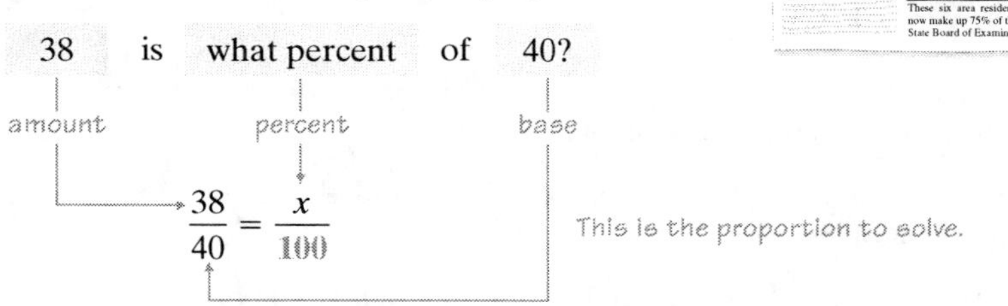

$$\frac{38}{40} = \frac{x}{100}$$

Self Check 4

4 is what percent of 80? 5%

Now Try **Problems 27 and 79**

Teaching Example 4 34 is what percent of 40?
Answer:
85%

To make the calculations easier, it is helpful to simplify the ratio $\frac{38}{40}$ at this time.

$\frac{19}{20} = \frac{x}{100}$	On the left side, simplify: $\frac{38}{40} = \frac{\overset{1}{\not{2}} \cdot 19}{\underset{1}{\not{2}} \cdot 20} = \frac{19}{20}$.
$19 \cdot 100 = 20 \cdot x$	To solve the proportion, find the cross products: $\frac{19}{20} = \frac{x}{100}$. Then set them equal.
$1{,}900 = 20 \cdot x$	To simplify the left side of the equation, do the multiplication: $19 \cdot 100 = 1{,}900$.
$\frac{1{,}900}{20} = \frac{\overset{1}{\not{20}} \cdot x}{\underset{1}{\not{20}}}$	To undo the multiplication by 20 and isolate x on the right side, divide both sides of the equation by 20. Then remove the common factor of 20 from the numerator and denominator.
$95 = x$	On the left side, divide 1,900 by 20.

$$\begin{array}{r} 95 \\ 20\overline{)1{,}900} \\ -1\,80 \\ \hline 100 \\ -100 \\ \hline 0 \end{array}$$

We have found that 38 is 95% of 40. That is, 95% of the wells mentioned in the newspaper article were declared safe.

Self Check 5

9 is what percent of 16? 56.25%

Now Try **Problem 31**

Teaching Example 5 5 is what percent of 16?

Answer:
31.25%

EXAMPLE 5 14 is what percent of 32?

Strategy We will identify the percent, the base, and the amount and write a percent proportion of the form $\frac{\text{amount}}{\text{base}} = \frac{\text{percent}}{100}$.

WHY Then we can solve the proportion to find the unknown percent.

Solution First, we write the percent proportion.

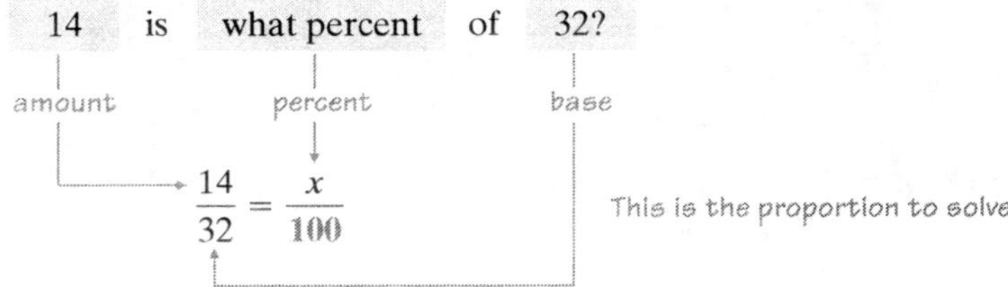

To make the calculations easier, it is helpful to simplify the ratio $\frac{14}{32}$ at this time.

$\frac{7}{16} = \frac{x}{100}$	On the left side, simplify: $\frac{14}{32} = \frac{\overset{1}{\not{2}} \cdot 7}{\underset{1}{\not{2}} \cdot 16} = \frac{7}{16}$.
$7 \cdot 100 = 16 \cdot x$	To solve the proportion, find the cross products: $\frac{7}{16} = \frac{x}{100}$. Then set them equal.
$700 = 16 \cdot x$	To simplify the left side of the equation, do the multiplication: $7 \cdot 100 = 700$.
$\frac{700}{16} = \frac{\overset{1}{\not{16}} \cdot x}{\underset{1}{\not{16}}}$	To undo the multiplication by 16 and isolate x on the right side, divide both sides of the equation by 16. Then remove the common factor of 16 from the numerator and denominator.
$43.75 = x$	On the left side, divide 700 by 16.

$$\begin{array}{r} 43.75 \\ 16\overline{)700.00} \\ -64 \\ \hline 60 \\ -48 \\ \hline 12\,0 \\ -11\,2 \\ \hline 80 \\ -80 \\ \hline 0 \end{array}$$

Thus, 14 is 43.75% of 32.

Self Check 6

What percent of 5 is 8.5? 170%

Now Try **Problem 35**

EXAMPLE 6 What percent of 6 is 7.5?

Strategy We will identify the percent, the base, and the amount and write a percent proportion of the form $\frac{\text{amount}}{\text{base}} = \frac{\text{percent}}{100}$.

WHY Then we can solve the proportion to find the unknown percent.

Solution First, we write the percent proportion.

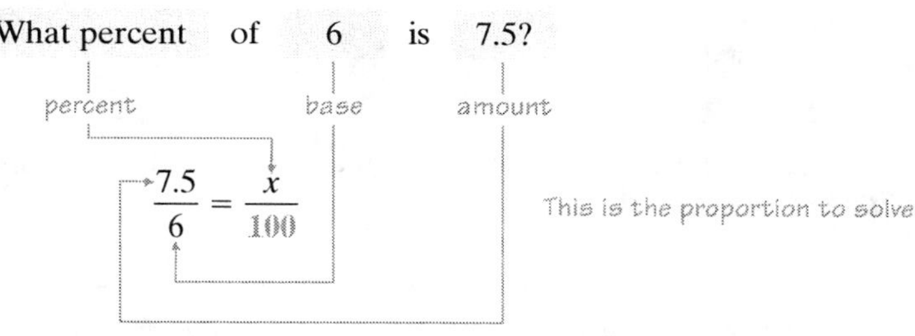

$$\frac{7.5}{6} = \frac{x}{100}$$ This is the proportion to solve.

$7.5 \cdot 100 = 6 \cdot x$ To solve the proportion, find the cross products: $\frac{7.5}{6} = \frac{x}{100}$. Then set them equal.

$750 = 6 \cdot x$ To simplify the left side of the equation, do the multiplication: $7.5 \cdot 100 = 750$.

$\frac{750}{6} = \frac{\overset{1}{\cancel{6}} \cdot x}{\underset{1}{\cancel{6}}}$ To undo the multiplication by 6 and isolate x on the right side, divide both sides of the equation by 6. Then remove the common factor of 6 from the numerator and denominator.

$125 = x$ On the left side, divide 750 by 6.

$$\begin{array}{r} 125 \\ 6\overline{)750} \\ -6 \\ \hline 15 \\ -12 \\ \hline 30 \\ -30 \\ \hline 0 \end{array}$$

Thus, 7.5 is 125% of 6.

Teaching Example 6 What percent of 7 is 9.1?
Answer:
130%

4 Solve percent proportions to find the base.

Recall the State Board of Examiners problem from the newspaper example in the introduction to this section. We can write and solve a percent proportion to find the unknown base.

EXAMPLE 7 6 is 75% of what number?

Strategy We will identify the percent, the base, and the amount and write a percent proportion of the form $\frac{\text{amount}}{\text{base}} = \frac{\text{percent}}{100}$.

WHY Then we can solve the proportion to find the unknown number.

Solution First, we write the percent proportion.

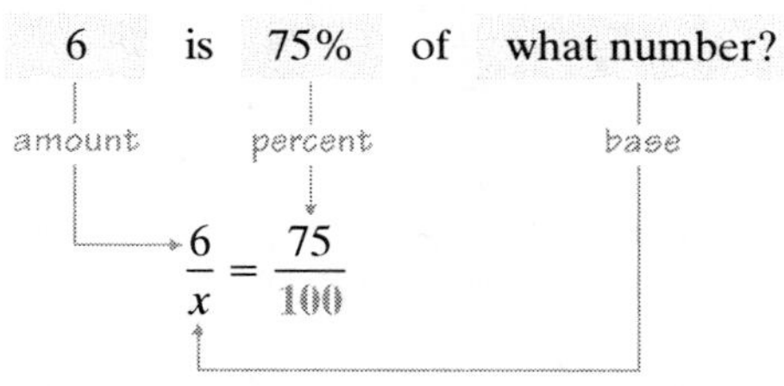

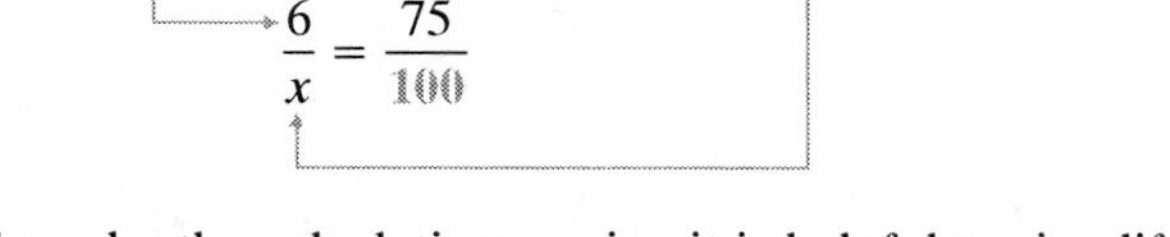

$$\frac{6}{x} = \frac{75}{100}$$

To make the calculations easier, it is helpful to simplify the ratio $\frac{75}{100}$ at this time.

$\frac{6}{x} = \frac{3}{4}$ Simplify: $\frac{75}{100} = \frac{3 \cdot \overset{1}{\cancel{25}}}{4 \cdot \underset{1}{\cancel{25}}} = \frac{3}{4}$.

$6 \cdot 4 = x \cdot 3$ To solve the proportion, find the cross products: $\frac{6}{x} = \frac{3}{4}$. Then set them equal.

$24 = x \cdot 3$ To simplify the left side of the equation, do the multiplication: $6 \cdot 4 = 24$.

Self Check 7

3 is 5% of what number? 60

Now Try **Problem 39**

Teaching Example 7 7 is 35% of what number?
Answer:
20

$$\frac{24}{3} = \frac{x \cdot \overset{1}{\cancel{3}}}{\underset{1}{\cancel{3}}}$$ To undo the multiplication by 3 and isolate x on the right side, divide both sides of the equation by 3. Then remove the common factor of 3 from the numerator and denominator.

$$8 = x$$ On the left side, divide 24 by 3.

Thus, 6 is 75% of 8. That is, there are 8 members on the State Board of Examiners mentioned in the newspaper article.

Self Check 8

150 is $66\frac{2}{3}$% of what number? 225

Now Try **Problems 43 and 83**

Teaching Example 8 22.6 is $33\frac{1}{3}$% of what number?

Answer:
67.8

EXAMPLE 8 31.5 is $33\frac{1}{3}$% of what number?

Strategy We will identify the percent, the base, and the amount and write a percent proportion of the form $\frac{\text{amount}}{\text{base}} = \frac{\text{percent}}{100}$.

WHY Then we can solve the proportion to find the unknown number.

Solution First, we write the percent proportion.

31.5 (amount) is $33\frac{1}{3}$% (percent) of what number? (base)

$$\frac{31.5}{x} = \frac{33\frac{1}{3}}{100}$$

To make the calculations easier, it is helpful to write the mixed number $33\frac{1}{3}$ as the improper fraction $\frac{100}{3}$.

$$\frac{31.5}{x} = \frac{\frac{100}{3}}{100}$$ Write $33\frac{1}{3}$ as $\frac{100}{3}$.

$$31.5 \cdot 100 = x \cdot \frac{100}{3}$$ To solve the proportion, find the cross products: $\frac{31.5}{x} = \frac{\frac{100}{3}}{100}$. Then set them equal.

$$3{,}150 = x \cdot \frac{100}{3}$$ To simplify the left side of the equation, do the multiplication: $31.5 \cdot 100 = 3{,}150$.

$$\frac{3{,}150}{\frac{100}{3}} = \frac{x \cdot \frac{\overset{1}{\cancel{100}}}{\cancel{3}}}{\frac{\cancel{100}}{\underset{1}{\cancel{3}}}}$$ To undo the multiplication by $\frac{100}{3}$ and isolate x on the right side, divide both sides of the equation by $\frac{100}{3}$. Then remove the common factor of $\frac{100}{3}$ from the numerator and denominator.

$$3{,}150 \div \frac{100}{3} = x$$ On the left side, the fraction bar indicates division.

$$\frac{3{,}150}{1} \cdot \frac{3}{100} = x$$ On the left side, write 3,150 as a fraction: $\frac{3{,}150}{1}$. Then use the rule for dividing fractions: Multiply by the reciprocal of $\frac{100}{3}$, which is $\frac{3}{100}$.

$$\frac{9{,}450}{100} = x$$ Multiply the numerators. Multiply the denominators.

$$94.50 = x$$ Divide 9,450 by 100 by moving the understood decimal point in 9,450 two places to the left.

Thus, 31.5 is $33\frac{1}{3}$% of 94.5.

To solve percent application problems, we often have to rewrite the facts of the problem in percent sentence form before we can translate to an equation.

EXAMPLE 9 *Rentals* In an apartment complex, 198 of the units are currently occupied. If this represents an 88% occupancy rate, how many units are in the complex?

Strategy We will carefully read the problem and use the given facts to write them in the form of a percent sentence.

WHY Then we can write and solve a percent proportion to find the unknown number of units in the complex.

Solution An occupancy rate of 88% means that 88% of the units are occupied. Thus, the 198 units that are currently occupied are 88% of some unknown number of units in the complex, and we can write:

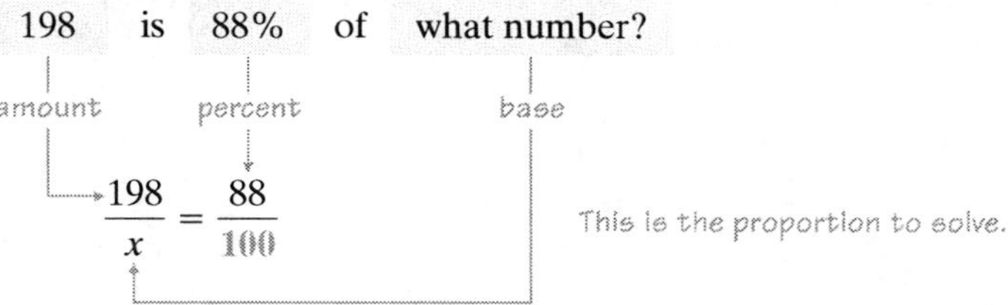

To make the calculations easier, it is helpful to simplify the ratio $\frac{88}{100}$ at this time.

$$\frac{198}{x} = \frac{22}{25}$$ On the right side, simplify: $\frac{88}{100} = \frac{\overset{1}{\cancel{4}} \cdot 22}{\underset{1}{\cancel{4}} \cdot 25} = \frac{22}{25}$.

$$198 \cdot 25 = x \cdot 22$$ Find the cross products. Then set them equal.

$$4{,}950 = x \cdot 22$$ To simplify the left side, do the multiplication: $198 \cdot 25 = 4{,}950$.

$$\frac{4{,}950}{22} = \frac{x \cdot \overset{1}{\cancel{22}}}{\underset{1}{\cancel{22}}}$$ To undo the multiplication by 22 and isolate x on the right side, divide both sides of the equation by 22. Then remove the common factor of 22 from the numerator and denominator.

$$225 = x$$ On the left side, divide 4,950 by 22.

$$\begin{array}{r} 198 \\ \times 25 \\ \hline 990 \\ 3960 \\ \hline 4{,}950 \end{array} \qquad \begin{array}{r} 225 \\ 22\overline{)4{,}950} \\ -44 \\ \hline 55 \\ -44 \\ \hline 110 \\ -110 \\ \hline 0 \end{array}$$

The apartment complex has 225 units, of which 198, or 88%, are occupied.

Self Check 9

CAPACITY OF A GYM A total of 784 people attended a graduation in a high school gymnasium. If this was 98% of capacity, what is the total capacity of the gym? 800 people

Now Try **Problem 81**

Teaching Example 9
CLOSED CLASSES On the first day of classes, 36 of the algebra sections offered by a college mathematics department were closed. If this represented 72% of all the sections of algebra, what is the total number of algebra sections offered that semester?
Answer:
50 classes

5 Read circle graphs.

Percents are used with **circle graphs,** or **pie charts,** as a way of presenting data for comparison. In the figure below, the entire circle represents the total amount of electricity generated in the United States in 2008. The pie-shaped pieces of the graph show the relative sizes of the energy sources used to generate the electricity. For example, we see that the greatest amount of electricity (50%) was generated from coal. Note that if we add the percents from all categories (50% + 3% + 7% + 18% + 20% + 2%), the sum is 100%.

The 100 tick marks equally spaced around the circle serve as a visual aid when constructing a circle graph. For example, to represent hydropower as 7%, a line was drawn from the center of the circle to a tick mark. Then we counted off 7 ticks and drew a second line from the center to that tick to complete the pie-shaped wedge.

Sources of Electricity in the United States, 2008

Other 2%
Nuclear 20%
Coal 50%
Natural gas 18%
Hydropower 7%
Petroleum 3%

Source: Energy Information Administration

Self Check 10

PRESIDENTIAL ELECTIONS Results from the 2004 U.S. presidential election are shown in the circle graph below. Find the number of states won by President Bush.

31 states

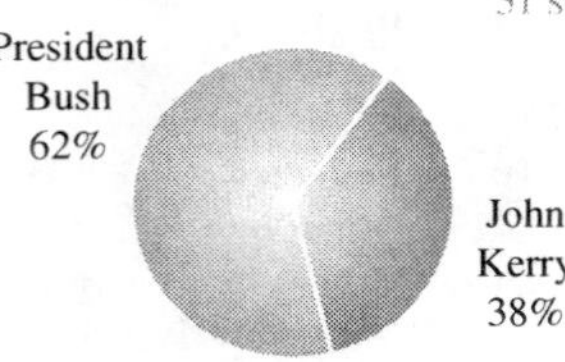

2004 Presidential Election
States won by each candidate

Now Try **Problem 85**

Teaching Example 10
HOUSING At the end of 2007, approximately 110 million housing units in the United States were occupied. Use the information in the following circle graph to find the number of millions of units that were owner occupied in 2007.

2007 Housing Inventory

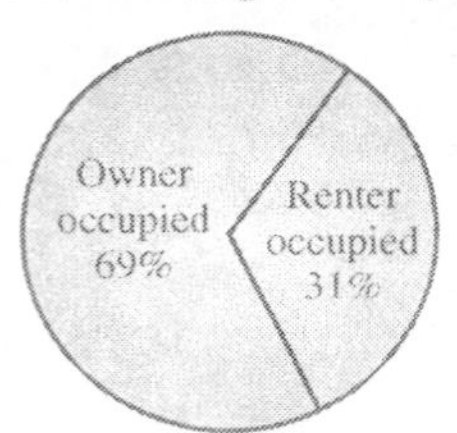

Source: The U.S. Census Bureau

Answer:
75.9 million housing units

EXAMPLE 10 *Presidential Elections*

Results from the 2008 U.S. presidential election are shown in the circle graph to the right. Find the number of states won by Barack Obama.

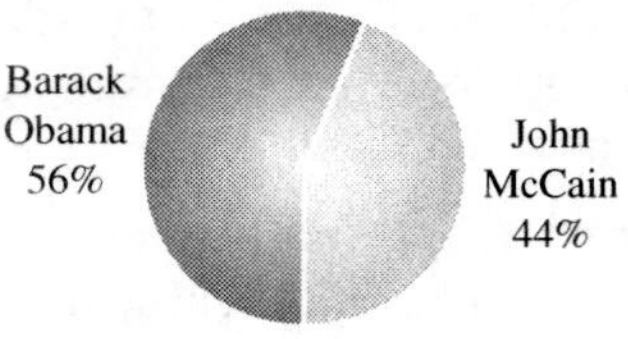

2008 Presidential Election
States won by each candidate

Strategy We will rewrite the facts of the problem in percent sentence form.

WHY Then we can translate the sentence to a percent equation (or percent proportion) to find the number of states won by Barack Obama.

Solution The circle graph shows that Barack Obama won 56% of the 50 states. Thus, the percent is 56% and the base is 50. One way to find the unknown amount is to write and then solve a percent equation.

What number	is	56%	of	50?	
↓	↓	↓	↓	↓	
x	$=$	56%	$\cdot$	50	Translate to a percent equation.

Now we perform the multiplication on the right side of the equation.

$x = 0.56 \cdot 50$ Write 56% as a decimal: 56% = 0.56.

$x = 28$ Do the multiplication.

$$\begin{array}{r} 50 \\ \times 0.56 \\ \hline 3\,00 \\ 25\,00 \\ \hline 28.00 \end{array}$$

Thus, Barack Obama won 28 of the 50 states in the 2008 U.S. presidential election.

Another way to find the unknown amount is to write and then solve a percent proportion.

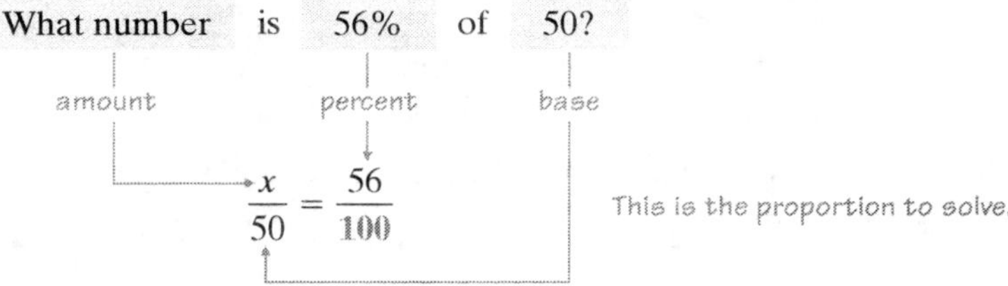

$$\frac{x}{50} = \frac{56}{100}$$ This is the proportion to solve.

To make the calculations easier, it is helpful to simplify the ratio $\frac{56}{100}$ at this time.

$\frac{x}{50} = \frac{14}{25}$ On the right side, simplify: $\frac{56}{100} = \frac{\overset{1}{\cancel{4}} \cdot 14}{\underset{1}{\cancel{4}} \cdot 25} = \frac{14}{25}$.

$x \cdot 25 = 50 \cdot 14$ Find the cross products: $\frac{x}{50} = \frac{14}{25}$. Then set them equal.

$x \cdot 25 = 700$ To simplify the right side, do the multiplication: $50 \cdot 14 = 700$.

$\frac{x \cdot \overset{1}{\cancel{25}}}{\underset{1}{\cancel{25}}} = \frac{700}{25}$ To undo the multiplication by 25 and isolate x on the left side, divide both sides of the equation by 25. Then remove the common factor of 25 from the numerator and denominator.

$x = 28$ On the right side, divide 700 by 25.

$$\begin{array}{r} 50 \\ \times 14 \\ \hline 200 \\ 500 \\ \hline 700 \end{array}$$

$$\begin{array}{r} 28 \\ 25\overline{)700} \\ -50 \\ \hline 200 \\ -200 \\ \hline 0 \end{array}$$

As we would expect, the percent proportion method gives the same answer as the percent equation method. Barack Obama won 28 of the 50 states in the 2008 U.S. presidential election. ■

THINK IT THROUGH *Community College Students*

"When the history of American higher education is updated years from now, the story of our current times will highlight the pivotal role community colleges played in developing human capital and bolstering the nation's educational system."

Community College Survey of Student Engagement, 2007

More than 310,000 students responded to the 2007 Community College Survey of Student Engagement. Some results are shown below. Study each circle graph and then complete its legend.

Enrollment in Community Colleges

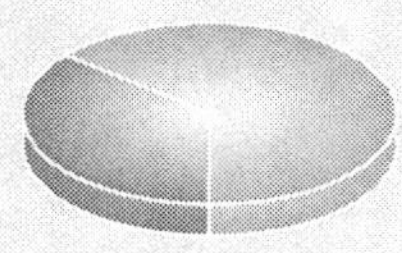

64% are enrolled in college part time.

?

36% are enrolled in college full time

Community College Students Who Work More Than 20 Hours per Week

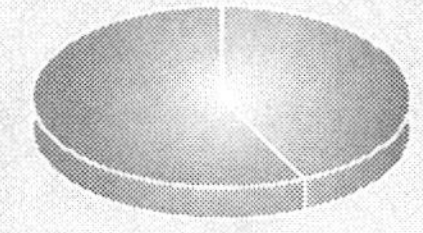

57% of the students work more than 20 hours per week.

?

43% of the students work less than 20 hours per week.

Community College Students Who Discussed Their Grades or Assignments with an Instructor

45% often or very often

45% sometimes

?

10% never

ANSWERS TO SELF CHECKS

1. a. $x = 33\% \cdot 80$ or $\frac{x}{80} = \frac{33}{100}$ **b.** $x \cdot 55 = 6$ or $\frac{6}{55} = \frac{x}{100}$ **c.** $172\% \cdot x = 4$ or $\frac{4}{x} = \frac{172}{100}$ **2.** 144 **3.** 192.72 **4.** 5% **5.** 56.25% **6.** 170% **7.** 60 **8.** 225 **9.** 800 people **10.** 31 states

SECTION 3.8 STUDY SET

VOCABULARY

Fill in the blanks.

1. We call "What number is 15% of 25?" a percent sentence. It translates to the percent equation $x = 15\% \cdot 25$.

2. The key words in a percent sentence translate as follows:

- is translates to an equal symbol =
- of translates to multiplication that is shown with a raised dot ·
- what *number* or what *percent* translates to an unknown number that is represented by a variable.

3. When we find the value of the variable that makes a percent equation true, we say that we have solved the equation.

▶ **4.** In the percent sentence "45 is 90% of 50," 45 is the amount, 90% is the percent, and 50 is the base.

5. The amount is part of the base. The base is the standard of comparison—it represents the whole of some quantity.

6. a. *Amount is to base as percent is to 100:*

$$\frac{\text{amount}}{\text{base}} = \frac{\text{percent}}{100}$$

b. *Part is to whole as percent is to 100:*

$$\frac{\text{part}}{\text{whole}} = \frac{\text{percent}}{100}$$

7. The cross products for the proportion $\frac{24}{x} = \frac{36}{100}$ are $24 \cdot 100$ and $x \cdot 36$.

8. In a circle graph, pie-shaped wedges are used to show the division of a whole quantity into its component parts.

CONCEPTS

9. Fill in the blanks to complete the percent equation (formula):

Amount = percent · base

or

Part = percent · whole

10. a. Without doing the calculation, tell whether 12% of 55 is more than 55 or less than 55. less

b. Without doing the calculation, tell whether 120% of 55 is more than 55 or less than 55. more

11. CANDY SALES The circle graph shows the percent of the total candy sales for each of four holiday seasons in 2008. What is the sum of all the percents? 100%

Percent of Total Candy Sales, 2008

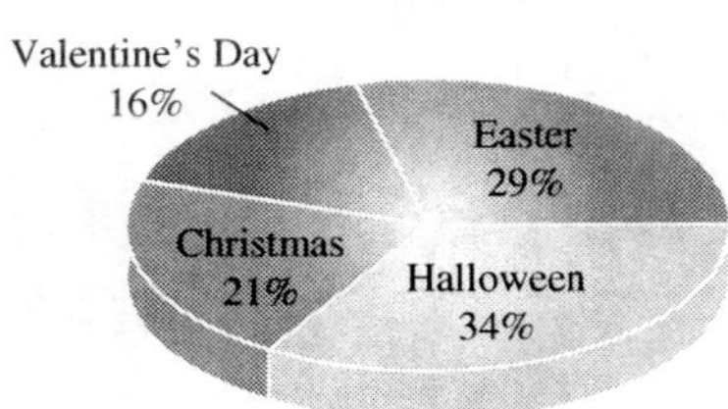

Source: National Confectioners Association, Annual Industry Review, 2009

12. SMARTPHONES The circle graph shows the percent U.S. market share for the leading smartphone companies. What is the sum of all the percents? 100%

U.S. Smartphone Marketshare

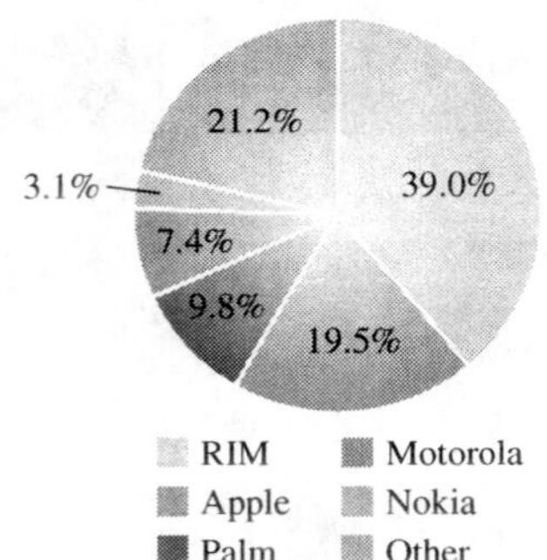

NOTATION

13. When computing with percents, we must change the percent to a decimal or a fraction. Change each percent to a decimal.

a. 12% 0.12

b. 5.6% 0.056

c. 125% 1.25

d. $\frac{1}{4}\%$ 0.0025

14. When computing with percents, we must change the percent to a decimal or a fraction. Change each percent to a fraction.

a. $33\frac{1}{3}\%$ $\frac{1}{3}$

b. $66\frac{2}{3}\%$ $\frac{2}{3}$

c. $16\frac{2}{3}\%$ $\frac{1}{6}$

d. $83\frac{1}{3}\%$ $\frac{5}{6}$

GUIDED PRACTICE

Translate each percent sentence to a percent equation or percent proportion. Do not solve. See Example 1.

15. a. What number is 7% of 16? $x = 7\% \cdot 16$ $\frac{x}{16} = \frac{7}{100}$

b. 125 is what percent of 800? $125 = x \cdot 800$ $\frac{125}{800} = \frac{x}{100}$

c. 1 is 94% of what number? $1 = 94\% \cdot x$ $\frac{1}{x} = \frac{94}{100}$

16. a. What number is 28% of 372? $x = 28\% \cdot 372$ $\frac{x}{372} = \frac{28}{100}$

b. 9 is what percent of 21? $9 = x \cdot 21$ $\frac{9}{21} = \frac{x}{100}$

c. 4 is 17% of what number? $4 = 17\% \cdot x$ $\frac{4}{x} = \frac{17}{100}$

17. a. 5.4% of 99 is what number? $5.4\% \cdot 99 = x$ $\frac{x}{99} = \frac{5.4}{100}$

b. 75.1% of what number is 15? $75.1\% \cdot x = 15$ $\frac{15}{x} = \frac{75.1}{100}$

c. What percent of 33.8 is 3.8? $x \cdot 33.8 = 3.8$ $\frac{3.8}{33.8} = \frac{x}{100}$

18. a. 1.5% of 3 is what number? $1.5\% \cdot 3 = x$ $\frac{x}{3} = \frac{1.5}{100}$

b. 49.2% of what number is 100? $49.2\% \cdot x = 100$ $\frac{100}{x} = \frac{49.2}{100}$

c. What percent of 100.4 is 50.2? $x \cdot 100.4 = 50.2$ $\frac{50.2}{100.4} = \frac{x}{100}$

Translate to a percent equation or percent proportion and then solve to find the unknown number. See Example 2.

19. What is 34% of 200? 68

20. What is 48% of 600? 288

21. What is 88% of 150? 132

22. What number is 52% of 350? 182

Translate to a percent equation or percent proportion and then solve to find the unknown number. See Example 3.

23. What number is 224% of 7.9? 17.696

24. What number is 197% of 6.3? 12.411

25. What number is 105% of 23.2? 24.36

26. What number is 228% of 34.5? 78.66

Translate to a percent equation or percent proportion and then solve to find the unknown number. See Example 4.

27. 8 is what percent of 32? 25%

28. 9 is what percent of 18? 50%

29. 51 is what percent of 60? 85%

30. 52 is what percent of 80? 65%

Translate to a percent equation or percent proportion and then solve to find the unknown number. See Example 5.

31. 5 is what percent of 8? 62.5%

32. 7 is what percent of 8? 87.5%

33. 7 is what percent of 16? 43.75%

34. 11 is what percent of 16? 68.75%

Translate to a percent equation or percent proportion and then solve to find the unknown number. See Example 6.

35. What percent of 60 is 66? 110%

36. What percent of 50 is 56? 112%

37. What percent of 24 is 84? 350%

38. What percent of 14 is 63? 450%

Translate to a percent equation or percent proportion and then solve to find the unknown number. See Example 7.

39. 9 is 30% of what number? 30

40. 8 is 40% of what number? 20

41. 36 is 24% of what number? 150

42. 24 is 16% of what number? 200

Translate to a percent equation or percent proportion and then solve to find the unknown number. See Example 8.

43. 19.2 is $33\frac{1}{3}\%$ of what number? 57.6

44. 32.8 is $33\frac{1}{3}\%$ of what number? 98.4

45. 48.4 is $66\frac{2}{3}\%$ of what number? 72.6

46. 56.2 is $16\frac{2}{3}\%$ of what number? 337.2

TRY IT YOURSELF

Translate to a percent equation or percent proportion and then solve to find the unknown number.

47. What percent of 40 is 0.5? 1.25%

48. What percent of 15 is 0.3? 2%

49. 7.8 is 12% of what number? 65

50. 39.6 is 44% of what number? 90

51. $33\frac{1}{3}\%$ of what number is 33? 99

52. $66\frac{2}{3}\%$ of what number is 28? 42

53. What number is 36% of 250? 90

54. What number is 82% of 300? 246

55. 16 is what percent of 20? 80%

56. 13 is what percent of 25? 52%

57. What number is 0.8% of 12? 0.096

58. What number is 5.6% of 40? 2.24

59. 3.3 is 7.5% of what number? 44

60. 8.4 is 20% of what number? 42

61. What percent of 0.05 is 1.25? 2,500%

62. What percent of 0.06 is 2.46? 4,100%

63. 102% of 105 is what number? 107.1

64. 210% of 66 is what number? 138.6

65. $9\frac{1}{2}\%$ of what number is 5.7? 60

66. $\frac{1}{2}\%$ of what number is 5,000? 1,000,000

67. What percent of 8,000 is 2,500? 31.25%

68. What percent of 3,200 is 1,400? 43.75%

69. Find $7\frac{1}{4}\%$ of 600. 43.5

70. Find $1\frac{3}{4}\%$ of 800. 14

APPLICATIONS

71. DOWNLOADING The message on the computer monitor screen shown below indicates that 24% of the 50K bytes of information that the user has decided to view have been downloaded to her computer at that time. Find the number of bytes of information that have been downloaded. (50K stands for 50,000.) 12K bytes = 12,000 bytes

72. LUMBER The rate of tree growth for walnut trees is about 3% per year. If a walnut tree has 400 board feet of lumber that can be cut from it, how many more board feet will it produce in a year? (*Source:* Iowa Department of Natural Resources) 12 board ft

73. REBATES A telephone company offered its customers a rebate of 20% of the cost of all long-distance calls made in the month of July. One customer's long-distance calls for July are shown below.

a. Find the total amount of the customer's long-distance charges for July. $20.75

b. How much will this customer receive in the form of a rebate for these calls? $4.15

Date	Time	Place called	Min.	Amount
Jul 4	3:48 P.M.	Denver	47	$3.80
Jul 9	12:00 P.M.	Detroit	68	$7.50
Jul 20	8:59 A.M.	San Diego	70	$9.45
July Totals			185	?

74. PRICE GUARANTEES To assure its customers of low prices, the Home Club offers a "10% Plus" guarantee. If the customer finds the same item selling for less somewhere else, he or she receives the difference in price, plus 10% of the difference. A woman bought miniblinds at the Home Club for $120 but later saw the same blinds on sale for $98 at another store.

a. What is the difference in the prices of the miniblinds? $22

b. What is 10% of the difference in price? $2.20

c. How much money can the woman expect to receive if she takes advantage of the "10% Plus" guarantee from the Home Club? $24.20

75. ENLARGEMENTS The enlarge feature on a copier is set at 180%, and a 1.5-inch wide picture is to be copied. What will be the width of the enlarged picture? 2.7 in.

76. COPY MACHINES The reduce feature on a copier is set at 98%, and a 2-inch wide picture is to be copied. What will be the width of the reduced picture? 1.96 in.

77. DRIVER'S LICENSE On the written part of his driving test, a man answered 28 out of 40 questions correctly. If 70% correct is passing, did he pass the test? yes

78. HOUSING A general budget rule of thumb is that your rent or mortgage payment should be less than 30% of your income. Together, a couple earns $4,500 per month and they pay $1,260 in rent. Are they following the budget rule of thumb for housing? yes (28%)

79. INSURANCE The cost to repair a car after a collision was $4,000. The automobile insurance policy paid the entire bill except for a $200 deductible, which the driver paid. What percent of the cost did he pay? 5%

80. FLOOR SPACE A house has 1,200 square feet on the first floor and 800 square feet on the second floor.

a. What is the total square footage of the house? 2,000 sq ft

b. What percent of the square footage of the house is on the first floor? 60%

81. CHILD CARE After the first day of registration, 84 children had been enrolled in a new day care center. That represented 70% of the available slots. What was the maximum number of children the center could enroll? 120

82. RACING PROGRAMS One month before a stock car race, the sale of ads for the official race program was slow. Only 12 pages, or 60% of the available pages, had been sold. What was the total number of pages devoted to advertising in the program? 20

83. WATER POLLUTION A 2007 study found that about 4,500 kilometers, or $33\frac{1}{3}\%$ of China's Yellow River and its tributaries were not fit for any use. What is the combined length of the river and its tributaries? (*Source:* Discovermagazine.com) 13,500 km

84. FINANCIAL AID The National Postsecondary Student Aid Study found that in 2008 about 14 million, or $66\frac{2}{3}\%$, of the nation's undergraduate students received some type of financial aid. How many undergraduate students were there in 2008? 21 million

85. GOVERNMENT SPENDING The circle graph below shows the breakdown of federal spending for fiscal year 2007. If the total spending was approximately $2,700 billion, how many dollars were spent on Social Security, Medicare, and other retirement programs? $1,026 billion

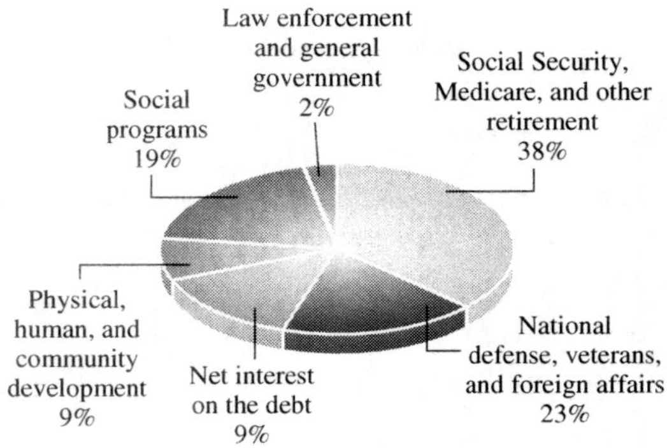

Source: 2008 Federal Income Tax Form 1040

86. WASTE The circle graph below shows the types of trash U.S. residents, businesses, and institutions generated in 2007. If the total amount of trash produced that year was about 254 million tons, how many million tons of yard trimmings was there? 35.512 million tons

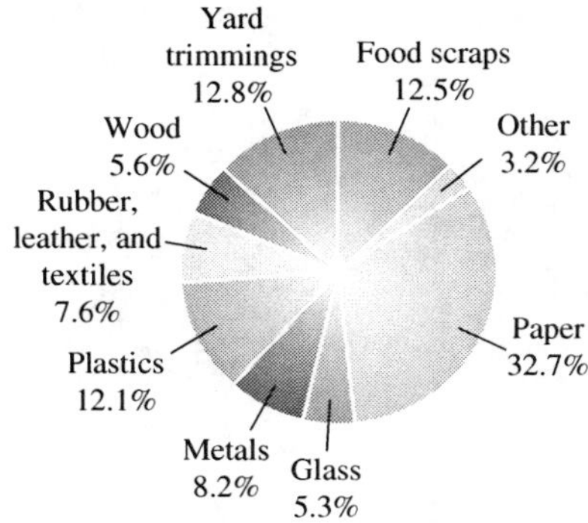

Source: Environmental Protection Agency

87. PRODUCT PROMOTION To promote sales, a free 6-ounce bottle of shampoo is packaged with every large bottle. Use the information on the package to find how many ounces of shampoo the large bottle contains. 24 oz

88. NUTRITION FACTS The nutrition label on a package of corn chips is shown.

a. How many milligrams of sodium are in one serving of chips? 240 mg

b. According to the label, what percent of the daily value of sodium is this? 12%

c. What daily value of sodium intake is considered healthy? 2,000 mg

Nutrition Facts
Serving Size: 1 oz. (28g/About 29 chips)
Servings Per Container: About 11

Amount Per Serving
Calories 160 Calories from Fat 90

	% Daily Value
Total fat 10g	**15%**
Saturated fat 1.5 g	**7%**
Cholesterol 0mg	**0%**
Sodium 240mg	**12%**
Total carbohydrate 15g	**5%**
Dietary fiber 1g	**4%**
Sugars less than 1g	
Protein 2g	

89. MIXTURES Complete the table to find the number of gallons of sulfuric acid in each of two storage tanks.

	Gallons of solution in tank	% Sulfuric acid	Gallons of sulfuric acid in tank
Tank 1	60	50%	30
Tank 2	40	30%	12

90. THE ALPHABET What percent of the English alphabet do the vowels a, e, i, o, and u make up? (Round to the nearest 1 percent.) 19%

91. TIPS In August of 2006, a customer left Applebee's employee Cindy Kienow of Hutchinson, Kansas, a \$10,000 tip for a bill that was approximately \$25. What percent tip is this? (*Source:* cbsnews.com) 40,000%

92. ELECTIONS In Los Angeles City Council races, if no candidate receives more than 50% of the vote, a runoff election is held between the first- and second-place finishers.

a. How many total votes were cast? 17,177

b. Determine whether there must be a runoff election for District 10. yes

City council	District 10
Nate Holden	8,501
Madison T. Shockley	3,614
Scott Suh	2,630
Marsha Brown	2,432

Use a circle graph to illustrate the given data. A circle divided into 100 sections is provided to help in the graphing process.

93. ENERGY Draw a circle graph to show what percent of the total U.S. energy produced in 2007 was provided by each source.

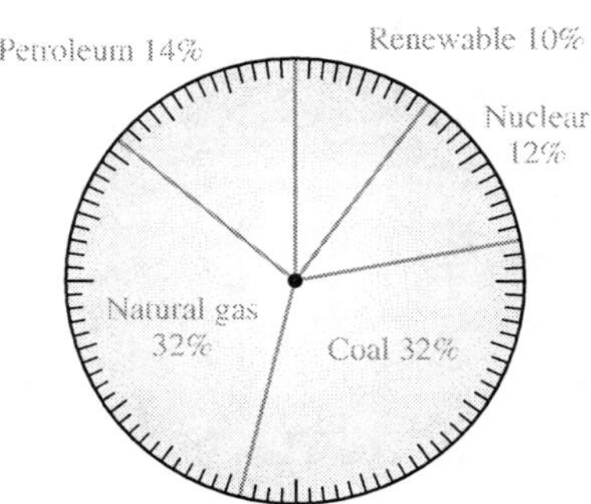

Renewable	10%
Nuclear	12%
Coal	32%
Natural gas	32%
Petroleum	14%

Source: Energy Information Administration

94. GREENHOUSE GASSES Draw a circle graph to show what percent of the total U.S. greenhouse gas emissions in 2007 came from each economic sector.

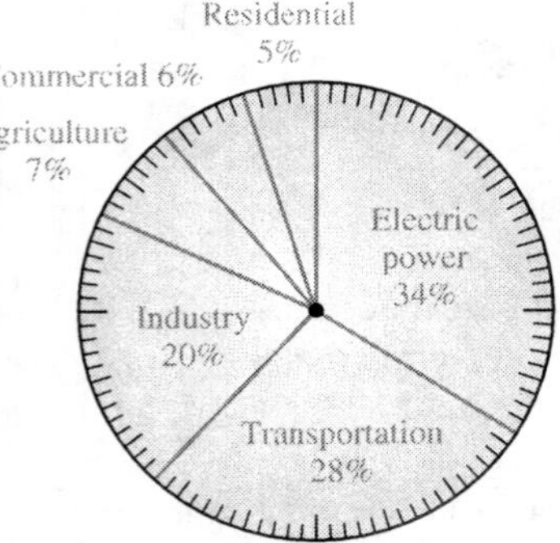

Electric power	34%
Transportation	28%
Industry	20%
Agriculture	7%
Commercial	6%
Residential	5%

Source: Environmental Protection Agency, *Time Magazine,* June 8, 2009

95. GOVERNMENT INCOME Complete the following table by finding what percent of total federal government income in 2007 each source provided. Then draw a circle graph for the data.

Total Income, Fiscal Year 2007: $2,600 Billion

Source of income	Amount	Percent of total
Social Security, Medicare, unemployment taxes	$832 billion	32%
Personal income taxes	$1,118 billion	43%
Corporate income taxes	$338 billion	13%
Excise, estate, customs taxes	$156 billion	6%
Borrowing to cover deficit	$156 billion	6%

Source: 2008 Federal Income Tax Form

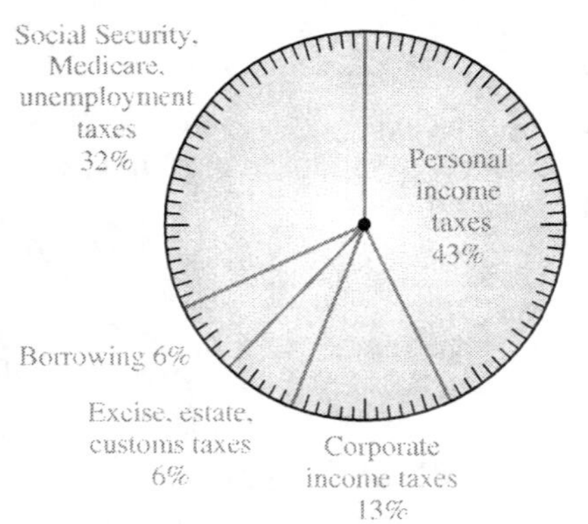

96. WATER USAGE The per-person indoor water use in the typical single family home is about 70 gallons per day. Complete the following table. Then draw a circle graph for the data.

Use	Gallons per person per day	Percent of total daily use
Showers	11.9	17%
Clothes washer	15.4	22%
Dishwasher	0.7	1%
Toilets	18.9	27%
Baths	1.4	2%
Leaks	9.8	14%
Faucets	10.5	15%
Other	1.4	2%

Source: American Water Works Association

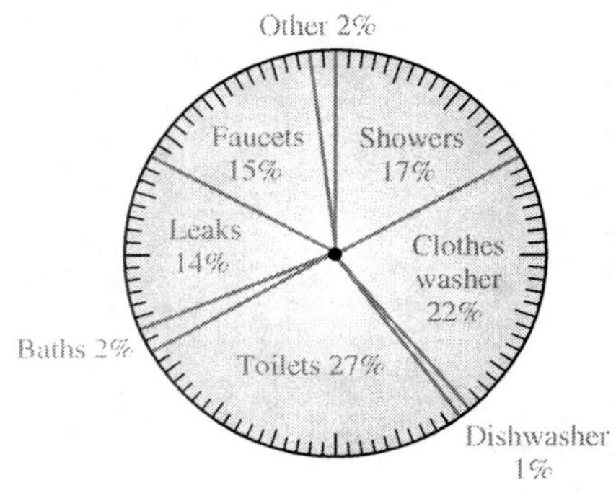

WRITING

97. Write a real-life situation that can be described by "9 is what percent of 20?"

98. Write a real-life situation that can be translated to $15 = 25\% \cdot x$.

99. Explain why 150% of a number is more than the number.

100. Explain why each of the following problems is easy to solve.

a. What is 9% of 100?

b. 16 is 100% of what number?

c. 27 is what percent of 27?

101. When solving percent problems, when is it best to write a given percent as a fraction instead of as a decimal?

102. Explain how to identify the amount, the percent, and the base in a percent problem.

REVIEW

103. Add: 2.78 + 6 + 9.09 + 0.3 18.17

104. Evaluate: $\sqrt{64} + 3\sqrt{9}$ 17

105. On the number line, which is closer to 5: the number 4.9 or the number 5.001? 5.001

106. Multiply: 34.5464 · 1,000 34,546.4

107. Evaluate: $(0.2)^3$ 0.008

108. Evaluate the formula $d = 4t$ for $t = 25$. 100

SECTION 3.9

Applications of Percent

Objectives

1. Calculate sales taxes, total cost, and tax rates.
2. Calculate commissions and commission rates.
3. Find the percent of increase or decrease.
4. Calculate the amount of discount, the sale price and the discount rate.

In this section, we discuss applications of percent. Three of them (taxes, commissions, and discounts) are directly related to purchasing. A solid understanding of these concepts will make you a better shopper and consumer. The fourth uses percent to describe increases or decreases of such things as population and unemployment.

1 Calculate sales taxes, total cost, and tax rates.

The department store sales receipt shown below gives a detailed account of what items were purchased, how many of each were purchased, and the price of each item.

Bradshaw's

Department Store #612

4	@	1.05	GIFTS	$ 4.20
1	@	1.39	BATTERIES	$ 1.39
1	@	24.85	TOASTER	$24.85
3	@	2.25	SOCKS	$ 6.75
2	@	9.58	PILLOWS	$19.16
SUBTOTAL				$56.35
SALES TAX @ 5.00%				$ 2.82
TOTAL				$59.17

The purchase price of the items bought

The sales tax on the items purchased

The total cost

The sales tax rate

The receipt shows that the $56.35 purchase price (labeled *subtotal*) was taxed at a rate of 5%. Sales tax of $2.82 was charged.

This example illustrates the following sales tax formula. Notice that the formula is based on the percent equation.

Finding the Sales Tax

The sales tax on an item is a percent of the purchase price of the item.

Sales tax = sales tax rate · purchase price
↑ amount = ↑ percent · ↑ base

Sales tax rates are usually expressed as a percent and, when necessary, sales tax dollar amounts are rounded to the nearest cent.

Self Check 1

SALES TAX What would the sales tax be if the \$56.35 purchase were made in a state that has a 6.25% state sales tax? \$3.52

Now Try **Problem 13**

Teaching Example 1
SALES TAX Find the sales tax on a purchase of \$64.50 if the sales tax rate is 7%.
Answer:
\$4.52

EXAMPLE 1 ***Sales Tax*** Find the sales tax on a purchase of \$56.35 if the sales tax rate is 5%. (This is the purchase on the sales receipt shown on the previous page.)

Strategy We will identify the sales tax rate and the purchase price.

WHY Then we can use the sales tax formula to find the unknown sales tax.

Solution The sales tax rate is 5% and the purchase price is \$56.35.

Sales tax = **sales tax rate** · **purchase price** This is the sales tax formula.
= 5% · \$56.35 Substitute 5% for the sales tax rate and \$56.35 for the purchase price.
= 0.05 · \$56.35 Write 5% as a decimal: 5% = 0.05.
= \$2.8175 Do the multiplication.

$$\begin{array}{r} \overset{3\,1\,\,2}{56.35} \\ \times 0.05 \\ \hline 2.8175 \end{array}$$

The rounding digit in the hundredths column is 1.
= \$2.8175 Prepare to round the sales tax to the nearest cent (hundredth) by identifying the rounding digit and test digit.
The test digit is 7.
≈ \$2.82 Since the test digit is 5 or greater, round up.

The sales tax on the \$56.35 purchase is \$2.82. The sales receipt shown on the previous page is correct.

Success Tip It is helpful to see the sales tax problem in Example 1 as a type of percent problem.

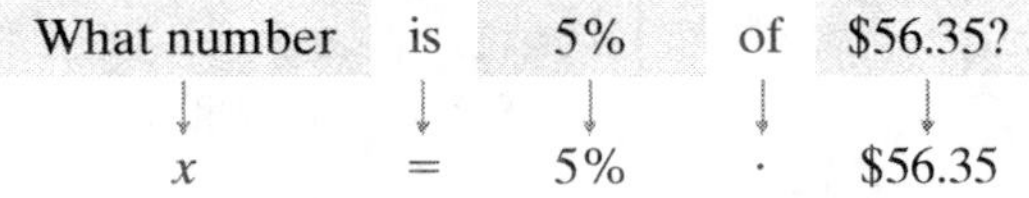

Look at the department store sales receipt once again. Note that the sales tax was added to the purchase price to get the total cost. This example illustrates the following formula for total cost.

Finding the Total Cost

The total cost of an item is the sum of its purchase price and the sales tax on the item.

Total cost = purchase price + sales tax

EXAMPLE 2 *Total Cost* Find the total cost of the child's car seat shown on the right if the sales tax rate is 7.2%.

Strategy First, we will find the sales tax on the child's car seat.

WHY Then we can add the purchase price and the sales tax to find the total of the car seat.

Solution The sales tax rate is 7.2% and the purchase price is $249.50.

Sales tax = sales tax rate · purchase price — This is the sales tax formula.

= 7.2% · $249.50 — Substitute 7.2% for the sales tax rate and $249.50 for the purchase price.

= 0.072 · $249.50 — Write 7.2% as a decimal: 7.2% = 0.072.

= $17.964 — Do the multiplication.

$$\begin{array}{r} 249.50 \\ \times\ 0.072 \\ \hline 49900 \\ 1746500 \\ \hline 17.96400 \end{array}$$

The rounding digit in the hundredths column is 6.

= $17.964 — Prepare to round the sales tax to the nearest cent (hundredth) by identifying the rounding digit and test digit.

The test digit is 4.

≈ $17.96 — Since the test digit is less than 5, round down.

Thus, the sales tax on the $249.50 purchase is $17.96. The total cost of the car seat is the sum of its purchase price and the sales tax.

Total cost = purchase price + sales tax — This is the formula for the total cost.

= $249.50 + $17.96 — Substitute $249.50 for the purchase price and $17.96 for the sales tax.

= $267.46 — Do the addition.

$$\begin{array}{r} \overset{1}{2}49.50 \\ +\ 17.96 \\ \hline 267.46 \end{array}$$

Self Check 2

TOTAL COST Find the total cost of a $179.95 baby stroller if the sales tax rate on the purchase is 3.2%. $185.71

Now Try **Problem 17**

Teaching Example 2
TOTAL COST Find the total cost of a $619.50 refrigerator if the sales tax rate on the purchase is 2.8%.
Answer:
$636.85

In addition to sales tax, we pay many other taxes in our daily lives. Income tax, gasoline tax, and Social Security tax are just a few.

EXAMPLE 3 *Withholding Tax* A waitress found that $11.04 was deducted from her weekly gross earnings of $240 for federal income tax. What withholding tax rate was used?

Strategy We will carefully read the problem and use the given facts to write them in the form of a percent sentence.

WHY Then we can translate the sentence into a percent equation (or percent proportion) and solve it to find the unknown withholding tax rate.

Solution There are two methods that can be used to solve this problem.

The percent equation method: Since the withholding tax of $11.04 is some unknown percent of her weekly gross earnings of $240, the percent sentence is:

$11.04	is	what percent	of	$240?
11.04	=	x	·	240

This is the percent equation to solve.

Self Check 3

INHERITANCE TAX A tax of $5,250 was paid on an inheritance of $15,000. What was the inheritance tax rate? 35%

Now Try **Problem 21**

Teaching Example 3
CITY INCOME TAX For the year 2008, a resident of Detroit, Michigan, paid $550 in city income tax on taxable earnings of $22,000. What is the Detroit city income tax rate?
Answer:
2.5%

$$\frac{11.04}{240} = \frac{x \cdot 240}{240}$$ To isolate x on the right side of the equation, divide both sides by 240.

$$0.046 = \frac{x \cdot \overset{1}{\cancel{240}}}{\underset{1}{\cancel{240}}}$$ To simplify the fraction on the right side of the equation, remove the common factor of 240 from the numerator and denominator. On the left side, divide 11.04 by 240.

$$\begin{array}{r} 0.046 \\ 240\overline{)11.0400} \\ -\ \ 0 \\ \hline 11\ 04 \\ -9\ 60 \\ \hline 1\ 440 \\ -1\ 440 \\ \hline 0 \end{array}$$

$$0.046 = x$$

$$0\,04.6\% = x$$ To write the decimal 0.046 as a percent, multiply it by 100 by moving the decimal point two places to the right, and then insert a % symbol.

$$4.6\% = x$$

The withholding tax rate was 4.6%.

The percent proportion method: Since the withholding tax of $11.04 is some unknown percent of her weekly gross earnings of $240, the percent sentence is:

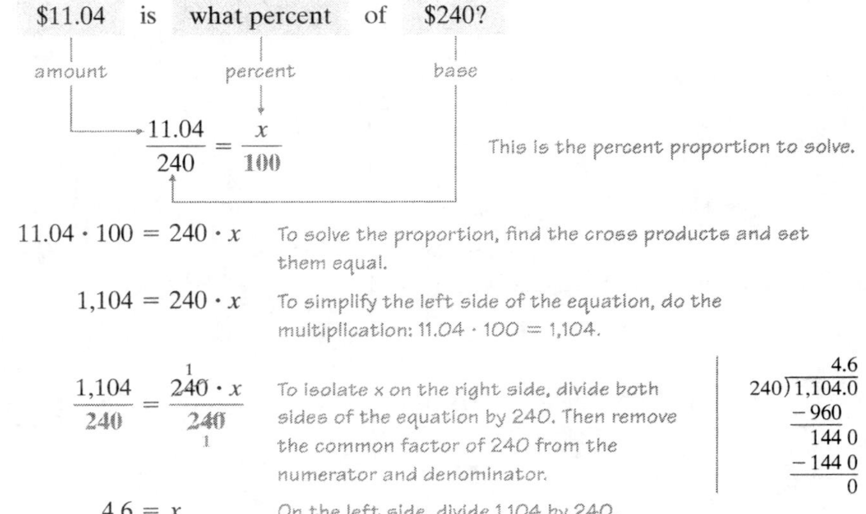

$$\frac{11.04}{240} = \frac{x}{100}$$ This is the percent proportion to solve.

$$11.04 \cdot 100 = 240 \cdot x$$ To solve the proportion, find the cross products and set them equal.

$$1{,}104 = 240 \cdot x$$ To simplify the left side of the equation, do the multiplication: 11.04 · 100 = 1,104.

$$\frac{1{,}104}{240} = \frac{\overset{1}{\cancel{240}} \cdot x}{\underset{1}{\cancel{240}}}$$ To isolate x on the right side, divide both sides of the equation by 240. Then remove the common factor of 240 from the numerator and denominator.

$$\begin{array}{r} 4.6 \\ 240\overline{)1{,}104.0} \\ -960 \\ \hline 144\ 0 \\ -144\ 0 \\ \hline 0 \end{array}$$

$$4.6 = x$$ On the left side, divide 1,104 by 240.

The withholding tax rate was 4.6%.

2 Calculate commissions and commission rates.

Instead of working for a salary or getting paid at an hourly rate, many salespeople are paid on **commission.** They earn a certain percent of the total dollar amount of the goods or services that they sell. The following formula to calculate a commission is based on the percent equation.

Finding the Commission

The amount of commission paid is a percent of the total dollar sales of goods or services.

$$\text{Commission} = \text{commission rate} \cdot \text{sales}$$

$$\text{amount} = \text{percent} \cdot \text{base}$$

EXAMPLE 4 *Appliance Sales* The commission rate for a salesperson at an appliance store is 16.5%. Find his commission from the sale of a refrigerator that costs $500.

Strategy We will identify the commission rate and the dollar amount of the sale.

WHY Then we can use the commission formula to find the unknown amount of the commission.

Solution The commission rate is 16.5% and the dollar amount of the sale is $500.

Commission = commission rate · sales This is the commission formula.

= 16.5% · $500 Substitute 16.5% for the commission rate and $500 for the sales.

= 0.165 · $500 Write 16.5% as a decimal: 16.5% = 0.165.

= $82.50 Do the multiplication.

$$\begin{array}{r} \overset{3\,2}{0.165} \\ \times\ 500 \\ \hline 82.500 \end{array}$$

The commission earned on the sale of the $500 refrigerator is $82.50.

Self Check 4

SELLING INSURANCE An insurance salesperson receives a 4.1% commission on each $120 premium paid by a client. What is the amount of the commission on this premium? $4.92

Now Try **Problem 25**

Teaching Example 4
SELLING REAL ESTATE A real estate agent earns a 3% commission on all sales. Find her commission if she sells a house for the listing price of $212,000.

Answer: $6,360

EXAMPLE 5 *Jewelry Sales* A jewelry salesperson earned a commission of $448 for selling a diamond ring priced at $5,600. Find the commission rate.

Strategy We will identify the commission and the dollar amount of the sale.

WHY Then we can use the commission formula to find the unknown commission rate.

Solution The commission is $448 and the dollar amount of the sale is $5,600.

Commission = commission rate · sales This is the commission formula.

$448 = x · $5,600 Substitute $448 for the commission and $5,600 for the sales. Let x represent the unknown commission rate.

$$\frac{448}{5{,}600} = \frac{x \cdot 5{,}600}{5{,}600}$$ We can drop the dollar sign. To undo the multiplication by 5,600 and isolate x on the right side of the equation, divide both sides by 5,600.

$$0.08 = \frac{x \cdot \overset{1}{\cancel{5{,}600}}}{\underset{1}{\cancel{5{,}600}}}$$ On the right side, remove the common factor of 5,600 from the numerator and denominator. On the left side, divide 448 by 5,600.

$$\begin{array}{r} 0.08 \\ 5{,}600\overline{)448.00} \\ -\,448\ 00 \\ \hline 0 \end{array}$$

$008\% = x$ To write the decimal 0.08 as a percent, multiply it by 100 by moving the decimal point two places to the right, and then insert a % symbol.

$8\% = x$

The commission rate paid the salesperson on the sale of the diamond ring was 8%.

Self Check 5

SELLING ELECTRONICS If the commission on a $430 digital camcorder is $21.50, what is the commission rate? 5%

Now Try **Problem 29**

Teaching Example 5
JEWELRY SALES A jewelry salesperson earned a commission of $78 for selling a pearl necklace priced at $1,300. Find the commission rate.

Answer: 6%

3 Find the percent of increase or decrease.

Percents can be used to describe how a quantity has changed. For example, consider the table on the right, which shows the number of television channels that the average U.S. home received in 2000 and 2007.

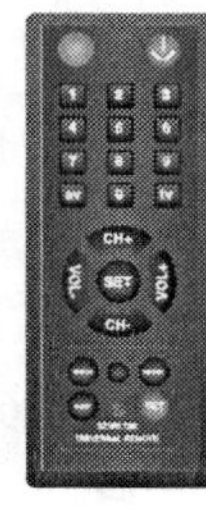

Year	Number of television channels that the average U.S. home received
2000	61
2007	119

Source: The Nielsen Company

From the table, we see that the number of television channels received increased considerably from 2000 to 2007. To describe this increase using a percent, we first subtract to find the **amount of increase.**

$119 - 61 = 58$ Subtract the number of TV channels received in 2000 from the number received in 2007.

Thus, the number of channels received increased by 58 from 2000 to 2007.

Next, we find what percent of the *original* 61 channels received in 2000 that the 58 channel increase represents. To do this, we translate the problem into a percent equation (or percent proportion) and solve it.

The percent equation method:

58	is	what percent	of	61?
↓	↓	↓	↓	↓
58	=	x	·	61

Translate.

$58 = x \cdot 61$ This is the equation to solve.

$\frac{58}{61} = \frac{x \cdot \overset{1}{\cancel{61}}}{\underset{1}{\cancel{61}}}$ To isolate x on the right side, divide both sides of the equation by 61. Then remove the common factor of 61 from the numerator and denominator.

$\frac{58}{61} = x$

$0.9508 \approx x$ On the left side of the equation, divide 58 by 61. The division does not terminate.

$95.08\% \approx x$ To write the decimal 0.9508 as a percent, multiply it by 100 by moving the decimal point two places to the right, and then insert a % symbol.

$95\% \approx x$ Round to the nearest one percent.

$$
\begin{array}{r}
0.9508 \\
61\overline{)58.0000} \\
-54\ 9 \\
\hline
3\ 10 \\
-3\ 05 \\
\hline
50 \\
-0 \\
\hline
500 \\
-488 \\
\hline
12
\end{array}
$$

The percent proportion method:

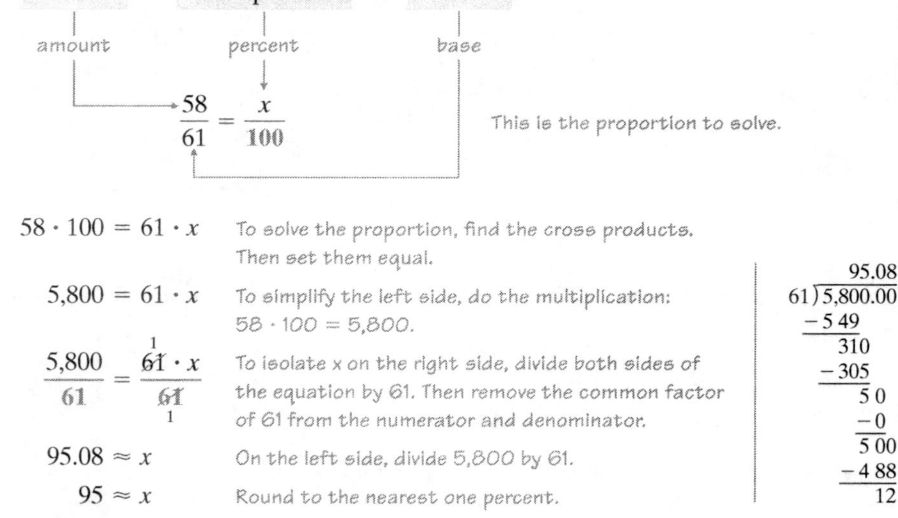

$\frac{58}{61} = \frac{x}{100}$ This is the proportion to solve.

$58 \cdot 100 = 61 \cdot x$ To solve the proportion, find the cross products. Then set them equal.

$5{,}800 = 61 \cdot x$ To simplify the left side, do the multiplication: $58 \cdot 100 = 5{,}800$.

$\frac{5{,}800}{61} = \frac{\overset{1}{\cancel{61}} \cdot x}{\underset{1}{\cancel{61}}}$ To isolate x on the right side, divide both sides of the equation by 61. Then remove the common factor of 61 from the numerator and denominator.

$95.08 \approx x$ On the left side, divide 5,800 by 61.

$95 \approx x$ Round to the nearest one percent.

$$
\begin{array}{r}
95.08 \\
61\overline{)5{,}800.00} \\
-5\ 49 \\
\hline
310 \\
-305 \\
\hline
5\ 0 \\
-0 \\
\hline
5\ 00 \\
-4\ 88 \\
\hline
12
\end{array}
$$

With either method, we see that there was a 95% increase in the number of television channels received by the average American home from 2000 to 2007.

EXAMPLE 6 *JFK* A 1996 auction included an oak rocking chair used by President John F. Kennedy in the Oval Office. The chair, originally valued at $5,000, sold for $453,500. Find the percent of increase in the value of the rocking chair.

Paul Schutzer/Time & Life Pictures/Getty Images

Strategy We will begin by finding the amount of increase in the value of the rocking chair.

WHY Then we can calculate what percent of the original $5,000 value of the chair that the increase represents.

Solution First, we find the amount of increase in the value of the rocking chair.

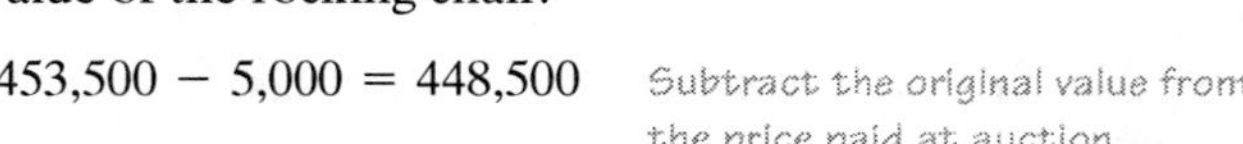

$453{,}500 - 5{,}000 = 448{,}500$ Subtract the original value from the price paid at auction.

The rocking chair increased in value by $448,500. Next, we find what percent of the original $5,000 value of the rocking chair the $448,500 increase represents by translating the problem into a percent equation (or percent proportion) and solving it.

The percent equation method:

$448,500 is what percent of $5,000?

$448{,}500 = x \cdot 5{,}000$ Translate.

$448{,}500 = x \cdot 5{,}000$ This is the equation to solve.

$\frac{448{,}500}{5{,}000} = \frac{x \cdot \overset{1}{\cancel{5{,}000}}}{\underset{1}{\cancel{5{,}000}}}$ To isolate x on the right side, divide both sides of the equation by 5,000. Then remove the common factor of 5,000 from the numerator and denominator.

$\frac{4{,}485}{50} = x$ Before performing the division on the left side of the equation, recall that there is a shortcut for dividing a dividend by a divisor when both end with zeros. Remove two of the ending zeros in the divisor 5,000 and remove the same number of ending zeros in the dividend 448,500.

$89.7 = x$ Divide 4,485 by 50.

$8970.\% = x$ To write the decimal 89.7 as a percent, multiply it by 100 by moving the decimal point two places to the right, and then insert a % symbol.

$8{,}970\% = x$

$$\begin{array}{r} 89.7 \\ 50\overline{)4{,}485.0} \\ -4\,00 \\ \hline 485 \\ -450 \\ \hline 35\,0 \\ -35\,0 \\ \hline 0 \end{array}$$

The percent proportion method:

$448,500 is what percent of $5,000?

amount percent base

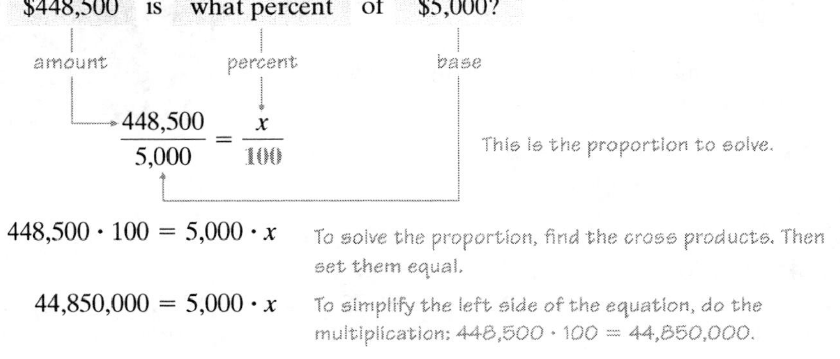

$\frac{448{,}500}{5{,}000} = \frac{x}{100}$ This is the proportion to solve.

$448{,}500 \cdot 100 = 5{,}000 \cdot x$ To solve the proportion, find the cross products. Then set them equal.

$44{,}850{,}000 = 5{,}000 \cdot x$ To simplify the left side of the equation, do the multiplication: $448{,}500 \cdot 100 = 44{,}850{,}000$.

Self Check 6

HOME SCHOOLING In one school district, the number of home-schooled children increased from 15 to 150 in 4 years. Find the percent of increase. 900%

Now Try **Problem 33**

Teaching Example 6
TALK RADIO Refer to the table below and find the percent increase in the number of news/talk radio stations from 2004 to 2008.

Year	Number of U.S. News/ Radio Stations*
2004	1,280
2008	1,360

(Source: *The World Almanac*, 2009)
*Number of stations rounded to the nearest ten

Answer:
6.25%

$$\frac{44{,}850{,}000}{5{,}000} = \frac{\overset{1}{\cancel{5{,}000}} \cdot x}{\underset{1}{\cancel{5{,}000}}}$$ To isolate x on the right side, divide both sides of the equation by 5,000. Then remove the common factor of 5,000 from the numerator and denominator.

$$\frac{44{,}850{,}000}{5{,}000} = x$$

$$\begin{array}{r} 8970 \\ 5\overline{)44{,}850} \\ -40 \\ \hline 48 \\ -45 \\ \hline 35 \\ -35 \\ \hline 0 \\ -0 \\ \hline 0 \end{array}$$

Before performing the division on the left side of the equation, recall that there is a shortcut for dividing a dividend by a divisor when both end with zeros.

$$\frac{44{,}850}{5} = x$$ Remove the three ending zeros in the divisor 5,000 and remove the same number of ending zeros in the dividend 44,850,000.

$$8{,}970 = x$$ Divide 44,850 by 5.

With either method, we see that there was an amazing 8,970% increase in the value of the Kennedy rocking chair. ■

Caution! The percent of increase (or decrease) is a percent of the *original number,* that is, the number before the change occurred. Thus, in Example 6, it would be incorrect to write a percent sentence that compares the increase to the *new value* of the Kennedy rocking chair.

$448,500 is what percent of $453,500?

Finding the Percent of Increase or Decrease

To find the percent of increase or decrease:

1. Subtract the smaller number from the larger to find the amount of increase or decrease.
2. Find what percent the amount of increase or decrease is of the original amount.

Self Check 7

REDUCING FAT INTAKE One serving of the original *Jif* peanut butter has 16 grams of fat per serving. The new *Jif Reduced Fat* product contains 12 grams of fat per serving. What is the percent decrease in the number of grams of fat per serving? 25%

***Now Try* Problem 37**

Teaching Example 7
INSURANCE COSTS A college student's good grades earned her a student discount on her car insurance premium. Find the percent of decrease if her annual premium was lowered from $1,050 to $924.

Answer:
12%

EXAMPLE 7 ***Commercials*** Jared Fogle credits his tremendous weight loss to exercise and a diet of low-fat Subway sandwiches. His maximum weight (reached in March of 1998) was 425 pounds. His current weight is about 187 pounds. Find the percent of decrease in his weight.

Zack Seckler/Getty Images

Strategy We will begin by finding the amount of decrease in Jared Fogle's weight.

WHY Then we can calculate what percent of his original 425-pound weight that the decrease represents.

Solution First, we find the amount of decrease in his weight.

$425 - 187 = 238$ Subtract his new weight from his weight before going on the weight-loss program.

His weight decreased by 238 pounds.

Next, we find what percent of his original 425 weight the 238-pound decrease represents by translating the problem into a percent equation (or percent proportion) and solving it.

The percent equation method:

238 is what percent of 425?

$238 = x \cdot 425$ Translate.

$238 = x \cdot 425$ This is the equation to solve.

$\frac{238}{425} = \frac{x \cdot \overset{1}{\cancel{425}}}{\underset{1}{\cancel{425}}}$ To isolate x on the right side, divide both sides of the equation by 425. Then remove the common factor of 425 from the numerator and denominator.

$0.56 = x$ Divide 238 by 425.

$$\begin{array}{r} 0.56 \\ 425\overline{)238.00} \\ -212\ 5 \\ \hline 25\ 50 \\ -25\ 50 \\ \hline 0 \end{array}$$

$056\% = x$ To write the decimal 0.56 as a percent, multiply it by 100 by moving the decimal point two places to the right, and then insert a % symbol.

$56\% = x$

The percent proportion method:

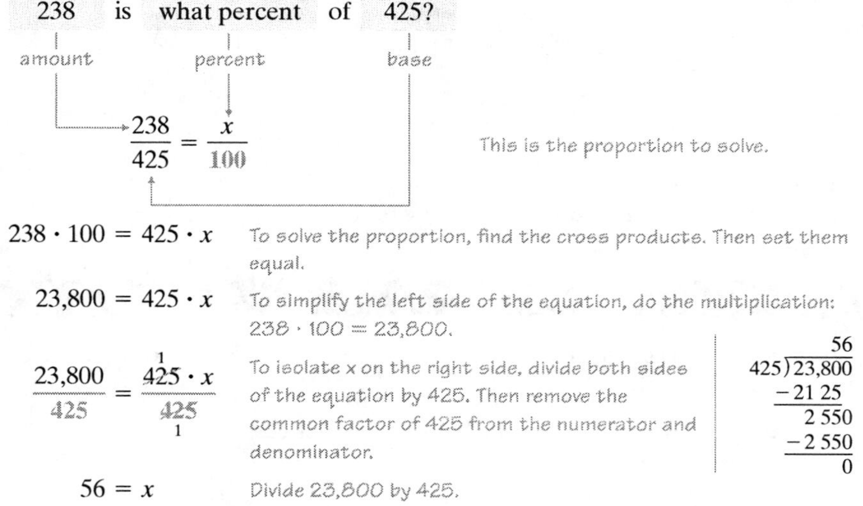

238 is what percent of 425?

238 → amount; what percent → percent; 425 → base

$\frac{238}{425} = \frac{x}{100}$ This is the proportion to solve.

$238 \cdot 100 = 425 \cdot x$ To solve the proportion, find the cross products. Then set them equal.

$23{,}800 = 425 \cdot x$ To simplify the left side of the equation, do the multiplication: $238 \cdot 100 = 23{,}800$.

$\frac{23{,}800}{425} = \frac{\overset{1}{\cancel{425}} \cdot x}{\underset{1}{\cancel{425}}}$ To isolate x on the right side, divide both sides of the equation by 425. Then remove the common factor of 425 from the numerator and denominator.

$$\begin{array}{r} 56 \\ 425\overline{)23{,}800} \\ -21\ 25 \\ \hline 2\ 550 \\ -2\ 550 \\ \hline 0 \end{array}$$

$56 = x$ Divide 23,800 by 425.

With either method, we see that there was a 56% decrease in Jared Fogle's weight.

THINK IT THROUGH *Studying Mathematics*

"All students, regardless of their personal characteristics, backgrounds, or physical challenges, must have opportunities to study—and support to learn—mathematics."

National Council of Teachers of Mathematics

The table below shows the number of students enrolled in Basic Mathematics classes at two-year colleges.

Year	1970	1975	1980	1985	1990	1995	2000	2005
Enrollment	57,000	100,000	146,000	142,000	147,000	134,000	122,000	104,000

Source: 2005 CBMS Survey of Undergraduate Programs

1. Over what five-year span was there the greatest percent increase in enrollment in Basic Mathematics classes? What was the percent increase?
1970–1975, about a 75% increase

2. Over what five-year span was there the greatest percent decrease in enrollment in Basic Mathematics classes? What was the percent increase?
2000–2005, about a 15% decrease

4 Calculate the amount of discount, the sale price, and the discount rate.

While shopping, you have probably noticed that many stores display signs advertising sales. Store managers have found that offering discounts attracts more customers. To be a smart shopper, it is important to know the vocabulary of discount sales.

The difference between the **original price** and the **sale price** of an item is called the **amount of discount,** or simply the **discount.** If the discount is expressed as a percent of the selling price, it is called the **discount rate.**

If we know the original price and the sale price of an item, we can use the following formula to find the amount of discount.

Finding the Discount

The amount of discount is the difference between the original price and the sale price.

Amount of discount = original price − sale price

If we know the original price of an item and the discount rate, we can use the following formula to find the amount of discount. Like several other formulas in this section, it is based on the percent equation.

Finding the Discount

The amount of discount is a percent of the original price.

Amount of discount = discount rate · original price

↑ amount = ↑ percent · ↑ base

We can use the following formula to find the sale price of an item that is being discounted.

Finding the Sale Price

To find the sale price of an item, subtract the discount from the original price.

Sale price = original price − discount

EXAMPLE 8 *Shoe Sales* Use the information in the advertisement shown on the previous page to find the amount of the discount on the pair of men's basketball shoes. Then find the sale price.

Strategy We will identify the discount rate and the original price of the shoes and use a formula to find the amount of the discount.

WHY Then we can subtract the discount from the original price to find the sale price of the shoes.

Solution From the advertisement, we see that the discount rate on the men's shoes is 25% and the original price is $89.80.

Amount of discount = **discount rate** · **original price** — This is the amount of discount formula.

= 25% · $89.80 — Substitute 25% for the discount rate and $89.80 for the original price.

= 0.25 · $89.80 — Write 25% as a decimal: 25% = 0.25.

= $22.45 — Do the multiplication.

$$\begin{array}{r} 89.80 \\ \times 0.25 \\ \hline 44900 \\ 179600 \\ \hline 22.4500 \end{array}$$

The discount on the men's shoes is $22.45. To find the sale price, we use subtraction.

Sale price = **original price** − **discount** — This is the sale price formula.

= $89.80 − $22.45 — Substitute $89.80 for the original price and $22.45 for the discount.

= $67.35 — Do the subtraction.

$$\begin{array}{r} {}^{7\,10} \\ 89.\cancel{8}\cancel{0} \\ -22.45 \\ \hline 67.35 \end{array}$$

The sale price of the men's basketball shoes is $67.35.

Self Check 8

SUNGLASSES SALES Sunglasses, regularly selling for $15.40, are discounted 15%. Find the amount of the discount. Then find the sale price. $2.31, $13.09

Now Try **Problem 41**

Teaching Example 8
BOOT SALES Find the amount of the discount on a pair of hiking boots if they are normally priced at $124.60, but are currently on sale for 15% off. Then find the sale price.
Answer:
$18.69, $105.91

EXAMPLE 9 *Discounts* Find the discount rate on the ladies' cross trainer shoes shown in the advertisement on the previous page. Round to the nearest one percent.

Strategy We will think of this as a percent-of-decrease problem.

WHY We want to find what percent of the $59.99 original price the amount of discount represents.

Solution From the advertisement, we see that the original price of the women's shoes is $59.99 and the sale price is $33.99. The discount (decrease in price) is found using subtraction.

$59.99 − $33.99 = $26 — Use the formula: Amount of discount = original price − sale price.

The shoes are discounted $26. Now we find what percent of the original price the $26 discount represents.

Amount of discount = discount rate · **original price** — This is the amount of discount formula.

26 = x · $59.99 — Substitute 26 for the amount of discount and $59.99 for the original price. Let x represent the unkown discount rate.

$$\frac{26}{59.99} = \frac{x \cdot 59.99}{59.99}$$

We can drop the dollar signs. To undo the multiplication by 59.99 and isolate x on the right side of the equation, divide both sides by 59.99.

Self Check 9

DINING OUT An early-bird special at a restaurant offers a $10.99 prime rib dinner for only $7.95 if it is ordered before 6 P.M. Find the rate of discount. Round to the nearest one percent. 28%

Now Try **Problem 45**

Teaching Example 9
FURNITURE SALES Find the discount rate on a desk lamp regularly priced at $89.95 that is on sale for $79.95. Round to the nearest one percent.
Answer:
11%

$0.433 \approx \frac{x \cdot \overset{1}{\cancel{59.99}}}{\underset{1}{\cancel{59.99}}}$ To simplify the fraction on the right side of the equation, remove the common factor of 59.99 from the numerator and denominator. On the left side, divide 26 by 59.99.

$$\begin{array}{r} 0.433 \\ 59.99\overline{)26.00.000} \\ -23\,99\,6 \\ \hline 2\,00\,40 \\ -1\,79\,97 \\ \hline 20\,430 \\ -17\,997 \\ \hline 2\,433 \end{array}$$

$043.3\% \approx x$ To write the decimal 0.433 as a percent, multiply it by 100 by moving the decimal point two places to the right, and then insert a % symbol.

$43\% \approx x$ Round to the nearest one percent.

To the nearest one percent, the discount rate on the women's shoes is 43%.

ANSWERS TO SELF CHECKS

1. \$3.52 **2.** \$185.71 **3.** 35% **4.** \$4.92 **5.** 5% **6.** 900% **7.** 25% **8.** \$2.31, \$13.09 **9.** 28%

SECTION 3.9 STUDY SET

VOCABULARY

Fill in the blanks.

1. Instead of working for a salary or getting paid at an hourly rate, some salespeople are paid on <u>commission</u>. They earn a certain percent of the total dollar amount of the goods or services they sell.
2. Sales tax <u>rates</u> are usually expressed as a percent.
3. **a.** When we use percent to describe how a quantity has increased compared to its original value, we are finding the percent of <u>increase</u>.
   b. When we use percent to describe how a quantity has decreased compared to its <u>original</u> value, we are finding the percent of decrease.
4. Refer to the advertisement below for a ceiling fan on sale.
   a. The <u>original</u> price of the ceiling fan was \$199.99.
   b. The amount of the <u>discount</u> is \$40.00.
   c. The discount <u>rate</u> is 20%.
   d. The <u>sale</u> price of the ceiling fan is \$159.00.

CONCEPTS

Fill in the blanks in each of the following formulas.

5. Sales tax = sales tax rate · <u>purchase price</u>
6. Total cost = <u>purchase price</u> + sales tax
7. Commission = commission rate · <u>sales</u>
8. **a.** Amount of discount = original price − <u>sale price</u>
   b. Amount of discount = <u>discount rate</u> · original price
   c. Sale price = <u>original price</u> − discount
9. **a.** The sales tax on an item priced at \$59.32 is \$4.75. What is the total cost of the item? \$64.07
   b. The original price of an item is \$150.99. The amout of discount is \$15.99. What is the sale price of the item? \$135.00
10. Round each dollar amount to the nearest cent.
    a. \$168.257 \$168.26
    b. \$57.234 \$57.23
    c. \$3.396 \$3.40
11. Fill in the blanks: To find the percent decrease, <u>subtract</u> the smaller number from the larger number to find the amount of decrease. Then find what percent that difference is of the <u>original</u> amount.

12. NEWSPAPERS The table below shows how the circulations of two daily newspapers changed from 2003 to 2007.

Daily Circulation

	Miami Herald	*USA Today*
2003	315,850	2,154,539
2007	255,844	2,293,137

Source: The World Almanac, 2009

a. What was the *amount of decrease* of the *Miami Herald*'s circulation? 60,006

b. What was the *amount of increase* of *USA Today*'s circulation? 138,598

GUIDED PRACTICE

Solve each problem to find the sales tax. See Example 1.

13. Find the sales tax on a purchase of \$92.70 if the sales tax rate is 4%. \$3.71

14. Find the sales tax on a purchase of \$33.60 if the sales tax rate is 8%. \$2.69

15. Find the sales tax on a purchase of \$83.90 if the sales tax rate is 5%. \$4.20

16. Find the sales tax on a purchase of \$234.80 if the sales tax is 2%. \$4.70

Solve each problem to find the total cost. See Example 2.

17. Find the total cost of a \$68.24 purchase if the sales tax rate is 3.8%. \$70.83

18. Find the total cost of a \$86.56 purchase if the sales tax rate is 4.3%. \$90.28

19. Find the total cost of a \$60.18 purchase if the sales tax rate is 6.4%. \$64.03

20. Find the total cost of a \$70.73 purchase if the sales tax rate is 5.9%. \$74.90

Solve each problem to find the tax rate. See Example 3.

21. SALES TAX The purchase price for a blender is \$140. If the sales tax is \$7.28, what is the sales tax rate? 5.2%

22. SALES TAX The purchase price for a camping tent is \$180. If the sales tax is \$8.64, what is the sales tax rate? 4.8%

23. SELF-EMPLOYED TAXES A business owner paid self-employment taxes of \$4,590 on a taxable income of \$30,000. What is the self-employment tax rate? 15.3%

24. CAPITAL GAINS TAXES A couple paid \$3,000 in capital gains tax on a profit of \$20,000 made from the sale of some shares of stock. What is the capital gains tax rate? 15%

Solve each problem to find the commission. See Example 4.

© iStockphoto.com/Cameron Pashak

25. SELLING SHOES A shoe salesperson earns a 12% commission on all sales. Find her commission if she sells a pair of dress shoes for \$95. \$11.40

26. SELLING CARS A used car salesperson earns an 11% commission on all sales. Find his commission if he sells a 2001 Chevy Malibu for \$4,800. \$528

27. EMPLOYMENT AGENCIES An employment counselor receives a 35% commission on the first week's salary of anyone that she places in a new job. Find her commission if one of her clients is hired as a secretary at \$480 per week. \$168

28. PHARMACEUTICAL SALES A medical sales representative is paid an 18% commission on all sales. Find her commission if she sells \$75,000 of Coumadin, a blood-thinning drug, to a pharmacy chain. \$13,500

Solve each problem to find the commission rate. See Example 5.

29. AUCTIONS An auctioneer earned a \$15 commission on the sale of an antique chair for \$750. What is the commission rate? 2%

30. SELLING TIRES A tire salesman was paid a \$28 commission after one of his customers purchased a set of new tires for \$560. What is the commission rate? 5%

31. SELLING ELECTRONICS If the commission on a \$500 laptop computer is \$20, what is the commission rate? 4%

32. SELLING CLOCKS If the commission on a \$600 grandfather clock is \$54, what is the commission rate? 9%

Solve each problem to find the percent of increase. See Example 6.

33. CLUBS The number of members of a service club increased from 80 to 88. What was the percent of increase in club membership? 10%

34. SAVINGS ACCOUNTS The amount of money in a savings account increased from \$2,500 to \$3,000. What was the percent of increase in the amount of money saved? 20%

35. RAISES After receiving a raise, the salary of a secretary increased from \$300 to \$345 dollars per week. What was the percent of increase in her salary? 15%

36. TUITION The tuition at a community college increased from \$2,500 to \$2,650 per semester. What was the percent of increase in the tuition? 6%

Solve each problem to find the percent of decrease. See Example 7.

37. TRAVEL TIME After a new freeway was completed, a commuter's travel time to work decreased from 30 minutes to 24 minutes. What was the percent of decrease in travel time? 20%

▶ **38.** LAYOFFS A printing company reduced the number of employees from 300 to 246. What was the percent of decrease in the number of employees? 18%

39. ENROLLMENT Thirty-six of the 40 students originally enrolled in an algebra class completed the course. What was the percent of decrease in the number of students in the class? 10%

40. DECLINING SALES One year, a pumpkin patch sold 1,200 pumpkins. The next year, they only sold 900 pumpkins. What was the percent of decrease in the number of pumpkins sold? 25%

Solve each problem to find the amount of the discount and the sale price. See Example 8.

41. DINNERWARE SALES Find the amount of the discount on a six-place dinnerware set if it regularly sells for $90, but is on sale for 33% off. Then find the sale price of the dinnerware set. $29.70, $60.30

▶ **42.** BEDDING SALES Find the amount of the discount on a $130 bedspread that is now selling for 20% off. Then find the sale price of the bedspread. $26, $104

43. MEN'S CLOTHING SALES 501 Levi jeans that regularly sell for $58 are now discounted 15%. Find the amount of the discount. Then find the sale price of the jeans. $8.70, $49.30

44. BOOK SALES At a bookstore, the list price of $23.50 for the *Merriam-Webster's Collegiate Dictionary* is crossed out, and a 30% discount sticker is pasted on the cover. Find the amount of the discount. Then find the sale price of the dictionary. $7.05, $16.45

Solve each problem to find the discount rate. See Example 9.

45. LADDER SALES Find the discount rate on an aluminum ladder regularly priced at $79.95 that is on sale for $64.95. Round to the nearest one percent. 19%

▶ **46.** OFFICE SUPPLIES SALES Find the discount rate on an electric pencil sharpener regularly priced at $49.99 that is on sale for $45.99. Round to the nearest one percent. 8%

47. DISCOUNT TICKETS The price of a one-way airline ticket from Atlanta to New York City was reduced from $209 to $179. Find the discount rate. Round to the nearest one percent. 14%

48. DISCOUNT HOTELS The cost of a one-night stay at a hotel was reduced from $245 to $200. Find the discount rate. Round to the nearest one percent. 18%

APPLICATIONS

49. SALES TAX The Utah state sales tax rate is 5.95%. Find the sales tax on a dining room set that sells for $900. $53.55

▶ **50.** SALES TAX Find the sales tax on a pair of jeans costing $40 if they are purchased in Missouri, which has a state sales tax rate of 4.225%. $1.69

51. SALES RECEIPTS Complete the sales receipt below by finding the subtotal, the sales tax, and the total cost of the purchase. $47.34, $2.84, $50.18

NURSERY CENTER

Your one-stop garden supply

3 @ 2.99	PLANTING MIX	$ 8.97
1 @ 9.87	GROUND COVER	$ 9.87
2 @ 14.25	SHRUBS	$28.50
	SUBTOTAL	$
	SALES TAX @ 6.00%	$
	TOTAL	$

▶ **52.** SALES RECEIPTS Complete the sales receipt below by finding all three prices, the subtotal, the sales tax, and the total cost of the purchase. $450.00, $180.00, $350.00, $980.00, $41.16, $1,021.16

McCOY'S FURNITURE

1 @ 450.00	SOFA	$
2 @ 90.00	END TABLES	$
1 @ 350.00	LOVE SEAT	$
	SUBTOTAL	$
	SALES TAX @ 4.20%	$
	TOTAL	$

53. ROOM TAX After checking out of a hotel, a man noticed that the hotel bill included an additional charge labeled *room tax*. If the price of the room was $129 plus a room tax of $10.32, find the room tax rate. 8%

▶ **54.** EXCISE TAX While examining her monthly telephone bill, a woman noticed an additional charge of $1.24 labeled *federal excise tax*. If the basic service charges for that billing period were $42, what is the federal excise tax rate? Round to the nearest one percent. 3%

55. GAMBLING For state authorized wagers (bets) placed with legal bookmakers and lottery operators, there is a federal excise tax on the wager. What is the excise tax rate if there is an excise tax of $5 on a $2,000 bet? 0.25%

56. BUYING FISHING EQUIPMENT There are federal exercise taxes on the retail price when purchasing fishing equipment. The taxes are intended to help pay for parks and conservation. What is the federal excise tax rate if there is an excise tax of $17.50 on a fishing rod and reel that has a retail price of $175? 10%

57. TAX HIKES In order to raise more revenue, some states raise the sales tax rate. How much additional money will be collected on the sale of a $15,000 car if the sales tax rate is raised 1%? $150

▶ **58.** FOREIGN TRAVEL Value-added tax (VAT) is a consumer tax on goods and services. Currently, VAT systems are in place all around the world. (The United States is one of the few nations not using a value-added tax system.) Complete the table by determining the VAT a traveler would pay in each country on a dinner that cost $25. Round to the nearest cent.

Country	VAT rate	Tax on a $25 dinner
Mexico	15%	$3.75
Germany	19%	$4.75
Ireland	21.5%	$5.38
Sweden	25%	$6.25

Source: www.worldwide-tax.com

59. PAYCHECKS Use the information on the paycheck stub to find the tax rate for the federal withholding, worker's compensation, Medicare, and Social Security taxes that were deducted from the gross pay. 8%, 3.75%, 1.2%, 6.2%

6286244

Issue date: 03-27-10

GROSS PAY	$360.00
TAXES	
FED. TAX	$ 28.80
WORK. COMP.	$ 13.50
MEDICARE	$ 4.32
SOCIAL SECURITY	$ 22.32
NET PAY	$291.06

▶ **60.** GASOLINE TAX In one state, a gallon of unleaded gasoline sells for $3.05. This price includes federal and state taxes that total approximately $0.64. Therefore, the price of a gallon of gasoline, before taxes, is $2.41. What is the tax rate on gasoline? Round to the nearest one percent. 27%

▶ **61.** POLICE FORCE A police department plans to increase its 80-person force to 84 persons. Find the percent increase in the size of the police force. 5%

62. COST-OF-LIVING INCREASES A woman making $32,000 a year receives a cost-of-living increase that raises her salary to $32,768 per year. Find the percent of increase in her yearly salary. 2.4%

63. LAKE SHORELINES Because of a heavy spring runoff, the shoreline of a lake increased from 5.8 miles to 7.6 miles. What was the percent of increase in the length of the shoreline? Round to the nearest one percent. 31%

▶ **64.** CROP DAMAGE After flooding damaged much of the crop, the cost of a head of lettuce jumped from $0.99 to $2.20. What percent of increase is this? Round to the nearest one percent. 122%

65. OVERTIME From May to June, the number of overtime hours for employees at a printing company increased from 42 to 106. What is the percent of increase in the number of overtime hours? Round to the nearest percent. 152%

66. TOURISM The graph below shows the number of international visitors (travelers) to the United States each year from 2002 to 2008.

a. The greatest percent of increase in the number of travelers was between 2003 and 2004. Find the percent increase. Round to the nearest one percent. 12%

b. The only decrease in the number of travelers was between 2002 and 2003. Find the percent decrease. Round to the nearest one percent. 6%

International Travel to the U.S.

Source: U.S. Department of Commerce

67. REDUCED CALORIES A company advertised its new, improved chips as having 96 calories per serving. The original style contained 150 calories. What percent of decrease in the number of calories per serving is this? 36%

68. CAR INSURANCE A student paid a car insurance premium of $420 every three months. Then the premium dropped to $370, because she qualified for a good-student discount. What was the percent of decrease in the premium? Round to the nearest percent. 12%

69. BUS PASSES To increase the number of riders, a bus company reduced the price of a monthly pass from $112 to $98. What was the percent of decrease in the cost of a bus pass? 12.5%

70. BASEBALL The illustration below shows the path of a baseball hit 110 mph, with a launch angle of 35 degrees, at sea level and at Coors Field, home of the Colorado Rockies. What is the percent of increase in the distance the ball travels at Coors Field? 10%

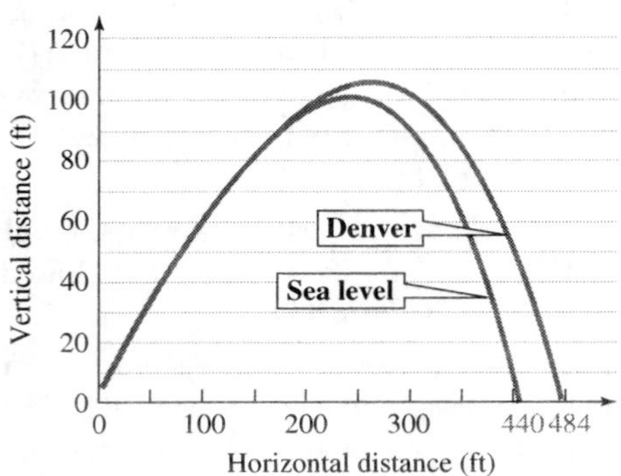

Source: Los Angeles Times, September 16, 1996

71. EARTH MOVING The illustration below shows the typical soil volume change during earth moving. (One cubic yard of soil fits in a cube that is 1 yard long, 1 yard wide, and 1 yard high.)

a. Find the percent of increase in the soil volume as it goes through step 1 of the process. 25%

b. Find the percent of decrease in the soil volume as it goes through step 2 of the process. 36%

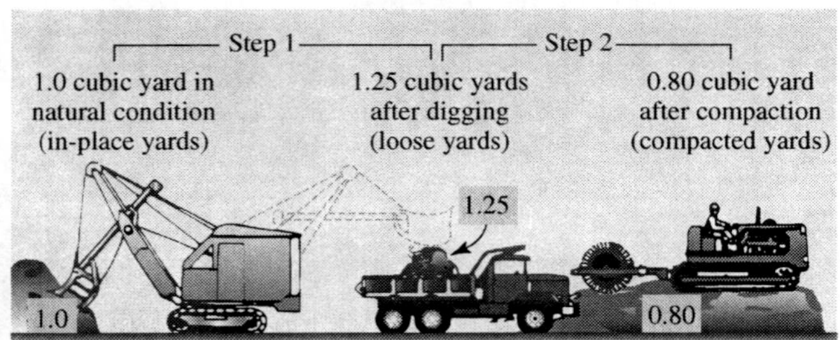

Source: U.S. Department of the Army

72. PARKING The management of a mall has decided to increase the parking area. The plans are shown in the next column. What will be the percent of increase in the parking area when the project is completed? 30%

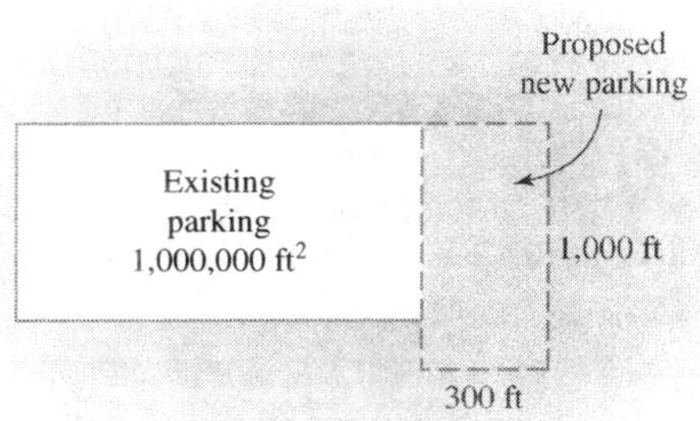

73. REAL ESTATE After selling a house for $98,500, a real estate agent split the 6% commission with another agent. How much did each person receive? $2,955

74. COMMISSIONS A salesperson for a medical supplies company is paid a commission of 9% for orders less than $8,000. For orders exceeding $8,000, she receives an additional 2% in commission on the total amount. What is her commission on a sale of $14,600? $1,606

75. SPORTS AGENTS A sports agent charges her clients a fee to represent them during contract negotiations. The fee is based on a percent of the contract amount. If the agent earned $37,500 when her client signed a $2,500,000 professional football contract, what rate did she charge for her services? 1.5%

76. ART GALLERIES An art gallery displays paintings for artists and receives a commission from the artist when a painting is sold. What is the commission rate if a gallery received $135.30 when a painting was sold for $820? 16.5%

77. WHOLE LIFE INSURANCE For the first 12 months, insurance agents earn a very large commission on the monthly premium of any whole life policy that they sell. After that, the commission rate is lowered significantly. Suppose on a new policy with monthly premiums of $160, an agent is paid monthly commissions of $144. Find the commission rate. 90%

78. TERM INSURANCE For the first 12 months, insurance agents earn a large commission on the monthly premium of any term life policy that they sell. After that, the commission rate is lowered significantly. Suppose on a new policy with monthly premiums of $180, an agent is paid monthly commissions of $81. Find the commission rate. 45%

79. CONCERT PARKING A concert promoter gets a commission of $33\frac{1}{3}\%$ of the revenue an arena receives from parking the night of the performance. How much can the promoter make if 6,000 cars are expected and parking costs $6 a car? $12,000

80. PARTIES A homemaker invited her neighbors to a kitchenware party to show off cookware and utensils. As party hostess, she received 12% of the total sales. How much was purchased if she received $41.76 for hosting the party? $348

81. WATCH SALE Refer to the advertisement below.

a. Find the amount of the discount on the watch. $7.99

b. Find the sale price of the watch. $31.96

SALE
WATCHES
Regularly
$39.95
Now
20% OFF

82. SCOOTER SALE Refer to the advertisement below.

a. Find the amount of the discount on the scooter. $108

b. Find the sale price of the scooter. $492

83. SEGWAYS Find the discount rate on a Segway PT shown in the advertisement. Round to the nearest one percent. 6%

84. FAX MACHINES An HP 3180 fax machine, regularly priced at $160, is on sale for $116. What is the discount rate? 27.5%

85. DISC PLAYERS What are the sale price and the discount rate for a Blu-ray disc player that regularly sells for $399.97 and is being discounted $50? Round to the nearest one percent. $349.97, 13%

▶ 86. CAMCORDER SALE What are the sale price and the discount rate for a camcorder that regularly sells for $559.97 and is being discounted $80? Round to the nearest one percent. $479.97, 14%

87. REBATES Find the discount rate and the new price for a case of motor oil if a shopper receives the manufacturer's rebate mentioned in the advertisement. Round to the nearest one percent. 23%, $11.88

▶ 88. DOUBLE COUPONS Find the discount, the discount rate, and the reduced price for a box of cereal that normally sells for $3.29 if a shopper presents the coupon at a store that doubles the value of the coupon. $0.70, about 21%, $2.59

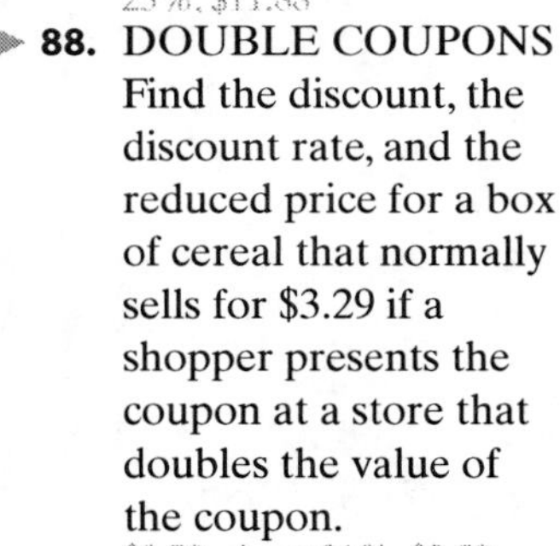

89. TV SHOPPING Determine the Home Shopping Network (HSN) price of the ring described in the illustration if it sells it for 55% off of the retail price. Ignore shipping and handling costs. $76.50

Item 169-117
2.75 lb ctw
10K
Blue Topaz
Ring
6, 7, 8, 9, 10
Retail value $170
HSN Price
$??.??
S&H $5.95

▶ 90. INFOMERCIALS The host of a TV infomercial says that the suggested retail price of a rotisserie grill is $249.95 and that it is now offered "for just 4 easy payments of only $39.95." What is the discount, and what is the discount rate? $90.15, about 36%

91. RING SALE What does a ring regularly sell for if it has been discounted 20% and is on sale for $149.99? (*Hint:* The ring is selling for 80% of its regular price.) $187.49

▶ 92. BLINDS SALE What do vinyl blinds regularly sell for if they have been discounted 55% and are on sale for $49.50? (*Hint:* The blinds are selling for 45% of their regular price.) $110

WRITING

93. Explain the difference between a sales tax and a sales tax rate.

94. List the pros and cons of working on commission.

95. Suppose the price of an item increases $25 from $75 to $100. Explain why the following percent sentence *cannot* be used to find the percent of increase in the price of the item.

25 is what percent of 100?

▶ 96. Explain how to find the sale price of an item if you know the regular price and the discount rate.

REVIEW

97. Multiply: $-5(-5)(-2)$ -50

98. Divide: $\frac{-320}{40}$ -8

99. Subtract: $-4 - (-7)$ 3

100. Add: $-17 + 6 + (-12)$ -23

101. Evaluate: $|-5 - 8|$ 13

102. Evaluate: $\sqrt{25} - \sqrt{16}$ 1

Module 4: Expressions, Linear Equations, Linear Inequalities

DMA 040

Note: A vocation opener will be added here.

Objectives

1. Identify terms and coefficients of terms.
2. Write word phrases as algebraic expressions.
3. Analyze problems to determine hidden operations.
4. Evaluate algebraic expressions.

SECTION 4.1
Algebraic Expressions

Since problems in algebra are often presented in words, the ability to interpret what you read is important. In this section, we will introduce several strategies that will help you translate English words into mathematical symbols.

1 Identify terms and coefficients of terms.

Recall that variables and/or numbers can be combined with the operations of arithmetic to create **algebraic expressions.** Addition symbols separate expressions into parts called *terms.* For example, the expression $x + 8$ has two terms.

x	$+$	8
First term		Second term

Since subtraction can be written as addition of the opposite, the expression $a^2 - 3a - 9$ has three terms.

$a^2 - 3a - 9 =$	a^2	$+$	$(-3a)$	$+$	(-9)
	First term		Second term		Third term

In general, a **term** is a product or quotient of numbers and/or variables. A single number or variable is also a term. Examples of terms are:

$$4, \quad y, \quad 6r, \quad -w^3, \quad 3.7x^5, \quad \frac{3}{n}, \quad -15ab^2$$

> ***The Language of Algebra*** By the commutative property of multiplication, $r6 = 6r$ and $-15b^2a = -15ab^2$. However, we usually write the numerical factor first and the variable factors in alphabetical order.

The numerical factor of a term is called the **coefficient** of the term. For instance, the term $6r$ has a coefficient of 6 because $6r = 6 \cdot r$. The coefficient of $-15ab^2$ is -15 because $-15ab^2 = -15 \cdot ab^2$. More examples are shown.

A term such as 4, that consists of a single number, is called a **constant term.**

Term	Coefficient	
$8y^2$	8	
$-0.9pq$	-0.9	
$\frac{3}{4}b$	$\frac{3}{4}$	This term could be written $\frac{3b}{4}$.
$-\frac{x}{6}$	$-\frac{1}{6}$	Because $-\frac{x}{6} = -\frac{1x}{6} = -\frac{1}{6} \cdot x$
x	1	Because $x = 1x$
$-t$	-1	Because $-t = -1t$
27	27	

The Language of Algebra Terms such as x and y have *implied* coefficients of 1. *Implied* means suggested without being precisely expressed.

EXAMPLE 1 Identify the coefficient of each term in the following expression: $7x^2 - x + 6$

Strategy We will begin by writing the subtraction as addition of the opposite. Then we will determine the numerical factor of each term.

WHY Addition symbols separate expressions into terms.

Solution

If we write $7x^2 - x + 6$ as $7x^2 + (-x) + 6$, we see that it has three terms: $7x^2$, $-x$, and 6. The numerical factor of each term is its coefficient.

The coefficient of $7x^2$ is 7 because $7x^2$ means $7 \cdot x^2$.

The coefficient of $-x$ is -1 because $-x$ means $-1 \cdot x$.

The coefficient of the constant 6 is 6.

Self Check 1

Identify the coefficient of each term in the expression: $p^3 - 12p^2 + 3p - 4$ 1, −12, 3, −4

Now Try **Problem 15**

Teaching Example 1 Identify the coefficient of each term in the expression: $-3x^2 + x - 5$
Answer:
−3, 1, −5

It is important to be able to distinguish between the *terms* of an expression and the *factors* of a term.

EXAMPLE 2 Is m used as a *factor* or a *term* in each expression?

a. $m + 6$ **b.** $8m$

Strategy We will begin by determining whether m is involved in an addition or a multiplication.

WHY Addition symbols separate expressions into *terms.* A *factor* is a number being multiplied.

Solution

a. Since m is added to 6, m is a term of $m + 6$.

b. Since m is multiplied by 8, m is a factor of $8m$.

Self Check 2

Is b used as a *factor* or a *term* in each expression?

a. $-27b$ factor

b. $5a + b$ term

Now Try **Problem 21**

Teaching Example 2 Is a used as a factor or a term in each expression?
a. $32a$ **b.** $a + 9$
Answers:
a. factor **b.** term

2 Write word phrases as algebraic expressions.

In the following tables, we list some words and phrases that are used to indicate addition, subtraction, multiplication, and division, and we show how they can be translated to form algebraic expressions.

Addition

The phrase	Translates to
the sum of a and 8	$a + 8$
4 plus c	$4 + c$
16 added to m	$m + 16$
4 more than t	$t + 4$
20 greater than F	$F + 20$
T increased by r	$T + r$
exceeds y by 35	$y + 35$

Subtraction

The phrase	Translates to
the difference of 23 and P	$23 - P$
550 minus h	$550 - h$
18 less than w	$w - 18$
7 decreased by j	$7 - j$
M reduced by x	$M - x$
12 subtracted from L	$L - 12$
5 less f	$5 - f$

Caution! Be careful when translating subtraction. Order is important. For example, when translating the phrase "18 less than w," the terms are reversed.

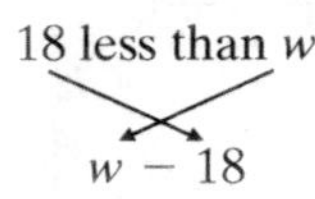

Multiplication

The phrase	Translates to
the product of 4 and x	$4x$
20 times B	$20B$
twice r	$2r$
triple the profit P	$3P$
$\frac{3}{4}$ of m	$\frac{3}{4}m$

Division

The phrase	Translates to
the quotient of R and 19	$\frac{R}{19}$
s divided by d	$\frac{s}{d}$
the ratio of c to d	$\frac{c}{d}$
k split into 4 equal parts	$\frac{k}{4}$

Caution! The phrase *greater than* is used to indicate addition. The phrase *is greater than* refers to the symbol $>$. Similarly, the phrase *less than* indicates subtraction, and the phrase *is less than* refers to the symbol $<$.

Self Check 3

Write each phrase as an algebraic expression:

a. 80 cents less than t cents $t - 80$

b. $\frac{2}{3}$ of the time T $\frac{2}{3}T$

c. the difference of twice a and 15 $2a - 15$

Now Try **Problems 23, 25, 35**

Teaching Example 3 Write each phrase as an algebraic expression.
a. 5 feet less than x feet
b. twice w
c. 4 feet more than twice b
Answer:
a. $x - 5$ b. $2w$
c. $2b + 4$

EXAMPLE 3 Write each phrase as an algebraic expression.

a. The sum of the length l and the width 20

b. 5 less than the capacity c

c. The product of the weight w and 2,000, increased by 300

Strategy We will read each phrase and pay close attention to key words that can be translated to mathematical operations. We will refer to the tables as a guide if needed.

WHY Key phrases can be translated to mathematical symbols.

Solution

a. Key word: *sum* **Translation:** add

The phrase translates to $l + 20$.

b. Key phrase: *less than* **Translation:** subtract

The capacity c is to be made less, so we subtract 5 from it: $c - 5$.

c. Key word: *product* **Translation:** multiply

Key phrase: *increased by* **Translation:** add

The weight w is to be multiplied by 2,000, and then 300 is to be added to the product: $2{,}000w + 300$.

When solving problems, we often begin by letting a variable stand for an unknown quantity.

EXAMPLE 4 *Food Preparation* A butcher trims 4 ounces of fat from a roast that originally weighed x ounces. Write an algebraic expression that represents the weight of the roast after it is trimmed.

Strategy We will start by letting x represent the original weight of the roast. Then we will look for a key word or phrase to write an expression that represents the trimmed weight of the roast.

WHY The weight after trimming is related to the original weight of the roast.

Solution

We let $x =$ the original weight of the roast (in ounces).

Key word: *trimmed* **Translation:** subtract

After 4 ounces of fat have been trimmed, the weight of the roast is $(x - 4)$ ounces.

Self Check 4

When a secretary rides the bus to work, it takes her m minutes. If she drives her own car, her travel time exceeds this by 15 minutes. How can we represent the time it takes her to get to work by car? $(m + 15)$ minutes

Now Try **Problem 42**

Teaching Example 4 When a student studies for his math class, it takes him t minutes. If he is studying for a test, his study time exceeds this by 120 minutes. How can we represent the time he spends studying for a test?
Answer:
$t + 120$

EXAMPLE 5 *Competitive Swimming* The swimming pool to the right is x feet wide. If it is to be sectioned into 8 equally wide swimming lanes, write an algebraic expression that represents the width of each lane.

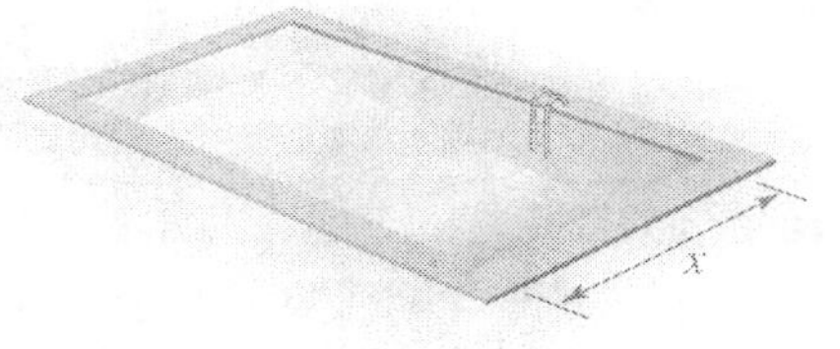

Strategy We start by letting x represent the width of the swimming pool. Then we will look for key words or phrases to write an expression that represents the width of each lane.

WHY The width of each lane is related to the width of the pool.

Solution

We let $x =$ the width of the swimming pool (in feet).

Key phrase: *sectioned into 8 equally wide lanes* **Translation:** divide

The width of each lane is $\frac{x}{8}$ feet.

Self Check 5

A handyman estimates that it will take the same amount of time to sand as it will to paint some kitchen cabinets. If the entire job takes x hours, how can we express the time it will take him to do the painting? $\frac{x}{2}$ hours

Now Try **Problem 45**

Teaching Example 5 The semester tuition cost for a total of 15 credit hours is x dollars. Write an expression that represents the cost of each credit hour.
Answer:
$\frac{x}{15}$

When we are solving problems, the variable to be used is rarely specified. We must decide what the unknown quantities are and how they will be represented using variables. The following examples illustrate how to approach these situations.

Self Check 6

A candy bar has twice the number of calories as a serving of pears. Write an expression that represents the number of calories in a candy bar.

Now Try **Problem 47**

Self Check 6 Answers
x = the number of calories in a serving of pears, $2x$ = the number of calories in a candy bar

Teaching Example 6 A delivery of x cases of pies, each containing 8 pies, is made to a fundraiser. Write an expression for the number of pies delivered to the fundraiser.
Answer:
x = the number of cases of pies
$8x$ = the number of pies

EXAMPLE 6 *Collectibles* The value of a collectible doll is three times that of an antique toy truck. Write an expression that represents the value of the doll.

Strategy We start by letting x represent the value of the toy truck. Then we will look for key words or phrases to write an expression that represents the value of the antique doll.

WHY The value of the doll is related to the value of the toy truck.

Solution

There are two unknown quantities. Since the doll's value is related to the truck's value, we will let x = the value of the toy truck in dollars.

Key phrase: 3 *times* **Translation:** multiply by 3

The value of the doll is $\$3x$.

Caution! A variable is used to represent an unknown number. Therefore, in Example 6, it would be incorrect to write, "Let x = toy truck," because the truck is not a number. We need to write, "Let x = the *value* of the toy truck."

Self Check 7

Part of a \$900 donation to a college went to the scholarship fund, the rest to the building fund. Choose a variable to represent the amount donated to one of the funds. Then write an expression that represents the amount donated to the other fund.

Now Try **Problem 52**

Self Check 7 Answers
s = amount donated to scholarship fund in dollars, $900 - s$ = amount donated to building fund

Teaching Example 7 Part of a \$2000 investment is to be invested in an account paying $3\frac{1}{2}\%$, and the rest in an account paying 4%. Choose a variable to represent the amount invested at $3\frac{1}{2}\%$. Write an expression that represents the amount invested at 4%.
Answer: x = amount invested at $3\frac{1}{2}\%$,
$2000 - x$ = amount invested at 4%

EXAMPLE 7 *Painting* A 10-inch-long paintbrush has two parts: a handle and bristles. Choose a variable to represent the length of one of the parts. Then write an expression to represent the length of the other part.

Strategy There are two approaches. We can let h = the length of the handle or we can let b = the length of the bristles.

WHY Both the length of the handle and the length of the bristles are unknown, however we do know the entire length of the paintbrush.

Solution

Refer to the drawing on the top. If we let h = the length of the handle (in inches), then the length of the bristles is $10 - h$.

Now refer to the drawing on the bottom. If we let b = the length of the bristles (in inches), then the length of the handle is $10 - b$.

Self Check 8

The number of votes received by the incumbent in an election was 55 fewer than three times the number the challenger received. Write an expression that represents the number of votes received by the incumbent.

Now Try **Problem 53**

EXAMPLE 8 *Student Enrollments* In the second semester, student enrollment in a retraining program at a college was 32 more than twice that of the first semester. Write an expression that represents the student enrollment in the second semester.

Strategy We start by letting x represent the enrollment in the first semester. Then we will look for a key word or phrase to write an expression to represent the second-semester enrollment.

WHY The second-semester enrollment is related to the first-semester enrollment.

Solution

Since the second-semester enrollment is expressed in terms of the first-semester enrollment, we let x = the enrollment in the first semester.

Key phrase: *more than* **Translation:** add

Key word: *twice* **Translation:** multiply by 2

The enrollment for the second semester is $2x + 32$.

Self Check 8 Answers
x = the number of votes received by the challenger, $3x - 55$ = the number of votes received by the incumbent

Teaching Example 8 The cost of the tuition at a small private college is $500 more than 3 times the tuition at a state university. Write an expression that represents the tuition cost at the small private college.
Answer:
x = the tuition at the state university, $3x + 500$ = the tuition at the small private college

3 Analyze problems to determine hidden operations.

When analyzing problems, we aren't always given key words or key phrases to help establish what mathematical operation to use. Sometimes a careful reading of the problem is needed to determine the hidden operations.

EXAMPLE 9 *Disney Theme Parks* Disneyland, located in Anaheim, California, was in operation 16 years before the opening of Walt Disney World, in Orlando, Florida. Euro Disney, in Paris, France, was constructed 21 years after Disney World. Use algebraic expressions to express the ages (in years) of each of these Disney attractions.

Strategy We start by letting x represent the age of Disney World.

WHY The ages of Disneyland and Euro Disney are related to the age of Disney World.

Solution

The ages of Disneyland and Euro Disney are both related to the age of Walt Disney World. Therefore, we will let x = the age of Walt Disney World.

In carefully reading the problem, we find that Disneyland was built 16 years *before* Disney World, so its age is more than that of Disney World.

Key phrase: *more than* **Translation:** add

In years, the age of Disneyland is $x + 16$. Euro Disney was built 21 years *after* Disney World, so its age is less than that of Disney World.

Key phrase: *less than* **Translation:** subtract

In years, the age of Euro Disney is $x - 21$. The results are summarized in the table.

Attraction	Age
Disneyland	$x + 16$
Disney World	x
Euro Disney	$x - 21$

Self Check 9

Kayla worked 5 more hours preparing her tax return than she did on her daughter's return. Kayla's son's return took her 2 more hours to prepare than her daughter's. Write an expression to represent the hours she spent on each return.

Now Try **Problem 57**

Self Check 9 Answers
Daughter's: x
Kayla's: $x + 5$
Son's: $x + 2$

Teaching Example 9 Tom is 3 years older than Joan. Carly is 5 years younger than Joan. Write an algebraic expression to express the ages of Tom, Joan, and Carly.
Answer:
Tom: $x + 3$
Joan: x
Carly: $x - 5$

EXAMPLE 10 How many months are in x years?

Strategy There are no key words, so we must carefully analyze the problem to write an expression that represents the number of months in x years. We will begin by considering some specific cases.

WHY When no key words are present, it is helpful to work with specifics to get a better understanding of the relationship between the two quantities.

Solution

Let's calculate the number of months in 1 year, 2 years, and 3 years. When we write the results in a table, a pattern is apparent.

Self Check 10

Complete the table. How many days is h hours?

Number of hours	Number of days
24	1
48	2
72	3
h	$\frac{h}{24}$

Now Try **Problem 59**

Teaching Example 10 How many seconds are in x minutes?
Answer:
$60x$

Number of years	Number of months
1	12
2	24
3	36
x	$12x$

We multiply the number of years by 12 to find the number of months.

Therefore, if x = the number of years, the number of months is $12 \cdot x$ or $12x$.

Some problems deal with quantities that have value. In these problems, we must distinguish between *the number of* and *the value of* the unknown quantity. For example, to find the value of 3 quarters, we multiply the number of quarters by the value (in cents) of one quarter. Therefore, the value of 3 quarters is $3 \cdot 25$ cents = 75 cents.

The same distinction must be made if the number is unknown. For example, the value of n nickels is not n cents. The value of n nickels is $n \cdot 5$ cents = $(5n)$ cents. For problems of this type, we will use the relationship

Number · value = total value

Self Check 11

Find the value of

a. six fifty-dollar savings bonds

b. t one-hundred-dollar savings bonds

c. $x - 4$ one-thousand-dollar savings bonds

Now Try **Problem 62**

Self Check 11 Answers
a. \$300 **b.** \$100t **c.** \$1,000$(x - 4)$

Teaching Example 11 Find the value of
a. 7 nickels
b. t \$50 bills
c. $x + 3$ \$20 bills
Answers:
a. 35¢ **b.** \$50t
c. \$20$(x + 3)$

EXAMPLE 11 Find the total value of

a. five dimes **b.** q quarters **c.** $x + 1$ half-dollars

Strategy We will find the total value (in cents) of each collection of coins by multiplying the number of coins by the value of one coin.

WHY Number · value = total value

Solution

To find the total value (in cents) of each collection of coins, we multiply the number of coins by the value (in cents) of one coin, as shown in the table.

Type of Coin	Number	· Value	= Total Value
Dime	5	10	50
Quarter	q	25	$25q$
Half-dollar	$x + 1$	50	$50(x + 1)$

← $q \cdot 25$ is written $25q$.

4 Evaluate algebraic expressions.

To **evaluate an algebraic expression,** we replace each variable with a given number value. (When we replace a variable with a number, we say we are **substituting** for the variable.) Then we do the necessary calculations following the rules for the order of operations. For example, to evaluate $x^2 - 2x + 1$ for $x = 3$, we begin by substituting 3 for x.

$$x^2 - 2x + 1 = 3^2 - 2(3) + 1 \quad \text{Substitute 3 for } x.$$
$$= 9 - 2(3) + 1 \quad \text{Evaluate the exponential expression: } 3^2 = 9.$$
$$= 9 - 6 + 1 \quad \text{Perform the multiplication: } 2(3) = 6.$$
$$= 4 \quad \text{Working left to right, perform the subtraction and then the addition.}$$

We say that 4 is the **value** of this expression when $x = 3$.

Caution! When replacing a variable with its numerical value, use parentheses around the replacement number to avoid possible misinterpretation. For example, when substituting 5 for x in $2x + 1$, we show the multiplication using parentheses: $2(5) + 1$. If we don't show the multiplication, we could misread the expression as $25 + 1$.

EXAMPLE 12 Evaluate each expression for $x = 3$ and $y = -4$:
a. $-y$ **b.** $-3(y + x^2)$

Strategy We will replace x with 3 and y with -4 and then evaluate the expression using the order of operations.

WHY To evaluate an expression means to find its numerical value, once we know the values of the variable(s).

Solution

a. $-y = -(-4)$ Substitute -4 for y.
$= 4$ The opposite of -4 is 4.

b. $-3(y + x^2) = -3(-4 + 3^2)$ Substitute 3 for x and -4 for y.
$= -3(-4 + 9)$ Work within the parentheses first. Evaluate the exponential expression.
$= -3(5)$ Perform the addition within the parentheses.
$= -15$

Self Check 12

Evaluate each expression for $x = -2$ and $y = 3$: **a.** $-x$ **b.** $5(x - y)$

Now Try **Problem 63**

Self Check 12 Answers
a. 2 b. -25

Teaching Example 12 Evaluate: $-5(3y + 2x^2)$ when $x = -3$ and $y = 2$.
Answer:
-120

EXAMPLE 13 *Temperature Conversion* The expression $\frac{9C + 160}{5}$ converts a temperature in degrees Celsius (represented by C) to a temperature in degrees Fahrenheit. Convert -170°C, the coldest temperature on the moon, to degrees Fahrenheit.

Strategy We will replace C in the expression with -170 and evaluate it using the order of operations.

WHY The expression evaluated at $C = -170$ converts -170°C to degrees Fahrenheit.

Solution

To convert -170°C to degrees Fahrenheit, we evaluate the algebraic expression for $C = -170$.

$\frac{9C + 160}{5} = \frac{9(-170) + 160}{5}$ Substitute -170 for C.

$= \frac{-1{,}530 + 160}{5}$ Perform the multiplication.

$= \frac{-1{,}370}{5}$ Perform the addition.

$= -274$ Perform the division.

In degrees Fahrenheit, the coldest temperature on the moon is -274°.

Self Check 13

On January 22, 1943, the temperature in Spearfish, South Dakota changed from -20°C to 7.2°C in two minutes. Convert -20°C to degrees Fahrenheit.

Now Try **Problem 75**

Self Check 13 Answer
-4°F

Teaching Example 13 Convert 7.2°C to degrees Fahrenheit.
Answer:
44.96°F

Using Your CALCULATOR Evaluating Algebraic Expressions

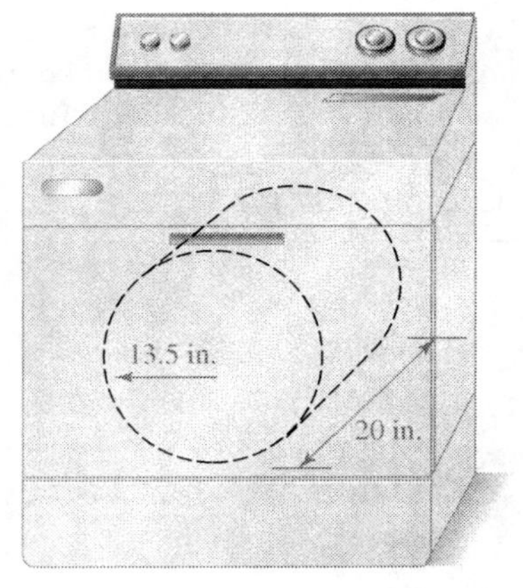

The rotating drum of a clothes dryer is a cylinder. To find the capacity of the dryer, we can find its volume by evaluating the algebraic expression $\pi r^2 h$, where r represents the radius and h represents the height of the drum. (Here, the cylinder is lying on its side.) If we substitute 13.5 for r and 20 for h, we obtain $\pi(13.5)^2(20)$. Using a scientific calculator, we can evaluate the expression by entering these numbers and pressing these keys.

[π] [×] 13.5 [x^2] [×] 20 [=] 11451.10522

Using a graphing or direct-entry calculator, we can evaluate the expression by entering these numbers and pressing these keys.

[2nd] [π] [×] 13.5 [x^2] [×] 20 [ENTER]

π*13.5²*20
11451.10522

To the nearest cubic inch, the capacity of the dryer is 11,451 in.^{3}.

Self Check 14

In Example 14, suppose the initial velocity is 112 feet per second, so the height of the rocket is given by $112t - 16t^2$. Complete the table to find out how many seconds after launch it would hit the ground. 7 sec

t	$112t - 16t^2$
1	96
3	192
5	160
7	0

Now Try **Problem 82**

Teaching Example 14 Suppose the initial velocity is 160 feet per second, so the height of the rocket is given by the expression $160t - 16t^2$. Complete the table to find out how many seconds after launch it would hit the ground.

t	$160t - 16t^2$
1	144
5	400
10	0

Answer: 10 seconds

EXAMPLE 14 *Rocketry* If a toy rocket is shot into the air with an initial velocity of 80 feet per second, its height (in feet) after t seconds in flight is given by the algebraic expression

$$80t - 16t^2$$

How many seconds after the launch will it hit the ground?

Strategy We will substitute positive values for t, the time in flight, until we find the one that gives a height of 0.

WHY When the toy rocket is on the ground, its height above the ground is 0.

Solution

We can substitute positive values for t, the time in flight, until we find the one that gives a height of 0. At that time, the rocket will be on the ground. We will begin by finding the height after the rocket has been in flight for 1 second ($t = 1$) and record the result in a table.

$$\begin{aligned} 80t - 16t^2 &= 80(1) - 16(1)^2 \quad \text{Substitute 1 for } t. \\ &= 64 \end{aligned}$$

After 1 second in flight, the height of the rocket is 64 feet. We continue to pick more values of t until we find out when the height is 0.

As we evaluate $80t - 16t^2$ for various values of t, we can show the results in a **table of values.** In the column headed "t," we list each value of the variable to be used in the evaluations. In the column headed "$80t - 16t^2$," we write the result of each evaluation.

t	$80t - 16t^2$
1	64
2	96
3	96
4	64
5	0

Evaluate for $t = 2$:
$80t - 16t^2 = 80(2) - 16(2)^2 = 96$
Evaluate for $t = 3$:
$80t - 16t^2 = 80(3) - 16(3)^2 = 96$
Evaluate for $t = 4$:
$80t - 16t^2 = 80(4) - 16(4)^2 = 64$
Evaluate for $t = 5$:
$80t - 16t^2 = 80(5) - 16(5)^2 = 0$

Since the height of the rocket is 0 when $t = 5$, the rocket will hit the ground in 5 seconds.

The two columns of a table of values are sometimes headed with the terms **input** and **output,** as shown. The t-values are the inputs into the expression $80t - 16t^2$, and the resulting values are thought of as the outputs.

Input	Output
1	64
2	96
3	96
4	64
5	0

ANSWERS TO SELF CHECKS

1. 1, −12, 3, −4 **2. a.** factor **b.** term **3. a.** $t - 80$ **b.** $\frac{2}{3}T$ **c.** $2a - 15$ **4.** $m + 15$ minutes **5.** $\frac{x}{2}$ hours **6.** x = the number of calories in a serving of pears, $2x$ = the number of calories in a candy bar **7.** s = amount donated to scholarship fund in dollars, $900 - s$ = amount donated to building fund **8.** x = the number of votes received by the challenger, $3x - 55$ = the number of votes received by the incumbent **9.** Daughter's: x, Kayla's: $x + 5$, son's: $x + 2$ **10.** 1, 2, 3; $\frac{h}{24}$ **11. a.** \$300 **b.** \$100t **c.** \$1,000($x - 4$) **12. a.** 2 **b.** −25 **13.** −4°F **14.** 7 sec (the heights are 96, 192, 160, and 0)

SECTION 4.1 STUDY SET

VOCABULARY

Fill in the blanks.

1. To evaluate an algebraic expression, we substitute the values for the variables and then apply the rules for the order of operations.

2. Variables and/or numbers can be combined with the operation symbols of addition, subtraction, multiplication, and division to create algebraic expressions.

3. $2x + 5$ is an example of an algebraic expression, whereas $2x + 5 = 7$ is an example of an equation.

▶ **4.** When we evaluate an algebraic expression, such as $5x - 8$, for several values of x, we can keep track of the results in an input/output table.

▶ Selected exercises available online at **www.webassign.net/brookscole**

CONCEPTS

5. Write two algebraic expressions that contain the variable x and the numbers 6 and 20.
$6 + 20x$, $\frac{6 - x}{20}$ (answers may vary)

6. a. Complete the table to determine how many days are in w weeks.

Number of weeks	Number of days
1	7
2	14
3	21
w	$7w$

b. Complete the table to answer this question: s seconds is how many minutes?

Number of seconds	Number of minutes
60	1
120	2
180	3
s	$\frac{s}{60}$

7. When evaluating $3x - 6$ for $x = 4$, what misunderstanding can occur if we don't write parentheses around 4 when it is substituted for the variable? We would obtain $34 - 6$; it looks like 34, not 3(4).

▶ **8.** If the knife shown is 12 inches long, write an expression for the length of the blade. $(12 - h)$ in.

9. a. In the illustration, the weight of the van is 500 pounds less than twice the weight of the car. If the car weighs x pounds, write an expression that represents the weight of the van. $2x - 500$

b. If the actual weight of the car is 2,000 pounds, what is the weight of the van? 3,500 lb

▶ **10.** See the illustration.

a. If we let b = the length of the beam, write an expression for the length of the pipe. $b - 15$

b. If we let p = the length of the pipe, write an expression for the length of the beam. $p + 15$

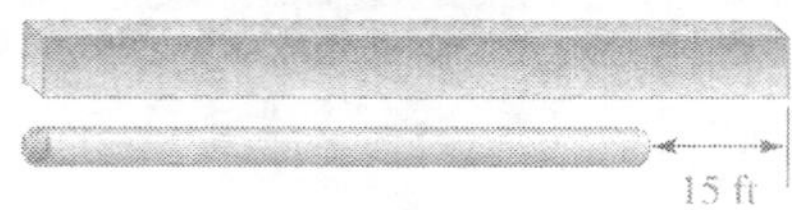

11. Complete the table.

Type of coin	Number ·	Value in cents =	Total value in cents
Nickel	6	5	30
Dime	d	10	$10d$
Half dollar	$x + 5$	50	$50(x + 5)$

12. If $x = -9$, find the value of

a. $-x$ 9 **b.** $-(-x)$ -9

c. $-x^2$ -81 **d.** $(-x)^2$ 81

NOTATION

Complete each evaluation.

13. Evaluate the expression $9a - a^2$ for $a = 5$.

$$\begin{aligned} 9a - a^2 &= 9(5) - (5)^2 \\ &= 9(5) - 25 \\ &= 45 - 25 \\ &= 20 \end{aligned}$$

▶ **14.** Evaluate $\frac{4x^2 - 3y}{9(x - y)}$ when $x = 4$ and $y = -3$.

$$\begin{aligned} \frac{4x^2 - 3y}{9(x - y)} &= \frac{4(4)^2 - 3(-3)}{9[4 - (-3)]} \\ &= \frac{4(16) - 3(-3)}{9(7)} \\ &= \frac{(64) - (-9)}{63} \\ &= \frac{73}{63} \end{aligned}$$

GUIDED PRACTICE

Identify the coefficient of each term in the expression. See Example 1.

15. $4x^2 - 5x + 7$ 4, -5, 7 ▶ **16.** $-8x^2 + 3x - 2$ -8, 3, -2

17. $9x^2 - 4x$ 9, -4 **18.** $-5x^2 + 6$ -5, 6

Is n used as a factor or a term in each expression? See Example 2.

19. $n - 4$ term **20.** $3n - 4$ factor

▶ **21.** $-5n^2 - 4n + 3$ factor **22.** $5m^2 + n$ term

Write each phrase as an algebraic expression. If no variable is given, use x as the variable. See Example 3.

▶ **23.** The sum of the length l and 15 $l + 15$

24. The difference of a number and 10 $x - 10$

25. The product of a number and 50 $50x$

▶ **26.** Three-fourths of the population p $\frac{3}{4}p$

27. The ratio of the amount won w and lost l $\frac{w}{l}$

28. The tax t added to c $c + t$

29. P increased by p $P + p$

30. 21 less than the total height h $h - 21$

31. The square of k minus 2,005 $k^2 - 2{,}005$

▶ **32.** s subtracted from S $S - s$

33. J reduced by 500 $J - 500$

34. Twice the attendance a $2a$

35. 1,000 split n equal ways $\frac{1{,}000}{n}$

36. Exceeds the cost c by 25,000 $c + 25{,}000$

37. 90 more than the current price p $p + 90$

38. 64 divided by the cube of y $\frac{64}{y^3}$

Write an algebraic expression that represents each quantity.
See Example 4.

39. A model's skirt is x inches long. The designer then lets the hem down 2 inches. How can we express the length (in inches) of the altered skirt? $(x + 2)$ in.

40. A caterer always prepares food for 10 more people than the order specifies. If p people are to attend a reception, write an expression for the number of people she should prepare for. $p + 10$

41. Last year a club sold x candy bars for a fundraiser. This year they want to sell 150 more than last year. Write an expression for the number of candy bars they want to sell this year. $x + 150$

42. The tag on a new pair of 36-inch-long jeans warns that after washing, they will shrink x inches in length. Express the length (in inches) of the jeans after they are washed. $(36 - x)$ in.

Write an algebraic expression that represents each quantity.
See Example 5.

43. A soft-drink manufacturer produced c cans of cola during the morning shift. Write an expression for how many six-packs of cola can be assembled from the morning shift's production. $\frac{c}{6}$

44. A student has a paper to type that contains x words. If the student can type 60 words per minute, write an expression for the number of minutes it will take for her to type the paper. $\frac{x}{60}$

45. A walking path is x feet wide and is striped down the middle. Write an expression for the width of each lane of the path. $\frac{x}{2}$

46. Tickets to a musical cost a total of $\$t$ for 5 tickets. Write an expression for the cost of one ticket to the musical. $\frac{t}{5}$

Write an algebraic expression that represents each quantity.
See Example 6.

47. A caravan of b cars, each carrying 5 people, traveled to the state capital for a political rally. Express how many people were in the car caravan. $5b$

48. Tickets to a circus cost \$5 each. Express how much tickets will cost for a family of x people if they also pay for two of their neighbors. $\$5(x + 2)$

49. A rectangle is twice as long as it is wide. If the rectangle's width is w, write an expression for the length. $2w$

50. If each egg is worth e¢, express the value (in cents) of a dozen eggs. $12e$¢

Write an algebraic expression that represents each quantity.
See Examples 7–8.

51. A 12-foot board is to be cut into two pieces. Choose a variable to represent the length of one piece. Then write an expression that represents the other piece. x ft, $(12 - x)$ ft

52. Part of a \$10,000 investment is to be invested in an account paying 2% interest, and the rest in an account paying 3%. Choose a variable to represent the amount invested at 2%. Then write an expression that represents the amount invested at 3%. $\$x$, $\$(10{,}000 - x)$

53. The number of runners in a marathon this year is 25 more than twice the number that participated last year. Write an expression that represents the number of marathon runners this year. $2x + 25$

54. In the second year of operation, a bakery sold 31 more than three times the number of cakes it sold the first year. Write an expression that represents the number of cakes the bakery sold the second year of operation. $3x + 31$

Write an algebraic expression that represents each quantity.
See Example 9.

55. IBM was founded 80 years before Apple Computer. Dell Computer Corporation was founded 9 years after Apple.
   a. Let x represent the age (in years) of one of the companies. Write algebraic expressions to represent the ages (in years) of the other two companies.
   x = age of Apple, $x + 80$ = age of IBM, $x - 9$ = age of Dell
   b. On April 1, 2008, Apple Computer Company was 32 years old. How old were the other two companies then?
   IBM: 112 years, Dell: 23 years

56. Abraham Lincoln was inaugurated 60 years after Thomas Jefferson. Barack Obama was inaugurated 208 years after Jefferson. Write algebraic expressions to represent the year of inauguration of each of these presidents.
Jefferson: x, Lincoln: $x + 60$, Obama $x + 208$

57. Florida became a state 27 years after Illinois. California became a state 32 years after Illinois. Write algebraic expressions to represent the year of statehood of each of these states.
Illinois: x, Florida: $x + 27$, California: $x + 32$

58. Minnesota became a state 13 years after Texas. Arizona became a state 67 years after Texas. Write algebraic expressions to represent the year of statehood of each of these states.
Texas: x, Minnesota: $x + 13$, Arizona: $x + 67$

Write an algebraic expression that represents each quantity. See Examples 10–11.

59. How many minutes are there in

a. 5 hours 300

b. h hours? $60h$

▶ **60.** A woman watches television x hours a day. Express the number of hours she watches TV

a. in a week $7x$

b. in a year $365x$

61. a. How many feet are in y yards? $3y$

b. How many yards are in f feet? $\frac{f}{3}$

▶ **62.** A sales clerk earns \$$x$ an hour. How much does he earn in

a. an 8-hour day? \$$8x$

b. a 40-hour week? \$$40x$

Evaluate each expression, for $x = 3$, $y = -2$, and $z = -4$. See Example 12.

63. $(3 + x)y$ -12

▶ **64.** $(4 + z)y$ 0

65. $3y^2 - 6y - 4$ 20

▶ **66.** $-z^2 - z - 12$ -24

67. $(4x)^2 + 3y^2$ 156

68. $4x^2 + (3y)^2$ 72

69. $(x + y)^2 - |z + y|$ -5

70. $[(z - 1)(z + 1)]^2$ 225

71. $-\frac{2x + y^3}{y + 2z}$ $-\frac{1}{5}$

▶ **72.** $-\frac{2z^2 - y}{2x - y^2}$ -17

73. $\frac{yz + 4x}{2z + y}$ -2

74. $\frac{5y + z}{z - x}$ 2

Evaluate each formula for the given values. See Example 13.

▶ **75.** $b^2 - 4ac$ for $a = -1, b = 5$, and $c = -2$ 17

76. $a^2 + 2ab + b^2$ for $a = -5$ and $b = -1$ 36

77. $\frac{n}{2}[2a + (n - 1)d]$ for $n = 10, a = -4$, and $d = 6$ 230

78. $\frac{a(1 - r^n)}{1 - r}$ for $a = -5, r = 2$, and $n = 3$ -35

Complete each table. See Example 14.

79.

x	$x^3 - 1$
0	-1
-1	-2
-3	-28

80.

g	$g^2 - 7g + 1$
0	1
7	1
-10	171

▶ **81.**

s	$\frac{5s + 36}{s}$
1	41
6	11
-12	2

82.

a	$2{,}500a + a^3$
2	5,008
4	10,064
-5	$-12{,}625$

83.

Input x	Output $2x - \frac{x}{2}$
100	150
-300	-450

84.

Input x	Output $\frac{x}{3} + \frac{x}{4}$
12	7
-36	-21

85.

x	$(x + 1)(x + 5)$
-1	0
-5	0
-6	5

86.

x	$\frac{1}{x + 8}$
-7	1
-9	-1
-8	undefined

TRY IT YOURSELF

Translate each phrase into an algebraic expression.

87. The total of 35, h, and 300 $35 + h + 300$

88. x decreased by 17 $x - 17$

▶ **89.** 680 fewer than the entire population p $p - 680$

90. Triple the number of expected participants x $3x$

91. The product of d and 4, decreased by 15 $4d - 15$

92. Forty-five more than the quotient of y and 6 $\frac{y}{6} + 45$

93. Twice the sum of 200 and t $2(200 + t)$

▶ **94.** The square of the quantity 14 less than x $(x - 14)^2$

95. The absolute value of the difference of a and 2 $|a - 2|$

▶ **96.** The absolute value of a, decreased by 2 $|a| - 2$

97. Four more than twice x $2x + 4$

98. Five less than twice w $2w - 5$

APPLICATIONS

▶ **99.** ROCKETRY The algebraic expression $64t - 16t^2$ gives the height of a toy rocket (in feet) t seconds after being launched. Find the height of the rocket for each of the times shown in the table.

t	h
0	0
1	48
2	64
3	48
4	0

100. GROWING SOD To determine the number of square feet of sod *remaining* in a field after filling an order, the manager of a sod farm uses the expression $20{,}000 - 3s$ (where s is the number of 1-foot-by-3-foot strips the customer has ordered). To sod a soccer field, a city orders 7,000 strips of sod. Evaluate the expression for this value of s and explain the result.
$-1{,}000$, the sod farm is short 1,000 ft^2 needed to fill the city's order.

Strips of sod, cut and ready to be loaded on a truck for delivery

101. ANTIFREEZE The expression

$$\frac{5(F - 32)}{9}$$

converts a temperature in degrees Fahrenheit (given as F) to degrees Celsius. Convert the temperatures listed on the container of antifreeze below to degrees Celsius. Round to the nearest degree. −37°C, −64°C

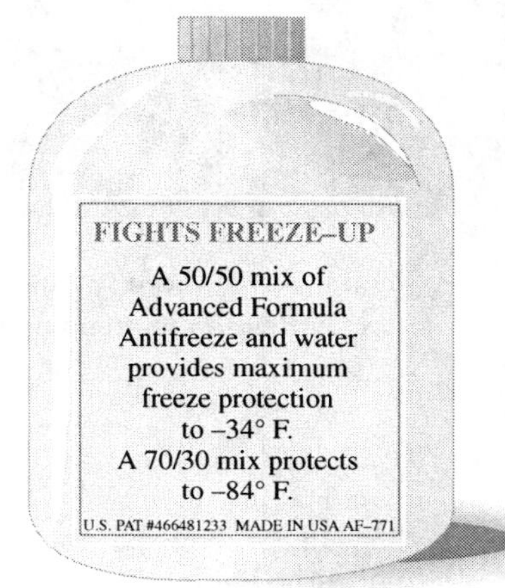

102. TEMPERATURE ON MARS On Mars, maximum summer temperatures can reach 20°C. However, daily temperatures average −33°C. Convert each of these temperatures to degrees Fahrenheit. See Example 13 (page 89). Round to the nearest degree. 68°F, −27°F

103. TOOLS The utility knife blade shown is in the shape of a trapezoid. Find the area of the front face of the blade. The expression $\frac{1}{2}h(b + d)$ gives the area of a trapazoid. $1\frac{23}{64}$ in.^{2}

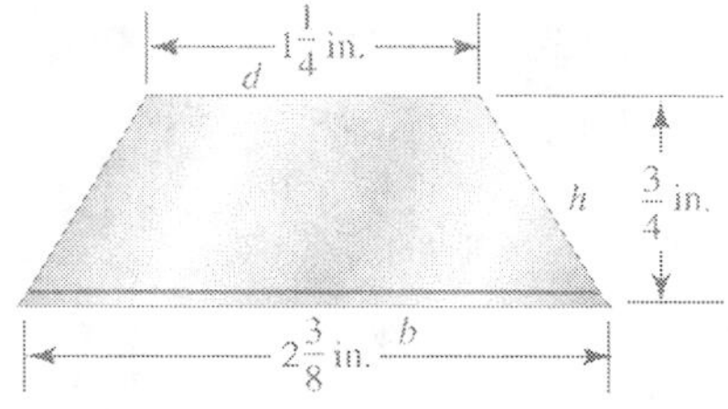

104. TRUMPET MUTES The expression

$$\pi[b^2 + d^2 + (b + d)s]$$

can be used to find the total surface area of the trumpet mute shown. Evaluate the expression for the given dimensions to find the number of square inches of cardboard (to the nearest tenth) used to make the mute. 77.8 in.^{2}

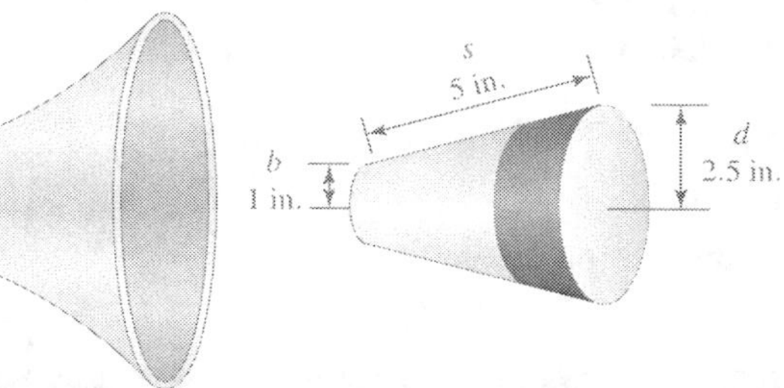

105. LANDSCAPING A grass strip is to be planted around a tree, as shown. Find the number of square feet of sod to order by evaluating the expression $\pi(R^2 - r^2)$. Round to the nearest square foot. 235 ft^2

106. ENERGY CONSERVATION A fiberglass blanket wrapped around a water heater helps prevent heat loss. Find the number of square feet of heater surface the blanket covers by evaluating the algebraic expression $2\pi rh$, where r is the radius and h is the height. Round to the nearest square foot. 69 ft^2

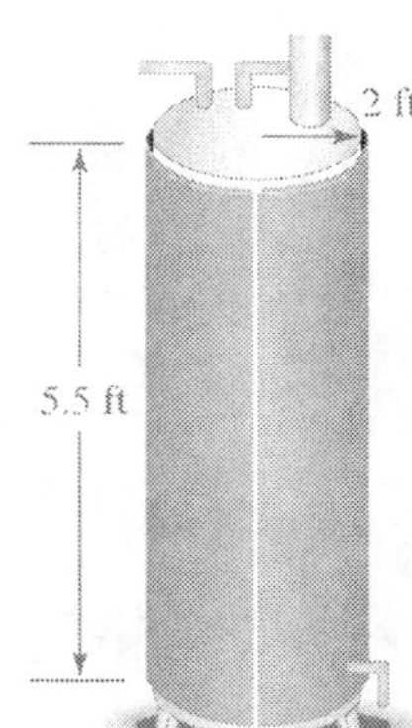

WRITING

107. What is an algebraic expression? Give some examples.

108. What is a variable? How are variables used in this section?

109. In this section, we substituted a number for a variable. List some other uses of the word *substitute* that you encounter in everyday life.

110. Explain why d dimes are not worth d cents.

REVIEW

111. Simplify: -0 0

112. Is the statement $-5 > -4$ true or false? false

113. Evaluate: $\left|-\frac{2}{3}\right|$ $\frac{2}{3}$

114. Evaluate: $2^3 \cdot 3^2$ 72

115. Write $c \cdot c \cdot c \cdot c$ in exponential form. c^4

116. Evaluate: $15 + 2[15 - (12 - 10)]$ 41

117. Find the mean (average) of the three test scores 84, 93, and 72. 83

118. Fill in the blanks: In the multiplication statement $5 \cdot x = 5x$, 5 and x are called factors, and $5x$ is called the product.

Objectives

1 Simplify products.

2 Use the distributive property.

3 Identify like terms.

4 Combine like terms.

SECTION 4.2

Simplifying Algebraic Expressions Using Properties of Real Numbers

In algebra, we often simplify algebraic expressions. To **simplify an algebraic expression,** we use properties of algebra to write the expression in an equivalent, less complicated form.

1 Simplify products.

Two properties that are often used to simplify algebraic expressions are the associative and commutative properties of multiplication. Recall that the associative property of multiplication enables us to change the *grouping of factors* involved in a multiplication. The commutative property of multiplication enables us to change the *order of the factors.*

As an example, let's consider the expression $8(4x)$ and simplify it as follows:

$$8(4x) = 8 \cdot (4 \cdot x) \quad 4x = 4 \cdot x$$

$$= (8 \cdot 4) \cdot x \quad \text{Use the associative property of multiplication to group 4 with 8 instead of with } x.$$

$$= 32x \quad \text{Perform the multiplication within the parentheses: } 8 \cdot 4 = 32.$$

Since $8(4x) = 32x$, we say that $8(4x)$ simplifies to $32x$. To verify that $8(4x)$ and $32x$ are **equivalent expressions** (represent the same number), we can evaluate each expression for several choices of x. For each value of x, the results should be the same.

If $x = 10$		If $x = -3$	
$8(4x) = 8[4(10)]$	$32x = 32(10)$	$8(4x) = 8[4(-3)]$	$32x = 32(-3)$
$= 8(40)$	$= 320$	$= 8(-12)$	$= -96$
$= 320$		$= -96$	

Self Check 1

Simplify each expression:

a. $9 \cdot 6s$ **b.** $8\left(\frac{7}{8}h\right)$

c. $21p(-3q)$ **d.** $-4(6m)(-2m)$

EXAMPLE 1 Simplify each expression:

a. $15a(-7)$ **b.** $5\left(\frac{4}{5}x\right)$ **c.** $-5r(-6s)$ **d.** $3(7p)(-5p)$

Strategy We will use the commutative and associative properties of multiplication to reorder and regroup the factors.

WHY We want to group the numerical factors of the expression together so that we can find their product.

Solution

a. $15a(-7) = 15(-7)a$ — Use the commutative property of multiplication to change the order of the factors.

$= -105a$ — Working left to right, perform the multiplications.

b. $5\left(\frac{4}{5}x\right) = \left(5 \cdot \frac{4}{5}\right)x$ — Use the associative property of multiplication to group the numbers.

$= 4x$ — Multiply: $5 \cdot \frac{4}{5} = \frac{5}{1} \cdot \frac{4}{5} = \frac{\overset{1}{\cancel{5}} \cdot 4}{1 \cdot \underset{1}{\cancel{5}}} = 4$.

c. We note that the expression contains two variables.

$-5r(-6s) = [-5(-6)][r \cdot s]$ — Use the commutative and associative properties of multiplication to group the numbers and group the variables.

$= 30rs$ — Perform the multiplications within the brackets: $-5(-6) = 30$ and $r \cdot s = rs$.

d. $3(7p)(-5p) = [3(7)(-5)](p \cdot p)$ — Use the commutative and associative properties of multiplication to change the order and to regroup the factors.

$= -105p^2$ — Perform the multiplication within the grouping symbols: $3(7)(-5) = -105$ and $p \cdot p = p^2$.

Now Try **Problem 33**

Self Check 1 Answers

a. $54s$ **b.** $7h$ **c.** $-63pq$ **d.** $48m^2$

Teaching Example 1 Simplify each expression:

a. $3 \cdot 4x$

b. $\frac{1}{2}(6x)$

c. $5x(-2y)$

d. $-3(-4x)(2y)$

Answers:

a. $12x$ **b.** $3x$

c. $-10xy$ **d.** $24xy$

Success Tip By the commutative property of multiplication, we can change the order of the factors.

2 Use the distributive property.

To introduce the **distributive property,** we will consider the expression $4(5 + 3)$, which can be evaluated in two ways.

Method 1. Rules for the order of operations: We compute the sum within the parentheses first.

$4(5 + 3) = 4(8)$ — Perform the addition within the parentheses first.

$= 32$ — Perform the multiplication.

Method 2. The distributive property: We multiply both 5 and 3 by 4, and then we add the results.

$4(5 + 3) = 4(5) + 4(3)$ — Distribute the multiplication by 4.

$= 20 + 12$ — Perform the multiplications.

$= 32$ — Perform the addition.

Notice that each method gives a result of 32.

We can interpret the distributive property geometrically. The figure on the next page shows three rectangles that are divided into squares. Since the area of the rectangle on the left-hand side of the equals sign can be found by multiplying its width by its length, its area is $4(5 + 3)$ square units. We can evaluate this expression, or we can count squares; either way, we see that the area is 32 square units.

The area shown on the right-hand side is the sum of the areas of two rectangles: $4(5) + 4(3)$. Either by evaluating this expression or by counting squares, we see that this area is also 32 square units. Therefore,

$$4(5 + 3) = 4(5) + 4(3)$$

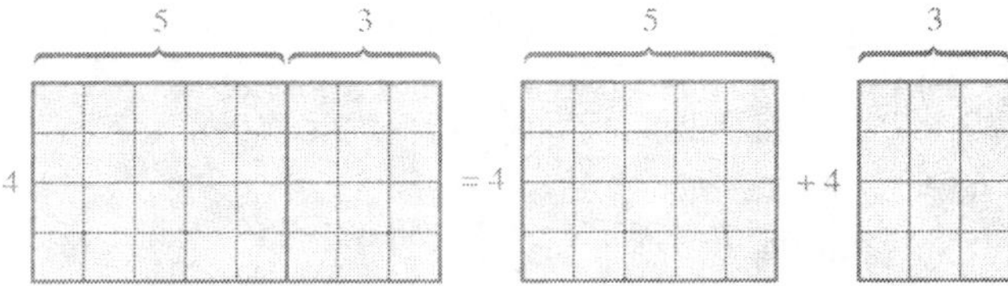

The following figure shows the general case where the width is a and the length is $b + c$.

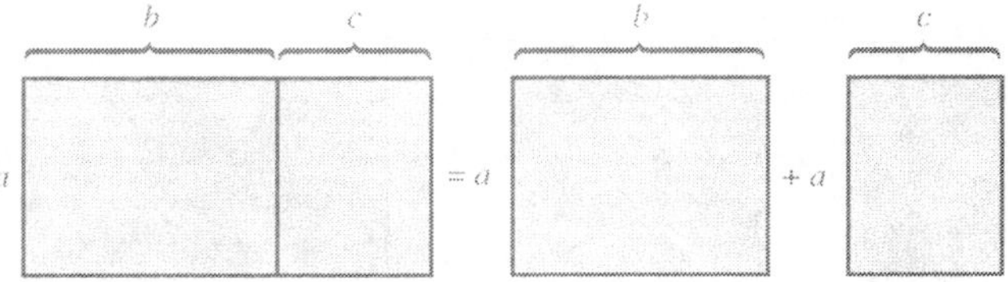

Using the figure as a basis, we can now state the distributive property in symbols.

The Distributive Property

For any real numbers, a, b, and c,

$$a(b + c) = ab + ac$$

Since subtraction is the same as adding the opposite, the distributive property also holds for subtraction.

The Distributive Property

For any real numbers, a, b, and c,

$$a(b - c) = ab - ac$$

To illustrate one use of the distributive property, let's consider the expression $5(x + 2)$. Since we are not given the value of x, we cannot add x and 2 within the parentheses. However, we can distribute the multiplication by the factor of 5 that is outside the parentheses to x and to 2 and add those products.

$5(x + 2) = 5(x) + 5(2)$ Distribute the multiplication by 5.

$= 5x + 10$ Perform the multiplications.

Caution! Since the expression $5(x + 2)$ contains parentheses, some students are tempted to perform the addition within the parentheses first. However, we cannot add x and 2, because we do not know the value of x. Instead, we should multiply $x + 2$ by 5, which requires the use of the distributive property.

EXAMPLE 2 Multiply: **a.** $3(x - 8)$ **b.** $-12(a + 1)$ **c.** $-6(-3y - 8)$

Strategy We will use the distributive property to multiply each term within the parentheses by the factor outside the parentheses.

WHY In each case, we cannot simplify the expression within the parentheses.

Solution

a. $3(x - 8) = 3(x) - 3(8)$ Distribute the multiplication by 3.

$= 3x - 24$ Perform the multiplications.

b. $-12(a + 1) = -12(a) + (-12)(1)$ Distribute the multiplication by −12.

$= -12a + (-12)$ Perform the multiplications.

$= -12a - 12$ Write the addition of −12 as subtraction of 12.

c. $-6(-3y - 8) = -6(-3y) - (-6)(8)$ Distribute the multiplication by −6.

$= 18y - (-48)$ Perform the multiplications.

$= 18y + 48$ Add the opposite of −48, which is 48.

Caution! A common mistake is to forget to distribute the multiplication over each of the terms within the parentheses.

$3(3b - 4) = 9b - 4$

Self Check 2

Multiply:

a. $5(p + 2)$ $5p + 10$

b. $4(t - 1)$ $4t - 4$

c. $-8(2x - 4)$ $-16x + 32$

Now Try **Problem 39**

Teaching Example 2 Multiply:
a. $7(a - 2)$ **b.** $-5(m + 7)$
c. $-4(2x - 5)$
Answers:
a. $7a - 14$ **b.** $-5m - 35$
c. $-8x + 20$

Caution! The fact that an expression contains parentheses does not necessarily mean that the distributive property can be applied. For example, the distributive property does not apply to the expressions:

$6(5x)$ or $6(-7 \cdot y)$ Here a product is multiplied by 6. Simplifying, we have $6(5x) = 30x$ and $6(-7 \cdot y) = -42y$.

However, the distributive property does apply to the expressions:

$6(5 + x)$ or $6(-7 - y)$ Here a sum and a difference are multiplied by 6. Distributing the 6, we have $6(5 + x) = 30 + 6x$ and $6(-7 - y) = -42 - 6y$.

To use the distributive property to simplify $-(x + 10)$, we note that the negative sign in front of the parentheses represents -1.

The − sign represents −1.

$-(x + 10) = -1(x + 10)$

$= -1(x) + (-1)(10)$ Distribute the multiplication by −1.

$= -x + (-10)$ Multiply: $-1(x) = -x$ and $(-1)(10) = -10$.

$= -x - 10$ Write the addition of −10 as a subtraction.

EXAMPLE 3 Simplify: $-(-12 - 3p)$

Strategy We will use the distributive property to multiply each term within the parentheses by -1.

WHY The "−" symbol outside the parentheses represents a factor of -1.

Self Check 3

Simplify: $-(-5x + 18)$ $5x - 18$

Now Try **Problem 49**

Teaching Example 3 Simplify: $-(-4a - 5)$
Answer: $4a + 5$

Solution

$-(-12 - 3p)$

$= -1(-12 - 3p)$ Change the − sign in front of the parentheses to −1.

$= -1(-12) - (-1)(3p)$ Distribute the multiplication by −1.

$= 12 - (-3p)$ Multiply: $-1(-12) = 12$ and $(-1)(3p) = -3p$.

$= 12 + 3p$ To subtract $-3p$, add the opposite of $-3p$, which is $3p$.

Success Tip Notice that distributing the multiplication by −1 changes the sign of each term within the parentheses.

Since multiplication is commutative, we can write the distributive property in the following forms.

$$(b + c)a = ba + ca \qquad (b - c)a = ba - ca$$

Self Check 4

Multiply: $(-6x - 24y)\frac{1}{3}$

Now Try **Problem 54**

Self Check 4 Answers
$-2x - 8y$

Teaching Example 4 Multiply: $(4x - 3)(2)$
Answer:
$8x - 6$

EXAMPLE 4 Multiply: $(6x + 4y)\frac{1}{2}$

Strategy We will use the distributive property to multiply each term within the parentheses by the factor outside the parentheses.

WHY In each case, we cannot simplify the expression within the parentheses.

Solution

$(6x + 4y)\frac{1}{2} = (6x)\frac{1}{2} + (4y)\frac{1}{2}$ Distribute the multiplication by $\frac{1}{2}$.

$= 3x + 2y$ Multiply: $(6x)\frac{1}{2} = \left(6 \cdot \frac{1}{2}\right)x = 3x$ and $(4y)\frac{1}{2} = \left(4 \cdot \frac{1}{2}\right)y = 2y$.

The distributive property can be extended to situations in which there are more than two terms within parentheses.

The Extended Distributive Property

For any real numbers, a, b, and c,

$$a(b + c + d) = ab + ac + ad \quad \text{and} \quad a(b - c - d) = ab - ac - ad$$

Self Check 5

Multiply: $-0.7(2r + 5s - 8)$

Now Try **Problem 57**

Self Check 5 Answers
$-1.4r - 3.5s + 5.6$

Teaching Example 5 Multiply: $-0.4(3m - 2n + 5)$
Answer:
$-1.2m + 0.8n - 2$

EXAMPLE 5 Multiply: $-0.3(3a - 4b + 7)$

Strategy We will use the distributive property to multiply each term within the parentheses by the factor outside the parentheses.

WHY We cannot simplify the expression within the parentheses.

Solution

$-0.3(3a - 4b + 7)$

$= -0.3(3a) - (-0.3)(4b) + (-0.3)(7)$ Distribute the multiplication by −0.3.

$= -0.9a - (-1.2b) + (-2.1)$ Perform the three multiplications.

$= -0.9a + 1.2b + (-2.1)$ To subtract $-1.2b$, add its opposite, which is $1.2b$.

$= -0.9a + 1.2b - 2.1$ Write the addition of -2.1 as a subtraction.

3 Identify like terms.

The expression $5p + 7q - 3p + 12$, which can be written $5p + 7q + (-3p) + 12$, contains four terms, $5p$, $7q$, $-3p$, and 12. Since the variable of $5p$ and $-3p$ are the same, we say that these terms are **like** or **similar terms.**

Like Terms (Similar Terms)

Like terms (or **similar terms**) are terms with exactly the same variables raised to exactly the same powers. Any numbers (called **constants**) in an expression are considered to be like terms.

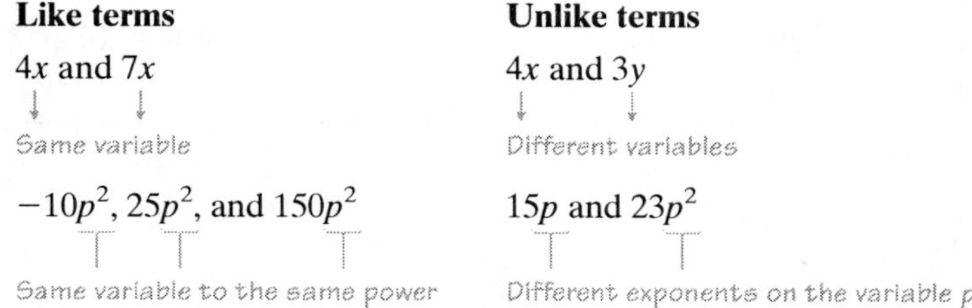

Caution! It is important to be able to distinguish between a *term* of an expression and a *factor* of a term. Terms are separated by + symbols. Factors are numbers and/or variables that are multiplied together. For example, x is a term of the expression $18 + x$, because x and 18 are separated by a + symbol. In the expression $18x + 9$, x is a factor of the term $18x$, because x and 18 are multiplied together.

EXAMPLE 6 List like terms:

a. $7r + 5 + 3r$ **b.** $x^4 - 6x^2 - 5$ **c.** $-7m + 7 - 2 + m$

Strategy First we will identify each term of the expression. Then we will look for terms that contain the same variable factors raised to exactly the same powers.

WHY If terms contain the same variables raised to the same powers, they are like terms.

Solution

a. $7r + 5 + 3r$ contains the like terms $7r$ and $3r$.

b. $x^4 - 6x^2 - 5$ contains no like terms.

c. $-7m + 7 - 2 + m$ contains two pairs of like terms: $-7m$ and m are like terms, and the constants, 7 and -2, are like terms.

Self Check 6

List like terms:

a. $5x - 2y + 7y$

b. $-5pq + 17p - 12q - 2pq$

Now Try **Problem 59**

Self Check 6 Answers

a. $-2y$ and $7y$ b. $-5pq$ and $-2pq$

Teaching Example 6 List like terms:

a. $7 + 2x - 5x$

b. $r^2 + s^2 - 2rs + 5r^2 - rs$

Answers:

a. $2x$ and $-5x$

b. r^2 and $5r^2$, $-2rs$ and $-rs$

4 Combine like terms.

To add (or subtract) objects, they must have the same units. For example, we can add dollars to dollars and inches to inches, but we cannot add dollars to inches. The same is true when we work with terms of an algebraic expression. They can be added or subtracted only when they are like terms.

This expression can be simplified, because it contains like terms.

$3x + 4x$

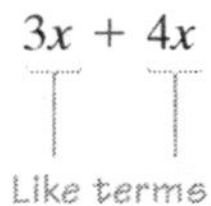

Like terms
The variable parts are identical.

This expression cannot be simplified, because its terms are not like terms.

$3x + 4y$

Unlike terms
The variable parts are not identical.

To simplify an expression containing like terms, we use the distributive property. For example, we can simplify $3x + 4x$ as follows:

$3x + 4x = (3 + 4)x$ Use the distributive property.

$= 7x$ Perform the addition within the parentheses: $3 + 4 = 7$.

We have simplified the expression $3x + 4x$ by **combining like terms.** The result is the equivalent expression $7x$. This example suggests the following general rule.

Combining Like Terms

To add or subtract like terms, combine their coefficients and keep the same variables with the same exponents.

Self Check 7

Simplify by combining like terms:

a. $5n + (-8n)$ $-3n$

b. $-1.2a^3 + 1.4a^3$ $0.2a^3$

Now Try **Problem 65**

Teaching Example 7 Simplify by combining like terms:

a. $-3x - 5x$

b. $2x^3 + 5x^3$

Answers:

a. $-8x$

b. $7x^3$

EXAMPLE 7 Simplify by combining like terms:

a. $-8p + (-12p)$ **b.** $0.5s^2 - 0.3s^2$

Strategy We will use the distributive property in reverse to add (or subtract) the coefficients of the like terms. We will keep the variable factors raised to the same powers.

WHY To *combine like terms* means to add or subtract the like terms in an expression.

Solution

a. $-8p + (-12p) = -20p$ Add the coefficients of the like terms: $-8 + (-12) = -20$. Keep the variable p.

b. $0.5s^2 - 0.3s^2 = 0.2s^2$ Subtract: $0.5 - 0.3 = 0.2$. Keep the variable part s^2.

Self Check 8

Simplify: $8R + 7r - 14R - 21r$

Now Try **Problem 71**

Self Check 8 Answers

$-6R - 14r$

Teaching Example 8 Simplify: $5D + 3d - 7D + d$

Answer:

$-2D + 4d$

EXAMPLE 8 Simplify: $7P - 8p - 12P + 25p$

Strategy We will use the commutative property of addition to write the like terms next to each other. Keep in mind that an uppercase P and a lower case p are different variables.

WHY To *simplify* an expression we use properties of real numbers to write an equivalent expression in simpler form.

Solution

The uppercase P and the lowercase p are different variables. We can use the commutative property of addition to write like terms next to each other.

$7P - 8p - 12P + 25p$

$= 7P + (-8p) + (-12P) + 25p$ Rewrite each subtraction as the addition of the opposite.

$= 7P + (-12P) + (-8p) + 25p$ Use the commutative property of addition to write the like terms together.

$= -5P + 17p$ Combine like terms: $7P + (-12P) = -5P$ and $-8p + 25p = 17p$.

The expression in Example 8 contained two sets of like terms, and we rearranged the terms so that like terms were next to each other. With practice, you will be able to combine like terms without having to write them next to each other.

EXAMPLE 9 Simplify: $4(x + 5) - 3(2x - 4)$

Strategy First we will use the distributive property to remove the parentheses. Then we will identify any like terms and combine them.

WHY To *simplify* an expression we use properties of real numbers, such as the distributive property, to write an equivalent expression in simpler form.

Solution

$4(x + 5) - 3(2x - 4)$

$= 4x + 20 - 6x + 12$ Use the distributive property twice.

$= -2x + 32$ Combine like terms: $4x - 6x = -2x$ and $20 + 12 = 32$.

Self Check 9

Simplify: $-5(y - 4) + 2(4y + 6)$

Now Try **Problem 83**

Self Check 9 Answers

$3y + 32$

Teaching Example 9 Simplify: $3(4x - 2) - 5(x - 2)$

Answer:

$7x + 4$

ANSWERS TO SELF CHECKS

1. a. $54s$ **b.** $7h$ **c.** $-63pq$ **d.** $48m^2$ **2. a.** $5p + 10$ **b.** $4t - 4$ **c.** $-16x + 32$ **3.** $5x - 18$ **4.** $-2x - 8y$ **5.** $-1.4r - 3.5s + 5.6$ **6. a.** $-2y$ and $7y$ **b.** $-5pq$ and $-2pq$ **7. a.** $-3n$ **b.** $0.2a^3$ **8.** $-6R - 14r$ **9.** $3y + 32$

SECTION 4.2 STUDY SET

VOCABULARY

Fill in the blanks.

1. To simplify the expression $5(6x)$ means to write it in the simpler form $5(6x) = 30x$.
2. $5(6x)$ and $30x$ are equivalent expressions because for each value of x, they represent the same number.
3. To perform the multiplication $2(x + 8)$, we use the distributive property to remove parentheses.
4. Terms such as $7x^2$ and $5x^2$, which have the same variables raised to exactly the same powers, are called like terms.

CONCEPTS

5. What property does the equation $a(b + c) = ab + ac$ illustrate? distributive property
6. The illustration shows an application of the distributive property. Fill in the blanks.

$2(3 + 4) = 2(3) + 2(4)$

$2(3 + 4) \quad = \quad 2(3) \quad + \quad 2(4)$

Fill in the blanks.

7. $a(b + c + d) =$ $ab + ac + ad$
8. **a.** $2(x + 4) = 2x + 8$
   b. $2(x - 4) = 2x - 8$
9. **a.** $2(-x + 4) = -2x + 8$
   b. $2(-x - 4) = -2x - 8$
10. **a.** $-2(x + 4) = -2x - 8$
    b. $-2(x - 4) = -2x + 8$
11. **a.** $-2(-x + 4) = 2x - 8$
    b. $-2(-x - 4) = 2x + 8$
12. To add or subtract like terms, combine their coefficients and keep the same variables and exponents.
13. A board was cut into two pieces, as shown. Add the lengths of the two pieces. How long was the original board? $x + 20 - x = 20$, 20 ft

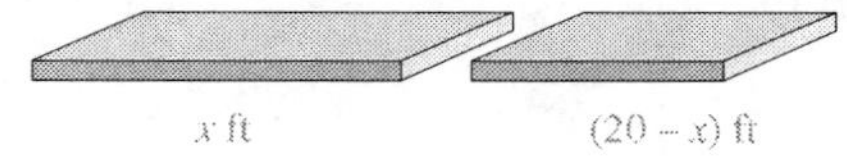

Selected exercises available online at www.webassign.net/brookscole

14. Let x = the number of miles driven on the first day of a 2-day driving trip. Translate the verbal model to mathematical symbols, and simplify by combining like terms. $x + x + 100 = 2x + 100$

The miles driven one day	plus	100 miles more than the miles driven on day 1.

15. Two angles are called **complementary angles** when the sum of their measures is 90°. Add the measures of the angles in illustration (a). Are they complementary angles? yes

16. Two angles are called **supplementary angles** if the sum of their measures is 180°. Add the measures of the angles in illustration (b). Are they supplementary angles? yes

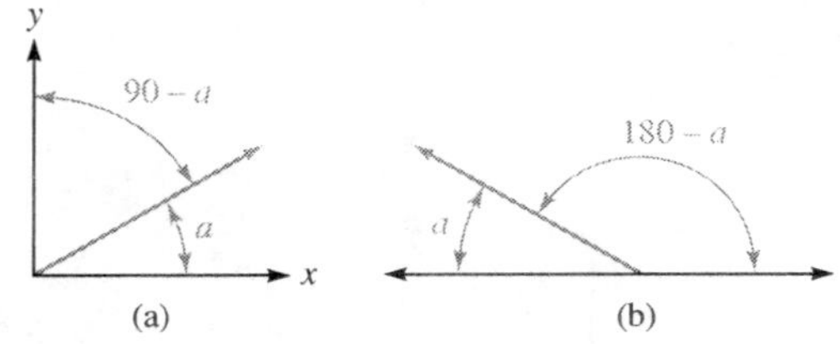

All angle measures are in degrees.

Simplify each expression, if possible.

▶ **17.** $5(2x)$ and $5 + 2x$ $10x$, can't be simplified

▶ **18.** $6(-7x)$ and $6 - 7x$ $-42x$, can't be simplified

▶ **19.** $2(3x)(3)$ and $2 + 3x + 3$ $18x$, $3x + 5$

▶ **20.** $-3(2x)(4)$ and $5 - 3x + 2$ $-24x$, $-3x + 7$

NOTATION

Complete each solution.

21. $7(a + 2) = 7 \cdot a + 7 \cdot 2$

$= 7a + 14$

22. $6(b - 5) + 12b + 7 = 6(b) - 6(5) + 12b + 7$

$= 6b - 30 + 12b + 7$

$= 6b + 12b - 30 + 7$

$= 18b - 23$

23. a. Are $2K$ and $3k$ like terms? no

b. Are $-d$ and d like terms? yes

24. Fill in the blank: $-(x + 10) = -1(x + 10)$

25. Write each expression using fewer symbols.

a. $5x - (-1)$ $5x + 1$ **b.** $16t + (-6)$ $16t - 6$

26. In the table in the next column, a student's answers to five problems are compared to the answers in the back of the book. Are the answers equivalent?

Student's answer	Book's answer	Equivalent?
$10x$	$10 + x$	no
$3 + y$	$y + 3$	yes
$5 - 8a$	$8a - 5$	no
$3(x) + 4$	$3(x + 4)$	no
$2x$	x^2	no

GUIDED PRACTICE

Simplify each expression. See Example 1.

27. $9(7m)$ $63m$

28. $12n(8)$ $96n$

29. $5(-7q)$ $-35q$

▶ **30.** $-7(5t)$ $-35t$

31. $12\left(\frac{5}{12}x\right)$ $5x$

32. $15\left(-\frac{4}{15}w\right)$ $-4w$

33. $(-5p)(-4b)$ $20bp$

▶ **34.** $(-7d)(-7c)$ $49cd$

35. $-5(4r)(-2r)$ $40r^2$

36. $7t(-4t)(-2)$ $56t^2$

37. $8q(-2q)(-3)$ $48q^2$

38. $-3m(-5m)(-2m)$ $-30m^3$

Multiply. See Example 2.

39. $5(x + 3)$ $5x + 15$

▶ **40.** $4(x + 2)$ $4x + 8$

▶ **41.** $-2(b - 1)$ $-2b + 2$

▶ **42.** $-7(p - 5)$ $-7p + 35$

43. $8(3t - 2)$ $24t - 16$

44. $9(2q + 1)$ $18q + 9$

45. $3(-5t - 4)$ $-15t - 12$

▶ **46.** $2(5x - 4)$ $10x - 8$

Multiply. See Example 3.

47. $-(r - 10)$ $-r + 10$

48. $-(h + 4)$ $-h - 4$

49. $-(x - 7)$ $-x + 7$

▶ **50.** $-(y + 1)$ $-y - 1$

Multiply. See Example 4.

51. $(3w - 6)\left(-\frac{2}{3}\right)$ $-2w + 4$

52. $(2y - 8)\frac{1}{2}$ $y - 4$

53. $(9x - 3y)\frac{2}{3}$ $6x - 2y$

▶ **54.** $(4p + 3q)\frac{3}{4}$ $3p + \frac{9}{4}q$

Multiply. See Example 5.

55. $17(2x - y + 2)$ $34x - 17y + 34$

▶ **56.** $-12(3a + 2b - 1)$ $-36a - 24b + 12$

57. $-0.1(-14 + 3p - t)$ $1.4 - 0.3p + 0.1t$

58. $-1.5(-x - y + 5)$ $1.5x + 1.5y - 7.5$

List all like terms, if any. See Example 6.

59. $8p + 7 - 5p$ $8p, -5p$

▶ **60.** $-7m - 3m + 5m$ $-7m, -3m, 5m$

61. $a^4 + 5a^2 - 7$ no like terms

62. $6q^2 + 3q - 5q^2 - 2q$ $6q^2$ and $-5q^2$, $3q$ and $-2q$

Simplify each expression by combining like terms. See Example 7.

63. $3x + 17x$ $20x$
64. $12y - 15y$ $-3y$
65. $8x^2 - 5x^2$ $3x^2$
66. $17x^2 + 3x^2$ $20x^2$
67. $-4x + 4x$ 0
68. $-16y + 16y$ 0
69. $-7b + 7b$ 0
70. $-2c + 2c$ 0

Simplify each expression by combining like terms. See Example 8.

71. $1.8h - 0.7h + p - 3p$ $1.1h - 2p$
72. $-5.7m + 4.3m + 3n - 1.2n$ $-1.4m + 1.8n$
73. $a + a + b$ $2a + b$
74. $-t - t - T - T$ $-2t - 2T$
75. $3x + 5x - 7x + 3y$ $x + 3y$
76. $-x + 3y + 2y$ $-x + 5y$
77. $-13x^2 + 2x^2 - 5y^2 + 2y^2$ $-11x^2 - 3y^2$
78. $-8x^3 - x^3 + 3y + 5y$ $-9x^3 + 8y$

Simplify each expression by combining like terms. See Example 9.

79. $(a + 2) - (a - b)$ $b + 2$
80. $3z + 2(Z - z) + Z$ $3Z + z$
81. $x(x + 3) - 3x^2$ $-2x^2 + 3x$
82. $2x + x(x - 3)$ $x^2 - x$
83. $-(c + 7) - 2(c - 3)$ $-3c - 1$
84. $-(z + 2) + 5(3 - z)$ $-6z + 13$
85. $-(c - 6) + 3(c + 1)$ $2c + 9$
86. $-2(m - 1) - 4(-2 + m)$ $-6m + 10$

TRY IT YOURSELF

Simplify.

87. $0.4(x - 4)$ $0.4x - 1.6$
88. $-2.2(2q + 1)$ $-4.4q - 2.2$
89. $2x + 4(X - x) + 3X$ $7X - 2x$
90. $3p - 6(p + z) + p$ $-2p - 6z$
91. $0 - 3x$ $-3x$
92. $0 - 4a$ $-4a$
93. $0 - (-t)$ t
94. $0 - (-2y)$ $2y$
95. $\frac{3}{5}t + \frac{1}{5}t$ $\frac{4}{5}t$
96. $\frac{3}{16}x - \frac{5}{16}x$ $-\frac{1}{8}x$
97. $(2y - 1)6$ $12y - 6$
98. $(3w - 5)5$ $15w - 25$
99. $3(y - 3) + 4(y + 1)$ $7y - 5$
100. $-5(a - 2) - 4(a + 1)$ $-9a + 6$
101. $8\left(\frac{3}{4}y\right)$ $6y$
102. $27\left(\frac{2}{3}x\right)$ $18x$
103. $-0.2r - (-0.6r)$ $0.4r$
104. $-1.1m - (-2.4m)$ $1.3m$
105. $2z + 5(z - 3)$ $7z - 15$
106. $12(m + 11) - 11$ $12m + 121$

APPLICATIONS

107. THE AMERICAN RED CROSS In 1891, Clara Barton founded the Red Cross. Its symbol is a white flag bearing a red cross. If each side of the cross in the illustration has length x, write an algebraic expression for the perimeter (the total distance around the outside) of the cross. $12x$

108. BILLIARDS Billiard tables vary in size, but all tables are twice as long as they are wide.

a. If the following billiard table is x feet wide, write an expression involving x that represents its length. $2x$ ft

b. Write an expression for the perimeter of the table. $6x$ ft

109. PING-PONG Write an expression for the perimeter of the table shown in the illustration. $(4x + 8)$ ft

110. SEWING Write an expression for the length of the blue trim needed to outline a pennant with the given side lengths. $(5x - 30)$ cm

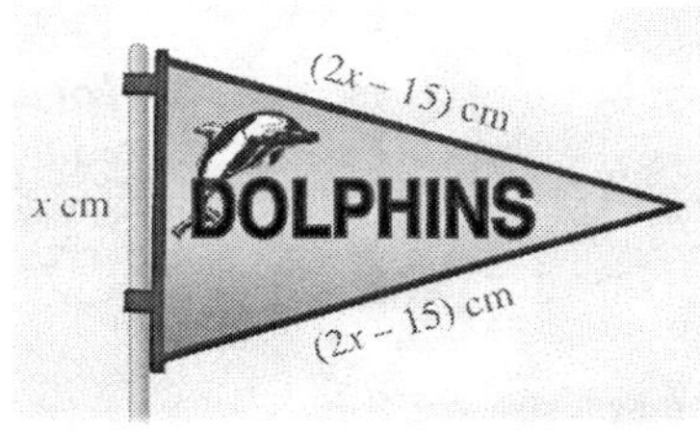

WRITING

111. Explain why the distributive property applies to $2(3 + x)$ but not to $2(3x)$.
112. Explain why $3x^2y$ and $5x^2y$ are like terms, and explain why $3x^2y$ and $5xy^2$ are not like terms.
113. Distinguish between a *factor* and a *term* of an algebraic expression. Give examples.
114. Describe how to combine like terms.

REVIEW

Evaluate each expression for $x = -3$, $y = -5$, and $z = 0$.

115. $x^2z(y^3 - z)$ 0
116. $|y^3 - z|$ 125
117. $\dfrac{x - y^2}{2y - 1 + x}$ 2
118. $\dfrac{2y + 1}{x} - x$ 6

Teaching Guide: Refer to the Instructor's Resource Binder to find activities, worksheets on key concepts, more examples, instruction tips, overheads, and assessments.

SECTION 4.3 Solving Equations Using Properties of Equality

Objectives

1. Determine whether a number is a solution.
2. Use the addition property of equality.
3. Use the subtraction property of equality.
4. Use the multiplication property of equality.
5. Use the division property of equality.

In this section, we introduce four fundamental properties of equality that are used to solve equations.

1 Determine whether a number is a solution.

An **equation** is a statement indicating that two expressions are equal. An example is $x + 5 = 15$. The equal symbol $=$ separates the equation into two parts: The expression $x + 5$ is the **left side** and 15 is the **right side.** The letter x is the **variable** (or the **unknown**). The sides of an equation can be reversed, so we can write $x + 5 = 15$ or $15 = x + 5$.

- An equation can be true: $6 + 3 = 9$
- An equation can be false: $2 + 4 = 7$
- An equation can be neither true nor false. For example, $x + 5 = 15$ is neither true nor false because we don't know what number x represents.

An equation that contains a variable is made true or false by substituting a number for the variable. If we substitute 10 for x in $x + 5 = 15$, the resulting equation is true: $10 + 5 = 15$. If we substitute 1 for x, the resulting equation is false: $1 + 5 = 15$. A number that makes an equation true when substituted for the variable is called a **solution** and it is said to **satisfy** the equation. Therefore, 10 is a solution of $x + 5 = 15$, and 1 is not. The **solution set** of an equation is the set of all numbers that make the equation true.

> ***The Language of Algebra*** It is important to know the difference between an equation and an expression. An equation contains an $=$ symbol and an expression does not.

Self Check 1

Is 25 a solution of $10 - x = 35 - 2x$? yes

Now Try **Problem 19**

Teaching Example 1 Is -2 a solution of $4x - 2 = 3x - 4$?
Answer:
yes

EXAMPLE 1 Is 9 a solution of $3y - 1 = 2y + 7$?

Strategy We will substitute 9 for each y in the equation and evaluate the expression on the left side and the expression on the right side separately.

WHY If a true statement results, 9 is a solution of the equation. If we obtain a false statement, 9 is not a solution.

Solution

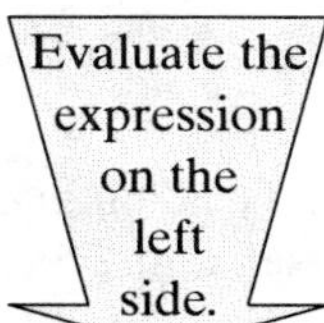

$$3y - 1 = 2y + 7$$
$$3(9) - 1 \stackrel{?}{=} 2(9) + 7$$
$$27 - 1 \stackrel{?}{=} 18 + 7$$
$$26 = 25$$

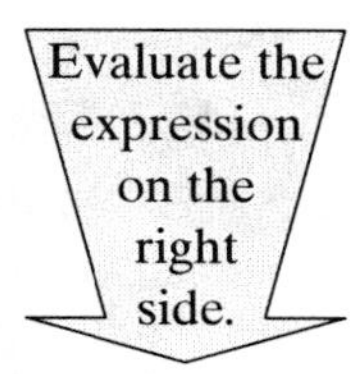

Since $26 = 25$ is false, 9 is not a solution of $3y - 1 = 2y + 7$.

2 Use the addition property of equality.

To **solve an equation** means to find all values of the variable that make the equation true. We can develop an understanding of how to solve equations by referring to the scales shown on the next page.

The first scale represents the equation $x - 2 = 3$. The scale is in balance because the weights on the left side and right side are equal. To find x, we must add 2 to the left side. To keep the scale in balance, we must also add 2 to the right side. After doing this, we see that x grams is balanced by 5 grams. Therefore, x must be 5. We say that we have solved the equation $x - 2 = 3$ and that the solution is 5.

In this example, we solved $x - 2 = 3$ by transforming it to a simpler *equivalent equation*, $x = 5$.

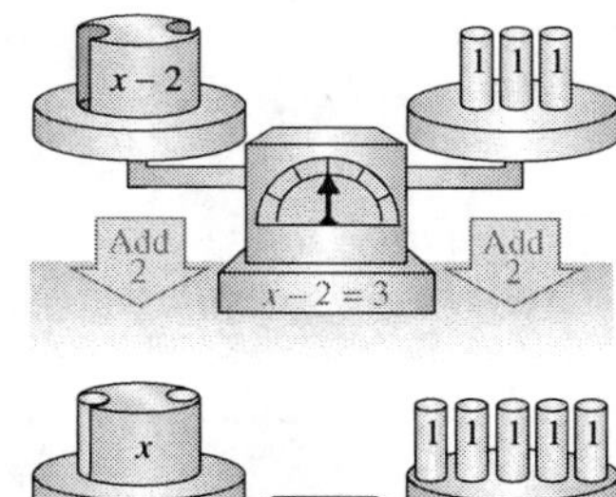

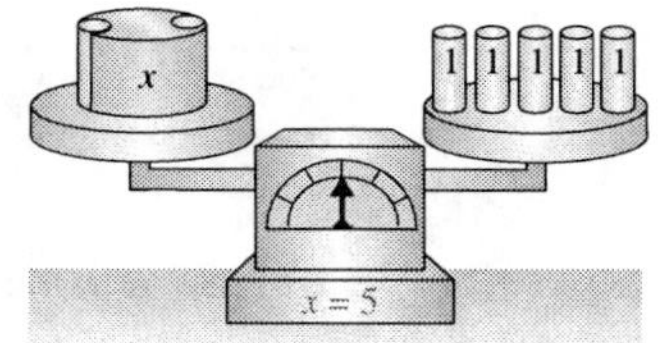

Equivalent Equations

Equations with the same solutions are called **equivalent equations.**

The procedure that we used suggests the following property of equality.

Addition Property of Equality

Adding the same number to both sides of an equation does not change its solution.

For any real numbers a, b, and c,

if $a = b$, then $a + c = b + c$

When we use this property, the resulting equation is *equivalent to the original one.* We will now show how it is used to solve $x - 2 = 3$ algebraically.

EXAMPLE 2 Solve: $x - 2 = 3$

Strategy We will use a property of equality to isolate the variable on one side of the equation.

WHY To solve the original equation, we want to find a simpler equivalent equation of the form $x =$ a number, whose solution is obvious.

Solution

We will use the addition property of equality to isolate x on the left side of the equation. We can undo the subtraction of 2 by adding 2 to both sides.

Self Check 2

Solve: $n - 16 = 33$ 49

Now Try **Problem 37**

Teaching Example 2 Solve: $x - 5 = -1$

Answer:

4

$x - 2 = 3$ This is the equation to solve.

$x - 2 + 2 = 3 + 2$ Add 2 to both sides.

$x + 0 = 5$ The sum of a number and its opposite is zero: $-2 + 2 = 0$.

$x = 5$ When 0 is added to a number, the result is the same number.

Since 5 is obviously the solution of the equivalent equation $x = 5$, the solution of the original equation, $x - 2 = 3$, is also 5. To check this result, we substitute 5 for x in the original equation and simplify.

$x - 2 = 3$

$5 - 2 \stackrel{?}{=} 3$ Substitute 5 for x.

$3 = 3$ True

Since the statement is true, 5 is the solution. A more formal way to present this result is to write the solution within braces as a solution set: {5}.

The Language of Algebra We solve equations by writing a series of steps that result in an equivalent equation of the form

$x = a\ number$

or

$a\ number = x$

We say the variable is *isolated* on one side of the equation. *Isolated* means alone or by itself.

Self Check 3

Solve: **a.** $-5 = b - 38$ 33

b. $-20 + n = 29$ 49

Now Try **Problems 39 and 43**

Teaching Example 3 Solve: $-3 = a - 9$

Answer: 6

EXAMPLE 3 Solve: **a.** $-19 = y - 7$ **b.** $-27 + y = -3$

Strategy We will use a property of equality to isolate the variable on one side of the equation.

WHY To solve the original equation, we want to find a simpler equivalent equation of the form $y =$ **a number** or **a number** $= y$, whose solution is obvious.

Solution

a. To isolate y on the right side, we use the addition property of equality. We can undo the subtraction of 7 by adding 7 to both sides.

$-19 = y - 7$ This is the equation to solve.

$-19 + 7 = y - 7 + 7$ Add 7 to both sides.

$-12 = y$ The sum of a number and its opposite is zero: $-7 + 7 = 0$.

Check: $-19 = y - 7$ This is the original equation.

$-19 \stackrel{?}{=} -12 - 7$ Substitute -12 for y.

$-19 = -19$ True

Since the statement is true, the solution is -12. The solution set is $\{-12\}$.

b. To isolate y, we use the addition property of equality. We can eliminate -27 on the left side by adding its opposite (additive inverse) to both sides.

$-27 + y = -3$ The equation to solve.

$-27 + y + 27 = -3 + 27$ Add 27 to both sides.

$y = 24$ The sum of a number and its opposite is zero: $-27 + 27 = 0$.

Check: $-27 + y = -3$ This is the original equation.

$-27 + 24 \stackrel{?}{=} -3$ Substitute 24 for y.

$-3 = -3$ True

The solution is 24. The solution set is {24}.

Caution! After checking a result, be careful when stating your conclusion. Here, it would be incorrect to say:

The solution is -3.

The number we were checking was 24, not -3.

3 Use the subtraction property of equality.

Since any subtraction can be written as an addition by adding the opposite of the number to be subtracted, the following property is an extension of the addition property of equality.

Subtraction Property of Equality

Subtracting the same number from both sides of an equation does not change its solution.

For any real numbers a, b, and c,

if $a = b$, then $a - c = b - c$

When we use this property, the resulting equation is equivalent to the original one.

EXAMPLE 4

Solve: **a.** $x + \frac{1}{8} = \frac{7}{4}$ **b.** $54.9 + x = 45.2$

Strategy We will use a property of equality to isolate the variable on one side of the equation.

WHY To solve the original equation, we want to find a simpler equivalent equation of the form $x =$ a number, whose solution is obvious.

Solution

a. To isolate x, we use the subtraction property of equality. We can undo the addition of $\frac{1}{8}$ by subtracting $\frac{1}{8}$ from both sides.

$$x + \frac{1}{8} = \frac{7}{4}$$ This is the equation to solve.

$$x + \frac{1}{8} - \frac{1}{8} = \frac{7}{4} - \frac{1}{8}$$ Subtract $\frac{1}{8}$ from both sides.

$$x = \frac{7}{4} - \frac{1}{8}$$ On the left side, $\frac{1}{8} - \frac{1}{8} = 0$.

$$x = \frac{7}{4} \cdot \frac{2}{2} - \frac{1}{8}$$ Build $\frac{7}{4}$ so that it has a denominator of 8.

$$x = \frac{14}{8} - \frac{1}{8}$$ Multiply the numerators and multiply the denominators.

$$x = \frac{13}{8}$$ Subtract the numerators. Write the result over the common denominator 8.

Verify that $\frac{13}{8}$ is the solution by substituting it for x in the original equation and simplifying.

Self Check 4

Solve: **a.** $x + \frac{4}{15} = \frac{11}{5}$ $\frac{29}{15}$

b. $0.7 + a = 0.2$ -0.5

Now Try **Problems 49 and 51**

Teaching Example 4 Solve:
a. $x + \frac{1}{3} = \frac{3}{4}$
b. $36.25 + x = 48.36$
Answers:
a. $\frac{5}{12}$ b. 12.11

b. To isolate x, we use the subtraction property of equality. We can undo the addition of 54.9 by subtracting 54.9 from both sides.

$54.9 + x = 45.2$ This is the equation to solve.

$54.9 + x - 54.9 = 45.2 - 54.9$ Subtract 54.9 from both sides.

$x = -9.7$ On the left side, $54.9 - 54.9 = 0$.

Check: $54.9 + x = 45.2$ This is the original equation.

$54.9 + (-9.7) \stackrel{?}{=} 45.2$ Substitute -9.7 for x.

$45.2 = 45.2$ True

The solution is -9.7. The solution set is $\{-9.7\}$.

4 Use the multiplication property of equality.

The first scale shown below represents the equation $\frac{x}{3} = 25$. The scale is in balance because the weights on the left side and right side are equal. To find x, we must triple (multiply by 3) the weight on the left side. To keep the scale in balance, we must also triple the weight on the right side. After doing this, we see that x is balanced by 75. Therefore, x must be 75.

The procedure that we used suggests the following property of equality.

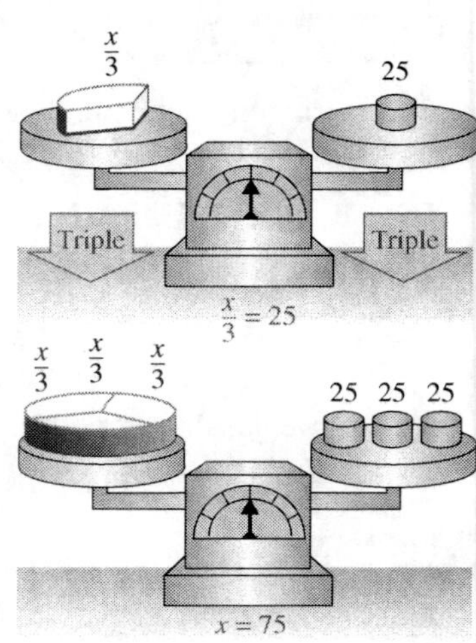

Multiplication Property of Equality

Multiplying both sides of an equation by the same nonzero number does not change its solution.

For any real numbers a, b, and c, where c is not 0,

if $a = b$, then $ca = cb$

When we use this property, the resulting equation is equivalent to the original one. We will now show how it is used to solve $\frac{x}{3} = 25$ algebraically.

Self Check 5

Solve: $\frac{b}{24} = 3$ 72

Now Try **Problem 53**

Teaching Example 5 Solve: $\frac{y}{4} = 12$
Answer:
48

EXAMPLE 5 Solve: $\dfrac{x}{3} = 25$

Strategy We will use a property of equality to isolate the variable on one side of the equation.

WHY To solve the original equation, we want to find a simpler equivalent equation of the form $x =$ **a number**, whose solution is obvious.

Solution

To isolate x, we use the multiplication property of equality. We can undo the division by 3 by multiplying both sides by 3.

$\frac{x}{3} = 25$ This is the equation to solve.

$3 \cdot \frac{x}{3} = 3 \cdot 25$ Multiply both sides by 3.

$\frac{3x}{3} = 75$ Do the multiplications.

$1x = 75$ Simplify $\frac{3x}{3}$ by removing the common factor of 3 in the numerator and denominator: $\frac{3}{3} = 1$.

$x = 75$ The coefficient 1 need not be written since $1x = x$.

If we substitute 75 for x in $\frac{x}{3} = 25$, we obtain the true statement $25 = 25$. This verifies that 75 is the solution. The solution set is {75}.

Since the product of a number and its reciprocal (or multiplicative inverse) is 1, we can solve equations such as $\frac{2}{3}x = 6$, where the coefficient of the variable term is a fraction, as follows.

EXAMPLE 6 Solve: **a.** $\frac{2}{3}x = 6$ **b.** $-\frac{5}{4}x = 3$

Strategy We will use a property of equality to isolate the variable on one side of the equation.

WHY To solve the original equation, we want to find a simpler equivalent equation of the form $x =$ a number, whose solution is obvious.

Solution

a. Since the coefficient of x is $\frac{2}{3}$, we can isolate x by multiplying both sides of the equation by the reciprocal of $\frac{2}{3}$, which is $\frac{3}{2}$.

$\frac{2}{3}x = 6$ This is the equation to solve.

$\frac{3}{2} \cdot \frac{2}{3}x = \frac{3}{2} \cdot 6$ To undo the multiplication by $\frac{2}{3}$, multiply both sides by the reciprocal of $\frac{2}{3}$.

$\left(\frac{3}{2} \cdot \frac{2}{3}\right)x = \frac{3}{2} \cdot 6$ Use the associative property of multiplication to group $\frac{3}{2}$ and $\frac{2}{3}$.

$1x = 9$ On the left, $\frac{3}{2} \cdot \frac{2}{3} = 1$. On the right, $\frac{3}{2} \cdot 6 = \frac{18}{2} = 9$.

$x = 9$ The coefficient 1 need not be written since $1x = x$.

Check: $\frac{2}{3}x = 6$ This is the original equation.

$\frac{2}{3}(9) \stackrel{?}{=} 6$ Substitute 9 for x in the original equation.

$6 = 6$ On the left side, $\frac{2}{3}(9) = \frac{18}{3} = 6$.

Since the statement is true, 9 is the solution. The solution set is {9}.

The Language of Algebra Variable terms with fractional coefficients can be written in two ways. For example:

$\frac{2x}{3} = \frac{2}{3}x$ and $-\frac{5a}{4} = -\frac{5}{4}a$

b. To isolate x, we multiply both sides by the reciprocal of $-\frac{5}{4}$, which is $-\frac{4}{5}$.

Self Check 6

Solve: **a.** $\frac{7}{2}x = 21$ 6

b. $-\frac{3}{8}b = 2$ $-\frac{16}{3}$

Now Try **Problems 61 and 67**

Teaching Example 6 Solve:
a. $\frac{5}{6}x = 10$
b. $-\frac{2}{3}x = 5$
Answers:
a. 12 b. $-\frac{15}{2}$

$-\frac{5}{4}x = 3$	This is the equation to solve.
$-\frac{4}{5}\left(-\frac{5}{4}x\right) = -\frac{4}{5}(3)$	To undo the multiplication by $-\frac{5}{4}$, multiply both sides by the reciprocal of $-\frac{5}{4}$.
$1x = -\frac{12}{5}$	On the left side, $-\frac{4}{5}\left(-\frac{5}{4}\right) = 1$. On the right side, $-\frac{4}{5}(3) = -\frac{12}{5}$.
$x = -\frac{12}{5}$	The coefficient 1 need not be written since $1x = x$.

The solution is $-\frac{12}{5}$. Verify that this is correct by checking.

5 Use the division property of equality.

Since any division can be rewritten as a multiplication by multiplying by the reciprocal, the following property is a natural extension of the multiplication property.

Division Property of Equality

Dividing both sides of an equation by the same nonzero number does not change its solution.

For any real numbers a, b, and c, where c is not 0,

$$\text{if } a = b, \text{ then } \frac{a}{c} = \frac{b}{c}$$

When we use this property, the resulting equation is equivalent to the original one.

Self Check 7

Solve: **a.** $16x = 176$ 11

b. $10.04 = -0.4r$ -25.1

Now Try **Problems 69 and 79**

Teaching Example 7 Solve:
a. $3y = 21$ b. $-3.25 = -2.6y$
Answers:
a. 7 b. 1.25

EXAMPLE 7 Solve: **a.** $2t = 80$ **b.** $-6.02 = -8.6t$

Strategy We will use a property of equality to isolate the variable on one side of the equation.

WHY To solve the original equation, we want to find a simpler equivalent equation of the form $t =$ **a number** or **a number** $= t$, whose solution is obvious.

Solution

a. To isolate t on the left side, we use the division property of equality. We can undo the multiplication by 2 by dividing both sides of the equation by 2.

$2t = 80$	This is the equation to solve.
$\frac{2t}{2} = \frac{80}{2}$	Use the division property of equality: Divide both sides by 2.
$1t = 40$	Simplify $\frac{2t}{2}$ by removing the common factor of 2 in the numerator and denominator: $\frac{2}{2} = 1$.
$t = 40$	The product of 1 and any number is that number: $1t = t$.

If we substitute 40 for t in $2t = 80$, we obtain the true statement $80 = 80$. This verifies that 40 is the solution. The solution set is $\{40\}$.

The Language of Algebra Since division by 2 is the same as multiplication by $\frac{1}{2}$, we can also solve $2t = 80$ using the multiplication property of equality. We could also isolate t by multiplying both sides by the *multiplicative inverse* of 2, which is $\frac{1}{2}$:

$$\frac{1}{2} \cdot 2t = \frac{1}{2} \cdot 80$$

b. To isolate t on the right side, we use the division property of equality. We can undo the multiplication by -8.6 by dividing both sides by -8.6.

$$-6.02 = -8.6t$$ This is the equation to solve.

$$\frac{-6.02}{-8.6} = \frac{-8.6t}{-8.6}$$ Use the division property of equality: Divide both sides by -8.6.

$$0.7 = t$$ Do the division: $8.6\overline{)6.02}$. The quotient of two negative numbers is positive.

The solution is 0.7. Verify that this is correct by checking.

Success Tip It is usually easier to multiply on each side if the coefficient of the variable term is a *fraction,* and divide on each side if the coefficient is an *integer* or *decimal.*

EXAMPLE 8 Solve: $-x = 3$

Strategy The variable x is not isolated, because there is a $-$ sign in front of it. Since the term $-x$ has an understood coefficient of -1, the equation can be written as $-1x = 3$. We need to select a property of equality and use it to isolate the variable on one side of the equation.

WHY To find the solution of the original equation, we want to find a simpler equivalent equation of the form $x =$ **a number**, whose solution is obvious.

Solution

To isolate x, we can either multiply or divide both sides by -1.

Multiply both sides by −1:

$-x = 3$ The equation to solve

$-1x = 3$ Write: $-x = -1x$

$(-1)(-1x) = (-1)3$

$1x = -3$

$x = -3$ $1x = x$

Divide both sides by −1:

$-x = 3$ The equation to solve

$-1x = 3$ Write: $-x = -1x$

$\frac{-1x}{-1} = \frac{3}{-1}$

$1x = -3$ On the left side, $\frac{-1}{-1} = 1$.

$x = -3$ $1x = x$

Check:

$-x = 3$ This is the original equation.

$-(-3) \stackrel{?}{=} 3$ Substitute -3 for x.

$3 = 3$ On the left side, the opposite of -3 is 3.

Since the statement is true, -3 is the solution. The solution set is $\{-3\}$.

Self Check 8

Solve: $-h = -12$ 12

Now Try **Problem 81**

Teaching Example 8 Solve: $-a = -3$
Answer:
3

ANSWERS TO SELF CHECKS

1. Yes **2.** 49 **3. a.** 33 **b.** 49 **4. a.** $\frac{29}{15}$ **b.** -0.5 **5.** 72 **6. a.** 6 **b.** $-\frac{16}{3}$ **7. a.** 11 **b.** -25.1 **8.** 12

SECTION 4.3 STUDY SET

VOCABULARY

Fill in the blanks.

1. An equation, such as $x + 1 = 7$, is a statement indicating that two expressions are equal.
2. Any number that makes an equation true when substituted for the variable is said to satisfy the equation. Such numbers are called solutions.
3. To solve an equation means to find all values of the variable that make the equation true.
4. To solve an equation, we isolate the variable on one side of the equal symbol.
5. Equations with the same solutions are called equivalent equations.
6. To check the solution of an equation, we substitute the value for the variable in the original equation and determine whether the result is a true statement.

CONCEPTS

7. Given $x + 6 = 12$:
   a. What is the left side of the equation? $x + 6$
   b. Is this equation true, false, or neither? neither
   c. Is 5 the solution? no
   d. Does 6 satisfy the equation? yes
8. For each equation, determine what operation is performed on the variable. Then explain how to undo that operation to isolate the variable.
   a. $x - 8 = 24$ subtraction of 8; add 8
   b. $x + 8 = 24$ addition of 8; subtract 8 or add -8
   c. $\frac{x}{8} = 24$ division by 8; multiply by 8
   d. $8x = 24$ multiplication by 8; divide by 8 or multiply by $\frac{1}{8}$
9. Complete the following properties of equality.
   a. If $a = b$, then

   $$a + c = b + c \text{ and } a - c = b - c$$

   b. If $a = b$, then $ca = cb$ and $\frac{a}{c} = \frac{b}{c}$ $(c \neq 0)$
10. a. To solve $\frac{h}{10} = 20$, do we multiply both sides of the equation by 10 or 20? 10
    b. To solve $4k = 16$, do we subtract 4 from both sides of the equation or divide both sides by 4? divide both sides by 4
11. Simplify each expression.
    a. $x + 7 - 7$ x
    b. $y - 2 + 2$ y
    c. $\frac{5t}{5}$ t
    d. $6 \cdot \frac{h}{6}$ h
12. a. To solve $-\frac{4}{5}x = 8$, we can multiply both sides by the reciprocal of $-\frac{4}{5}$. What is the reciprocal of $-\frac{4}{5}$? $-\frac{5}{4}$
    b. What is $-\frac{5}{4}\left(-\frac{4}{5}\right)$? 1

NOTATION

Complete each solution to solve the equation.

13. $$\begin{aligned} x - 5 &= 45 \\ x - 5 + 5 &= 45 + 5 \\ x &= 50 \end{aligned}$$

    Check: $$\begin{aligned} x - 5 &= 45 \\ 50 - 5 &\stackrel{?}{=} 45 \\ 45 &= 45 \text{ True} \end{aligned}$$

    50 is the solution.

14. $$\begin{aligned} 8x &= 40 \\ \frac{8x}{8} &= \frac{40}{8} \\ x &= 5 \end{aligned}$$

    Check: $$\begin{aligned} 8x &= 40 \\ 8(5) &\stackrel{?}{=} 40 \\ 40 &= 40 \text{ True} \end{aligned}$$

    5 is the solution.

15. a. What does the symbol $\stackrel{?}{=}$ mean? is possibly equal to
    b. If you solve an equation and obtain $50 = x$, can you write $x = 50$? yes
16. Fill in the blank: $-x = -1x$

GUIDED PRACTICE

Check to determine whether the given number is a solution of the equation. See Example 1.

17. 6, $x + 12 = 28$ no
18. 110, $x - 50 = 60$ yes
19. -8, $2b + 3 = -15$ no
20. -2, $5t - 4 = -16$ no
21. 5, $0.5x = 2.9$ no
22. 3.5, $1.2 + x = 4.7$ yes
23. -6, $33 - \frac{x}{2} = 30$ no
24. -8, $\frac{x}{4} + 98 = 100$ no
25. -2, $|c - 8| = 10$ yes
26. -45, $|30 - r| = 15$ no
27. 12, $3x - 2 = 4x - 5$ no
28. 5, $5y + 8 = 3y - 2$ no
29. -3, $x^2 - x - 6 = 0$ no
30. -2, $y^2 + 5y - 3 = 0$ no
31. 1, $\frac{2}{a + 1} + 5 = \frac{12}{a + 1}$ yes
32. 4, $\frac{2t}{t - 2} - \frac{4}{t - 2} = 1$ no

Selected exercises available online at www.webassign.net/brookscole

33. $\frac{3}{4}, x - \frac{1}{8} = \frac{5}{8}$ yes

34. $\frac{7}{3}, -4 = a + \frac{5}{3}$ no

35. $-3, (x - 4)(x + 3) = 0$ yes

36. $5, (2x + 1)(x - 5) = 0$ yes

Use a property of equality to solve each equation. Then check the result. See Examples 2–4.

37. $a - 5 = 66$ 71

▶ **38.** $x - 34 = 19$ 53

39. $9 = p - 9$ 18

40. $3 = j - 88$ 91

41. $x - 1.6 = -2.5$ −0.9

42. $y - 1.2 = -1.3$ −0.1

43. $-3 + a = 0$ 3

44. $-1 + m = 0$ 1

45. $d - \frac{1}{9} = \frac{7}{9}$ $\frac{8}{9}$

46. $\frac{7}{15} = b - \frac{1}{15}$ $\frac{8}{15}$

47. $x + 7 = 10$ 3

48. $y + 15 = 24$ 9

49. $s + \frac{1}{5} = \frac{4}{25}$ $-\frac{1}{25}$

▶ **50.** $\frac{1}{6} = h + \frac{4}{3}$ $-\frac{7}{6}$

51. $3.5 + f = 1.2$ −2.3

52. $9.4 + h = 8.1$ −1.3

Use a property of equality to solve each equation. Then check the result. See Example 5.

53. $\frac{x}{15} = 3$ 45

▶ **54.** $\frac{y}{7} = 12$ 84

55. $0 = \frac{v}{11}$ 0

56. $\frac{d}{49} = 0$ 0

57. $\frac{d}{-7} = -3$ 21

58. $\frac{c}{-2} = -11$ 22

59. $\frac{y}{0.6} = -4.4$ −2.64

▶ **60.** $\frac{y}{0.8} = -2.9$ −2.32

Use a property of equality to solve each equation. Then check the result. See Example 6.

61. $\frac{4}{5}t = 16$ 20

62. $\frac{11}{15}y = 22$ 30

63. $\frac{2}{3}c = 10$ 15

▶ **64.** $\frac{9}{7}d = 81$ 63

65. $-\frac{7}{2}r = 21$ −6

66. $-\frac{4}{5}s = 36$ −45

67. $-\frac{5}{4}h = -5$ 4

68. $-\frac{3}{8}t = -3$ 8

Use a property of equality to solve each equation. Then check the result. See Example 7.

▶ **69.** $4x = 16$ 4

70. $5y = 45$ 9

71. $63 = 9c$ 7

▶ **72.** $40 = 5t$ 8

73. $23b = 23$ 1

▶ **74.** $16 = 16h$ 1

75. $-8h = 48$ −6

76. $-9a = 72$ −8

77. $-100 = -5g$ 20

78. $-80 = -5w$ 16

▶ **79.** $-3.4y = -1.7$ 0.5

80. $-2.1x = -1.26$ 0.6

Use a property of equality to solve each equation. Then check the result. See Example 8.

81. $-x = 18$ −18

▶ **82.** $-y = 50$ −50

83. $-n = \frac{4}{21}$ $-\frac{4}{21}$

84. $-w = \frac{11}{16}$ $-\frac{11}{16}$

TRY IT YOURSELF

Solve each equation. Then check the result.

85. $8.9 = -4.1 + t$ 13

▶ **86.** $7.7 = -3.2 + s$ 10.9

87. $-2.5 = -m$ 2.5

88. $-1.8 = -b$ 1.8

89. $-\frac{9}{8}x = 3$ $-\frac{8}{3}$

90. $-\frac{14}{3}c = 7$ $-\frac{3}{2}$

91. $\frac{3}{4} = d + \frac{1}{10}$ $\frac{13}{20}$

92. $\frac{5}{9} = r + \frac{1}{6}$ $\frac{7}{18}$

93. $-15x = -60$ 4

▶ **94.** $-14x = -84$ 6

95. $-10 = n - 5$ −5

▶ **96.** $-8 = t - 2$ −6

97. $\frac{h}{-40} = 5$ −200

▶ **98.** $\frac{x}{-7} = 12$ −84

99. $a - 93 = 2$ 95

100. $18 = x - 3$ 21

APPLICATIONS

101. SYNTHESIZERS To find the unknown angle measure, which is represented by x, solve the equation $x + 115 = 180$. 65°

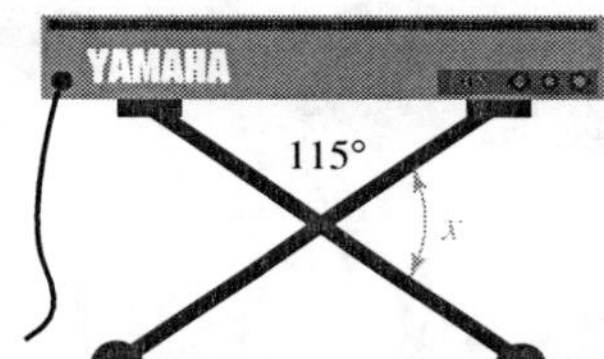

102. STOP SIGNS To find the measure of one angle of the stop sign, which is represented by x, solve the equation $8x = 1{,}080$. 135°

103. SHARING THE WINNING TICKET When a 2006 Florida Lotto Jackpot was won by a group of 16 nurses employed at a Southwest Florida Medical Center, each received \$375,000. To find the amount of the jackpot, which is represented by x, solve the equation $\frac{x}{16} = 375{,}000$. \$6,000,000

104. TENNIS Billie Jean King won 40 Grand Slam tennis titles in her career. This is 14 less than the all-time leader, Martina Navratilova. To find the number of titles won by Navratilova, which is represented by x, solve the equation $40 = x - 14$. 54

WRITING

105. What does it mean to solve an equation?

106. When solving an equation, we *isolate* the variable on one side of the equation. Write a sentence in which the word *isolate* is used in a different context.

107. Explain the error in the following work.

Solve:
$$x + 2 = 40$$
$$x + 2 - 2 = 40$$
$$x = 40$$

108. After solving an equation, how do we check the result?

REVIEW

109. Evaluate $-9 - 3x$ for $x = -3$. 0

110. Evaluate: $-5^2 + (-5)^2$ 0

111. Translate to symbols: Subtract x from 45 $45 - x$

112. Evaluate: $\dfrac{2^3 + 3(5 - 3)}{15 - 4 \cdot 2}$ 2

Objectives

1. Use more than one property of equality to solve equations.
2. Simplify expressions to solve equations.
3. Clear equations of fractions and decimals.
4. Identify identities and contradictions.

SECTION 4.4 More about Solving Equations

We have solved simple equations by using properties of equality. We will now expand our equation-solving skills by considering more complicated equations. We want to develop a general strategy that can be used to solve any kind of *linear equation in one variable*.

Linear Equation in One Variable

A **linear equation in one variable** can be written in the form

$$ax + b = c$$

where a, b and c are real numbers and $a \neq 0$.

1 Use more than one property of equality to solve equations.

Sometimes we must use several properties of equality to solve an equation. For example, on the left side of $2x + 6 = 10$, the variable x is multiplied by 2, and then 6 is added to that product. To isolate x, we use the order of operations rules in reverse. First, we undo the addition of 6, and then we undo the multiplication by 2.

$2x + 6 = 10$	This is the equation to solve.
$2x + 6 - 6 = 10 - 6$	To undo the addition of 6, subtract 6 from both sides.
$2x = 4$	Do the subtractions.
$\dfrac{2x}{2} = \dfrac{4}{2}$	To undo the multiplication by 2, divide both sides by 2.
$x = 2$	Do the divisions.

The solution is 2.

The Language of Algebra We subtract 6 from both sides to isolate the *variable term,* $2x$. Then we divide both sides by 2 to isolate the *variable,* x.

Self Check 1

Solve: $8x - 13 = 43$ 7

Now Try **Problem 15**

Teaching Example 1 Solve: $-15x + 3 = 48$
Answer:
-3

EXAMPLE 1 Solve: $-12x + 5 = 17$

Strategy First we will use a property of equality to isolate the *variable term* on one side of the equation. Then we will use a second property of equality to isolate the *variable* itself.

WHY To solve the original equation, we want to find a simpler equivalent equation of the form $x = $ **a number**, whose solution is obvious.

Solution

- To isolate the variable term, $-12x$, we subtract 5 from both sides to undo the addition of 5.
- To isolate the variable, x, we divide both sides by -12 to undo the multiplication by -12.

	$-12x + 5 = 17$	This is the equation to solve.
	$-12x + 5 - 5 = 17 - 5$	Use the subtraction property of equality: Subtract 5 from both sides to isolate the variable term $-12x$.
	$-12x = 12$	Do the subtractions: $5 - 5 = 0$ and $17 - 5 = 12$.
	$\frac{-12x}{-12} = \frac{12}{-12}$	Use the division property of equality: Divide both sides by -12 to isolate x.
	$x = -1$	Do the divisions.
Check:	$-12x + 5 = 17$	This is the original equation.
	$-12(-1) + 5 \stackrel{?}{=} 17$	Substitute -1 for x.
	$12 + 5 \stackrel{?}{=} 17$	Do the multiplication on the left side.
	$17 = 17$	True

The solution is -1. The solution set is $\{-1\}$.

Caution! When checking solutions, always use the original equation.

EXAMPLE 2

Solve: $\frac{5}{8}m - 2 = -12$

Strategy We will use properties of equality to isolate the variable on one side of the equation.

WHY To solve the original equation, we want to find a simpler equivalent equation of the form $m = \text{a number}$, whose solution is obvious.

Solution

We note that the coefficient of m is $\frac{5}{8}$ and proceed as follows.

- To isolate the variable term $\frac{5}{8}m$, we add 2 to both sides to undo the subtraction of 2.
- To isolate the variable, m, we multiply both sides by $\frac{8}{5}$ to undo the multiplication by $\frac{5}{8}$.

$\frac{5}{8}m - 2 = -12$	This is the equation to solve.
$\frac{5}{8}m - 2 + 2 = -12 + 2$	Use the addition property of equality: Add 2 to both sides to isolate the variable term $\frac{5}{8}m$.
$\frac{5}{8}m = -10$	Do the additions: $-2 + 2 = 0$ and $-12 + 2 = -10$.
$\frac{8}{5}\left(\frac{5}{8}m\right) = \frac{8}{5}(-10)$	Use the multiplication property of equality: Multiply both sides by $\frac{8}{5}$ (which is the reciprocal of $\frac{5}{8}$) to isolate m.
$m = -16$	On the left side: $\frac{8}{5}\left(\frac{5}{8}\right) = 1$ and $1m = m$. On the right side: $\frac{8}{5}(-10) = -\frac{8 \cdot 2 \cdot \cancel{5}}{\cancel{5}} = -16$.

The solution is -16. Verify this by substituting -16 into the original equation. The solution set is $\{-16\}$.

Self Check 2

Solve: $\frac{7}{12}a - 6 = -27$ -36

Now Try **Problem 21**

Teaching Example 2 Solve: $\frac{4}{7}a - 5 = 7$

Answer:
21

Self Check 3

Solve: $-6.6 - m = -2.7$ -3.9

Now Try **Problem 35**

Teaching Example 3 Solve: $-2.4 = -1.1 - x$
Answer:
1.3

EXAMPLE 3 Solve: $-0.2 = -0.8 - y$

Strategy First, we will use a property of equality to isolate the variable term on one side of the equation. Then we will use a second property of equality to isolate the variable itself.

WHY To solve the original equation, we want to find a simpler equivalent equation of the form **a number** $= y$, whose solution is obvious.

Solution

To isolate the variable term $-y$ on the right side, we eliminate -0.8 by adding 0.8 to both sides.

$$-0.2 = -0.8 - y \quad \text{This is the equation to solve.}$$

$$-0.2 + 0.8 = -0.8 - y + 0.8 \quad \text{Add 0.8 to both sides to isolate } -y.$$

$$0.6 = -y \quad \text{Do the additions.}$$

Since the term $-y$ has an understood coefficient of -1, the equation can be written as $0.6 = -1y$. To isolate y, we can either multiply both sides or divide both sides by -1. If we choose to divide both sides by -1, we proceed as follows.

$$0.6 = -1y$$

$$\frac{0.6}{-1} = \frac{-1y}{-1} \quad \text{To undo the multiplication by } -1\text{, divide both sides by } -1.$$

$$-0.6 = y$$

The solution is -0.6. Verify this by substituting -0.6 into the original equation.

2 Simplify expressions to solve equations.

When solving equations, we should simplify the expressions that make up the left and right sides before applying any properties of equality. Often, that involves removing parentheses and/or combining like terms.

Self Check 4

Solve: **a.** $4(a + 2) - a = 11$ 1

b. $9x - 5(x - 9) = 1$ -11

Now Try **Problems 45 and 47**

Teaching Example 4 Solve:
a. $4(x + 1) - 5x = 3$
b. $7y - 3(y - 2) = -6$
Answers:
a. 1 **b.** -3

EXAMPLE 4 Solve: **a.** $3(k + 1) - 5k = 0$ **b.** $8a - 2(a - 7) = 68$

Strategy We will use the distributive property along with the process of combining like terms to simplify the left side of each equation.

WHY It's best to simplify each side of an equation before using a property of equality.

Solution

a. $3(k + 1) - 5k = 0$ This is the equation to solve.

$$3k + 3 - 5k = 0 \quad \text{Distribute the multiplication by 3.}$$

$$-2k + 3 = 0 \quad \text{Combine like terms: } 3k - 5k = -2k.$$

$$-2k + 3 - 3 = 0 - 3 \quad \text{To undo the addition of 3, subtract 3 from both sides. This isolates the variable term } -2k.$$

$$-2k = -3 \quad \text{Do the subtractions: } 3 - 3 = 0 \text{ and } 0 - 3 = -3$$

$$\frac{-2k}{-2} = \frac{-3}{-2} \quad \text{To undo the multiplication by } -2\text{, divide both sides by } -2. \text{ This isolates the variable } k.$$

$$k = \frac{3}{2} \quad \text{Simplify: } \frac{-3}{-2} = \frac{3}{2}.$$

Check:

$$3(k + 1) - 5k = 0 \quad \text{This is the original equation.}$$

$$3\left(\frac{3}{2} + 1\right) - 5\left(\frac{3}{2}\right) \stackrel{?}{=} 0 \quad \text{Substitute } \tfrac{3}{2} \text{ for } k.$$

$$3\left(\frac{5}{2}\right) - 5\left(\frac{3}{2}\right) \stackrel{?}{=} 0 \quad \text{Do the addition within the parentheses. Think of 1 as } \tfrac{2}{2} \text{ and then add: } \tfrac{3}{2} + \tfrac{2}{2} = \tfrac{5}{2}.$$

$$\frac{15}{2} - \frac{15}{2} \stackrel{?}{=} 0 \quad \text{Do the multiplications.}$$

$$0 = 0 \quad \text{True}$$

The solution is $\frac{3}{2}$ and the solution set is $\{\frac{3}{2}\}$.

> ***Caution!*** To check a result, we evaluate each side of the equation following the order of operations rules.

b.

$8a - 2(a - 7) = 68$	This is the equation to solve.
$8a - 2a + 14 = 68$	Distribute the multiplication by −2.
$6a + 14 = 68$	Combine like terms: $8a - 2a = 6a$.
$6a + 14 - 14 = 68 - 14$	To undo the addition of 14, subtract 14 from both sides. This isolates the variable term $6a$.
$6a = 54$	Do the subtractions.
$\frac{6a}{6} = \frac{54}{6}$	To undo the multiplication by 6, divide both sides by 6. This isolates the variable a.
$a = 9$	Do the divisions.

The solution is 9. Verify this by substituting 9 into the original equation.

When solving an equation, if variables appear on both sides, we can use the addition (or subtraction) property of equality to get all variable terms on one side and all constant terms on the other.

EXAMPLE 5 Solve: $3x - 15 = 4x + 36$

Strategy There are variable terms ($3x$ and $4x$) on both sides of the equation. We will eliminate $3x$ from the left side of the equation by subtracting $3x$ from both sides.

WHY To solve for x, all the terms containing x must be on the same side of the equation.

Solution

$3x - 15 = 4x + 36$	This is the equation to solve.
$3x - 15 - 3x = 4x + 36 - 3x$	Subtract $3x$ from both sides to isolate the variable term on the right side.
$-15 = x + 36$	Combine like terms: $3x - 3x = 0$ and $4x - 3x = x$.
$-15 - 36 = x + 36 - 36$	To undo the addition of 36, subtract 36 from both sides.
$-51 = x$	Do the subtractions.

Self Check 5

Solve: $30 + 6n = 4n - 2$ −16

Now Try **Problem 57**

Teaching Example 5 Solve: $5x - 4 = 6x + 10$
Answer: −14

Check:

$$3x - 15 = 4x + 36$$ The original equation.

$$3(-51) - 15 \stackrel{?}{=} 4(-51) + 36$$ Substitute −51 for x.

$$-153 - 15 \stackrel{?}{=} -204 + 36$$ Do the multiplications.

$$-168 = -168$$ True

The solution is −51 and the solution set is {−51}.

3 Clear equations of fractions and decimals.

Equations are usually easier to solve if they don't involve fractions. We can use the multiplication property of equality to clear an equation of fractions by multiplying both sides of the equation by the least common denominator.

Self Check 6

Solve: $\frac{1}{4}x + \frac{1}{2} = -\frac{1}{8}$ $-\frac{5}{2}$

Now Try **Problem 63**

Teaching Example 6 Solve: $\frac{1}{10}x + \frac{4}{5} = \frac{1}{2}$

Answer:

−3

EXAMPLE 6 Solve: $\frac{1}{6}x + \frac{5}{2} = \frac{1}{3}$

Strategy To clear the equations of fractions, we will multiply both sides by their LCD.

WHY It's easier to solve an equation that involves only integers.

Solution

$$\frac{1}{6}x + \frac{5}{2} = \frac{1}{3}$$ This is the equation to solve.

$$6\left(\frac{1}{6}x + \frac{5}{2}\right) = 6\left(\frac{1}{3}\right)$$ Multiply both sides by the LCD of $\frac{1}{6}$, $\frac{5}{2}$, and $\frac{1}{3}$, which is 6. Don't forget the parentheses.

$$6\left(\frac{1}{6}x\right) + 6\left(\frac{5}{2}\right) = 6\left(\frac{1}{3}\right)$$ On the left side, distribute the multiplication by 6.

$$x + 15 = 2$$ Do each multiplication: $6\left(\frac{1}{6}\right) = 1$, $6\left(\frac{5}{2}\right) = \frac{30}{2} = 15$, and $6\left(\frac{1}{3}\right) = \frac{6}{3} = 2$.

$$x + 15 - 15 = 2 - 15$$ To undo the addition of 15, subtract 15 from both sides.

$$x = -13$$

Check the solution by substituting −13 for x in $\frac{1}{6}x + \frac{5}{2} = \frac{1}{3}$.

Caution! Before multiplying both sides of an equation by the LCD, enclose the left and right sides with parentheses or brackets.

$$\left(\frac{1}{6}x + \frac{5}{2}\right) = \left(\frac{1}{3}\right)$$

If an equation contains decimals, it is often convenient to multiply both sides by a power of 10 to change the decimals in the equation to integers.

Self Check 7

Solve:

$(15{,}000 - x)\,0.08x + 0.07 = 1{,}110$ 6,000

Now Try **Problem 71**

EXAMPLE 7 Solve: $0.04(12) + 0.01x = 0.02(12 + x)$

Strategy To clear the equations of decimals, we will multiply both sides by a carefully chosen power of 10.

WHY It's easier to solve an equation that involves only integers.

Solution

The equation contains the decimals 0.04, 0.01, and 0.02. Since the greatest number of decimal places in any one of these numbers is two, we multiply both sides of the equation by 10^2 or 100. This changes 0.04 to 4, and 0.01 to 1, and 0.02 to 2.

$$0.04(12) + 0.01x = 0.02(12 + x)$$

$$100[0.04(12) + 0.01x] = 100[0.02(12 + x)]$$ Multiply both sides by 100. Don't forget the brackets.

$$100 \cdot 0.04(12) + 100 \cdot 0.01x = 100 \cdot 0.02(12 + x)$$ Distribute the multiplication by 100.

$$4(12) + 1x = 2(12 + x)$$ Multiply each decimal by 100 by moving its decimal point 2 places to the right.

$$48 + x = 24 + 2x$$ Distribute the multiplication by 2.

$$48 + x - 24 - x = 24 + 2x - 24 - x$$ Subtract 24 and x from both sides.

$$24 = x$$ Simplify each side.

$$x = 24$$

The solution is 24. Check by substituting 24 for x in the original equation.

Teaching Example 7 Solve: $0.03(15) + 0.03x = 0.04(5 + x)$
Answer:
25

The previous examples suggest the following strategy for solving equations. It is important to note that not every step is needed to solve every equation.

Strategy for Solving Linear Equations in One Variable

1. **Clear the equation of fractions or decimals:** Multiply both sides by the LCD to clear fractions or multiply both sides by a power of 10 to clear decimals.
2. **Simplify each side of the equation:** Use the distributive property to remove parentheses, and then combine like terms on each side.
3. **Isolate the variable term on one side:** Add (or subtract) to get the variable term on one side of the equation and a number on the other using the addition (or subtraction) property of equality.
4. **Isolate the variable:** Multiply (or divide) to isolate the variable using the multiplication (or division) property of equality.
5. **Check the result:** Substitute the possible solution for the variable in the *original* equation to see if a true statement results.

EXAMPLE 8

Solve: $\dfrac{7m + 5}{5} = -4m + 1$

Strategy We will follow the steps of the equation-solving strategy to solve the equation.

WHY This is the most efficient way to solve a linear equation in one variable.

Solution

$$\frac{7m + 5}{5} = -4m + 1$$ This is the equation to solve.

Step 1 $$5\left(\frac{7m + 5}{5}\right) = 5(-4m + 1)$$ Clear the equation of the fraction by multiplying both sides by 5.

Self Check 8

Solve: $6c + 2 = \dfrac{18 - c}{9}$ 0

Now Try **Problem 79**

Teaching Example 8 Solve: $\dfrac{4x + 9}{2} = 3x + 1$
Answer:
$\frac{7}{2}$

Step 2 $7m + 5 = -20m + 5$ — On the left side, remove the common factor 5 in the numerator and denominator. On the right side, distribute the multiplication by 5.

Step 3 $7m + 5 + 20m = -20m + 5 + 20m$ — To eliminate the term $-20m$ on the right side, add $20m$ to both sides.

$27m + 5 = 5$ — Combine like terms: $7m + 20m = 27m$ and $-20m + 20m = 0$.

$27m + 5 - 5 = 5 - 5$ — To isolate the term $27m$, undo the addition of 5 by subtracting 5 from both sides.

$27m = 0$ — Do the subtractions.

Step 4 $\frac{27m}{27} = \frac{0}{27}$ — To isolate m, undo the multiplication by 27 by dividing both sides by 27.

$m = 0$ — 0 divided by any nonzero number is 0.

Step 5 Substitute 0 for m in $\frac{7m + 5}{5} = -4m + 1$ to check that the solution is 0.

> ***Caution!*** Remember that when you multiply one side of an equation by a nonzero number, you must multiply the other side of the equation by the same number.

4 Identify identities and contradictions.

Each of the equations in Examples 1 through 8 had exactly one solution. However, some equations have no solutions while others have infinitely many solutions.

A linear equation in one variable that is true for all values of the variable is an **identity.** One example is the equation

$x + x = 2x$ — If we substitute -10 for x, we get the true statement $-20 = -20$. If we substitute 7 for x, we get $14 = 14$, and so on.

Since we can replace x with any number and the equation will be true, all real numbers are solutions of $x + x = 2x$. This equation has infinitely many solutions. Its solution set is written as {all real numbers}.

An equation that is not true for any values of its variable is called a **contradiction.** One example is

$x = x + 1$ — No number is 1 greater than itself.

Since $x = x + 1$ has no solutions, its solution set is the **empty set,** or **null set,** and is written as $\varnothing$.

Self Check 9

Solve:
$3(x + 5) - 4(x + 4) = -x - 1$

Now Try **Problem 87**

Self Check 9 Answer
All real numbers; the equation is an identity

EXAMPLE 9 Solve: $3(x + 8) + 5x = 2(12 + 4x)$

Strategy We will follow the steps of the equation-solving strategy to solve the equation.

WHY This is the most efficient way to solve a linear equation in one variable.

Solution

$3(x + 8) + 5x = 2(12 + 4x)$ — This is the equation to solve.

$3x + 24 + 5x = 24 + 8x$ — Distribute the multiplication by 3 and by 2.

$$8x + 24 = 24 + 8x$$ Combine like terms: $3x + 5x = 8x$. Note that the sides of the equation are identical.

$$8x - 8x + 24 = 24 + 8x - 8x$$ To eliminate the term $8x$ on the right side, subtract $8x$ from both sides.

$$24 = 24$$ Combine like terms on both sides: $8x - 8x = 0$.

In this case, the terms involving x drop out and the result is true. This means that any number substituted for x in the original equation will give a true statement. Therefore, *all real numbers* are solutions and this equation is an identity.

Teaching Example 9 Solve: $4(x - 3) + 3x = 12(x - 1) - 5x$
Answer:
All real numbers, the equation is an identity.

Success Tip Note that at the step $8x + 24 = 24 + 8x$ we know that the equation is an identity.

EXAMPLE 10 Solve: $3(d + 7) - d = 2(d + 10)$

Strategy We will follow the steps of the equation-solving strategy to solve the equation.

WHY This is the most efficient way to solve a linear equation in one variable.

Solution

$$3(d + 7) - d = 2(d + 10)$$ This is the equation to solve.

$$3d + 21 - d = 2d + 20$$ Distribute the multiplication by 3 and by 2.

$$2d + 21 = 2d + 20$$ Combine like terms: $3d - d = 2d$.

$$2d + 21 - 2d = 2d + 20 - 2d$$ To eliminate the term $2d$ on the right side, subtract $2d$ from both sides.

$$21 = 20$$ Combine like terms on both sides: $2d - 2d = 0$.

In this case, the terms involving d drop out and the result is false. This means that any number that is substituted for d in the original equation will give a false statement. Since this equation has *no solution,* it is a contradiction.

Self Check 10
Solve:
$-4(c - 3) + 2c = 2(10 - c)$

Now Try **Problem 89**

Self Check 10 Answer
No solution; the equation is a contradiction

Teaching Example 10 Solve: $3(y + 2) - 2y = 4(y - 3) - 3y$
Answer:
No solution, the equation is a contradiction.

The Language of Algebra *Contradiction* is a form of the word *contradict,* meaning conflicting ideas. During a trial, evidence might be introduced that *contradicts* the testimony of a witness.

ANSWERS TO SELF CHECKS

1. 7 **2.** −36 **3.** −3.9 **4. a.** 1 **b.** −11 **5.** −16 **6.** $-\frac{5}{2}$ **7.** 6,000 **8.** 0 **9.** All real numbers; the equation is an identity **10.** No solution; the equation is a contradiction

SECTION 4.4 STUDY SET

VOCABULARY

Fill in the blanks.

1. $3x + 8 = 10$ is an example of a linear equation in one variable.
2. To solve $\frac{s}{3} + \frac{1}{4} = -\frac{1}{2}$, we can clear the equation of the fractions by multiplying both sides by 12.
3. A linear equation in one variable that is true for all values of the variable is an identity.
4. An equation that is not true for any values of its variable is called a contradiction.

▶ Selected exercises available online at
www.webassign.net/brookscole

CONCEPTS

Fill in the blanks.

5. To solve $3x - 5 = 1$, we first undo the subtraction of 5 by adding 5 to both sides. Then we undo the multiplication by 3 by dividing both sides by 3.

6. To solve $\frac{x}{2} + 3 = 5$, we can undo the addition of 3 by subtracting 3 from both sides. Then we can undo the division by 2 by multiplying both sides by 2.

7. a. Combine like terms on the left side of $6x - 8 - 8x = -24$. $-2x - 8 = -24$
   b. Distribute and then combine like terms on the right side of $-20 = 4(3x - 4) - 9x$. $-20 = 3x - 16$

8. Is -2 a solution of the equation?
   a. $6x + 5 = 7$ No b. $8(x + 3) = 8$ Yes

9. Multiply.
   a. $20\left(\frac{3}{5}x\right)$ $12x$ b. $100 \cdot 0.02x$ $2x$

10. By what must you multiply both sides of $\frac{2}{3} - \frac{1}{2}b = -\frac{4}{3}$ to clear it of fractions? 6

11. By what must you multiply both sides of $0.7x + 0.3(x - 1) = 0.5x$ to clear it of decimals? 10

12. a. Simplify: $3x + 5 - x$ $2x + 5$
    b. Solve: $3x + 5 = 9$ $\frac{4}{3}$
    c. Evaluate $3x + 5 - x$ for $x = 9$. 23
    d. Check: Is -1 a solution of $3x + 5 - x = 9$? No

NOTATION

Complete the solution.

13. Solve:

$$\begin{aligned} 2x - 7 &= 21 \\ 2x - 7 + 7 &= 21 + 7 \\ 2x &= 28 \\ \frac{2x}{2} &= \frac{28}{2} \\ x &= 14 \end{aligned}$$

Check:

$$\begin{aligned} 2x - 7 &= 21 \\ 2(14) - 7 &\stackrel{?}{=} 21 \\ 28 - 7 &\stackrel{?}{=} 21 \\ 21 &= 21 \end{aligned}$$

14 is the solution.

14. A student multiplied both sides of $\frac{3}{4}t + \frac{5}{8} = \frac{1}{2}t$ by 8 to clear it of fractions, as shown below. Explain his error in showing this step. $8\left(\frac{3}{4}t + \frac{5}{8}\right) = 8 \cdot \frac{1}{2}t$

$$8 \cdot \frac{3}{4}t + \frac{5}{8} = 8 \cdot \frac{1}{2}t$$

GUIDED PRACTICE

Solve each equation and check the result. See Examples 1–2.

15. $2x + 5 = 17$ 6
16. $3x - 5 = 13$ 6
17. $5q - 2 = 23$ 5
18. $4p + 3 = 43$ 10
19. $-33 = 5t + 2$ -7
20. $-55 = 3w + 5$ -20
21. $\frac{5}{6}k - 5 = 10$ 18
22. $\frac{2}{5}c - 12 = 2$ 35
23. $-\frac{7}{16}h + 28 = 21$ 16
24. $-\frac{5}{8}h + 25 = 15$ 16
25. $\frac{t}{3} + 2 = 6$ 12
26. $\frac{x}{5} - 5 = -12$ -35
27. $-3p + 7 = -3$ $\frac{10}{3}$
28. $-2r + 8 = -1$ $\frac{9}{2}$
29. $-5 - 2d = 0$ $-\frac{5}{2}$
30. $-8 - 3c = 0$ $-\frac{8}{3}$
31. $2(-3) + 4y = 14$ 5
32. $4(-1) + 3y = 8$ 4
33. $0.7 - 4y = 1.7$ -0.25
34. $0.3 - 2x = -0.9$ 0.6

Solve each equation and check the result. See Example 3.

35. $1.2 - x = -1.7$ 2.9
36. $0.6 = 4.1 - x$ 3.5
37. $-6 - y = -2$ -4
38. $-1 - h = -9$ 8

Solve each equation and check the result. See Example 4.

39. $3(2y - 2) - y = 5$ $\frac{11}{5}$
40. $2(-3a + 2) + a = 2$ $\frac{2}{5}$
41. $4(5b) + 2(6b - 1) = -34$ -1
42. $9(x + 11) + 5(13 - x) = 0$ -41
43. $-(4 - m) = -10$ -6
44. $-(6 - t) = -12$ -6
45. $10.08 = 4(0.5x + 2.5)$ 0.04
46. $-3.28 = 8(1.5y - 0.5)$ 0.06
47. $6a - 3(3a - 4) = 30$ -6
48. $16y - 8(3y - 2) = -24$ 5
49. $-(19 - 3s) - (8s + 1) = 35$ -11
50. $2(3x) - 5(3x + 1) = 58$ -7

Solve each equation and check the result. See Example 5.

51. $5x = 4x + 7$ 7
52. $3x = 2x + 2$ 2
53. $8y + 44 = 4y$ -11
54. $9y + 36 = 6y$ -12
55. $60r - 50 = 15r - 5$ 1
56. $100f - 75 = 50f + 75$ 3
57. $8y - 2 = 4y + 16$ $\frac{9}{2}$
58. $7 + 3w = 4 + 9w$ $\frac{1}{2}$
59. $2 - 3(x - 5) = 4(x - 1)$ 3
60. $2 - (4x + 7) = 3 + 2(x + 2)$ -2
61. $3(A + 2) = 2(A - 7)$ -20
62. $9(T - 1) = 6(T + 2) - T$ $\frac{21}{4}$

Solve each equation and check the result. See Example 6.

63. $\frac{1}{8}y - \frac{1}{2} = \frac{1}{4}$ 6
64. $\frac{1}{15}x - \frac{4}{5} = \frac{2}{3}$ 22
65. $\frac{1}{3} = \frac{5}{6}x + \frac{2}{9}$ $\frac{2}{15}$
66. $\frac{2}{3} = -\frac{2}{3}x + \frac{3}{4}$ $\frac{1}{8}$

67. $\frac{1}{6}y + \frac{1}{4}y = -1$ $-\frac{12}{5}$

68. $\frac{1}{3}x + \frac{1}{4}x = -2$ $-\frac{24}{7}$

69. $\frac{2}{3}y + 2 = \frac{1}{5} + y$ $\frac{27}{5}$

70. $\frac{2}{5}x + 1 = \frac{1}{3} + x$ $\frac{10}{9}$

Solve each equation and check the result. See Example 7.

71. $0.06(s + 9) - 1.24 = -0.08s$ 5

72. $0.08(x + 50) - 0.16x = 0.04(50)$ 25

73. $0.09(t + 50) + 0.15t = 52.5$ 200

74. $0.08(x - 100) = 44.5 - 0.07x$ 350

75. $0.06(a + 200) + 0.1a = 172$ 1,000

76. $0.03x + 0.05(6{,}000 - x) = 280$ 1,000

77. $0.4b - 0.1(b - 100) = 70$ 200

78. $0.105x + 0.06(20{,}000 - x) = 1{,}740$ 12,000

Solve each equation and check the result. See Example 8.

79. $\frac{10 - 5s}{3} = s$ $\frac{5}{4}$

80. $\frac{40 - 8s}{5} = -2s$ -20

81. $\frac{7t - 9}{16} = t$ -1

82. $\frac{11r + 68}{3} = -3$ -7

83. $\frac{5(1 - x)}{6} = -x + 1$ 1

84. $\frac{3(14 - u)}{8} = -3u + 6$ $\frac{2}{7}$

85. $\frac{3(d - 8)}{4} = \frac{2(d + 1)}{3}$ 80

86. $\frac{3(c - 2)}{2} = \frac{2(2c + 3)}{5}$ 6

Solve each equation, if possible. See Examples 9–10.

87. $8x + 3(2 - x) = 5x + 6$ all real numbers

88. $5(x + 2) = 5x - 2$ no solution

89. $-3(s + 2) = -2(s + 4) - s$ no solution

90. $21(b - 1) + 3 = 3(7b - 6)$ all real numbers

91. $2(3z + 4) = 2(3z - 2) + 13$ no solution

92. $x + 7 = \frac{2x + 6}{2} + 4$ all real numbers

93. $4(y - 3) - y = 3(y - 4)$ all real numbers

94. $5(x + 3) - 3x = 2(x + 8)$ no solution

TRY IT YOURSELF

Solve each equation, if possible. Check the result.

95. $3x - 8 - 4x - 7x = -2 - 8$ $\frac{1}{4}$

96. $-6t - 7t - 5t - 1 = 12 - 3$ $-\frac{5}{9}$

97. $0.05a + 0.01(90) = 0.02(a + 90)$ 30

98. $0.03x + 0.05(2{,}000 - x) = 99.5$ 25

99. $\frac{3(b + 2)}{2} = \frac{4b - 10}{4}$ -11

100. $\frac{2(5a - 7)}{4} = \frac{9(a - 1)}{3}$ -1

101. $4(a - 3) = -2(a - 6) + 6a$ no solution

102. $9(t + 2) = -6(t - 3) + 15t$ all real numbers

103. $10 - 2y = 8$ 1

104. $7 - 7x = -21$ 4

105. $2n - \frac{3}{4}n = \frac{1}{2}n + \frac{13}{3}$ $\frac{52}{9}$

106. $\frac{5}{6}n + 3n = -\frac{1}{3}n - \frac{11}{9}$ $-\frac{22}{75}$

107. $-\frac{2}{3}z + 4 = 8$ -6

108. $-\frac{7}{5}x + 9 = -5$ 10

109. $-2(9 - 3s) - (5s + 2) = -25$ -5

110. $4(x - 5) - 3(12 - x) = 7$ 9

WRITING

111. To solve $3x - 4 = 5x + 1$, one student began by subtracting $3x$ from both sides. Another student solved the same equation by first subtracting $5x$ from both sides. Will the students get the same solution? Explain why or why not.

112. What does it mean to clear an equation such as $\frac{1}{4} + \frac{1}{2}x = \frac{3}{8}$ of the fractions?

113. Explain the error in the following solution.

Solve:
$$2x + 4 = 30$$
$$\frac{2x}{2} + 4 = \frac{30}{2}$$
$$x + 4 = 15$$
$$x + 4 - 4 = 15 - 4$$
$$x = 11$$

114. Write an equation that is an identity. Explain why every real number is a solution.

REVIEW

Name the property that is used.

115. $x \cdot 9 = 9x$ commutative property of multiplication

116. $4 \cdot \frac{1}{4} = 1$ multiplicative inverse property

117. $(x + 1) + 2 = x + (1 + 2)$ associative property of addition

118. $2(30y) = (2 \cdot 30)y$ associative property of multiplication

Objectives

1. Apply the steps of a problem-solving strategy.
2. Solve consecutive integer problems.
3. Solve geometry problems.

SECTION 4.5
Problem Solving

In this section, you will see that algebra is a powerful tool that can be used to solve a wide variety of real-world problems.

1 Apply the steps of a problem-solving strategy.

To become a good problem solver, you need a plan to follow, such as the following five-step strategy.

> ***The Language of Algebra*** A **strategy** is a careful plan or method. For example, a businessman might develop a new advertising *strategy* to increase sales or a long distance runner might have a *strategy* to win a marathon.

Strategy for Problem Solving

1. **Analyze the problem** by reading it carefully. What information is given? What are you asked to find? What vocabulary is given? Often, a diagram or table will help you visualize the facts of the problem.
2. **Form an equation** by picking a variable to represent the numerical value to be found. Then express all other unknown quantities as expressions involving that variable. Key words or phrases can be helpful. Finally, translate the words of the problem into an equation.
3. **Solve the equation.**
4. **State the conclusion** using a complete sentence. Be sure to include the units (such as feet, seconds, or pounds) in your answer.
5. **Check the result** using the original wording of the problem, not the equation that was formed in step 2.

Self Check 1

The Mountain-Bay State Park Bike Trail in Northeast Wisconsin is 76 miles long. A couple rode the trail in four days. Each day they rode 2 miles more than the previous day. How many miles did they ride each day?

Now Try **Problem 16**

Self Check 1 Answer
16 mi, 18 mi, 20 mi, and 22 mi

Teaching Example 1 A mountain climber wants to cut a 213 foot rope into three pieces. If each piece is to be 2 feet longer than the previous one, how long is each piece?
Answer:
69 ft, 71 ft, and 73 ft

EXAMPLE 1 *California Coastline*

The first part of California's magnificent 17-Mile Drive begins at the Pacific Grove entrance and continues to Seal Rock. It is 1 mile longer than the second part of the drive, which extends from Seal Rock to the Lone Cypress. The final part of the tour winds through the Monterey Peninsula, eventually returning to the entrance. This part of the drive is 1 mile longer than four times the length of the second part. How long is each part of 17-Mile Drive?

Analyze The drive is composed of three parts. We need to find the length of each part. We can straighten out the winding 17-Mile Drive and model it with a line segment.

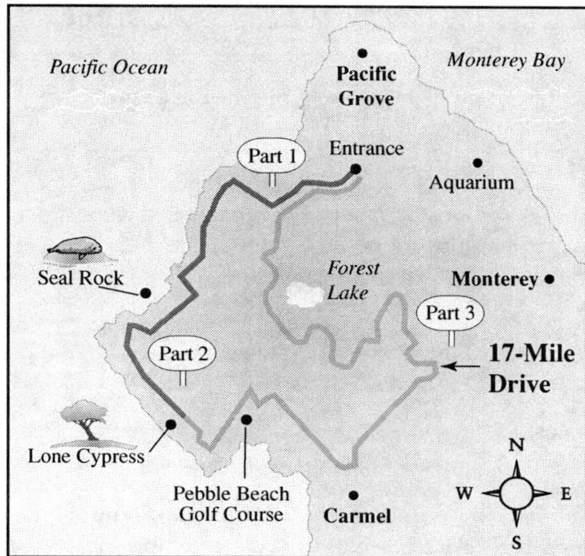

Form Since the lengths of the first part and of the third part of the drive are related to the length of the second part, we will let x represent the length of that part. We then express the other lengths in terms of x. Let

x = the length of the second part of the drive
$x + 1$ = the length of the first part of the drive
$4x + 1$ = the length of the third part of the drive

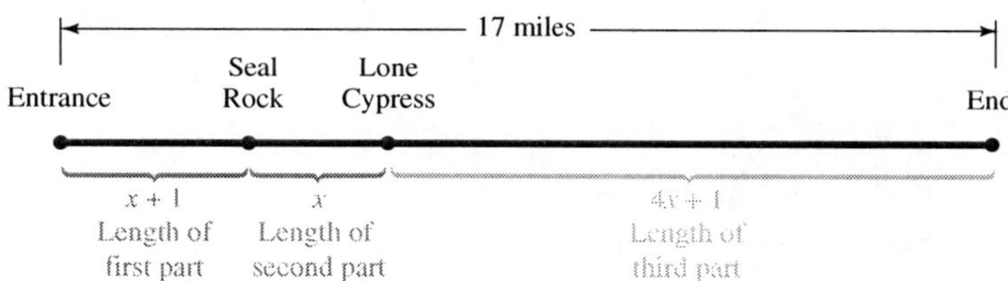

The sum of the lengths of the three parts must be 17 miles.

The length of part 1	plus	the length of part 2	plus	the length of part 3	equals	the total length.
$x + 1$	$+$	x	$+$	$4x + 1$	$=$	17

Solve

$$x + 1 + x + 4x + 1 = 17$$

$6x + 2 = 17$ Combine like terms: $x + x + 4x = 6x$ and $1 + 1 = 2$.

$6x = 15$ To undo the addition of 2, subtract 2 from both sides.

$\frac{6x}{6} = \frac{15}{6}$ To isolate x, undo the multiplication by 6 by dividing both sides by 6.

$x = 2.5$ Do the divisions.

Recall that x represents the length of the second part of the drive. To find the lengths of the first and third parts, we evaluate $x + 1$ and $4x + 1$ for $x = 2.5$.

First part of drive	***Third part of drive***	
$x + 1 = 2.5 + 1$	$4x + 1 = 4(2.5) + 1$	Substitute 2.5 for x.
$= 3.5$	$= 11$	

State The first part of the drive is 3.5 miles long, the second part is 2.5 miles long, and the third part is 11 miles long.

Check Since 3.5 mi + 2.5 mi + 11 mi = 17 mi, the answers check.

Self Check 2

A school club had their motto screenprinted on the front of T-shirts. They were charged $5 per shirt plus a one-time setup fee of $20. If the project cost $255, how many T-shirts were printed? 47

Now Try **Problem 21**

Teaching Example 2 A youth soccer league had shirts printed up for each of the players. They were charged $18 per shirt plus a one time setup fee of $20. If the total due was $4232, how many shirts were printed?
Answer:
234

EXAMPLE 2 *Computer Logos* A trucking company had their logo embroidered on the front of baseball caps. They were charged $8.90 per hat plus a one-time setup fee of $25. If the project cost $559, how many hats were embroidered?

ALL STAR TRUCKING

Analyze

- It cost $8.90 to have a logo embroidered on a hat.
- The setup charge was $25.
- The project cost $559.
- We are to find the number of hats that were embroidered.

Form Let $x =$ the number of hats that were embroidered. If x hats are embroidered, at a cost of $8.90 per hat, the cost to embroider all of the hats is $x \cdot \$8.90$ or $\$8.90x$. Now we translate the words of the problem into an equation.

The cost to embroider on hat	times	the number of hats	plus	the setup charge	equals	the total cost.
8.90	$\cdot$	x	+	25	=	559

Solve

$$8.90x + 25 = 559$$

$$8.90x = 534 \quad \text{To undo the addition of 25, subtract 25 from both sides.}$$

$$\frac{8.90x}{8.90} = \frac{534}{8.90} \quad \text{To isolate } x\text{, undo the multiplication by 8.90 by dividing both sides by 8.90.}$$

$$x = 60 \quad \text{Do the divisions.}$$

State The company had 60 hats embroidered.

Check The cost to embroider 60 hats is 60($8.90) = $534. When the $25 setup charge is added, we get $534 + $25 = $559. The answer checks.

Success Tip The *Form* step is often the hardest. To help, write a **verbal model** of the situation (shown here in blue) and then translate it into an equation.

Self Check 3

A farmer is going to sell one of his Black Angus cattle at an auction and would like to make $2,597 after paying a 6% commission to the auctioneer. For what selling price will the farmer make this amount of money? $2,762.77

Now Try **Problem 27**

Teaching Example 3 A homeowner is planning on selling his home. He wants to get $240,975 after paying a $5\frac{1}{2}$% commission. What selling price is needed to meet his requirement?
Answer: $255,000

EXAMPLE 3 *Auctions* A classic car owner is going to sell his 1960 Chevy Impala at an auction. He wants to make $46,000 after paying an 8% commission to the auctioneer. For what selling price (called the "hammer price") will the car owner make this amount of money?

Analyze When the commission is subtracted from the selling price of the car, the owner wants to have $46,000 left.

Form Let $x =$ the selling price of the car. The amount of the commission is 8% of x, or $0.08x$. Now we translate the words of the problem to an equation.

The selling price of the car	minus	the auctioneer's commission	should be	$46,000.
x	−	$0.08x$	=	46,000

Solve

$$x - 0.08x = 46{,}000$$

$$0.92x = 46{,}000 \quad \text{Combine like terms: } 1.00x - 0.08x = 0.92x.$$

$$\frac{0.92x}{0.92} = \frac{46{,}000}{0.92} \quad \text{To isolate } x \text{, undo the multiplication by 0.92 by dividing both sides by 0.92.}$$

$$x = 50{,}000 \quad \text{Do the divisions.}$$

State The owner will make \$46,000 if the car sells for \$50,000.

Check An 8% commission on \$50,000 is 0.08(\$50,000) = \$4,000. The owner will keep \$50,000 − \$4,000 = \$46,000. The answer checks.

2 Solve consecutive integer problems.

Integers that follow one another, such as 15 and 16, are called **consecutive integers.** They are 1 unit apart. **Consecutive even integers** are even integers that differ by 2 units, such as 12 and 14. Similarly, **consecutive odd integers** differ by 2 units, such as 9 and 11. When solving consecutive integer problems, if we let x = the first integer, then

- two consecutive integers are x and $x + 1$
- two consecutive even integers are x and $x + 2$
- two consecutive odd integers are x and $x + 2$

EXAMPLE 4 *U.S. History* The year George Washington was chosen president and the year the Bill of Rights went into effect are consecutive odd integers whose sum is 3,580. Find the years.

Analyze We need to find two consecutive odd integers whose sum is 3,580. From history, we know that Washington was elected president first and the Bill of Rights went into effect later.

Form Let x = the first odd integer (the date when Washington was chosen president). The next odd integer is 2 *greater than* x, therefore $x + 2$ = the next larger odd integer (the date when the Bill of Rights went into effect).

The first odd integer	plus	the second odd integer	is	3,580.
x	$+$	$x + 2$	$=$	3,580

Solve

$$x + x + 2 = 3{,}580$$

$$2x + 2 = 3{,}580 \quad \text{Combine like terms: } x + x = 2x.$$

$$2x = 3{,}578 \quad \text{To undo the addition of 2, subtract 2 from both sides.}$$

$$x = 1{,}789 \quad \text{To isolate } x \text{, undo the multiplication by 2 by dividing both sides by 2.}$$

State George Washington was chosen president in the year 1789. The Bill of Rights went into effect in 1789 + 2 = 1791.

Check 1789 and 1791 are consecutive odd integers whose sum is 1789 + 1791 = 3,580. The answers check.

Self Check 4

The definitions of the words *little* and *lobby* are on back-to-back pages in a dictionary. If the sum of the page numbers is 1,159, on what page can the definition of *little* be found? 579

Now Try **Problem 33**

Teaching Example 4 The birth years of the three children in a family are consecutive even integers. The sum of the integers is 5982. Find the year of each child's birth.
Answer:
1992, 1994, 1996

The Language of Algebra *Consecutive* means following one after the other in order. Elton John holds the record for the most *consecutive* years with a song on the Top 50 music chart: 31 years (1970 to 2000).

3 Solve geometry problems.

Self Check 5

A rectangular counter for the customer service department of a store is 6 feet longer than it is wide. If the perimeter is 32 feet, find the outside dimensions of the counter. 5 ft by 11 ft

Now Try **Problem 39**

Teaching Example 5 A woman has 28 meters of fencing to make a rectangular kennel. If the kennel is to be 6 meters longer than it is wide, find its dimensions.
Answer:
4 m by 10 m

EXAMPLE 5 *Crime Scenes* Police used 400 feet of yellow tape to fence off a rectangular-shaped lot for an investigation. Fifty less feet of tape was used for each width as for each length. Find the dimensions of the lot.

Analyze Since the yellow tape surrounded the lot, the concept of perimeter applies. Recall that the formula for the perimeter of a rectangle is $P = 2l + 2w$. We also know that the width of the lot is 50 feet less than the length.

Form Since the width of the lot is given in terms of the length, we let l = the length of the lot. Then $l - 50$ = the width. Using the perimeter formula, we have:

2	times	the length	plus	2	times	the width	is	the perimeter.
2	$\cdot$	l	$+$	2	$\cdot$	$(l - 50)$	$=$	400

Solve

$2l + 2(l - 50) = 400$ Write the parentheses so that the entire expression $l - 50$ is multiplied by 2.

$2l + 2l - 100 = 400$ Distribute the multiplication by 2.

$4l - 100 = 400$ Combine like terms: $2l + 2l = 4l$.

$4l = 500$ To undo the subtraction of 100, add 100 to both sides.

$l = 125$ To isolate l, undo the multiplication by 4 by dividing both sides by 4.

State The length of the lot is 125 feet and width is $125 - 50 = 75$ feet.

Check The width (75 feet) is 50 less than the length (125 feet). The perimeter of the lot is $2(125) + 2(75) = 250 + 150 = 400$ feet. The answers check.

Self Check 6

The perimeter of an isosceles triangle is 32 cm. If the base is 8 cm, find the length of each remaining side. 12 cm, 12 cm

Now Try **Problem 43**

Teaching Example 6 The perimeter of an isosceles triangle is 24 cm. If the base is 6 cm, find the length of each remaining side.
Answer: 9 cm, 9 cm

EXAMPLE 6 *Isosceles Triangles* If the vertex angle of an isosceles triangle is 56°, find the measure of each base angle.

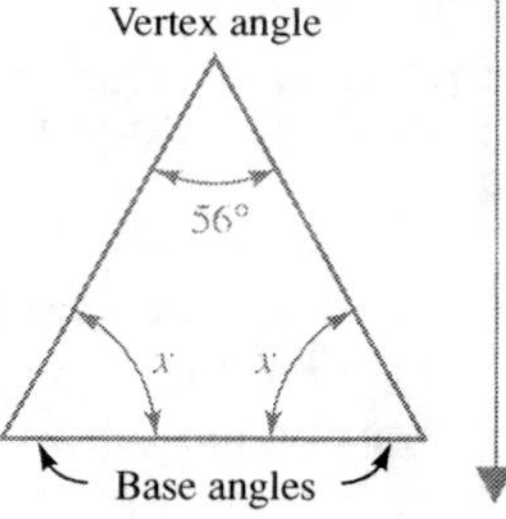

Analyze An **isosceles triangle** has two sides of equal length, which meet to form the **vertex angle.** In this case, the measurement of the vertex angle is 56°. We can sketch the triangle as shown. The **base angles** opposite the equal sides are also equal. We need to find their measure.

Form If we let x = the measure of one base angle, the measure of the other base angle is also x. Since the sum of the angles of any triangle is 180°, the sum of the base angles and the vertex angle is 180°. We can use this fact to form the equation.

One base angle	plus	the other base angle	plus	the vertex angle	is	180°.
x	$+$	x	$+$	56	$=$	180

Solve

$x + x + 56 = 180$

$2x + 56 = 180$ Combine like terms: $x + x = 2x$.

$2x = 124$ To undo the addition of 56, subtract 56 from both sides.

$x = 62$ To isolate x, undo the multiplication by 2 by dividing both sides by 2.

State The measure of each base angle is 62°.

Check Since 62° + 62° + 56° = 180°, the answer checks.

ANSWERS TO SELF CHECKS

1. 16 mi, 18 mi, 20 mi, 22 mi **2.** 47 **3.** \$2,762.77 **4.** 579 **5.** 5 ft by 11 ft **6.** 12 cm, 12 cm

SECTION 4.5 STUDY SET

VOCABULARY

Fill in the blanks.

1. Integers that follow one another, such as 7 and 8, are called consecutive integers.
2. An isosceles triangle is a triangle with two sides of the same length.
3. The equal sides of an isosceles triangle meet to form the vertex angle. The angles opposite the equal sides are called base angles, and they have equal measures.
4. When asked to find the dimensions of a rectangle, we are to find its length and width.

CONCEPTS

5. A 17-foot pipe is cut into three sections. The longest section is three times as long as the shortest, and the middle-sized section is 2 feet longer than the shortest. Complete the diagram.

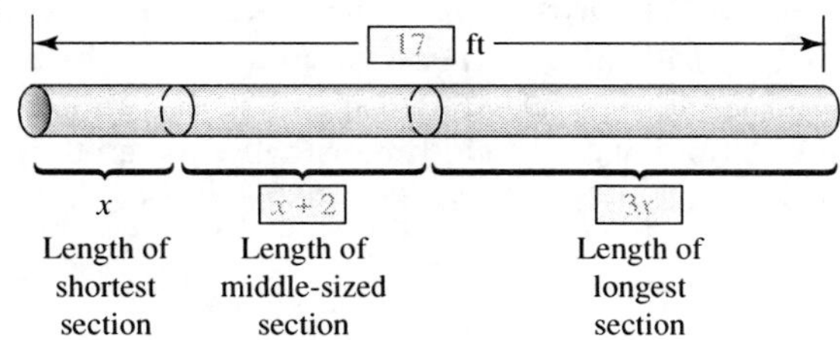

6. It costs \$28 per hour to rent a trailer. Write an expression that represents the cost to rent the trailer for x hours. \$28x
7. A realtor is paid a 3% commission on the sale of a house. Write an expression that represents the amount of the commission if a house sells for \$$x$. \$0.03x
8. The perimeter of the rectangle is 15 feet. Fill in the blanks: $2(5x - 1) + 2x = 15$

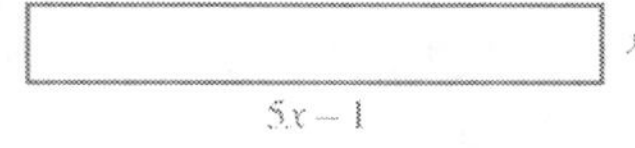

9. What is the sum of the measures of the angles of any triangle? 180°
10. What is x? 25

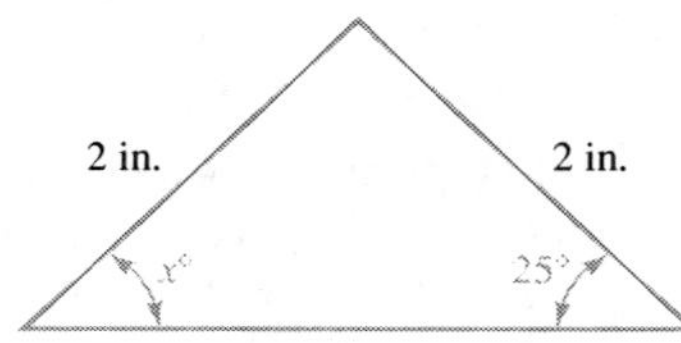

NOTATION

11. **a.** If x represents an integer, write an expression for the next largest integer. $x + 1$

Selected exercises available online at www.webassign.net/brookscole

b. If x represents an odd integer, write an expression for the next largest odd integer. $x + 2$

12. What does 45° mean? 45 degrees

GUIDED PRACTICE

See Examples 1–3.

13. A 12-foot board has been cut into two sections, one twice as long as the other. How long is each section? 4 ft, 8 ft

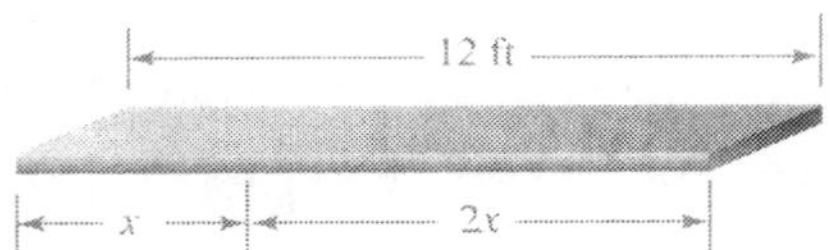

14. The robotic arm will extend a total distance of 18 feet. Find the length of each section. 5 ft, 9 ft, 4 ft

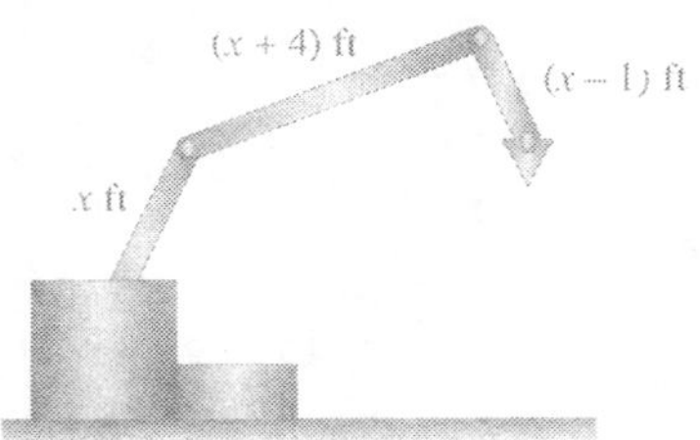

15. NATIONAL PARKS The Natchez Trace Parkway is a historical 444-mile route from Natchez, Mississippi, to Nashville, Tennessee. A couple drove the Trace in four days. Each day they drove 6 miles more than the previous day. How many miles did they drive each day? 102 mi, 108 mi, 114 mi, 120 mi

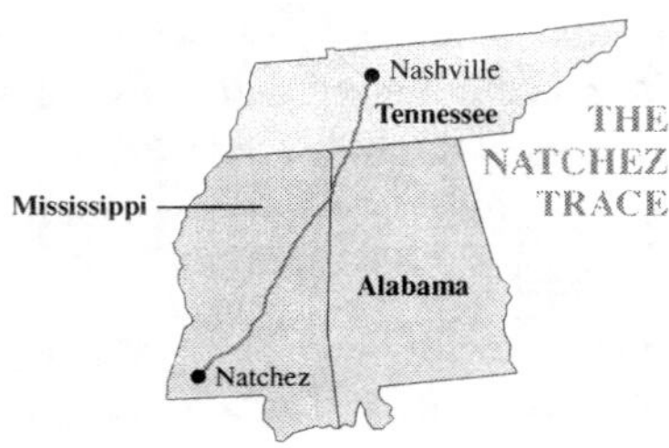

16. TOURING A rock group plans to travel for a total of 38 weeks, making three concert stops. They will be in Japan for 4 more weeks than they will be in Australia. Their stay in Sweden will be 2 weeks shorter than that in Australia. How many weeks will they be in each country? Australia: 12 wk, Japan: 16 wk, Sweden: 10 wk

17. SOLAR HEATING Refer to the illustration in the next column. One solar panel is 3.4 feet wider than the other. Find the width of each panel. 7.3 ft, 10.7 ft

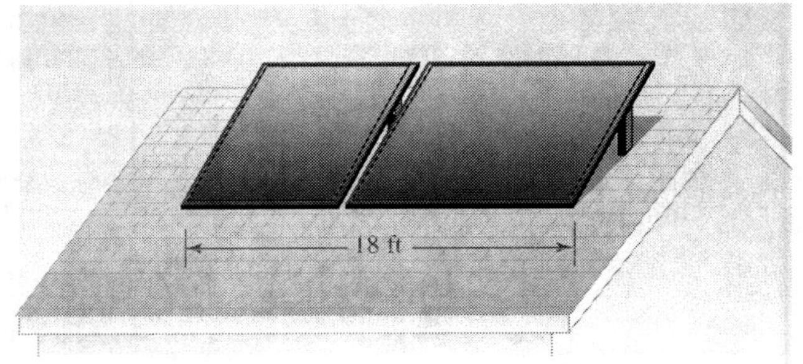

18. ACCOUNTING Determine the 2005 income of Abercrombie & Fitch Company for each quarter from the data in the graph. in millions of dollars: $40, $57, $72, $165

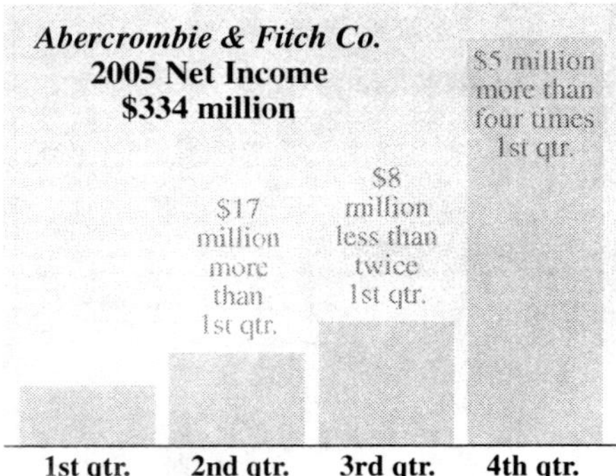

19. COUNTING CALORIES A slice of pie with a scoop of ice cream has 850 calories. The calories in the pie alone are 100 more than twice the calories in the ice cream alone. How many calories are in each food? 250 calories in ice cream, 600 calories in pie

20. WASTE DISPOSAL Two tanks hold a total of 45 gallons of a toxic solvent. One tank holds 6 gallons more than twice the amount in the other. How many gallons does each tank hold? 13 gal, 32 gal

21. CONCERTS The fee to rent a concert hall is $2,250 plus $150 per hour to pay for the support staff. For how many hours can an orchestra rent the hall and stay within a budget of $3,300? 7

22. TRUCK MECHANICS An engine repair cost a truck owner $1,185 in parts and labor. If the parts were $690 and the mechanic charged $45 per hour, how many hours did the repair take? 11

23. FIELD TRIPS It costs a school $65 a day plus $0.25 per mile to rent a 15-passenger van. If the van is rented for two days, how many miles can be driven on a $275 budget? 580

24. DECORATIONS A party supply store charges a set-up fee of $80 plus 35¢ per balloon to make a balloon arch. A business has $150 to spend on decorations for their grand opening. How many balloons can they have in the arch? (*Hint:* 35¢ = $0.35.) 200

25. TUTORING High school students enrolling in a private tutoring program must first take a placement test (cost $25) before receiving tutoring (cost $18.75 per hour). If a family has set aside $400 to get their child extra help, how many hours of tutoring can they afford? 20

26. DATA CONVERSION The *Books2Bytes* service converts old print books to Microsoft Word electronic files for $20 per book plus $2.25 per page. If it cost $1,201.25 to convert a novel, how many pages did the novel have? 525

27. CATTLE AUCTIONS A cattle rancher is going to sell one of his prize bulls at an auction and would like to make $45,500 after paying a 9% commission to the auctioneer. For what selling price will the rancher make this amount of money? $50,000

28. LISTING PRICE At what price should a home be listed if the owner wants to make $567,000 on its sale after paying a 5.5% real estate commission? $600,000

29. SAVINGS ACCOUNTS The balance in a savings account grew by 5% in one year, to $5,512.50. What was the balance at the beginning of the year? $5,250

30. AUTO INSURANCE Between the years 2000 and 2006, the average cost for auto insurance nationwide grew 27%, to $867. What was the average cost in 2000? Round to the nearest dollar. $683

Consecutive integer problems See Example 4.

31. SOCCER Ronaldo of Brazil and Gerd Mueller of Germany rank 1 and 2, respectively, with the most goals scored in World Cup play. The number of goals Ronaldo and Mueller have scored are consecutive integers that total 29. Find the number of goals scored by each man. Ronaldo: 15, Mueller: 14

32. DICTIONARIES The definitions of the words *job* and *join* are on back-to-back pages in a dictionary. If the sum of those page numbers is 1,411, on what page can the definition of *job* be found? 705

33. TV HISTORY *Friends* and *Leave It to Beaver* are two of the most popular television shows of all time. The number of episodes of each show are consecutive even integers whose sum is 470. If there are more episodes of *Friends*, how many episodes of each were there? *Friends*: 236, *Leave It to Beaver*: 234

34. VACATIONS The table in the next column shows the average number of vacation days an employed adult receives for selected countries. Complete the table. (The numbers of days are listed in descending order.)

Average number of vacation days per year

Country	Days
Italy	42
France	37
Germany	35
U.S.	13

Consecutive odd integers whose sum is 72.

Source: *The World Almanac*, 2006

35. CELEBRITY BIRTHDAYS Elvis Presley, George Foreman, and Kirstie Alley have birthdays (in that order) on consecutive even-numbered days in January. The sum of the calendar dates of their birthdays is 30. Find each birthday. Jan. 8, 10, 12

36. LOCKS The three numbers of the combination for a lock are consecutive integers, and their sum is 81. Find the combination. 26, 27, 28

Geometry problems See Examples 5–6.

37. TENNIS The perimeter of a regulation singles tennis court is 210 feet and the length is 3 feet less than three times the width. What are the dimensions of the court? width: 27 ft, length: 78 ft

38. SWIMMING POOLS The seawater Orthlieb Pool in Casablanca, Morocco, is the largest swimming pool in the world. With a perimeter of 1,110 meters, this rectangular-shaped pool is 30 meters longer than 6 times its width. Find its dimensions. 75 m by 480 m

39. ART The *Mona Lisa* was completed by Leonardo da Vinci in 1506. The length of the picture is 11.75 inches shorter than twice the width. If the perimeter of the picture is 102.5 inches, find its dimensions. 21 in. by 30.25 in.

40. NEW YORK CITY Central Park, which lies in the middle of Manhattan, is rectangular-shaped and has a 6-mile perimeter. The length is 5 times the width. What are the dimensions of the park? width: 0.5 mi, length: 2.5 mi

41. ENGINEERING A truss is in the form of an isosceles triangle. Each of the two equal sides is 4 feet shorter than the third side. If the perimeter is 25 feet, find the lengths of the sides. 7 ft, 7 ft, 11 ft

42. FIRST AID A sling is in the shape of an isosceles triangle with a perimeter of 144 inches. The longest side of the sling is 18 inches longer than either of the other two sides. Find the lengths of each side. 60 in., 42 in., 42 in.

43. TV TOWERS The two guy wires supporting a tower form an isosceles triangle with the ground. Each of the base angles of the triangle is 4 times the third angle (the vertex angle). Find the measure of the vertex angle. 20°

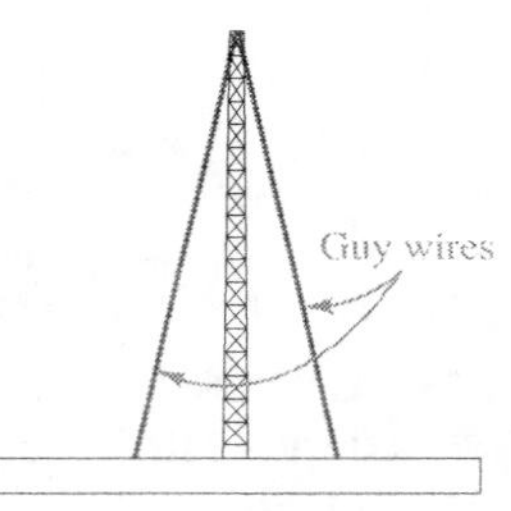

44. CLOTHESLINES A pair of damp jeans are hung in the middle of a clothesline to dry. Find $x°$, the angle that the clothesline makes with the horizontal. 11°

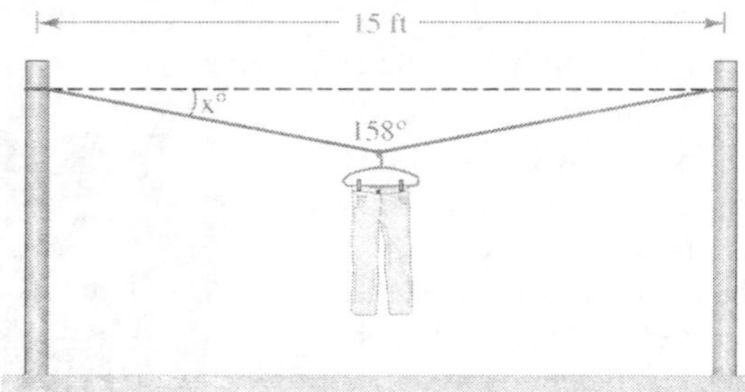

45. MOUNTAIN BICYCLES For the bicycle frame shown in the next column, the angle that the horizontal crossbar makes with the seat support is 15° less than twice the angle at the steering column. The angle at the pedal gear is 25° more than the angle at the steering column. Find these three angle measures. 42.5°, 70°, 67.5°

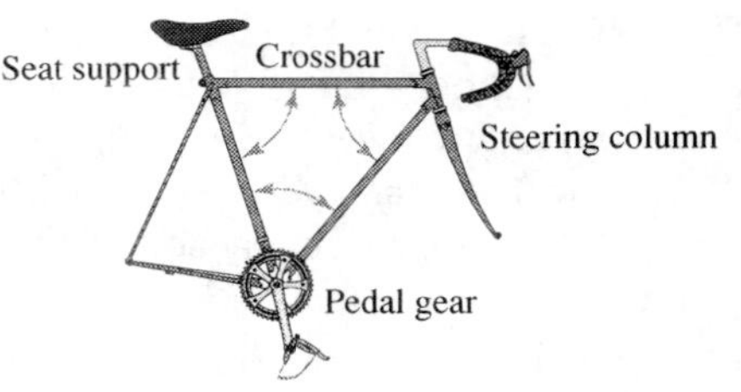

46. TRIANGLES The measure of $\angle 1$ (read as angle 1) of a triangle is one-half that of $\angle 2$. The measure of $\angle 3$ is equal to the sum of the measures of $\angle 1$ and $\angle 2$. Find each angle measure. 30°, 60°, 90°

47. COMPLEMENTARY ANGLES Two angles are called ***complementary angles*** when the sum of their measures is 90°. Find the measures of the complementary angles shown in the illustration. 22°, 68°

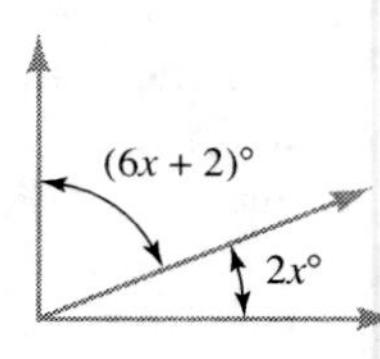

48. SUPPLEMENTARY ANGLES Two angles are called ***supplementary angles*** when the sum of their measures is 180°. Find the measures of the supplementary angles shown in the illustration. 40°, 140°

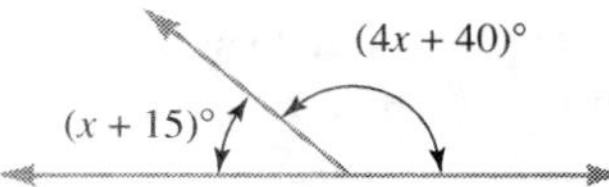

WRITING

49. Create a geometry problem that could be answered by solving the equation $2w + 2(w + 5) = 26$.

50. What information do you need to know to answer the following question?

A business rented a copy machine for \$85 per month plus 4¢ for every copy made. How many copies can be made each month?

51. Make a list of words and phrases that translate to an equal symbol =.

52. Define the word *strategy*.

REVIEW

Solve.

53. $\frac{5}{8}x = -15$ −24

54. $\frac{12x + 24}{13} = 36$ 37

55. $\frac{3}{4}y = \frac{2}{5}y - \frac{3}{2}y - 2$ $-\frac{40}{37}$

56. $6 + 4(1 - x) = 3(x + 1)$ 1

57. $4.2(y - 4) - 0.6y = -13.2$ 1

58. $16 - 8(b + 4) = 24b + 64$ $-\frac{5}{2}$

SECTION 4.6
More about Problem Solving

Objectives

1. Solve investment problems.
2. Solve uniform motion problems.
3. Solve liquid mixture problems.
4. Solve dry mixture problems.
5. Solve number-value problems.

In this section, we will solve problems that involve money, motion, and mixtures. Tables are a helpful way to organize the information given in these problems.

1 Solve investment problems.

To find the amount of *simple interest* I an investment earns, we use the formula $I = Prt$, where P is the principal (the amount invested), r is the annual interest rate, and t is the time in years.

EXAMPLE 1 *Paying Tuition* A college student invested the $12,000 inheritance he received and decided to use the annual interest earned to pay his tuition cost of $945. The highest rate offered by a bank at that time was 6% annual simple interest. At this rate, he could not earn the needed $945, so he invested some of the money in a riskier, but more profitable, investment offering a 9% return. How much did he invest at each rate?

Analyze We know that $12,000 was invested for 1 year at two rates: 6% and 9%. We are asked to find the amount invested at each rate so that the total return would be $945.

Form Let $x =$ the amount invested at 6%. Then $12{,}000 - x =$ the amount invested at 9%. To organize the facts of the problem, we enter the principal, rate, time, and interest earned in a table.

Step 1: List each investment in a row of the table.

Bank				
Riskier investment				

Step 2: Label the columns using $I = Prt$ reversed and also write Total:.

	P	$\cdot\ r$	$\cdot\ t =$	I
Bank				
Riskier investment				
				Total:

Step 3: Enter the rates, times, and total interest.

	P	$\cdot\ r$	$\cdot\ t =$	I
Bank		**0.06**	**1**	
Riskier investment		**0.09**	**1**	
				Total: **945**

Self Check 1

A student invested $4,200 in certificates of deposit, one at 2% and the other at 3%. Find the amount invested at each rate if the first year combined interest income from the two investments was $102.

Now Try **Problem 17**

Self Check 1 Answer
$2,400 at 2%, $1,800 at 3%

Teaching Example 1 A professor has $15,000 to invest for 1 year, some at 8% and the rest at 7%. If she will earn $1,110 from these investments, how much did she invest at each rate?
Answer:
$6,000 at 8%, $9,000 at 7%

Step 4: Enter each unknown principal.

	P	$\cdot\ r$	$\cdot\ t =$	I
Bank	x	0.06	1	
Riskier investment	**12,000 − x**	0.09	1	
				Total: 945

Step 5: In the last column, multiply P, r, and t to obtain expressions for the interest earned.

	P	$\cdot\ r$	$\cdot\ t =$	I
Bank	x	0.06	1	**0.06x**
Riskier investment	$12{,}000 - x$	0.09	1	**0.09(12,000 − x)**
				Total: 945

← This is $x \cdot 0.06 \cdot 1$.

This is $(12{,}000 - x) \cdot 0.09 \cdot 1$.

Use the information in this column to form an equation.

The interest earned at 6%	plus	the interest earned at 9%	equals	the total interest.
$0.06x$	$+$	$[0.09(12{,}000 - x)]$	$=$	945

Solve

$$0.06x + 0.09(12{,}000 - x) = 945$$

$$100[0.06x + 0.09(12{,}000 - x)] = 100(945)$$ Multiply both sides by 100 to clear the equation of decimals.

$$100(0.06x) + 100(0.09)(12{,}000 - x) = 100(945)$$ Distribute the multiplication by 100.

$$6x + 9(12{,}000 - x) = 94{,}500$$ Do the multiplications by 100.

$$6x + 108{,}000 - 9x = 94{,}500$$ Use the distributive property.

$$-3x + 108{,}000 = 94{,}500$$ Combine like terms.

$$-3x = -13{,}500$$ Subtract 108,000 from both sides.

$$x = 4{,}500$$ To isolate x, divide both sides by -3.

State The student invested \$4,500 at 6% and \$12,000 − \$4,500 = \$7,500 at 9%.

Check The first investment earned 0.06(\$4,500), or \$270. The second earned 0.09(\$7,500), or \$675. Since the total return was \$270 + \$675 = \$945, the answers check.

2 Solve uniform motion problems.

If we know the rate r at which we will be traveling and the time t we will be traveling at that rate, we can find the distance d traveled by using the formula $d = rt$.

EXAMPLE 2 *Rescues at Sea* A cargo ship, heading into port, radios the Coast Guard that it is experiencing engine trouble and that its speed has dropped to 3 knots (this is 3 sea miles per hour). Immediately, a Coast Guard cutter leaves port and speeds at a rate of 25 knots directly toward the disabled ship, which is 56 sea miles away. How long will it take the Coast Guard to reach the ship? (Sea miles are also called nautical miles.)

Analyze We know the *rate* of each ship (25 knots and 3 knots), and we know that they must close a *distance* of 56 sea miles between them. We don't know the *time* it will take to do this.

Form Let t = the time it takes the Coast Guard to reach the cargo ship. During the rescue, the ships don't travel at the same rate, but they do travel for the same amount of time. Therefore, t also represents the travel time for the cargo ship.

We enter the rates, the variable t for each time, and the total distance traveled by the ships (56 sea miles) in the table. To fill in the last column, we use the formula $r \cdot t = d$ twice to find an expression for each distance traveled: $25 \cdot t = 25t$ and $3 \cdot t = 3t$.

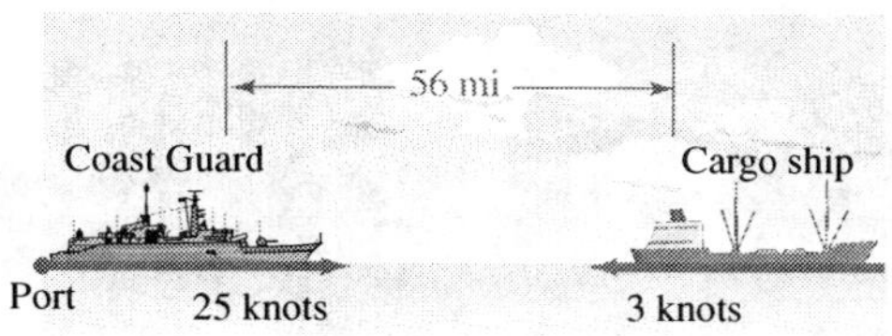

	r	$\cdot\ t$	$= d$
Coast Guard cutter	25	t	$25t$
Cargo ship	3	t	$3t$
		Total: 56	

Multiply $r \cdot t$ to obtain an expression for each distance traveled.

Use the information in this column to form an equation.

The distance the cutter travels	plus	the distance the ship travels	equals	the original distance between the ships.
$25t$	$+$	$3t$	$=$	56

Solve

$$25t + 3t = 56$$

$$28t = 56 \quad \text{Combine like terms: } 25t + 3t = 28t.$$

$$t = \frac{56}{28} \quad \text{To isolate } t \text{, divide both sides by 28.}$$

$$t = 2 \quad \text{Do the division.}$$

State The ships will meet in 2 hours.

Check In 2 hours, the Coast Guard cutter travels $25 \cdot 2 = 50$ sea miles, and the cargo ship travels $3 \cdot 2 = 6$ sea miles. Together, they travel $50 + 6 = 56$ sea miles. Since this is the original distance between the ships, the answer checks.

Success Tip A sketch is helpful when solving uniform motion problems.

Self Check 2

Two search-and-rescue teams leave base at the same time looking for a lost boy. The first team, on foot, heads north at 2 mph, and the other, on horseback, heads south at 4 mph. How long will it take them to search a distance of 21 miles between them? 3.5 hr

Now Try **Problem 27**

Teaching Example 2 A car leaves Rockford traveling toward Wausau at the rate of 55 mph. At the same time, another car leaves Wausau traveling toward Rockford at the rate of 50 mph. How long will it take them to meet if the cities are 157.5 miles apart?
Answer:
$1\frac{1}{2}$ hr

Self Check 3

A car leaves a vacation spot traveling at 50 mph. Half an hour later, their friends leave the same spot in a second car traveling at 60 mph. How long will it take the second car to catch up with their friends? 2.5 hr

Now Try **Problem 31**

Teaching Example 3 A bus carrying a group of campers leaves Normal, Illinois, traveling at a rate of 45 miles per hour. Half an hour later a car leaves Normal traveling at 65 miles per hour with camping gear that the campers forgot. How long will it take the car to catch the bus?
Answer:
1.625 hr or ≈ 1 hr, 38 min

EXAMPLE 3 *Concert Tours* While on tour, a country music star travels by bus. Her musical equipment is carried in a truck. How long will it take her bus, traveling 60 mph, to overtake the truck, traveling at 45 mph, if the truck had a $1\frac{1}{2}$-hour head start to her next concert location?

Analyze We know the rate of each vehicle (60 mph and 45 mph) and that the truck began the trip $1\frac{1}{2}$ or 1.5 hours earlier than the bus. We need to determine how long it will take the bus to catch up to the truck.

Form Let t = the time it takes the bus to overtake the truck. With a 1.5-hour head start, the truck is on the road longer than the bus. Therefore, $t + 1.5$ = the truck's travel time.

We enter each rate and time in the table, and use the formula $r \cdot t = d$ twice to fill in the distance column.

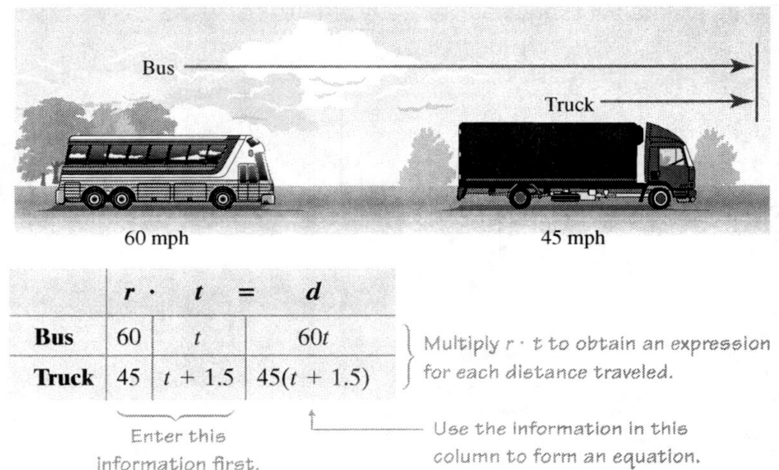

	r ·	t =	d
Bus	60	t	$60t$
Truck	45	$t + 1.5$	$45(t + 1.5)$

Multiply $r \cdot t$ to obtain an expression for each distance traveled.

Enter this information first.

Use the information in this column to form an equation.

When the bus overtakes the truck, they will have traveled the same distance.

The distance traveled by the bus	is the same as	the distance traveled by the truck.
$60t$	$=$	$45(t + 1.5)$

Solve

$60t = 45(t + 1.5)$

$60t = 45t + 67.5$ Distribute the multiplication by 45: $45(1.5) = 67.5$.

$15t = 67.5$ Subtract $45t$ from both sides: $60t - 45t = 15t$.

$t = 4.5$ To isolate t, divide both sides by 15: $\frac{67.5}{15} = 4.5$.

State The bus will overtake the truck in 4.5 or $4\frac{1}{2}$ hours.

Check In 4.5 hours, the bus travels $60(4.5) = 270$ miles. The truck travels for $1.5 + 4.5 = 6$ hours at 45 mph, which is $45(6) = 270$ miles. Since the distance traveled are the same, the answer checks.

Success Tip We used 1.5 hrs for the head start because it is easier to solve $60t = 45(t + 1.5)$ than $60t = 45\left(t + 1\frac{1}{2}\right)$.

3 Solve liquid mixture problems.

We now discuss how to solve mixture problems. In the first type, a liquid mixture of a desired strength is made from two solutions with different concentrations.

EXAMPLE 4 *Mixing Solutions* A chemistry experiment calls for a 30% sulfuric acid solution. If the lab supply room has only 50% and 20% sulfuric acid solutions, how much of each should be mixed to obtain 12 liters of a 30% acid solution?

Analyze The 50% solution is too strong and the 20% solution is too weak. We must find how much of each should be combined to obtain 12 liters of a 30% solution.

Form If $x =$ the number of liters of the 50% solution used in the mixture, the remaining $(12 - x)$ liters must be the 20% solution. The amount of pure sulfuric acid in each solution is given by

Amount of solution · strength of the solution = amount of pure sulfuric acid

A table and sketch are helpful in organizing the facts of the problem.

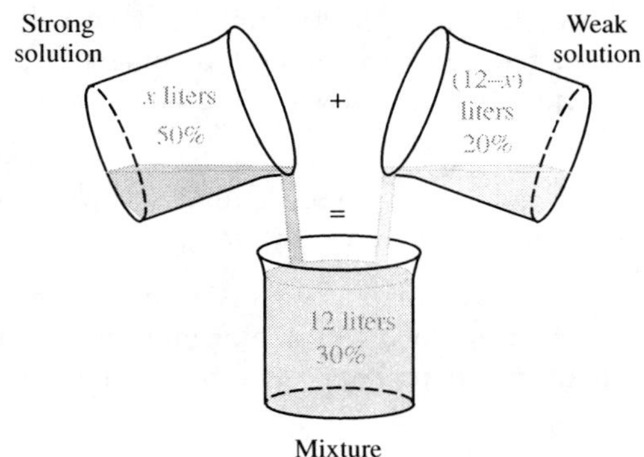

	Amount ·	Strength =	Amount of pure sulfuric acid
Strong	x	0.50	$0.50x$
Weak	$12 - x$	0.20	$0.20(12 - x)$
Mixture	12	0.30	$12(0.30)$

Multiply amount · strength three times to fill in this column.

Enter this information first.

Use the information in this column to form an equation.

The sulfuric acid in the 50% solution	plus	the sulfuric acid in the 20% solution	equals	the sulfuric acid in the mixture.
$0.50x$	$+$	$0.20(12 - x)$	$=$	$12(0.30)$

Solve

$$0.50x + 0.20(12 - x) = 12(0.30)$$

$$0.5x + 2.4 - 0.2x = 3.6 \quad \text{Distribute the multiplication by 0.20.}$$

$$0.3x + 2.4 = 3.6 \quad \text{Combine like terms: } 0.5x - 0.2x = 0.3x.$$

$$0.3x = 1.2 \quad \text{Subtract 2.4 from both sides.}$$

$$x = 4 \quad \text{To isolate } x \text{, undo the multiplication by 0.3 by dividing both sides by 0.3: } \frac{1.2}{0.3} = 4.$$

Self Check 4

How many gallons of a 3% salt solution must be mixed with a 7% salt solution to obtain 25 gallons of a 5.4% salt solution? 10 gal

Now Try **Problem 39**

Teaching Example 4 Cream is approximately 22% butterfat. How many gallons of cream must be mixed with milk testing at 2% butterfat to get 20 gallons of milk containing 4% butterfat?
Answer:
2 gal

State 4 liters of 50% solution and $12 - 4 = 8$ liters of 20% solution should be used.

Check The amount of acid in 4 liters of the 50% solution is $0.50(4) = 2.0$ liters and the amount of acid in 8 liters of the 20% solution is $0.20(8) = 1.6$ liters. Thus, the amount of acid in these two solutions is $2.0 + 1.6 = 3.6$ liters. The amount of acid in 12 liters of the 30% mixture is also $0.30(12) = 3.6$ liters. Since the amounts of acid are equal, the answers check.

> ***Success Tip*** The strength *(concentration)* of a mixture is always between the strengths of the two solutions used to make it.

4 Solve dry mixture problems.

In another type of mixture problem, a dry mixture of a specified value is created from two differently priced ingredients.

Self Check 5

Candy worth \$1.90 per pound is to be mixed with 60 lb of a second candy selling for \$1.20 per pound. How many pounds of the \$1.90 per pound mixture should be used to make a mixture worth \$1.48 per pound?

Now Try **Problem 45**

Self Check 5 Answer
40 lb

Teaching Example 5 The owner of a store wants to make a mixture of two candies to use up 10 pounds of candy that sells for \$3.10 per pound. How many pounds of candy that sells for \$2.95 per pound should be mixed with the more expensive candy to obtain a mixture that cost \$3.00 per pound?
Answer:
20 lb

EXAMPLE 5 *Snack Foods* Because cashews priced at \$9 per pound were not selling, a produce clerk decided to combine them with less expensive peanuts and sell the mixture for \$7 per pound. How many pounds of peanuts, selling at \$6 per pound, should be mixed with 50 pounds of cashews to obtain such a mixture?

Analyze We need to determine how many pounds of peanuts to mix with 50 pounds of cashews to obtain a mixture worth \$7 per pound.

Form Let $x =$ the number of pounds of peanuts to use in the mixture. Since 50 pounds of cashews will be combined with the peanuts, the mixture will weigh $50 + x$ pounds. The value of the mixture and of each of its ingredients is given by

Amount · the price = the total value

We can organize the facts of the problem in a table.

	Amount	· Price	= Total value
Peanuts	x	6	$6x$
Cashews	50	9	450
Mixture	$50 + x$	7	$7(50 + x)$

Multiply amount · price three times to fill in this column.

Enter this information first.

Use the information in this column to form an equation.

The value of the peanuts	plus	the value of the cashews	equals	the value of the mixture.
$6x$	$+$	450	$=$	$7(50 + x)$

Solve

$$6x + 450 = 7(50 + x)$$

$$6x + 450 = 350 + 7x \quad \text{Distribute the multiplication by 7.}$$

$$450 = 350 + x \quad \text{To eliminate the term } 6x \text{ on the left side, subtract } 6x \text{ from both sides: } 7x - 6x = x.$$

$$100 = x \quad \text{To isolate } x \text{, subtract 350 from both sides.}$$

State 100 pounds of peanuts should be used in the mixture.

Check The value of 100 pounds of peanuts, at \$6 per pound, is $100(6) = \$600$ and the value of 50 pounds of cashews, at \$9 per pound, $50(9) = \$450$. Thus, the value of these two amounts is \$1,050. Since the value of 150 pounds of the mixture, at \$7 per pound, is also $150(7) = \$1{,}050$, the answer checks.

5 Solve number-value problems.

When problems deal with collections of different items having different values, we must distinguish between the *number of* and the *value of* the items. For these problems, we will use the fact that

Number · value = total value

EXAMPLE 6 *Dining Area Improvements* A restaurant owner needs to purchase some tables, chairs, and dinner plates for the dining area of her establishment. She plans to buy four chairs and four plates for each new table. She also plans to buy 20 additional plates in case of breakage. If a table costs \$100, a chair \$50, and a plate \$5, how many of each can she buy if she takes out a loan for \$6,500 to pay for the new items?

Analyze We know the *value* of each item: Tables cost \$100, chairs cost \$50, and plates cost \$5 each. We need to find the *number* of tables, chairs, and plates she can purchase for \$6,500.

Form The number of chairs and plates she needs depends on the number of tables she buys. So we let t = the number of tables to be purchased. Since every table requires four chairs and four plates, she needs to order $4t$ chairs. Because 20 additional plates are needed, she should order $(4t + 20)$ plates. We can organize the facts of the problem in a table.

	Number ·	Value =	Total value
Tables	t	100	$100t$
Chairs	$4t$	50	$50(4t)$
Plates	$4t + 20$	5	$5(4t + 20)$
			Total: 6,500

Multiply number · value three times to fill in this column.

Enter this information first.

Use the information in this column to form an equation.

The value of the tables	plus	the value of the chairs	plus	the value of the plates	equals	the value of the purchase.
$100t$	+	$50(4t)$	+	$5(4t + 20)$	=	6,500

Solve

$$100t + 50(4t) + 5(4t + 20) = 6{,}500$$

$$100t + 200t + 20t + 100 = 6{,}500 \quad \text{Do the multiplications and distribute.}$$

$$320t + 100 = 6{,}500 \quad \text{Combine like terms: } 100t + 200t + 20t = 320t.$$

$$320t = 6{,}400 \quad \text{Subtract 100 from both sides.}$$

$$t = 20 \quad \text{To isolate } t \text{, divide both sides by 320.}$$

Self Check 6

A small electronics store sells iPods for \$189, iPod skins for \$32, and iTunes cards for \$15. If they place an order for three times as many iPods as skins and 6 times as many iTunes cards as skins, how many of each did they order if the total before shipping and tax totaled \$2,756?

***Now Try* Problem 53**

Self Check 6 Answer
12 iPods, 4 skins, 24 cards

Teaching Example 6 Tickets to a concert cost \$4 for students, \$7 for adults, and \$5 for seniors. Twice as many students as adults and half as many seniors as adults attended the concert. If the total receipts were \$875, how many students attended the concert?
Answer:
100 students

To find the number of chairs and plates to buy, we evaluate $4t$ and $4t + 20$ for $t = 20$.

Chairs: $4t = 4(20)$ $= 80$ **Plates:** $4t + 20 = 4(20) + 20$ $= 100$ Substitute 20 for t.

State The owner needs to buy 20 tables, 80 chairs, and 100 plates.

Check The total value of 20 tables is 20($100) = $2,000, the total value of 80 chairs is 80($50) = $4,000, and the total value of 100 plates is 100($5) = $500. Because the total purchase is $2,000 + $4,000 + $500 = $6,500, the answers check.

ANSWERS TO SELF CHECKS

1. $2,400 at 2%, $1,800 at 3% **2.** 3.5 hr **3.** 2.5 hr **4.** 10 gal **5.** 40 lb **6.** 12 iPods, 4 skins, 24 cards

SECTION 4.6 STUDY SET

VOCABULARY

Fill in the blanks.

1. Problems that involve depositing money are called investment problems, and problems that involve moving vehicles are called uniform motion problems.

2. Problems that involve combining ingredients are called mixture problems, and problems that involve collections of different items having different values are called number-value problems.

CONCEPTS

3. Complete the *principal column* given that part of $30,000 is invested in stocks and the rest in art. $30{,}000 - x$

	P ·	r ·	$t = I$
Stocks	x		
Art	?		

4. A man made two investments that earned a combined annual interest of $280. Complete the table and then form an equation for this investment problem. $0.04x + 0.06(6{,}000 - x) = 280$

	P ·	r ·	$t =$	I
Bank	x	0.04	1	$0.04x$
Stocks	$6{,}000 - x$	0.06	1	$0.06(6{,}000 - x)$
				Total: 280

5. Complete the *rate column* given that the eastbound plane flew 150 mph slower than the westbound plane. $r - 150$

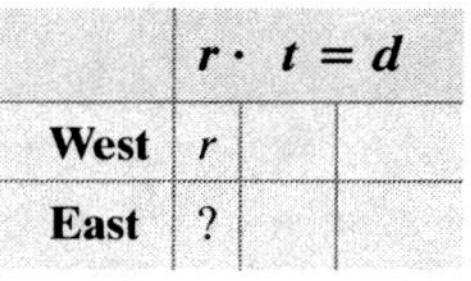

	r ·	$t =$	d
West	r		
East	?		

6. a. Complete the *time column* given that a runner wants to overtake a walker and the walker had a $\frac{1}{2}$-hour head start. $t + 0.5$

	r ·	$t =$	d
Runner		t	
Walker		?	

b. Complete the *time column* given that part of a 6-hour drive was in fog and the other part was in clear conditions. $6 - t$

	r ·	$t =$	d
Foggy		t	
Clear		?	

7. A husband and wife drive in opposite directions to work. Their drives last the same amount of time and their workplaces are 80 miles apart. Complete the table and then form an equation for this distance problem. $35t + 45t = 80$

	r ·	$t =$	d
Husband	35	t	$35t$
Wife	45	t	$45t$
			Total: 80

8. a. How many gallons of acetic acid are there in barrel 2? (See the figure on the next page.) 16.8 gal

b. Suppose the contents of the two barrels are poured into an empty third barrel. How many gallons of liquid will the third barrel contain? $x + 42$

c. Estimate the strength of the solution in the third barrel: 15%, 35%, or 60% acid? 35%

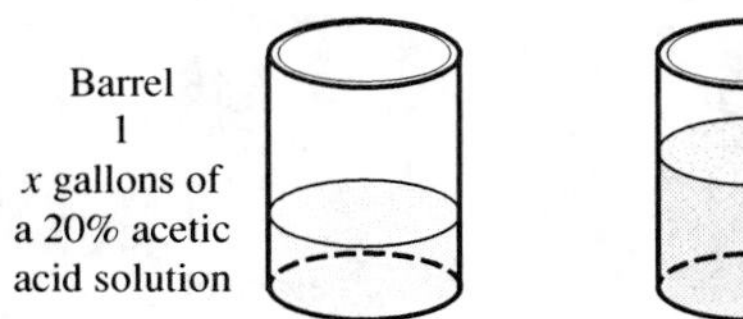

9. **a.** Two antifreeze solutions are combined to form a mixture. Complete the table and then form an equation for this mixture problem.
$0.50(6) + 0.25x = 0.30(6 + x)$

	Amount	· Strength	= Pure antifreeze
Strong	6	0.50	$0.50(6)$
Weak	x	0.25	$0.25x$
Mixture	$6 + x$	0.30	$0.30(6 + x)$

b. Two oil-and-vinegar salad dressings are combined to make a new mixture. Complete the table and then form an equation for this mixture problem.
$0.06x + 0.03(10 - x) = 0.05(10)$

	Amount	· Strength	= Pure vinegar
Strong	x	0.06	$0.06x$
Weak	$10 - x$	0.03	$0.03(10 - x)$
Mixture	10	0.05	$0.05(10)$

10. The value of all the nylon brushes that a paint store carries is $670. Complete the table and then form an equation for this number-value problem.
$8x + 5x + 7(x + 10) = 670$

	Number	· Value	= Total value
1-inch	$2x$	4	$8x$
2-inch	x	5	$5x$
3-inch	$x + 10$	7	$7(x + 10)$
			Total: 670

NOTATION

11. Write 6% and 15.2% in decimal form. 0.06, 0.152

12. By what power of 10 should each decimal be multiplied to make it a whole number?

a. 0.08 100 **b.** 0.162 1,000

GUIDED PRACTICE

Solve each equation. See Example 1.

13. $0.18x + 0.45(12 - x) = 0.36(12)$ 4

14. $0.12x + 0.20(4 - x) = 0.6$ 2.5

15. $0.08x + 0.07(15{,}000 - x) = 1{,}110$ 6,000

16. $0.108x + 0.07(16{,}000 - x) = 1{,}500$ 10,000

APPLICATIONS

Investment problems. See Example 1.

17. CORPORATE INVESTMENTS The financial board of a corporation invested $25,000 overseas, part at 4% and part at 7% annual interest. Find the amount invested at each rate if the first-year combined income from the two investments was $1,300. $15,000 at 4%, $10,000 at 7%

18. LOANS A credit union loaned out $50,000, part at an annual rate of 5% and the rest at an annual rate of 8%. They collected combined simple interest of $3,400 from the loans that year. How much was loaned out at each rate? $20,000 at 5%, $30,000 at 8%

19. OLD COINS A salesperson used her $3,500 year-end bonus to purchase some old coins, with hopes of earning 15% annual interest on the gold coins and 12% annual interest on the silver coins. If she saw return on her investment of $480 the first year, how much did she invest in each type of coin? silver: $1,500, gold: $2,000

20. HIGH-RISK COMPANIES An investment club used funds totaling $200,000 to invest in a bio-tech company and in an ethanol plant, with hopes of earning 11% and 14% annual interest, respectively. Their hunch paid off. The club made a total of $24,250 interest the first year. How much was invested at each rate? $125,000 at 11%, $75,000 at 14%

21. RETIREMENT A professor wants to supplement her pension with investment interest. If she invests $28,000 at 6% interest, how much would she have to invest at 7% to achieve a goal of $3,500 per year in supplemental income? $26,000

22. EXTRA INCOME An investor wants to receive $1,000 annually from two investments. He has put $4,500 in a money market account paying 4% annual interest. How much should he invest in a stock fund that pays 10% annual interest to achieve his goal? $8,200

23. 1099 FORMS The form on the next page shows the interest income Terrell Washington earned in 2008 from two savings accounts. He deposited a total of $15,000 at the first of that year, and made no further deposits or withdrawals. How much money did he deposit in account 822 and in account 721? 822: $9,000, 721: $6,000

USA HOME SAVINGS **2008**

This is important tax information and is being furnished to the Internal Revenue Service.

RECIPIENT'S name

TERRELL WASHINGTON

Account Number	Annual Percent Yield	Interest earned
822	5%	?
721	4.5%	?

FORM 1099 **Total Interest Income $720.00**

24. INVESTMENT PLANS A financial planner recommends a plan for a client who has $65,000 to invest. (See the chart.) At the end of the presentation, the client asks, "How much will be invested at each rate?" Answer this question using the given information. $42,200 at 12%, $22,800 at 6.2%

25. INVESTMENTS Equal amounts are invested in each of three accounts paying 7%, 8%, and 10.5% annually. If one year's combined interest income is $1,249.50, how much is invested in each account? $4,900

26. PERSONAL LOANS Maggy lent her brother some money at 2% annual interest. She lent her sister twice as much money at half of the interest rate. In one year, Maggy collected combined interest of $200 from her brother and sister. How much did she lend each of them? brother: $5,000, sister: $10,000

Uniform motion problems. See Examples 2–3.

27. TORNADOES During a storm, two teams of scientists leave a university at the same time in vans to search for tornadoes. The first team travels east at 20 mph and the second travels west at 25 mph. If their radios have a range of up to 90 miles, how long will it be before they lose radio contact? (See the next column.) 2 hr

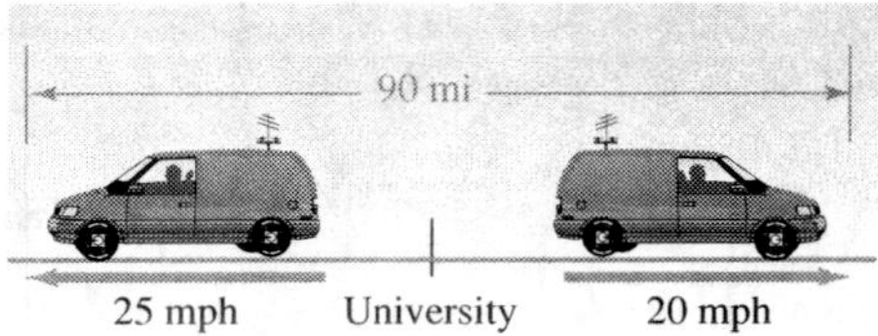

28. UNMANNED AIRCRAFT Two remotely controlled unmanned aircraft are launched in opposite directions. One flies east at 78 mph and the other west at 82 mph. How long will it take the aircraft to fly a combined distance of 560 miles? 3.5 hr

29. HELLO/GOODBYE A husband and wife work different shifts at the same plant. When the husband leaves from work to make the 20-mile trip home, the wife leaves their home and drives to work. They travel on the same road. The husband's driving rate is 45 mph and the wife's is 35 mph. How long into their drives can they wave at each other when passing on the road? $\frac{1}{4}$ hr = 15 min

30. AIR TRAFFIC CONTROL An airliner leaves Berlin, Germany, headed for Montreal, Canada, flying at an average speed of 450 mph. At the same time, an airliner leaves Montreal headed for Berlin, averaging 500 mph. If the airports are 3,800 miles apart, when will the air traffic controllers have to make the pilots aware that the planes are passing each other? 4 hr into the flights

31. CYCLING A cyclist leaves his training base for a morning workout, riding at the rate of 18 mph. One and one-half hours later, his support staff leaves the base in a car going 45 mph in the same direction. How long will it take the support staff to catch up with the cyclist? 1 hr

32. PARENTING How long will it take a mother, running at 4 feet per second, to catch up with her toddler, running down the sidewalk at 2 feet per second, if the child had a 5-second head start? 5 sec

33. ROAD TRIPS A car averaged 40 mph for part of a trip and 50 mph for the remainder. If the 5-hour trip covered 210 miles, for how long did the car average 40 mph? 4 hr

34. CROSS-TRAINING An athlete runs up a set of stadium stairs at a rate of 2 stairs per second, immediately turns around, and then descends the same stairs at a rate of 3 stairs per second. If the workout takes 90 seconds, how long does it take him to run up the stairs? 54 sec

35. WINTER DRIVING A trucker drove for 4 hours before he encountered icy road conditions. He reduced his speed by 20 mph and continued driving for 3 more hours. Find his average speed during the first part of the trip if the entire trip was 325 miles. 55 mph

36. SPEED OF TRAINS Two trains are 330 miles apart, and their speeds differ by 20 mph. Find the speed of each train if they are traveling toward each other and will meet in 3 hours. 65 mph, 45 mph

Liquid mixture problems. See Example 4.

37. SALT SOLUTIONS How many gallons of a 3% salt solution must be mixed with 50 gallons of a 7% solution to obtain a 5% solution? 50 gal

38. PHOTOGRAPHY A photographer wishes to mix 2 liters of a 5% acetic acid solution with a 10% solution to get a 7% solution. How many liters of 10% solution must be added? $1\frac{1}{3}$ liters

39. MAKING CHEESE To make low-fat cottage cheese, milk containing 4% butterfat is mixed with milk containing 1% butterfat to obtain 15 gallons of a mixture containing 2% butterfat. How many gallons of each milk must be used? 4%: 5 gal, 1%: 10 gal

40. ANTIFREEZE How many quarts of a 10% antifreeze solution must be mixed with 16 quarts of a 40% antifreeze solution to make a 30% solution? 8 quarts

41. PRINTING A printer has ink that is 8% cobalt blue color and ink that is 22% cobalt blue color. How many ounces of each ink are needed to make 1 gallon (64 ounces) of ink that is 15% cobalt blue color? 32 ounces of 8%, 32 ounces of 22%

42. FLOOD DAMAGE One website recommends a 6% chlorine bleach–water solution to remove mildew. A chemical lab has 3% and 15% chlorine bleach–water solutions in stock. How many gallons of each should be mixed to obtain 100 gallons of the mildew spray? 75 gallons of 3%, 25 gallons of 15%

43. INTERIOR DECORATING The colors on the paint chip card below are created by adding different amounts of orange tint to a white latex base. How many gallons of Desert Sunrise should be mixed with 1 gallon of Bright Pumpkin to obtain Cool Cantaloupe? 6 gal

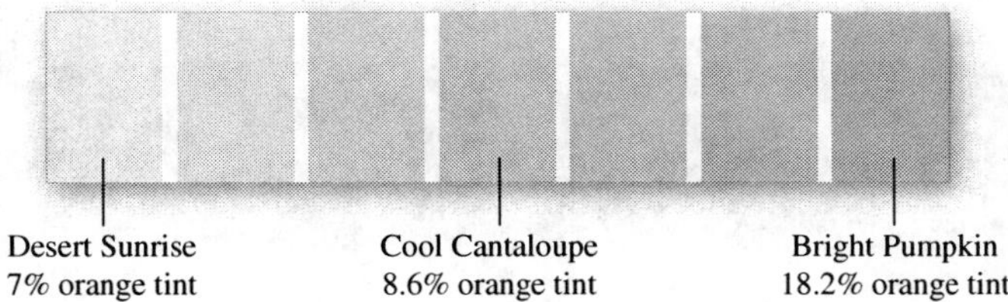

44. ANTISEPTICS A nurse wants to add water to 30 ounces of a 10% solution of benzalkonium chloride to dilute it to an 8% solution. How much water must she add? (*Hint:* Water is 0% benzalkonium chloride.) 7.5 oz

Dry mixture problems

45. LAWN SEED A store sells bluegrass seed for $6 per pound and ryegrass seed for $3 per pound. How much ryegrass must be mixed with 100 pounds of bluegrass to obtain a blend that will sell for $5 per pound? 50 lb

46. COFFEE BLENDS A store sells regular coffee for $8 a pound and gourmet coffee for $14 a pound. To get rid of 40 pounds of the gourmet coffee, a shopkeeper makes a blend to put on sale for $10 a pound. How many pounds of regular coffee should he use? 80 lb

47. RAISINS How many scoops of natural seedless raisins costing $3.45 per scoop must be mixed with 20 scoops of golden seedless raisins costing $2.55 per scoop to obtain a mixture costing $3 per scoop? 20 scoops

48. FERTILIZER Fertilizer with weed control costing $38 per 50-pound bag is to be mixed with a less expensive fertilizer costing $6 per 50-pound bag to make 16 bags of fertilizer that can be sold for $28 per bag. How many bags of cheaper fertilizer should be used? 5 bags

49. PACKAGED SALAD How many 10-ounce bags of Romaine lettuce must be mixed with fifty 10-ounce bags of Iceberg lettuce to obtain a blend that sells for $2.50 per ten-ounce bag? 15

50. MIXING CANDY Lemon drops worth $3.80 per pound are to be mixed with jelly beans that cost $2.40 per pound to make 100 pounds of a mixture worth $2.96 per pound. How many pounds of each candy should be used? 40 lb lemon drops, 60 lb jelly beans

51. BRONZE A pound of tin is worth $1 more than a pound of copper. Four pounds of tin are mixed with 6 pounds of copper to make bronze that sells for $3.65 per pound. How much is a pound of tin worth? $4.25

52. SNACK FOODS A bag of peanuts is worth $.30 less than a bag of cashews. Equal amounts of peanuts and cashews are used to make 40 bags of a mixture that sells for $1.05 per bag. How much is a bag of cashews worth? $1.20

Number-value problems. See Example 6.

53. RENTALS The owners of an apartment building rent equal numbers of 1-, 2-, and 3-bedroom units. The monthly rent for a 1-bedroom is \$550, a 2-bedroom is \$700, and a 3-bedroom is \$900. If the total monthly income is \$36,550, how many of each type of unit are there? 17

54. WAREHOUSING A store warehouses 40 more portables than big-screen TV sets, and 15 more consoles than big-screen sets. The monthly storage cost for a portable is \$1.50, a console is \$4.00, and a big-screen is \$7.50. If storage for all the televisions costs \$276 per month, how many big-screen sets are in stock? 12

55. SOFTWARE Three software applications are priced as shown. Spreadsheet and database programs sold in equal numbers, but 15 more word processing applications were sold than the other two combined. If the three applications generated sales of \$72,000, how many spreadsheets were sold? 90

Software	Price
Spreadsheet	\$150
Database	\$195
Word processing	\$210

56. INVENTORIES With summer approaching, the number of air conditioners sold is expected to be double that of stoves and refrigerators combined. Stoves sell for \$350, refrigerators for \$450, and air conditioners for \$500, and sales of \$56,000 are expected. If stoves and refrigerators sell in equal numbers, how many of each appliance should be stocked? 20 stoves, 20 refrigerators, 80 air conditioners

57. PIGGY BANKS When a child emptied his coin bank, he had a collection of pennies, nickels, and dimes. There were 20 more pennies than dimes and the number of nickels was triple the number of dimes. If the coins had a value of \$5.40, how many of each type coin were in the bank? 40 pennies, 20 dimes, 60 nickels

58. WISHING WELLS A scuba diver, hired by an amusement park, collected \$121 in nickels, dimes, and quarters at the bottom of a wishing well. There were 500 nickels, and 90 more quarters than dimes. How many quarters and dimes were thrown into the wishing well? dimes: 210, quarters: 300

59. BASKETBALL Epiphanny Prince, of New York, scores 113 points in a high school game on February 1, 2006, breaking a national prep record that was held by Cheryl Miller. Prince made 46 more 2-point baskets than 3-point baskets, and only 1 free throw. How many 2-point and 3-point baskets did she make? 2-pointers: 50, 3-pointers: 4

60. MUSEUM TOURS The admission prices for the Coca-Cola Museum in Atlanta are shown. A family purchased 3 more children's tickets than adult tickets, and 1 less senior ticket than adult tickets. The total cost of the tickets was \$73. How many of each type of ticket did they purchase? adult: 3, senior: 2, child: 6

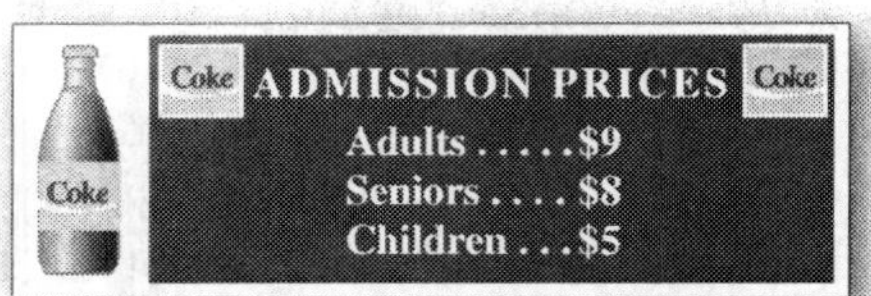

WRITING

61. Create a mixture problem of your own, and solve it.

62. Is it possible to mix a 10% sugar solution with a 20% sugar solution to get a 30% sugar solution? Explain.

REVIEW

Multiply.

63. $-25(2x - 5)$ $-50x + 125$

64. $-12(3a + 4b - 32)$ $-36a - 48b + 384$

65. $-(3x - 3)$ $-3x + 3$

66. $\frac{1}{2}(4b - 8)$ $2b - 4$

67. $(4y - 4)4$ $16y - 16$

68. $3(5t + 1)2$ $30t + 6$

SECTION 4.7 Solving Inequalities

Objectives

1. Determine whether a number is a solution of an inequality.
2. Graph solution sets and use interval notation.
3. Solve linear inequalities.
4. Solve compound inequalities.
5. Solve inequality applications.

In our daily lives, we often speak of one value being *greater than* or *less than* another. For example, a sick child might have a temperature *greater than* 98.6°F or a granola bar might contain *less than* 2 grams of fat.

In mathematics, we use *inequalities* to show that one expression is greater than or is less than another expression.

1 Determine whether a number is a solution of an inequality.

An **inequality** is a statement that contains one or more of the following symbols.

Inequality Symbols

$<$ is less than $>$ is greater than $\neq$ is not equal to
$\leq$ is less than or equal to $\geq$ is greater than or equal to

An inequality can be true, false, or neither true nor false. For example,

- $9 \geq 9$ is true because $9 = 9$.
- $37 < 24$ is false.
- $x + 1 > 5$ is neither true nor false because we don't know what number x represents.

An inequality that contains a variable can be made true or false depending on the number that is substituted for the variable. If we substitute 10 for x in $x + 1 > 5$, the resulting inequality is true: $10 + 1 > 5$. If we substitute 1 for x, the resulting inequality is false: $1 + 1 > 5$. A number that makes an inequality true is called a **solution** of the inequality, and we say that the number *satisfies* the inequality. Thus, 10 is a solution of $x + 1 > 5$ and 1 is not.

The Language of Algebra Because $<$ requires one number to be strictly less than another number and $>$ requires one number to be strictly greater than another number, $<$ and $>$ are called *strict inequalities.*

In this section, we will find the solutions of *linear inequalities in one variable.*

Linear Inequality in One Variable

A **linear inequality in one variable** can be written in one of the following forms where a, b, and c are real numbers and $a \neq 0$.

$$ax + b > c \qquad ax + b \geq c \qquad ax + b < c \qquad ax + b \leq c$$

EXAMPLE 1 Is 9 a solution of $2x + 4 \leq 21$?

Strategy We will substitute 9 for x and evaluate the expression on the left side.

WHY If a true statement results, 9 is a solution of the inequality. If we obtain a false statement, 9 is not a solution.

Solution

$2x + 4 \leq 21$

$2(9) + 4 \overset{?}{\leq} 21$ Substitute 9 for x. Read $\overset{?}{\leq}$ as "is possibly less than or equal to."

$18 + 4 \overset{?}{\leq} 21$

$22 \leq 21$ This inequality is false.

The statement $22 \leq 21$ is false because neither $22 < 21$ nor $22 = 21$ is true. Therefore, 9 is not a solution.

Self Check 1

Is 2 a solution of $3x - 1 \geq 0$? yes

Now Try **Problem 13**

Teaching Example 1 Is -3 a solution of $4x + 5 \leq -6$?
Answer:
yes

2 Graph solution sets and use interval notation.

The **solution set** of an inequality is the set of all numbers that make the inequality true. Some solution sets are easy to determine. For example, if we replace the variable in $x > -3$ with a number greater than -3, the resulting inequality will be true. Because there are infinitely many real numbers greater than -3, it follows that $x > -3$ has infinitely many solutions. Since there are too many solutions to list, we use **set-builder notation** to describe the solutions set.

$\{x \mid x > -3\}$ Read as "the set of all x such that x is greater than −3."

We can illustrate the solution set by **graphing the inequality** on a number line. To graph $x > -3$, a **parenthesis** or **open circle** is drawn on the endpoint -3 to indicate that -3 is not part of the graph. Then we shade all of the points on the number line to the right of -3. The right arrowhead is also shaded to show that the solutions continue forever to the right.

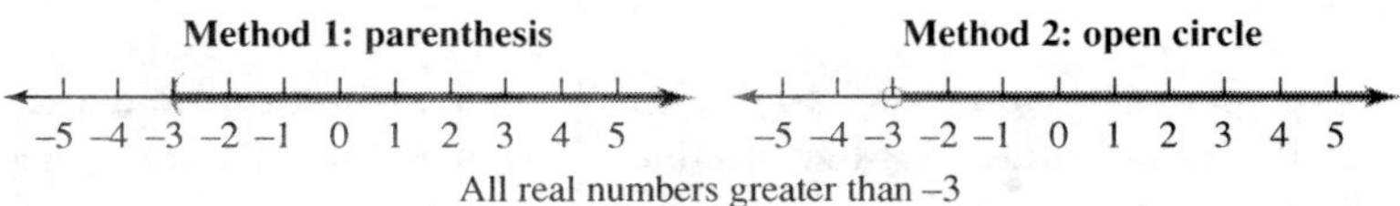

All real numbers greater than –3

The graph of $x > -3$ is an example of an **interval** on the number line. We can write intervals in a compact form called **interval notation.**

The interval notation that represents the graph of $x > -3$ is $(-3, \infty)$. As on the number line, a left parenthesis is written next to -3 to indicate that -3 is not included in the interval. The **positive infinity symbol** ∞ that follows indicates that the interval continues without end to the right. With this notation, *a parenthesis is always used next to an infinity symbol.*

The illustration below shows the relationship between the symbols used to graph an interval and the corresponding interval notation. If we begin at -3 and move to the right, the shaded arrowhead on the graph indicates that the interval approaches positive infinity ∞.

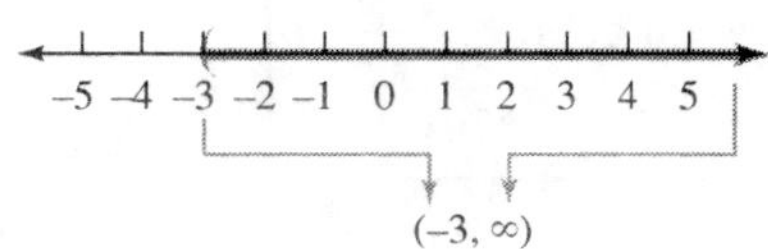

We now have three ways to describe the solution set of an inequality.

Set-builder notation	***Number line graph***	***Interval notation***
$\{x \mid x > -3\}$	–5 –4 –3 –2 –1 0 1 2 3 4 5	$(-3, \infty)$

> ***Success Tip*** The *infinity* symbol ∞ does not represent a number. It indicates that an interval extends to the right without end.

Self Check 2

Graph: $x \geq 0$ $[0, \infty)$

–1 0 1

Now Try **Problem 17**

EXAMPLE 2 Graph: $x \leq 2$

Strategy We need to determine which real numbers, when substituted for x, would make $x \leq 2$ a true statement.

WHY To graph $x \leq 2$ means to draw a "picture" of all of the values of x that make the inequality true.

Solution

If we replace x with a number less than or equal to 2, the resulting inequality will be true. To graph the solution set, a **bracket** or a **closed circle** is drawn at the endpoint 2 to indicate that 2 is part of the graph. Then we shade all of the points on the number line to the left of 2 and the left arrowhead.

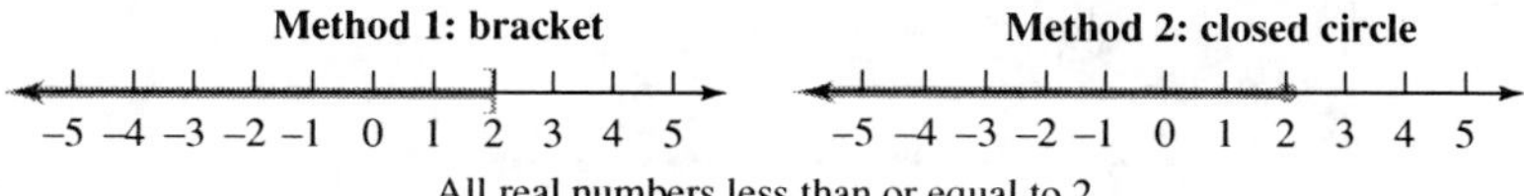

The interval is written as $(-\infty, 2]$. The right bracket indicates that 2 is included in the interval. The **negative infinity symbol** $-\infty$ shows that the interval continues forever to the left. The illustration below shows the relationship between the symbols used to graph the interval and the corresponding interval notation.

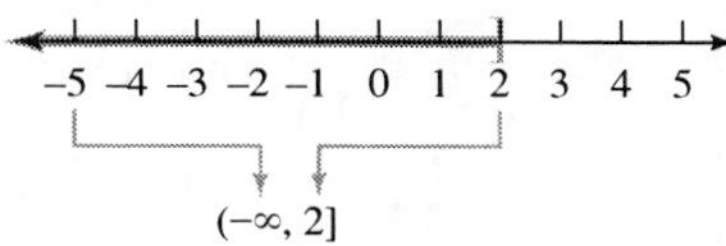

Teaching Example 2 Graph: $x > -1$
Answer:

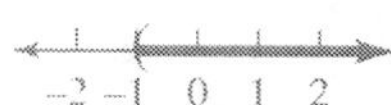

3 Solve linear inequalities.

To **solve an inequality** means to find all values of the variable that make the inequality true. As with equations, there are properties that we can use to solve inequalities.

Addition and Subtraction Properties of Inequality

Adding the same number to, or subtracting the same number from, both sides of an inequality does not change its solutions.

For any real numbers a, b, and c,

If $a < b$, then $a + c < b + c$.
If $a < b$, then $a - c < b - c$.

Similar statements can be made for the symbols $\leq$, $>$, and $\geq$.

After applying one of these properties, the resulting inequality is equivalent to the original one. **Equivalent inequalities** have the same solution set.

Like equations, inequalities are solved by isolating the variable on one side.

EXAMPLE 3 Solve $x + 3 > 2$. Write the solution set in interval notation and graph it.

Strategy We will use a property of inequality to isolate the variable on one side.

WHY To solve the original inequality, we want to find a simpler equivalent inequality of the form $x >$ a number or $x <$ a number, whose solution is obvious.

Solution
We will use the subtraction property of inequality to isolate x on the left side of the inequality. We can undo the addition of 3 by subtracting 3 from both sides.

Self Check 3

Solve $x - 3 < -2$. Write the solution set in interval notation and graph it. $(-\infty, 1)$

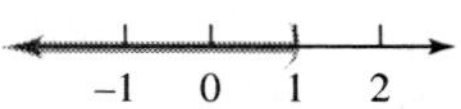

Now Try **Problem 25**

Teaching Example 3 Solve $x - 5 \leq 3$. Write the answer in interval notation.
Answer:
$x \leq 8$, $(-\infty, 8]$

$$x + 3 > 2 \quad \text{This is the inequality to solve.}$$
$$x + 3 - 3 > 2 - 3 \quad \text{Subtract 3 from both sides.}$$
$$x > -1$$

All real numbers greater than -1 are solutions of $x + 3 > 2$. The solution set can be written in set-builder notation as $\{x \mid x > -1\}$ and in interval notation as $(-1, \infty)$. The graph of the solution set is shown below.

Since there are infinitely many solutions, we cannot check all of them.

As an informal check, we can pick some numbers in the graph, say 0 and 30, substitute each number for x in the original inequality, and see whether true statements result.

Check:

$x + 3 > 2$		$x + 3 > 2$	
$0 + 3 \overset{?}{>} 2$	Substitute 0 for x.	$30 + 3 \overset{?}{>} 2$	Substitute 30 for x.
$3 > 2$	True	$33 > 2$	True

The solution set appears to be correct.

Caution! Since we use parentheses and brackets in interval notation, we will use them to graph inequalities. Note that parentheses, not brackets, are written next to ∞ and $-\infty$ because there is no endpoint.

$(-3, \infty)$ $\quad$ $(-\infty, 2]$

As with equations, there are properties for multiplying and dividing both sides of an inequality by the same number. To develop what is called *the multiplication property of inequality,* we consider the true statement $2 < 5$. If both sides are multiplied by a positive number, such as 3, another true inequality results.

$$2 < 5 \quad \text{This inequality is true.}$$
$$3 \cdot 2 < 3 \cdot 5 \quad \text{Multiply both sides by 3.}$$
$$6 < 15 \quad \text{This inequality is true.}$$

However, if we multiply both sides of $2 < 5$ by a negative number, such as -3, the direction of the inequality symbol is reversed to produce another true inequality.

$$2 < 5 \quad \text{This inequality is true.}$$
$$-3 \cdot 2 > -3 \cdot 5 \quad \text{Multiply both sides by } -3 \text{ and reverse the direction of the inequality.}$$
$$-6 > -15 \quad \text{This inequality is true.}$$

The inequality $-6 > -15$ is true because -6 is to the right of -15 on the number line.

Dividing both sides of an inequality by the same negative number also requires that the direction of the inequality symbol be reversed.

$$-4 < 6 \quad \text{This inequality is true.}$$
$$\frac{-4}{-2} > \frac{6}{-2} \quad \text{Divide both sides by } -2 \text{ and change } < \text{ to } >.$$
$$2 > -3 \quad \text{This inequality is true.}$$

These examples illustrate the multiplication and division properties of inequality.

Multiplication and Division Properties of Inequality

Multiplying or dividing both sides of an inequality by the same positive number does not change its solutions.

For any real numbers a, b, and c, where c is positive,

$$\text{If } a < b, \quad \text{then } ac < bc. \qquad \text{If } a < b, \quad \text{then } \frac{a}{c} < \frac{b}{c}.$$

If we multiply or divide both sides of an inequality by a negative number, the direction of the inequality symbol must be reversed for the inequalities to have the same solutions.

For any real numbers a, b, and c, where c is negative,

$$\text{If } a < b, \quad \text{then } ac > bc. \qquad \text{If } a < b, \text{ then } \frac{a}{c} > \frac{b}{c}.$$

Similar statements can be made for the symbols $\leq$, $>$, and $\geq$.

EXAMPLE 4 Solve each inequality. Write the solution set in interval notation and graph it. **a.** $-\frac{3}{2}t \geq -12$ **b.** $-5t < 55$

Strategy We will use a property of inequality to isolate the variable on one side.

WHY To solve the original inequality, we want to find a simpler equivalent inequality, whose solution is obvious.

Solution

a. To undo the multiplication by $-\frac{3}{2}$, we multiply both sides by the reciprocal, which is $-\frac{2}{3}$.

$-\frac{3}{2}t \geq -12$ This is the inequality to solve.

$-\frac{2}{3}\left(-\frac{3}{2}t\right) \leq -\frac{2}{3}(-12)$ Multiply both sides by $-\frac{2}{3}$. Since we are multiplying both sides by a negative number, reverse the direction of the inequality.

$t \leq 8$ Do the multiplications.

The solution set is $(-\infty, 8]$ and it is graphed as shown.

6 7 8 9

b. To undo the multiplication by -5, we divide both sides by -5.

$-5t < 55$ This is the inequality to solve.

$\frac{-5t}{-5} > \frac{55}{-5}$ To isolate t, undo the multiplication by -5 by dividing both sides by -5. Since we are dividing both sides by a negative number, reverse the direction of the inequality.

$t > -11$

The solution set is $(-11, \infty)$ and it is graphed as shown.

−12 −11 −10 −9

Self Check 4

Solve each inequality. Write the solution set in interval notation and graph it.

a. $-\frac{h}{20} \leq 10$ $[-200, \infty)$

−200 0 200

b. $-12a > -144$ $(-\infty, 12)$

10 11 12 13

Now Try **Problems 31 and 33**

Teaching Example 4 Solve each inequality. Write the solution set in interval notation and graph it.

a. $-\frac{5}{3}x \geq 10$

b. $-6x < 12$

Answers:

a. $x \leq -6$, $(-\infty, -6]$ −8 −7 −6

b. $x > -2$, $(-2, \infty)$ −3 −2 −1

Self Check 5

Solve $-13 < 2r - 7$. Write the solution set in interval notation and graph it. $(-3, \infty)$

-4 -3 -2 -1

Now Try **Problem 39**

Teaching Example 5 Solve $3 > 4x + 11$. Write the solution set in interval notation and graph it.
Answer:
$x < -2$, $(-\infty, -2)$

-3 -2 -1

EXAMPLE 5 Solve $-5 > 3x + 7$. Write the solution set in interval notation and graph it.

Strategy First we will use a property of inequality to isolate the *variable term* on one side. Then we will use a second property of inequality to isolate the *variable* itself.

WHY To solve the original inequality, we want to find a simpler equivalent inequality of the form $x >$ **a number** or $x <$ **a number**, whose solution is obvious.

Solution

$-5 > 3x + 7$ This is the inequality to solve.

$-5 - 7 > 3x + 7 - 7$ To isolate the variable term, 3x, undo the addition of 7 by subtracting 7 from both sides.

$-12 > 3x$ Do the subtractions.

$\frac{-12}{3} > \frac{3x}{3}$ To isolate x, undo the multiplication by 3 by dividing both sides by 3.

$-4 > x$ Do the divisions.

To determine the solution set, it is useful to rewrite the inequality $-4 > x$ in an equivalent form with the variable on the left side. If -4 is greater than x, it follows that x must be less than -4.

$x < -4$

The solution set is $(-\infty, -4)$, whose graph is shown below.

-6 -5 -4 -3

Self Check 6

Solve $-9n + 1.8 > -17.1$. Write the solution set in interval notation and graph it. $(-\infty, 2.1)$

2.1

1 2 3

Now Try **Problem 47**

Teaching Example 6 Solve $-4.2 - 2x < 3.6$. Write the solution set in interval notation and graph it.
Answer:
$x > -3.9$, $(-3.9, \infty)$

-3.9

-4 -3 -2 -1 0 1

EXAMPLE 6 Solve $5.1 - 3k < 19.5$. Write the solution set in interval notation and graph it.

Strategy We will use properties of inequality to isolate the variable on one side.

WHY To solve the original inequality, we want to find a simpler equivalent inequality of the form $k >$ **a number** or $k <$ **a number**, whose solution is obvious.

Solution

$5.1 - 3k < 19.5$ This is the inequality to solve.

$5.1 - 3k - 5.1 < 19.5 - 5.1$ To isolate $-3k$ on the left side, subtract 5.1 from both sides.

$-3k < 14.4$ Do the subtractions.

$\frac{-3k}{-3} > \frac{14.4}{-3}$ To isolate k, undo the multiplication by -3 by dividing both sides by -3 and reverse the direction of the $<$ symbol.

$k > -4.8$ Do the divisions.

The solution set is $(-4.8, \infty)$, whose graph is shown below.

-4.8

-6 -5 -4 -3

The equation solving strategy on page 163 can be applied to inequalities. However, when solving inequalities, we must remember to *change the direction of the inequality symbol when multiplying or dividing both sides by a negative number.*

EXAMPLE 7 Solve $8(y + 1) \geq 2(y - 4) + y$. Write the solution set in interval notation and graph it.

Strategy We will follow the steps of the equation-solving strategy (adapted to inequalities) to solve the inequality.

WHY This is the most efficient way to solve a linear inequality in one variable.

Solution

$8(y + 1) \geq 2(y - 4) + y$	This is the inequality to solve.
$8y + 8 \geq 2y - 8 + y$	Distribute the multiplication by 8 and by 2.
$8y + 8 \geq 3y - 8$	Combine like terms: $2y + y = 3y$.
$8y + 8 - 3y \geq 3y - 8 - 3y$	To eliminate $3y$ from the right side, subtract $3y$ from both sides.
$5y + 8 \geq -8$	Combine like terms on both sides.
$5y + 8 - 8 \geq -8 - 8$	To isolate $5y$, undo the addition of 8 by subtracting 8 from both sides.
$5y \geq -16$	Do the subtractions.
$\frac{5y}{5} \geq \frac{-16}{5}$	To isolate y, undo the multiplication by 5 by dividing both sides by 5. Do not reverse the direction of the $\geq$ symbol.
$y \geq -\frac{16}{5}$	

The solution set is $\left[-\frac{16}{5}, \infty\right)$. To graph it, we note that $-\frac{16}{5} = -3\frac{1}{5}$.

Self Check 7

Solve $5(b - 2) \geq -(b - 3) + 2b$. Write the solution set in interval notation and graph it. $\left[\frac{13}{4}, \infty\right)$

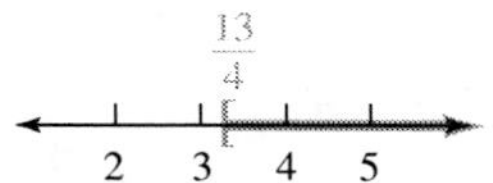

Now Try **Problem 53**

Teaching Example 7 Solve $4(x - 2) < 2(x + 1) + x$. Write the solution set in interval notation and graph it.
Answer:
$x < 10$, $(-\infty, 10)$
8 9 10

4 Solve compound inequalities.

Two inequalities can be combined into a **compound inequality** to show that an expression lies between two fixed values. For example, $-2 < x < 3$ is a combination of

$$-2 < x \qquad \text{and} \qquad x < 3$$

It indicates that x is greater than -2 and that x is also less than 3. The solution set of $-2 < x < 3$ consists of all numbers that lie between -2 and 3, and we write it as $(-2, 3)$. The graph of the compound inequality is shown below.

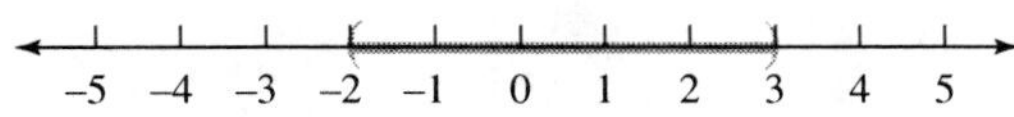

EXAMPLE 8 Graph: $-4 \leq x < 0$

Strategy We need to determine which real numbers, when substituted for x, would make $-4 \leq x < 0$ a true statement.

WHY To graph $-4 \leq x < 0$ means to draw a "picture" of all of the values of x that make the compound inequality true.

Self Check 8

Graph $-2 \leq x < 1$ and write the solution set in interval notation.

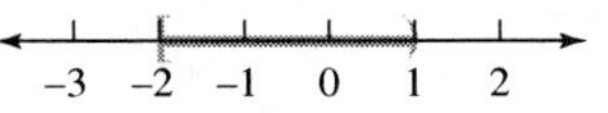

Now Try **Problem 61**

Self Check 8 Answer
$[-2, 1)$

Teaching Example 8 Graph: $-3 < x \leq 4$
Answer:

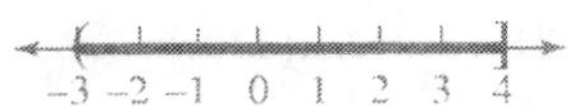

Solution

If we replace the variable in $-4 \leq x < 0$ with a number between -4 and 0, including -4, the resulting compound inequality will be true. Therefore, the solution set is the interval $[-4, 0)$. To graph the interval, we draw a bracket at -4, a parenthesis at 0, and shade in between.

To check, we pick a number in the graph, such as -2, and see whether it satisfies the inequality. Since $-4 \leq -2 < 0$ is true, the answer appears to be correct.

> ***Success Tip*** Note that the two inequality symbols in $-4 \leq x < 0$ point in the same direction and point to the smaller number.

To solve compound inequalities, we isolate the variable in the middle part of the inequality. To do this, we apply the properties of inequality to all *three* parts of the inequality.

Self Check 9

Solve $-6 \leq 3(t + 2) \leq 6$. Write the solution set in interval notation and graph it. $[-4, 0]$

Now Try Problem 69

Teaching Example 9 Solve $-6 < 3(x + 1) \leq 9$. Write the solution set in interval notation and graph it.
Answer:
$-3 < x \leq 2$, $(-3, 2]$

EXAMPLE 9 Solve $-4 < 2(x - 1) \leq 4$. Write the solution set in interval notation and graph it.

Strategy We will use properties of inequality to isolate the variable by itself as the middle part of the inequality.

WHY To solve the original inequality, we want to find a simpler equivalent inequality of the form a number $< x \leq$ a number, whose solution is obvious.

Solution

$-4 < 2(x - 1) \leq 4$	This is the compound inequality to solve.
$-4 < 2x - 2 \leq 4$	Distribute the multiplication by 2.
$-4 + 2 < 2x - 2 + 2 \leq 4 + 2$	To isolate 2x, undo the subtraction of 2 by adding 2 to all three parts.
$-2 < 2x \leq 6$	Do the additions.
$\frac{-2}{2} < \frac{2x}{2} \leq \frac{6}{2}$	To isolate x, we undo the multiplication by 2 by dividing all three parts by 2.
$-1 < x \leq 3$	Do the divisions.

The solution set is $(-1, 3]$ and its graph is shown.

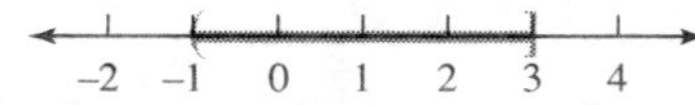

> ***Success Tip*** Think of interval notation as a way to tell someone how to draw the graph, from left to right, giving them only a "start" and a "stop" instruction.

5 Solve inequality applications.

When solving problems, phrases such as "not more than," or "should exceed" suggest that the problem involves an inequality rather than an equation.

The Language of Algebra Some phrases that suggest an inequality are:

surpass: $>$ at least: $\geq$
not exceed: $\leq$ at most: $\leq$
between: $< \quad <$

EXAMPLE 10 *Grades* A student has scores of 72%, 74%, and 78% on three exams. What percent score does he need on the last exam to earn a grade of no less than B (80%)?

Analyze We know three scores. We are to find what the student must score on the last exam to earn a grade of B or higher.

Form an Inequality We can let $x =$ the score on the fourth (and last) exam. To find the average grade, we add the four scores and divide by 4. To earn a grade of *no less than* B, the student's average must be *greater than or equal to* 80%.

The average of the four grades	must be no less than	80.
$\frac{72 + 74 + 78 + x}{4}$	$\geq$	80

Solve

$$\frac{224 + x}{4} \geq 80$$ Combine like terms in the numerator: $72 + 74 + 78 = 224$.

$$4\left(\frac{224 + x}{4}\right) \geq 4(80)$$ To clear the inequality of the fraction, multiply both sides by 4.

$$224 + x \geq 320$$ Simplify each side.

$$x \geq 96$$ To isolate x, undo the addition of 224 by subtracting 224 from both sides.

State To earn a B, the student must score 96% or better on the last exam. Assuming the student cannot score higher than 100% on the exam, the solution set is written as [96, 100]. The graph is shown below.

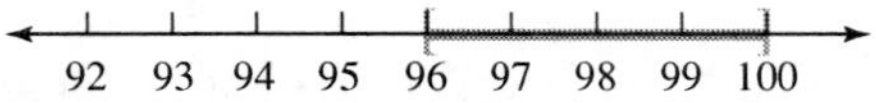

92 93 94 95 96 97 98 99 100

Check Pick some numbers in the interval, and verify that the average of the four scores will be 80% or greater.

Self Check 10

A student has scores of 78%, 82%, and 76% on three exams. What percent score does he need on the last test to earn a grade of no less than a B (80%)? 84%

Now Try **Problem 99**

Teaching Example 10 A student has scores of 68%, 67%, and 72% on three exams. What percent score does he need on the last test to earn a grade of no less than a C (70%)?
Answer:
73% or better

ANSWERS TO SELF CHECKS

1. Yes **2.** $[0, \infty)$ −1 0 1 **3.** $(-\infty, 1)$ −1 0 1 2
4. a. $[-200, \infty)$ −200 0 200 **b.** $(-\infty, 12)$ 10 11 12 13
5. $(-3, \infty)$ −4 −3 −2 −1 **6.** $(-\infty, 2.1)$ 2.1 1 2 3
7. $\left[\frac{13}{4}, \infty\right)$ $\frac{13}{4}$ 2 3 4 5 **8.** $[-2, 1)$ −3 −2 −1 0 1 2
9. $[-4, 0]$ −5 −4 −3 −2 −1 0 1 **10.** 84%

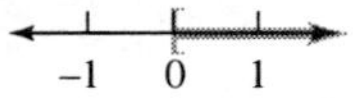

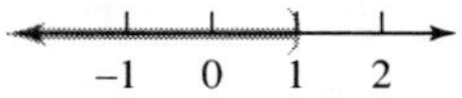

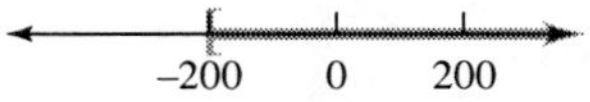

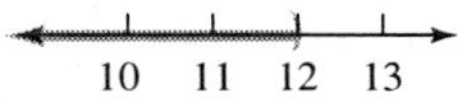

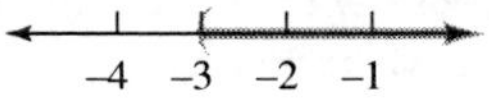

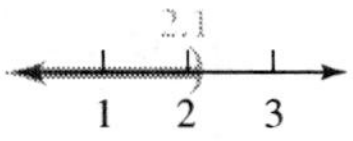

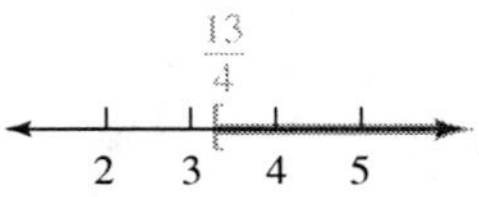

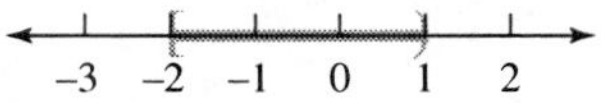

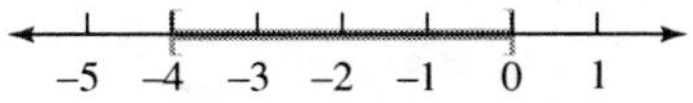

SECTION 4.7 STUDY SET

VOCABULARY

Fill in the blanks.

1. An inequality is a statement that contains one of the symbols: $>$, $\geq$, $<$, or $\leq$.
2. To solve an inequality means to find all the values of the variable that make the inequality true.
3. The solution set of $x > 2$ can be expressed in interval notation as $(2, \infty)$.
4. The inequality $-4 < x \leq 10$ is an example of a compound inequality.

CONCEPTS

Fill in the blanks.

5. **a.** Adding the same number to both sides of an inequality does not change the solutions.
   b. Multiplying or dividing both sides of an inequality by the same positive number does not change the solutions.
   c. If we multiply or divide both sides of an inequality by a negative number, the direction of the inequality symbol must be reversed for the inequalities to have the same solutions.
6. To solve $-4 \leq 2x + 1 < 3$, properties of inequality are applied to all three parts of the inequality.
7. Rewrite the inequality $32 < x$ in an equivalent form with the variable on the left side. $x > 32$
8. The solution set of an inequality is graphed below. Which of the four numbers, 3, -3, 2, and 4.5, when substituted for the variable in that inequality, would make it true? 3, 4.5

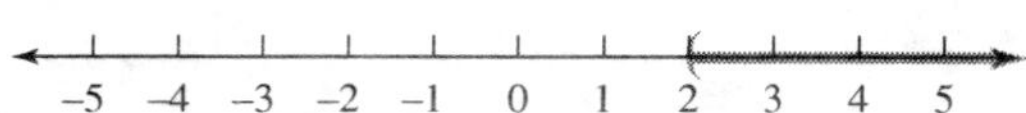

NOTATION

9. Write each symbol.
   a. is less than or equal to $\leq$
   b. infinity ∞
   c. bracket [or]
   d. is greater than $>$
10. Consider the graph of the interval $[4, 8)$.
    a. Is the endpoint 4 included or not included in the graph? included
    b. Is the endpoint 8 included or not included in the graph? not included

Complete the solution to solve each inequality.

11.
$$4x - 5 \geq 7$$
$$4x - 5 + 5 \geq 7 + 5$$
$$4x \geq 12$$
$$\frac{4x}{4} \geq \frac{12}{4}$$
$$x \geq 3 \qquad \text{Solution set: } [3, \infty)$$

12.
$$-6x > 12$$
$$\frac{-6x}{-6} < \frac{12}{-6}$$
$$x < -2 \qquad \text{Solution set: } (-\infty, -2)$$

GUIDED PRACTICE

See Example 1.

13. Determine whether each number is a solution of $3x - 2 > 5$.
    a. 5 yes **b.** -4 no
14. Determine whether each number is a solution of $3x + 7 < 4x - 2$.
    a. 12 yes **b.** 9 no
15. Determine whether each number is a solution of $-5(x - 1) \geq 2x + 12$.
    a. 1 no **b.** -1 yes
16. Determine whether each number is a solution of $\frac{4}{5}a \geq -2$.
    a. $-\frac{5}{4}$ yes **b.** -15 no

Graph each inequality and describe the graph using interval notation. See Example 2.

17. $x < 5$ $(-\infty, 5)$

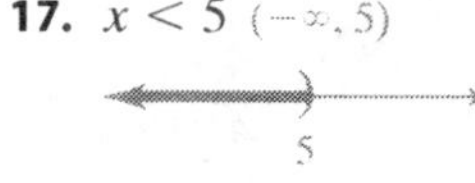

18. $x \geq -2$ $[-2, \infty)$

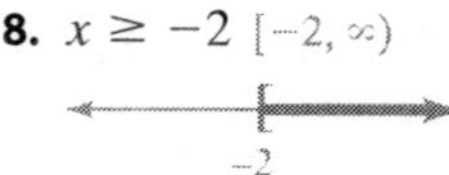

19. $-3 < x \leq 1$ $(-3, 1]$

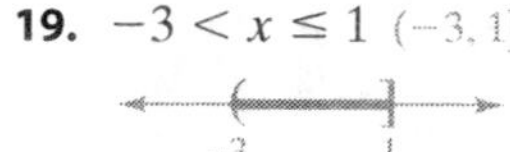

20. $-4 \leq x \leq 2$ $[-4, 2]$

Write the inequality that is represented by each graph. Then describe the graph using interval notation.

21. $x < -1$, $(-\infty, -1)$
22. $x \geq 2$, $[2, \infty)$

Selected exercises available online at www.webassign.net/brookscole

23. Number line: −7, 2 $\quad -7 < x \le 2, (-7, 2]$

24. Number line: 4, 6 $\quad 4 < x \le 6, (4, 6]$

Solve each inequality. Write the solution set in interval notation and graph it. See Examples 3–4.

25. $x + 2 > 5$
$(3, \infty)$
3

26. $x + 5 \ge 2$
$[-3, \infty)$
−3

27. $g - 30 \ge -20$
$[10, \infty)$
10

28. $h - 18 \le -3$
$(-\infty, 15]$
15

29. $8h < 48$
$(-\infty, 6)$

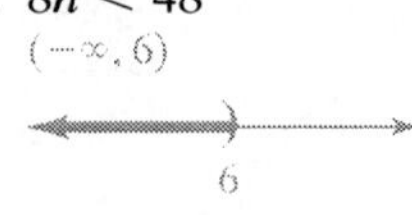

30. $2t > 22$
$(11, \infty)$
11

31. $-\frac{3}{16}x \ge -9$
$(-\infty, 48]$
48

32. $-\frac{7}{8}x \le 21$
$[-24, \infty)$
−24

33. $-3y \le -6$
$[2, \infty)$

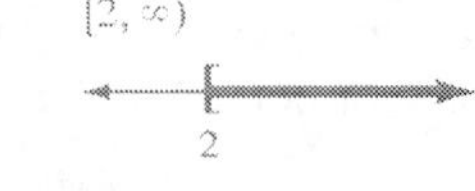

34. $-6y \ge -6$
$(-\infty, 1]$
1

35. $\frac{2}{3}x \ge 2$
$[3, \infty)$

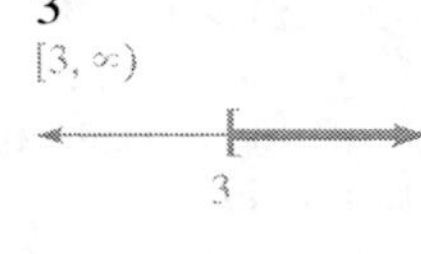

36. $\frac{3}{4}x < 3$
$(-\infty, 4)$
4

Solve each inequality. Write the solution set in interval notation and graph it. See Examples 5–6.

37. $9x + 1 > 64$
$(7, \infty)$
7

38. $4x + 8 < 32$
$(-\infty, 6)$
6

39. $0.5 \ge 2x - 0.3$
$(-\infty, 0.4]$

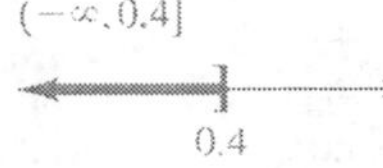

40. $0.8 > 7x - 0.04$
$(-\infty, 0.12)$
0.12

41. $\frac{x}{8} - (-9) \ge 11$
$[16, \infty)$

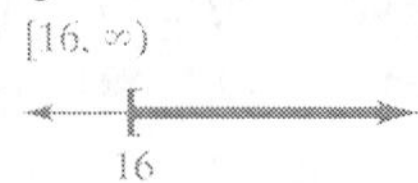

42. $\frac{x}{6} - (-12) > 14$
$(12, \infty)$
12

43. $\frac{m}{-42} - 1 > -1$
$(-\infty, 0)$

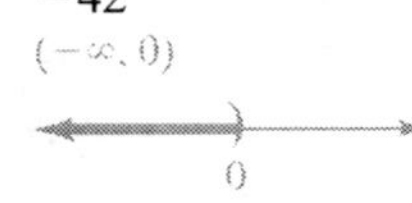

44. $\frac{a}{-25} + 3 < 3$
$(0, \infty)$

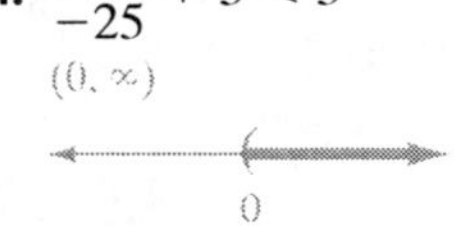

45. $-x - 3 \le 7$
$[-10, \infty)$
−10

46. $-x - 9 > 3$
$(-\infty, -12)$
−12

47. $-3x - 7 > -1$
$(-\infty, -2)$

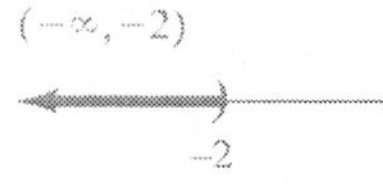

48. $-5x + 7 \le 12$
$[-1, \infty)$
−1

Solve each inequality. Write the solution set in interval notation and graph it. See Example 7.

49. $9a + 4 > 5a - 16$
$(-5, \infty)$

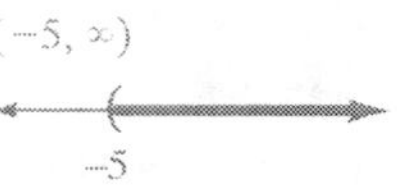

50. $8t + 1 < 4t - 19$
$(-\infty, -5)$
−5

51. $0.4x \le 0.1x + 0.45$
$(-\infty, 1.5]$

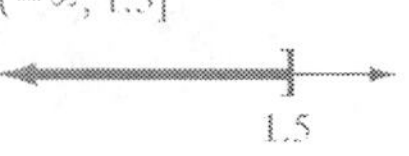

52. $0.9s \le 0.3s + 0.54$
$(-\infty, 0.9]$
0.9

53. $8(5 - x) \le 10(8 - x)$
$(-\infty, 20]$
20

54. $17(3 - x) \ge 3 - 13x$
$(-\infty, 12]$
12

55. $8x + 4 > -(3x - 4)$
$(0, \infty)$
0

56. $7x + 6 \ge -(x - 6)$
$[0, \infty)$
0

57. $\frac{1}{2} + \frac{n}{5} > \frac{3}{4}$
$\left(\frac{5}{4}, \infty\right)$
5/4

58. $\frac{1}{3} + \frac{c}{5} > -\frac{3}{2}$
$\left(-\frac{55}{6}, \infty\right)$
−55/6

59. $\frac{6x + 1}{4} \le x + 1$
$\left(-\infty, \frac{3}{2}\right]$
3/2

60. $\frac{3x - 10}{5} \le x + 4$
$[-15, \infty)$
−15

Solve each compound inequality. Write the solution set in interval notation and graph it. See Examples 8–9.

61. $2 < x - 5 < 5$
$(7, 10)$
7 10

62. $-8 < t - 8 < 8$
$(0, 16)$
0 16

63. $0 \le x + 10 \le 10$
$[-10, 0]$

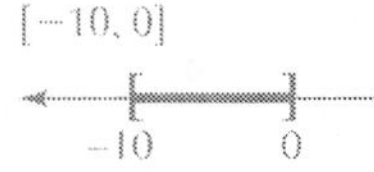

64. $-9 \le x + 8 < 1$
$[-17, -7)$
−17 −7

65. $-3 \le \frac{c}{2} \le 5$
$[-6, 10]$
−6 10

66. $-12 < \frac{b}{3} < 0$
$(-36, 0)$

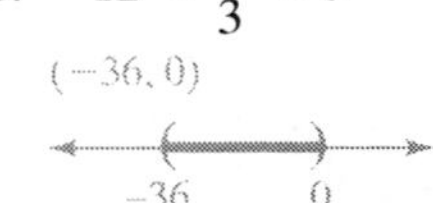

67. $3 \le 2x - 1 < 5$
$[2, 3)$
2 3

68. $4 < 3x - 5 \le 7$
$(3, 4]$
3 4

69. $-9 < 6x + 9 \le 45$
$(-3, 6]$
−3 6

70. $-30 \le 10d + 20 < 90$
$[-5, 7)$
−5 7

▶ **71.** $6 < -2(x - 1) < 12$
$(-5, -2)$
−5 −2

72. $4 \le -4(x - 2) < 20$
$(-3, 1]$
−3 1

TRY IT YOURSELF

Solve each inequality or compound inequality. Write the solution set in interval notation and graph it.

73. $6 - x \le 3(x - 1)$
$\left[\frac{9}{4}, \infty\right)$
9/4

74. $3(3 - x) \ge 6 + x$
$\left(-\infty, \frac{3}{4}\right]$
3/4

75. $\frac{y}{4} + 1 \le -9$
$(-\infty, -40]$
−40

76. $\frac{r}{8} - 7 \ge -8$
$[-8, \infty)$
−8

77. $0 < 5(x + 2) \le 15$
$(-2, 1]$
−2 1

78. $-18 \le 9(x - 5) < 27$
$[3, 8)$
3 8

79. $-1 \le -\frac{1}{2}n$
$(-\infty, 2]$
2

80. $-3 \ge -\frac{1}{3}t$
$[9, \infty)$
9

81. $-m - 12 > 15$
$(-\infty, -27)$
−27

82. $-t + 5 < 10$
$(-5, \infty)$
−5

83. $-\frac{2}{3} \ge \frac{2y}{3} - \frac{3}{4}$
$\left(-\infty, \frac{1}{8}\right]$
1/8

84. $-\frac{2}{9} \ge \frac{5x}{6} - \frac{1}{3}$
$\left(-\infty, \frac{2}{15}\right]$
2/15

85. $9x + 13 \ge 2x + 6x$
$[-13, \infty)$
−13

▶ **86.** $7x - 16 < 2x + 4x$
$(-\infty, 16)$
16

87. $7 < \frac{5}{3}a + (-3)$
$(6, \infty)$
6

▶ **88.** $5 < \frac{7}{2}a + (-9)$
$(4, \infty)$
4

89. $-8 \le \frac{y}{8} - 4 \le 2$
$[-32, 48]$
−32 48

90. $6 < \frac{m}{16} + 7 < 8$
$(-16, 16)$
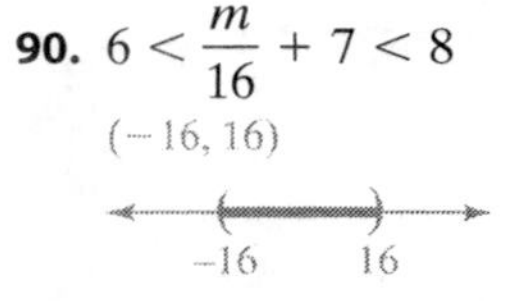
−16 16

91. $-2(2x - 3) > 17$
$\left(-\infty, -\frac{11}{4}\right)$
−11/4

92. $-3(x + 0.2) < 0.3$
$(-0.3, \infty)$
−0.3

93. $\frac{5}{3}(x + 1) \ge -x + \frac{2}{3}$
$\left[-\frac{3}{8}, \infty\right)$
−3/8

94. $\frac{5}{2}(7x - 15) \ge \frac{11}{2}x - \frac{3}{2}$
$[3, \infty)$
3

95. $2x + 9 \le x + 8$
$(-\infty, -1]$
−1

96. $3x + 7 \le 4x - 2$
$[9, \infty)$
9

97. $-7x + 1 < -5$
$\left(\frac{6}{7}, \infty\right)$
6/7

98. $-3x - 10 \ge -5$
$\left(-\infty, -\frac{5}{3}\right]$
−5/3

APPLICATIONS

▶ **99.** GRADES A student has test scores of 68%, 75%, and 79% in a government class. What must she score on the last exam to earn a B (80% or better) in the course? 98% or better

▶ **100.** OCCUPATIONAL TESTING An employment agency requires applicants average at least 70% on a battery of four job skills tests. If an applicant scored 70%, 74%, and 84% on the first three exams, what must he score on the fourth test to maintain a 70% or better average? 52% or better

101. GAS MILEAGE A car manufacturer produces three models in equal quantities. One model has an economy rating of 17 miles per gallon, and the second model is rated for 19 mpg. If government regulations require the manufacturer to have a fleet average that exceeds 21 mpg, what economy rating is required for the third model? more than 27 mpg

▶ **102.** SERVICE CHARGES When the average daily balance of a customer's checking account falls below $500 in any week, the bank assesses a $5 service charge. The table shows the daily balances of one customer. What must Friday's balance be to avoid the service charge? $869.20 or more

Day	Balance
Monday	$540.00
Tuesday	$435.50
Wednesday	$345.30
Thursday	$310.00

103. GEOMETRY The perimeter of an equilateral triangle is at most 57 feet. What could the length of a side be? (*Hint:* All three sides of an equilateral triangle are equal.) 19 ft or less

104. GEOMETRY The perimeter of a square is no less than 68 centimeters. How long can a side be? 17 cm or more

105. COUNTER SPACE A rectangular counter is being built for the customer service department of a store. Designers have determined that the outside perimeter of the counter (shown in red) needs to exceed 30 feet. Determine the acceptable values for x. more than 5 ft

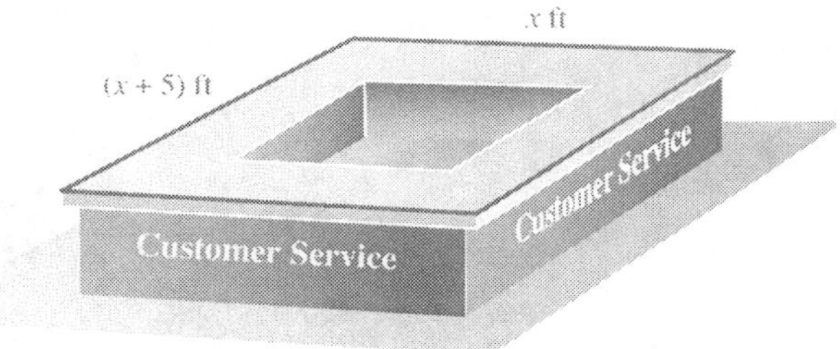

106. NUMBER PUZZLES What numbers satisfy the condition: Four more than three times the number is at most 10? $x \le 2$

107. GRADUATIONS It costs a student \$18 to rent a cap and gown and 80 cents for each graduation announcement that she orders. If she doesn't want her spending on these graduation costs to exceed \$50, how many announcements can she order? 40 or less

108. TELEPHONES A cellular telephone company has currently enrolled 36,000 customers in a new calling plan. If an average of 1,200 people are signing up for the plan each day, in how many days will the company surpass their goal of having 150,000 customers enrolled? 96 days

109. WINDOWS An architect needs to design a triangular-shaped bathroom window that has an area no greater than 100 in.^{2}. If the base of the window must be 16 inches long, what window heights will meet this condition? 12.5 in. or less

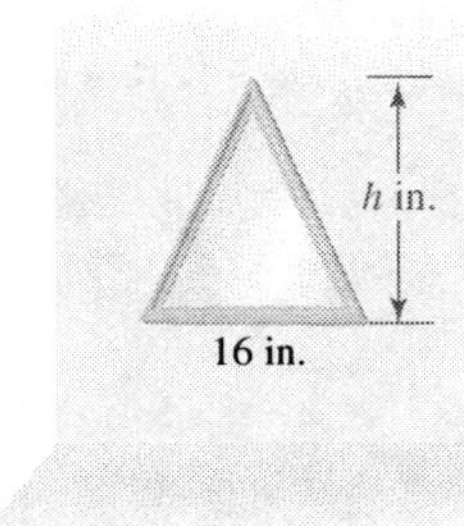

110. ROOM TEMPERATURES To hold the temperature of a room between 19° and 22° Celsius, what Fahrenheit temperatures must be maintained? (*Hint:* Use the formula $C = \frac{5}{9}(F - 32)$.) $66.2° < F < 71.6°$

111. INFANTS The graph is used to classify the weight of a baby boy from birth to 1 year. Estimate the weight range for boys in the following classifications, using a compound inequality:

a. 10 months old, "heavy" $26 \text{ lb} \le w \le 31 \text{ lb}$

b. 5 months old, "light" $12 \text{ lb} \le w \le 14 \text{ lb}$

c. 8 months old, "average" $18.5 \text{ lb} \le w \le 20.5 \text{ lb}$

d. 3 months old, "moderately light" $11 \text{ lb} \le w \le 13 \text{ lb}$

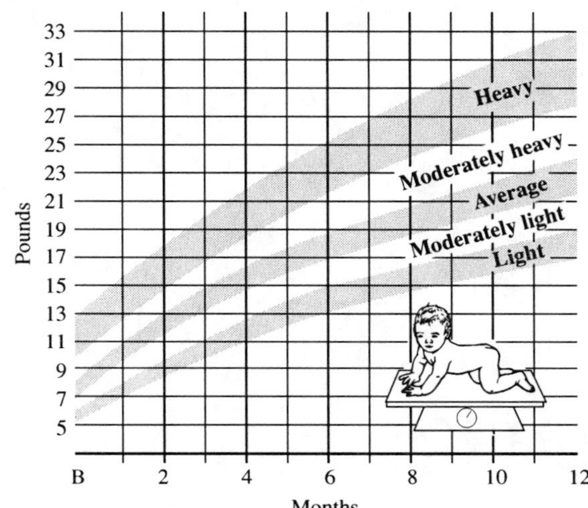

Source: Based on data from *Better Homes and Gardens Baby Book* (Meredith Corp., 1969)

112. NUMBER PUZZLES What *whole* numbers satisfy the condition: Twice the number decreased by 1 is between 50 and 60? 26, 27, 28, 29, 30

WRITING

113. Explain why multiplying both sides of an inequality by a negative number reverses the direction of the inequality.

114. Explain the use of parentheses and brackets for graphing intervals.

REVIEW

Complete each table.

115.

x	$x^2 - 3$
−2	1
0	−3
3	6

116.

x	$\frac{x}{3} + 2$
−6	0
0	2
12	6

Module 5: Graphs and Equations of Lines

DMA 050

Kim Steele/Photodisc/Getty Images

from Campus to Careers

Postal Service Mail Carrier

Mail carriers follow schedules as they collect and deliver mail to homes and businesses. They must have the ability to quickly and accurately compare similarities and differences among sets of letters, numbers, objects, pictures, and patterns. They also need to have strong problem-solving skills to redirect mislabeled letters and packages. Mail carriers weigh items on postal scales and make calculations with money as they read postage rate tables.

In **Problem 19** of **Study Set 5.1**, you will see how a mail carrier must be able to read a postal rate table and know American units of weight to determine the cost to send a package using priority mail.

JOB TITLE:
Postal Service Mail Carrier

EDUCATION: A high school diploma (or equivalent) and a passing score on a written exam are required.

JOB OUTLOOK: Competition for jobs is high since positions usually come open only upon retirement of current mail carriers.

ANNUAL EARNINGS: Average (mean) salary $46,970

FOR MORE INFORMATION:
http://stats.bls.gov/oco/ocos141.HTM

Objectives

1. Read tables.
2. Read bar graphs.
3. Read pictographs.
4. Read circle graphs.
5. Read line graphs.
6. Read histograms and frequency polygons.

SECTION 5.1
Reading Graphs and Tables

We live in an information age. Never before have so many facts and figures been right at our fingertips. Since information is often presented in the form of tables or graphs, we need to be able to read and make sense of data displayed in that way.

The following **table, bar graph,** and **circle graph** (or **pie chart**) show the results of a shopper survey. A large sample of adults were asked how far in advance they typically shop for a gift. In the bar graph, the length of a bar represents the percent of responses for a given shopping method. In the circle graph, the size of a colored region represents the percent of responses for a given shopping method.

Shopper Survey

How far in advance gift givers typically shop

A Table

Survey responses

Time in advance	Percent
A month or longer	8%
Within a month	12%
Within 3 weeks	12%
Within 2 weeks	23%
Within a week	41%
The same day as giving it	4%

A Bar Graph

Survey responses

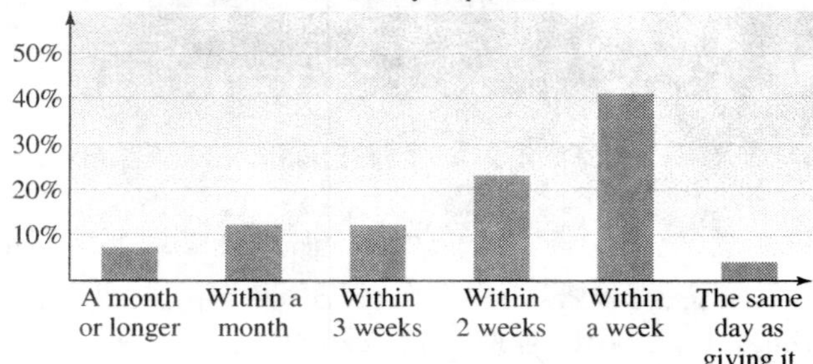

A Circle Graph

Survey responses

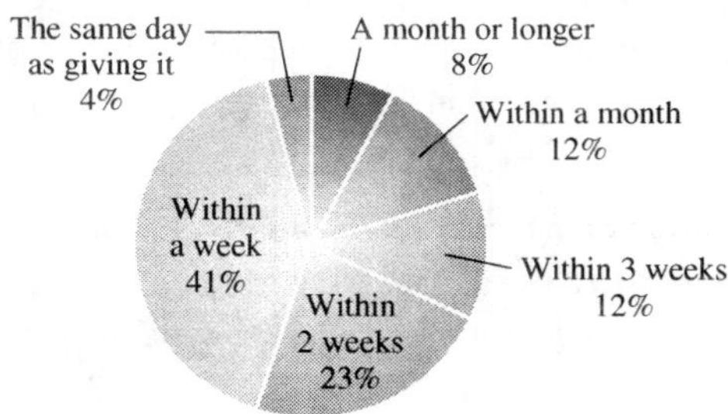

(*Source:* Harris interactive online study via QuickQuery for Gifts.com)

It is often said that a picture is worth a thousand words. That is the case here, where the graphs display the results of the survey more clearly than the table. It's easy to see from the graphs that most people shop within a week of when they need to purchase a gift. It is also apparent that same-day shopping for a gift was the least popular response. That information also appears in the table, but it is just not as obvious.

1 Read tables.

Data are often presented in tables, with information organized in **rows** and **columns.** To read a table, we must find the *intersection* of the row and column that contains the desired information.

EXAMPLE 1 *Postal Rates* Refer to the table of priority mail postal rates (from 2009) below. Find the cost of mailing an $8\frac{1}{2}$-pound package by priority mail to postal zone 4.

Postage Rate for Priority Mail 2009

Weight Not Over (pounds)	Zones						
	Local, 1 & 2	**3**	**4**	**5**	**6**	**7**	**8**
1	$4.95	$4.95	$4.95	$4.95	$4.95	$4.95	$4.95
2	4.95	5.20	5.75	7.10	7.60	8.10	8.70
3	5.50	6.25	7.10	9.05	9.90	10.60	11.95
4	6.10	7.10	8.15	10.80	11.95	12.95	14.70
5	6.85	8.15	9.45	12.70	13.75	15.20	17.15
6	7.55	9.25	10.75	14.65	15.50	17.50	19.60
7	8.30	10.30	12.05	16.55	17.30	19.75	22.05
8	8.80	10.70	13.10	17.95	18.80	21.70	24.75
9	9.25	11.45	**13.95**	19.15	20.30	23.60	27.55
10	9.90	12.35	15.15	20.75	22.50	25.90	29.95
11	10.55	13.30	16.40	22.40	24.75	28.20	32.40
12	11.20	14.20	17.60	24.00	26.95	30.50	34.80

Strategy We will read the number at the intersection of the 9th row and the column labeled Zone 4.

WHY Since $8\frac{1}{2}$ pounds is more than 8 pounds, we cannot use the 8th row. Since $8\frac{1}{2}$ pounds does not exceed 9 pounds, we use the 9th row of the table.

Solution

The number at the intersection of the 9th row (in red) and the column labeled Zone 4 (in blue) is 13.95 (in purple). This means it would cost $13.95 to mail the $8\frac{1}{2}$-pound package by priority mail.

Self Check 1

POSTAL RATES Refer to the table of priority mail postal rates. Find the cost of mailing a 3.75-pound package by priority mail to postal zone 8. $14.70

***Now Try* Problem 17**

Teaching Example 1 POSTAL RATES Refer to the table of priority mail postal rates. Find the cost of mailing a $5\frac{3}{4}$-pound package by priority mail to postal zone 6.
Answer:
$15.50

2 Read bar graphs.

Another popular way to display data is to use a **bar graph** with bars drawn vertically or horizontally. The relative heights (or lengths) of the bars make for easy comparisons of values. A horizontal or vertical line used for reference in a bar graph is called an **axis.** The **horizontal axis** and the **vertical axis** of a bar graph serve to frame the graph, and they are scaled in units such as years, dollars, minutes, pounds, and percent.

Self Check 2

SPEED OF ANIMALS Refer to the bar graph of Example 2.

a. What is the maximum speed of a giraffe? 32 mph

b. How much greater is the maximum speed of a coyote compared to that of a reindeer? 11 mph

c. Which animals listed in the graph have a maximum speed that is slower than that of a domestic cat? a chicken and an elephant

Now Try **Problem 21**

Teaching Example 2 SPEED OF ANIMALS Refer to the bar graph of Example 2.

a. What is the maximum speed of a chicken?

b. How much greater is the maximum speed of a zebra compared to that of an elephant?

c. What two animals have the same maximum speed?

Answers:

a. 9 mph

b. 15 mph

c. a giraffe and a reindeer

Federico Veronesi/ Getty Images

EXAMPLE 2 *Speed of Animals* The following bar graph shows the maximum speeds for several animals over a given distance.

a. What animal in the graph has the fastest maximum speed?

b. What animal in the graph has the slowest maximum speed?

c. How much greater is the maximum speed of a lion compared to that of a coyote?

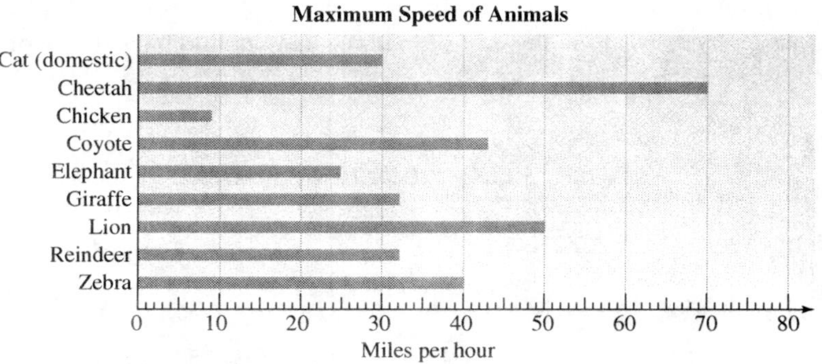

Strategy We will locate the name of each desired animal on the vertical axis and move right to the end of its corresponding bar.

WHY Then we can extend downward and read the animal's maximum speed on the horizontal axis scale.

Solution

a. The longest bar in the graph has a length of 70 units and corresponds to a cheetah. Of all the animals listed in the graph, the cheetah has the fastest maximum speed at 70 mph.

b. The shortest bar in the graph has a length of approximately 9 units and corresponds to a chicken. Of all the animals listed in the graph, the chicken has the slowest maximum speed at 9 mph.

c. The length of the bar that represents a lion's maximum speed is 50 units long and the length of the bar that represents a coyote's maximum speed appears to be 43 units long. To find how much greater is the maximum speed of a lion compared to that of a coyote, we subtract

$$50 \text{ mph} - 43 \text{ mph} = 7 \text{ mph}$$ Subtract the coyote's maximum speed from the lion's maximum speed.

The maximum speed of a lion is about 7 mph faster than the maximum speed of a coyote.

To compare sets of related data, groups of two (or three) bars can be shown. For **double-bar** or **triple-bar graphs**, a **key** is used to explain the meaning of each type of bar in a group.

EXAMPLE 3 *The U.S. Economy* The following bar graph shows the total income generated by three sectors of the U.S. economy in each of three years.

a. What income was generated by retail sales in 2000?

b. Which sector of the economy consistently generated the most income?

c. By what amount did the income from the wholesale sector increase from 1990 to 2007?

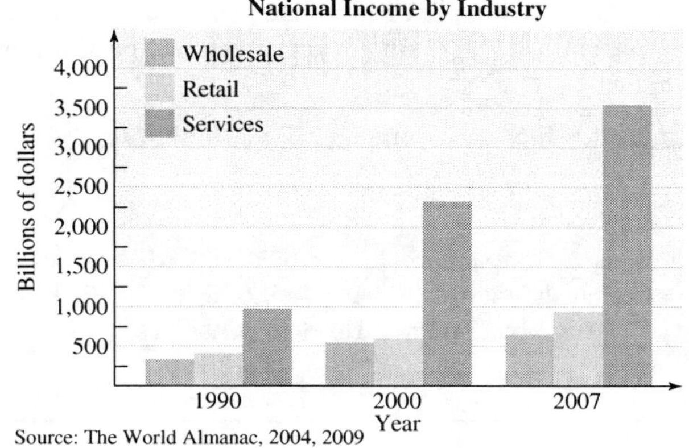

Source: The World Almanac, 2004, 2009

Strategy To answer questions about years, we will locate the correct colored bar and look at the *horizontal axis* of the graph. To answer questions about the income, we will locate the correct colored bar and extend to the left to look at the *vertical axis* of the graph.

WHY The years appear on the horizontal axis. The height of each bar, representing income in billions of dollars, is measured on the scale on the vertical axis.

Solution

a. The second group of bars indicates income in the year 2000. According to the color key, the blue bar of that group shows the retail sales. Since the vertical axis is scaled in units of \$250 billion, the height of that bar is approximately 500 plus one-half of 250, or 125. Thus, the height of the blue bar is approximately $500 + 125 = 625$, which represents \$625 billion in retail sales in 2000.

b. In each group, the green bar is the tallest. That bar, according to the color key, represents the income from the services sector of the economy. Thus, services consistently generated the most income.

c. According to the color key, the orange bar in each group shows income from the wholesale sector. That sector generated about \$260 billion of income in 1990 and \$700 billion in income in 2007. The amount of increase is the difference of these two quantities.

\$700 billion − \$260 billion = \$440 billion   *Subtract the 1990 wholesale income from the 2007 wholesale income.*

Wholesale income increased by about \$440 billion between 1990 and 2007.

Self Check 3

THE U.S. ECONOMY Refer to the bar graph of Example 3.

a. What income was generated by retail sales in 1990? about \$400 billion

b. What income was generated by the wholesale sector in 2007? about \$700 billion

c. In 2000, by what amount did the income from the services sector exceed the income from the retail sector? about \$170 billion

Now Try **Problems 25 and 31**

Teaching Example 3 THE U.S. ECONOMY Refer to the bar graph of Example 3.

a. What income was generated by wholesale sales in 2000?

b. What income was generated by the services sector in 1990?

c. By what amount did the income from the services sector increase from 1990 through 2007?

Answers:

a. about \$600 billion

b. about \$900 billion

c. about \$2,600 billion

3 Read pictographs.

A **pictograph** is like a bar graph, but the bars are made from pictures or symbols. A **key** tells the meaning (or value) of each symbol.

EXAMPLE 4 *Pizza Deliveries*

The pictograph on the right shows the number of pizzas delivered to the three residence halls on a college campus during final exam week. In the graph, what information does the top row of pizzas give?

Pizzas ordered during final exam week

Men's residence hall

Women's residence hall

Co-ed residence hall

= 12 pizzas

Self Check 4

PIZZA DELIVERIES In the pictograph of Example 4, what information does the last row of pizzas give? 33 pizzas were delivered to the co-ed residence hall.

Now Try **Problems 33 and 35**

Teaching Example 4 PIZZA DELIVERIES In the pictograph of Example 4, what information does the middle row of pizzas give?
Answer:
54 pizzas were delivered to the women's residence hall.

Strategy We will count the number of complete pizza symbols that appear in the top row of the graph, and we will estimate what fractional part of a pizza symbol also appears in that row.

WHY The key indicates that each complete pizza symbol represents one dozen (12) pizzas.

Solution
The top row contains 3 complete pizza symbols and what appears to be $\frac{1}{4}$ of another. This means that the men's residence hall ordered $3 \cdot 12$, or 36 pizzas, plus approximately $\frac{1}{4}$ of 12, or about 3 pizzas. This totals 39 pizzas.

Caution! One drawback of a pictograph is that it can be difficult to determine what fractional amount is represented by a portion of a symbol. For example, if the CD shown to the right represents 1,000 units sold, we can only estimate that the partial CD symbol represents about 600 units sold.

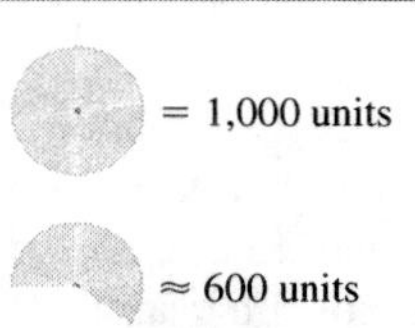

4 Read circle graphs.

In **a circle graph**, regions called **sectors** are used to show what part of the whole each quantity represents.

The Language of Mathematics A *sector* has the shape of a slice of pizza or a slice of pie. Thus, circle graphs are also called **pie charts.**

Self Check 5

GOLD PRODUCTION Refer to the circle graph of Example 5. To the nearest tenth of a million, how many ounces of gold did Russia produce in 2008? 5.5 million ounces

Now Try **Problems 37, 41, and 43**

Teaching Example 5 GOLD PRODUCTION Refer to the circle graph of Example 5.
a. What percent of the total was the combined production of Australia, the United States, and Canada in 2008?
b. How many ounces of gold did South Africa produce in 2008?
Answers:
a. 24% b. 7.8 million ounces

EXAMPLE 5 *Gold Production* The circle graph to the right gives information about world gold production. The entire circle represents the world's total production of 78 million troy ounces in 2008. Use the graph to answer the following questions.

a. What percent of the total was the combined production of the United States and Canada?

b. What percent of the total production came from sources other than those listed?

c. To the nearest tenth of a million, how many ounces of gold did China produce in 2008?

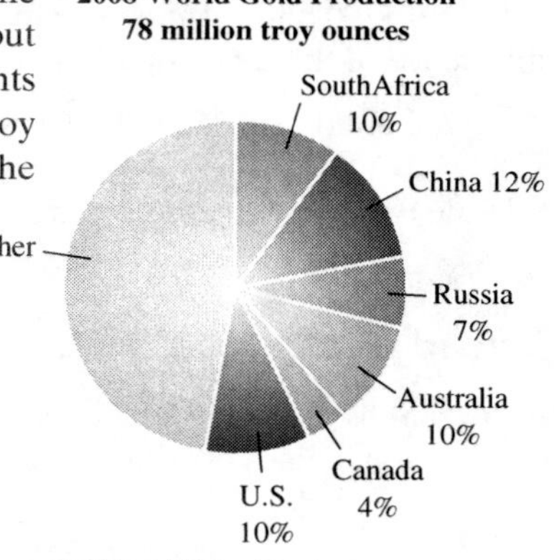

Strategy We will look for the key words in each problem.

WHY Key words tell us what operation (addition, subtraction, multiplication, or division) must be performed to answer each question.

Solution

a. The key word *combined* indicates addition. According to the graph, the United States produced 10% and Canada produced 4% of the total amount of gold in 2008. Together, they produced 10% + 4%, or 14% of the total.

b. The phrase *from sources other than those listed* indicates subtraction. To find the percent of gold produced by countries that are not listed, we add the contributions of all the listed sources and subtract that total from 100%.

$$100\% - (10\% + 12\% + 7\% + 10\% + 4\% + 10\%) = 100\% - 53\% = 47\%$$

Countries that are not listed in the graph produced 47% of the world's total production of gold in 2008.

c. From the graph we see that China produced 12% of the world's gold in 2008. To find the number of ounces produced by China (the amount), we use the method for solving percent problems.

What number	is	12%	of	78?	This is the percent sentence. The units are millions of ounces.
↓	↓	↓	↓	↓	
x	$=$	12%	$\cdot$	78	Translate to a percent equation.

Now we perform the multiplication on the right side of the equation.

$x = 0.12 \cdot 78$ Write 12% as a decimal: 12% = 0.12.

$x = 9.36$ Do the multiplication.

$$\begin{array}{r} 78 \\ \times\, 0.12 \\ \hline 156 \\ 780 \\ \hline 9.36 \end{array}$$

Rounded to the nearest tenth of a million, China produced 9.4 million ounces of gold in 2008.

5 Read line graphs.

Another type of graph, called a **line graph,** is used to show how quantities change with time. From such a graph, we can determine when a quantity is increasing and when it is decreasing.

> ***The Language of Mathematics*** The symbol ⫲ is often used when graphing to show a break in the scale on an axis. Such a break enables us to omit large portions of empty space on a graph.

EXAMPLE 6 *ATMs* The line graph below shows the number of automated teller machines (ATMs) in the United States for the years 2000 through 2007. Use the graph to answer the following questions.

a. How many ATMs were there in the United States in 2001?

b. Between which two years was there the greatest increase in the number of ATMs?

c. When did the number of ATMs decrease?

d. Between which two years did the number of ATMs remain about the same?

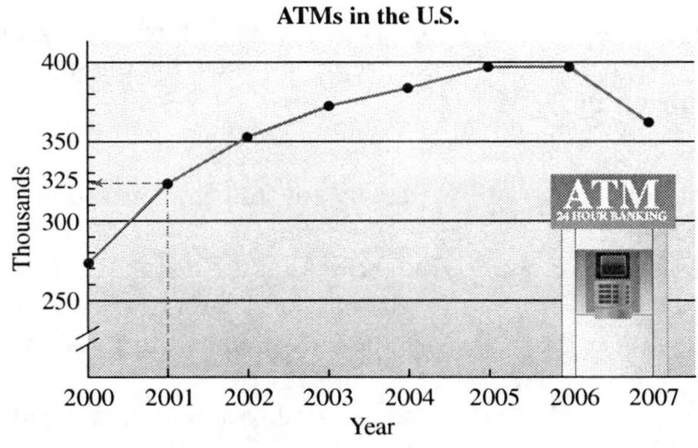

Source: The Federal Reserve and *ATM & Debit News*

Self Check 6

ATMS Refer to the line graph of Example 6.

a. Find the increase in the number of ATMs between 2002 and 2003. about 20,000

b. How many more ATMs were there in the United States in 2007 as compared to 2000? about 90,000

Now Try **Problems 45, 47, and 51**

Teaching Example 6 ATMS Refer to the line graph of Example 6.

a. How many ATMs were there in the United States in 2005?

b. Find the increase in the number of ATMs between 2000 and 2001.

c. In which year did the number of ATMs first exceed 350,000?

Answers:

a. about 395,000

b. about 55,000

c. 2002

Strategy We will determine whether the graph is rising, falling, or is horizontal.

WHY When the graph rises as we read from left to right, the number of ATMs is increasing. When the graph falls as we read from left to right, the number of ATMs is decreasing. If the graph is horizontal, there is no change in the number of ATMs.

Solution

a. To find the number of ATMs in 2001, we follow the dashed blue line from the label 2001 on the horizontal axis straight up to the line graph. Then we extend directly over to the scale on the vertical axis, where the arrowhead points to approximately 325. Since the vertical scale is in thousands of ATMs, there were about 325,000 ATMs in 2001 in the United States.

b. This line graph is composed of seven line segments that connect pairs of consecutive years. The steepest of those seven segments represents the greatest increase in the number of ATMs. Since that segment is between the 2000 and 2001, the greatest increase in the number of ATMs occurred between 2000 and 2001.

c. The only line segment of the graph that falls as we read from left to right is the segment connecting the data points for the years 2006 and 2007. Thus, the number of ATMs decreased from 2006 to 2007.

d. The line segment connecting the data points for the years 2005 and 2006 appears to be horizontal. Since there is little or no change in the number of ATMS for those years, the number of ATMs remained about the same from 2005 to 2006. ■

Two quantities that are changing with time can be compared by drawing both lines on the same graph.

Self Check 7

TRAINS In the graph for Exercise 7, what is train 1 doing at time D? Train 1, which had been stopped, is beginning to move.

Now Try **Problems 53, 55, and 59**

Teaching Example 7 TRAINS Refer to the line graph of Example 7.

a. Which train had traveled farther at time A?
b. Which train had traveled farther at time D?
c. Was train 2 moving or was it stopped at time B?
d. Immediately after time E, which train was traveling faster?

Answers:
a. train 1
b. train 2
c. stopped
d. train 1

EXAMPLE 7 *Trains* The line graph below shows the movements of two trains. The horizontal axis represents time, and the vertical axis represents the distance that the trains have traveled.

a. How are the trains moving at time A?

b. At what time (A, B, C, D, or E) are both trains stopped?

c. At what times have both trains traveled the same distance?

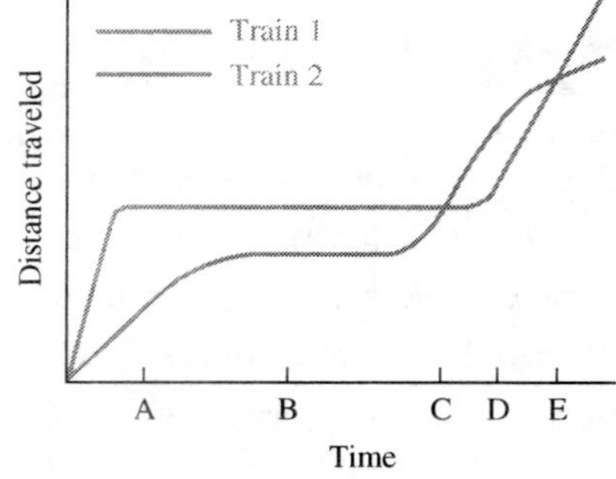

Strategy We will determine whether the graphs are rising or are horizontal. We will also consider the relative positions of the graphs for a given time.

WHY A rising graph indicates the train is moving and a horizontal graph means it is stopped. For any given time, the higher graph indicates that the train it represents has traveled the greater distance.

Solution

The movement of train 1 is represented by the red line, and that of train 2 is represented by the blue line.

a. At time A, the blue line is rising. This shows that the distance traveled by train 2 is increasing. Thus, at time A, train 2 is moving. At time A, the red line is horizontal. This indicates that the distance traveled by train 1 is not changing: At time A, train 1 is stopped.

b. To find the time at which both trains are stopped, we find the time at which both the red and the blue lines are horizontal. At time B, both trains are stopped.

c. At any time, the height of a line gives the distance a train has traveled. Both trains have traveled the same distance whenever the two lines are the same height—that is, at any time when the lines intersect. This occurs at times C and E.

6 Read histograms and frequency polygons.

A company that makes vitamins is sponsoring a program on a cable TV channel. The marketing department must choose from three advertisements to show during the program.

1. Children talking about a chewable vitamin that the company makes.
2. A college student talking about an active-life vitamin that the company makes.
3. A grandmother talking about a multivitamin that the company makes.

A survey of the viewing audience records the age of each viewer, counting the number in the 6-to-15-year-old age group, the 16-to-25-year-old age group, and so on. The graph of the data is displayed in a special type of bar graph called a **histogram,** as shown on the right. The vertical axis, labeled **Frequency**, indicates the number of viewers in each age group. For example, the histogram shows that 105 viewers are in the 36-to-45-year-old age group.

Age of Viewers of a Cable TV Channel

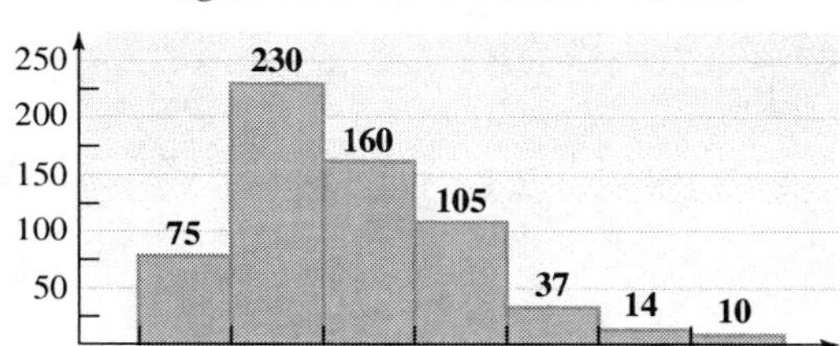

A histogram is a bar graph with three important features.

1. The bars of a histogram touch.
2. Data values never fall at the edge of a bar.
3. The widths of each bar are equal and represent a range of values.

The width of each bar of a histogram represents a range of numbers called a **class interval.** The histogram above has 7 class intervals, each representing an age span of 10 years. Since most viewers are in the 16-to-25-year-old age group, the marketing department decides to advertise the active-life vitamins in commercials that appeal to young adults.

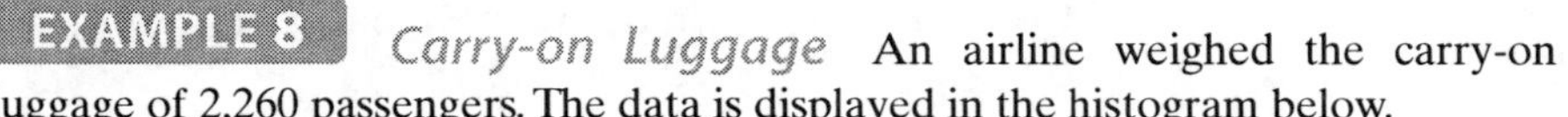

EXAMPLE 8 *Carry-on Luggage* An airline weighed the carry-on luggage of 2,260 passengers. The data is displayed in the histogram below.

a. How many passengers carried luggage in the 8-to-11-pound range?

b. How many carried luggage in the 12-to-19-pound range?

Weight of Carry-on Luggage

Frequency: 1,100 900 700 500 300 100

Bars: 120, 430, 970, 540, 200

Weight (lb): 3.5 7.5 11.5 15.5 19.5 23.5

Strategy We will examine the scale on the horizontal axis of the histogram and identify the interval that contains the given range of weight for the carry-on luggage.

WHY Then we can read the height of the corresponding bar to answer the question.

Solution

a. The second bar, with edges at 7.5 and 11.5 pounds, corresponds to the 8-to-11-pound range. Use the height of the bar (or the number written there) to determine that 430 passengers carried such luggage.

b. The 12-to-19-pound range is covered by two bars. The total number of passengers with luggage in this range is 970 + 540, or 1,510.

Self Check 8

CARRY-ON LUGGAGE Refer to the histogram of Example 8. How many passengers carried luggage in the 20-to-23-pound range? 200

Now Try **Problem 61**

Teaching Example 8 CARRY-ON LUGGAGE Refer to the histogram of Example 8.

a. How many passengers carried luggage in the 4-to-7-pound range?

b. How many passengers carried luggage in the 8-to-19-pound range?

Answers:

a. 120 **b.** 1,940

A special line graph, called a **frequency polygon,** can be constructed from the carry-on luggage histogram by joining the center points at the top of each bar. (See the graphs below.) On the horizontal axis, we write the coordinate of the middle value of each bar. After erasing the bars, we get the frequency polygon shown on the right below.

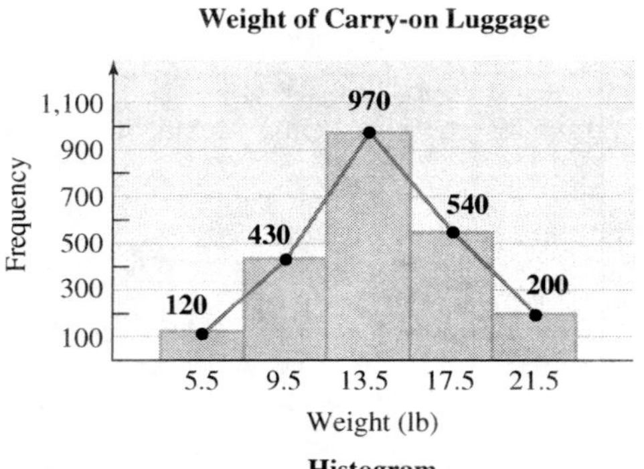

Histogram

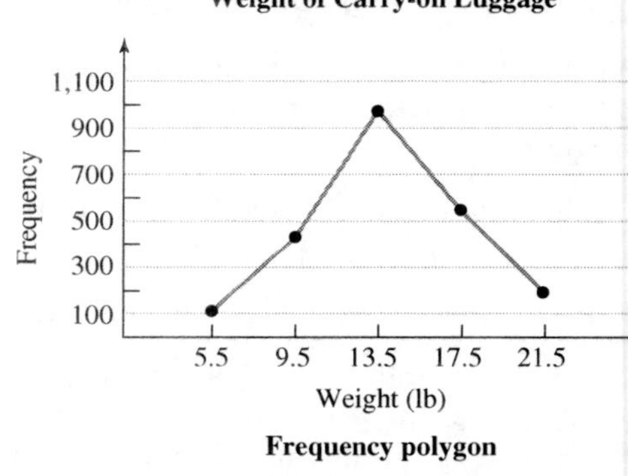

Frequency polygon

ANSWERS TO SELF CHECKS

1. \$14.70 **2. a.** 32 mph **b.** 11 mph **c.** a chicken and an elephant **3. a.** about \$400 billion **b.** about \$700 billion **c.** about \$170 billion **4.** 33 pizzas were delivered to the co-ed residence hall. **5.** 5.5 million ounces **6. a.** about 20,000 **b.** about 90,000 **7.** Train 1, which had been stopped, is beginning to move. **8.** 200

SECTION 5.1 STUDY SET

VOCABULARY

For problems 1-6, refer to graphs a through f below. Fill in the blanks with the correct letter.

1. Graph _(a)_ is a bar graph.

2. Graph _(e)_ is a circle graph.

3. Graph _(c)_ is a pictograph.

▶ **4.** Graph _(f)_ is a line graph.

5. Graph _(d)_ is a histogram.

6. Graph _(b)_ is a frequency polygon.

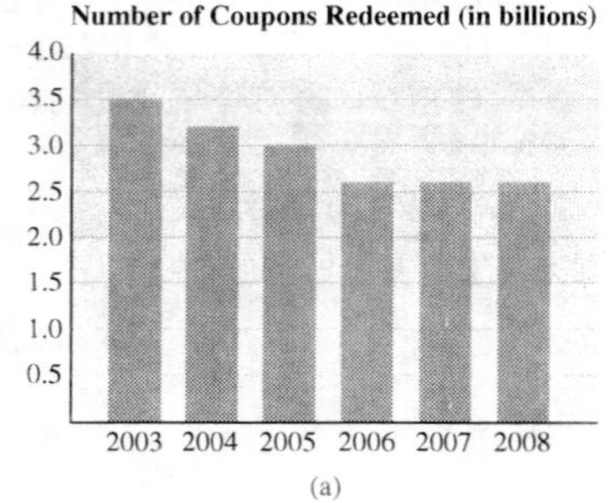

(a)

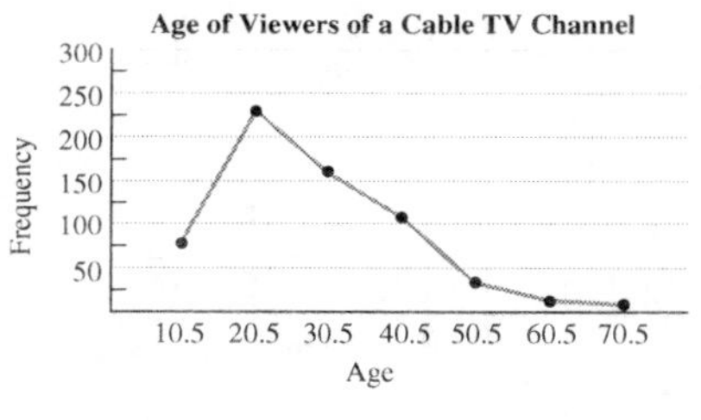

(b)

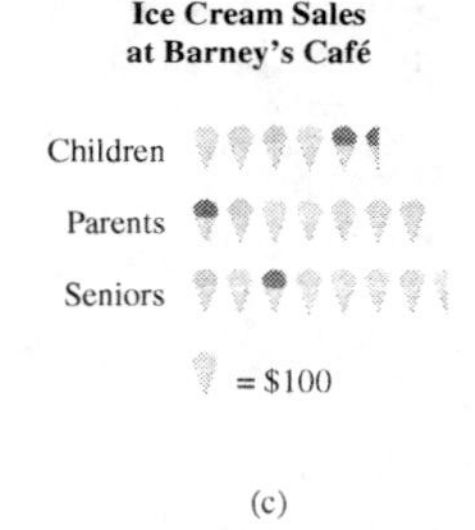

(c)

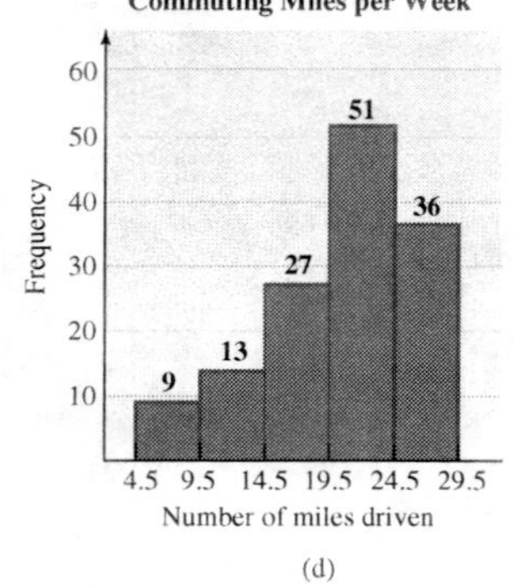

(d)

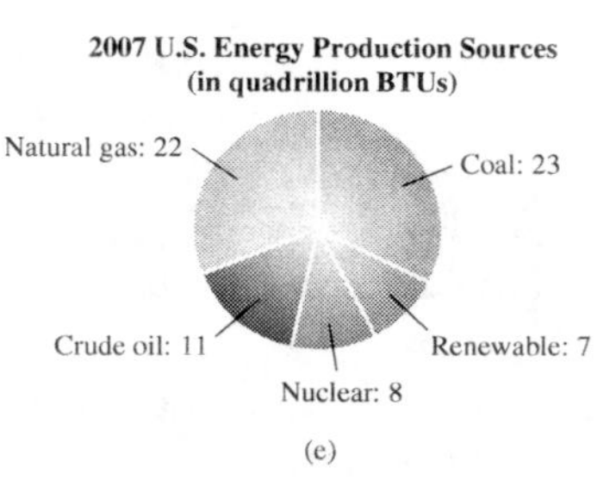

(e)

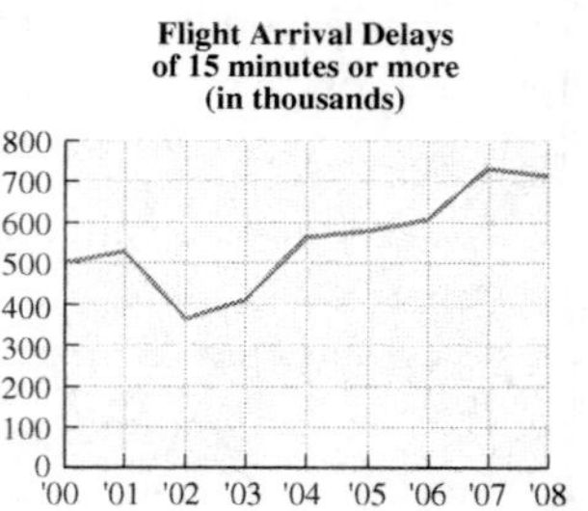

(f)

7. A horizontal or vertical line used for reference in a bar graph is called an axis.

8. In a circle graph, slice-of-pie–shaped figures called sectors are used to show what part of the whole each quantity represents.

CONCEPTS

Fill in the blanks.

9. To read a table, we must find the intersection of the row and column that contains the desired information.

10. The horizontal axis and the vertical axis of a bar graph serve to frame the graph, and they are scaled in units such as years, dollars, minutes, pounds, and percent.

11. A pictograph is like a bar graph, but the bars are made from pictures or symbols.

12. Line graphs are often used to show how a quantity changes with time. On such graphs, we can easily see when a quantity is increasing and when it is decreasing.

13. A histogram is a bar graph with three important features.
    - The bars of a histogram touch.
    - Data values never fall at the edge of a bar.
    - The widths of the bars of a histogram are equal and represent a range of values.

14. A frequency polygon can be constructed from a histogram by joining the center points at the top of each bar.

NOTATION

15. If the symbol [bus] =1,000 buses, estimate what the symbol [half bus] represents. about 500 buses

16. Fill in the blank: The symbol ⫳ is used when graphing to show a break in the scale on an axis.

GUIDED PRACTICE

Refer to the postal rate table on page 595 to answer the following questions. See Example 1.

17. Find the cost of using priority mail to send a package weighing $7\frac{1}{4}$ pounds to zone 3. \$10.70

▶ 18. Find the cost of sending a package weighing $2\frac{1}{4}$ pounds to zone 5 by priority mail. \$9.05

19. A woman wants to send a birthday gift and an anniversary gift to her brother, who lives in zone 6, using priority mail. One package weighs 2 pounds 9 ounces, and the other weighs 3 pounds 8 ounces. Suppose you are the woman's mail carrier and she asks you how much money will be saved by sending both gifts as one package instead of two. Make the necessary calculations to answer her question. (Hint: 16 ounces = 1 pound.) \$4.55 (\$21.85 - \$17.30)

from Campus to Careers
Postal Service Mail Carrier

Kim Steele/Photodisc/Getty Images

20. Juan wants to send a package weighing 6 pounds 1 ounce to a friend living in zone 2. Standard postage would be \$3.25. How much could he save by sending the package standard postage instead of priority mail? \$5.05

Refer to the bar graph below to answer the following questions. See Example 2.

21. List the top three most commonly owned pets in the United States. fish, cat, dog

▶ 22. There are four types of pets that are owned in approximately equal numbers. What are they? birds, horses, reptiles, small animals

23. Together, are there more pet dogs and cats than pet fish? no

24. How many more pet cats are there than pet dogs? about 15 million

Total Number of Pets Owned in the United States, 2009

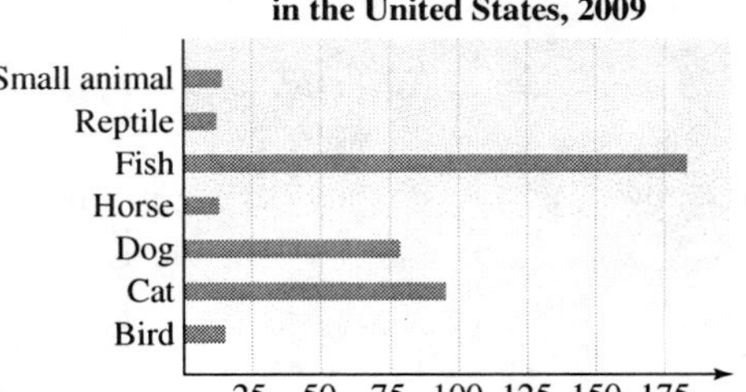

Source: National Pet Owners Survey, AAPA

Refer to the bar graph on the next page to answer the following questions. See Example 3.

25. For the years shown in the graph, has the production of zinc always exceeded the production of lead? yes

26. Estimate how many times greater the amount of zinc produced in 2000 was compared to the amount of lead produced that year? about 3 times greater

27. What is the sum of the amounts of lead produced in 1990, 2000, and 2007? about 10,000,000 metric tons

28. For which metal, lead or zinc, has the production remained about the same over the years? lead

29. In what years was the amount of zinc produced at least twice that of lead? 1990, 2000, 2007

30. Find the difference in the amount of zinc produced in 2007 and the amount produced in 2000. about 2,000,000 metric tons

31. By how many metric tons did the amount of zinc produced increase between 1990 and 2007? 4,000,000 metric tons

32. Between which two years did the production of lead decrease? 1990 and 2000

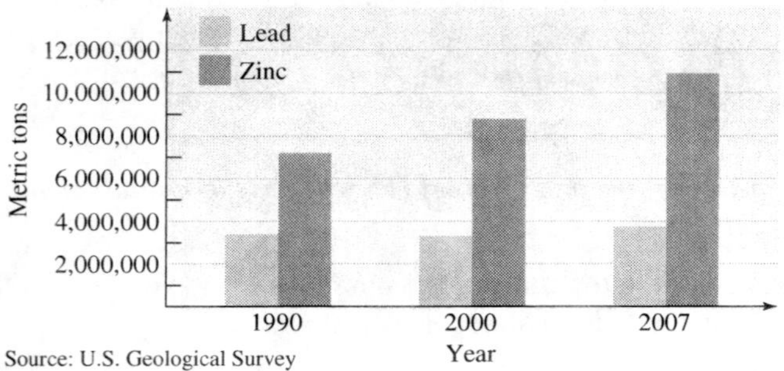

Refer to the pictograph below to answer the following questions. See Example 4.

33. Which group (children, parents, or seniors) spent the most money on ice cream at Barney's Café? seniors

34. How much money did parents spend on ice cream? \$700

35. How much more money did seniors spend than parents? \$50

36. How much more money did seniors spend than children? \$200

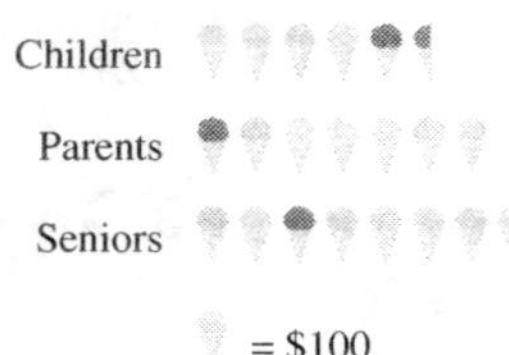

Refer to the circle graph in the next column to answer the following questions. See Example 5.

37. Of the languages in the graph, which is spoken by the greatest number of people? Chinese

38. Do more people speak Spanish or French? Spanish

39. Together, do more people speak English, French, Spanish, Russian, and German combined than Chinese? no

40. Three pairs of languages shown in the graph are spoken by groups of the same size. Which pairs of languages are they? French and German (1%), Hindu and Arabic (3%), English and Spanish (5%)

41. What percent of the world's population speak a language other than the eight shown in the graph? 62%

42. What percent of the world's population speak Russian or English? 7%

43. To the nearest one million, how many people in the world speak Chinese? 1,219,000,000

44. To the nearest one million, how many people in the world speak Arabic? 203,000,000

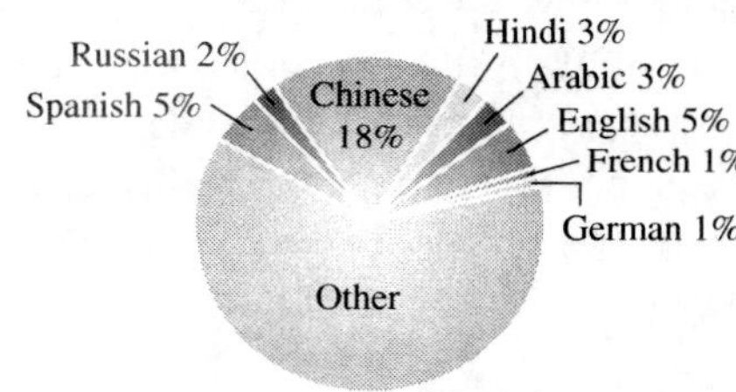

Refer to the line graph on the next page to answer the following questions. See Example 6.

45. How many U.S. ski resorts were in operation in 2004? 493

46. How many U.S. ski resorts were in operation in 2008? 481

47. Between which two years was there a decrease in the number of ski resorts in operation? (*Hint:* there is more than one answer.) 2002 to 2003; 2004 to 2005; 2005 to 2006; 2007 to 2008

48. Between which two years was there an increase in the number of ski resorts in operation? (*Hint:* there is more than one answer.) 2001 to 2002; 2003 to 2004; 2006 to 2007

49. For which two years were the number of ski resorts in operation the same? 2001 and 2003

50. Find the difference in the number of ski resorts in operation in 2001 and 2008. 9 fewer resorts in 2008

51. Between which two years was there the greatest decrease in the number of ski resorts in operation? What was the decrease? 2005 to 2006; a decrease of 14 resorts

52. Between which two years was there the greatest increase in the number of ski resorts in operation? What was the increase? 2006 to 2007; an increase of 7 resorts

Source: National Ski Area Assn.

Refer to the line graph below to answer the following questions. See Example 7.

53. Which runner ran faster at the start of the race? 1

54. At time A, which runner was ahead in the race? 1

55. At what time during the race were the runners tied for the lead? B

56. Which runner stopped to rest first? 1

57. Which runner dropped his watch and had to go back to get it? 1

58. At which of these times (A, B, C, D, E) was runner 1 stopped and runner 2 running? A and D

59. Describe what was happening at time E. Who was running? Who was stopped? Runner 1 was running; runner 2 was stopped.

60. Which runner won the race? 2

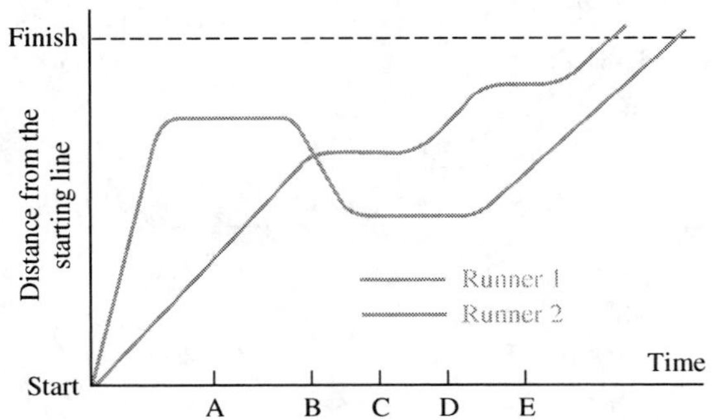

Refer to the histogram and frequency polygon below to answer the following questions. See Example 8.

61. COMMUTING MILES An insurance company collected data on the number of miles its employees drive to and from work. The data are presented in the histogram below.

a. How many employees have a commute that is in the range of 15 to 19 miles per week? 27

b. How many employees commute 14 miles or less per week? 22

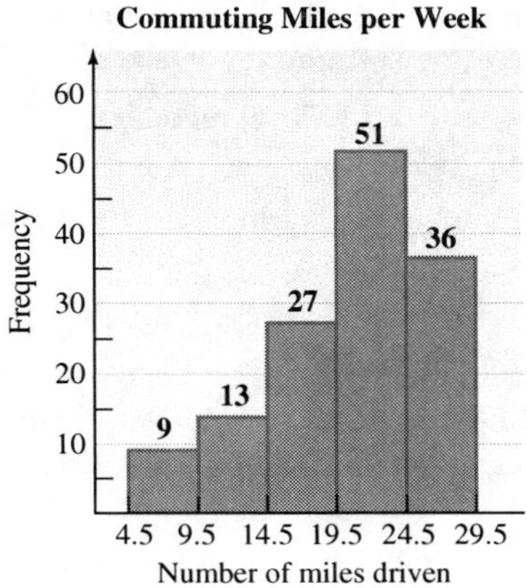

62. NIGHT SHIFT STAFFING A hospital administrator surveyed the medical staff to determine the number of room calls during the night. She constructed the frequency polygon below.

a. On how many nights were there about 30 room calls? 90

b. On how many nights were there about 60 room calls? 10

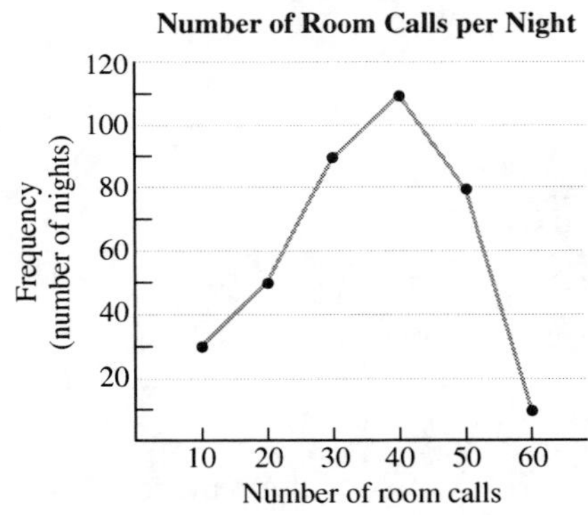

TRY IT YOURSELF

Refer to the 2008 federal income tax table below.

63. FILING A SINGLE RETURN Herb is single and has an adjusted income of $79,250. Compute his federal income tax. $16,168.25

64. FILING A JOINT RETURN Raul and his wife have a combined adjusted income of $57,100. Compute their federal income tax if they file jointly. $7,762.50

65. TAX-SAVING STRATEGY Angelina is single and has an adjusted income of $53,000. If she gets married, she will gain other deductions that will reduce her income by $2,000, and she can file a joint return.

a. Compute her federal income tax if she remains single. $9,593.75

b. Compute her federal income tax if she gets married. $6,847.50

c. How much will she save in federal income tax by getting married? $2,746.25

66. THE MARRIAGE PENALTY A single man with an adjusted income of $80,000 is dating a single woman with an adjusted income of $75,000.

a. Find the amount of federal income tax each person would pay on their adjusted income. man: $16,378.25; woman: $15,093.75

b. Add the results from part a. $31,472

c. If they get married and file a joint return, how much federal income tax will they have to pay on their combined adjusted incomes? $32,144

d. Would they have saved on their federal income taxes if they did not get married and paid as two single persons? Find the amount of the "marriage penalty." yes; $672

Refer to the following bar graph.

67. In which year was the largest percent of flights cancelled? Estimate the percent. 2000; about 3.2%

68. In which year was the smallest percent of flights cancelled? Estimate the percent. 2002; about 1.3%

69. Did the percent of cancelled flights increase or decrease between 2006 and 2007? By how much? increase; about 1%

70. Did the percent of cancelled flights increase or decrease between 2007 and 2008? By how much? decrease; about 0.2%

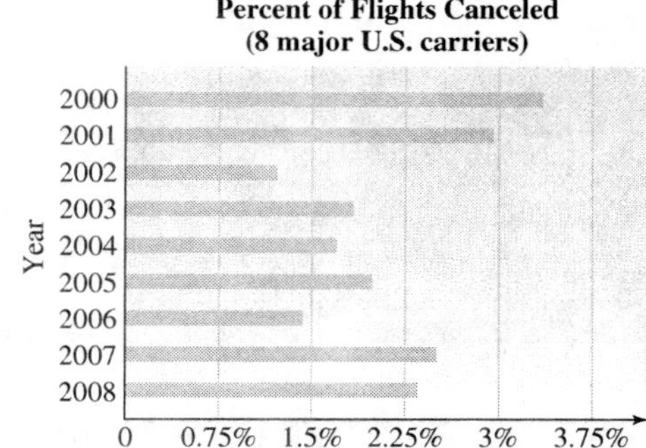

Source: Bureau of Transportation Statistics

Revised 2008 Tax Rate Schedules

	If TAXABLE INCOME		The TAX is		
		THEN			
	Is Over	But Not Over	This Amount	Plus This %	Of the Amount Over
SCHEDULE X—					
Single	$0	$8,025	$0.00	10%	$0.00
	$8,025	$32,550	$802.50	15%	$8,025
	$32,550	$78,850	$4,481.25	25%	$32,550
	$78,850	$164,550	$16,056.25	28%	$78,850
	$164,550	$357,700	$40,052.25	33%	$164,550
	$357,700	—	$103,791.75	35%	$357,700
SCHEDULE Y-1—					
Married Filing	$0	$16,050	$0.00	10%	$0.00
Jointly or	$16,050	$65,100	$1,605.00	15%	$16,050
Qualifying	$65,100	$131,450	$8,962.50	25%	$65,100
Widow(er	$131,450	$200,300	$25,550.00	28%	$131,450
	$200,300	$357,700	$44,828.00	33%	$200,300
	$357,700	—	$96,770.00	35%	$357,700

Refer to the following line graph, which shows the altitude of a small private airplane.

71. How did the plane's altitude change between times B and C? it increased
72. At what time did the pilot first level off the airplane? A
73. When did the pilot first begin his descent to land the airplane? D
74. How did the plane's altitude change between times D and E? it decreased

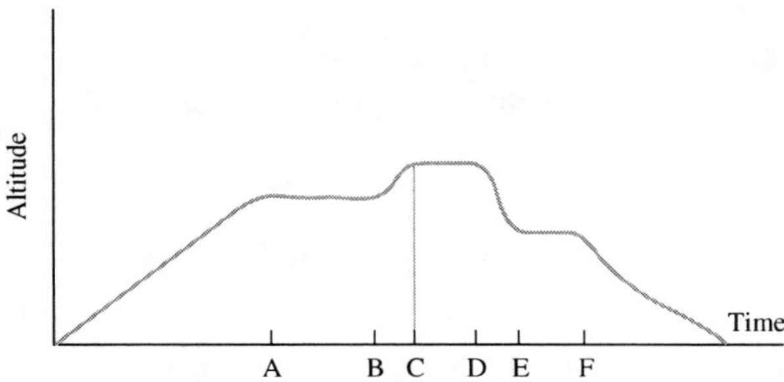

Refer to the following double-bar graph.

75. In which categories of moving violations have violations decreased since last month? reckless driving and failure to yield
76. Last month, which violation occurred most often? following too closely
77. This month, which violation occurred least often? reckless driving
78. Which violation has shown the greatest decrease in number since last month? failure to yield

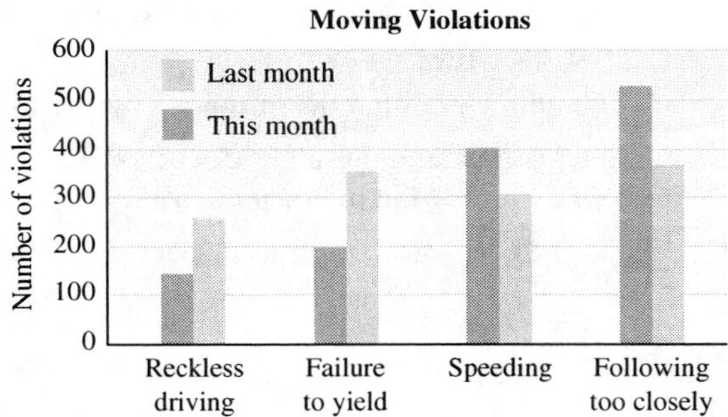

Refer to the following line graph.

79. What were the average weekly earnings in mining for the year 1980? about $440
80. What were the average weekly earnings in construction for the year 1980? about $390
81. Were the average weekly earnings in mining and construction ever the same? no
82. What was the difference in a miner's and a construction worker's weekly earnings in 1995? about $75
83. In the period between 2005 and 2008, which occupation's weekly earnings were increasing more rapidly, the miner's or the construction worker's? the miner's
84. Did the weekly earnings of a miner or a construction worker ever decrease over a five-year span? no
85. In the period from 1980 to 2008, which workers received the greatest increase in weekly earnings? the miners
86. In what five-year span was the miner's increase in weekly earnings the smallest? 1990 to 1995

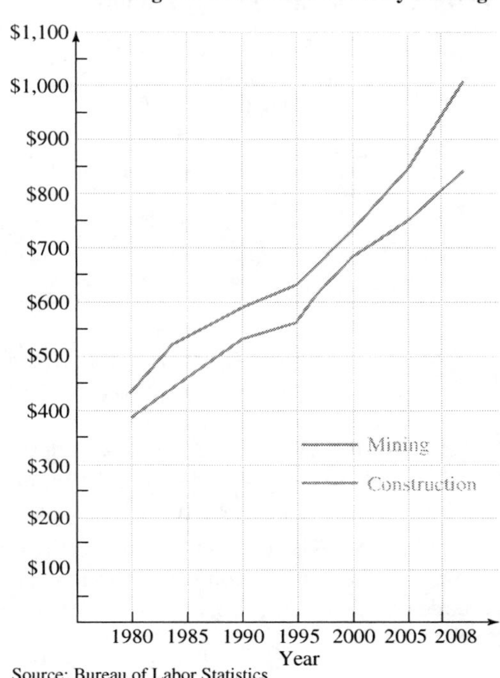

Refer to the following pictograph.

87. What is the daily parking rate for Midtown New York? about $42
88. What is the daily parking rate for Boston? about $33
89. How much more would it cost to park a car for five days in Boston compared to five days in San Francisco? about $30
90. How much more would it cost to park a car for five days in Midtown New York compared to five days in Boston? about $45

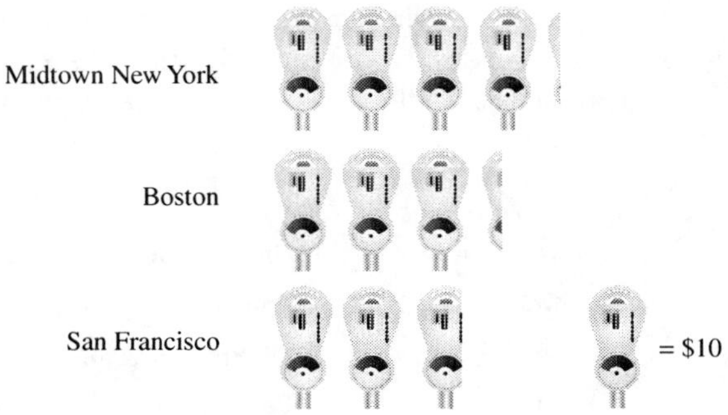

Refer to the following circle graph.

91. What percent of U.S. energy production comes from nuclear energy? Round to the nearest percent. 11%

92. What percent of U.S. energy production comes from natural gas? Round to the nearest percent. 31%

93. What percent of the total energy production comes from renewable and nuclear combined? 21%

94. By what percent does energy produced from coal exceed that produced from crude oil? about 17%

2007 U.S. Energy Production Sources (in quadrillion BTUs)

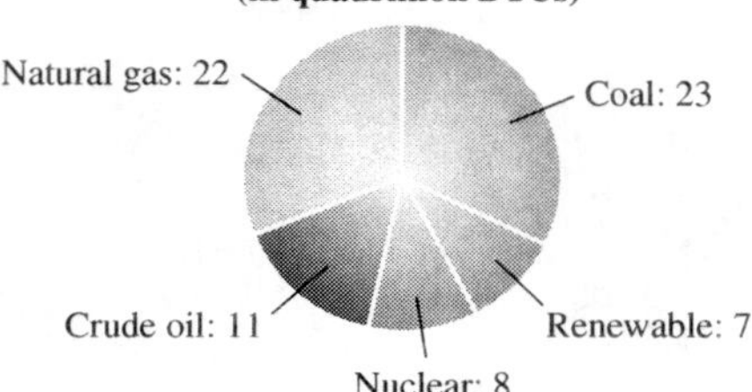

Total production: 71 quadrillion BTUs

Source: Energy Information Administration

95. NUMBER OF U.S. FARMS Use the data in the table below to make a bar graph showing the number of U.S. farms for selected years from 1950 through 2007.

96. SIZE OF U.S. FARMS Use the data in the table below to make a line graph showing the average acreage of U.S. farms for selected years from 1950 through 2007.

Year	Number of U.S. farms (in millions)	Average size of U.S. farms (acres)
1950	5.6	213
1960	4.0	297
1970	2.9	374
1980	2.4	426
1990	2.1	460
2000	2.2	436
2007	2.1	449

Source: U.S. Dept. of Agriculture

97. COUPONS Each coupon value shown in the table below provides savings for shoppers. Make a line graph that relates the original price (in dollars, on the horizontal axis) to the sale price (in dollars, on the vertical axis).

Coupon value: amount saved	Original price of the item
$10	$100, but less than $250
$25	$250, but less than $500
$50	$500 or more

98. DENTISTRY To study the effect of fluoride in preventing tooth decay, researchers counted the number of fillings in the teeth of 28 patients and recorded these results:

3, 7, 11, 21, 16, 22, 18, 8, 12, 3, 7, 2, 8, 19, 12, 19, 12, 10, 13, 10, 14, 15, 14, 14, 9, 10, 12, 13

Tally the results by completing the table. Then make a histogram. The first bar extends from 0.5 to 5.5, the second bar from 5.5 to 10.5, and so on.

Number of fillings	Frequency
1–5	3
6–10	8
11–15	11
16–20	4
21–25	2

WRITING

99. What kind of presentation (table, bar graph, line graph, circle graph, pictograph, or histogram) is most appropriate for displaying each type of information? Explain your choices.

- The percent of students at a college, classified by major
- The percent of biology majors at a college each year since 1970
- The number of hours a group of students spent studying for final exams
- The ethnic populations of the ten largest cities
- The average annual salary of corporate executives for ten major industries

▶ **100.** Explain why a histogram is a special type of bar graph.

REVIEW

101. Write the prime numbers between 10 and 30. 11, 13, 17, 19, 23, 29

102. Write the first ten composite numbers. 4, 6, 8, 9, 10, 12, 14, 15, 16, 18

103. Write the even whole numbers less than 6 that are not prime. 0, 4

104. Write the odd whole numbers less than 20 that are not prime. 1, 9, 15

SECTION 5.2

The Rectangular Coordinate System

Objectives

1. Construct a rectangular coordinate system.
2. Plot ordered pairs and determine the coordinates of a point.
3. Graph paired data.
4. Read line graphs.
5. Read step graphs.

It is often said, "A picture is worth a thousand words." In this section, we will show how numerical relationships can be described using mathematical pictures called **graphs.** We will also show how graphs are constructed and how we can obtain information from them.

1 Construct a rectangular coordinate system.

When designing the Gateway Arch in St. Louis, architects created a mathematical model called a **rectangular coordinate graph.** This graph, shown below, is drawn on a grid called a **rectangular coordinate system.** This coordinate system is also called a **Cartesian coordinate system,** after the 17th-century French mathematician René Descartes.

© David R. Frazier Photolibrary Inc./Alamy

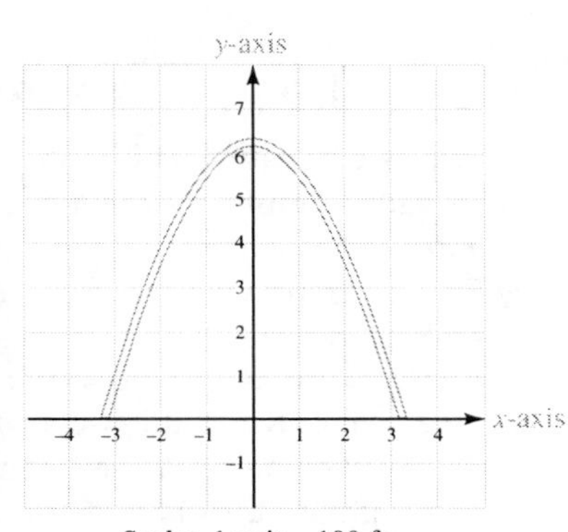

Scale: 1 unit = 100 ft

A rectangular coordinate system is formed by two perpendicular number lines. The horizontal number line is called the ***x*-axis,** and the vertical number line is called the ***y*-axis.** On the x-axis, the positive direction is to the right. On the y-axis, the positive direction is upward. The scale on each axis should fit the data. For example, the axes of the graph of the arch are scaled in units of 100 feet.

> ***Success Tip*** If no scale is indicated on the axes, we assume that the axes are scaled in units of 1.

The point where the axes intersect is called the **origin.** This is the zero point on each axis. The axes form a **coordinate plane,** and they divide it into four regions called **quadrants,** which are numbered counterclockwise using Roman numerals as shown to the right. The axes are not considered to be in any quadrant.

Each point in a coordinate plane can be identified by an **ordered pair** of real numbers x and y written in the form (x, y).

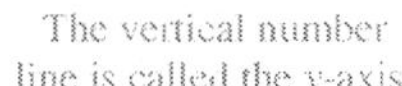

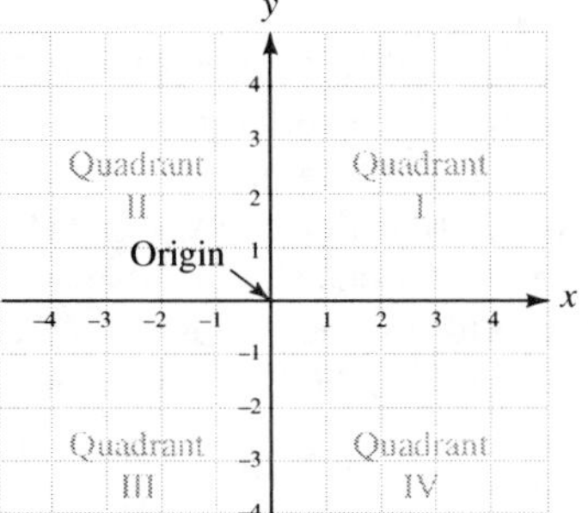

The first number, x, in the pair is called the **x-coordinate,** and the second number, y, is called the **y-coordinate.** The numbers in the pair are called the **coordinates** of the point. Some examples of such pairs are $(3, -4)$, $\left(-1, \frac{3}{2}\right)$, and $(0, 2.5)$.

$(3, -4)$

↑ The x-coordinate is listed first.

↑ The y-coordinate is listed second.

> ***Caution!*** Do not be confused by this new use of parentheses. The notation $(3, -4)$ represents a point on the coordinate plane, whereas $3(-4)$ indicates multiplication. Also, don't confuse the ordered pair with interval notation.

2 Plot ordered pairs and determine the coordinates of a point.

The process of locating a point in the coordinate plane is called **graphing** or **plotting** the point. In the figure to the right, we use two blue arrows to show how to graph the point with coordinates of $(3, -4)$. Since the x-coordinate, 3, is positive, we start at the origin and move 3 units to the *right* along the x-axis. Since the y-coordinate, -4, is negative, we then move *down* 4 units and draw a dot. The graph of $(3, -4)$ lies in quadrant IV.

Two red arrows are used to show how to plot the point $(-4, 3)$. We start at the origin, move 4 units to the *left* along the x-axis, and then move *up* 3 units and draw a dot. The graph of $(-4, 3)$ lies in quadrant II.

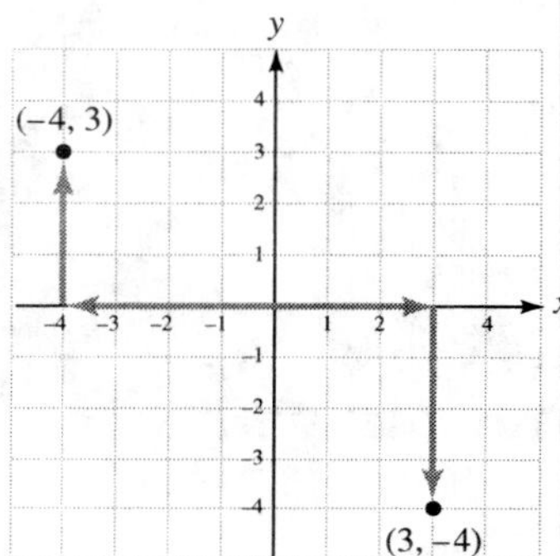

> ***The Language of Algebra*** Note that the point with coordinates $(3, -4)$ is not the same as the point with coordinates $(-4, 3)$. Since the order of the coordinates of a point is important, we call the pairs **ordered pairs.**

In the figure to the right, we see that the points $(-4, 0)$, $(0, 0)$, and $(2, 0)$ lie on the x-axis. In fact, all points with a y-coordinate of zero will lie on the x-axis. We also see that the points $(0, -3)$, $(0, 0)$, and $(0, 3)$ lie on the y-axis. All points with an x-coordinate of zero lie on the y-axis. We can also see that the coordinates of the origin are $(0, 0)$.

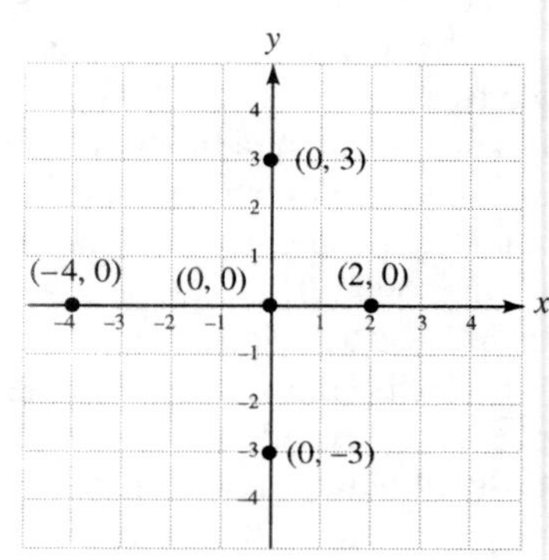

EXAMPLE 1 Plot each point. Then state the quadrant in which it lies or the axis on which it lies. **a.** $(-2, 3)$ **b.** $\left(-1, -\frac{3}{2}\right)$ **c.** $(0, 2.5)$ **d.** $(4, 2)$

Strategy We will start at the origin and move the corresponding number of units right or left for the x-coordinate, then move the corresponding number of units up or down for the y-coordinate, to locate the point. Draw a dot at the point.

WHY The coordinates of a point determine its location on the coordinate plane.

Solution

a. Since the x-coordinate, -2, is negative, we start at the origin and move 2 units to the *left* along the x-axis. Since the y-coordinate, 3, is positive, we then move *up* 3 units and draw a dot. The point lies in quadrant II.

b. To plot $\left(-1, -\frac{3}{2}\right)$, we begin at the origin and move 1 unit to the *left* and $\frac{3}{2}$ $\left(\text{or } 1\frac{1}{2}\right)$ units *down*. The point lies in quadrant III.

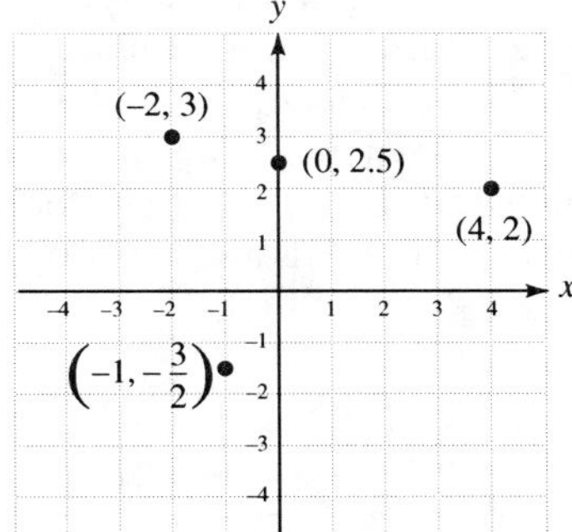

c. To graph $(0, 2.5)$, we begin at the origin and do not move right or left, because the x-coordinate is 0. Since the y-coordinate is positive, we move 2.5 units *up*. The point lies on the y-axis.

d. To graph $(4, 2)$, we begin at the origin and move 4 units to the *right* and 2 units *up*. The point lies in quadrant I.

Self Check 1

Plot the points:
a. $(2, -2)$ **b.** $(-4, 0)$
c. $\left(1.5, \frac{5}{2}\right)$ **d.** $(0, 5)$

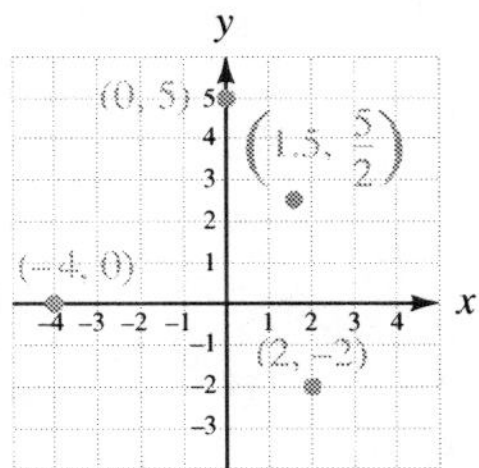

Now Try **Problem 21**

Teaching Example 1 Plot each point. Then state the quadrant in which it lies or the axis on which it lies.
a. $(4, -5)$ **b.** $\left(-2, -\frac{5}{2}\right)$ **c.** $(4, 0)$
Answers:
a. QIV **b.** QIII **c.** x-axis

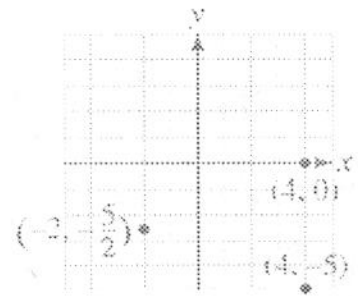

EXAMPLE 2 Find the coordinates of points A, B, C, D, and E plotted in figure (a) below.

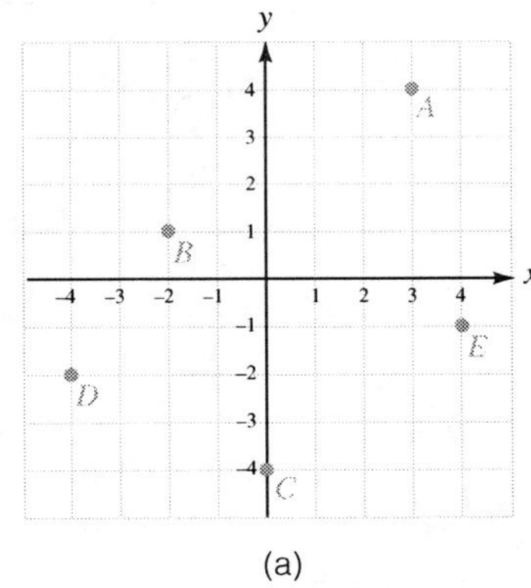

(a)

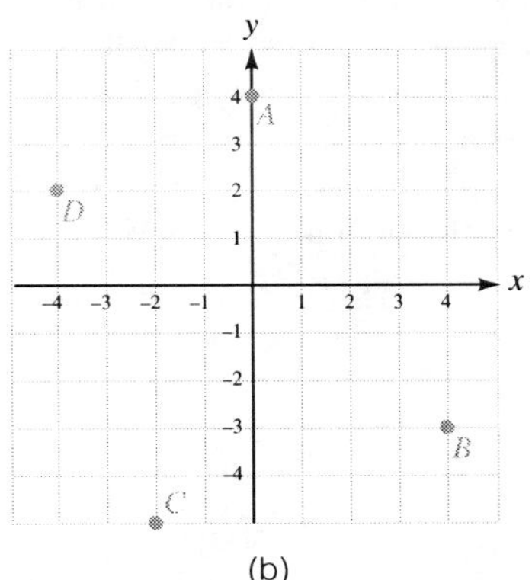

(b)

Strategy We will start at the origin and count to the right or left on the x-axis, and then up or down to reach each point.

WHY The right or left movement gives the x-coordinate and the up or down movement gives the y-coordinate of the point.

Solution

To find the coordinates of point A, we start at the origin, move 3 units to the right on the x-axis, and then 4 units up. The coordinates of point A are $(3, 4)$. The coordinates of the other points are found in the same manner: $B(-2, 1)$, $C(0, -4)$, $D(-4, -2)$, $E(4, -1)$.

Self Check 2

Find the coordinates of each point in figure (b).

Now Try **Problem 25**

Self Check 2 Answer
$A(0, 4)$, $B(4, -3)$, $C(-2, -5)$, $D(-4, 2)$

Teaching Example 2 Find the coordinates of points A, B, C, D, and E.
Answers:
$A(4, 1)$, $B(2, -3)$, $C(-3, 0)$, $D(-2, -4)$, $E(-1, 4)$

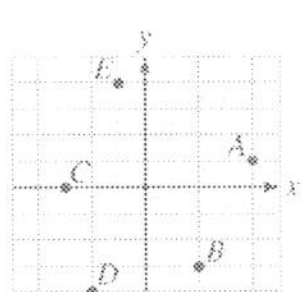

3 Graph paired data.

Every day, we deal with quantities that are related:

- The time it takes to cook a turkey depends on the weight of the turkey.
- Our weight depends on how much we eat.
- The amount of water in a tub depends on how long the water has been running.

We can use graphs to visualize such relationships. For example, suppose we know the number of gallons of water that are in a tub at several time intervals after the water has been turned on. We can list that information in a **table.**

The information in the table can be used to construct a graph that shows the relationship between the amount of water in the tub and the time the water has been running. Since the amount of water in the tub depends on the time, we will associate *time* with the x-axis and *amount of water* with the y-axis.

At various times, the amount of water in the tub was measured and recorded in the table.

Time (min)	Water in tub (gal)	
0	0	→ (0, 0)
1	8	→ (1, 8)
3	24	→ (3, 24)
4	32	→ (4, 32)

↑ x-coordinate ↑ y-coordinate

↑ The data in the table can be expressed as ordered pairs (x, y).

To construct the graph below we plot the four ordered pairs and draw a straight line through the resulting data points. The y-axis is scaled in larger units (4 gallons) because the data range from 0 to 32 gallons.

From the graph, we can see that the amount of water in the tub steadily increases as the water is allowed to run. We can also use the graph to make observations about the amount of water in the tub at other times. For example, the dashed line on the graph shows that in 5 minutes, the tub will contain 40 gallons of water.

x	y	(x, y)
0	0	(0, 0)
1	8	(1, 8)
3	24	(3, 24)
4	32	(4, 32)

The data can be listed in a table with headings x, y, and (x, y).

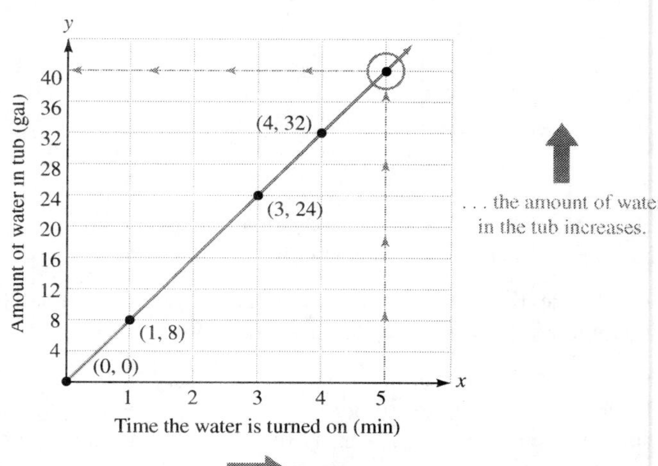

4 Read line graphs.

Since graphs are a popular way to present information, the ability to read and interpret them is very important.

EXAMPLE 3 *TV Shows* The graph shows the number of people in an audience before, during, and after the taping of a television show. On the x-axis, zero represents the time when taping began. Use the graph to answer the following questions and complete the table.

a. How many people were in the audience when taping began?

b. What was the size of the audience 10 minutes before taping began?

c. At what times were there exactly 100 people in the audience?

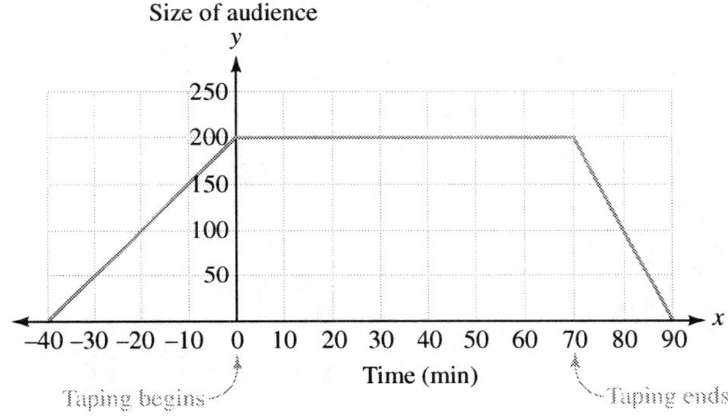

Strategy We will use an ordered pair of the form (*time, size of audience*) to describe each situation mentioned in parts a, b, and c.

WHY The coordinates of specific points on the graph can be used to answer each of these questions.

Solution

Time (min) x	Size of audience y
0	200
−10	150
−20	100
80	100

a. The time when taping began is represented by 0 on the x-axis. The point on the graph directly above 0 is (0, 200). The y-coordinate indicates that 200 people were in the audience when the taping began. We enter this result in the table at the right.

b. Ten minutes before taping began is represented by -10 on the x-axis. The point on the graph directly above -10 is $(-10, 150)$. The y-coordinate indicates that 150 people were in the audience 10 minutes before the taping began. We enter this result in the table.

c. We can draw a horizontal line passing through 100 on the y-axis. Since this line intersects the graph twice, at $(-20, 100)$ and at $(80, 100)$, there are two times when 100 people were in the audience. The x-coordinates of the points tell us those times: 20 minutes before taping began and 80 minutes after. Enter these results in the table.

Self Check 3

Use the graph to answer the following questions.

a. At what times were there exactly 50 people in the audience?

b. What was the size of the audience that watched the taping?

c. How long did it take for the audience to leave the studio after the taping ended?

Now Try **Problems 33 and 34**

Self Check 3 Answers

a. 30 min before and 85 min after taping began

b. 200

c. 20 min

Teaching Example 3 Use the graph to answer the following questions.

a. How many people were in the audience 80 minutes after taping began?

b. At what time before taping was there exactly 150 people in the audience?

Answers:

a. 100 people

b. 10 min. before taping began

5 Read step graphs.

The graph below shows the cost of renting a trailer for different periods of time. For example, the cost of renting the trailer for 4 days is \$60, which is the y-coordinate of the point (4, 60). The cost of renting the trailer for a period lasting over 4 and up to 5 days jumps to \$70. Since the jumps in cost form steps in the graph, we call this graph a **step graph.**

Self Check 4

Use the information in the figure of Example 4 to answer the following:

a. Find the cost of renting the trailer for 1 day. \$20

b. Find the cost of renting the trailer for $4\frac{1}{2}$ days. \$70

c. How long can you rent the trailer if you have \$40? 2 days

Now Try **Problems 41 and 43**

Teaching Example 4 Use the information in the figure to answer the following questions.

a. Find the cost of renting the trailer for 6 days.

b. Find the cost of renting the trailer for $2\frac{1}{2}$ days.

c. How long can you rent the trailer if you have \$70?

Answers:

a. \$80 b. \$50 c. 5 days

EXAMPLE 4 Use the information in the figure to answer the following questions. Write the results in a table.

a. Find the cost of renting the trailer for 2 days.

b. Find the cost of renting the trailer for $5\frac{1}{2}$ days.

c. How long can you rent the trailer if you have \$50?

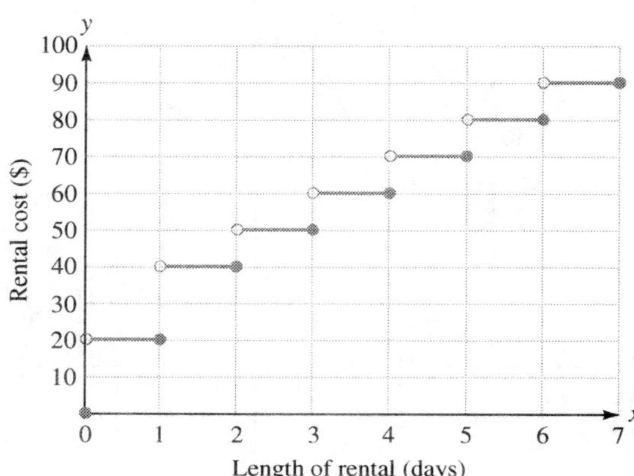

Strategy We will use an ordered pair of the form (*days, rental cost*) to describe each situation mentioned in parts a, b, and c.

WHY The coordinates of specific points on the graph can be used to answer each of these questions.

Solution

a. The solid dot at the end of each step indicates the rental cost for 1, 2, 3, 4, 5, 6, or 7 days. Each open circle indicates that that point is not on the graph. We locate 2 days on the x-axis and move up to locate the point on the graph directly above the 2. Since the point has coordinates (2, 40), a 2-day rental would cost \$40. We enter this result in the table below.

b. We locate $5\frac{1}{2}$ days on the x-axis and move straight up to locate the point with coordinates $\left(5\frac{1}{2}, 80\right)$, which indicates that a $5\frac{1}{2}$-day rental would cost \$80. We then enter this result in the table.

c. We draw a horizontal line through the point labeled 50 on the y-axis. Since this line intersects one step in the graph, we can look down to the x-axis to find the x-values that correspond to a y-value of 50. From the graph, we see that the trailer can be rented for more than 2 and up to 3 days for \$50. The point has coordinates (3, 50). Enter the results in the table.

Length of rental (days) x	Cost (dollars) y
2	40
$5\frac{1}{2}$	80
3	50

ANSWERS TO SELF CHECKS

1.

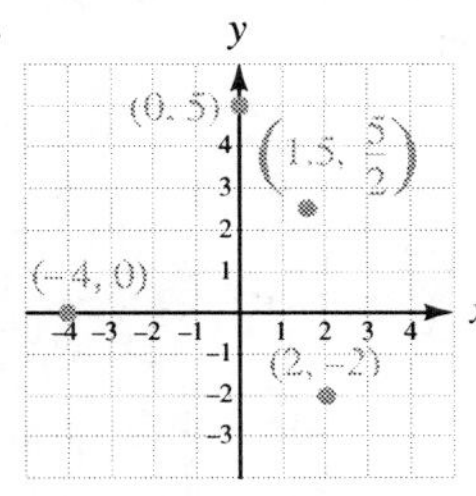

2. $A(0, 4)$, $B(4, -3)$, $C(-2, -5)$, $D(-4, 2)$ **3. a.** 30 min before and 85 min after taping began **b.** 200 **c.** 20 min **4. a.** \$20 **b.** \$70 **c.** 2 days

SECTION 5.2 STUDY SET

VOCABULARY

Fill in the blanks.

1. The point with coordinates (4, 2) can be graphed on a rectangular coordinate system.
2. On the rectangular coordinate system, the horizontal number line is called the *x*-axis and the vertical number line is called the *y*-axis.
3. On the rectangular coordinate system, the point (0, 0) where the axes cross is called the origin.
4. On the rectangular coordinate system, the axes form the coordinate plane.
5. The *x*- and *y*-axes divide the coordinate plane into four regions called quadrants.
6. The pair of numbers (−1, −5) is called an ordered pair.
7. In the ordered pair $\left(-\frac{3}{2}, -5\right)$, $-\frac{3}{2}$ is called the *x*-coordinate and −5 is called the *y*-coordinate.
8. The process of locating the position of a point on a coordinate plane is called graphing or plotting the point.

CONCEPTS

Fill in the blanks.

9. To plot the point with coordinates (−5, 4.5), we start at the origin and move 5 units to the left and then move 4.5 units up.
10. To plot the point with coordinates $\left(6, -\frac{3}{2}\right)$, we start at the origin and move 6 units to the right and then move $\frac{3}{2}$ units down.
11. Do (3, 2) and (2, 3) represent the same point? no
12. In the ordered pair (4, 5), is the number 4 associated with the horizontal or the vertical axis? horizontal
13. In which quadrant do points with a negative *x*-coordinate and a positive *y*-coordinate lie? quadrant II
14. In which quadrant do points with a positive *x*-coordinate and a negative *y*-coordinate lie? quadrant IV
15. In the following illustration, fill in the missing coordinate of each highlighted point on the graph of the circle.
    a. (4, 3)
    b. (3, −4)
    c. (5, 0)
    d. (−3, −4)
    e. (−5, 0)
    f. (0, 5)

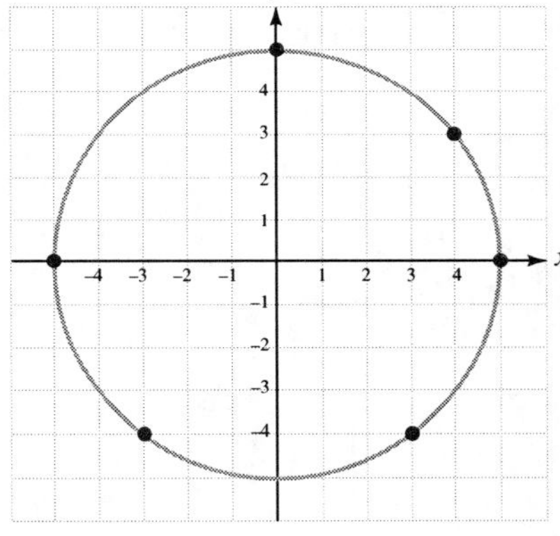

16. In the following illustration, fill in the missing coordinate of each point on the graph of the line.
    a. (−4, 3)
    b. (2, 0)
    c. (−2, 2)
    d. (4, −1)
    e. (0, 1)

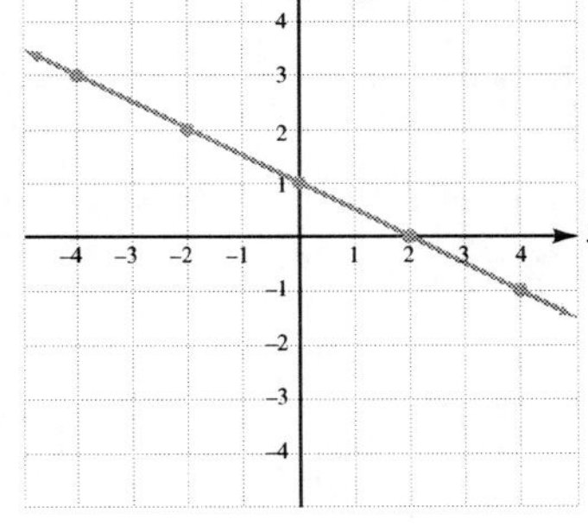

NOTATION

17. Explain the difference between (3, 5), 3(5), and 5(3 + 5).
(3, 5) is an ordered pair, 3(5) indicates multiplication, and 5(3 + 5) is an expression containing grouping symbols.

▶ Selected exercises available online at www.webassign.net/brookscole

18. In the table, which column contains values associated with the vertical axis of a graph? the 2nd column

x	y
2	0
5	-2
-1	$-\frac{1}{2}$

19. Do these ordered pairs name the same point?

$\left(2.5, -\frac{7}{2}\right), \left(2\frac{1}{2}, -3.5\right), \left(2.5, -3\frac{1}{2}\right)$ yes

20. Do these ordered pairs name the same point?

$(-1.25, 4), \left(-1\frac{1}{4}, 4.0\right), \left(-\frac{5}{4}, 4\right)$ yes

GUIDED PRACTICE

Plot each point on the grid provided. See Example 1.

21. $(-3, 4)$
$(4, 3.5)$
$\left(-2, -\frac{5}{2}\right)$

22. $(0, -4)$
$\left(\frac{3}{2}, 0\right)$
$(3, -4)$

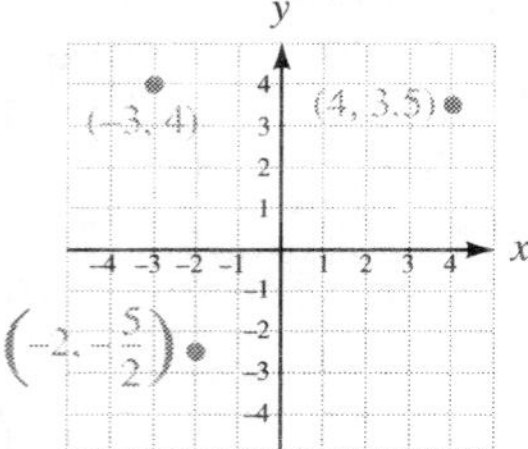

23. $(4, 4)$
$(0.5, -3)$
$(-4, -4)$

24. $(0, 0)$
$(0, 3)$
$(-2, 0)$
$(0, -1)$

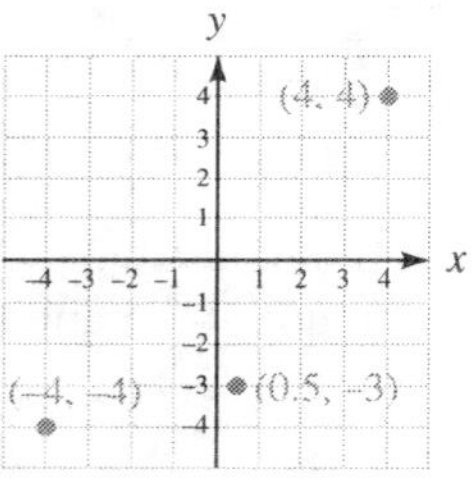

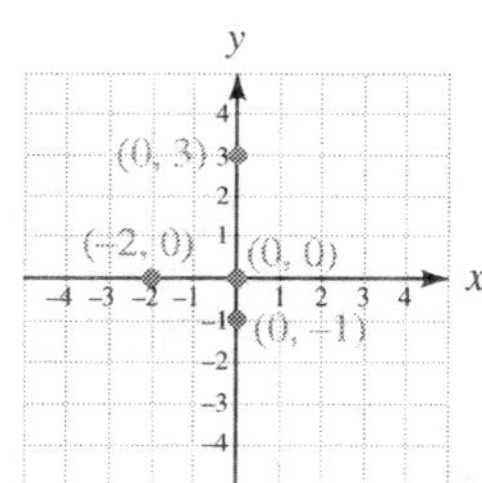

Refer to the illustration and determine the coordinates of each point. See Example 2.

25. A (2, 3)

26. B (−3, 4)

27. C (−3, −4)

28. D (4, −4)

29. E (0, 0)

30. F (4, 0)

31. G (−4, 0)

32. H $\left(\frac{3}{2}, -\frac{5}{2}\right)$

The graph in the illustration gives the heart rate of a woman before, during, and after an aerobic workout. Use the graph to answer problems 33–40. See Example 3.

33. What information does the point $(-10, 60)$ give us? 10 min before the workout, her heart rate was 60 beats/min.

34. After beginning her workout, how long did it take the woman to reach her training-zone heart rate? 10 min

35. What was the woman's heart rate half an hour after beginning the workout? 150 beats/min

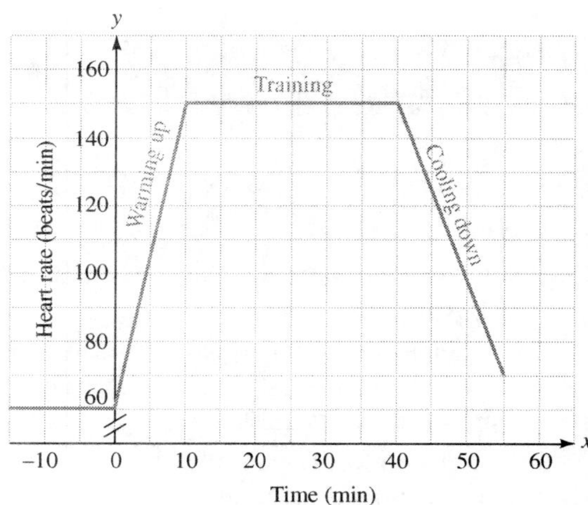

36. For how long did the woman work out at her training zone? 30 min

37. At what time was her heart rate 100 beats per minute? approximately 5 min and 50 min after starting

38. How long was her cool-down period? 15 min

39. What was the difference in the woman's heart rate before the workout and after the cool-down period? 10 beats/min faster after cool-down

40. What was her approximate heart rate 8 minutes after beginning? about 135 beats/min

The graph in the illustration on the next page gives the charges for renting a video for certain lengths of time. Use the graph to answer problems 41–44. See Example 4.

41. Find the charge for a 1-day rental. \$2

42. Find the charge for a 2-day rental. \$4

43. What is the charge if a tape is kept for 5 days? \$7

44. What is the charge if a tape is kept for a week? \$9

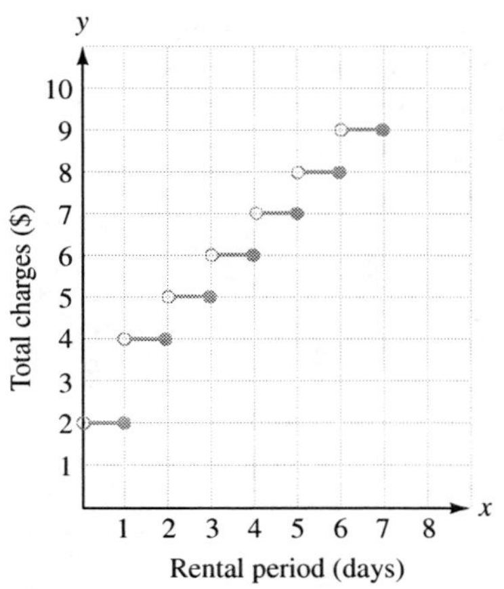

APPLICATIONS

45. BRIDGE CONSTRUCTION Find the coordinates of each rivet, weld, and anchor. rivets: (−6, 0), (−2, 0), (2, 0), (6, 0); welds: (−4, 3), (0, 3), (4, 3); anchors: (−6, −3), (6, −3)

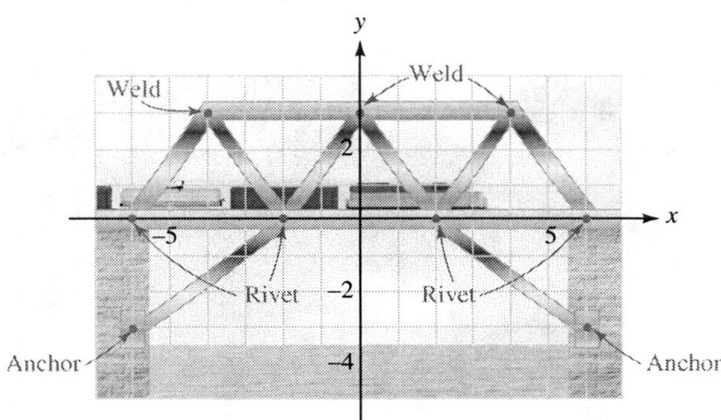

46. GOLF A golfer is videotaped and then has her swing displayed on a computer monitor so that it can be analyzed. Give the coordinates of the points that are highlighted in red. (6, 10), (−7, 4.5), (−5, 11)

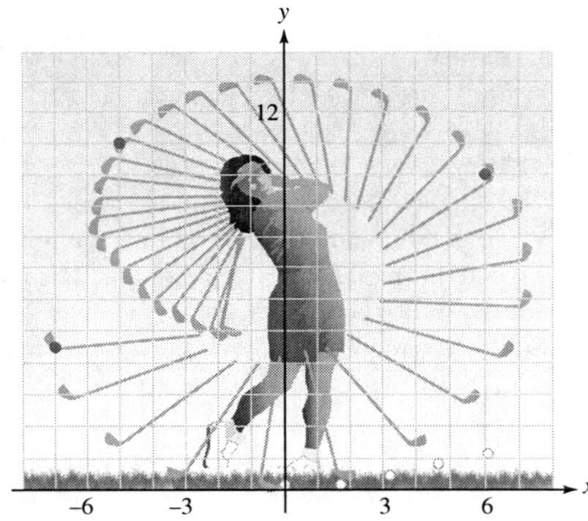

47. GAMES In the game Battleship, the player uses coordinates to drop depth charges from a battleship to hit a hidden submarine. What coordinates should be used to make three hits on the exposed submarine shown? Express each answer in the form (letter, number). (G, 2), (G, 3), (G, 4)

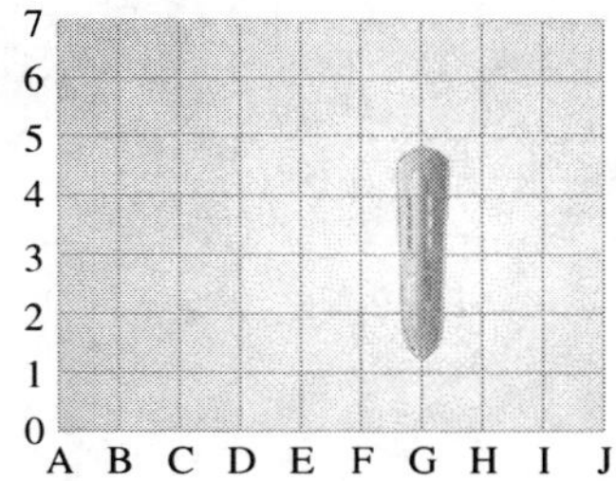

48. MAPS Use coordinates of the form (number, letter) to locate each position on the following map: Rockford, Forreston, Harvard, and the intersection of state Highway 251 and U.S. Highway 30. Rockford (5, B), Forreston (2, C), Harvard (7, A), intersection (5, E)

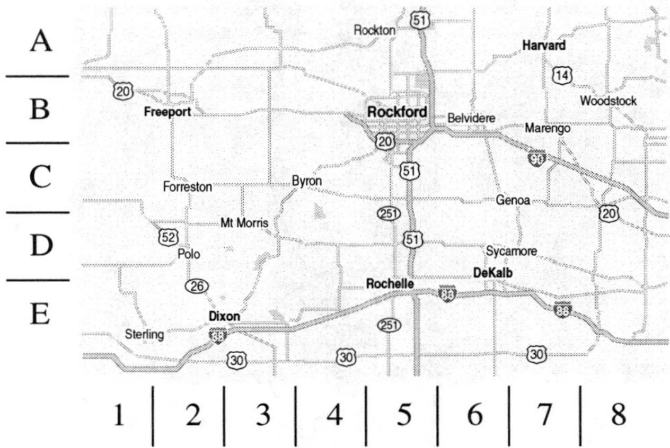

49. WATER PRESSURE The graph shows how the path of a stream of water changes when the hose is held at two different angles.

a. At which angle does the stream of water shoot up higher? How much higher? 60°, 4 ft

b. At which angle does the stream of water shoot out farther? How much farther? 30°, 4 ft

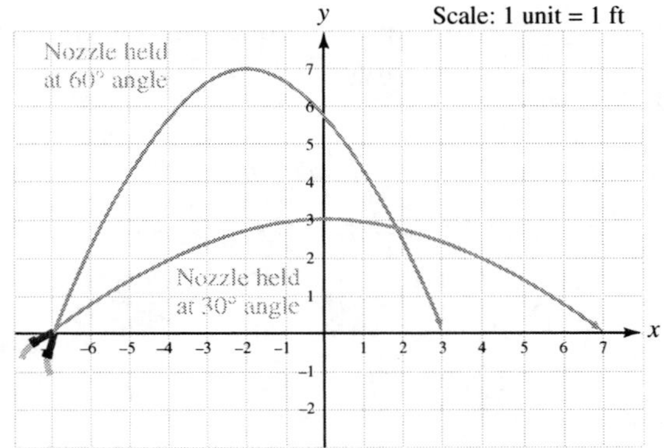

50. MEDICINE Scoliosis is a lateral curvature of the spine that can be detected when a grid is superimposed over an X-ray. In the illustration, find the coordinates of the center points of the indicated vertebrae. Note that T3 means the third thoracic vertebra, L4 means the fourth lumbar vertebra, and so on. T3(2, 21), T6(3, 16), T9(3, 10), T11(2.5, 6.5), L1(1, 2.5), L2(0, 0), L4(−1, −5), L5(0, −8)

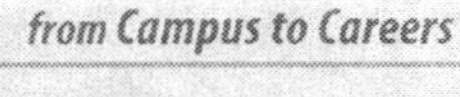

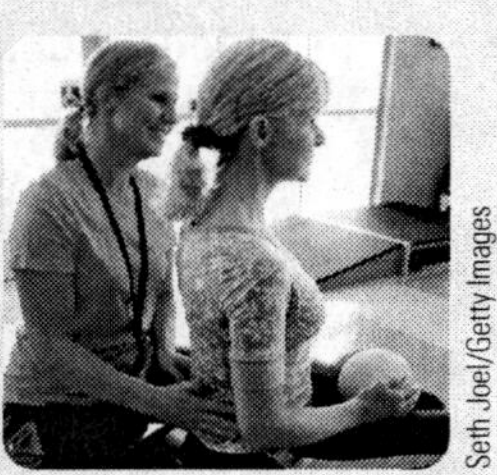
Seth Joel/Getty Images

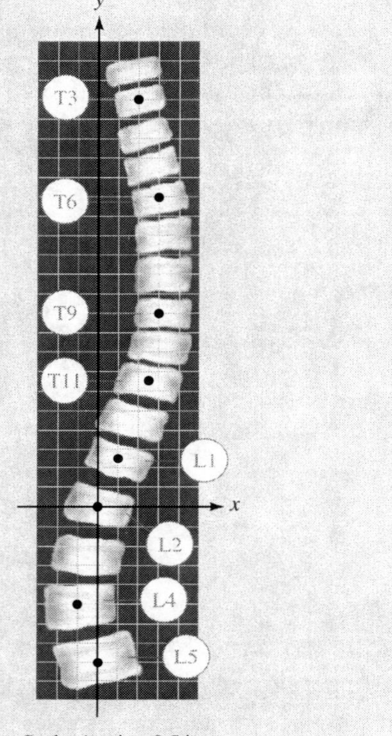

Scale: 1 unit = 0.5 in.

51. DENTISTRY Dentists describe teeth as being located in one of four quadrants as shown below:

a. How many teeth are located in the upper left quadrant? 8

b. Why would the upper left quadrant appear on the right in the illustration? It represents the patient's left side.

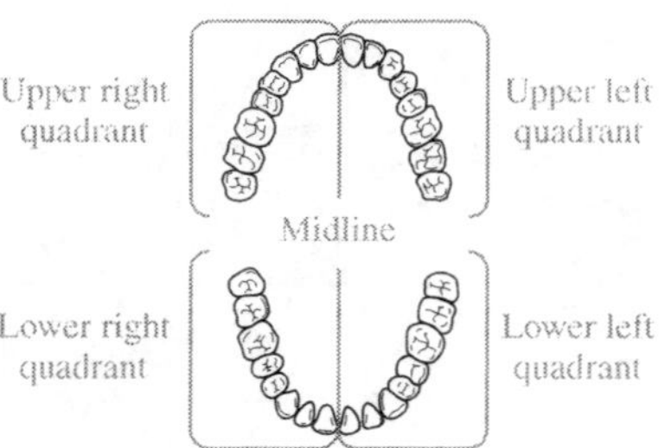

52. GAS MILEAGE The following table gives the number of miles (y) that a truck can be driven on x gallons of gasoline. Plot the ordered pairs and draw a line connecting the points.

x	y
2	10
3	15
5	25

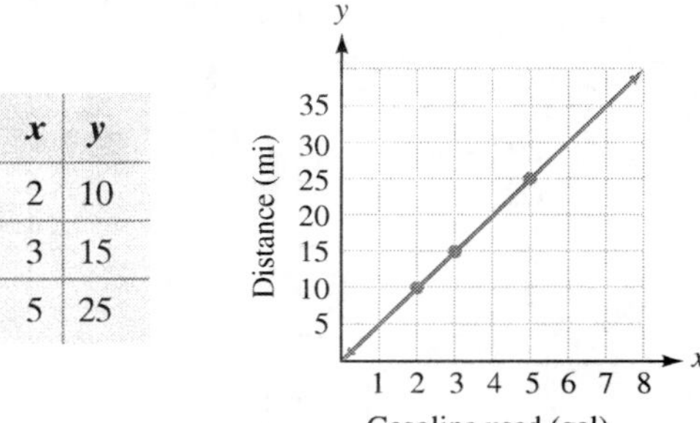

a. Estimate how far the truck can go on 7 gallons of gasoline. 35 mi

b. How many gallons of gas are needed to travel a distance of 20 miles? 4 gal

c. How far can the truck go on 6.5 gallons of gasoline? 32.5 mi

53. VALUE OF A CAR The following table shows the value y (in thousands of dollars) of a car that is x years old. Plot the ordered pairs and draw a line connecting the points.

x	y
3	7
4	5.5
5	4

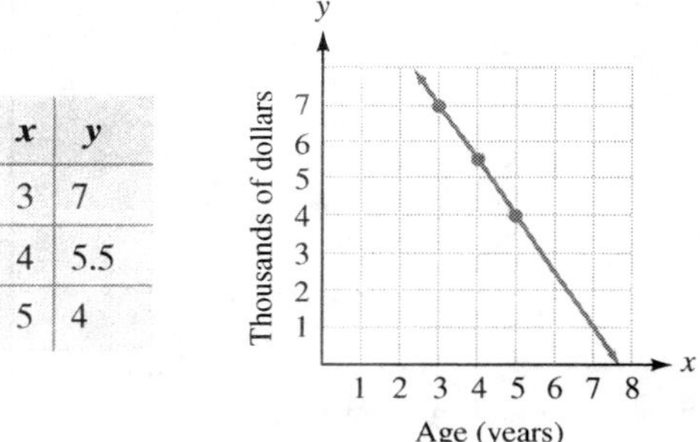

a. What does the point (3, 7) on the graph tell you? A 3-year-old car is worth $7,000.

b. Estimate the value of the car when it is 7 years old. $1,000

c. After how many years will the car be worth $2,500? 6

54. BOATING The table on the next page shows the cost to rent a sailboat for a given number of hours. Plot the data in the table as ordered pairs. Then draw a line through the points.

a. How much will it cost to rent the boat for 3 hours? $25

b. For how long can the boat be rented for \$60? 10 hr

Rental time (hr)	Cost (\$)
2	20
4	30
6	40

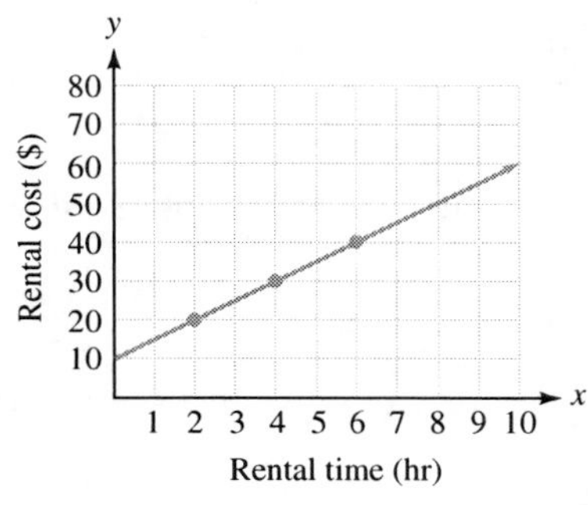

WRITING

55. Explain why the point $(-3, 3)$ is not the same as the point $(3, -3)$.

56. Explain what is meant when we say that the rectangular coordinate graph of the St. Louis Gateway Arch is made up of *infinitely many* points.

57. Explain how to plot the point $(-2, 5)$.

58. Explain why the coordinates of the origin are $(0, 0)$.

REVIEW

59. Evaluate: $-3 - 3(-5)$ 12

60. Evaluate: $(-5)^2 + (-5)$ 20

61. What is the opposite of -8? 8

62. Simplify: $|-1 - 9|$ 10

63. Solve: $-4x + 7 = -21$ 7

64. Solve $P = 2l + 2w$ for w. $w = \frac{P - 2l}{2}$

65. Evaluate $(x + 1)(x + y)^2$ for $x = -2$ and $y = -5$. -49

66. Simplify: $-6(x - 3) - 2(1 - x)$ $-4x + 16$

SECTION 5.3
Graphing Linear Equations

Objectives

1. Determine whether an ordered pair is a solution of an equation.
2. Complete ordered-pair solutions of equations.
3. Construct a table of solutions.
4. Graph equations by plotting points.
5. Graph equations that use different variables.

In this section, we will discuss equations that contain two variables. These equations are often used to describe relationships between two quantities. To see a mathematical picture of these relationships, we will construct graphs of their equations.

1 Determine whether an ordered pair is a solution of an equation.

We have previously solved **equations in one variable.** For example, $x - 4 = 3$ is an equation in x. If we add 4 to both sides, we see that $x = 7$ is the solution. To check this, we replace x with 7 and note that the result is a true statement: $3 = 3$.

In this chapter, we extend our equation-solving skills to find solutions of **equations in two variables.** To begin, let's consider $y = x - 1$, an equation in x and y.

A solution of $y = x - 1$ is a pair of values, one for x and one for y, that make the equation true. For example, suppose x is 5 and y is 4. Then we have:

$y = x - 1$ This is the original equation.

$4 \stackrel{?}{=} 5 - 1$ Substitute 5 for x and 4 for y.

$4 = 4$ True

Since $4 = 4$ is a true statement, the ordered pair $(5, 4)$ is a solution, and we say that $(5, 4)$ **satisfies** the equation. In general, a *solution of an equation in two variables* is an ordered pair of numbers that makes the equation a true statement.

EXAMPLE 1 Is the ordered pair $(-1, -3)$ a solution of $y = x - 1$?

Strategy We will substitute -1 for x and -3 for y and see whether the resulting equation is true.

WHY An ordered pair is a *solution* of $y = x - 1$ if replacing the variables with the values of the ordered pair results in a true statement.

Self Check 1

Is $(9, 8)$ a solution of $y = x - 1$? yes

Now Try **Problem 17**

Teaching Example 1 Is $(-5, -4)$ a solution of $y = x - 1$?
Answer: no

Solution

$y = x - 1$ This is the original equation.

$-3 \stackrel{?}{=} -1 - 1$ Substitute −1 for x and −3 for y.

$-3 = -2$ Perform the subtraction: $-1 - 1 = -2$. False

Since $-3 = -2$ is a false statement, $(-1, -3)$ is not a solution of $y = x - 1$.

Self Check 2

Is $(-2, 5)$ a solution of $y = x^2$? no

Now Try **Problem 19**

Teaching Example 2 Is (7, 14) a solution of $y = x^2$?
Answer:
no

EXAMPLE 2 Is the ordered pair $(-6, 36)$ a solution of $y = x^2$?

Strategy We will substitute −6 for x and 36 for y and see whether the resulting equation is true.

WHY An ordered pair is a *solution* of $y = x^2$ if replacing the variables with the values of the ordered pair results in a true statement.

Solution

We substitute −6 for x and 36 for y and see whether the resulting equation is a true statement.

$y = x^2$ This is the original equation.

$36 \stackrel{?}{=} (-6)^2$ Substitute −6 for x and 36 for y.

$36 = 36$ Find the power: $(-6)^2 = 36$. True

Since the equation $36 = 36$ is true, $(-6, 36)$ is a solution of $y = x^2$.

Language of Algebra Equations in two variables often involve the variables x and y. However, other letters can be used. For example, $a - 3b = 6$ and $n = 2m + 1$ are equations in two variables.

2 Complete ordered-pair solutions of equations.

If only one of the values of an ordered-pair solution is known, we can substitute it into the equation to determine the other value.

Self Check 3

Complete the solution $(-3, \quad)$ of the equation $y = 2x - 4$. $(-3, -10)$

Now Try **Problem 26**

Teaching Example 3 Complete the solution (2, _) of the equation $y = 2x - 4$
Answer:
(2, 0)

EXAMPLE 3 Complete the solution $(-4, \quad)$ of the equation $y = -x + 2$.

Strategy We will substitute the known x-coordinate of the solution into the given equation.

WHY We can use the resulting equation in one variable to find the unknown y-coordinate of the solution.

Solution

In the ordered pair $(-4, \quad)$, the x-value is −4; the y-value is not known. To find y, we substitute −4 for x in the equation and evaluate the right side.

$y = -x + 2$ This is the original equation.

$y = -(-4) + 2$ Substitute −4 for x.

$y = 4 + 2$ The opposite of −4 is 4.

$y = 6$ This is the missing y-coordinate of the solution.

The completed ordered pair is $(-4, 6)$.

3 Construct a table of solutions.

To find a solution of an equation in x and y, we can select a number, substitute it for x, and find the corresponding value of y. For example, to find a solution of the equation $y = x - 1$, we can let $x = -4$ (called the **input value**), substitute -4 for x, and solve for y (called the **output value**).

$y = x - 1$ This is the original equation.
$y = -4 - 1$ Substitute the input -4 for x.
$y = -5$ The output is -5.

$y = x - 1$		
x	y	(x, y)
-4	-5	$(-4, -5)$

The ordered pair $(-4, -5)$ is a solution. We list this ordered pair in red in the **table of solutions** (or **table of values**).

To find another solution of $y = x - 1$, we select another value of x, say -2, and find the corresponding y-value.

$y = x - 1$ This is the original equation.
$y = -2 - 1$ Substitute the input -2 for x.
$y = -3$ The output is -3.

$y = x - 1$		
x	y	(x, y)
-4	-5	$(-4, -5)$
-2	-3	$(-2, -3)$

A second solution is $(-2, -3)$, and we list it in the table of solutions.

If we let $x = 0$, we can find a third ordered pair that satisfies $y = x - 1$.

$y = x - 1$ This is the original equation.
$y = 0 - 1$ Substitute the input 0 for x.
$y = -1$ The output is -1.

$y = x - 1$		
x	y	(x, y)
-4	-5	$(-4, -5)$
-2	-3	$(-2, -3)$
0	-1	$(0, -1)$

A third solution is $(0, -1)$, which we also add to the table of solutions.

If we let $x = 2$, we can find a fourth solution.

$y = x - 1$ This is the original equation.
$y = 2 - 1$ Substitute the input 2 for x.
$y = 1$ The output is 1.

$y = x - 1$		
x	y	(x, y)
-4	-5	$(-4, -5)$
-2	-3	$(-2, -3)$
0	-1	$(0, -1)$
2	1	$(2, 1)$

A fourth solution is $(2, 1)$, and we add it to the table of solutions.

If we let $x = 4$, we have

$y = x - 1$ This is the original equation.
$y = 4 - 1$ Substitute the input 4 for x.
$y = 3$ The output is 3.

A fifth solution is $(4, 3)$.

Since we can choose any real number for x, and since any choice of x will give a corresponding value of y, it is apparent that the equation $y = x - 1$ has *infinitely many solutions.* We have found five of them: $(-4, -5)$, $(-2, -3)$, $(0, -1)$, $(2, 1)$, and $(4, 3)$.

$y = x - 1$		
x	y	(x, y)
-4	-5	$(-4, -5)$
-2	-3	$(-2, -3)$
0	-1	$(0, -1)$
2	1	$(2, 1)$
4	3	$(4, 3)$

$y = x - 1$		
x	y	(x, y)
-4	-5	$(-4, -5)$
-2	-3	$(-2, -3)$
0	-1	$(0, -1)$
2	1	$(2, 1)$
4	3	$(4, 3)$

4 Graph equations by plotting points.

To graph the equation $y = x - 1$, we plot the ordered pairs listed in the table of solutions on a rectangular coordinate system, as shown in figure (a). We can see that the five points lie on a line.

We then draw a line through the points, because the graph of any solution of $y = x - 1$ will lie on this line. The arrowheads show that the line continues forever in both directions. The line is a picture of all the solutions of the equation $y = x - 1$. This line is called the **graph of the equation.** See figure (b).

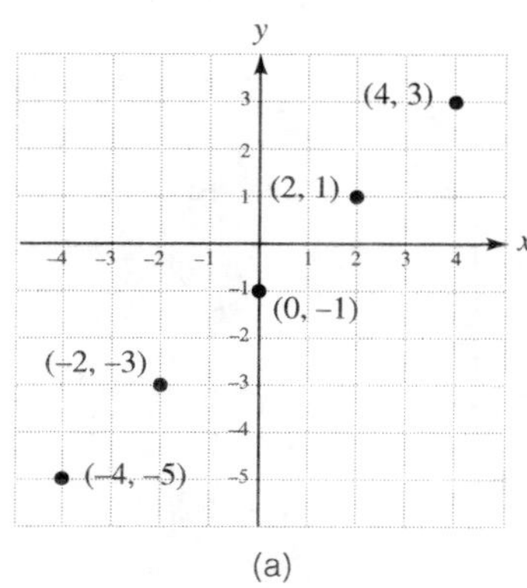

(a)

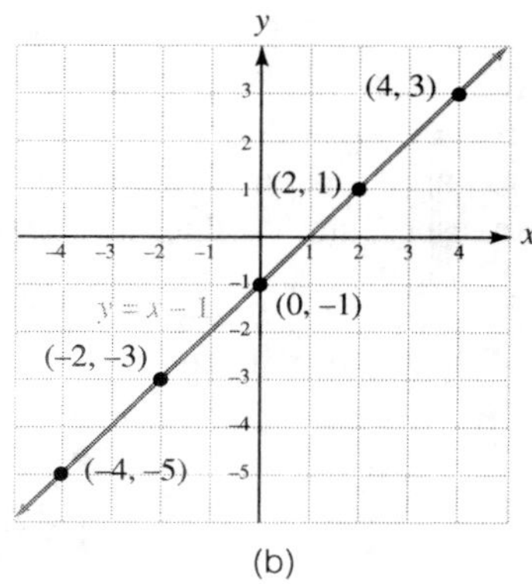

(b)

To graph an equation in x and y, we follow these steps.

Graphing an Equation in x and y

1. Make a table of solutions containing several ordered pairs of numbers (x, y) that satisfy the equation. Do this by picking values for x and finding the corresponding values for y.
2. Plot each ordered pair on a rectangular coordinate system.
3. Carefully draw a line or smooth curve through the points.

Since we will usually choose a number for x and then find the corresponding value of y, the value of y depends on x. For this reason, we call y the **dependent variable** and x the **independent variable.** The value of the independent variable is the input value, and the value of the dependent variable is the output value.

Self Check 4

Graph: $y = -3x + 1$

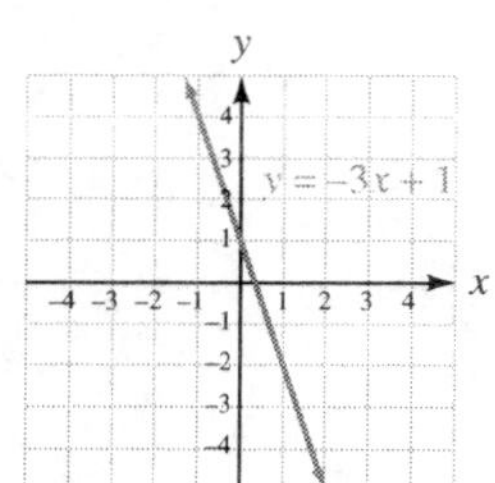

Now Try **Problem 33**

EXAMPLE 4 Graph: $y = -2x - 2$

Strategy We will find several solutions of the equation, plot them on a rectangular coordinate system, and then draw a graph passing through the points.

WHY To *graph* an equation in two variables means to make a drawing that represents all of its solutions.

Solution

To make a table of solutions, we choose numbers for x and find the corresponding values of y. If $x = -3$, we have

$y = -2x - 2$ This is the original equation.

$y = -2(-3) - 2$ Substitute -3 for x.

$y = 6 - 2$ Perform the multiplication: $-2(-3) = 6$.

$y = 4$ Perform the subtraction.

Thus, $x = -3$ and $y = 4$ is a solution. In a similar manner, we find the corresponding y-values for x-values of $-2, -1, 0,$ and 1 and record the results in the table of solutions. After plotting the ordered pairs, we draw a line through the points to get the graph shown.

$y = -2x - 2$		
x	y	(x, y)
−3	4	(−3, 4)
−2	2	(−2, 2)
−1	0	(−1, 0)
0	−2	(0, −2)
1	−4	(1, −4)

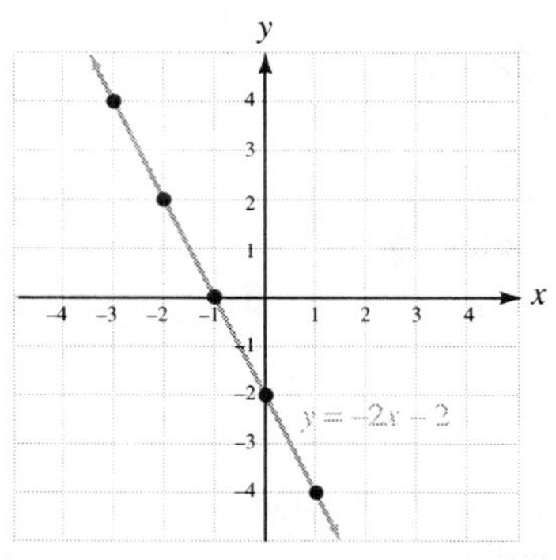

Teaching Example 4 Graph $y = -x + 2$.
Answer:

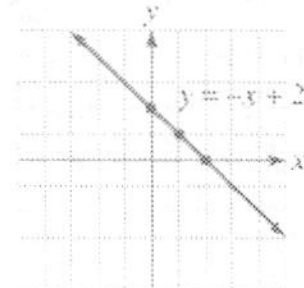

EXAMPLE 5 Graph: $y = x^2$

Strategy We will find several solutions of the equation, plot them on a rectangular coordinate system, and then draw a graph passing through the points.

WHY To *graph* an equation in two variables means to make a drawing that represents all of its solutions.

Solution

To make a table of solutions, we will choose numbers for x and find the corresponding values of y. If $x = -3$, we have

$y = x^2$ This is the original equation.

$y = (-3)^2$ Substitute the input −3 for x.

$y = 9$ The output is 9.

Thus, $x = -3$ and $y = 9$ is a solution. In a similar manner, we find the corresponding y-values for x-values of $-2, -1, 0, 1, 2,$ and 3. If we plot the ordered pairs listed in the table and join the points with a smooth curve, we get the graph shown in the figure, which is called a **parabola.**

$y = x^2$		
x	y	(x, y)
−3	9	(−3, 9)
−2	4	(−2, 4)
−1	1	(−1, 1)
0	0	(0, 0)
1	1	(1, 1)
2	4	(2, 4)
3	9	(3, 9)

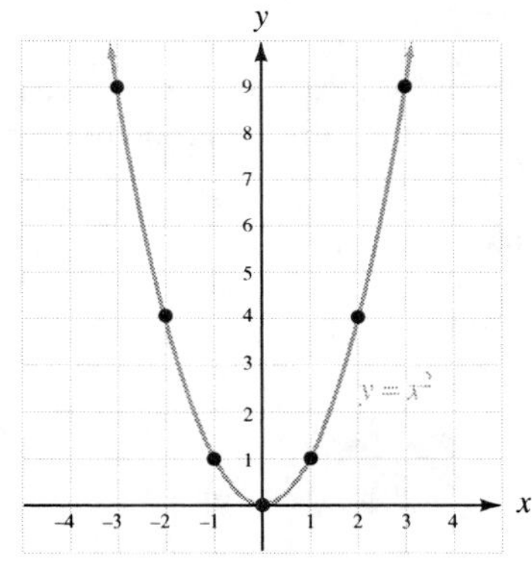

Self Check 5

Graph $y = x^2 - 2$ and compare the result to the graph of $y = x^2$. What do you notice?

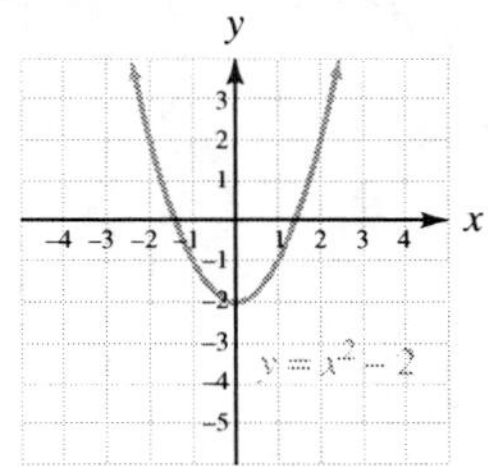

Now Try **Problem 37**

Self Check 5 Answer
The graph has the same shape, but is 2 units lower.

Teaching Example 5 Graph $y = x^2 + 3$ and compare the result to the graph of $y = x^2$. What do you notice?
Answer:
The graph has the same shape, but 3 units higher.

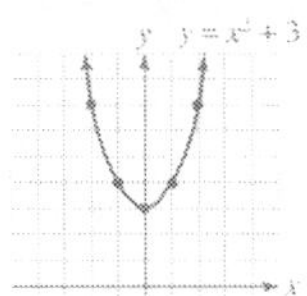

Success Tip When selecting x-values for a table of solutions, a rule of thumb is to choose some negative numbers, some positive numbers, and 0. When $x = 0$, the computations to find y are usually quite simple.

Self Check 6

Graph $y = |x| + 2$ and compare the result to the graph of $y = |x|$. What do you notice?

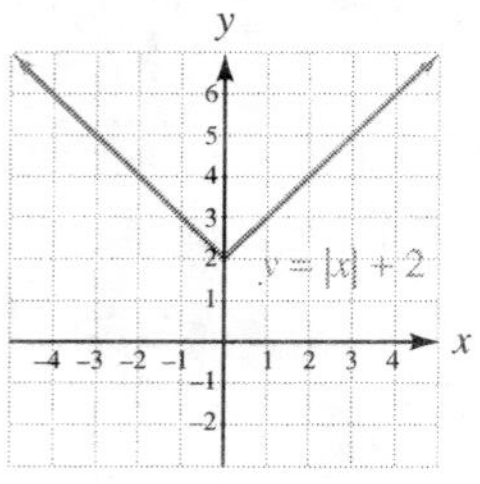

Now Try **Problem 43**

Self Check 6 Answer
The graph has the same shape, but is 2 units higher.

Teaching Example 6 Graph $y = |x| - 1$ and compare the result to the graph of $y = |x|$. What do you notice?
Answer:
The graph has the same shape, but 1 unit lower.

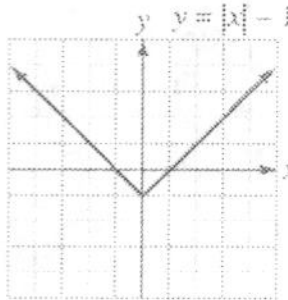

EXAMPLE 6 Graph: $y = |x|$

Strategy We will find several solutions of the equation, plot them on a rectangular coordinate system, and then draw a graph passing through the points.

WHY To *graph* an equation in two variables means to make a drawing that represents all of its solutions.

Solution
To make a table of solutions, we will choose numbers for x and find the corresponding values of y. If $x = -5$, we have

$y = |x|$ This is the original equation.
$y = |-5|$ Substitute the input −5 for x.
$y = 5$ The output is 5.

The ordered pair $(-5, 5)$ satisfies the equation. This pair and several others that satisfy the equation are listed in the table of solutions in the figure. If we plot the ordered pairs in the table, we see that they lie in a "V" shape. We join the points to complete the graph shown in the figure.

$y = \|x\|$		
x	**y**	**(x, y)**
−5	5	(−5, 5)
−4	4	(−4, 4)
−3	3	(−3, 3)
−2	2	(−2, 2)
−1	1	(−1, 1)
0	0	(0, 0)
1	1	(1, 1)
2	2	(2, 2)
3	3	(3, 3)

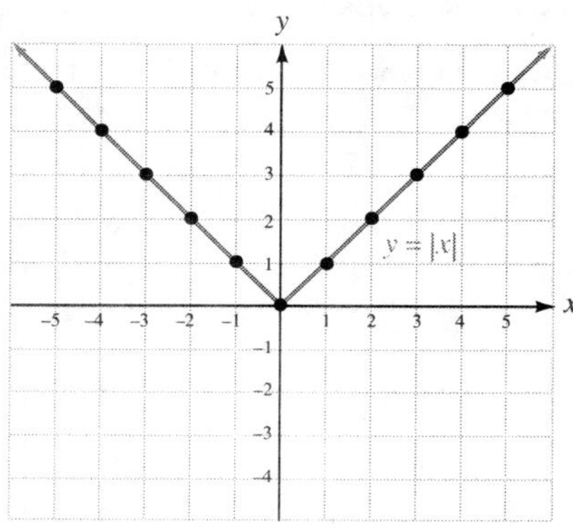

Self Check 7

Graph $y = (x - 2)^3$ and compare the result to the graph of $y = x^3$. What do you notice?

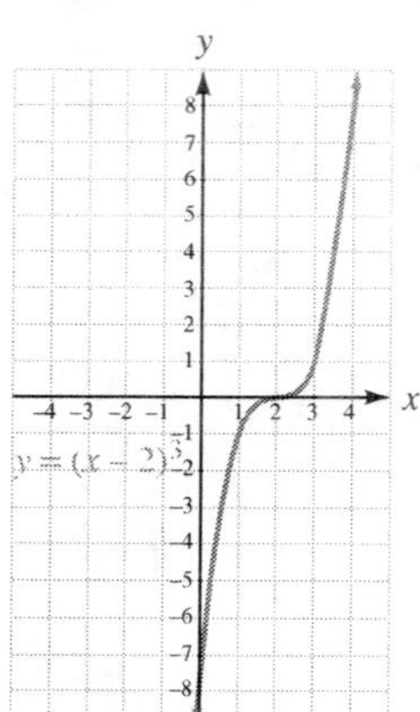

Now Try **Problem 45**

Self Check 7 Answer
The graph has the same shape but is 2 units to the right.

EXAMPLE 7 Graph: $y = x^3$

Strategy We will find several solutions of the equation, plot them on a rectangular coordinate system, and then draw a graph passing through the points.

WHY To *graph* an equation in two variables means to make a drawing that represents all of its solutions.

Solution
If we let $x = -2$, we have

$y = x^3$ This is the original equation.
$y = (-2)^3$ Substitute the input −2 for x.
$y = -8$ The output is −8.

The ordered pair $(-2, -8)$ satisfies the equation. This ordered pair and several others that satisfy the equation are listed in the table of solutions in the figure on the next page. Plotting the ordered pairs and joining them with a smooth curve gives us the graph shown in the figure.

$y = x^3$		
x	y	(x, y)
−2	−8	(−2, −8)
−1	−1	(−1, −1)
0	0	(0, 0)
1	1	(1, 1)
2	8	(2, 8)

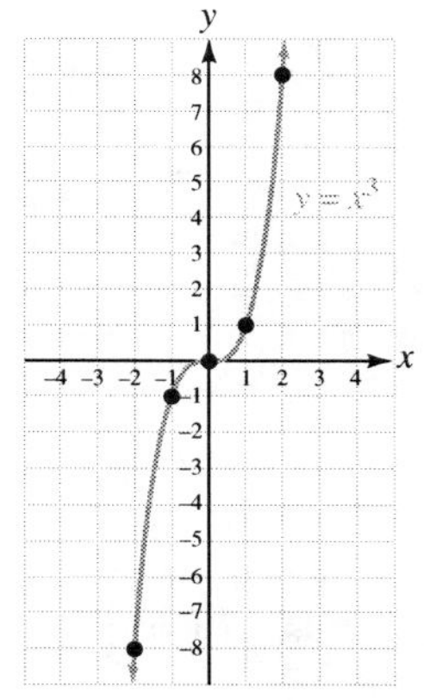

Teaching Example 7 Graph $y = (x + 1)^3$ and compare the result to the graph of $y = x^3$. What do you notice?

Answer:
The graph has the same shape but is 1 unit to the left.

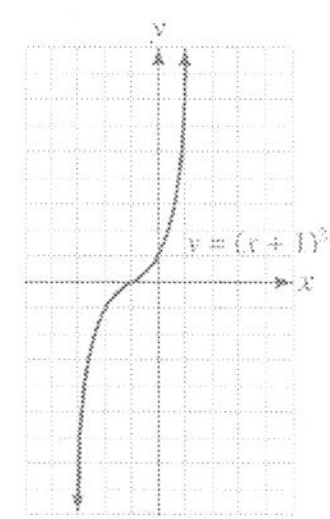

Using Your CALCULATOR Using a Graphing Calculator to Graph an Equation

We have graphed equations by making tables of solutions and plotting points. The task of graphing is much easier when we use a graphing calculator. The instructions in this discussion will be general in nature. For specific details about your calculator, please consult your owner's manual.

The viewing window
All graphing calculators have a viewing **window,** used to display graphs. The **standard window** has settings of

$$\text{Xmin} = -10, \quad \text{Xmax} = 10, \quad \text{Ymin} = -10, \quad \text{and} \quad \text{Ymax} = 10$$

which indicate that the minimum x- and y-coordinates used in the graph will be -10 and that the maximum x- and y-coordinates will be 10.

Graphing an equation
To graph the equation $y = x - 1$ using a graphing calculator, we press the [Y =] key and enter the right-hand side of the equation after the symbol Y_1. The display will show the equation

$$\text{Y}_1 = x - 1$$

Then we press the [GRAPH] key to produce the graph in figure (a) shown on the next page.

Next, we will graph the equation $y = |x - 4|$. Since absolute values are always nonnegative, the minimum y-value is zero. To obtain a reasonable viewing window, we press the [WINDOW] key and set the Ymin value slightly lower, at Ymin $= -3$. We set Ymax to be 10 units greater than Ymin, at Ymax $= 7$. The minimum value of y occurs when $x = 4$. To center the graph in the viewing window, we set the Xmin and Xmax values 5 units to the left and right of 4. Therefore, Xmin $= -1$ and Xmax $= 9$.

After entering the right-hand side of the equation, we obtain the graph in figure (b) shown on the next page. Consult your owner's manual to learn how to enter an absolute value.

(continued)

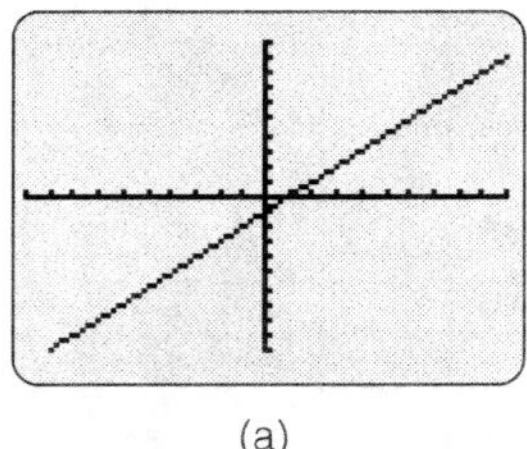

(a)

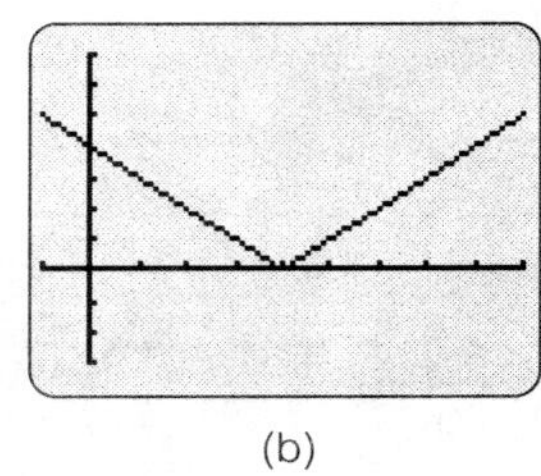

(b)

Changing the viewing window:
The choice of viewing windows is extremely important when graphing equations. To show this, let's graph $y = x^2 - 25$ with x-values from -1 to 6 and y-values from -5 to 5.

To graph this equation, we set the x and y window values and enter the right-hand side of the equation. The display will show

$$Y_1 = x^2 - 25$$

Then we press the GRAPH key to produce the graph shown in figure (c). Although the graph appears to be a straight line, it is not. Actually, we are seeing only part of a parabola. If we pick a viewing window with x-values of -6 to 6 and y-values of -30 to 2, as in figure (d), we can see that the graph is a parabola.

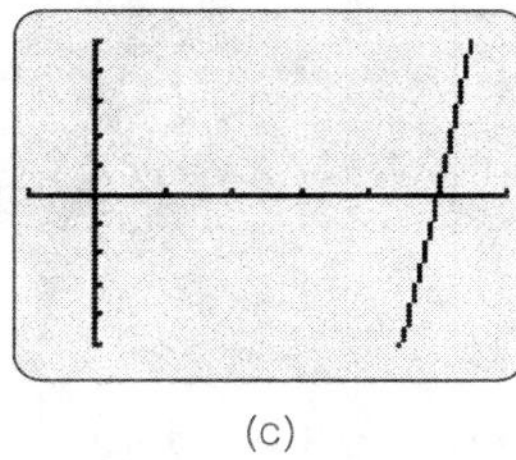

(c)

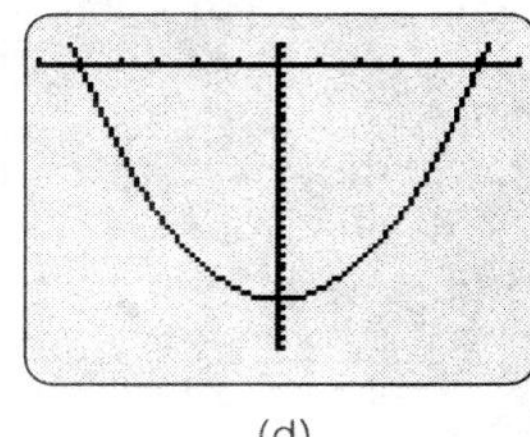

(d)

Use a graphing calculator to graph each equation. Use a viewing window of $x = -5$ to 5 and $y = -5$ to 5.

1. $y = 2.1x - 1.1$ 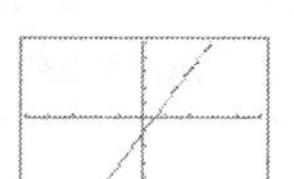

2. $y = 1.12x^2 - 1$ 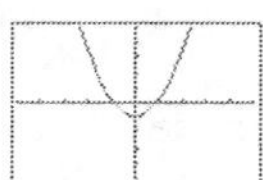

3. $y = |x + 0.7|$ 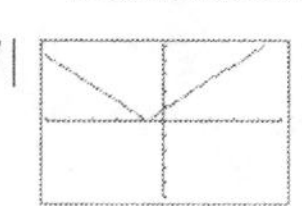

4. $y = 0.1x^3 + 1$ 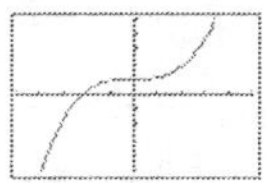

Graph each equation in a viewing window of $x = -4$ to 4 and $y = -4$ to 4. Each graph is not what it first appears to be. Pick a better viewing window and find a better representation of the true graph.

5. $y = -x^3 - 8.2$ 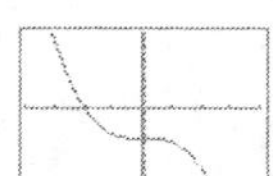

6. $y = -|x - 4.01|$ 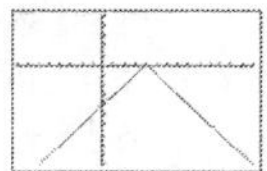

7. $y = x^2 + 5.9$ 

8. $y = -x + 7.95$ 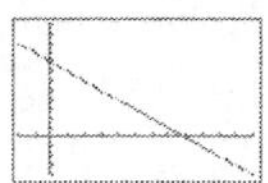

5 Graph equations that use different variables.

We will often encounter equations with variables other than x and y. When we make tables of solutions and graph these equations, we must know which is the independent variable (the input values) and which is the dependent variable (the output values). The independent variable is usually associated with the horizontal axis of the coordinate system, and the dependent variable is usually associated with the vertical axis.

EXAMPLE 8 *Speed Limits* In some states, the maximum speed limit on a U.S. interstate highway is 75 mph. The distance covered by a vehicle traveling at 75 mph depends on the time the vehicle travels at that speed. This relationship is described by the equation $d = 75t$, where d represents the distance (in miles) and t represents the time (in hours). Graph the equation.

Strategy We will find several solutions of the equation, plot them on a rectangular coordinate system, and then draw a graph passing through the points.

WHY We can use the graph to estimate the distance traveled (in miles) after traveling an amount of time at 75 mph.

Solution

Since d depends on t in the equation $d = 75t$, t is the independent variable (the input) and d is the dependent variable (the output). Therefore, we choose values for t and find the corresponding values of d. Since t represents the time spent traveling at 75 mph, we choose no negative values for t.

If $t = 0$, we have

$d = 75t$	This is the original equation.
$d = 75(0)$	Substitute the input 0 for t.
$d = 0$	Perform the multiplication.

The pair $t = 0$ and $d = 0$, or (0, 0), is a solution. This ordered pair and others that satisfy the equation are listed in the table of solutions shown below. If we plot the ordered pairs and draw a line through them, we obtain the graph shown in the figure. From the graph, we see (as expected) that the distance covered steadily increases as the traveling time increases.

$d = 75t$		
t	d	(t, d)
0	0	(0, 0)
1	75	(1, 75)
2	150	(2, 150)
3	225	(3, 225)
4	300	(4, 300)
5	375	(5, 375)

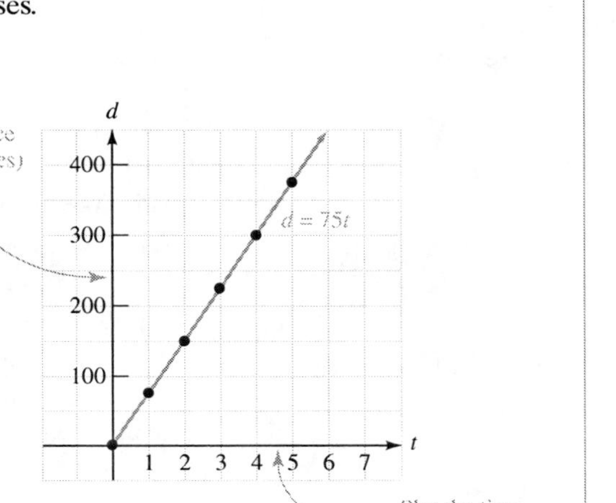

Self Check 8

If the maximum speed limit on a rural highway is 55 mph, the formula for the distance traveled in t time is $d = 55t$. Graph the equation.

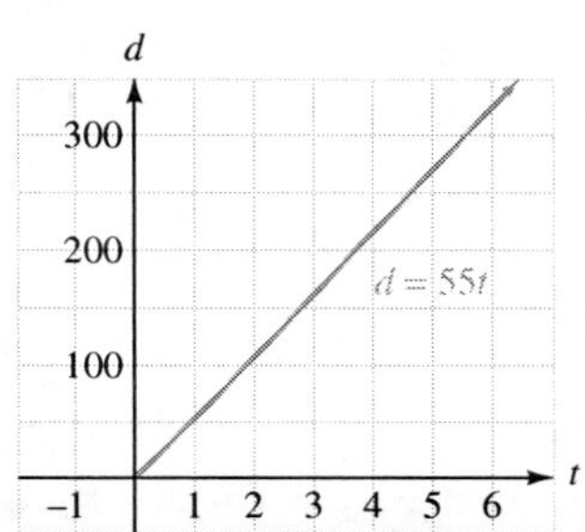

Now Try **Problem 49**

Teaching Example 8 If the maximum speed limit on a U.S. interstate highway is 65 mph, the formula for the distance traveled in t time is $d = 65t$. Graph the equation.

Answer:

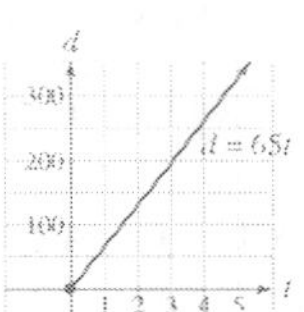

ANSWERS TO SELF CHECKS

1. yes **2.** no **3.** $(-3, -10)$

4.

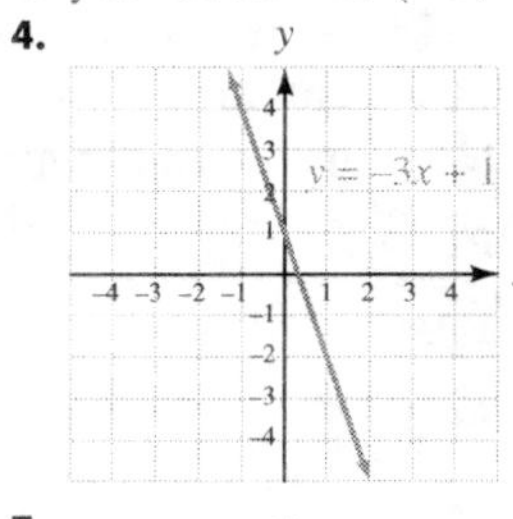

5.

6.

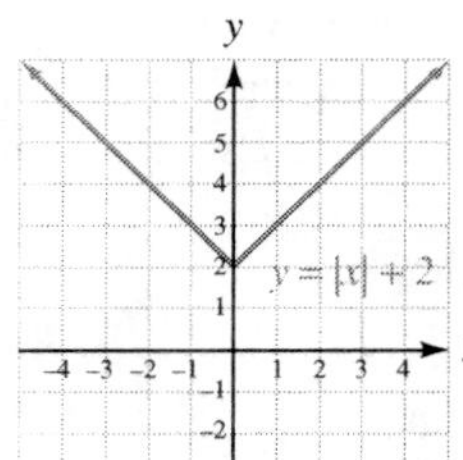

7.

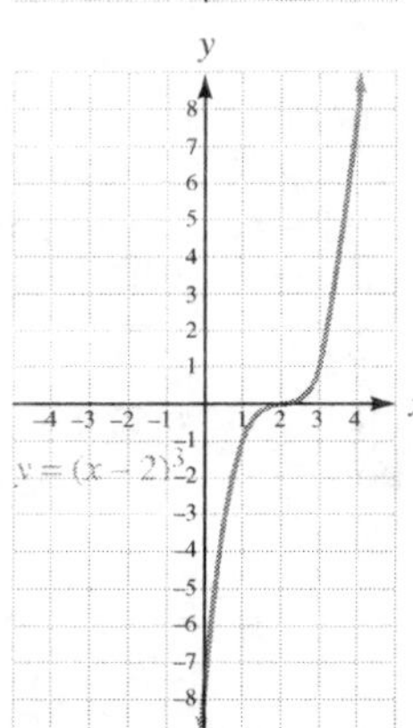

8.

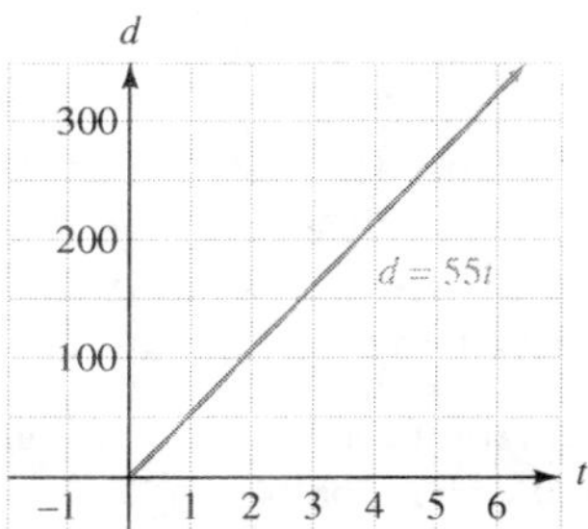

SECTION 5.3 STUDY SET

VOCABULARY

Fill in the blanks.

1. The equation $7 = -2x + 5$ is an equation in one variable. The equation $y = x + 1$ is an equation in two variables, x and y.

2. An ordered pair is a solution of an equation if the numbers in the ordered pair satisfy the equation.

3. When constructing a table of solutions, the values of x are the input values and the values of y are the output values.

4. In equations containing the variables x and y, x is called the independent variable and y is called the dependent variable.

CONCEPTS

5. Consider the equation: $y = -2x + 6$

a. How many variables does the equation contain? 2

b. Does the ordered pair $(4, -2)$ satisfy the equation? yes

c. Is $(-3, 12)$ a solution of the equation? yes

d. How many solutions does this equation have? infinitely many

6. To graph an equation, five solutions were found, they were plotted (in black), and a straight line was drawn through them, as shown. From the graph, determine three other solutions of the equation.
$(1, 4), (3, 2), (5, 0)$ (answers may vary)

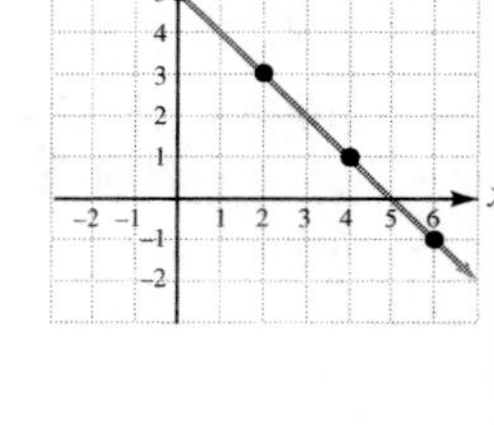

7. Fill in the blanks: The graph of $y = -x + 5$ is shown in Problem 6. Every point on the graph represents an ordered-pair solution of $y = -x + 5$, and every ordered-pair solution is a point on the graph.

8. Consider the graph of an equation shown below.

a. If the coordinates of point M are substituted into the equation, is the result a true or false statement? true

b. If the coordinates of point N are substituted into the equation, is the result a true or false statement? false

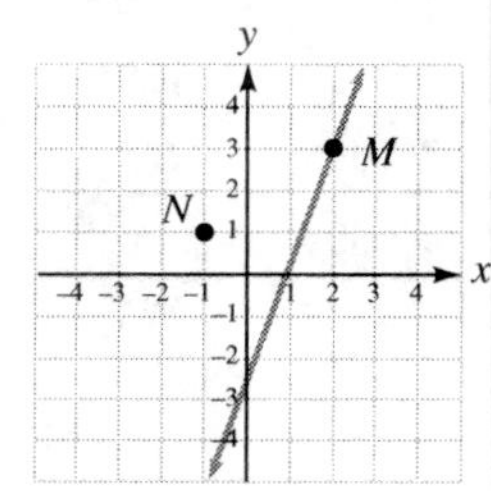

Selected exercises available online at www.webassign.net/brookscole

9. Complete the table.

$y = x^3$	
x (inputs)	**y (outputs)**
0	0
−1	−1
−2	−8
1	1
2	8

10. What is wrong with the graph of $y = x - 3$ shown below?
The line is too short, and arrowheads are not drawn on both ends of the line.

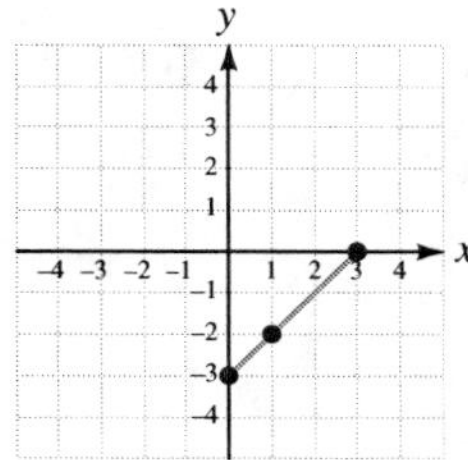

11. To graph $y = -x + 1$, a student constructed a table of solutions and plotted the ordered pairs as shown. Instead of drawing a crooked line through the points, what should he have done?
He should have checked his computations. At least one of his "solutions" is wrong.

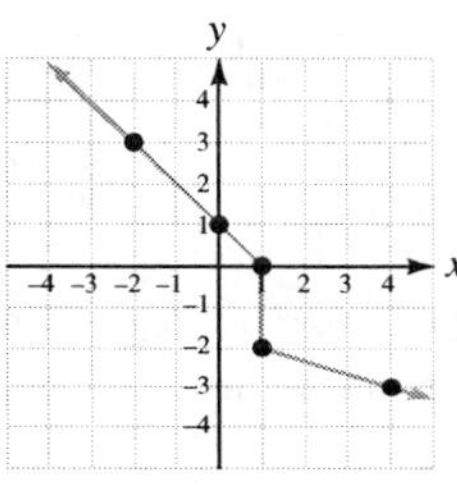

12. To graph $y = x^2 - 4$, a table of solutions is constructed and a graph is drawn, as shown. Explain the error made here.

$y = x^2 - 4$		
x	**y**	**(x, y)**
0	−4	(0, −4)
2	0	(2, 0)

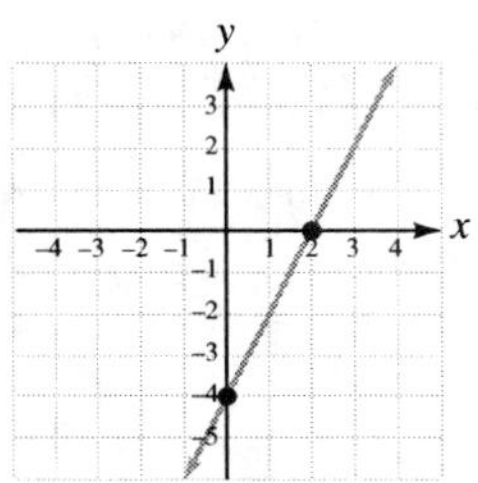

Not enough ordered pairs were found—the correct graph is a parabola.

13. Explain the error with the graph of $y = x^2$ shown in the illustration.
A smooth curve should be drawn through the points.

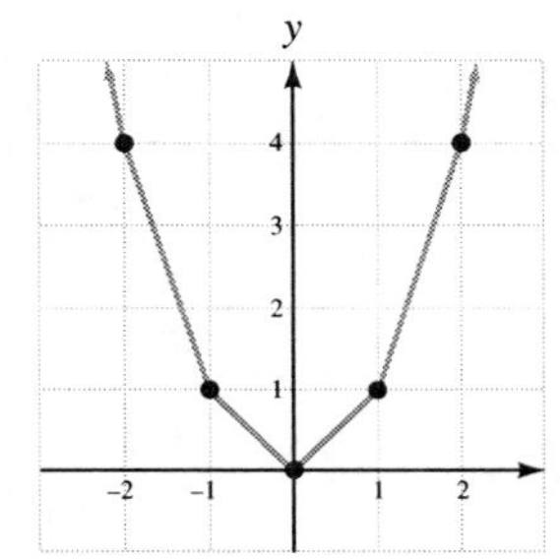

14. Several solutions of an equation are listed in the table of solutions. When graphing them, with what variable should the horizontal and vertical axes of the graph be labeled? horizontal: *t*, vertical: *s*

t	*s*	**(t, s)**
0	4	(0, 4)
1	5	(1, 5)
2	10	(2, 10)

NOTATION

Complete each solution.

15. Verify that $(-2, 6)$ satisfies $y = -x + 4$.

$$y = -x + 4$$
$$6 \stackrel{?}{=} -(-2) + 4$$
$$6 \stackrel{?}{=} 2 + 4$$
$$6 = 6$$

16. For the equation $y = |x - 2|$, if $x = -3$, find y.

$$y = |x - 2|$$
$$y = |-3 - 2|$$
$$y = |-5|$$
$$y = 5$$

GUIDED PRACTICE

Determine whether the ordered pair satisfies the equation. See Examples 1–2.

17. $y = 2x - 4$, $(4, 4)$ yes

18. $y = -3x + 1$, $(2, -4)$ no

19. $y = x^2$, $(8, 48)$ no

20. $y = -x^2 + 2$, $(1, 1)$ yes

21. $y = |x - 2|$, $(4, -3)$ no

22. $y = |x + 3|$, $(0, 3)$ yes

23. $y = x^3 + 1$, $(-2, -7)$ yes

24. $y = -x^3 - 1$, $(1, -2)$ yes

Complete the solution of each equation. See Example 3.

25. $y = 3x - 4$, $(1, ?)$ $(1, -1)$

26. $y = \frac{1}{2}x - 3$, $(2, ?)$ $(2, -2)$

27. $y = -5x + 3$, $(-3, ?)$ $(-3, 18)$

28. $y = -\frac{2}{5}x - 1$, $(-5, ?)$ $(-5, 1)$

Complete each table. See Objective 3.

29.

$y = x - 3$	
x	**y**
0	−3
1	−2
−2	−5

30.

$y = \|x - 3\|$	
x	**y**
0	3
−1	4
3	0

31.

$y = x^2 - 3$	
Input	**Output**
0	−3
2	1
−2	1

▶ **32.**

$y = x + 1$	
Input	**Output**
0	1
2	3
−1	0

Construct a table of solutions and graph each equation. See Example 4.

33. $y = 2x - 3$

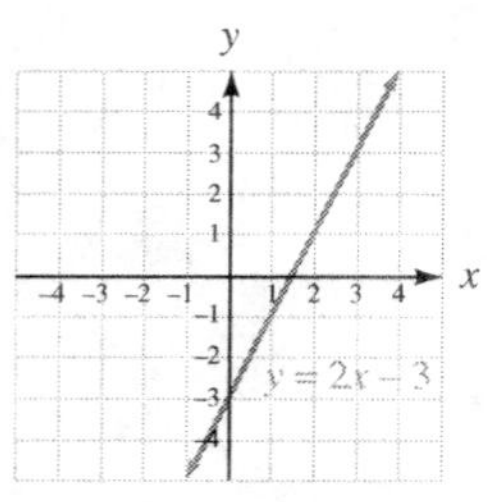

▶ **34.** $y = 3x + 1$

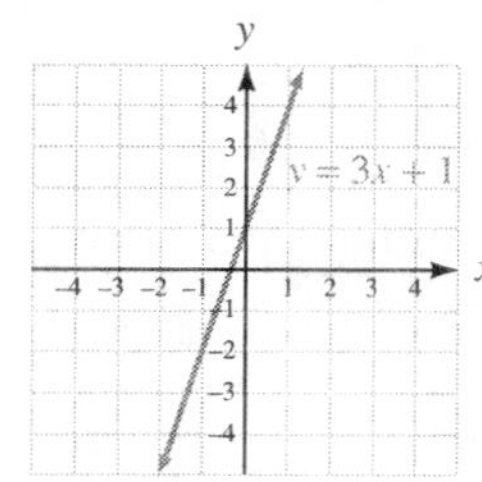

▶ **35.** $y = -2x + 1$

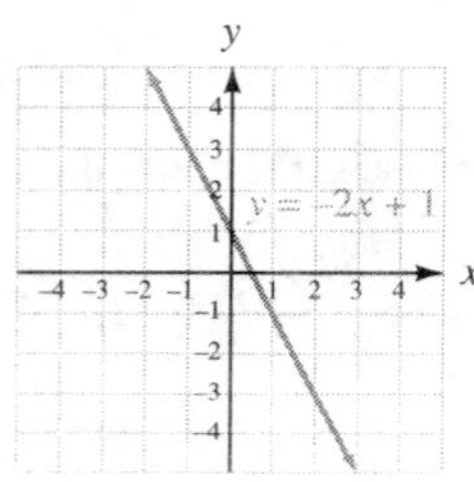

36. $y = -3x + 2$

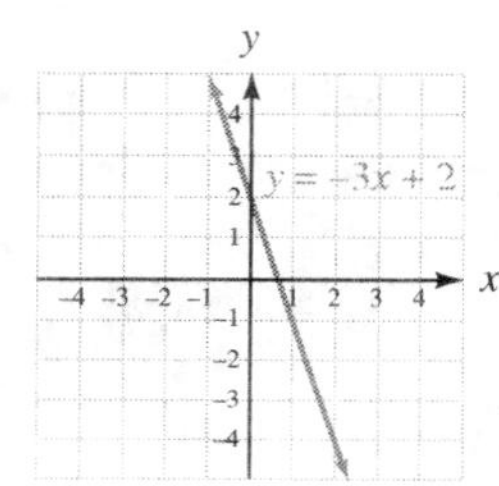

Construct a table of solutions and graph each equation. Compare the result to the graph of $y = x^2$. See Example 5.

37. $y = x^2 + 1$
1 unit higher

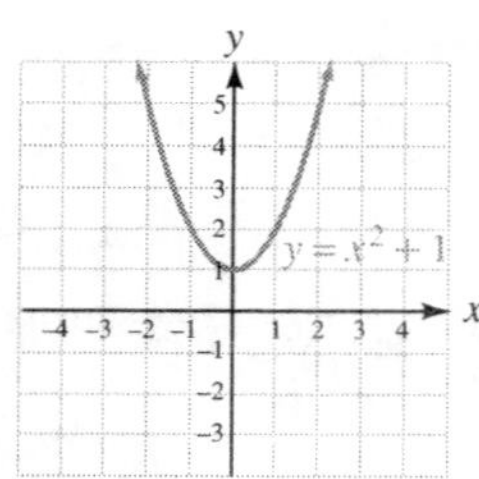

▶ **38.** $y = -x^2$
It is turned upside down.

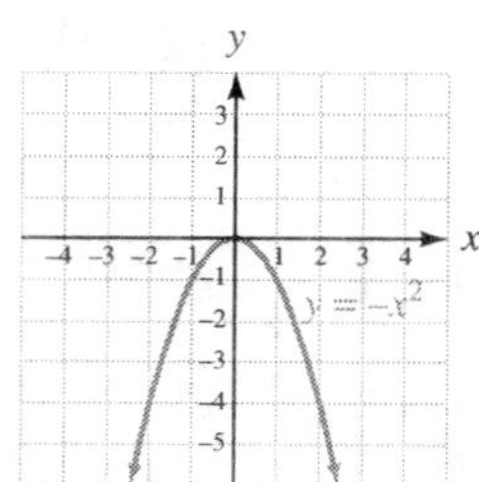

39. $y = (x - 2)^2$
2 units to the right

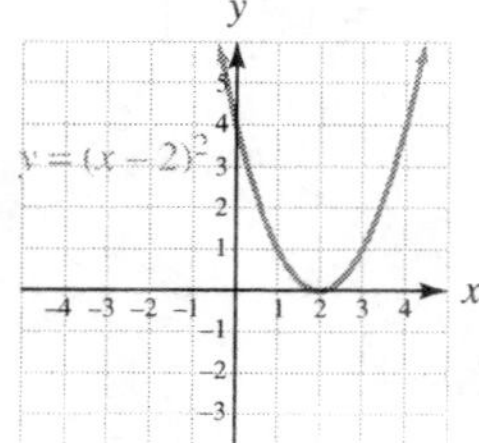

▶ **40.** $y = (x + 2)^2$
2 units to the left

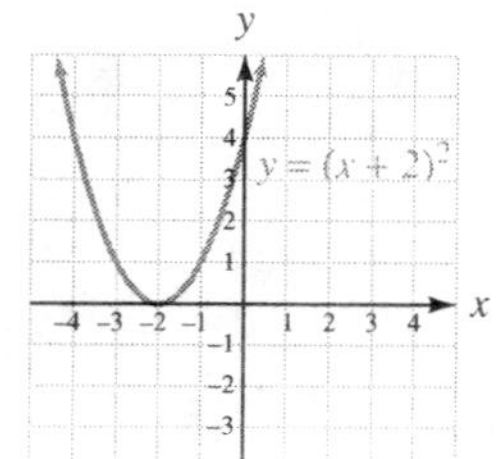

Construct a table of solutions and graph each equation. Compare the result to the graph of $y = |x|$. See Example 6.

41. $y = -|x|$
It is turned upside down.

▶ **42.** $y = |x| - 2$
2 units lower

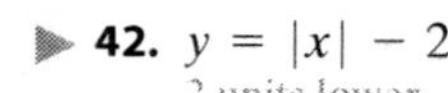

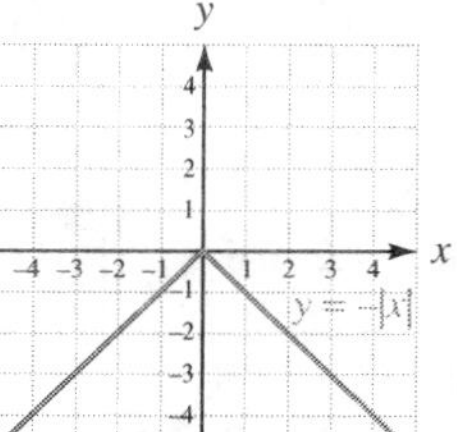

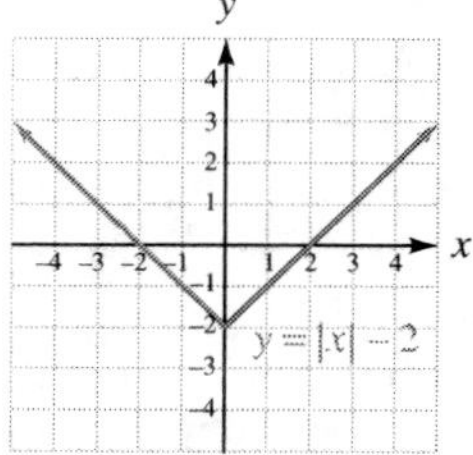

43. $y = |x + 2|$
2 units to the left

▶ **44.** $y = |x - 2|$
2 units to the right

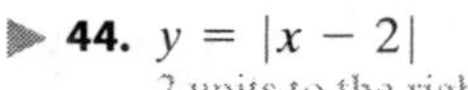

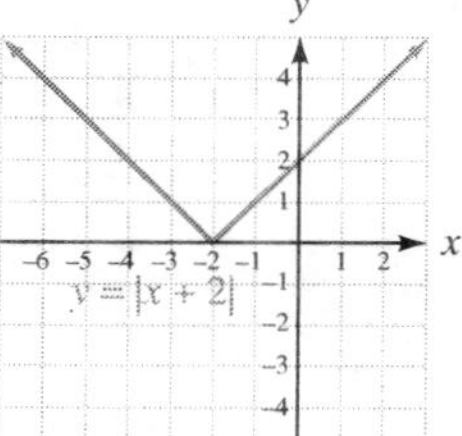

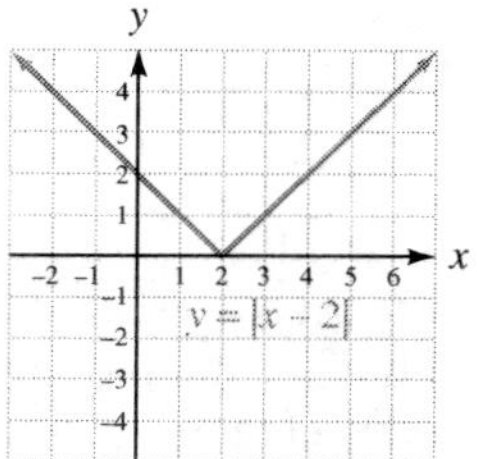

Construct a table of solutions and graph each equation. Compare the result to the graph of $y = x^3$. See Example 7.

45. $y = -x^3$
It is turned upside down.

▶ **46.** $y = x^3 + 2$
2 units higher

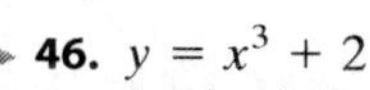

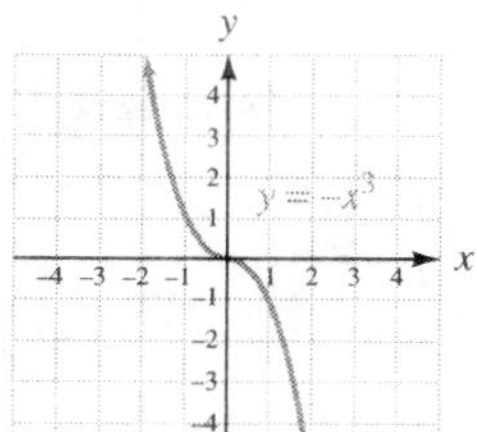

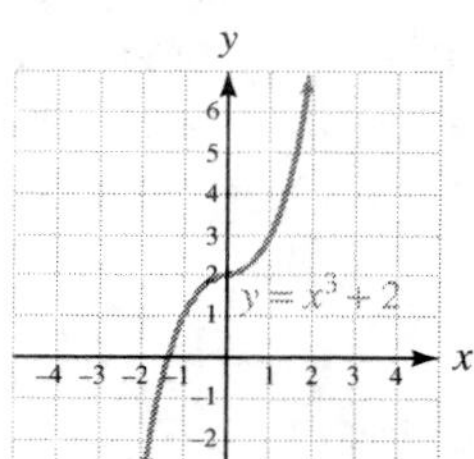

47. $y = x^3 - 2$
2 units lower

▶ **48.** $y = (x + 2)^3$
2 units to the left

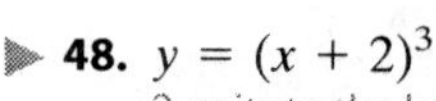

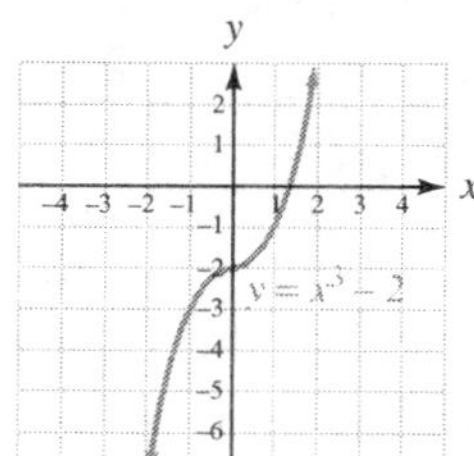

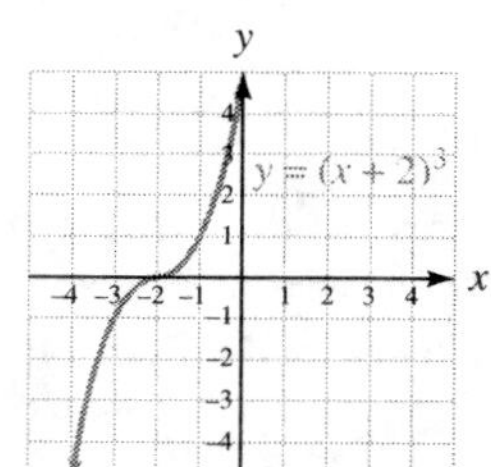

APPLICATIONS

See Example 8.

49. BILLIARDS The path traveled by the black 8 ball is described by the equations $y = 2x - 4$ and $y = -2x + 12$. Construct a table of solutions for $y = 2x - 4$ using the x-values 1, 2, and 4. Do the same for $y = -2x + 12$ using the x-values 4, 6, and 8. Then graph the path of the 8 ball.

x	1	2	4	4	6	8
y	−2	0	4	4	0	−4

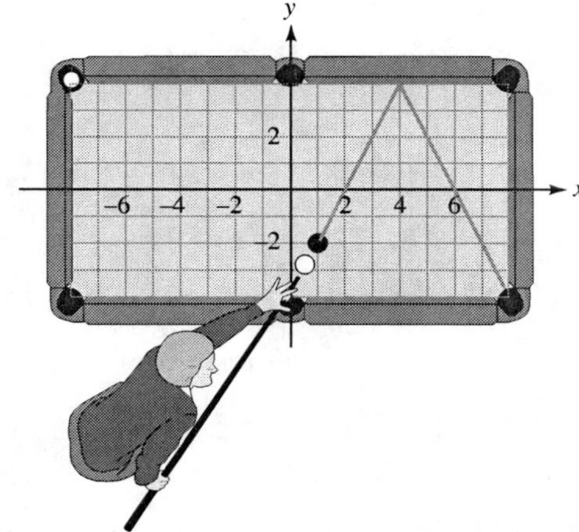

50. TABLE TENNIS The illustration shows the path traveled by a Ping-Pong ball as it bounces off the table. Use the information in the illustration to complete the table.

x	−7	−3	1	3	5
y	2	0	2	3	4

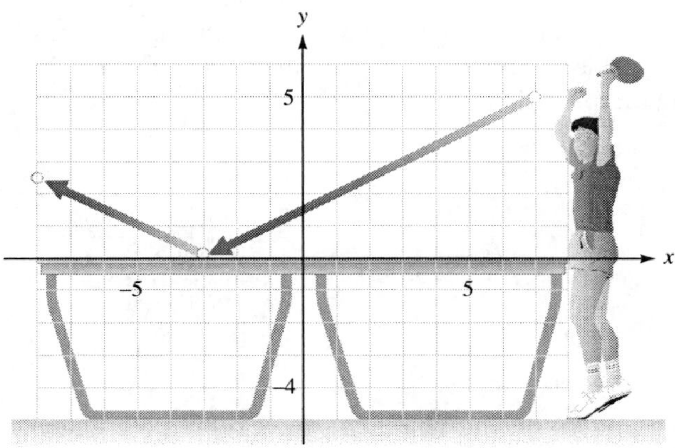

51. SUSPENSION BRIDGES The suspension cables of a bridge hang in the shape of a parabola, as shown in the next column. Use the information in the illustration to complete the table.

x	0	2	4	−2	−4
y	0	1	4	1	4

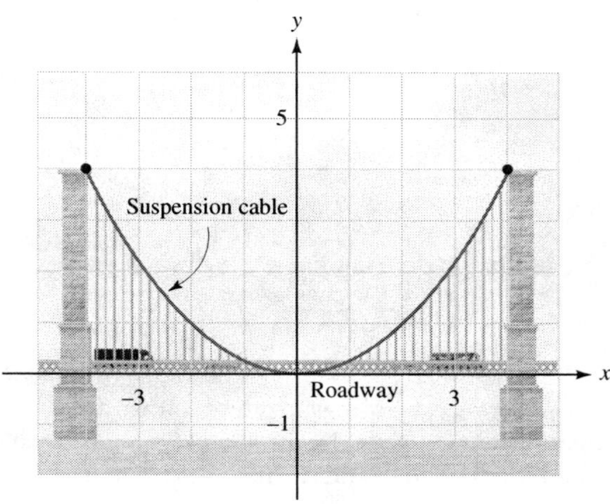

52. FIRE BOATS A stream of water from a high-pressure hose on a fire boat travels in the shape of a parabola. Use the information in the graph to complete the table.

x	1	2	3	4
y	3	4	3	0

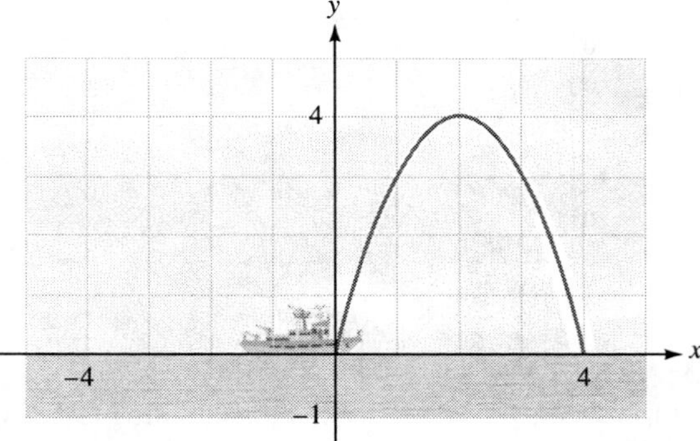

53. MANUFACTURING The graph on the next page shows the relationship between the length l (in inches) of a machine bolt and the cost C (in cents) to manufacture it.

a. What information does the point (2, 8) on the graph give us?
It costs 8¢ to make a 2-in. bolt.

b. How much does it cost to make a 7-inch bolt?
12¢

c. What length bolt is the least expensive to make?
a 4-in. bolt

d. Describe how the cost changes as the length of the bolt increases. It decreases as the length increases to 4 in., then increases as the length increases to 7 in.

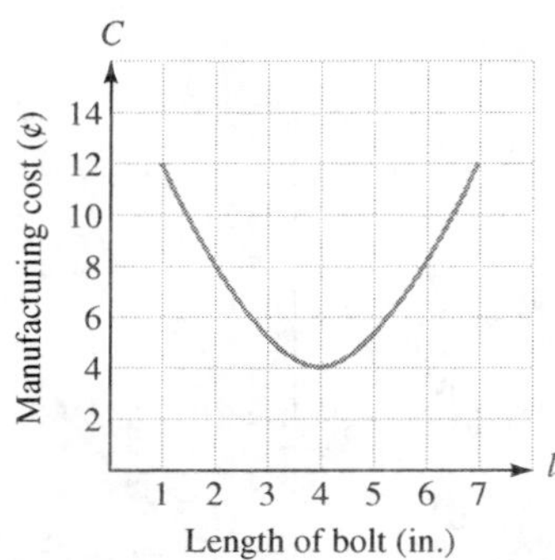

54. SOFTBALL The following graph shows the relationship between the distance d (in feet) traveled by a batted softball and the height h (in feet) it attains.

a. What information does the point (40, 40) on the graph give us?
After the ball has traveled 40 ft, its height is 40 ft.

b. At what distance from home plate does the ball reach its maximum height?
100 ft

c. Where will the ball land?
200 ft from home plate

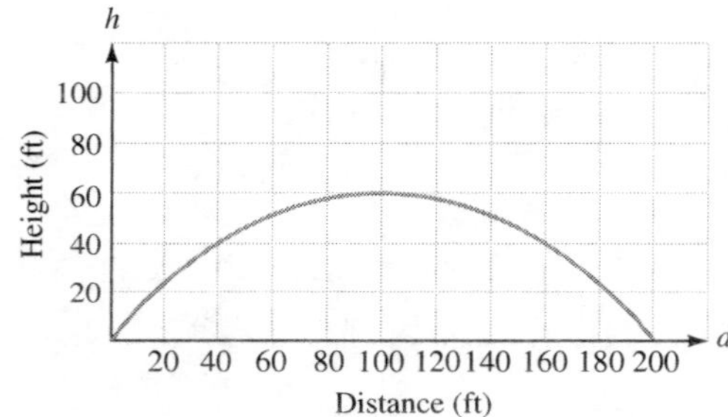

55. MARKET VALUE OF A HOUSE The following graph shows the relationship between the market value v of a house and the time t since it was purchased.

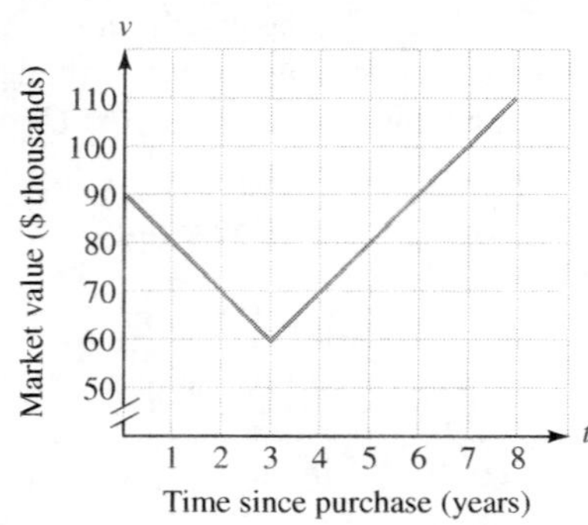

a. What was the purchase price of the house? $90,000

b. When did the value of the house reach its lowest point? the 3rd yr after being bought

c. When did the value of the house begin to surpass the purchase price? after the 6th yr

d. Describe how the market value of the house changed over the 8-year period.
It decreased in value for 3 yr to a low of $60,000, then increased in value for 5 yr to a high of $110,000.

56. POLITICAL SURVEYS The following graph shows the relationship between the percent P of those surveyed who rated their senator's job performance as satisfactory or better and the time t she had been in office.

a. When did her job performance rating reach a maximum? the 8th month after being elected

b. When was her job performance rating at or above the 60% mark? between the 4th and 12th months

c. Describe how her job performance rating changed over the 12-month period.
After the election, it increased for 8 mo to a high of 70%. Then it decreased for 4 mo.

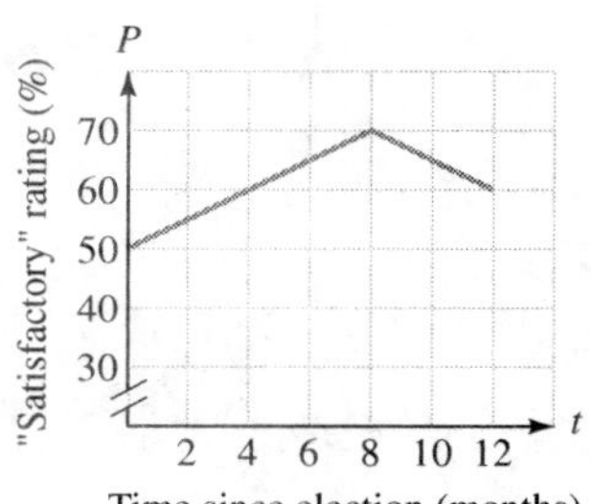

WRITING

57. What is a table of solutions?

58. To graph an equation in two variables, how many solutions of the equation must be found?

59. Give an example of an equation in one variable and an equation in two variables. How do their solutions differ?

60. When we say that $(-2, -6)$ is a solution of $y = x - 4$, what do we mean?

61. On a quiz, students were asked to graph $y = 3x - 1$. One student made the table of solutions on the left. Another student made the one on the right. Which table is incorrect? Or could they both be correct? Explain.

x	y	(x, y)
0	-1	$(0, -1)$
2	5	$(2, 5)$
3	8	$(3, 8)$
4	11	$(4, 11)$
5	14	$(5, 14)$

x	y	(x, y)
-2	-7	$(-2, -7)$
-1	-4	$(-1, -4)$
1	2	$(1, 2)$
-3	-10	$(-3, -10)$
2	5	$(2, 5)$

62. What does it mean when we say that an equation in two variables has infinitely many solutions?

REVIEW

63. Solve: $\frac{x}{8} = -12$ -96

64. Combine like terms: $3t - 4T + 5T - 6t$ $-3t + T$

65. Is $\frac{x + 5}{6}$ an expression or an equation? an expression

66. What formula is used to find the perimeter of a rectangle? $P = 2l + 2w$

67. What number is 0.5% of 250? 1.25

68. Solve: $-3x + 5 > -7$ $x < 4$

69. Find: $-2.5 - (-2.6)$ 0.1

70. Evaluate: $(-5)^3$ -125

SECTION 5.4 Intercepts

Objectives

1 Identify linear equations.

2 Complete ordered-pair solutions of linear equations.

3 Graph linear equations by plotting points.

4 Graph linear equations by the intercept method.

5 Identify and graph horizontal and vertical lines.

6 Use graphs of linear equations to solve applied problems.

1 Identify linear equations.

We have previously graphed the equations shown below. The graph of the equation $y = x - 1$ is a line, and we call it a **linear equation.** Since the graphs of $y = x^2$, $y = |x|$, and $y = x^3$ are *not* lines, they are **nonlinear equations.**

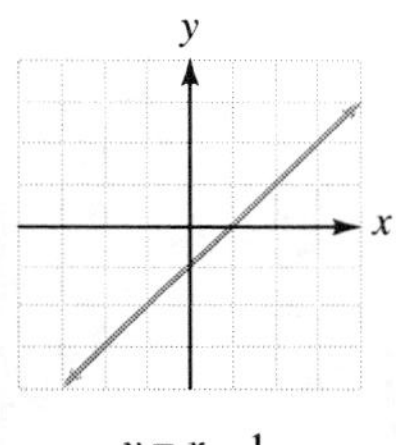

$y = x - 1$
Linear equation
(a)

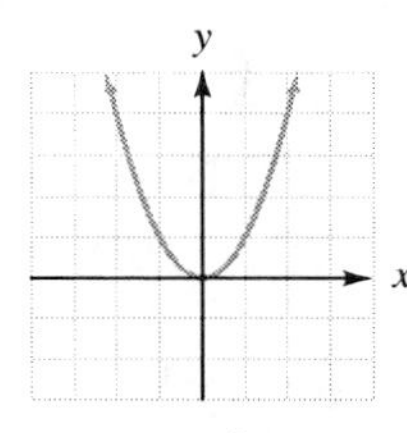

$y = x^2$
Nonlinear equation
(b)

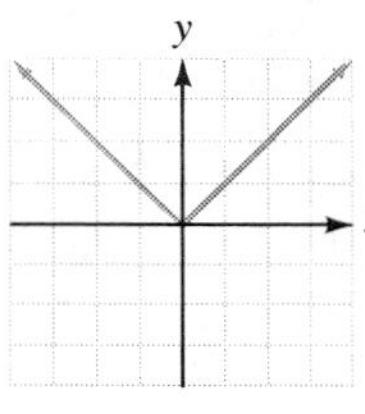

$y = |x|$
Nonlinear equation
(c)

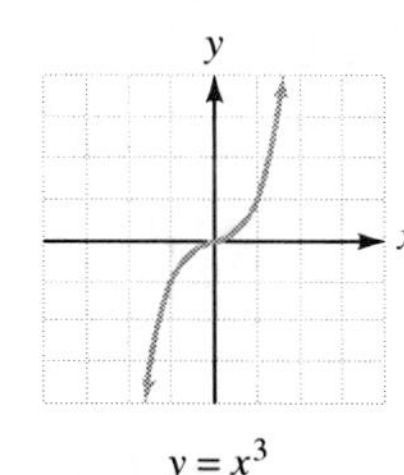

$y = x^3$
Nonlinear equation
(d)

In this section, we will discuss how to graph linear equations and show how to use their graphs to solve problems.

Any equation, such as $y = x - 1$, whose graph is a straight line is called a **linear equation in x and y.** Some other examples of linear equations are

$$y = \frac{1}{2}x + 2, \quad 3x - 2y = 8, \quad 5y - x + 2 = 0, \quad y = 4, \quad \text{and} \quad x = -3$$

A linear equation in x and y is any equation that can be written in a special form, called **general** (or **standard**) form.

General Form of a Linear Equation

If A, B, and C represent real numbers, the equation

$Ax + By = C$ (both A and B are not zero)

is called the **general form** (or **standard form**) of the equation of a line.

Whenever possible, we will write the general form $Ax + By = C$ so that A, B, and C are integers and $A \geq 0$. Note that in a linear equation in x and y, the exponents on x and y are 1.

Self Check 1

Which of the following are linear equations and which are nonlinear?

a. $y = |x|$ nonlinear

b. $-x = 6 - y$ linear

c. $y = x$ linear

Now Try **Problems 38 and 40**

Teaching Example 1 Which of the following are linear equations and which are nonlinear?
a. $y = 2x + 3$
b. $3x = -y + 7$
c. $y = |x| + 3$
Answers:
a. linear b. linear c. nonlinear

EXAMPLE 1 Which of the following equations are linear equations?

a. $3x = 1 - 2y$ **b.** $y = x^3 + 1$ **c.** $y = -\frac{1}{2}x$

Strategy We will try to write each equation in general form $Ax + By = C$. We will also note the exponents on x and y.

WHY If we can write an equation in general form $Ax + By = C$, it is a linear equation. If the exponents on x or y are not 1, the equation is nonlinear.

Solution

a. Since the equation $3x = 1 - 2y$ can be written in $Ax + By = C$ form, it is a linear equation.

$3x = 1 - 2y$ This is the original equation.

$3x + 2y = 1 - 2y + 2y$ Add 2y to both sides.

$3x + 2y = 1$ Simplify the right-hand side: $-2y + 2y = 0$.

Here $A = 3$, $B = 2$, and $C = 1$.

b. Since the exponent on x in $y = x^3 + 1$ is 3, the equation is a nonlinear equation.

c. Since the equation $y = -\frac{1}{2}x$ can be written in $Ax + By = C$ form, it is a linear equation.

$y = -\frac{1}{2}x$ This is the original equation.

$-2(y) = -2\left(-\frac{1}{2}x\right)$ Multiply both sides by -2 so that the coefficient of x will be 1.

$-2y = x$ Simplify the right-hand side: $-2\left(-\frac{1}{2}\right) = 1$.

$0 = x + 2y$ Add 2y to both sides.

$x + 2y = 0$ Write the equation in general form.

Here $A = 1$, $B = 2$, and $C = 0$.

2 Complete ordered-pair solutions of linear equations.

To find solutions of linear equations, we substitute arbitrary values for one variable and solve for the other.

Self Check 2

Complete the table of solutions for $3x + 2y = 5$.

x	y	(x, y)
3	−2	(3, −2)
5	−5	(5, −5)

Now Try **Problem 42**

Teaching Example 2 Complete the table of solutions for $2x - 5y = 10$.

x	y	(x, y)
10	2	(10, 2)
5	0	(5, 0)

EXAMPLE 2 Complete the table of solutions for $3x + 2y = 5$.

Strategy In each case we will substitute the known coordinate of the solution into the given equation.

WHY We can solve the resulting equation in one variable to find the unknown coordinate of the solution.

Solution

x	y	(x, y)
7		(7,)
	4	(, 4)

In the first row, we are given an x-value of 7. To find the corresponding y-value, we substitute 7 for x and solve for y.

$3x + 2y = 5$ This is the original equation.

$3(7) + 2y = 5$ Substitute 7 for x.

$21 + 2y = 5$ Perform the multiplication: $3(7) = 21$.

$2y = -16$ Subtract 21 from both sides: $5 - 21 = -16$.

$y = -8$ Divide both sides by 2.

A solution of $3x + 2y = 5$ is $(7, -8)$.

In the second row, we are given a y-value of 4. To find the corresponding x-value, we substitute 4 for y and solve for x.

$$3x + 2y = 5 \quad \text{This is the original equation.}$$
$$3x + 2(4) = 5 \quad \text{Substitute 4 for } y.$$
$$3x + 8 = 5 \quad \text{Perform the multiplication: } 2(4) = 8.$$
$$3x = -3 \quad \text{Subtract 8 from both sides: } 5 - 8 = -3.$$
$$x = -1 \quad \text{Divide both sides by 3.}$$

Another solution is $(-1, 4)$. The completed table is shown on the right.

x	y	(x, y)
7	−8	(7, −8)
−1	4	(−1, 4)

3 Graph linear equations by plotting points.

It is impossible to list the infinitely many solutions of a linear equation. However, to show all of its solutions, we can draw a mathematical "picture" of them. We call this picture the *graph of the equation.*

Graphing Linear Equations

1. Find three pairs (x, y) that satisfy the equation by picking arbitrary numbers for x and finding the corresponding values of y.
2. Plot each resulting pair (x, y) on a rectangular coordinate system. If the three points do not lie on a straight line, check your computations.
3. Draw the straight line passing through the points.

EXAMPLE 3 Graph: $y = -3x$

Strategy We will find three solutions of the equations, plot them on a rectangular coordinate system, and then draw a straight line passing through the points.

WHY To *graph* a linear equation in two variables means to make a drawing that represents all of its solutions.

Solution

To find three ordered pairs that satisfy the equation, we begin by choosing three x-values: −2, 0, and 2.

If $x = -2$	**If $x = 0$**	**If $x = 2$**
$y = -3x$	$y = -3x$	$y = -3x$
$y = -3(-2)$	$y = -3(0)$	$y = -3(2)$
$y = 6$	$y = 0$	$y = -6$

We enter the results in a table of solutions, plot the points, and draw a straight line through the points. The graph appears on the next page.

Self Check 3

Graph $y = -3x + 2$ and compare the result to the graph of $y = -3x$. What do you notice?

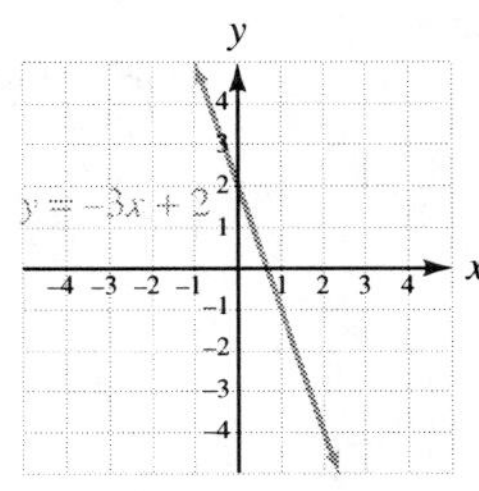

Now Try **Problem 45**

Self Check 3 Answer

It is a line 2 units above the graph of $y = -3x$.

Teaching Example 3 Graph $y = -3x - 3$ and compare the result to the graph of $y = -3x$. What do you notice?
Answer:
It is a line 3 units below the graph of $y = -3x$.

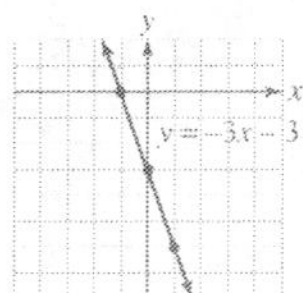

$y = -3x$		
x	y	(x, y)
-2	6	$(-2, 6)$
0	0	$(0, 0)$
2	-6	$(2, -6)$

↑ This point will serve as a check.

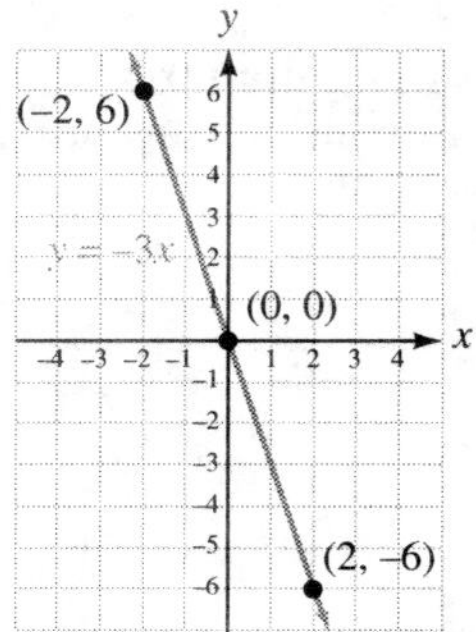

> ***Success Tip*** Since two points determine a line, only two points are needed to graph a linear equation. However, we will often plot a third point as a check. If the three points do not lie on a straight line, then at least one of them is in error.

When graphing linear equations, it is often easier to find solutions of the equation if it is first solved for y.

Self Check 4

Solve $3y = 3 + x$ for y. Then graph the equation.

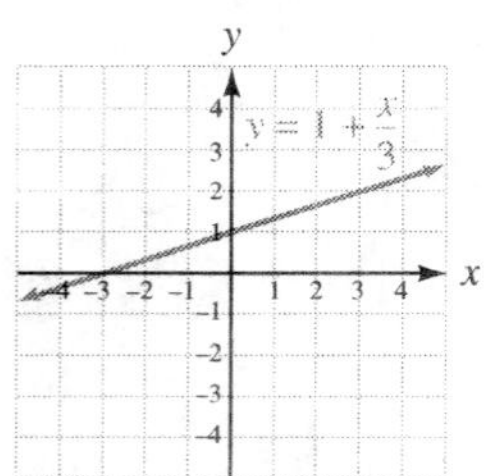

Now Try **Problem 53**

Self Check 4 Answer
$y = 1 + \frac{x}{3}$

Teaching Example 4 Solve $5y = 2x - 15$ for y. Then graph the equation.
Answer:
$y = \frac{2}{5}x - 3$

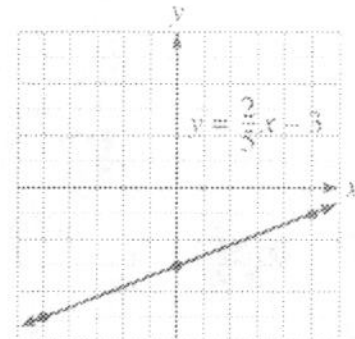

EXAMPLE 4 Graph: $2y = 4 - x$

Strategy We will use properties of equality to solve the given equation for y. Then we will use the point-plotting method of this section to graph the resulting equivalent equation.

WHY The calculations to find several solutions of a linear equation in two variables are usually easier when the equation is solved for y.

Solution

To solve for y, we undo the multiplication of 2 by dividing both sides by 2.

$$2y = 4 - x$$

$$\frac{2y}{2} = \frac{4}{2} - \frac{x}{2}$$ On the right-hand side, dividing each term by 2 is equivalent to dividing the entire side by 2: $\frac{4-x}{2} = \frac{4}{2} - \frac{x}{2}$.

$$y = 2 - \frac{x}{2}$$ Simplify: $\frac{4}{2} = 2$

Since each value of x will be divided by 2, we will choose values of x that are divisible by 2. Three such choices are -4, 0, and 4. If $x = -4$, we have

$$y = 2 - \frac{x}{2}$$

$$y = 2 - \frac{-4}{2}$$ Substitute -4 for x.

$$y = 2 - (-2)$$ Divide: $\frac{-4}{2} = -2$

$$y = 4$$ Perform the subtraction.

A solution is $(-4, 4)$. This pair and two others satisfying the equation are shown in the table on the next page. If we plot the points and draw a straight line through them, we will obtain the graph also shown on the next page.

$y = 2 - \frac{x}{2}$		
x	y	(x, y)
−4	4	(−4, 4)
0	2	(0, 2)
4	0	(4, 0)

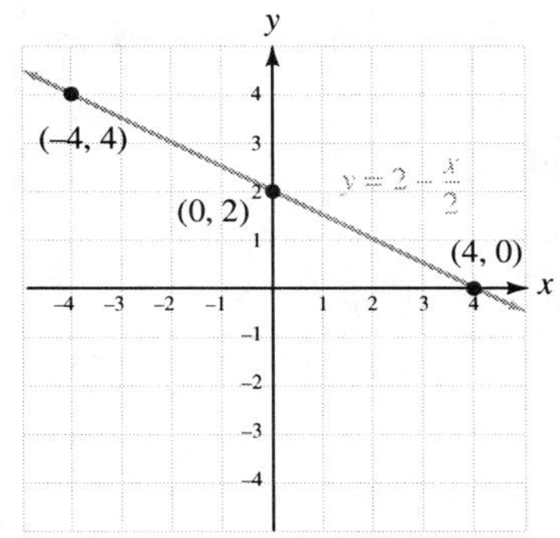

4 Graph linear equations by the intercept method.

In the figure to the right, the graph of $3x + 4y = 12$ intersects the y-axis at the point (0, 3); we call this point the **y-intercept** of the graph. Since the graph intersects the x-axis at (4, 0), the point (4, 0) is the **x-intercept.**

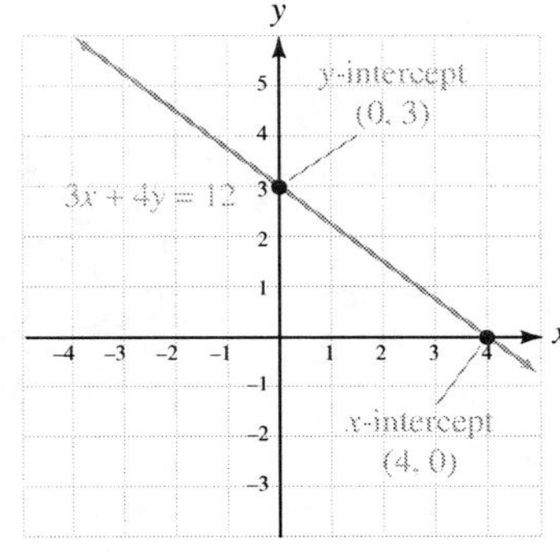

In general, we have the following definitions.

y- and x-intercepts

The **y-intercept** of a line is the point $(0, b)$ where the line intersects the y-axis. To find b, substitute 0 for x in the equation of the line and solve for y.

The **x-intercept** of a line is the point $(a, 0)$ where the line intersects the x-axis. To find a, substitute 0 for y in the equation of the line and solve for x.

Plotting the x- and y-intercepts of a graph and drawing a straight line through them is called the **intercept method of graphing a line.** This method is useful when graphing equations written in general form $Ax + By = C$.

EXAMPLE 5 Graph: $3x - 2y = 8$

Strategy We will let $y = 0$ to find the x-intercept of the graph. We will then let $x = 0$ to find the y-intercept.

WHY Since two points determine a line, the y-intercept and the x-intercept are enough information to graph this linear equation.

Solution

***x*-intercept: $y = 0$**

$$3x - 2y = 8$$

$$3x - 2(0) = 8 \quad \text{Substitute 0 for } y.$$

$$3x = 8 \quad \text{Simplify the left-hand side: } 2(0) = 0.$$

$$x = \frac{8}{3} \quad \text{Divide both sides by 3.}$$

Self Check 5

Graph $4x + 3y = 6$ using the intercept method.

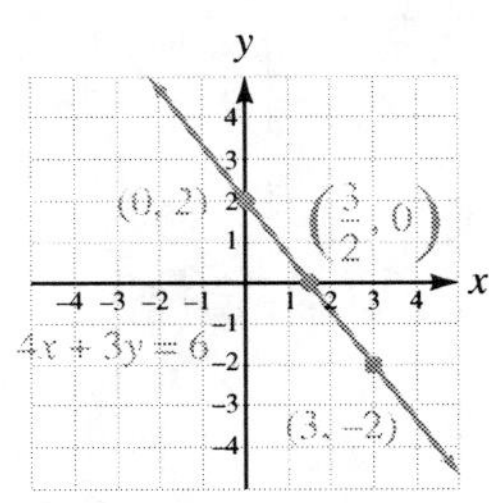

Now Try **Problem 59**

Teaching Example 5 Graph $2x - 3y = 6$ using the intercept method.
Answer:

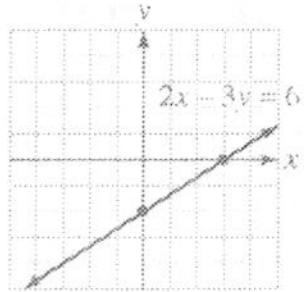

The x-intercept is $\left(\frac{8}{3}, 0\right)$, which can be written $\left(2\frac{2}{3}, 0\right)$. This ordered pair is entered in the table below.

y-intercept: $x = 0$.

$$3x - 2y = 8$$
$$3(0) - 2y = 8 \quad \text{Substitute 0 for x.}$$
$$-2y = 8 \quad \text{Simplify the left-hand side: } 3(0) = 0.$$
$$y = -4 \quad \text{Divide both sides by } -2.$$

The y-intercept is $(0, -4)$. It is entered in the table below. As a check, we find one more point on the line. If $x = 4$, then $y = 2$. We plot these three points and draw a straight line through them. The graph of $3x - 2y = 8$ is shown in the figure.

$3x - 2y = 8$

x	y	(x, y)
$\frac{8}{3} = 2\frac{2}{3}$	0	$\left(2\frac{2}{3}, 0\right)$
0	−4	$(0, -4)$
4	2	$(4, 2)$

↑ This point serves as a check.

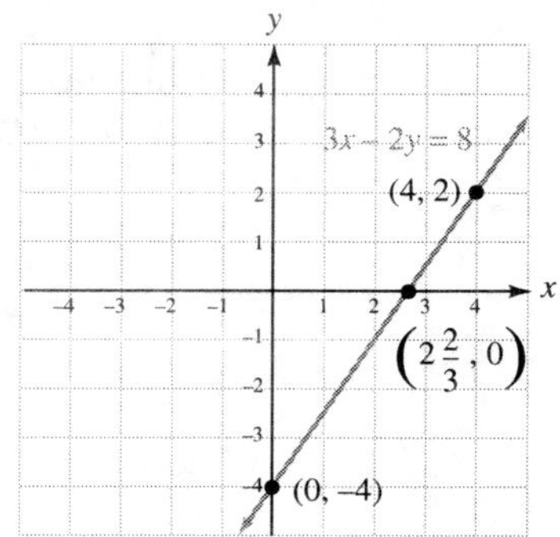

5 Identify and graph horizontal and vertical lines.

Equations such as $y = 4$ and $x = -3$ are linear equations, because they can be written in the general form $Ax + By = C$. For example, $y = 4$ is equivalent to $0x + 1y = 4$ and $x = -3$ is equivalent to $1x + 0y = -3$. We now discuss how to graph these types of linear equations.

Self Check 6

Graph: $y = -2$

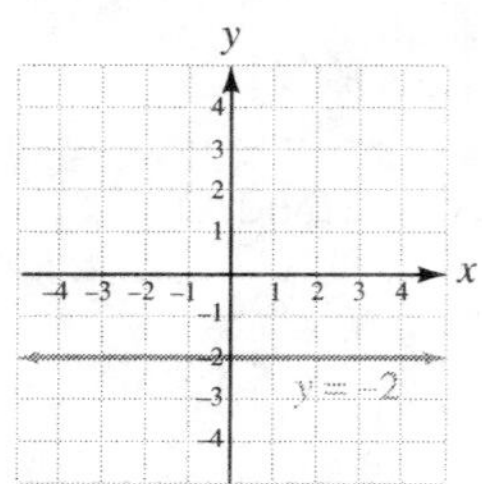

Now Try **Problem 62**

EXAMPLE 6 Graph: $y = 4$

Strategy To find three ordered-pair solutions of this equation to plot, we will select three values for x and use 4 for y each time.

WHY The given equation requires that $y = 4$.

Solution

We can write the equation in general form as $0x + y = 4$. Since the coefficient of x is 0, the numbers chosen for x have no effect on y. The value of y is always 4. For example, if $x = 2$, we have

$$0x + y = 4 \quad \text{This is the original equation, } y = 4\text{, written in general form.}$$
$$0(2) + y = 4 \quad \text{Substitute 2 for x.}$$
$$y = 4 \quad \text{Simplify the left side.}$$

The table of solutions shown on the next page contains three ordered pairs that satisfy the equation $y = 4$. If we plot the points and draw a straight line through them, the result is a horizontal line. The y-intercept is $(0, 4)$, and there is no x-intercept.

$y = 4$		
x	y	(x, y)
2	4	(2, 4)
−1	4	(−1, 4)
−3	4	(−3, 4)

↑ Note that each y-coordinate is 4.

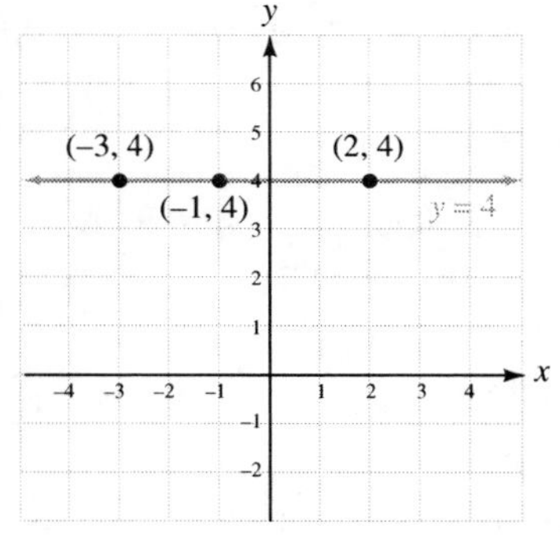

Teaching Example 6 Graph: $y = -3$
Answer:

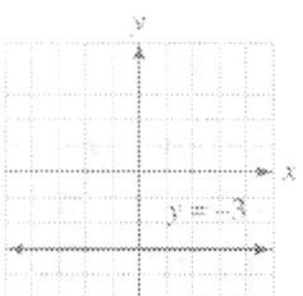

EXAMPLE 7 Graph: $x = -3$

Strategy To find three ordered-pair solutions of this equation to plot, we will select −3 for x each time and use three different values for y.

WHY The given equation requires that $x = -3$.

Solution

We can write the equation in general form as $x + 0y = -3$. Since the coefficient of y is 0, the numbers chosen for y have no effect on x. The value of x is always −3. For example, if $y = -2$, we have

$x + 0y = -3$ This is the original equation written in general form.

$x + 0(-2) = -3$ Substitute −2 for y.

$x = -3$ Simplify the left side.

The table of solutions shown below contains three ordered pairs that satisfy the equation $x = -3$. If we plot the points and draw a line through them, the result is a vertical line. The x-intercept is $(-3, 0)$, and there is no y-intercept.

$x = -3$		
x	y	(x, y)
−3	−2	(−3, −2)
−3	0	(−3, 0)
−3	3	(−3, 3)

↑ Note that each x-coordinate is −3.

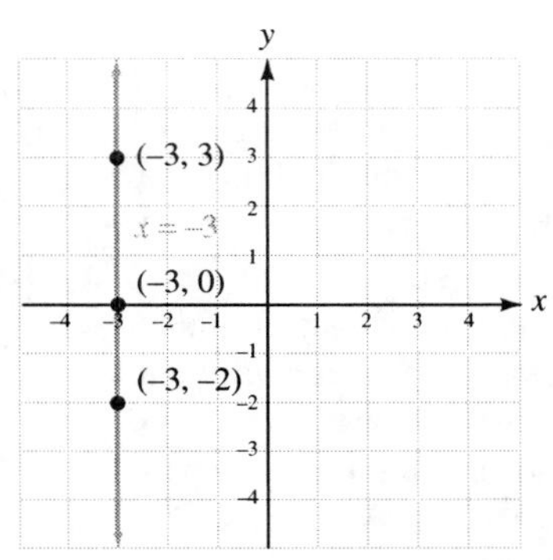

Self Check 7

Graph: $x = 4$

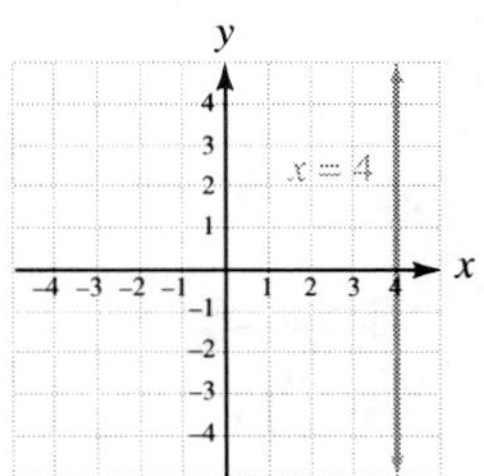

Now Try **Problem 64**

Teaching Example 7 Graph: $x = 2$
Answer:

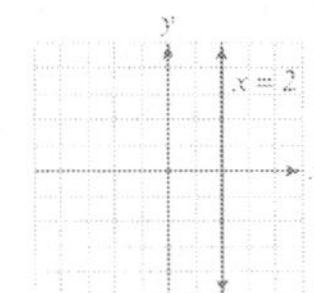

From the results of Examples 6 and 7, we have the following facts.

Equations of Horizontal and Vertical Lines

The equation $y = b$ represents the horizontal line that intersects the y-axis at $(0, b)$. If $b = 0$, the line is the x-axis.

The equation $x = a$ represents the vertical line that intersects the x-axis at $(a, 0)$. If $a = 0$, the line is the y-axis.

6 Use graphs of linear equations to solve applied problems.

Self Check 8

A laser tag business offers a party package that includes invitations, a party room, and 2 rounds of laser tag. The cost is \$15 plus \$10 per child. Write a linear equation that will give the cost for a party of any size, and then graph the equation. $c = 15 + 10n$

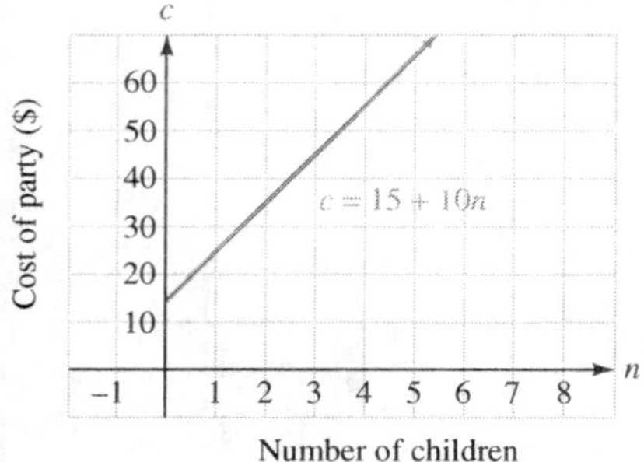

Now Try **Problem 62**

Teaching Example 8 The cost of embroidered hats is \$25 for a setup fee and \$15 per hat with the embroidered company logo. Write a linear equation that will give the cost for an order of any number of hats, and then graph the equation.
Answer:
$c = 25 + 15n$

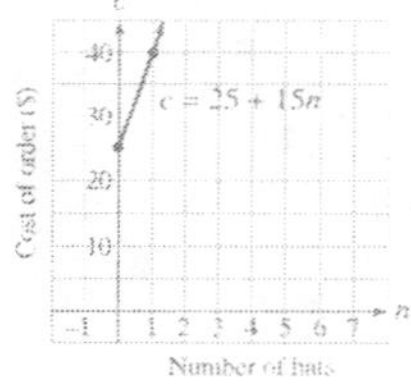

EXAMPLE 8 *Birthday Parties* A restaurant offers a party package that includes food, drinks, cake, and party favors for a cost of \$25 plus \$3 per child. Write a linear equation that will give the cost for a party of any size, and then graph the equation.

Strategy We will form an equation and use the plotting points method to graph the equation.

WHY The graph is a picture of all the solutions of the equation.

Solution

We can let c represent the cost of the party. The cost c is the sum of the basic charge of \$25 and the cost per child times the number of children attending. If the number of children attending is n, at \$3 per child, the total cost for the children is \$$3n$.

The cost	is	the basic \$25 charge	plus	\$3	times	the number of children.
c	$=$	25	$+$	3	$\cdot$	n

For the equation $c = 25 + 3n$, the independent variable (input) is n, the number of children. The dependent variable (output) is c, the cost of the party. We will find three points on the graph of the equation by choosing n-values of 0, 5, and 10 and finding the corresponding c-values. The results are shown in the table.

If $n = 0$
$c = 25 + 3(0)$
$c = 25$

If $n = 5$
$c = 25 + 3(5)$
$c = 25 + 15$
$c = 40$

If $n = 10$
$c = 25 + 3(10)$
$c = 25 + 30$
$c = 55$

$c = 25 + 3n$	
n	c
0	25
5	40
10	55

Next, we graph the points and draw a line through them. We don't draw an arrowhead on the left, because it doesn't make sense to have a negative number of children attend a party. Note that the c-axis is scaled in units of \$5 to accommodate costs ranging from \$0 to \$65. We can use the graph to determine the cost of a party of any size. For example, to find the cost of a party with 8 children, we locate 8 on the horizontal axis and then move up to find a point on the graph directly above the 8. Since the coordinates of that point are (8, 49), the cost for 8 children would be \$49.

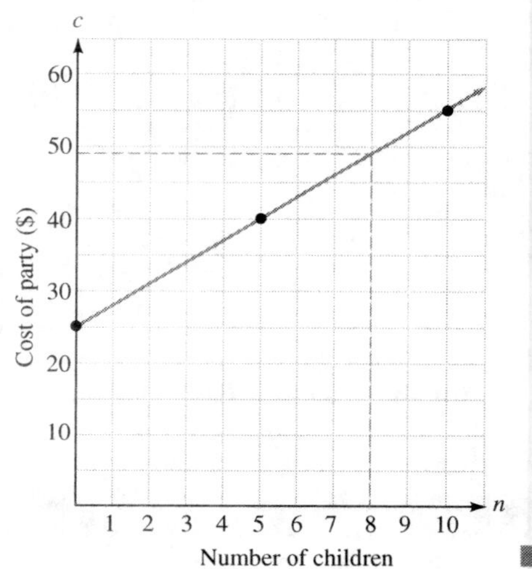

ANSWERS TO SELF CHECKS

1. a. nonlinear **b.** linear **c.** linear **2.** (3, −2), (5, −5)

3.

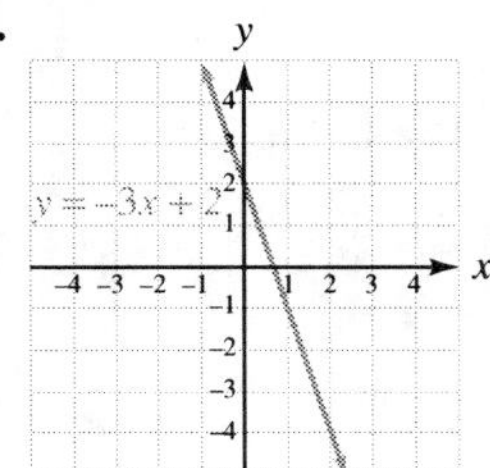

4.

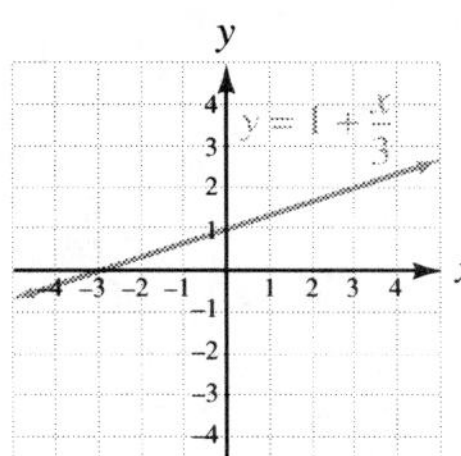

5.

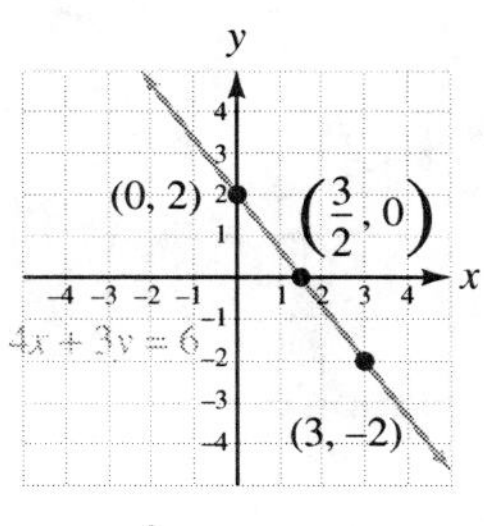

6.

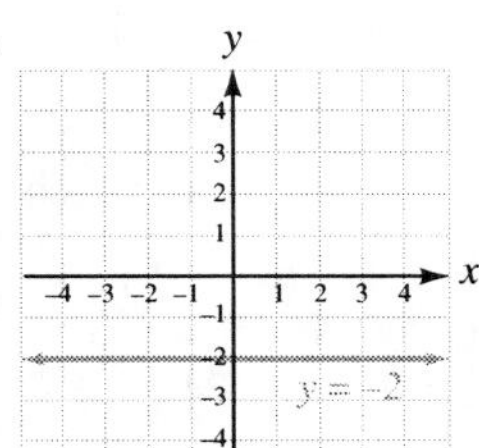

7.

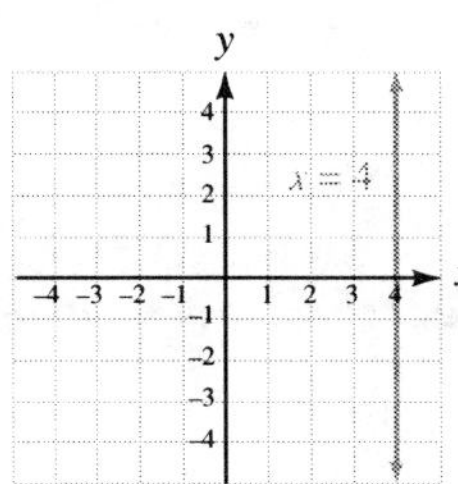

8.

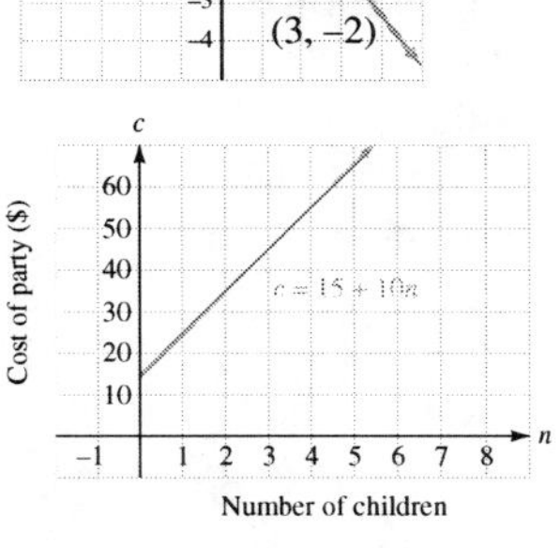

SECTION 5.4 STUDY SET

VOCABULARY

Fill in the blanks.

1. An equation whose graph is a line and whose variables are to the first power is called a linear equation.
2. The equation $Ax + By = C$ is the standard or general form of the equation of a line.
3. The y-intercept of a line is the point $(0, b)$ where the line intersects the y-axis.
4. The x-intercept of a line is the point $(a, 0)$ where the line intersects the x-axis.

CONCEPTS

Fill in the blanks.

5. To find the y-intercept of the graph of a linear equation, let x = 0 and solve for y.
6. To find the x-intercept of the graph of a linear equation, let y = 0 and solve for x.
7. Lines parallel to the y-axis are vertical lines.
8. Lines parallel to the x-axis are horizontal lines.
9. What is another name for the line $x = 0$? the y-axis
10. What is another name for the line $y = 0$? the x-axis

Find the power of each variable in Problems 11–13.

11. $y = 2x - 6$ y: 1st power, x: 1st power
12. $y = x^2 - 6$ y: 1st power, x: 2nd power
13. $y = x^3 + 2$ y: 1st power, x: 3rd power
14. In a linear equation in x and y, what are the exponents on x and y? 1

Consider the graph of a linear equation shown below.

15. Why will the coordinates of point A yield a true statement when substituted into the equation? because A is on the line
16. Why will the coordinates of point B yield a false statement when substituted into the equation? because B is not on the line

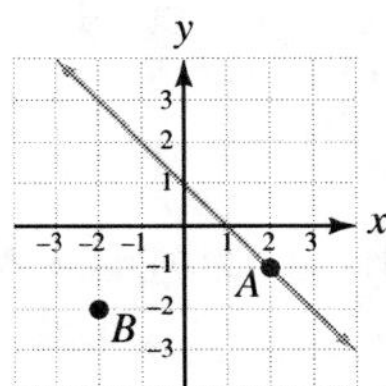

17. A student found three solutions of a linear equation and plotted them as shown. What conclusion can he make? He made a mistake. The points should lie on a straight line.

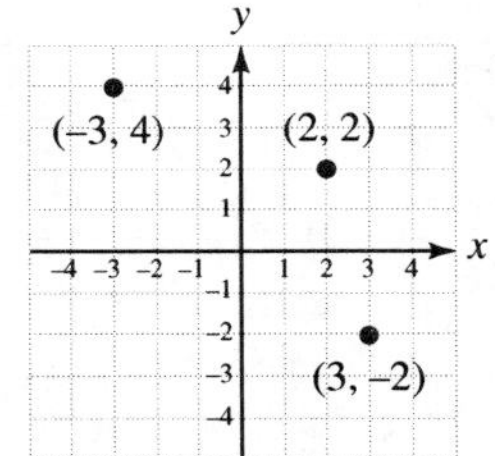

18. How many solutions are there for a linear equation in two variables? infinitely many

▶ Selected exercises available online at www.webassign.net/brookscole

19. Give the x-intercept of the graph on the right. $(-3, 0)$

20. Give the y-intercept of the graph on the right. $(0, -1)$

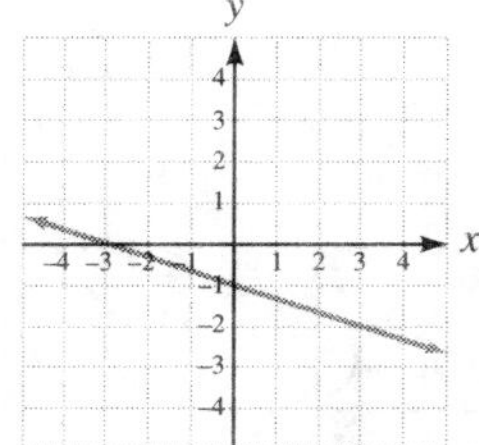

21. On the coordinate system below, draw the graph of a line with no x-intercept. Answers will vary.

22. On the coordinate system below, draw the graph of a line with no y-intercept. Answers will vary.

23. On the coordinate system below, draw a line with an x-intercept of $(2, 0)$. Answers will vary.

24. On the coordinate system to the right, draw a line with a y-intercept of $\left(0, -\frac{5}{2}\right)$.

Answers will vary.

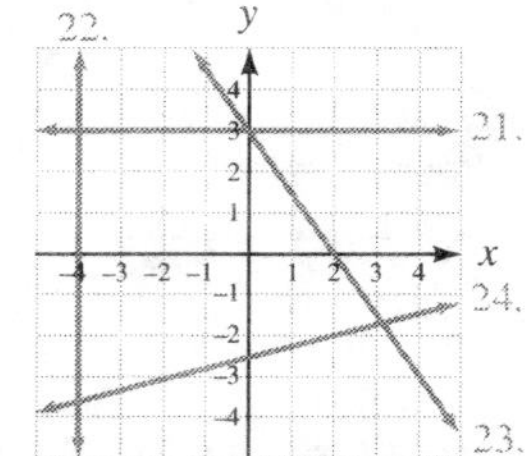

NOTATION

Write each equation in general form.

25. $4x = y + 6$
$4x - y = 6$

26. $2y = x$
$x - 2y = 0$

27. $x - 9 = -3y$
$x + 3y = 9$

28. $x = 12$
$x + 0y = 12$

Solve each equation for y.

29. $x + y = 8$
$y = 8 - x$

30. $2x - y = 8$
$y = 2x - 8$

31. $3x + \frac{y}{2} = 4$
$y = -6x + 8$

32. $y - 2 = 0$
$y = 2$

GUIDED PRACTICE

Classify each of the following as the graph of a linear equation or of a nonlinear equation. See Objective 1.

33.

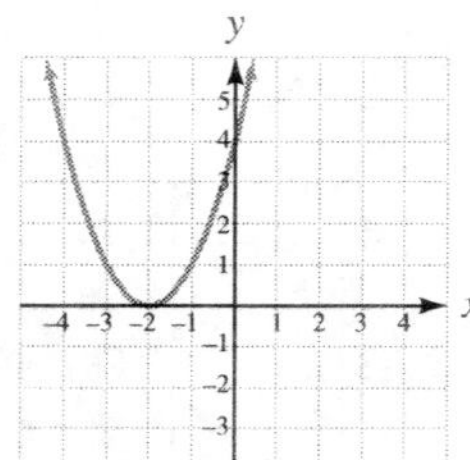

nonlinear

34.

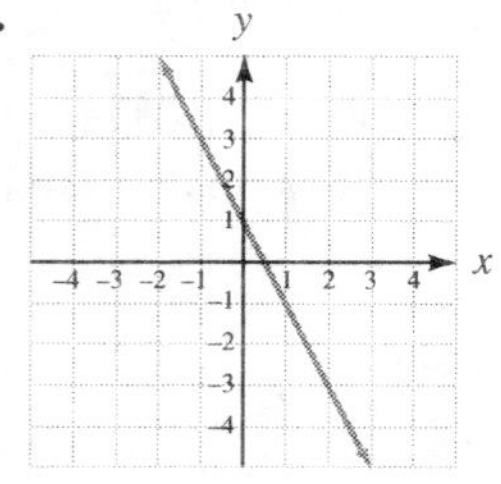

linear

35.

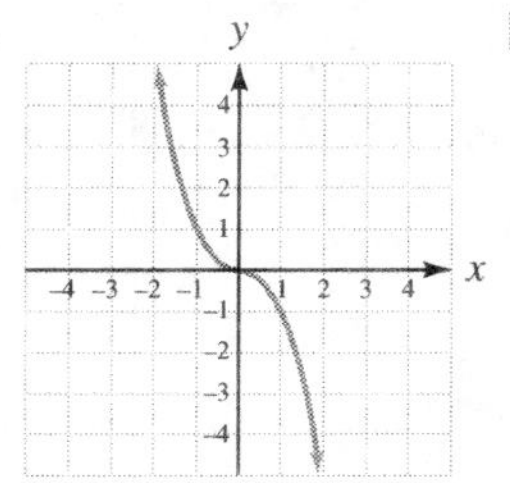

nonlinear

36.

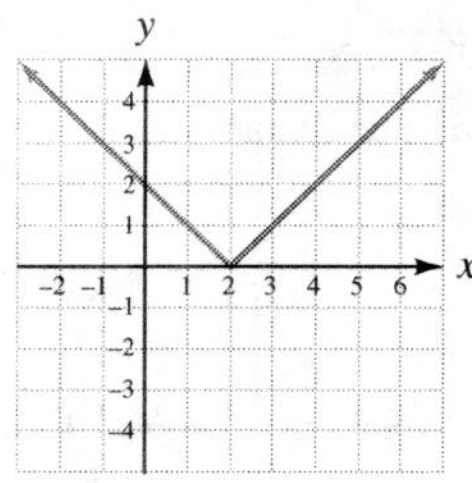

nonlinear

Classify each equation as linear or nonlinear. See Example 1.

37. $y = x^3$ nonlinear

38. $2x + 3y = 6$ linear

39. $y = -2$ linear

40. $y = |x + 2|$ nonlinear

Complete each table of solutions. See Example 2.

41. $5y = 2x + 10$

x	y
10	6
−5	0
5	4

42. $2x + 4y = 24$

x	y
4	4
−2	7
−4	8

43. $x - 2y = 4$

x	y
0	−2
4	0
1	$-\frac{3}{2}$

44. $5x - y = 3$

x	y
0	−3
$\frac{3}{5}$	0
1	2

Find three solutions of the equation and draw its graph. See Example 3.

45. $y = -x + 2$

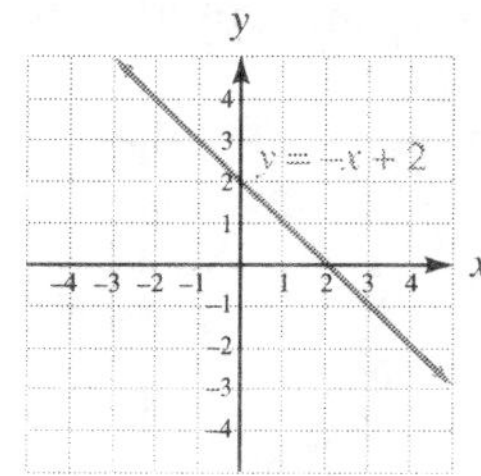

46. $y = -x - 1$

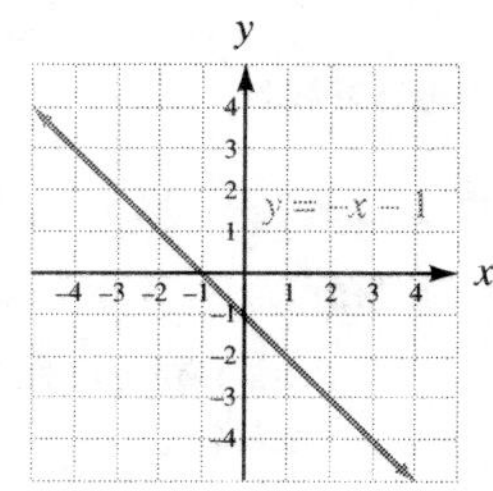

47. $y = 2x + 1$

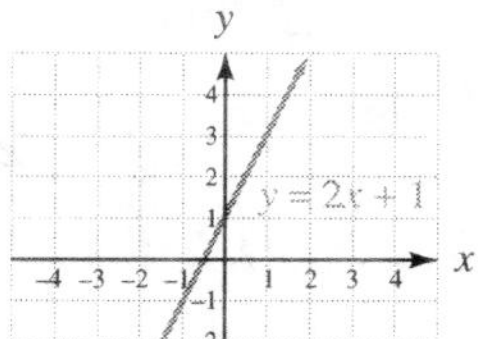

48. $y = 3x - 2$

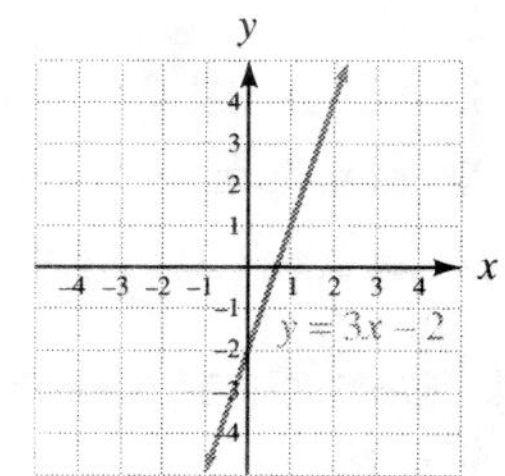

49. $y = x$

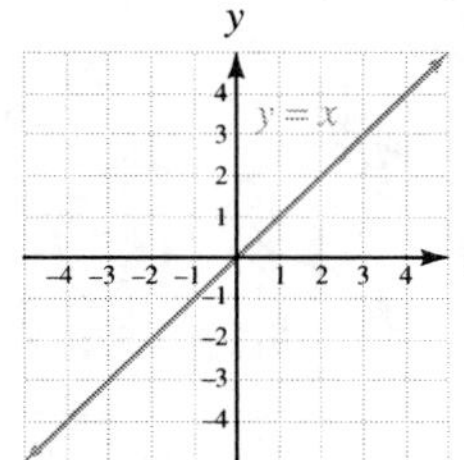

▶ **50.** $y = 3x$

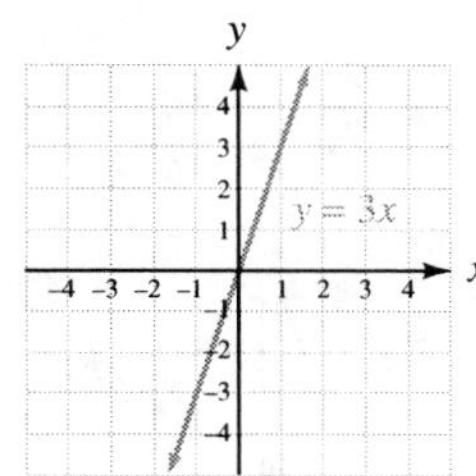

51. $y = -3x$

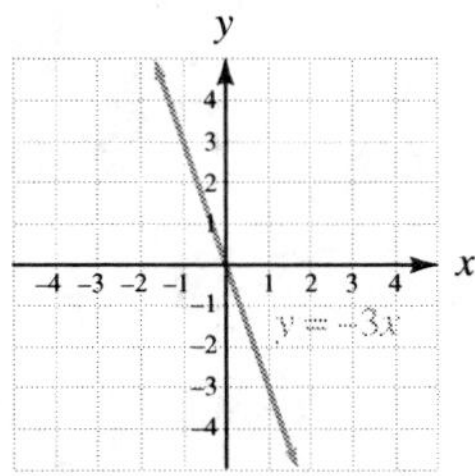

▶ **52.** $y = -2x$

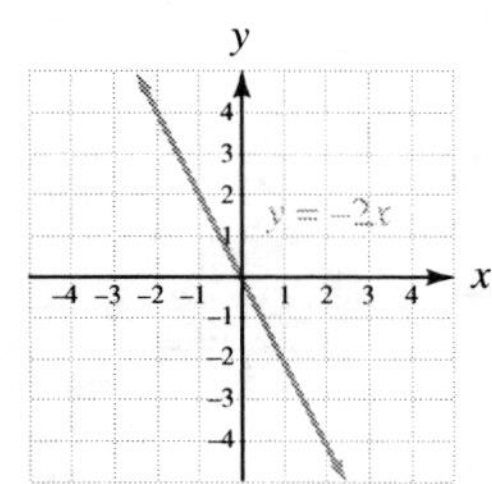

Solve each equation for y, find three solutions of the equation, and then draw its graph. See Example 4.

53. $2y = 4x - 6$

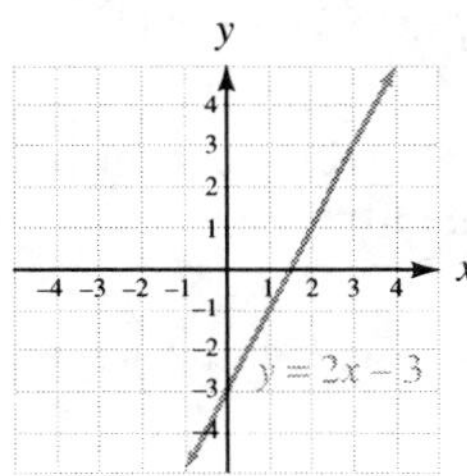

▶ **54.** $3y = 6x - 3$

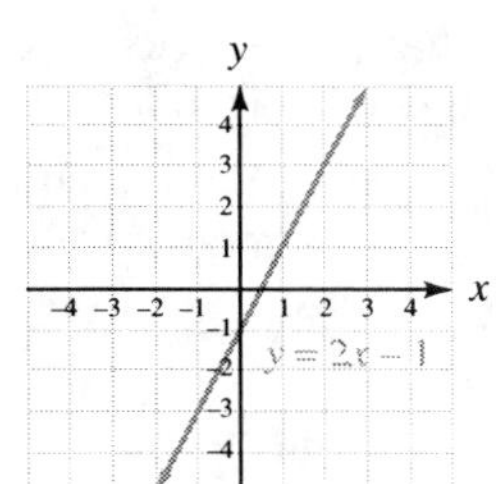

55. $2y = x - 4$

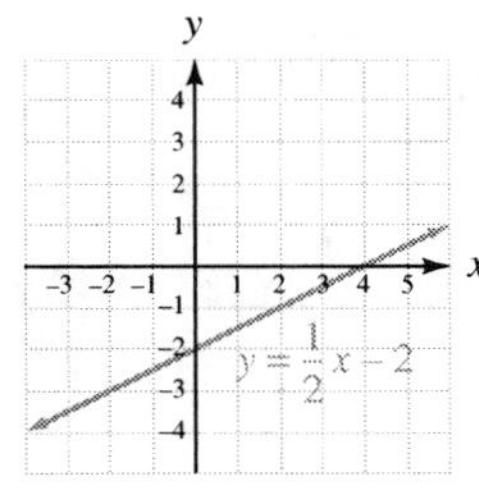

▶ **56.** $4y = x + 16$

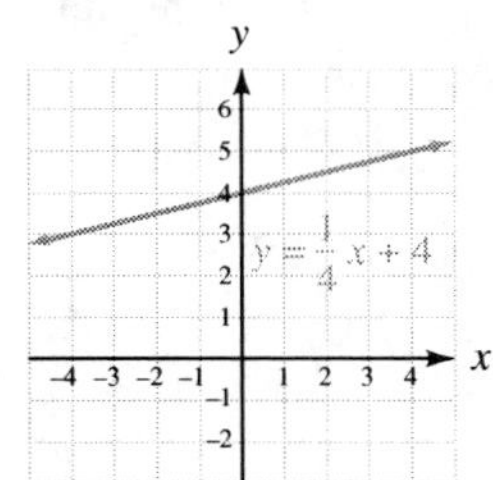

Graph each equation using the intercept method. See Example 5.

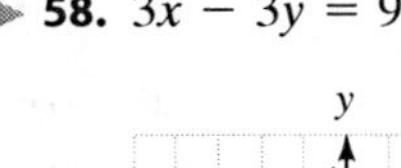

57. $2y - 2x = 6$

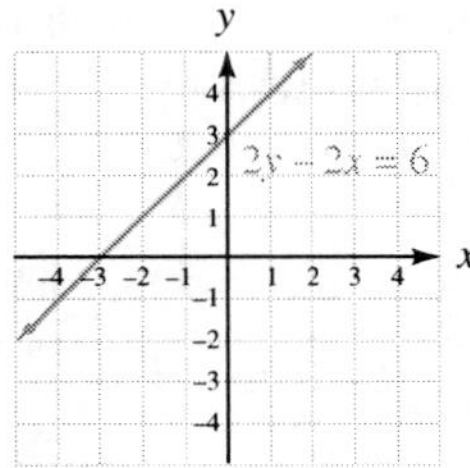

▶ **58.** $3x - 3y = 9$

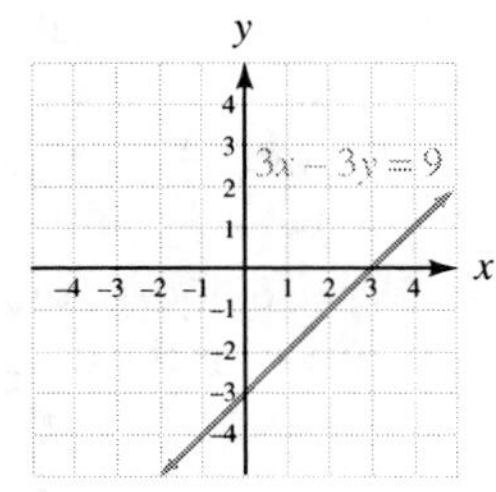

59. $4x + 5y = 20$

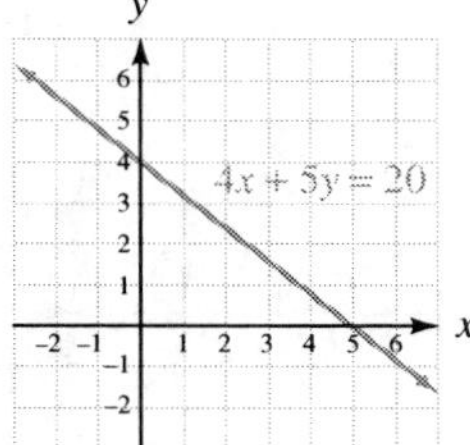

▶ **60.** $3x + y = -3$

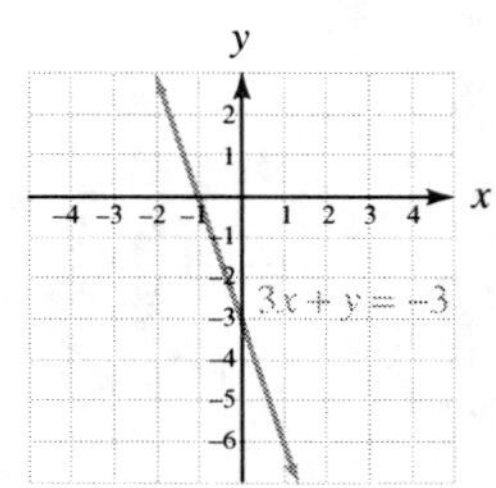

Graph each equation. See Examples 6–7.

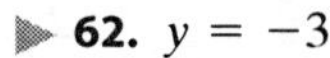

61. $y = 4$

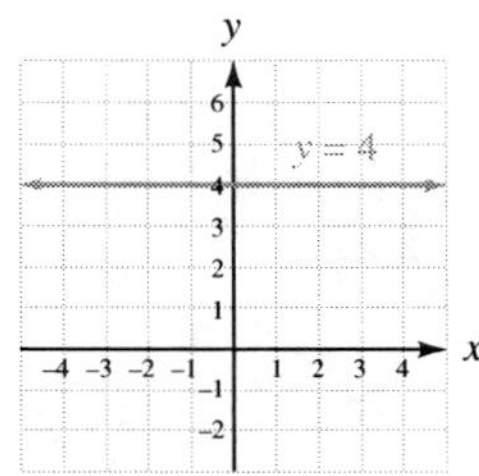

▶ **62.** $y = -3$

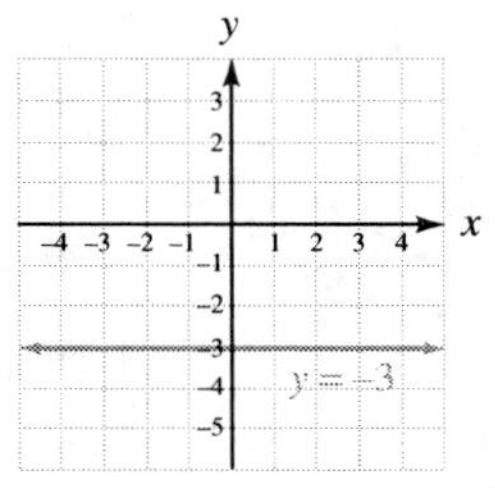

63. $x = -2$

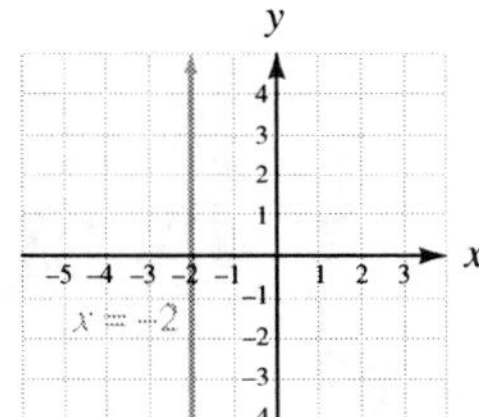

▶ **64.** $x = 5$

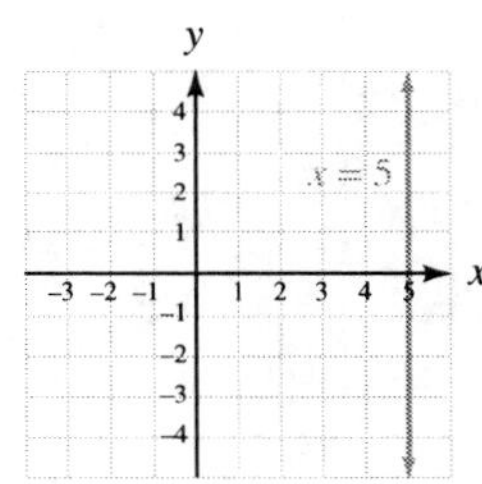

TRY IT YOURSELF

Graph each equation.

65. $15y + 5x = -15$

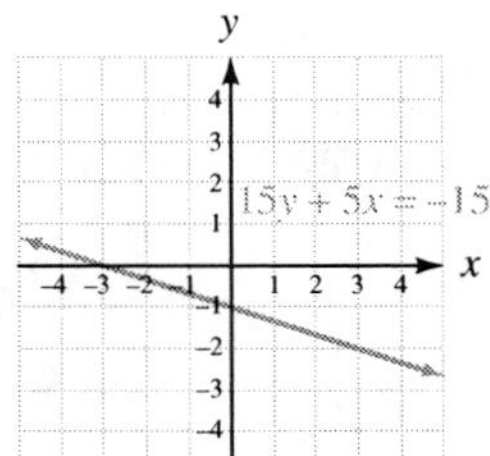

66. $8x + 4y = -24$

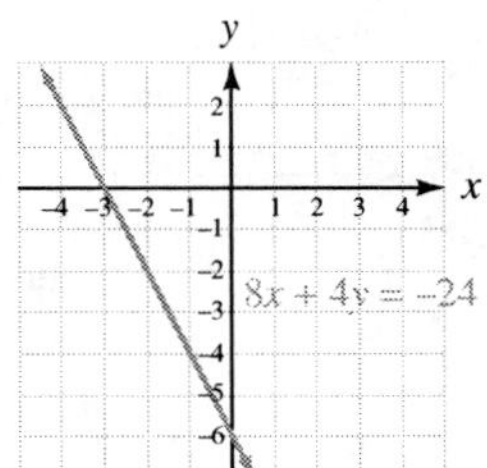

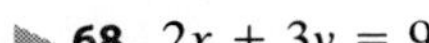

67. $3x + 4y = 8$

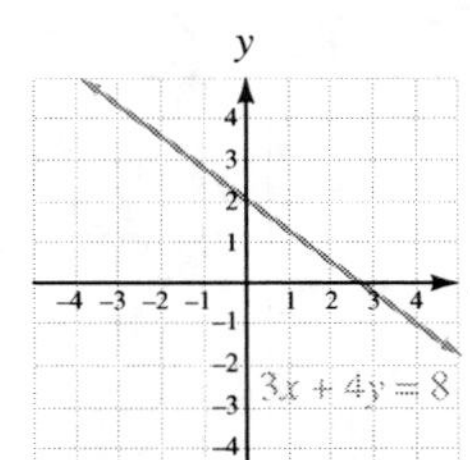

▶ **68.** $2x + 3y = 9$

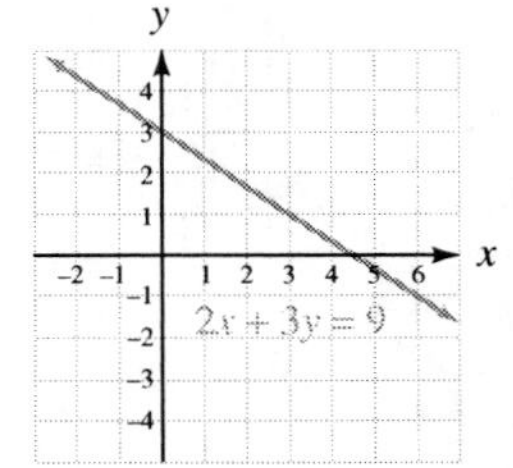

69. $y = \frac{x}{3}$

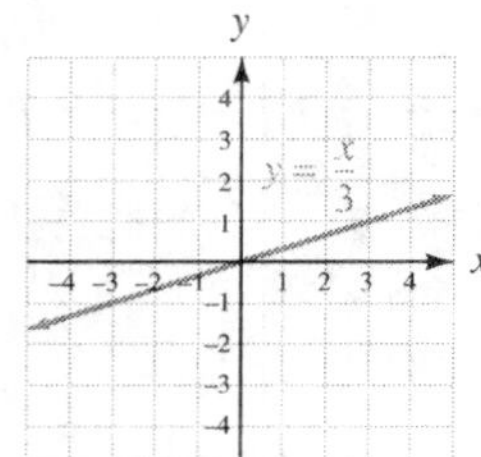

▶ 70. $y = -\frac{x}{3} - 1$

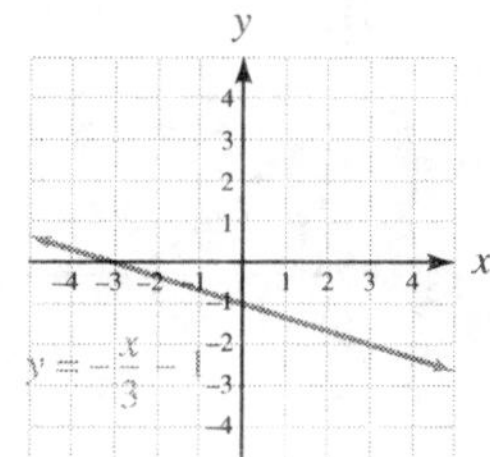

71. $-4y + 9x = -9$

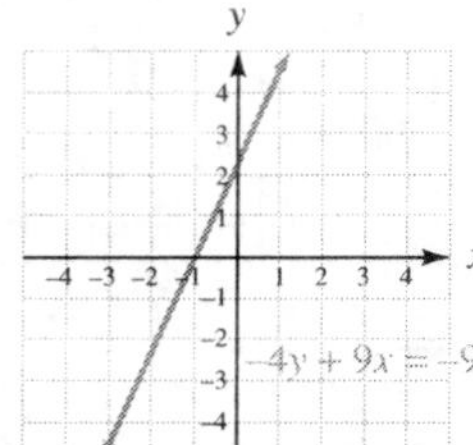

72. $-4y + 5x = -15$

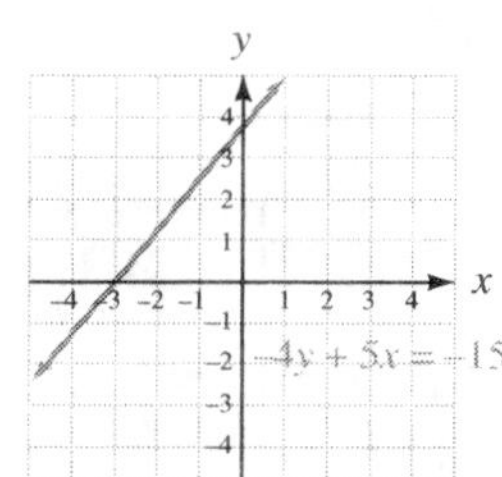

▶ 73. $3x + 4y = 12$

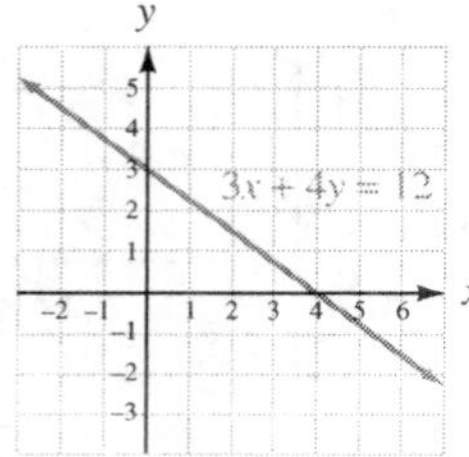

▶ 74. $4x - 3y = 12$

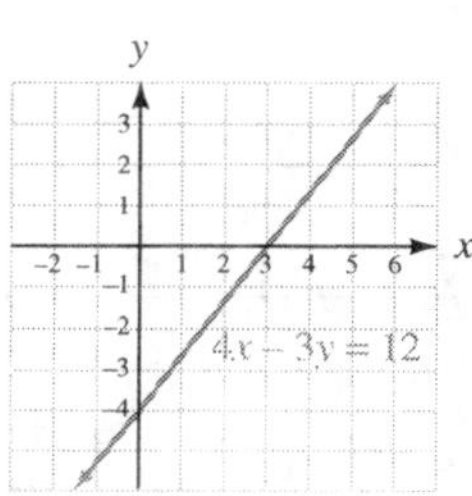

75. $y = -\frac{1}{2}$

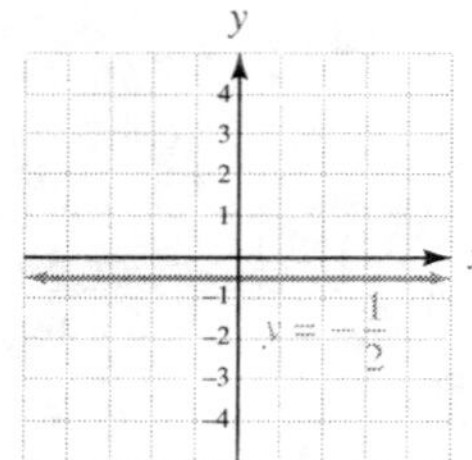

▶ 76. $y = \frac{5}{2}$

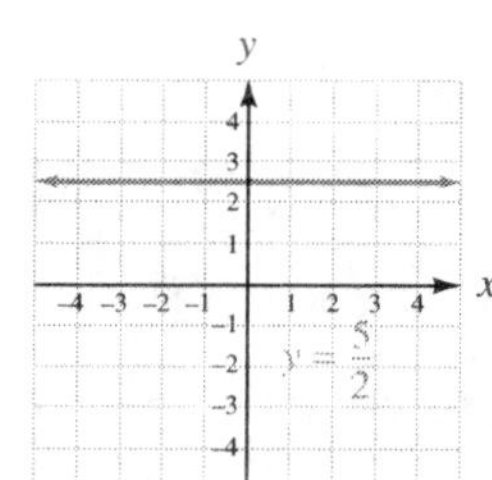

▶ 77. $x = \frac{4}{3}$

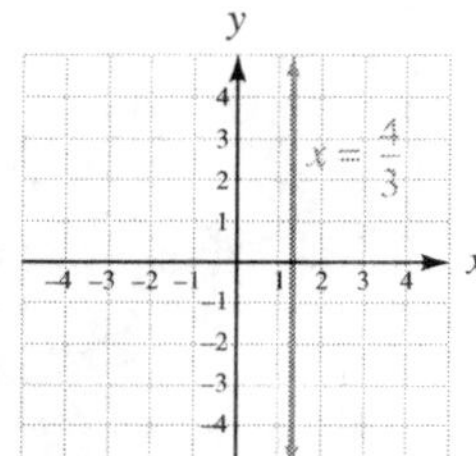

78. $x = -\frac{5}{3}$

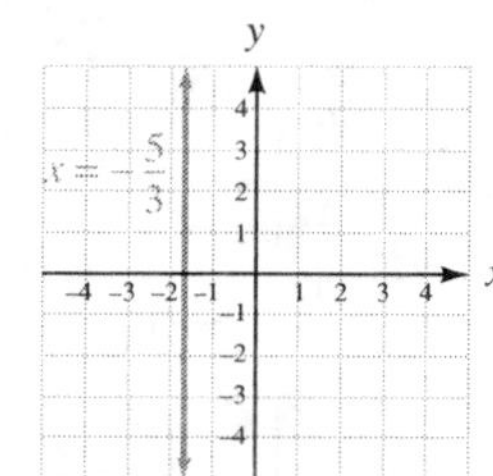

79. $y = -\frac{3}{2}x + 2$

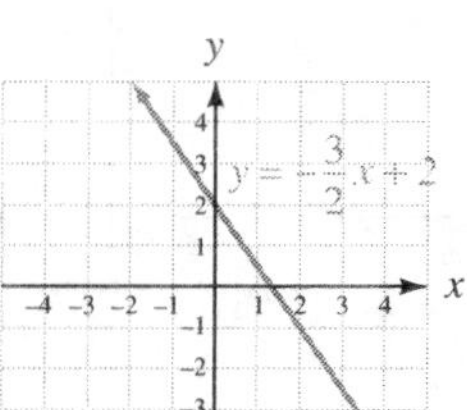

80. $y = \frac{2}{3}x - 2$

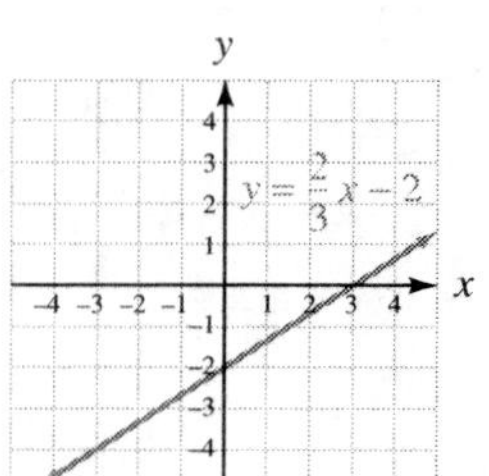

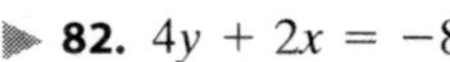

81. $2y + x = -2$

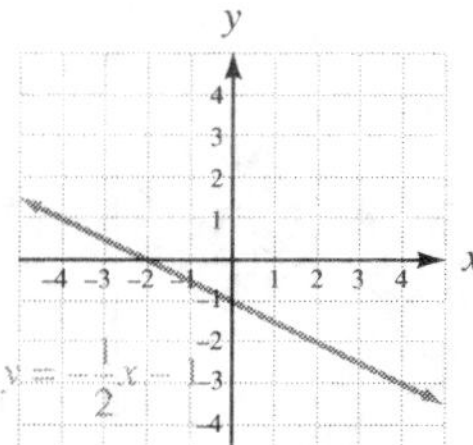

▶ 82. $4y + 2x = -8$

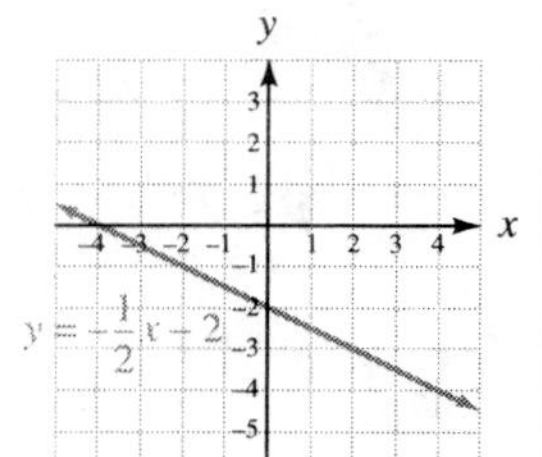

APPLICATIONS

▶ 83. EDUCATION COSTS Each semester, a college charges a services fee of \$50 plus \$25 for each unit taken by a student.

a. Write a linear equation that gives the total enrollment cost c for a student taking u units. $c = 50 + 25u$

b. Complete the table of solutions below and graph the equation.

c. Use the graph to find the total cost for a student taking 18 units the first semester and 12 units the second semester. \$850

d. What does the y-intercept of the line tell you? The service fee is \$50.

u	c
4	150
8	250
14	400

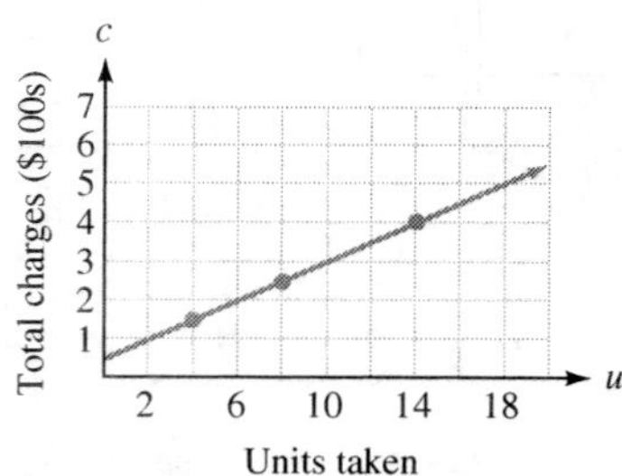

▶ 84. GROUP RATES To promote the sale of tickets for a cruise to Alaska, a travel agency reduces the regular ticket price of \$3,000 by \$5 for each individual traveling in the group.

a. Write a linear equation that would find the ticket price t for the cruise if a group of p people travel together. $t = 3{,}000 - 5p$

b. Complete the table of solutions on the next page and graph the equation.

c. As the size of the group increases, what happens to the ticket price? It decreases.

d. Use the graph to determine the cost of an individual ticket if a group of 25 will be traveling together. $2.875

p	t
10	2.950
30	2.850
60	2.700

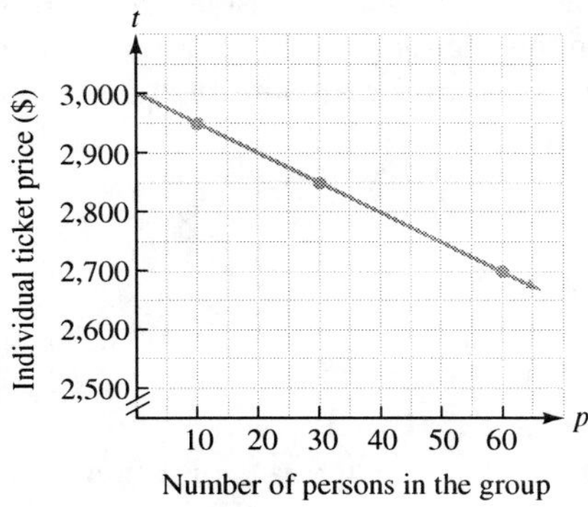

85. PHYSIOLOGY Physiologists have found that a woman's height h (in inches) can be approximated using the linear equation $h = 3.9r + 28.9$, where r represents the length of her radius bone in inches.

a. Complete the table of solutions. Round to the nearest tenth and then graph the equation.

b. Complete this sentence: From the graph, we see that the longer the radius bone, the ... taller the woman is.

c. From the graph, estimate the height of a woman whose radius bone is 7.5 inches long. 58 in.

r	h
7	56.2
8.5	62.1
9	64.0

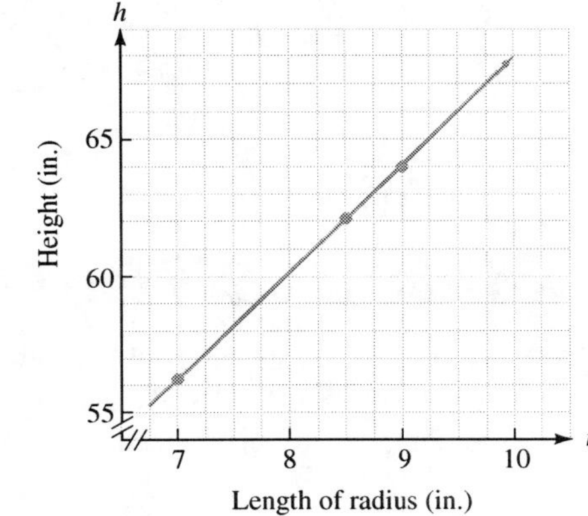

86. RESEARCH EXPERIMENTS A psychology major found that the time t (in seconds) that it took a white rat to complete a maze was related to the number of trials n the rat had been given. The resulting equation was $t = 25 - 0.25n$.

a. Complete the table of solutions and graph the equation.

b. Complete this sentence: From the graph, we see that the more trials the rat had, the ... less time it took it to complete the maze.

c. From the graph, estimate the time it will take the rat to complete the maze on its 32nd trial. 17 sec

n	t
4	24
12	22
16	21

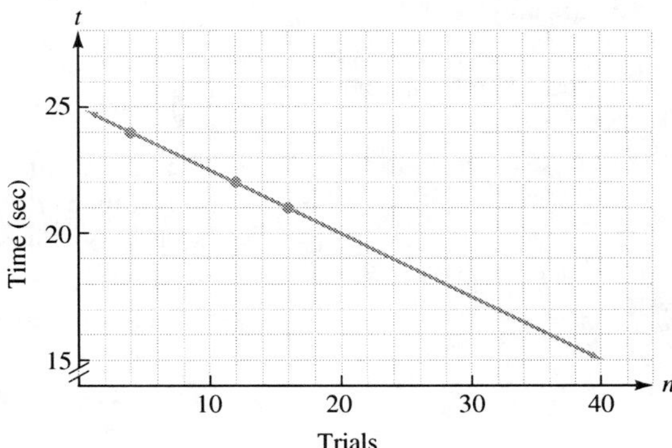

WRITING

87. A linear equation and a graph are two ways of mathematically describing a relationship between two quantities. Which do you think is more informative and why?

88. From geometry, we know that two points determine a line. Explain why it is a good practice when graphing linear equations to find and plot three points instead of just two.

89. How can we tell by looking at an equation whether its graph will be a straight line?

90. Can the x-intercept and the y-intercept of a line be the same point? Explain.

REVIEW

91. Simplify: $-(-5 - 4c)$ $5 + 4c$

92. Write the set of integers. $\{\ldots, -3, -2, -1, 0, 1, 2, 3, \ldots\}$

93. Solve: $\dfrac{x + 6}{2} = 1$ -4

94. Evaluate: $-2^2 + 2^2$ 0

95. Write a formula that relates profit, revenue, and costs. profit = revenue − costs

96. Find the volume, to the nearest tenth, of a sphere with radius 6 feet. 904.8 ft^3

97. Evaluate: $1 + 2[-3 - 4(2 - 8^2)]$ 491

98. Evaluate $\dfrac{x + y}{x - y}$ for $x = -2$ and $y = -4$. -3

Objectives

1. Find rates of change.
2. Find the slope of a line from its graph.
3. Find the slope of a line given two points.
4. Recognize positive and negative slope.
5. Find slopes of horizontal and vertical lines.
6. Use slope to graph a line.
7. Determine whether lines are parallel or perpendicular using slope.

SECTION 5.5
Slope and Rate of Change

Since our world is one of constant change, we must be able to describe change so that we can plan for the future. In this section, we will show how to describe the amount of change of one quantity in relation to the amount of change of another quantity by finding a **rate of change.**

1 Find rates of change.

The line graph in figure (a) below shows the number of business permits issued each month by a city over a 12-month period. From the shape of the graph, we can see that the number of permits issued *increased* each month.

For situations such as the one graphed in (a), it is often useful to calculate a rate of increase (called a **rate of change**). We do so by finding the **ratio** of the change in the number of business permits issued each month to the number of months over which that change took place.

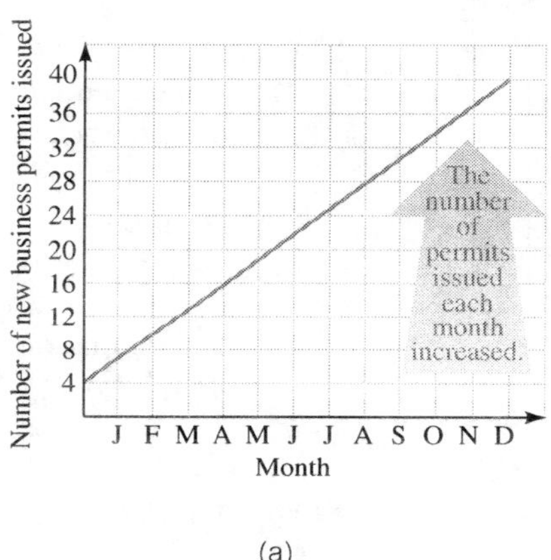

(a)

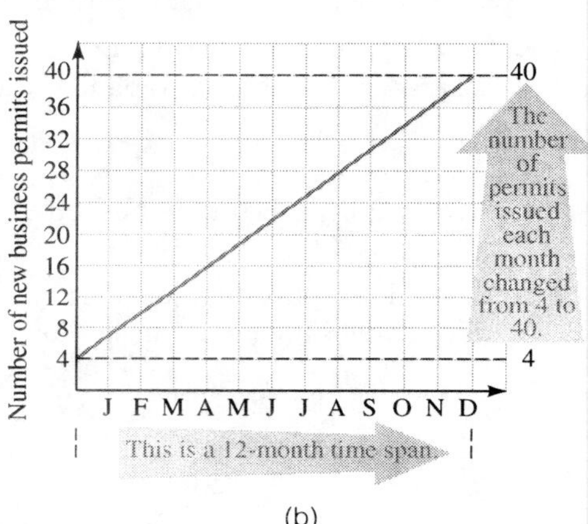

(b)

Ratios and Rates

A **ratio** is the quotient of two numbers or the quotient of two quantities with the same units. In symbols, if a and b represent two numbers, the ratio of a to b is $\frac{a}{b}$. Ratios that are used to compare quantities with different units are called **rates.**

In figure (b), we see that the number of permits issued prior to the month of January was 4. By the end of the year, the number of permits issued during the month of December was 40. This is a change of $40 - 4$, or 36, over a 12-month period. So we have

$$\text{Rate of change} = \frac{\text{change in number of permits issued each month}}{\text{change in time}}$$

The rate of change is a ratio.

$$= \frac{36 \text{ permits}}{12 \text{ months}}$$

$$= \frac{\overset{1}{\cancel{12}} \cdot 3 \text{ permits}}{\underset{1}{\cancel{12}} \text{ months}}$$ Factor 36 as 12 · 3 and remove the common factor of 12.

$$= \frac{3 \text{ permits}}{1 \text{ month}}$$

The number of business permits being issued increased at a rate of 3 per month, denoted as 3 permits/month.

> ***The Language of Algebra*** The preposition *per* means for each, or for every. When we say the rate of change is 3 permits *per* month, we mean 3 permits for each month.

EXAMPLE 1 The graph shows the number of subscribers to a newspaper. Find the rate of change in the number of subscribers over the first 5-year period. Write the rate in simplest form.

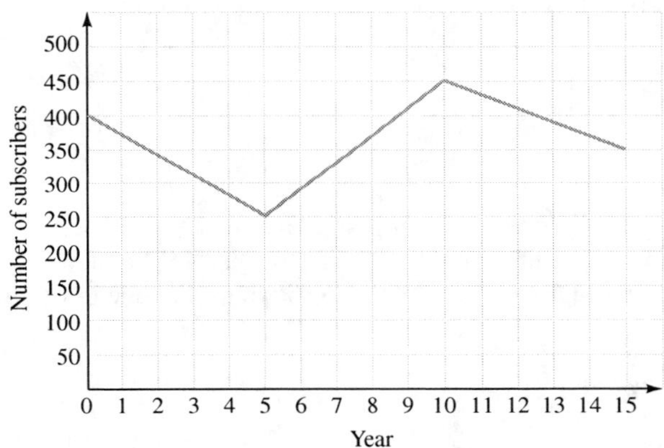

Strategy We will form a ratio of the change in the number of subscribers over the change in the time.

WHY The rate of change is given by this ratio.

Solution

$$\text{Rate of change} = \frac{\text{change in number of subscribers}}{\text{change in time}}$$ Set up the ratio.

$$= \frac{(250 - 400) \text{ subscribers}}{(5 - 0) \text{ years}}$$ Subtract the later number of subscribers from the earlier number of subscribers.

$$= \frac{-150 \text{ subscribers}}{5 \text{ years}}$$ $250 - 400 = -150$

$$= \frac{-30 \cdot \overset{1}{\cancel{5}} \text{ subscribers}}{\underset{1}{\cancel{5}} \text{ years}}$$ Factor -150 as $-30 \cdot 5$ and divide out the common factor of 5.

$$= \frac{-30 \text{ subscribers}}{1 \text{ year}}$$

The number of subscribers for the first 5 years *decreased* by 30 per year, as indicated by the negative sign in the result. We can write this as -30 subscribers/year.

Self Check 1

Find the rate of change in the number of subscribers over the second 5-year period. Write the rate in simplest form.

Now Try **Problem 25**

Self Check 1 Answer
40 subscribers/year

Teaching Example 1 Find the rate of change in the number of subscribers over the third 5-year period.
Answer:
-20 subscribers/year

2 Find the slope of a line from its graph.

The **slope of a nonvertical line** is a number that measures the line's steepness. We can calculate the slope by picking two points on the line and writing the ratio of the vertical change (called the **rise**) to the corresponding horizontal change (called the **run**) as we move from one point to the other. As an example, we will find the slope of the line that was used to describe the number of building permits issued and show that it gives the rate of change.

In the following figure, the line passes through points $P(0, 4)$ and $Q(12, 40)$. Moving along the line from point P to point Q causes the value of y to change from $y = 4$ to $y = 40$, an increase of $40 - 4 = 36$ units. We say that the *rise* is 36.

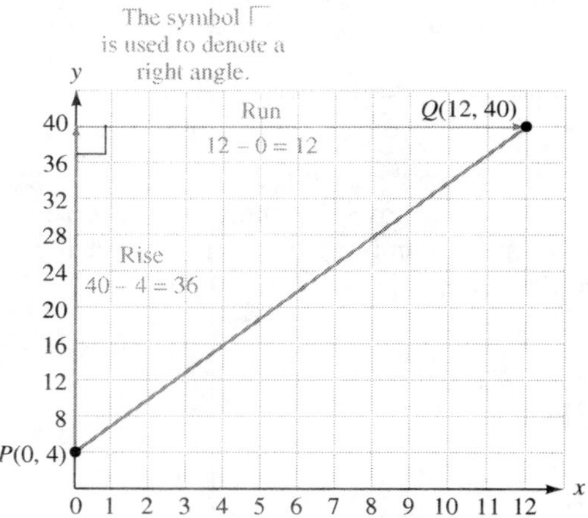

Moving from point P to point Q, the value of x increases from $x = 0$ to $x = 12$, an increase of $12 - 0 = 12$ units. We say that the *run* is 12. The slope of a line, usually denoted with the letter m, is defined to be the ratio of the change in y to the change in x.

$$m = \frac{\text{change in } y\text{-values}}{\text{change in } x\text{-values}}$$ Slope is a ratio.

$$= \frac{40 - 4}{12 - 0}$$ To find the change in y (the rise), subtract the y-values. To find the change in x (the run), subtract the x-values.

$$= \frac{36}{12}$$ Perform the subtractions.

$$= 3$$ Perform the division.

This is the same value we obtained when we found the rate of change of the number of business permits issued over the 12-month period. Therefore, by finding the slope of the line, we found a rate of change.

Self Check 2

Find the slope of the line using two points different from those used in Example 2. $-\frac{1}{2}$

Now Try **Problem 27**

Teaching Example 2 Find the slope of the line shown using $(-2, 1)$ and $(4, -2)$.
Answer:
The slope of the line is $-\frac{1}{2}$.

EXAMPLE 2 Find the slope of the line shown in figure (a).

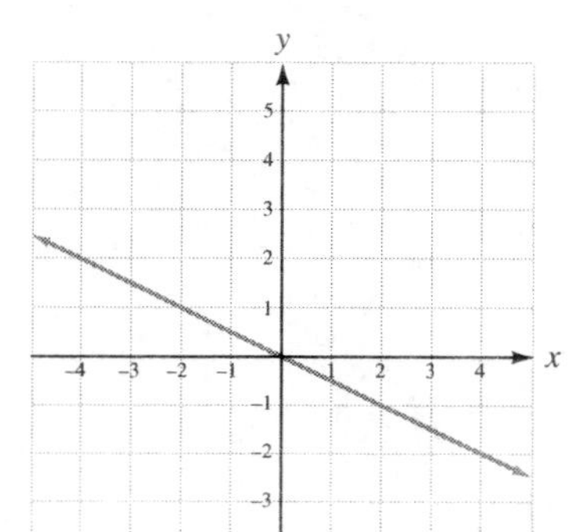

(a)

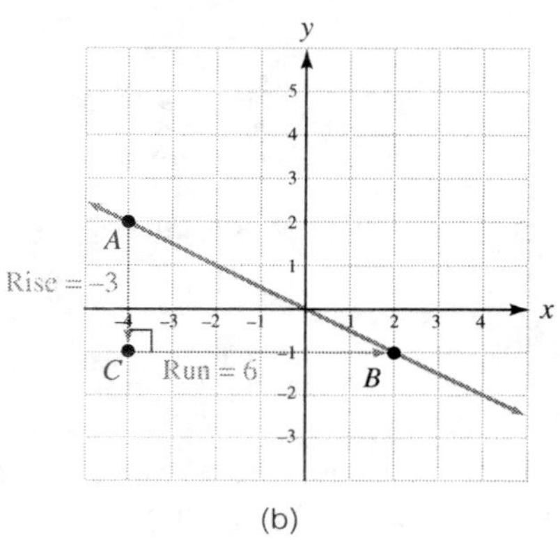

(b)

Strategy We will pick two points on the line, construct a slope triangle, and find the rise and the run. Then we will write the ratio of the rise to the run.

WHY The slope of a line is the ratio of the rise to the run.

Solution

We begin by choosing two points on the line—call them A and B—as shown in figure (b). One way to move from point A to point B is to start at point A and count *downward* 3 grid squares. Because this movement is downward, the rise is -3. Then, moving right, we count 6 grid squares to reach B. This indicates a run of 6. To find the slope of the line, we write a ratio of rise to run in simplified form. Usually the letter m is used to denote slope, so we have

$$m = \frac{\text{rise}}{\text{run}}$$ The slope of a line is the ratio of the rise to the run.

$$m = \frac{-3}{6}$$ From the slope triangle, the rise is -3 and the run is 6.

$$m = -\frac{1}{2}$$ Simplify the fraction.

The slope of the line is $-\frac{1}{2}$.

> ***Success Tip*** The answers from Example 2 and the Self Check illustrate an important fact about slope: *The same value for the slope of a line will result no matter which two points on the line are used to determine the rise and the run.*

3 Find the slope of a line given two points.

We can generalize the graphic method for finding slope to develop a slope formula. To begin, we select points P and Q on the line shown in the figure below. To distinguish between the coordinates of these points, we use **subscript notation.** Point P has coordinates (x_1, y_1), which are read as "x sub 1 and y sub 1." Point Q has coordinates (x_2, y_2), which are read as "x sub 2 and y sub 2."

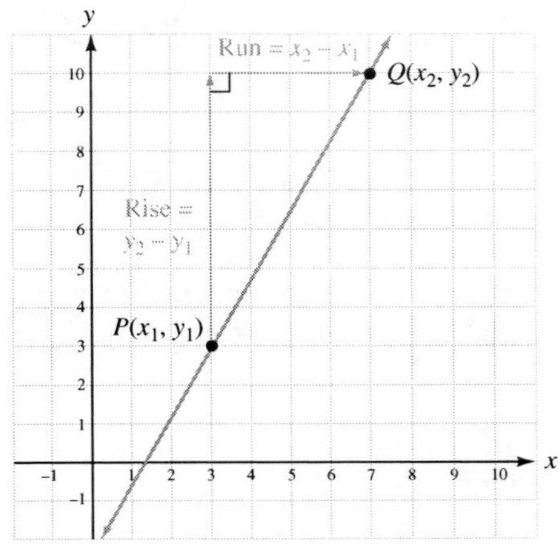

As we move from P to Q, the rise is the difference of the y-coordinates: $y_2 - y_1$. We call this difference the **change in y.** The run is the difference of the x-coordinates: $x_2 - x_1$. This difference is called the **change in x.** Since the slope is the ratio $\frac{\text{rise}}{\text{run}}$, we have the following formula for calculating slope.

Slope of a Nonvertical Line

The **slope** of a nonvertical line passing through points (x_1, y_1) and (x_2, y_2) is

$$m = \frac{\text{vertical change}}{\text{horizontal change}} = \frac{\text{rise}}{\text{run}} = \frac{\text{change in } y}{\text{change in } x} = \frac{y_2 - y_1}{x_2 - x_1} \quad \text{if } x_2 \neq x_1$$

Self Check 3

Find the slope of the line passing through (2, 1) and (4, 11). 5

Now Try **Problem 33**

Teaching Example 3 Find the slope of the line passing through (−2, −1) and (5, 1).
Answer:
$\frac{2}{7}$

EXAMPLE 3 Find the slope of the line passing through (1, 2) and (3, 8).

Strategy We will use the slope formula to find the slope of the line.

WHY We know the coordinates of two points on the line.

Solution

When using the slope formula, it makes no difference which point you call (x_1, y_1) and which point you call (x_2, y_2). If we let (x_1, y_1) be (**1**, **2**) and (x_2, y_2) be (3, 8), then

$$m = \frac{y_2 - y_1}{x_2 - x_1} \quad \text{This is the slope formula.}$$

$$m = \frac{8 - 2}{3 - 1} \quad \text{Substitute 8 for } y_2\text{, 2 for } y_1\text{, 3 for } x_2\text{, and 1 for } x_1.$$

$$m = \frac{6}{2} \quad \text{Do the subtractions.}$$

$$m = 3 \quad \text{Simplify. Think of this as a } \tfrac{3}{1} \text{ rise-to-run ratio.}$$

The slope of the line is 3. The graph of the line, including the slope triangle, is shown here. Note that we obtain the same value for the slope if we let $(x_1, y_1) = (3, 8)$ and $(x_2, y_2) = (1, 2)$.

$$m = \frac{y_2 - y_1}{x_2 - x_1} = \frac{2 - 8}{1 - 3} = \frac{-6}{-2} = 3$$

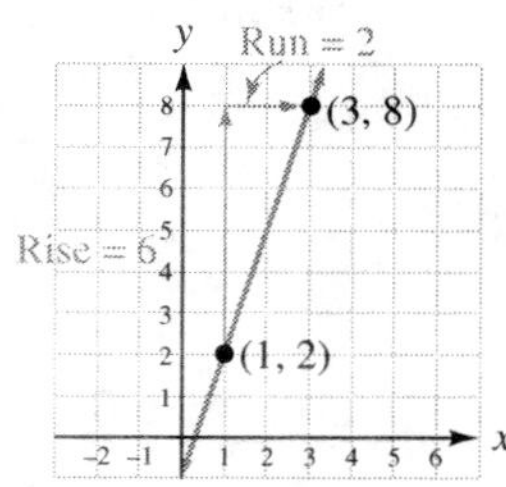

Caution! When finding the slope of a line, always subtract the y-values and the x-values in the same order. Otherwise your answer will have the wrong sign:

$$m \neq \frac{y_2 - y_1}{x_1 - x_2} \quad \text{and} \quad m \neq \frac{y_1 - y_2}{x_2 - x_1}$$

THINK IT THROUGH *Average Rate of Tuition Increase*

"Whatever happens in the future to the economy, whether up or down or more of the same, all current predictions point to a continuing rise over the coming decade in the cost of college education."

Daniel Silver in Show Me the Money, *News-Tribune*

The line graphed below approximates the average cost of tuition and fees at U.S. public two-year academic institutions for the years 1990–2003. Find the average rate of increase in cost over this time period by finding the slope of the line. $65 per year

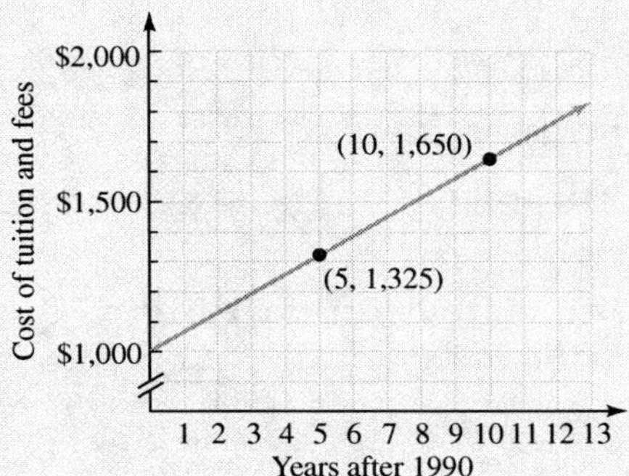

Source: The College Board

EXAMPLE 4

Find the slope of the line that passes through $(-2, 4)$ and $(5, -6)$ and draw its graph.

Strategy We will use the slope formula to find the slope of the line.

WHY We know the coordinates of two points on the line.

Solution

Since we know the coordinates of two points on the line, we can find its slope. If (x_1, y_1) is $(-2, 4)$ and (x_2, y_2) is $(5, -6)$, then

$$x_1 = -2 \quad \text{and} \quad x_2 = 5$$
$$y_1 = 4 \qquad\qquad y_2 = -6$$

$m = \dfrac{y_2 - y_1}{x_2 - x_1}$ This is the slope formula.

$m = \dfrac{-6 - 4}{5 - (-2)}$ Substitute -6 for y_2, 4 for y_1, 5 for x_2, and -2 for x_1.

$m = -\dfrac{10}{7}$ Simplify the numerator: $-6 - 4 = -10$. Simplify the denominator: $5 - (-2) = 7$.

The slope of the line is $-\frac{10}{7}$. The figure below shows the graph of the line. Note that the line falls from left to right—a fact that is indicated by its negative slope.

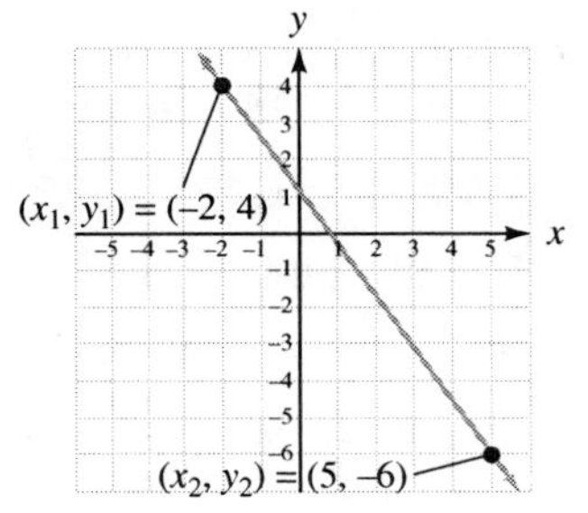

Self Check 4

Find the slope of the line that passes through $(-1, -2)$ and $(1, -7)$. $-\frac{5}{2}$

Now Try **Problem 39**

Teaching Example 4 Find the slope of the line that passes through $(3, -7)$ and $(1, -1)$.
Answer:
-3

4 Recognize positive and negative slope.

In Example 3, the slope of the line was positive (3). In Example 4, the slope of the line was negative $\left(-\frac{10}{7}\right)$. In general, lines that rise from left to right have a positive slope, and lines that fall from left to right have a negative slope, as shown below.

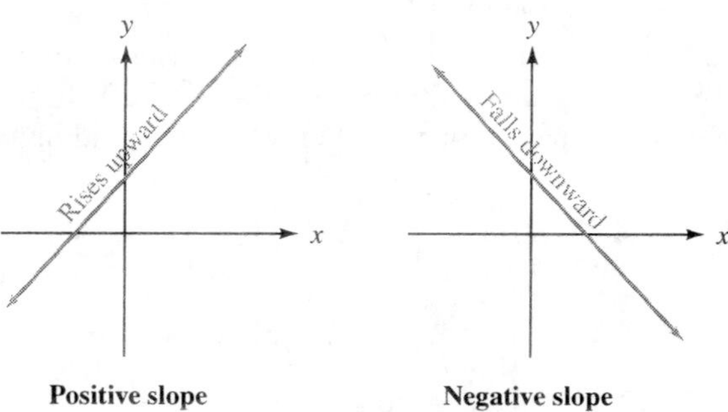

5 Find slopes of horizontal and vertical lines.

In the next two examples, we will calculate the slope of a horizontal line and show that a vertical line has no defined slope.

Self Check 5

Find the slope of the line $y = -2$. 0

Now Try **Problem 45**

Teaching Example 5 Find the slope of the line $y = -4$.
Answer:
0

EXAMPLE 5 Find the slope of the line $y = 3$.

Strategy We will find the coordinates of two points on the line.

WHY We can then use the slope formula to find the slope of the line.

Solution

To find the slope of the line $y = 3$, we need to know two points on the line. Graph the horizontal line $y = 3$ and label two points on the line: $(-2, 3)$ and $(3, 3)$.

If (x_1, y_1) is $(-2, 3)$ and (x_2, y_2) is $(3, 3)$, we have

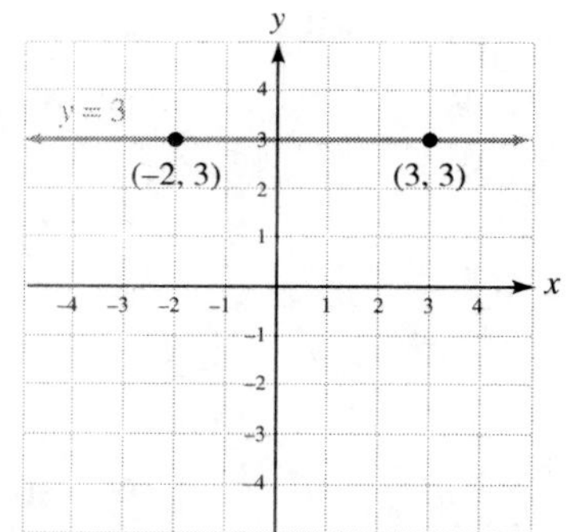

$$m = \frac{y_2 - y_1}{x_2 - x_1}$$ This is the slope formula.

$$m = \frac{3 - 3}{3 - (-2)}$$ Substitute 3 for y_2, 3 for y_1, 3 for x_2, and −2 for x_1.

$$m = \frac{0}{5}$$ Simplify the numerator and the denominator.

$$m = 0$$

The slope of the line $y = 3$ is 0. ■

The y-coordinates of any two points on any horizontal line will be the same, and the x-values will be different. Thus, the numerator of $\frac{y_2 - y_1}{x_2 - x_1}$ will always be zero, and the denominator will always be nonzero. Therefore, the slope of a horizontal line is zero.

Self Check 6

Find the slope of $x = 5$. undefined

Now Try **Problem 47**

EXAMPLE 6 If possible, find the slope of the line $x = -2$.

Strategy We will find the coordinates of two points on the line.

WHY We can then use the slope formula to find the slope of the line, if it exists.

Solution

To find the slope of the line $x = -2$, we need to know two points on the line. We graph the vertical line $x = -2$ and label two points on the line: $(-2, -1)$ and $(-2, 3)$.

If (x_1, y_1) is $(-2, -1)$ and (x_2, y_2) is $(-2, 3)$, we have

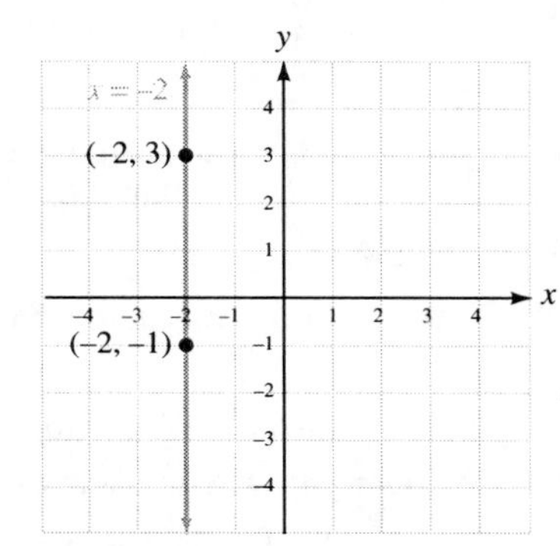

$$m = \frac{y_2 - y_1}{x_2 - x_1}$$ This is the slope formula.

$$m = \frac{3 - (-1)}{-2 - (-2)}$$ Substitute 3 for y_2, −1 for y_1, −2 for x_2, and −2 for x_1.

$$m = \frac{4}{0}$$ Simplify the numerator and the denominator.

Since division by zero is undefined, $\frac{4}{0}$ has no meaning. The slope of the line $x = -2$ is undefined.

Teaching Example 6 Find the slope of $x = 3$.
Answer:
undefined

The y-values of any two points on a vertical line will be different, and the x-values will be the same. Thus, the numerator of $\frac{y_2 - y_1}{x_2 - x_1}$ will always be nonzero, and the denominator will always be zero. Therefore, the slope of a vertical line is undefined.

We now summarize the results from Examples 5 and 6.

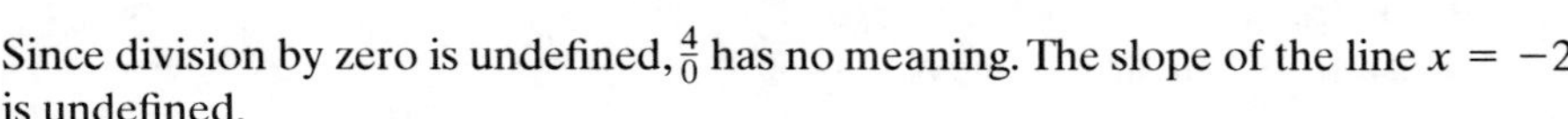

Slopes of Horizontal and Vertical Lines

Horizontal lines (lines with equations of the form $y = b$) have a slope of 0.

Vertical lines (lines with equations of the form $x = a$) have undefined slope.

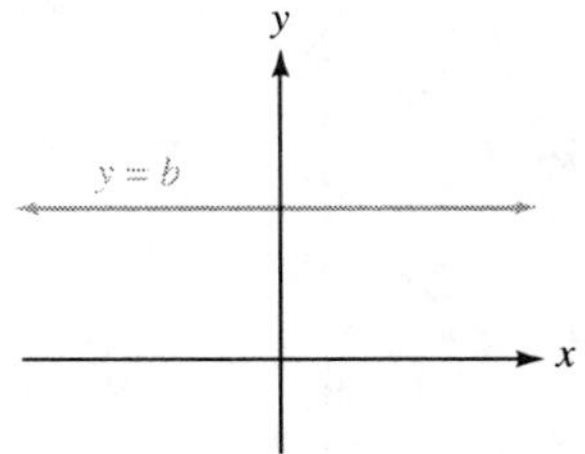

Horizontal line: 0 slope

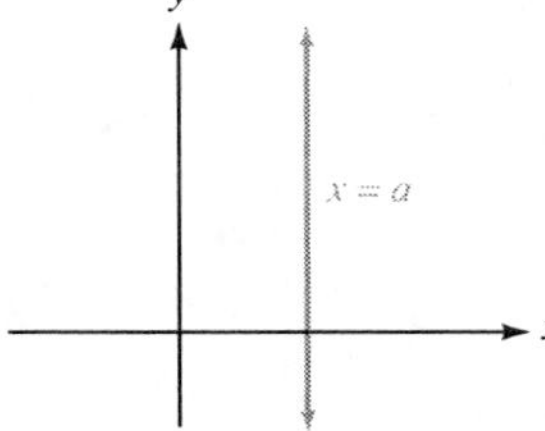

Vertical line: undefined slope

6 Use slope to graph a line.

We can graph a line whenever we know the coordinates of one point on the line and the slope of the line. For example, to graph the line that passes through $P(2, 4)$ and has a slope of 3, we first plot $P(2, 4)$, as in the figure. We can express the slope of 3 as a fraction: $3 = \frac{3}{1}$. Therefore, the line *rises* 3 units for every 1 unit it *runs* to the right. We can find a second point on the line by starting at $P(2, 4)$ and moving 3 units up (rise) and 1 unit to the right (run). This brings us to a point that we will call Q with coordinates $(2 + 1, 4 + 3)$ or $(3, 7)$. The required line passes through points P and Q.

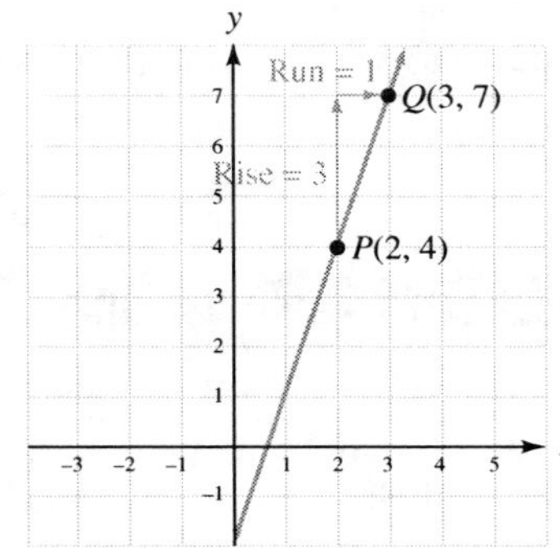

Self Check 7

Graph the line that passes through the point $(-4, 2)$ with slope -4.

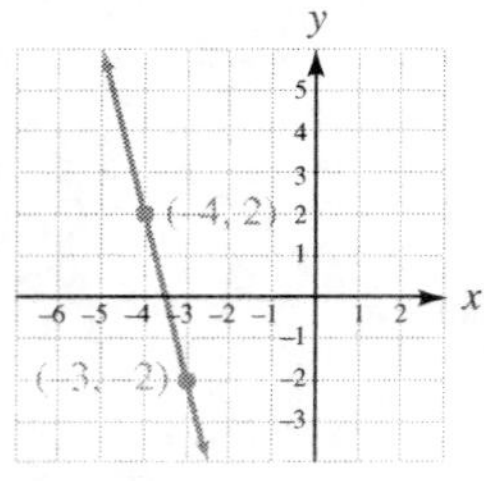

Now Try **Problem 49**

Teaching Example 7 Graph the line that passes through $(1, -3)$ with slope 4.
Answer:

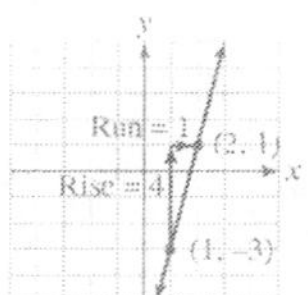

EXAMPLE 7 Graph the line that passes through the point $(-3, 4)$ with slope $-\frac{2}{5}$.

Strategy We will plot the given point and identify the rise and the run of the slope. Then we will start at the plotted point and find a second point on the line by forming a slope triangle.

WHY Once we locate two points on the line, we can draw the graph of the line.

Solution

We plot the point $(-3, 4)$ as shown in the figure to the right. Then, after writing the slope $-\frac{2}{5}$ as $\frac{-2}{5}$, we see that the *rise* is -2 and the *run* is 5. From the point $(-3, 4)$, we can find a second point on the line by moving 2 units down (rise) and then 5 units right (run). (A rise of -2 means to move down 2 units.) This brings us to the point with coordinates of $(2, 2)$. We then draw a line that passes through the two points.

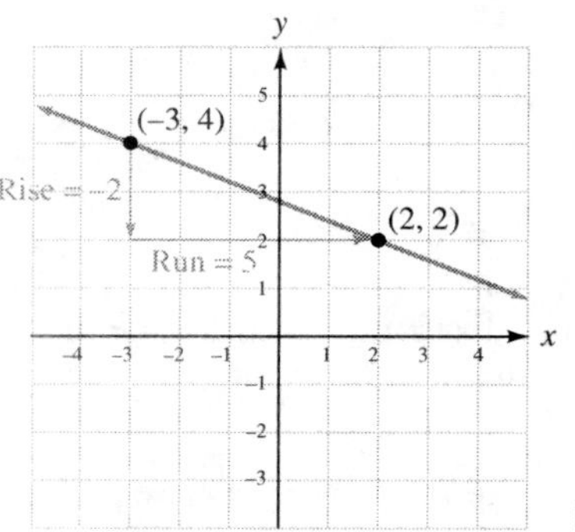

7 Determine whether lines are parallel or perpendicular using slope.

Two lines that lie in the same plane but do not intersect are called **parallel lines.** Parallel lines have the same slope and different y-intercepts. For example, the lines graphed in figure (a) are parallel because they both have slope $-\frac{2}{3}$.

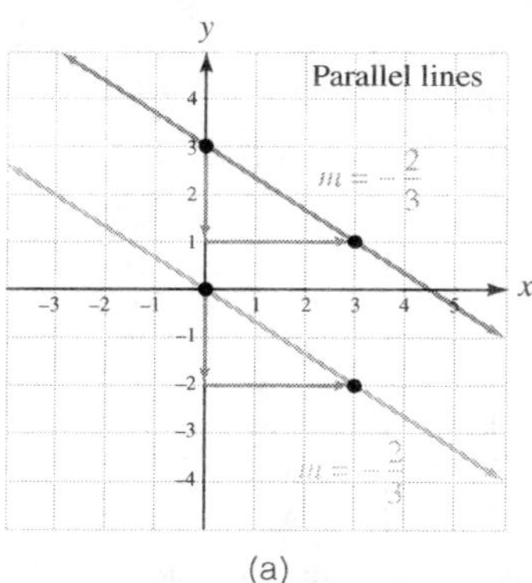

(a)

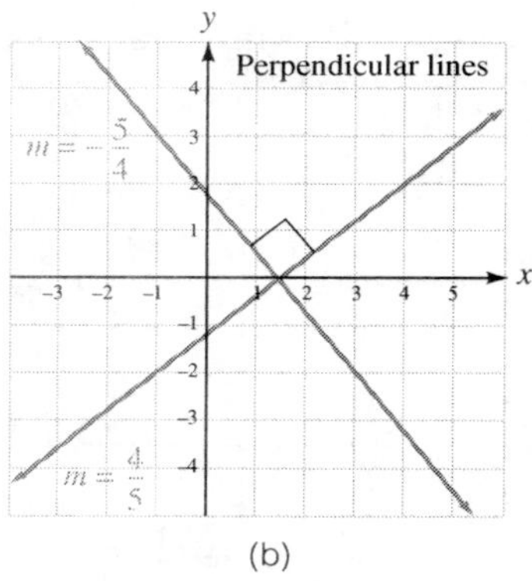

(b)

Lines that intersect to form four right angles (angles with measure 90°) are called **perpendicular lines.** If the product of the slopes of two lines is -1, the lines are perpendicular. This means that the slopes are **negative** (or **opposite**) **reciprocals.** In figure (b), we know that the lines with slopes $\frac{4}{5}$ and $-\frac{5}{4}$ are perpendicular because

$$\frac{4}{5}\left(-\frac{5}{4}\right) = -\frac{20}{20} = -1 \quad \frac{4}{5} \text{ and } -\frac{5}{4} \text{ are negative reciprocals.}$$

Slopes of Parallel and Perpendicular Lines

1. Two lines with the same slope are parallel.
2. Two lines are perpendicular if the product of the slopes is -1; that is, if their slopes are negative reciprocals.
3. Any horizontal line and any vertical line are perpendicular.

EXAMPLE 8 Determine whether the line that passes through (7, −9) and (10, 2) and the line that passes through (0, 1) and (3, 12) are parallel, perpendicular, or neither.

Strategy We will use the slope formula to find the slope of each line.

WHY If the slopes are equal, the lines are parallel. If the slopes are negative reciprocals, the lines are perpendicular. Otherwise, the lines are neither parallel nor perpendicular.

Solution

To calculate the slope of each line, we use the slope formula.

***The line through* (7, −9) *and* (10, 2):**

$$m = \frac{y_2 - y_1}{x_2 - x_1} = \frac{2 - (-9)}{10 - 7} = \frac{11}{3}$$

***The line through* (0, 1) *and* (3, 12):**

$$m = \frac{y_2 - y_1}{x_2 - x_1} = \frac{12 - 1}{3 - 0} = \frac{11}{3}$$

Since the slopes are the same, the lines are parallel.

Self Check 8

Determine whether the line that passes through (2, 1) and (6, 8) and the line that passes through (−1, 0) and (4, 7) are parallel, perpendicular, or neither. neither

Now Try **Problems 57 and 59**

Teaching Example 8 Determine whether the line that passes through (1, 4) and (5, −2) and the line that passes through (6, 2) and (9, 4) are parallel, perpendicular, or neither.
Answer:
perpendicular

EXAMPLE 9 Find the slope of a line perpendicular to the line passing through (1, −4) and (8, 4).

Strategy We will use the slope formula to find the slope of the line passing through (1, −4) and (8, 4).

WHY We can then form the negative reciprocal of the result to produce the slope of a line perpendicular to the given line.

Solution

The slope of the line that passes through (1, −4) and (8, 4) is

$$m = \frac{y_2 - y_1}{x_2 - x_1} = \frac{4 - (-4)}{8 - 1} = \frac{8}{7}$$

The slope of a line perpendicular to the given line has slope that is the negative (or opposite) reciprocal of $\frac{8}{7}$, which is $-\frac{7}{8}$.

Self Check 9

Find the slope of a line perpendicular to the line passing through (−4, 1) and (9, 5). $-\frac{13}{4}$

Now Try **Problem 67**

Teaching Example 9 Find the slope of a line perpendicular to the line passing through (−3, 4) and (5, 7).
Answer:
$-\frac{8}{3}$

ANSWERS TO SELF CHECKS

1. 40 subscribers/year **2.** $-\frac{1}{2}$ **3.** 5 **4.** $-\frac{5}{2}$ **5.** 0 **6.** undefined
7.

8. neither **9.** $-\frac{13}{4}$

SECTION 5.5 STUDY SET

VOCABULARY

Fill in the blanks.

1. A ratio is the quotient of two numbers.

▶ **2.** Ratios used to compare quantities with different units are called rates.

3. The slope of a line is defined to be the ratio of the change in y to the change in x.

▶ Selected exercises available online at **www.webassign.net/brookscole**

4. The vertical change between two points on a coordinate system is often called the rise.

5. The horizontal change between two points on a coordinate system is often called the run.

6. $m = \dfrac{\text{vertical change}}{\text{horizontal change}} = \dfrac{rise}{run} = \dfrac{change\ in\ y}{change\ in\ x}$

7. Two lines that lie in the same plane but do not intersect are called parallel lines.

8. The rate of change of a linear relationship can be found by finding the slope of the graph of the line.

CONCEPTS

Fill in the blanks.

9. Horizontal lines have a slope of 0.

10. Vertical lines have undefined slope.

11. A line with positive slope rises from left to right.

12. A line with negative slope falls from left to right.

In the following illustration, which line has

13. a positive slope? l_2

14. a negative slope? l_1

15. zero slope? l_4

16. undefined slope? l_3

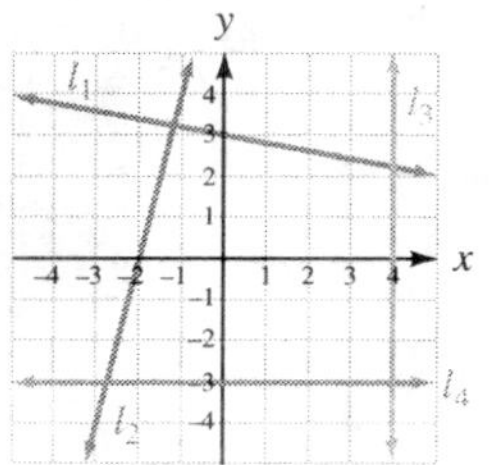

Consider the graph of the line in the following illustration:

17. Find its slope using points A and B. $\frac{1}{2}$

18. Find its slope using points B and C. $\frac{1}{2}$

19. Find its slope using points A and C. $\frac{1}{2}$

20. What observation is suggested by your answers to parts a, b, and c? When finding the slope of a line, any two points on the line give the same result.

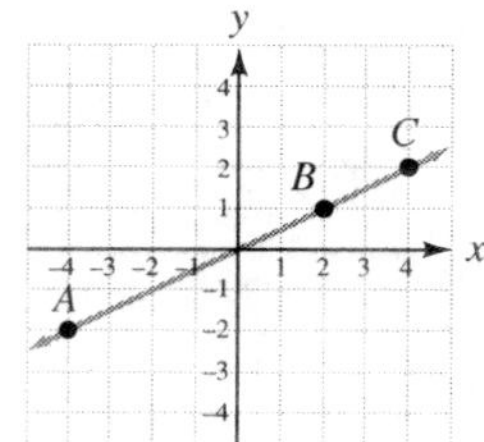

21. The following table shows the coordinates of two points on a line. Use the information to determine the slope of the graph of the line. −1

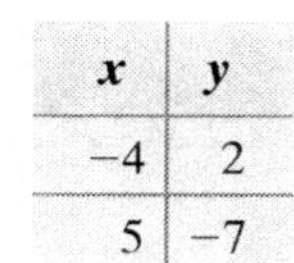

x	y
−4	2
5	−7

22. GROWTH RATES Use the graph to find the rate of change of a boy's height during the time shown. 3 in./yr

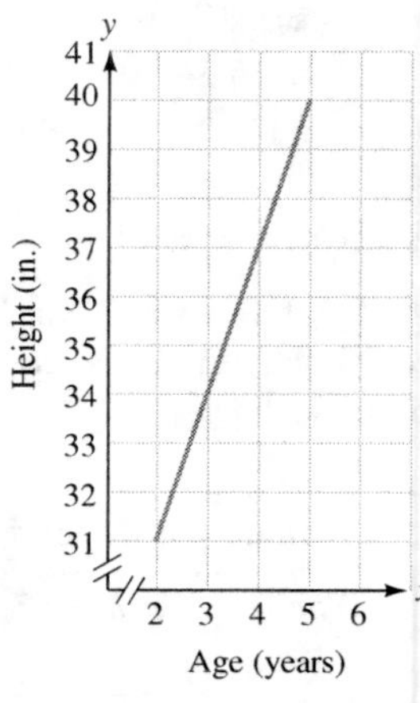

NOTATION

23. Write the formula used to find the slope of the line passing through (x_1, y_1) and (x_2, y_2). $m = \frac{y_2 - y_1}{x_2 - x_1}$

24. Explain the difference between y^2 and y_2. y^2 means $y \cdot y$ and y_2 means y sub 2.

GUIDED PRACTICE

Find the slope of each line. See Examples 1–2.

25.

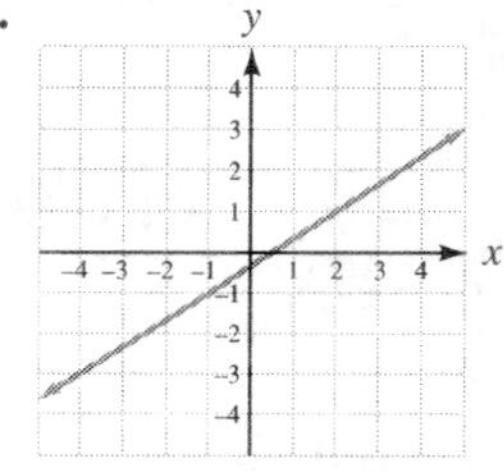

$m = \frac{2}{3}$

26.

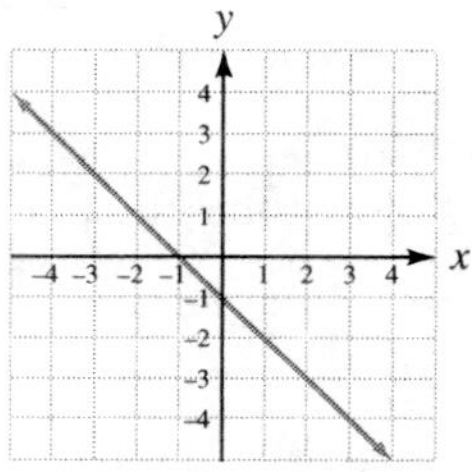

$m = -1$

27.

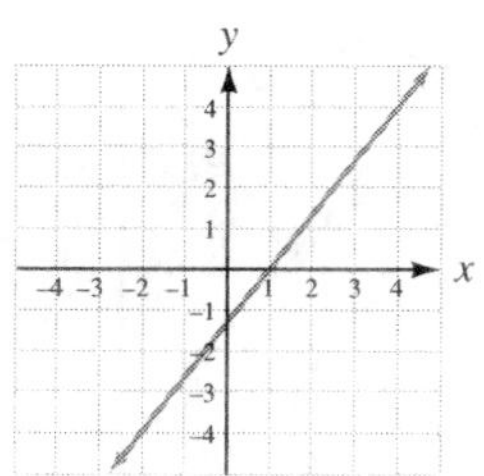

$m = \frac{4}{3}$

28.

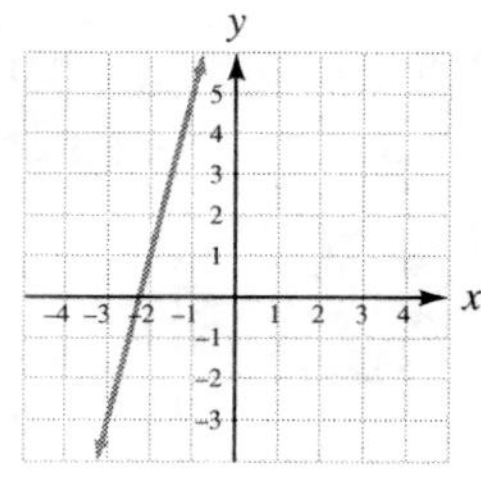

$m = 4$

29.

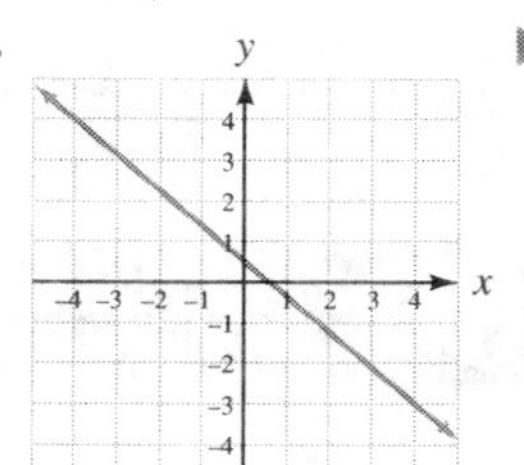

$m = -\frac{7}{8}$

30.

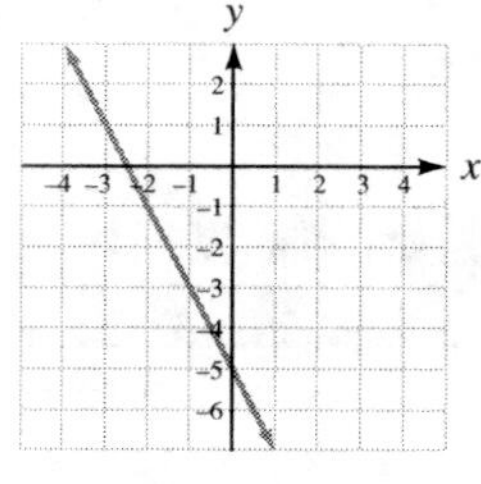

$m = -2$

31.

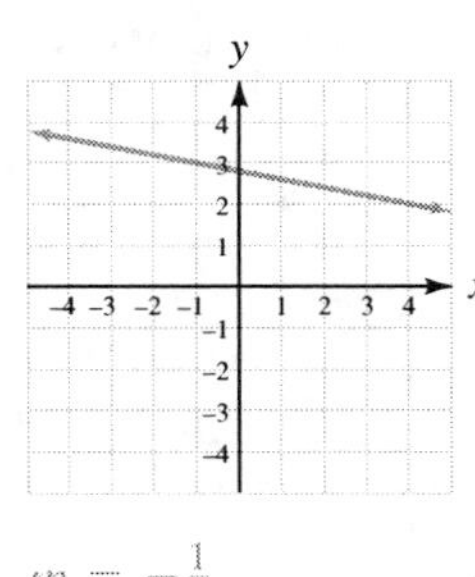

$m = -\frac{1}{5}$

32.

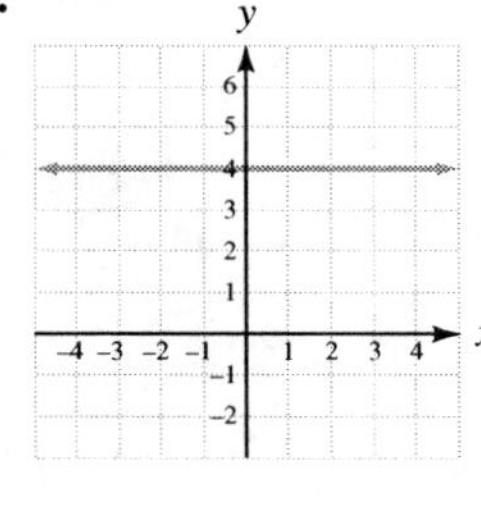

$m = 0$

Find the slope of the line passing through the given points, when possible. See Examples 3–4.

33. (2, 4) and (1, 3)
1

▶ **34.** (1, 3) and (2, 5)
2

35. (3, 4) and (2, 7)
−3

▶ **36.** (3, 6) and (5, 2)
−2

37. (0, 0) and (4, 5)
$\frac{5}{4}$

38. (4, 3) and (7, 8)
$\frac{5}{3}$

39. (−3, 5) and (−5, 6)
$-\frac{1}{2}$

▶ **40.** (6, −2) and (−3, 2)
$-\frac{4}{9}$

41. (5, 7) and (−4, 7)
0

▶ **42.** (−1, −12) and (6, −12)
0

43. (8, −4) and (8, −3)
undefined

▶ **44.** (−2, 8) and (−2, 15)
undefined

Find the slope of each line, if possible. See Examples 5–6.

▶ **45.** $y = 5$ 0

46. $x = -5$ undefined

▶ **47.** $x = 4$ undefined

48. $y = -7$ 0

Graph the line that passes through the given point and has the given slope. See Example 7.

49. (0, 0), $m = -4$

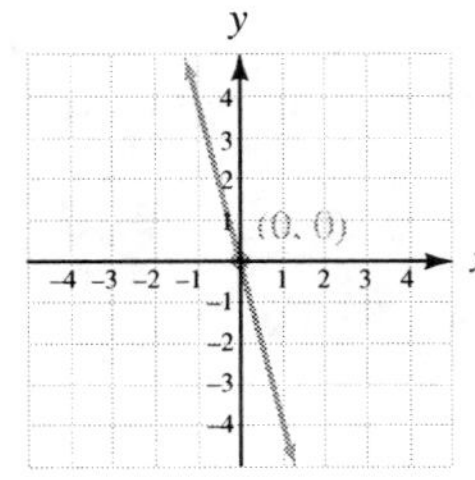

50. (0, 0), $m = 5$

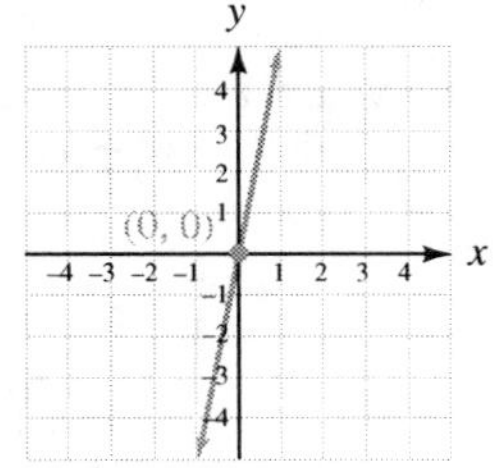

51. (−3, −3), $m = -\frac{3}{2}$

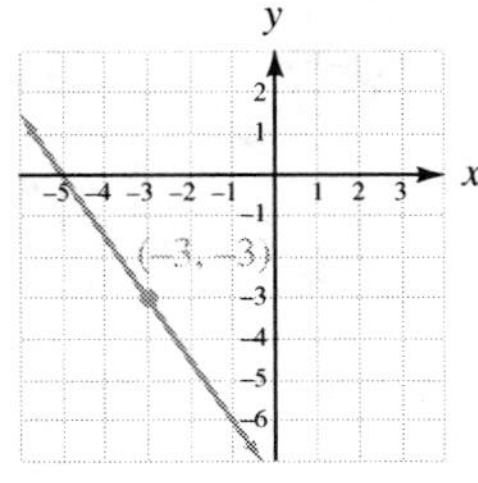

▶ **52.** (−2, −1), $m = \frac{4}{3}$

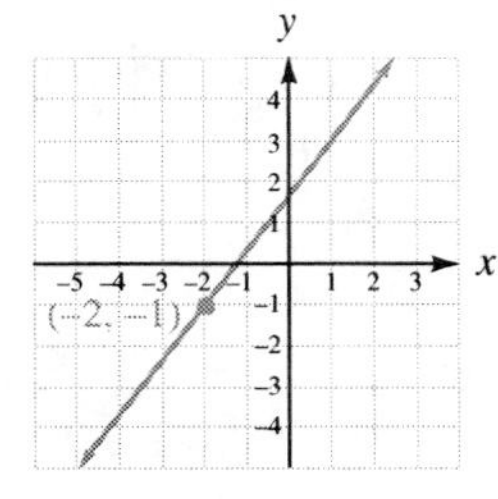

53. (−5, 1), $m = 0$

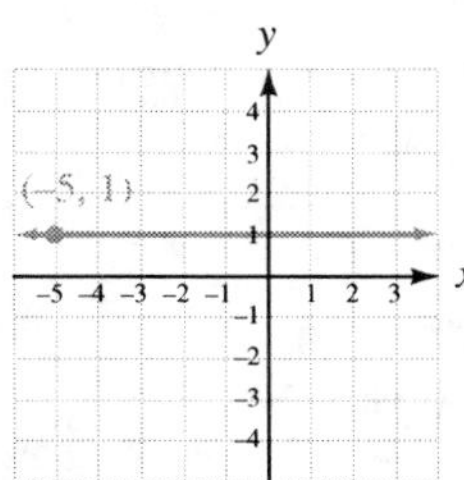

54. (0, 3), undefined slope

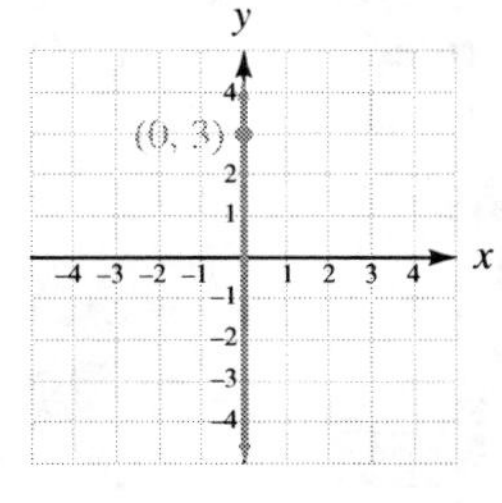

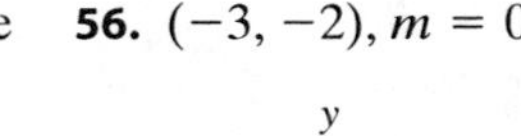

▶ **55.** (−1, −4), undefined slope

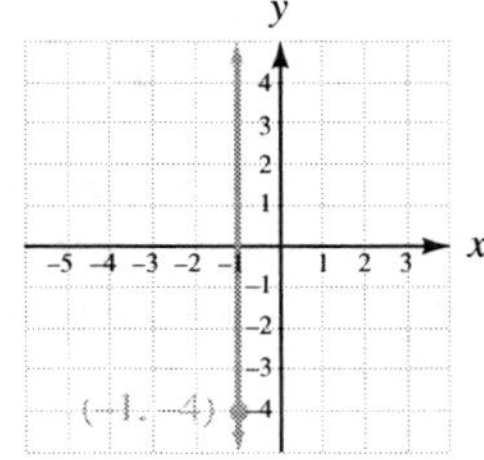

56. (−3, −2), $m = 0$

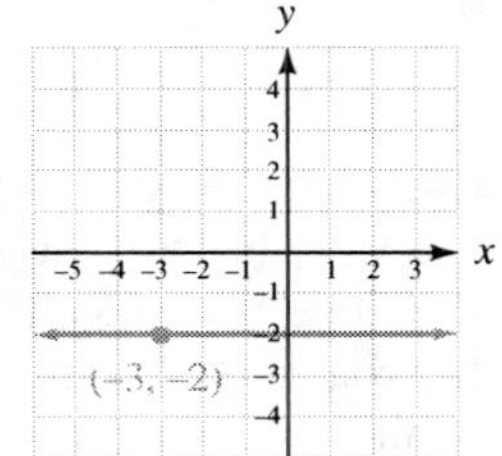

Determine whether the lines through each pair of points are parallel, perpendicular, or neither. See Example 8.

▶ **57.** (5, 3) and (1, 4)
(−3, −4) and (1, −5)
parallel

58. (2, 4) and (−1, −1)
(8, 0) and (11, 5)
parallel

▶ **59.** (−4, −2) and (2, −3)
(7, 1) and (8, 7)
perpendicular

60. (−2, 4) and (6, −7)
(−6, 4) and (5, 12)
perpendicular

61. (2, 2) and (4, −3)
(−3, 4) and (−1, 9)
neither

62. (−1, −3) and (2, 4)
(5, 2) and (8, −5)
neither

63. (4, 2) and (5, −3)
(−5, 3) and (−2, 9)
neither

64. (8, −3) and (8, −8)
(11, 3) and (22, 3)
perpendicular

Find the slope of a line perpendicular to the line passing through the given two points. See Example 9.

▶ **65.** (0, 0) and (5, −9) $\frac{5}{9}$

66. (0, 0) and (5, 12) $-\frac{5}{12}$

67. (−1, 7) and (1, 10) $-\frac{2}{3}$

68. (−7, 6) and (0, 4) $\frac{7}{2}$

APPLICATIONS

▶ **69.** POOL DESIGN Find the slope of the bottom of the swimming pool as it drops off from the shallow end to the deep end, as shown. $-\frac{2}{5}$

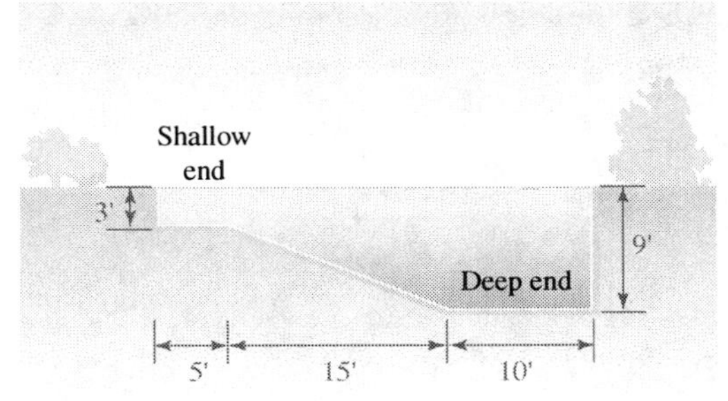

70. DRAINAGE To measure the amount of fall (slope) of a concrete patio slab, a 10-foot-long 2-by-4, a 1-foot ruler, and a level were used. Find the amount of fall in the slab. Explain what it means. $\frac{1}{40}$, 1-in. fall for every 40 in. of horizontal run

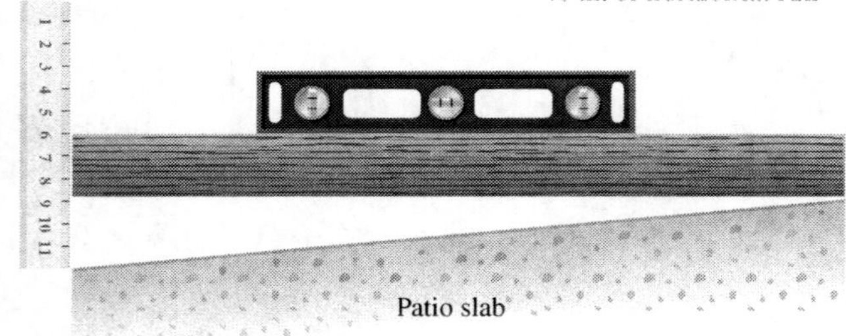

71. GRADE OF A ROAD The vertical fall of the road shown is 264 feet for a horizontal run of 1 mile. Find the slope of the decline and use that fact to complete the roadside warning sign for truckers. (*Hint:* 1 mile = 5,280 feet.) $\frac{1}{20}$, 5%

72. TREADMILLS For each height setting listed in the table, find the resulting slope of the jogging surface of the treadmill below. Express each incline as a percent.

Height setting	% incline
2 inches	4%
4 inches	8%
6 inches	12%

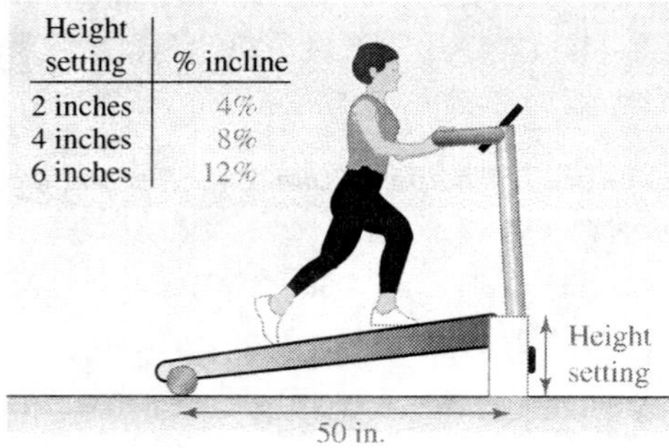

73. ACCESSIBILITY The illustration in the next column shows two designs to make the upper level of a stadium wheelchair-accessible.

a. Find the slope of the ramp in design 1. $\frac{1}{8}$

b. Find the slopes of the ramps in design 2. $\frac{1}{12}$

c. Give one advantage and one drawback of each design. 1: less expensive, steeper; 2: not as steep, more expensive

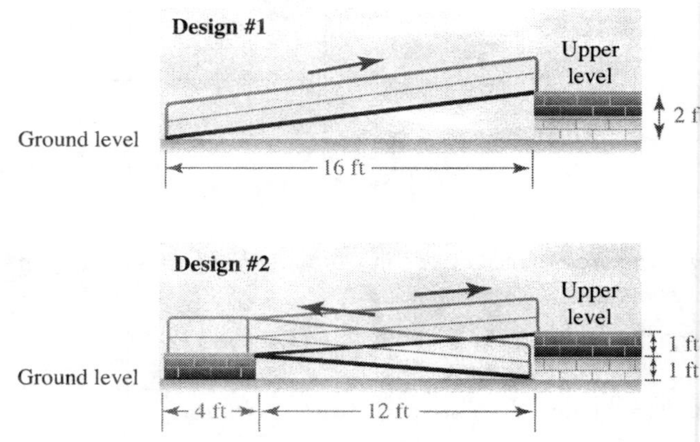

74. IRRIGATION The following graph shows the number of gallons of water remaining in a reservoir as water is discharged from it to irrigate a field. Find the rate of change in the number of gallons of water for the time the field was being irrigated. −875 gal/hr

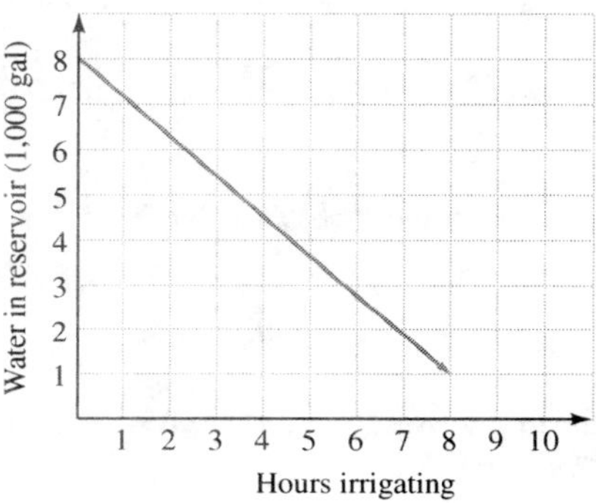

75. DEPRECIATION The following graph shows how the value of some sound equipment decreased over the years. Find the rate of change of its value during this time. −$2,500/year

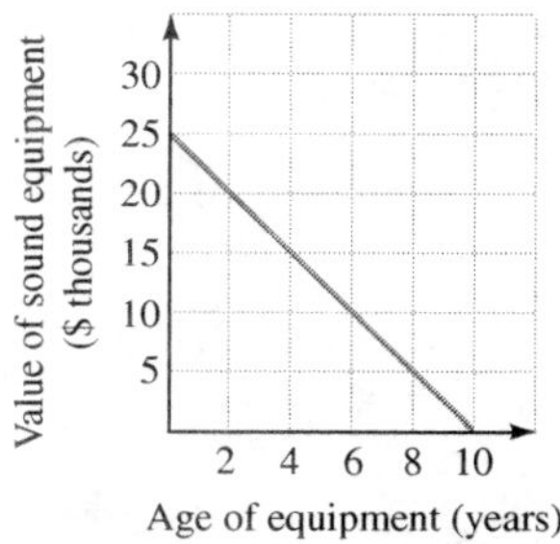

76. ARCHITECTURE Locate the coordinates of the peak of the roof if it is to have a pitch of $\frac{2}{5}$ and the roof line is to pass through the two points in black. (10, 10)

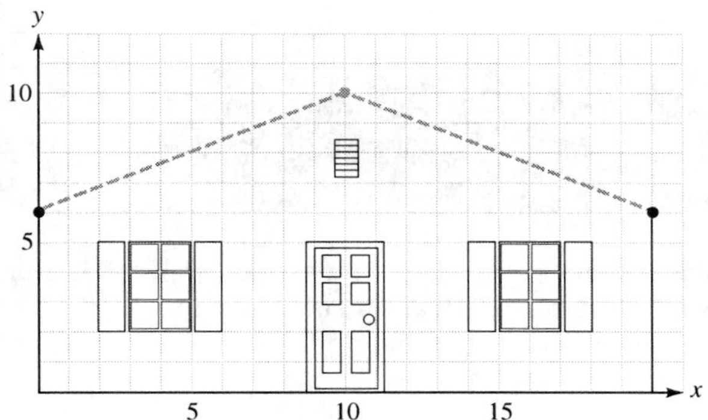

77. ENGINE OUTPUT Use the graph below to find the rate of change in the horsepower (hp) produced by an automobile engine for engine speeds in the range of 2,400 − 4,800 revolutions per minute (rpm). 3 hp/40 rpm

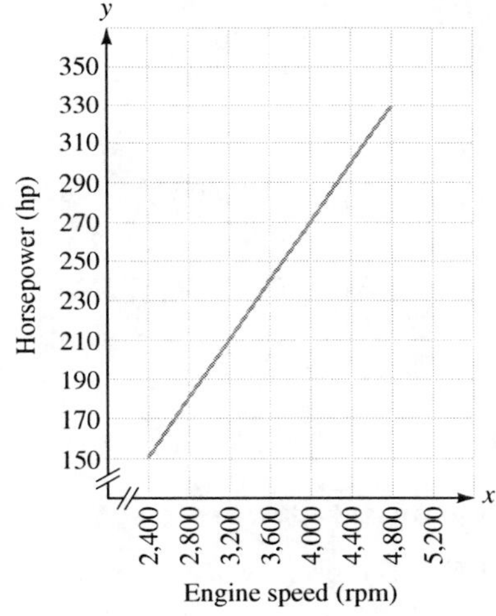

78. COMMERCIAL JETS Examine the graph and consider trips of more than 7,000 miles by a Boeing 777. Use a rate of change to estimate how the maximum payload decreases as the distance traveled increases. −15 lb/mi

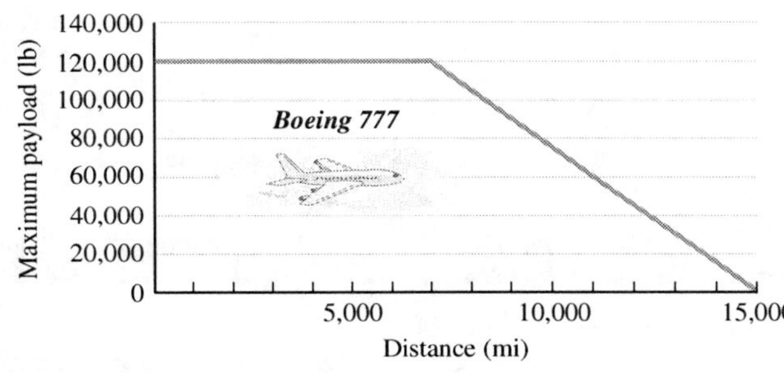

Based on data from Lawrence Livermore National Laboratory and *Los Angeles Times* (October 22, 1998).

79. MILK PRODUCTION The following graph approximates the amount of milk produced per cow in the United States for the years 1996–2005. Find the rate of change. 380 lb/yr

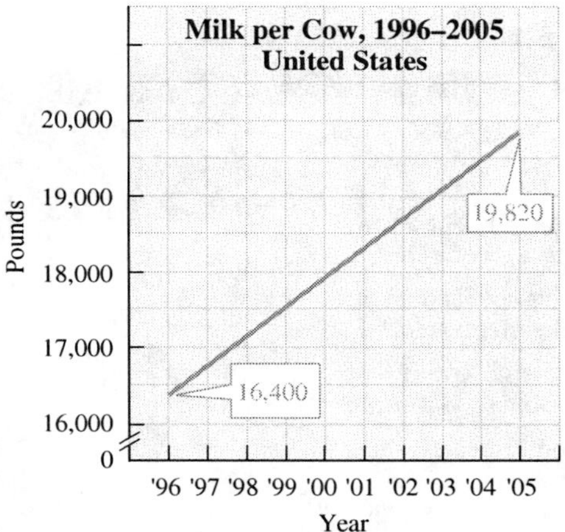

Source: United States Department of Agriculture

80. WAL-MART The graph below approximates the net sales of Wal-Mart for the years 1991–2006. Find the rate of change in sales for the years

a. 1991–1998 $11 billion per year

b. 1998–2006 $25 billion per year

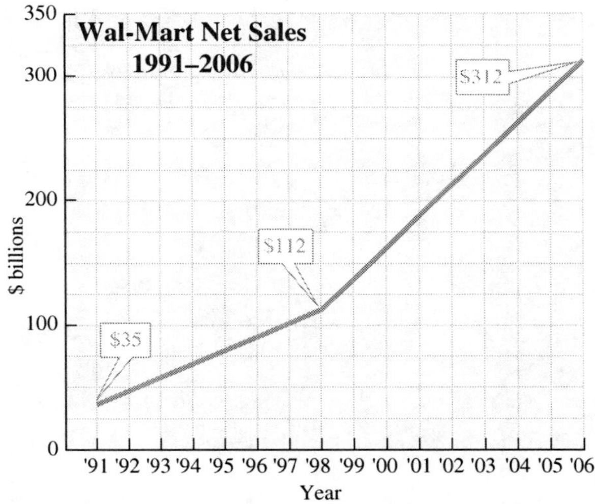

Based on data from the Wal-Mart 2006 Financial Summary

WRITING

81. Explain why the slope of a vertical line is undefined.

82. How do we distinguish between a line with positive slope and a line with negative slope?

83. Give an example of a rate of change that government officials might be interested in knowing so they can plan for the future needs of our country.

84. Explain the difference between a rate of change that is positive and one that is negative. Give an example of each.

REVIEW

85. In what quadrant does the point $(-3, 6)$ lie? quadrant II

86. What is the name given the point $(0, 0)$? origin

87. Is $(-1, -2)$ a solution of $y = x^2 + 1$? no

88. What basic shape does the graph of the equation $y = |x - 2|$ have? V-shape

89. Is the equation $y = 2x + 2$ linear or nonlinear? linear

90. Solve: $-3x \le 15$ $x \ge -5$

Objectives

1. Use slope–intercept form to identify the slope and y-intercept of a line.
2. Write a linear equation in slope–intercept form.
3. Use the slope and y-intercept to graph a linear equation.
4. Recognize parallel and perpendicular lines.
5. Use slope–intercept form to write an equation to model data.

SECTION 5.6 Slope–Intercept Form

Of all the ways in which a linear equation can be written, one form, called *slope–intercept form,* is probably the most useful. When an equation is written in this form, two important features of its graph are evident.

1 Use slope–intercept form to identify the slope and y-intercept of a line.

The graph of $y = -\frac{2}{3}x + 4$ shown in the figure enables us to see that the slope of the line is $-\frac{2}{3}$ and that the y-intercept is $(0, 4)$.

$y = -\frac{2}{3}x + 4$		
x	**y**	**(x, y)**
0	4	(0, 4)
3	2	(3, 2)

To find the slope of the line, we pick two points on the line, (0, 4) and (3, 2); draw a slope triangle; and count grid squares:

$$\text{slope} = \frac{\text{rise}}{\text{run}} = \frac{-2}{3} = -\frac{2}{3}$$

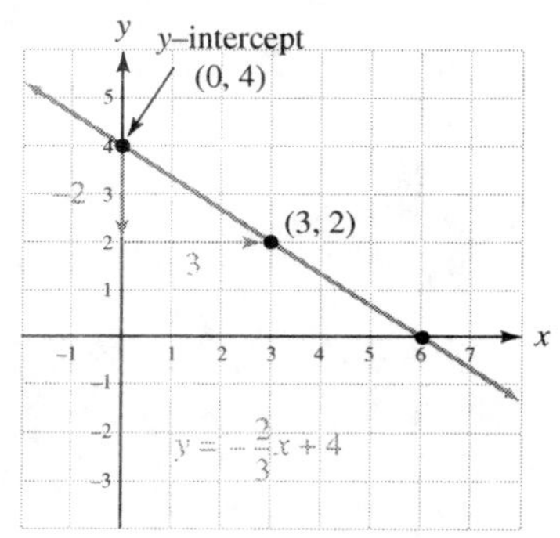

From the equation and the graph, we can make two observations:

- The graph crosses the y-axis at 4. This is the same as the constant term in $y = -\frac{2}{3}x + 4$
- The slope of the line is $-\frac{2}{3}$. This is the same as the coefficient of x in $y = -\frac{2}{3}x + 4$

$$y = -\frac{2}{3}x + 4$$

The slope of the line. is $-\frac{2}{3}$. The y-intercept is $(0, 4)$.

These observations suggest the following form of an equation of a line.

Slope-Intercept Form of the Equation of a Line

If a linear equation is written in the form

$$y = mx + b$$

the graph of the equation is a line with slope m and y-intercept $(0, b)$.

EXAMPLE 1 Find the slope and the y-intercept of the graph of each equation:

a. $y = 6x - 2$ **b.** $y = -\frac{5}{4}x$ **c.** $y = \frac{x}{2} + 6$

Strategy We will write each equation in slope–intercept form, $y = mx + b$.

WHY When the linear equations are written in slope–intercept form, the slope and the y-intercept of their graphs become apparent.

Solution

a. If we write the subtraction as the addition of the opposite, the equation will be in $y = mx + b$ form:

$$y = 6x + (-2)$$

Since $m = 6$ and $b = -2$, the slope of the line is 6 and the y-intercept is $(0, -2)$.

b. Writing $y = -\frac{5}{4}x$ in slope–intercept form, we have

$$y = -\frac{5}{4}x + 0$$

Since $m = -\frac{5}{4}$ and $b = 0$, the slope of the line is $-\frac{5}{4}$ and the y-intercept is $(0, 0)$.

c. Since $\frac{x}{2}$ means $\frac{1}{2}x$, we can rewrite $y = \frac{x}{2} + 6$ as

$$y = \frac{1}{2}x + 6$$

We see that $m = \frac{1}{2}$ and $b = 6$, so the slope of the line is $\frac{1}{2}$ and the y-intercept is $(0, 6)$.

Self Check 1

Find the slope and the y-intercept:

a. $y = -5x - 1$ $m = -5$, $(0, -1)$

b. $y = \frac{7}{8}x$ $m = \frac{7}{8}$, $(0, 0)$

c. $y = 5 - \frac{x}{3}$ $m = -\frac{1}{3}$, $(0, 5)$

Now Try **Problems 33 and 36**

Teaching Example 1 Find the slope and the y-intercept:

a. $y = 7x + 3$

b. $y = \frac{3}{5}x$

c. $y = 6 - \frac{2x}{3}$

Answers:

a. $m = 7$, $(0, 3)$

b. $m = \frac{3}{5}$, $(0, 0)$

c. $m = -\frac{2}{3}$, $(0, 6)$

Caution! If a linear equation is written in the form $y = mx + b$, the slope of the graph is the *coefficient* of x, not the term involving x. For example, it would be incorrect to say that the graph of $y = 5x + 1$ has a slope of $m = 5x$. Its graph has slope $m = 5$.

THINK IT THROUGH *Prospects for a Teaching Career*

"While student enrollments are rising rapidly, more than a million veteran teachers are nearing retirement. Experts predict that overall we will need more than 2 million new teachers in the next decade."

National Education Association, 2004

Have you ever thought about becoming a teacher? There will be plenty of openings in the future, especially for mathematics and science teachers. The equation

$$y = 865x + 11{,}100$$

approximates the average beginning teacher salary y, where x is the number of years after 1980. Graph the equation. What information about beginning teacher salaries is given by the slope of the line? By the y-intercept? What is the predicted average beginning teacher salary 5 years from now? *(Source: American Federation of Teachers)*

The rate of increase in beginning teacher salary is \$865 per year. In 1980, the average beginning teacher salary was \$11,100.

2 Write a linear equation in slope–intercept form.

The equation of any nonvertical line can be written in slope–intercept form. To do so, we apply the properties of equality to solve the equation for y.

Self Check 2

Find the slope and the y-intercept of the line determined by $8x - 2y = -2$. $m = 4$, $(0, 1)$

Now Try **Problem 41**

Teaching Example 2 Find the slope and the y-intercept of the line determined by $10x - 2y = 6$.
Answer:
$m = 5$, $(0, -3)$

EXAMPLE 2 Find the slope and the y-intercept of the line determined by $6x - 3y = 9$.

Strategy We will use the properties of equality to write each equation in slope–intercept form, $y = mx + b$.

WHY When the linear equations are written in slope–intercept form, the slope and the y-intercept of their graphs become apparent.

Solution
To find the slope and the y-intercept of the line, we write the equation in slope–intercept form by solving for y.

$$6x - 3y = 9$$

$$-3y = -6x + 9 \quad \text{Subtract } 6x \text{ from both sides.}$$

$$\frac{-3y}{-3} = \frac{-6x}{-3} + \frac{9}{-3}$$

To undo the multiplication by -3, divide both sides by -3. On the right-hand side, dividing each term by -3 is equivalent to dividing the entire side by -3: $\frac{-6x + 9}{-3} = \frac{-6x}{-3} + \frac{9}{-3}$

$$y = 2x - 3 \quad \text{Perform the divisions. Here, } m = 2 \text{ and } b = -3.$$

From the equation, we see that the slope is 2 and the y-intercept is $(0, -3)$. ■

3 Use the slope and y-intercept to graph a linear equation.

To graph $y = 2x - 3$, we plot the y-intercept $(0, -3)$, as shown. Since the slope is $\frac{\text{rise}}{\text{run}} = 2 = \frac{2}{1}$, the line rises 2 units for every unit it moves to the right. If we begin at $(0, -3)$ and move 2 units up (rise) and then 1 unit to the right (run), we locate the point $(1, -1)$, which is a second point on the line. We then draw a line through $(0, -3)$ and $(1, -1)$.

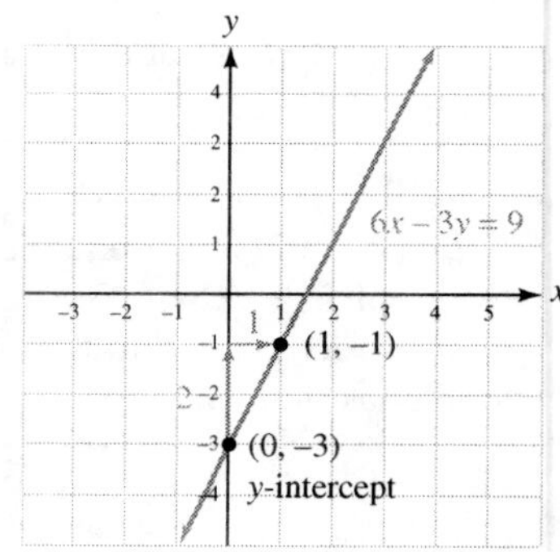

4 Recognize parallel and perpendicular lines.

The slope–intercept form enables us to quickly identify parallel and perpendicular lines.

Self Check 3

Determine whether the graphs of $y = -\frac{3}{2}x + 1$ and $y = \frac{3}{2}x + 4$ are parallel, perpendicular, or neither. neither

Now Try **Problems 45 and 46**

Teaching Example 3 Determine whether the graphs of $y = \frac{1}{5}x + 2$ and $y = -5x + 9$ are parallel, perpendicular, or neither.
Answer:
perpendicular

EXAMPLE 3 Determine whether the graphs of $y = -\frac{2}{3}x$ and $y = -\frac{2}{3}x + 3$ are parallel, perpendicular, or neither.

Strategy We will find the slope of each line and compare the slopes.

WHY If the slopes are equal, the lines are parallel. If the slopes are negative reciprocals, the lines are perpendicular. Otherwise, the lines are neither parallel nor perpendicular.

Solution
The graph of $y = -\frac{2}{3}x$ is a line with slope $-\frac{2}{3}$. The graph of $y = -\frac{2}{3}x + 3$ is a line with slope of $-\frac{2}{3}$. Since the slopes $-\frac{2}{3}$ and $-\frac{2}{3}$ are the same, the lines are parallel. ■

EXAMPLE 4 Are the graphs of $y = -5x + 6$ and $x - 5y = -10$ parallel, perpendicular, or neither?

Strategy We will find the slope of each line and then compare the slopes.

WHY If the slopes are equal, the lines are parallel. If the slopes are negative reciprocals, the lines are perpendicular. Otherwise, the lines are neither parallel nor perpendicular.

Solution
The graph of $y = -5x + 6$ is a line with slope -5. To find the slope of the graph of $x - 5y = -10$, we will write the equation in slope–intercept form.

$$x - 5y = -10$$

$$-5y = -x - 10 \quad \text{To eliminate } x \text{ from the left side, subtract } x \text{ from both sides.}$$

$$\frac{-5y}{-5} = \frac{-x}{-5} - \frac{10}{-5} \quad \text{To isolate } y\text{, undo the multiplication by } -5 \text{ by dividing both sides by } -5.$$

$$y = \frac{x}{5} + 2 \quad m = \frac{1}{5} \text{ because } \frac{x}{5} = \frac{1}{5}x.$$

The graph of $y = \frac{x}{5} + 2$ is a line with slope $\frac{1}{5}$. Since the slopes -5 and $\frac{1}{5}$ are negative reciprocals, the lines are perpendicular. This is verified by the fact that the product of their slopes is -1.

$$-5\left(\frac{1}{5}\right) = -\frac{5}{5} = -1$$

Self Check 4

Determine whether the graphs of $y = 4x + 6$ and $x - 4y = -8$ are parallel, perpendicular, or neither. neither

Now Try **Problem 49**

Teaching Example 4 Are the graphs of $2x + 3y = 6$ and $6y = -4x + 7$ parallel, perpendicular, or neither?
Answer:
parallel

> ***Success Tip*** Graphs are not necessary to determine if two lines are parallel, perpendicular, or neither. We simply examine the slopes of the lines.

5 Use slope–intercept form to write an equation to model data.

If we are given the slope and y-intercept of a line, we can write its equation, as in the next example.

EXAMPLE 5 *Limo Service* On weekends, a limousine service charges a fee of \$100, plus 50¢ per mile, for the rental of a stretch limo. Write a linear equation that describes the relationship between the rental cost and the number of miles driven. Graph the result.

Strategy We will determine the slope and the y-intercept of the graph of the equation from the given facts about the limo service.

WHY If we know the slope and y-intercept, we can use the slope–intercept form, $y = mx + b$, to write the equation to model the situation.

Solution
To write an equation describing this relationship, we will let x represent the number of miles driven and y represent the cost (in dollars). We can make two observations:

- The cost increases by 50¢ or \$0.50 for each mile driven. This is the *rate of change* of the rental cost to miles driven, and it will be the *slope* of the graph of the equation. Thus, $m = 0.50$.
- The basic fee is \$100. Before driving any miles (that is, when $x = 0$), the cost y is 100. The ordered pair (0, 100) will be the y-intercept of the graph of the equation. So we know that $b = 100$.

Self Check 5

To encourage larger orders, a screen printing service offers a \$0.02 per shirt discount from the normal cost of \$15 per shirt. Write a linear equation that determines the per shirt cost c of a shirt if n shirts are ordered.

Now Try **Problem 77**

Self Check 5 Answer
$c = -0.02n + 15$

Teaching Example 5 To promote group sales for an Alaskan cruise, a travel agency reduces the regular ticket price of \$4,500 by \$5 for each person traveling in the group. Write a linear equation that determines the per-person cost c of the cruise, if p people travel together.
Answer:
$c = -5p + 4500$

We substitute 0.50 for m and 100 for b in the slope–intercept form to get

$y = 0.50x + 100$ Here the cost y depends on x, the number of miles driven.

$m = 0.50$ $b = 100$

To graph $y = 0.50x + 100$, we plot its y-intercept, (0, 100). Since the slope is $0.50 = \frac{50}{100} = \frac{5}{10}$, we can start at (0, 100) and locate a second point on the line by moving 5 units up (rise) and then 10 units to the right (run). This point will have coordinates (0 + 10, 100 + 5) or (10, 105). We draw a straight line through these two points to get a graph that illustrates the relationship between the rental cost and the number of miles driven. We draw the graph only in quadrant I, because the number of miles driven is always positive.

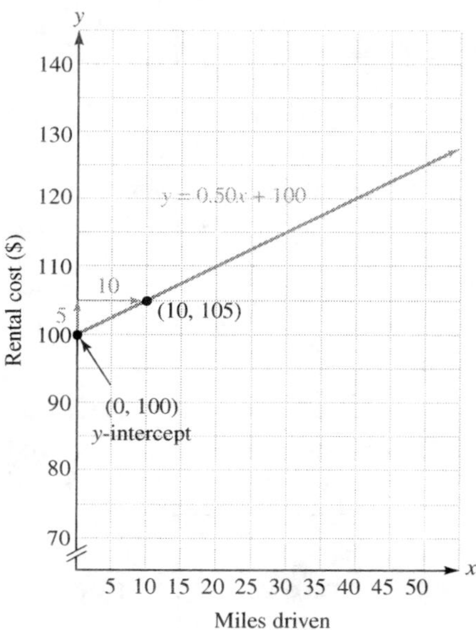

ANSWERS TO SELF CHECKS

1. a. $m = -5$, $(0, -1)$ **b.** $m = \frac{7}{8}$, $(0, 0)$ **c.** $m = -\frac{1}{3}$, $(0, 5)$ **2.** $m = 4$, $(0, 1)$ **3.** neither **4.** neither **5.** $c = -0.02n + 15$

SECTION 5.6 STUDY SET

VOCABULARY

Fill in the blanks.

1. The equation $y = mx + b$ is called the slope–intercept form for the equation of a line.

2. Parallel lines do not intersect. Perpendicular lines meet at right angles.

CONCEPTS

3. The graph of the linear equation $y = mx + b$ has a y-intercept of $(0, b)$ and a slope of m.

4. The numbers $\frac{5}{6}$ and $-\frac{6}{5}$ are negative reciprocals because their product is -1.

Determine whether each equation is in slope–intercept form.

5. $7x + 4y = 2$ no

6. $5y = 2x - 3$ no

7. $y = 6x + 1$ yes

8. $x = 4y - 8$ no

Determine the slope of the graph of each equation.

9. $y = \dfrac{-2x}{3} - 2$ $-\frac{2}{3}$

10. $y = \dfrac{x}{4} + 1$ $\frac{1}{4}$

Selected exercises available online at www.webassign.net/brookscole

11. $y = 2 - 8x$ -8

12. $y = 3x$ 3

13. $y = x$ 1

14. $y = -x$ -1

See the illustration.

15. What is the slope of the line? $-\frac{1}{2}$

16. What is the y-intercept of the line? $(0, -4)$

17. Write the equation of the line. $y = -\frac{1}{2}x - 4$

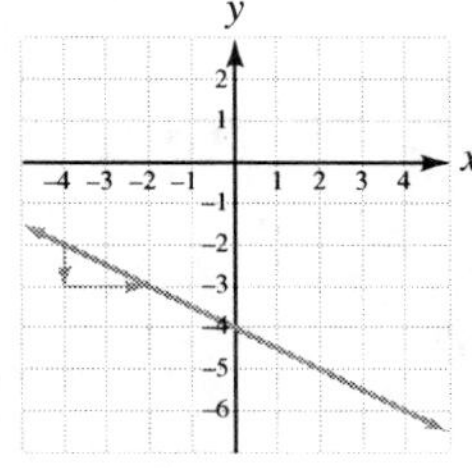

See the illustration.

18. What is the slope of the line? $\frac{5}{4}$

19. What is the y-intercept of the line? $(0, 0)$

20. Write the equation of the line. $y = \frac{5}{4}x$

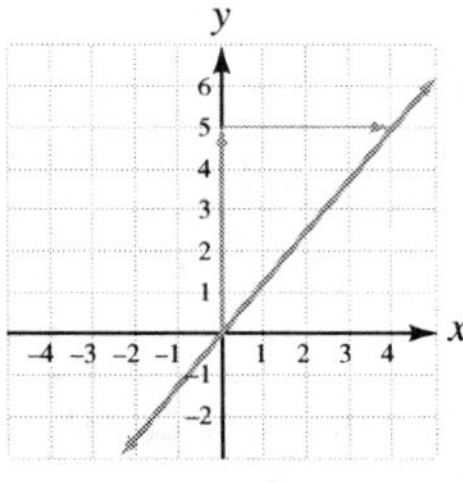

In the illustration, the slope of line l_1 is 2.

21. Determine the slope of line l_2. $-\frac{1}{2}$

22. Determine the slope of line l_3. 2

23. Determine the slope of line l_4. $-\frac{1}{2}$

24. Which lines have the same y-intercept? l_1 and l_2

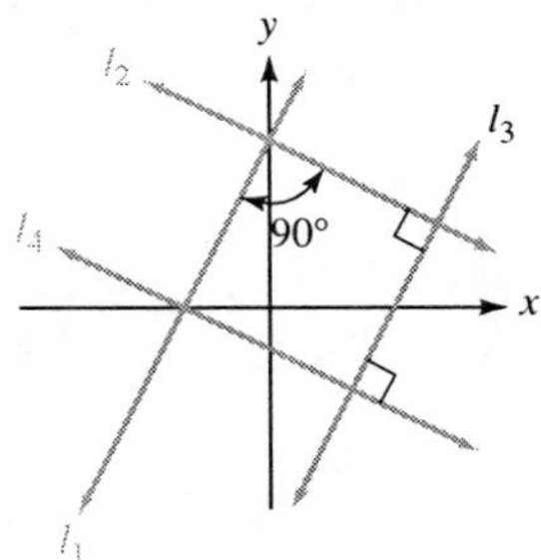

25. Determine the y-intercept of line l_1 in the illustration. $(0, 0)$

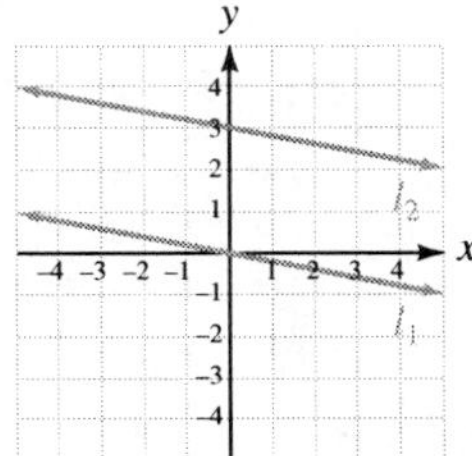

26. What do lines l_1 and l_2 have in common? How are they different? same slope, different y-intercepts

Without graphing, determine whether the graphs of each pair of lines are parallel, perpendicular, or neither.

27. $y = 0.5x - 3$, $y = \frac{1}{2}x + 3$ parallel

28. $y = 0.75x$, $y = -\frac{4}{3}x + 2$ perpendicular

29. $y = -x$, $y = -2x$ neither

30. $y = \dfrac{2}{3}x - 4$, $y = -\dfrac{3}{2}x + 4$ perpendicular

NOTATION

Complete each solution by solving the equation for y. Then find the slope and the y-intercept of its graph.

31.

$$\begin{aligned} 6x - 2y &= 10 \\ 6x - 6x - 2y &= -6x + 10 \\ -2y &= -6x + 10 \\ \frac{-2y}{-2} &= \frac{-6x}{-2} + \frac{10}{-2} \\ y &= 3x - 5 \end{aligned}$$

The slope is 3 and the y-intercept is $(0, -5)$.

32.

$$\begin{aligned} 2x + 5y &= 15 \\ 2x + 5y - 2x &= -2x + 15 \\ 5y &= -2x + 15 \\ \frac{5y}{5} &= \frac{-2x}{5} + \frac{15}{5} \\ y &= -\frac{2}{5}x + 3 \end{aligned}$$

The slope is $-\frac{2}{5}$ and the y-intercept is $(0, 3)$.

GUIDED PRACTICE

Find the slope and the y-intercept of the graph of each equation. See Examples 1–2.

33. $y = 4x + 2$ $4, (0, 2)$

34. $y = -4x - 2$ $-4, (0, -2)$

35. $y = \dfrac{x}{4} - \dfrac{1}{2}$ $\frac{1}{4}, \left(0, -\frac{1}{2}\right)$

36. $y = \frac{1}{2}x + 6$ $\frac{1}{2}, (0, 6)$

37. $4x - 2 = y$ $4, (0, -2)$

38. $6 - x = y$ $-1, (0, 6)$

39. $6y = x - 6$ $\frac{1}{6}, (0, -1)$

40. $6x - 1 = y$ $6, (0, -1)$

41. $4x - 3y = 12$ $\frac{4}{3}, (0, -4)$

42. $2x + 3y = 6$ $-\frac{2}{3}, (0, 2)$

43. $10x - 5y = 12$ $2, \left(0, -\frac{12}{5}\right)$

44. $7x + 4y = 16$ $-\frac{7}{4}, (0, 4)$

For each pair of equations, determine whether their graphs are parallel, perpendicular, or neither. See Examples 3–4.

45. $y = 6x + 8$
$y = 6x$
parallel

▶ **46.** $y = 3x - 15$
$y = -\frac{1}{3}x + 4$
perpendicular

▶ **47.** $y = x$
$y = -x$
perpendicular

48. $y = \frac{1}{2}x - \frac{4}{5}$
$y = 0.5x + 3$
parallel

▶ **49.** $y = -2x - 9$
$2x - y = 9$
neither

50. $y = \frac{3}{4}x + 1$
$4x - 3y = 15$
neither

51. $x - y = 12$
$-2x + 2y = -23$
parallel

52. $x = 9$
$y = 8$
perpendicular

TRY IT YOURSELF

Find the slope and the y-intercept of the graph of each equation.

53. $x + y = 8$
$-1, (0, 8)$

54. $x - y = -30$
$1, (0, 30)$

55. $2x + 3y = 6$
$-\frac{2}{3}, (0, 2)$

▶ **56.** $3x - 5y = 15$
$\frac{3}{5}, (0, -3)$

57. $3y - 13 = 0$
$0, \left(0, \frac{13}{3}\right)$

58. $-5y - 2 = 0$
$0, \left(0, -\frac{2}{5}\right)$

59. $y = -5x$
$-5, (0, 0)$

▶ **60.** $y = 14x$
$14, (0, 0)$

Write an equation of the line with the given slope and y-intercept. Then graph it.

61. $m = 5, (0, -3)$
$y = 5x - 3$

▶ **62.** $m = -2, (0, 1)$
$y = -2x + 1$

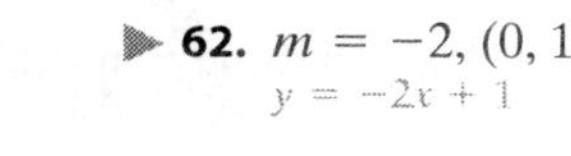

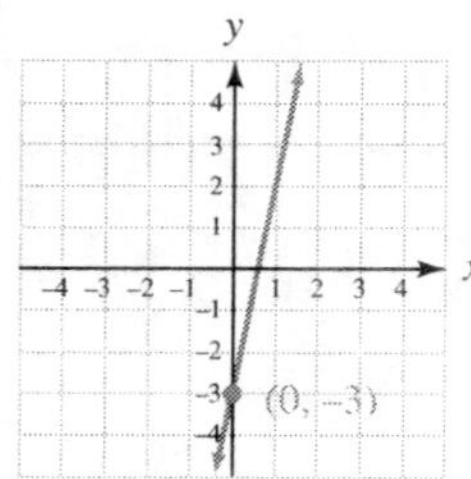

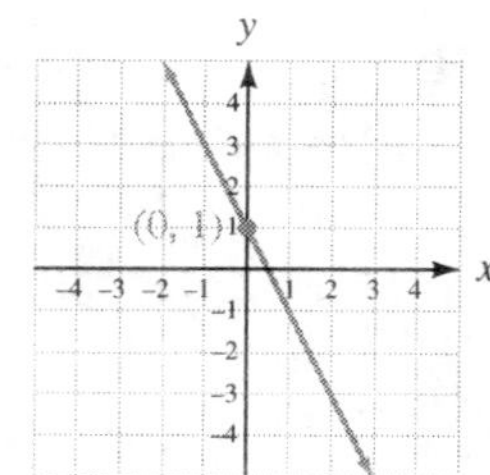

63. $m = \frac{1}{4}, (0, -2)$
$y = \frac{1}{4}x - 2$

64. $m = \frac{1}{3}, (0, -5)$
$y = \frac{1}{3}x - 5$

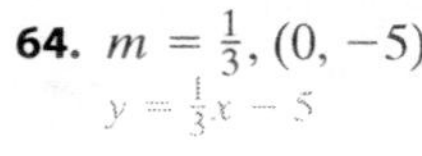

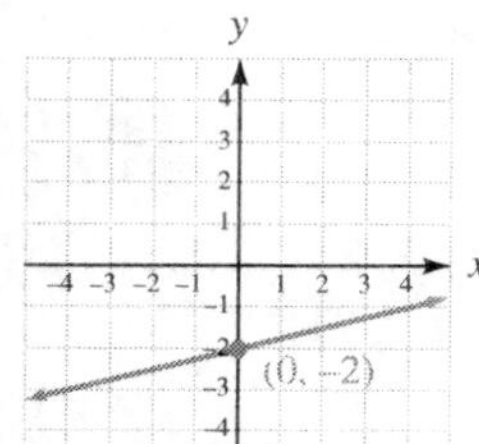

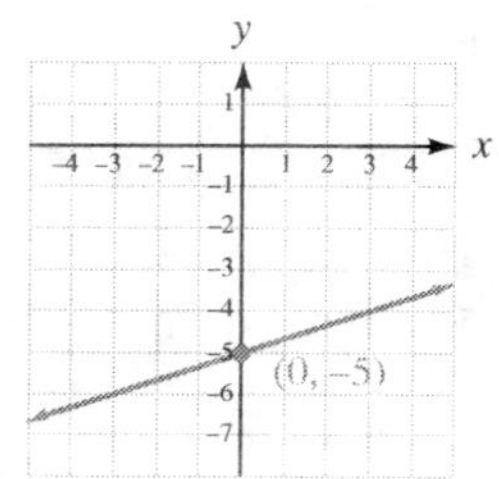

65. $m = -3, (0, 6)$
$y = -3x + 6$

▶ **66.** $m = 2, (0, 1)$
$y = 2x + 1$

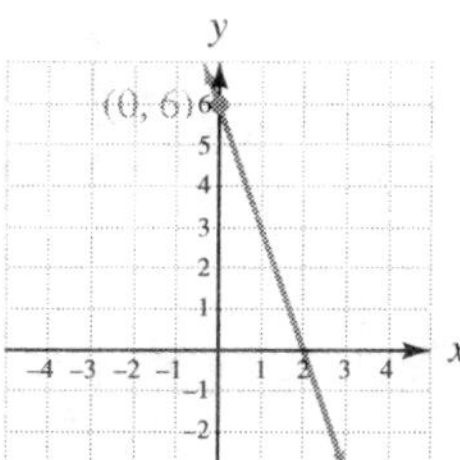

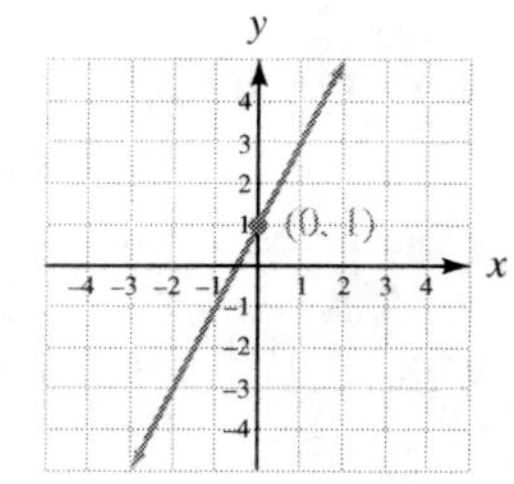

67. $m = -\frac{8}{3}, (0, 5)$
$y = -\frac{8}{3}x + 5$

▶ **68.** $m = -\frac{7}{6}, (0, 2)$
$y = -\frac{7}{6}x + 2$

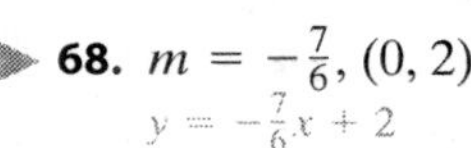

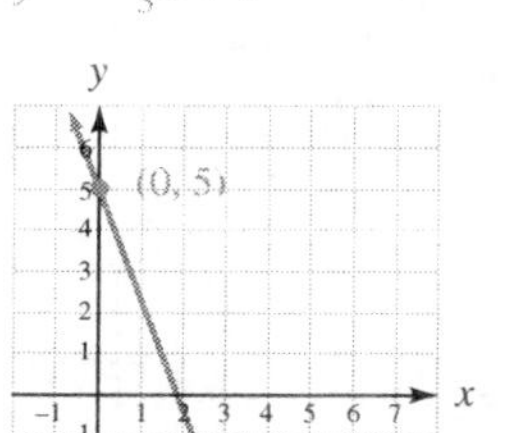

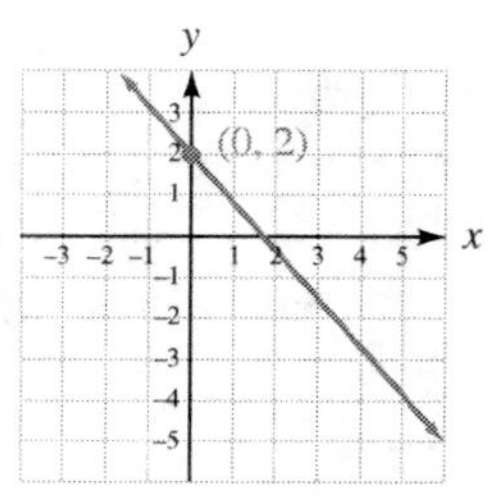

Find the slope and the y-intercept of the graph of each equation. Then graph it.

69. $y = 3x + 3$

70. $y = -3x + 5$

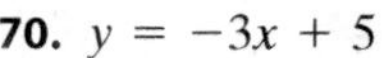

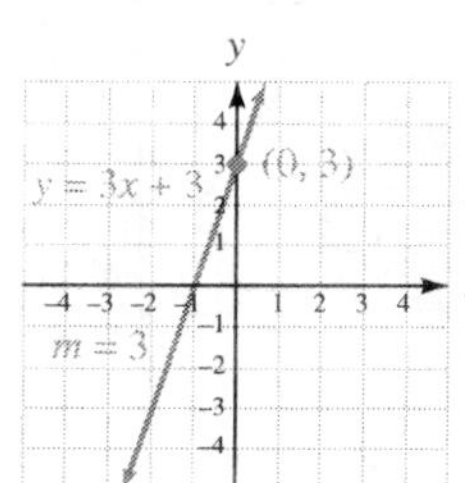

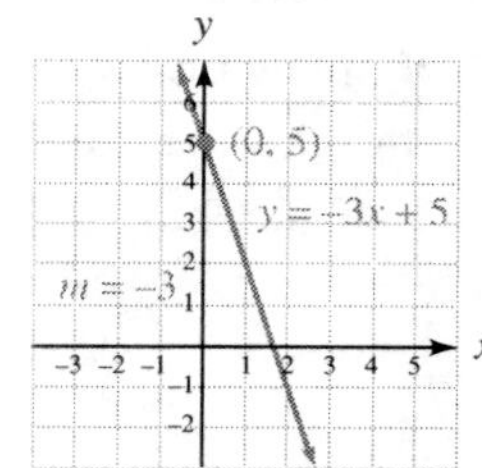

71. $y = -\frac{x}{2} + 2$

▶ **72.** $y = \frac{x}{3}$

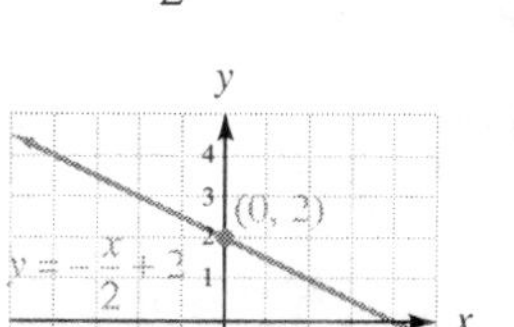

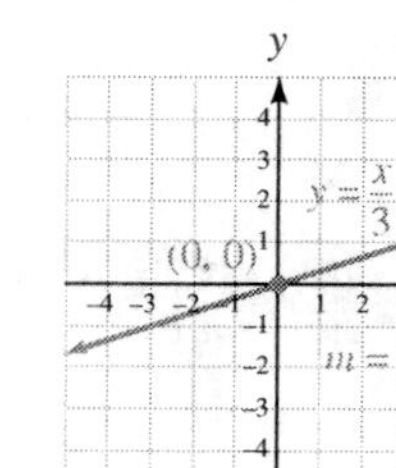

73. $3x + 4y = 16$

▶ **74.** $2x + 3y = 9$

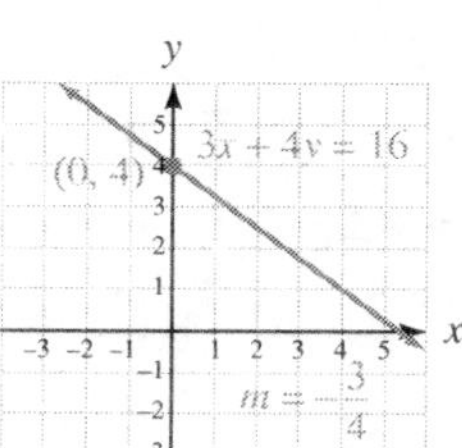

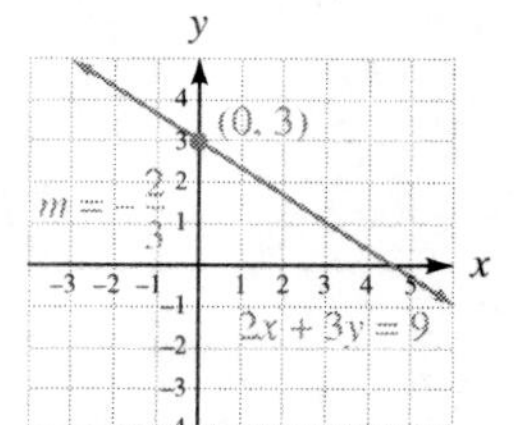

75. $10x - 5y = 5$

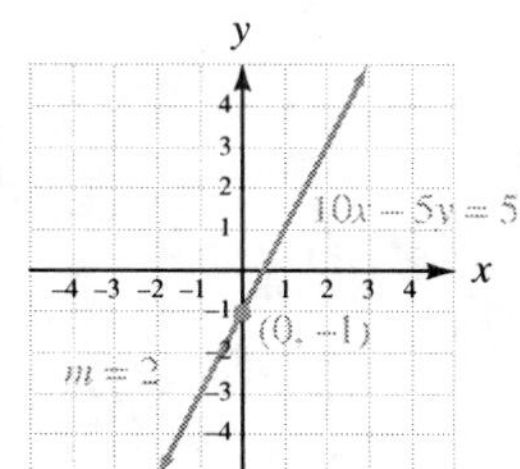

76. $4x - 2y = 6$

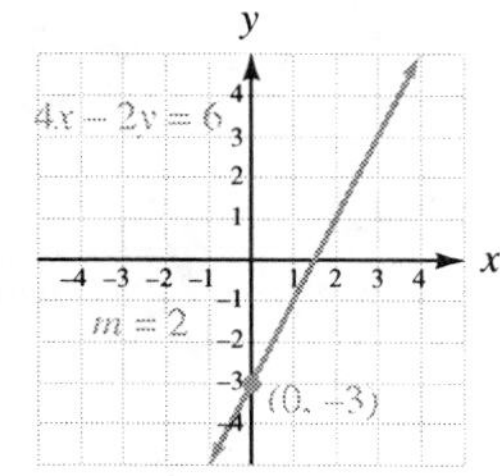

APPLICATIONS

See Example 5.

77. PRODUCTION COSTS A television production company charges a basic fee of \$5,000 and then \$2,000 an hour when filming a commercial.

a. Write a linear equation that describes the relationship between the total production costs y and the hours of filming x. $y = 2{,}000x + 5{,}000$

b. Use your answer to part a to find the production costs if a commercial required 8 hours of filming. \$21,000

78. COLLEGE FEES Each semester, students enrolling at a community college must pay tuition costs of \$20 per unit as well as a \$40 student services fee.

a. Write a linear equation that gives the total fees y to be paid by a student enrolling at the college and taking x units. $y = 20x + 40$

b. Use your answer to part a to find the enrollment cost for a student taking 12 units. \$280

79. CHEMISTRY EXPERIMENT The following illustration shows a portion of a student's chemistry lab manual. Use the information to write a linear equation relating the temperature y (in degrees Fahrenheit) of the compound to the time x (in minutes) elapsed during the lab procedure. $y = 5x - 10$

Chem. Lab #1 Aug. 13
Step 1: Removed compound from freezer @ −10°F.

Step 2: Used heating unit to raise temperature of compound 5° F every minute.

80. INCOME PROPERTY Use the information in the newspaper advertisement in the next column to write a linear equation that gives the amount of income y (in dollars) the apartment owner will receive when the unit is rented for x months. $y = 500x + 250$

APARTMENT FOR RENT
1 bedroom/1 bath, with garage
\$500 per month + \$250 nonrefundable security fee.

81. SALAD BAR For lunch, a delicatessen offers a "Salad and Soda" special where customers serve themselves at a well-stocked salad bar. The cost is \$1.00 for the drink and 20¢ an ounce for the salad.

a. Write a linear equation that will find the cost y of a lunch when a salad weighing x ounces is purchased. $y = 0.20x + 1.00$

b. Graph the equation using the grid below.

c. How would the graph from part b change if the delicatessen began charging \$2.00 for the drink? same slope, different y-intercept

d. How would the graph from part b change if the cost of the salad changed to 30¢ an ounce? same y-intercept, steeper slope

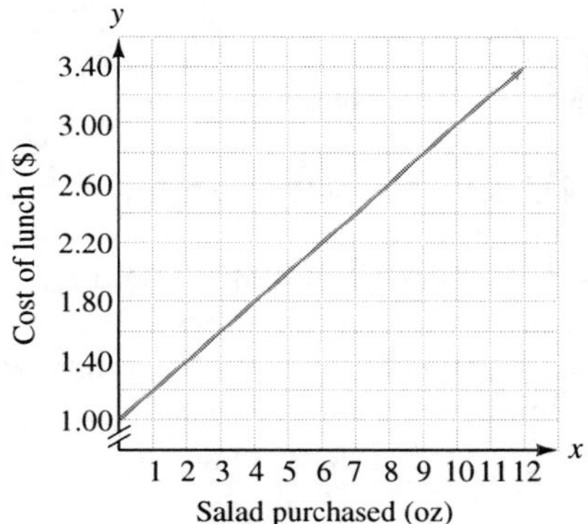

82. SEWING COSTS A tailor charges a basic fee of \$20 plus \$2.50 per letter to sew an athlete's name on the back of a jacket.

a. Write a linear equation that will find the cost y to have a name containing x letters sewn on the back of a jacket. $y = 2.50x + 20$

b. Graph the equation on the grid on the next page.

c. Suppose the tailor raises the basic fee to \$30. On your graph from part b, draw the new graph showing the increased cost.

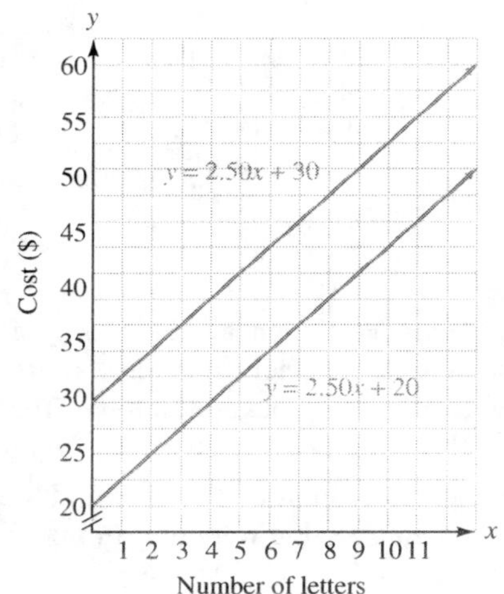

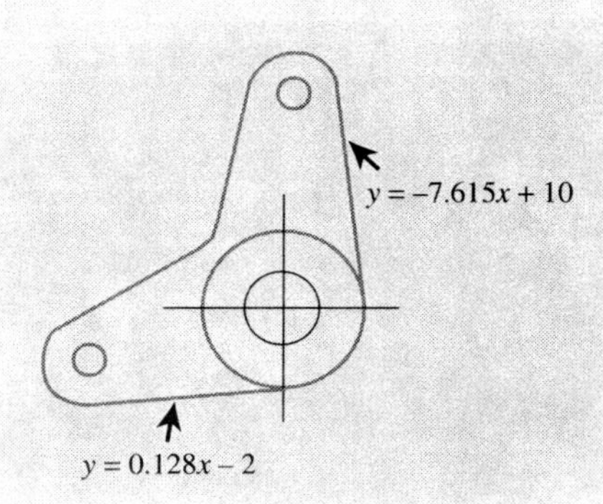

83. EMPLOYMENT SERVICE A policy statement of LIZCO, Inc., is shown below. Suppose a secretary had to pay an employment service \$500 to get placed in a new job at LIZCO. Write a linear equation that tells the secretary the actual cost y of the employment service to her x months after being hired. $y = -20x + 500$

> **Policy no. 23452**– A new hire will be reimbursed by LIZCO for any employment service fees paid by the employee at the rate of \$20 per month.

84. COMPUTER DRAFTING The illustration in the next column shows a computer-generated drawing of an automobile engine mount. When the designer clicks the mouse on a line of the drawing, the computer finds the equation of the line. Determine whether the two lines selected in the drawing are perpendicular. not quite: $(0.128)(-7.615) = -0.97472 \neq -1$

WRITING

85. Explain the advantages of writing the equation of a line in slope–intercept form ($y = mx + b$) as opposed to general form ($Ax + By = C$).

86. Why is $y = mx + b$ called the slope–intercept form of the equation of a line?

87. What is the minimum number of points needed to draw the graph of a line? Explain why.

88. List some examples of parallel and perpendicular lines that you see in your daily life.

REVIEW

89. Find the slope of the line passing through the points $(6, -2)$ and $(-6, 1)$. $-\frac{1}{4}$

90. Is $(3, -7)$ a solution of $y = 3x - 2$? no

91. Evaluate: $-4 - (-4)$ 0

92. Solve: $2(x - 3) = 3x$ -6

93. To evaluate $[-2(4 - 8) + 4^2]$, which operation should be performed first? subtraction

94. Translate to mathematical symbols: four less than twice the price p. $2p - 4$

95. What percent of 6 is 1.5? 25%

96. Is -6.75 a solution of $x + 1 > -9$? yes

Module 6: Polynomials and Quadratic Applications

DMA 060

© Robert E. Daemmrich/Getty Images

from Campus to Careers

Police Officer

People depend on the police to protect their lives and property. The job can be dangerous because police officers must arrest suspects and respond to emergencies. The daily activities of police officers can vary greatly depending on their specialty, such as patrol officer, game warden, or detective. Regardless of their duties, they must write reports and maintain records that will be needed if they testify in court.

In **Problem 80** of **Study Set 6.3,** you will see how police officers can compute the stopping distance of a car.

JOB TITLE:
Police Officer

EDUCATION: For many departments, two years of college or a college degree may be required. Physical education courses are helpful. Foreign language skills are desirable.

JOB OUTLOOK: Excellent—employment opportunities are expected to grow 11 percent through 2016.

ANNUAL EARNINGS: Median annual salary in 2007 was $50,330. Earnings often exceed their salary because of payments for overtime.

FOR MORE INFORMATION:
www.bls.gov/oco/ocos160.htm

Objectives

1. Identify bases and exponents.
2. Multiply exponential expressions that have like bases.
3. Divide exponential expressions that have like bases.
4. Raise exponential expressions to a power.
5. Find powers of products and quotients.

SECTION 6.1 Rules for Exponents

In this section, we will use the definition of exponent to develop some rules for simplifying expressions that contain exponents.

1 Identify bases and exponents.

We have used natural-number exponents to indicate repeated multiplication. For example,

$9^2 = 9 \cdot 9 = 81$ Write 9 as a factor 2 times.

$7^3 = 7 \cdot 7 \cdot 7 = 343$ Write 7 as a factor 3 times.

$(-2)^4 = (-2)(-2)(-2)(-2) = 16$ Write -2 as a factor 4 times.

$-2^4 = -(2 \cdot 2 \cdot 2 \cdot 2) = -16$ The $-$ sign in front of 2^4 means the opposite of 2^4.

These examples illustrate a definition for x^n, where n is a natural number.

Natural-Number Exponents

A natural-number exponent tells how many times its base is to be used as a factor. For any number x and any natural number n,

$$x^n = \overbrace{x \cdot x \cdot x \cdot \cdots \cdot x}^{n \text{ factors of } x}$$

In the **exponential expression** x^n, x is called the **base** and n is called the **exponent.** The entire expression is called a **power of x.**

base $\rightarrow x^n \leftarrow$ exponent

If an exponent is a natural number, it tells how many times its base is to be used as a factor. An exponent of 1 indicates that its base is to be used one time as a factor, an exponent of 2 indicates that its base is to be used two times as a factor, and so on. The base of an exponential expression can be a number, a variable, or a combination of numbers and variables.

$x^1 = x \qquad (y + 1)^2 = (y + 1)(y + 1) \qquad (-5s)^3 = (-5s)(-5s)(-5s)$

Self Check 1

Identify the base and the exponent:

a. $5x^4$ base: x, exponent: 4

b. $(5x)^4$ base: $5x$, exponent: 4

Now Try **Problems 25, 26, and 31**

Teaching Example 1 Identify the base and the exponent in each expression:
a. 12^3 b. $7x^{10}$
c. -4^3 d. $(7x)^9$
Answers:
a. base: 12, exponent: 3
b. base: x, exponent: 10
c. base: 4, exponent: 3
d. base: $7x$, exponent: 9

EXAMPLE 1 Identify the base and the exponent in each expression:

a. 7^6 **b.** $4x^3$ **c.** $-x^5$ **d.** $(2x)^4$

Strategy To identify the base and exponent, we will look for the exponent first. Then we will look for the base. We will report the base first, then the exponent.

WHY The exponent is the small raised number. The base is the number or variable directly in front of the exponent, unless there are parentheses.

Solution

a. In 7^6, the base is 7 and the exponent is 6.

b. $4x^3$ means $4 \cdot x^3$. The base is x and the exponent is 3.

c. $-x^5$ means $-1 \cdot x^5$. The base is x and the exponent is 5.

d. Because of the parentheses in $(2x)^4$, the base is $2x$ and the exponent is 4.

EXAMPLE 2 Write each expression in an equivalent form using an exponent:

a. $\frac{x}{5} \cdot \frac{x}{5} \cdot \frac{x}{5} \cdot \frac{x}{5}$ **b.** $4 \cdot y \cdot y \cdot y \cdot y \cdot y$

Strategy We will look for repeated factors and count the number of times each appears.

WHY We can use an exponent to represent repeated multiplication.

Solution

a. Since there are four repeated factors of $\frac{x}{5}$ in $\frac{x}{5} \cdot \frac{x}{5} \cdot \frac{x}{5} \cdot \frac{x}{5}$, the expression can be written as $\left(\frac{x}{5}\right)^4$.

b. Since there are 5 repeated factors of y, the expression can be written $4y^5$.

Self Check 2

Write as an exponential expression: $(a + b)(a + b)(a + b)(a + b)(a + b)(a + b)$

Now Try **Problems 33, 38, and 44**

Self Check 2 Answer
$(a + b)^6$

Teaching Example 2 Write each expression in an equivalent form using an exponent:
a. $3x \cdot 3x \cdot 3x \cdot 3x$
b. $3 \cdot x \cdot x \cdot x \cdot x$
Answers:
a. $(3x)^4$ b. $3x^4$

2 Multiply exponential expressions that have like bases.

To develop a rule for multiplying exponential expressions that have the same base, we consider the product $x^2 \cdot x^3$. Since the expression x^2 means that x is to be used as a factor two times, and the expression x^3 means that x is to be used as a factor three times, we have

$$x^2 \cdot x^3 = \underbrace{x \cdot x}_{\text{2 factors of } x} \cdot \underbrace{x \cdot x \cdot x}_{\text{3 factors of } x}$$

$$= \underbrace{x \cdot x \cdot x \cdot x \cdot x}_{\text{5 factors of } x}$$

$$= x^5$$

This example suggests the following rule:

Product Rule for Exponents

To multiply two exponential expressions that have the same base, keep the common base and add the exponents. If m and n represent natural numbers, then

$$x^m x^n = x^{m+n}$$

EXAMPLE 3 Simplify each expression:

a. $9^5(9^6)$ **b.** $x^3 \cdot x^4$ **c.** y^2y^4y **d.** $(c^2d^3)(c^4d^5)$ **e.** $(a + b)^4(a + b)^3$

Strategy We will identify exponential expressions that have the same base in each product. Then we will use the product rule for exponents to simplify the expression.

WHY The product rule for exponents is used to multiply exponential expressions that have the same base.

Solution

a. To simplify $9^5(9^6)$ means to write it in an equivalent form using one base and one exponent.

$9^5(9^6) = 9^{5+6}$ Use the product rule for exponents: Keep the common base, which is 9, and add the exponents.

$= 9^{11}$ Perform the addition. Since 9^{11} is a very large number, we will leave it in this form. We won't evaluate it.

Self Check 3

Simplify:
a. $7^8(7^7)$ 7^{15}
b. $z \cdot z^3$ z^4
c. $x^2x^3x^6$ x^{11}
d. $(s^4t^3)(s^4t^4)$ s^8t^7
e. $(r + s)^2(r + s)^5$ $(r + s)^7$

Now Try **Problems 45, 50, 57, and 60**

Teaching Example 3 Simplify:
a. $5^3(5^6)$ b. $a^3 \cdot a$ c. $y^2y^3y^5$
d. $(x^3y^2)(x^4y^3)$ e. $(a + b)^2(a + b)^4$
Answers:
a. 5^9 b. a^4 c. y^{10}
d. x^7y^5 e. $(a + b)^6$

b. $x^3 \cdot x^4 = x^{3+4}$ Keep the common base x and add the exponents.

$= x^7$ Perform the addition.

c. $y^2y^4y = y^{2+4}y$ Working from left to right, keep the common base y and add the exponents.

$= y^6y$ Perform the addition.

$= y^{6+1}$ Keep the common base and add the exponents.

$= y^7$ Perform the addition.

d. $(c^2d^3)(c^4d^5) = c^2d^3c^4d^5$ Use the associative property of multiplication.

$= c^2c^4d^3d^5$ Change the order of the factors.

$= c^{2+4}d^{3+5}$ Keep the common base c and add the exponents. Keep the common base d and add the exponents.

$= c^6d^8$ Perform the additions.

e. $(a + b)^4(a + b)^3 = (a + b)^{4+3}$ Keep the common base $(a + b)$ and add the exponents.

$= (a + b)^7$ Perform the addition.

Caution! We cannot use the product rule to simplify expressions like $3^2 \cdot 2^3$, where the bases are not the same. However, we can simplify this expression by doing the arithmetic: $3^2 \cdot 2^3 = 9 \cdot 8 = 72$.

THINK IT THROUGH ***PIN Code Choices***

"According to a Student Monitor LLC survey, ATM debit card ownership among college students has almost doubled from 30 percent to 57 percent in the past four years."

BYU Newsletter, Oct 2002

In 2002, there were 13.9 billion ATM transactions in the United States. On average, that's more than 38 million a day! Before each transaction, the card owner is required to enter his or her PIN (personal identification number). When an ATM card is issued, many financial institutions have the applicant select a four-digit PIN. There are 10 possible choices for the first digit of the PIN, 10 possible choices for the second digit, and so on. Write the total number of possible choices of a PIN as an exponential expression. Then evaluate the expression. $10^4 = 10{,}000$

3 Divide exponential expressions that have like bases.

To develop a rule for dividing exponential expressions that have the same base, we now consider the fraction

$$\frac{4^5}{4^2}$$

where the exponent in the numerator is greater than the exponent in the denominator.

We can simplify this fraction as follows:

$$\frac{4^5}{4^2} = \frac{4 \cdot 4 \cdot 4 \cdot 4 \cdot 4}{4 \cdot 4}$$ Write each expression without using exponents.

$$= \frac{\overset{1}{\cancel{4}} \cdot \overset{1}{\cancel{4}} \cdot 4 \cdot 4 \cdot 4}{\underset{1}{\cancel{4}} \cdot \underset{1}{\cancel{4}}}$$ Remove the common factors of 4.

$$= 4^3$$

We can quickly find this result if we keep the common base 4, and subtract the exponents on 4^5 and 4^2.

$$\frac{4^5}{4^2} = 4^{5-2} = 4^3$$

This example suggests another rule for exponents.

Quotient Rule for Exponents

To divide exponential expressions that have the same base, keep the common base and subtract the exponents. If m and n represent natural numbers, $m > n$, and $x \neq 0$, then

$$\frac{x^m}{x^n} = x^{m-n}$$

EXAMPLE 4 Simplify. Assume that there are no divisions by 0.

a. $\frac{20^{16}}{20^9}$ **b.** $\frac{x^4}{x^3}$ **c.** $\frac{a^3b^8}{ab^5}$

Strategy We will identify exponential expressions that have the same base in each quotient. Then we will use the quotient rule for exponents to simplify the expression.

WHY The quotient rule for exponents is used to divide exponential expressions that have the same base.

Solution

a. To simplify $\frac{20^{16}}{20^9}$ means to write it in an equivalent form using one base and one exponent.

$$\frac{20^{16}}{20^9} = 20^{16-9}$$ Use the quotient rule for exponents: Keep the common base, which is 20, and subtract the exponents.

$$= 20^7$$ Perform the subtraction.

b. $$\frac{x^4}{x^3} = x^{4-3}$$ Keep the common base x and subtract the exponents.

$$= x^1$$ Perform the subtraction.

$$= x$$

c. $$\frac{a^3b^8}{ab^5} = \frac{a^3}{a} \cdot \frac{b^8}{b^5}$$ Group the like bases together. Write a as a^1.

$$= a^{3-1}b^{8-5}$$ Keep the common base a and subtract the exponents. Keep the common base b and subtract the exponents.

$$= a^2b^3$$ Perform the subtractions.

Self Check 4

Simplify:

a. $\frac{55^{30}}{55^5}$ 55^{25}

b. $\frac{a^5}{a^3}$ a^2

c. $\frac{b^{15}c^4}{b^4c}$ $b^{11}c^3$

Now Try **Problems 62, 65, and 70**

Teaching Example 4 Simplify:
a. $\frac{13^{11}}{13^2}$ b. $\frac{x^8}{x^2}$ c. $\frac{y^4z^9}{yz^7}$
Answers:
a. 13^9 b. x^6 c. y^3z^2

Caution! Don't make the mistake of dividing the bases when using the quotient rule. Keep the *same* base and subtract the *exponents*.

$$\frac{20^{16}}{20^9} \neq 1^7$$

Self Check 5

Simplify: $\frac{b^2b^6b}{b^4b^4}$ b

Now Try **Problem 74**

Teaching Example 5 Simplify: $\frac{x^5x^3x}{x^2x^3}$

Answer:
x^4

EXAMPLE 5 Simplify: $\frac{a^3a^5a^7}{a^4a}$

Strategy We will use the product rule and quotient rule to write an equivalent expression using one base and one exponent.

WHY The expression involves multiplication and division of exponential expressions that have the same base.

Solution

We use the product rule for exponents to simplify the numerator and denominator separately and proceed as follows.

$\frac{a^3a^5a^7}{a^4a} = \frac{a^{15}}{a^5}$ In the numerator, keep the common base a and add the exponents. In the denominator, keep the common base a and add the exponents.

$= a^{15-5}$ Use the quotient rule for exponents: Keep the common base a and subtract the exponents.

$= a^{10}$ Perform the subtraction.

Success Tip Sometimes more than one rule for exponents is needed to simplify an expression.

It is important to pay close attention to the operation between the exponential expressions and then use the appropriate rules. To add or subtract exponential expressions, they must be like terms. To multiply or divide exponential expressions, only the bases need to be the same.

$x^2 + x^3$ The operation is addition and these are not like terms because the exponents are different. We cannot simplify the expression any further.

$x^4 + x^4 = 2x^4$ The operation is addition and these are like terms. We can simplify the expression by adding the numerical coefficients and keeping the variable expression.

$x^7 \cdot x^3 = x^{10}$ The operation is multiplication and the bases are the same. We keep the base and add the exponents.

$\frac{x^4}{x^3} = x$ The operation is division and the bases are the same. We keep the base and subtract the exponents. An exponent of 1 need not be written.

4 Raise exponential expressions to a power.

To find another rule for exponents, we consider the expression $(x^3)^4$, which can be written as $x^3 \cdot x^3 \cdot x^3 \cdot x^3$. Because each of the four factors of x^3 contains three factors of x, there are $4 \cdot 3$ (or 12) factors of x. This product can be written as x^{12}.

$$(x^3)^4 = x^3 \cdot x^3 \cdot x^3 \cdot x^3$$

$$= \underbrace{\overbrace{x \cdot x \cdot x \cdot x \cdot x \cdot x \cdot x \cdot x \cdot x \cdot x \cdot x \cdot x}^{12 \text{ factors of } x}}$$

$$= x^{12}$$

We can quickly find this result if we keep the base of x and multiply the exponents.

$$(x^3)^4 = x^{3 \cdot 4} = x^{12}$$

This illustrates the following rule for exponents:

Power Rule for Exponents

To raise an exponential expression to a power, keep the base and multiply the exponents. If m and n represent natural numbers, then

$$(x^m)^n = x^{m \cdot n} \quad \text{or, more simply,} \quad (x^m)^n = x^{mn}$$

EXAMPLE 6 Simplify each expression: **a.** $(2^3)^7$ **b.** $(z^8)^8$

Strategy In each case, we want to write an equivalent expression using one base and one exponent. We will use the power rule for exponents to do this.

WHY Each expression is a power of a power.

Solution

a. To simplify $(2^3)^7$ means to write it in an equivalent form using one base and one exponent.

$(2^3)^7 = 2^{3 \cdot 7}$ Keep the base of 2 and multiply the exponents.

$= 2^{21}$ Perform the multiplication.

b. $(z^8)^8 = z^{8 \cdot 8}$ Keep the base and multiply the exponents.

$= z^{64}$ Perform the multiplication.

Self Check 6

Simplify each expression:

a. $(5^4)^6$ 5^{24}

b. $(y^5)^2$ y^{10}

Now Try **Problems 78 and 84**

Teaching Example 6 Simplify:
a. $(7^3)^2$ b. $(a^4)^5$
Answers:
a. 7^6 b. a^{20}

EXAMPLE 7 Simplify each expression: **a.** $(x^2x^5)^2$ **b.** $(z^2)^4(z^3)^3$

Strategy In each case, we want to write an equivalent expression using one base and one exponent. We will use the product and power rules for exponents to do this.

WHY The expressions involve products and powers of exponential expressions that have the same base.

Solution

a. We begin by using the product rule for exponents. Then we use the power rule.

$(x^2x^5)^2 = (x^7)^2$ Within the parentheses, keep the base x and add the exponents.

$= x^{14}$ Keep the base x and multiply the exponents.

Self Check 7

Simplify each expression:

a. $(a^4a^3)^3$ a^{21}

b. $(a^3)^3(a^4)^2$ a^{17}

Now Try **Problems 86 and 90**

Teaching Example 7 Simplify each expression:
a. $(r^2r^3)^4$ b. $(b^2)^5(b^3)^2$
Answers:
a. r^{20} b. b^{16}

b. We begin by using the power rule for exponents twice. Then we use the product rule.

$(z^2)^4(z^3)^3 = z^8z^9$ For each power of z raised to a power, keep the base z and multiply the exponents.

$= z^{17}$ Keep the base z and add the exponents.

5 Find powers of products and quotients.

To develop two more rules for exponents, we consider the expression $(2x)^3$, which is a *power of the product* of 2 and x, and the expression $\left(\frac{2}{x}\right)^3$, which is a *power of the quotient* of 2 and x.

$$
\begin{aligned}
(2x)^3 &= (2x)(2x)(2x) \\
&= (2 \cdot 2 \cdot 2)(x \cdot x \cdot x) \\
&= 2^3x^3 \\
&= 8x^3
\end{aligned}
$$

$$\left(\frac{2}{x}\right)^3 = \left(\frac{2}{x}\right)\left(\frac{2}{x}\right)\left(\frac{2}{x}\right) \quad \text{Assume } x \neq 0$$

$$= \frac{2 \cdot 2 \cdot 2}{x \cdot x \cdot x} \quad \text{Multiply the numerators. Multiply the denominators.}$$

$$= \frac{2^3}{x^3}$$

$$= \frac{8}{x^3} \quad \text{Evaluate: } 2^3 = 8.$$

These examples illustrate the following rules for exponents:

Powers of a Product and a Quotient

To raise a product to a power, we raise each factor of the product to that power. To raise a fraction to a power, we raise both the numerator and the denominator to that power. If n represents a natural number, then

$$(xy)^n = x^ny^n \quad \text{and if} \quad y \neq 0, \quad \text{then} \quad \left(\frac{x}{y}\right)^n = \frac{x^n}{y^n}$$

Self Check 8

Simplify:

a. $(2t)^4$ $16t^4$

b. $(c^3d^4)^6$ $c^{18}d^{24}$

c. $(-3ab^5)^3$ $-27a^3b^{15}$

Now Try **Problems 94, 96, and 99**

Teaching Example 8 Simplify:
a. $(5x)^3$ b. $(a^4b^3)^3$ c. $(-4a^5b^3)^2$
Answers:
a. $125x^3$ b. $a^{12}b^9$ c. $16a^{10}b^6$

EXAMPLE 8 Simplify: **a.** $(3c)^3$ **b.** $(x^2y^3)^5$ **c.** $(-2a^3b)^2$

Strategy We will use the power of a product rule for exponents to write the simplified expression.

WHY Within each set of parentheses is a product, and each of those products is raised to a power.

Solution

a. Since $3c$ is the product of 3 and c, the expression $(3c)^3$ is a power of a product.

$(3c)^3 = 3^3c^3$ Use the power rule for products: Raise each factor of the product 3c to the 3rd power.

$= 27c^3$ Evaluate: $3^3 = 27$.

b. $(x^2y^3)^5 = (x^2)^5(y^3)^5$ Raise each factor of the product x^2y^3 to the 5th power.

$= x^{10}y^{15}$ For each power of a power, keep the base and multiply the exponents.

c. $(-2a^3b)^2 = (-2)^2(a^3)^2b^2$ Raise each of the three factors of the product $-2a^3b$ to the 2nd power.

$= 4a^6b^2$ Evaluate: $(-2)^2 = 4$. Keep the base a and multiply the exponents.

EXAMPLE 9 Simplify: $\dfrac{(a^3b^4)^2}{ab^5}$

Strategy We will use the power of a product rule and the quotient rule for exponents to write the simplified expression.

WHY The expression involves a power of a product and a quotient of exponential expressions that have the same base.

Solution

$$\frac{(a^3b^4)^2}{ab^5} = \frac{(a^3)^2(b^4)^2}{ab^5}$$ In the numerator, raise each factor within the parentheses to the 2nd power.

$$= \frac{a^6b^8}{ab^5}$$ In the numerator, for each power of a power, keep the base and multiply the exponents.

$$= a^{6-1}b^{8-5}$$ Keep each of the bases, a and b, and subtract the exponents.

$$= a^5b^3$$ Perform the subtractions.

Self Check 9

Simplify: $\dfrac{(c^4d^5)^3}{c^2d^3}$ $c^{10}d^{12}$

Now Try **Problem 101**

Teaching Example 9 Simplify: $\dfrac{(5x^3y^4)^2}{x^2y^3}$

Answer: $25x^4y^5$

EXAMPLE 10 Simplify: **a.** $\left(\dfrac{4}{k}\right)^3$ **b.** $\left(\dfrac{3x^2}{2y^3}\right)^5$

Strategy In each case, we will use the power of a quotient rule for exponents to simplify the expression.

WHY Each expression is a quotient raised to a power.

Solution

a. Since $\dfrac{4}{k}$ is the quotient of 4 and k, the expresion $\left(\dfrac{4}{k}\right)^3$ is a power of a quotient.

$$\left(\frac{4}{k}\right)^3 = \frac{4^3}{k^3}$$ Use the power rule for quotients: Raise the numerator and denominator to the 3rd power.

$$= \frac{64}{k^3}$$ Evaluate: $4^3 = 64$.

b. $$\left(\frac{3x^2}{2y^3}\right)^5 = \frac{(3x^2)^5}{(2y^3)^5}$$ Raise the numerator and the denominator to the 5th power.

$$= \frac{3^5(x^2)^5}{2^5(y^3)^5}$$ In the numerator and denominator, raise each factor within the parentheses to the 5th power.

$$= \frac{243x^{10}}{32y^{15}}$$ Evaluate 3^5 and 2^5. For each power of a power, keep the base and multiply the exponents.

Self Check 10

Simplify:

a. $\left(\dfrac{x}{7}\right)^3$ $\dfrac{x^3}{343}$

b. $\left(\dfrac{2x^3}{3y^2}\right)^4$ $\dfrac{16x^{12}}{81y^8}$

Now Try **Problems 106 and 107**

Teaching Example 10 Simplify: a. $\left(\dfrac{a}{3}\right)^4$ b. $\left(\dfrac{5x^3}{3y^4}\right)^3$

Answers: a. $\dfrac{a^4}{81}$ b. $\dfrac{125x^9}{27y^{12}}$

EXAMPLE 11 Simplify: $\dfrac{(5b)^9}{(5b)^6}$

Strategy We will use the quotient rule for exponents and then the power of a product rule.

WHY The expression involves division of exponential expressions that have the same base, $5b$.

Solution

$$\frac{(5b)^9}{(5b)^6} = (5b)^{9-6}$$ Keep the common base $5b$, and subtract the exponents.

$$= (5b)^3$$ Perform the subtraction.

$$= 5^3b^3$$ Raise each factor within the parentheses to the 3rd power.

$$= 125b^3$$ Evaluate: $5^3 = 125$.

Self Check 11

Simplify: $\dfrac{(-2h)^{20}}{(-2h)^{14}}$ $64h^6$

Now Try **Problem 109**

Teaching Example 11 Simplify: $\dfrac{(3x)^5}{(3x)^2}$

Answer: $27x^3$

The rules for natural-number exponents are summarized below.

Rules for Exponents

If n represents a natural number, then

$$x^n = \overbrace{x \cdot x \cdot x \cdot \cdots \cdot x}^{n \text{ factors of } x}$$

If m and n represent natural numbers and there are no divisions by zero, then

Exponent of 1	***Product Rule***	***Quotient Rule***
$x^1 = x$	$x^m x^n = x^{m+n}$	$\frac{x^m}{x^n} = x^{m-n}$
Power Rule	***Power of a Product***	***Power of a Quotient***
$(x^m)^n = x^{mn}$	$(xy)^n = x^n y^n$	$\left(\frac{x}{y}\right)^n = \frac{x^n}{y^n}$

ANSWERS TO SELF CHECKS

1. a. base: x, exponent: 4 **b.** base: $5x$, exponent: 4 **2.** $(a+b)^6$ **3. a.** 7^{15} **b.** z^4 **c.** x^{11} **d.** s^8t^7 **e.** $(r+s)^7$ **4. a.** 55^{25} **b.** a^2 **c.** $b^{11}c^3$ **5.** b **6. a.** 5^{24} **b.** y^{10} **7. a.** a^{21} **b.** a^{17} **8. a.** $16t^4$ **b.** $c^{18}d^{24}$ **c.** $-27a^3b^{15}$ **9.** $c^{10}d^{12}$ **10. a.** $\frac{x^3}{343}$ **b.** $\frac{16x^{12}}{81y^8}$ **11.** $64h^6$

SECTION 6.1 STUDY SET

VOCABULARY

Fill in the blanks.

1. The base of the exponential expression $(-5)^3$ is -5. The exponent is 3.
2. The exponential expression x^4 represents a repeated multiplication where x is to be written as a factor four times.
3. x^n is called a power of x.
4. The expression $(2x^2b)^5$ is a power of a product, and $\left(\frac{2x^2}{b}\right)^5$ is a power of a quotient.

CONCEPTS

Fill in the blanks.

5. $(3x)^4$ means $3x \cdot 3x \cdot 3x \cdot 3x$
6. Using an exponent, $(-5y)(-5y)(-5y)$ can be written as $(-5y)^3$.
7. $x^m x^n = x^{m+n}$
8. $(xy)^n = x^n y^n$
9. $\left(\frac{a}{b}\right)^n = \frac{a^n}{b^n}$
10. $(a^b)^c = a^{bc}$
11. $\frac{x^m}{x^n} = x^{m-n}$
12. $x = x^1$
13. $(x^m)^n = x^{mn}$
14. $(t^3)^2 = t^3 \cdot t^3$
15. Write a power of a product that has two factors. $(3x^2)^6$ (answers may vary)
16. Write a power of a quotient. $\left(\frac{3d^2}{b}\right)^2$ (answers may vary)
17. To simplify $(2y^3z^2)^4$, how many factors within the parentheses must be raised to the fourth power? 3
18. To simplify $\left(\frac{y^3}{z^2}\right)^4$ what two expressions must be raised to the fourth power? y^3 and z^2

NOTATION

Complete each solution.

19. $(x^4x^2)^3 = (x^6)^3$
$= x^{18}$
20. $\frac{a^3a^4}{a^2} = \frac{a^7}{a^2}$
$= a^{7-2}$
$= a^5$

▶ Selected exercises available online at **www.webassign.net/brookscole**

Evaluate each expression.

21. $(-4)^2$ 16 ▶ **22.** $(-5)^2$ 25

23. -4^2 -16 ▶ **24.** -5^2 -25

GUIDED PRACTICE

Identify the base and the exponent in each expression. See Example 1.

25. 4^3 base 4, exponent 3

26. $(-8)^2$ base -8, exponent 2

27. x^5 base x, exponent 5

28. $\left(\frac{5}{x}\right)^3$ base $\frac{5}{x}$, exponent 3

29. $(-3x)^2$ base $-3x$, exponent 2

▶ **30.** $-x^4$ base x, exponent 4

31. $-\frac{1}{3}y^6$ base y, exponent 6

▶ **32.** $3.14r^4$ base r, exponent 4

Write each expression in an equivalent form using an exponent. See Example 2.

33. $\frac{a}{3}\cdot\frac{a}{3}\cdot\frac{a}{3}$ $\left(\frac{a}{3}\right)^3$

34. $\frac{y}{4}\cdot\frac{y}{4}\cdot\frac{y}{4}\cdot\frac{y}{4}$ $\left(\frac{y}{4}\right)^4$

35. $-\frac{b}{6}\cdot\frac{b}{6}\cdot\frac{b}{6}\cdot\frac{b}{6}\cdot\frac{b}{6}$ $-\left(\frac{b}{6}\right)^5$

▶ **36.** $-\frac{c}{5}\cdot\frac{c}{5}\cdot\frac{c}{5}$ $-\left(\frac{c}{5}\right)^3$

37. $6\cdot x\cdot x\cdot x\cdot x\cdot x$ $6x^5$

38. $-3\cdot y\cdot y\cdot y$ $-3y^3$

39. $(4t)(4t)(4t)(4t)$ $(4t)^4$

40. $(-5u)(-5u)$ $(-5u)^2$

41. $-4\cdot t\cdot t\cdot t$ $-4t^3$

42. $-5\cdot u\cdot u$ $-5u^2$

43. $(x+y)(x+y)$ $(x+y)^2$

44. $(a+b)(a+b)(a+b)(a+b)$ $(a+b)^4$

Simplify each expression. See Example 3.

45. $12^3\cdot 12^4$ 12^7 ▶ **46.** $3^4\cdot 3^6$ 3^{10}

47. $(2^3)(2^2)$ 2^5 **48.** $(5^5)(5^3)$ 5^8

▶ **49.** $a^3\cdot a^3$ a^6 **50.** $m^7\cdot m^7$ m^{14}

51. x^4x^3 x^7 **52.** y^5y^2 y^7

53. a^3aa^5 a^9 **54.** b^2b^3b b^6

55. $y^3(y^2y^4)$ y^9 ▶ **56.** $(y^4y)y^6$ y^{11}

57. $(a^2b^3)(a^3b^3)$ a^5b^6 **58.** $(u^3v^5)(u^4v^5)$ u^7v^{10}

59. $(m+n)^2(m+n)^3$ $(m+n)^5$

60. $(c-d)^3(c-d)^4$ $(c-d)^7$

Simplify each expression. Assume there are no divisions by 0. See Example 4.

61. $\frac{8^{12}}{8^4}$ 8^8 **62.** $\frac{10^4}{10^2}$ 10^2

63. $\frac{12^{15}}{12^{12}}$ 12^3 **64.** $\frac{15^{17}}{15^{10}}$ 15^7

65. $\frac{x^{15}}{x^3}$ x^{12} ▶ **66.** $\frac{y^6}{y^3}$ y^3

67. $\frac{c^{10}}{c^9}$ c **68.** $\frac{h^{20}}{h^{10}}$ h^{10}

69. $\frac{x^2y^8}{xy^4}$ xy^4 **70.** $\frac{p^3q^8}{p^2q^6}$ pq^2

71. $\frac{c^3d^7}{cd}$ c^2d^6 ▶ **72.** $\frac{r^8s^9}{rs}$ r^7s^8

Simplify each expression. Assume there are no divisions by 0. See Example 5.

73. $\frac{m^2m^5m^7}{m^2m}$ m^{11} **74.** $\frac{p^3p^4p^5}{p^2p^6}$ p^4

75. $\frac{a^2a^3a^4}{a^4a^4}$ a ▶ **76.** $\frac{aa^2a^6}{a^2a^3}$ a^4

Simplify each expression. See Example 6.

77. $(3^2)^4$ 3^8 ▶ **78.** $(4^3)^3$ 4^9

79. $(2^3)^5$ 2^{15} **80.** $(5^4)^2$ 5^8

81. $(y^5)^3$ y^{15} **82.** $(b^3)^6$ b^{18}

83. $(m^{50})^{10}$ m^{500} **84.** $(n^{25})^4$ n^{100}

Simplify each expression. See Example 7.

85. $(x^2x^3)^5$ x^{25} **86.** $(y^3y^4)^4$ y^{28}

87. $(b^3b^4)^2$ b^{14} ▶ **88.** $(m^4m^2)^3$ m^{18}

89. $(y^3)^2(y^2)^4$ y^{14} **90.** $(b^4)^3(b^2)^2$ b^{16}

91. $(p^2)^3(p^3)^3$ p^{15} **92.** $(q^4)^2(q^2)^3$ q^{14}

Simplify each expression. See Example 8.

93. $(4p^3)^3$ $64p^9$ **94.** $(3n^2)^4$ $81n^8$

▶ **95.** $(a^3b^2)^3$ a^9b^6 **96.** $(r^3s^2)^2$ r^6s^4

97. $(p^2q^4)^2$ p^4q^8 **98.** $(r^3s^5)^3$ r^9s^{15}

▶ **99.** $(-2r^2s^3)^3$ $-8r^6s^9$ **100.** $(-3x^2y^4)^2$ $9x^4y^8$

Simplify each expression. See Example 9.

101. $\frac{(x^2y^3)^2}{xy^2}$ x^3y^4 **102.** $\frac{(a^3b^4)^3}{a^3b^4}$ a^6b^8

103. $\frac{(p^5q^2)^3}{p^{10}q^4}$ p^5q^2 ▶ **104.** $\frac{(m^5n^2)^3}{m^{12}n^3}$ m^3n^3

Simplify each expression. See Example 10.

105. $\left(\frac{a}{b}\right)^3$ $\frac{a^3}{b^3}$ ▶ **106.** $\left(\frac{r}{s}\right)^4$ $\frac{r^4}{s^4}$

107. $\left(\frac{2x^2}{y^3}\right)^5$ $\frac{32x^{10}}{y^{15}}$ **108.** $\left(\frac{3u^4}{2v^2}\right)^6$ $\frac{729u^{24}}{64v^{12}}$

Simplify each expression. See Example 11.

109. $\dfrac{(3z)^5}{(3z)^2}$ $27z^3$

110. $\dfrac{(2t)^{10}}{(2t)^5}$ $32t^5$

111. $\dfrac{(6k)^7}{(6k)^4}$ $216k^3$

112. $\dfrac{(-3a)^{12}}{(-3a)^{10}}$ $9a^2$

TRY IT YOURSELF

Simplify each expression. Assume there are no divisions by 0.

113. $xy^2 \cdot x^2y$ x^3y^3

114. $s^8t^2s^2t^7$ $s^{10}t^9$

115. $(3zz^2z^3)^5$ $243z^{30}$

116. $(4t^3t^6t^2)^2$ $16t^{22}$

117. $(x^5)^2(x^7)^3$ x^{31}

118. $(y^3y)^2(y^2)^2$ y^{12}

119. $(uv)^4$ u^4v^4

120. $(xy)^3$ x^3y^3

121. $\left(\dfrac{-2a}{b}\right)^5$ $-\dfrac{32a^5}{b^5}$

122. $\left(\dfrac{-2t}{3}\right)^4$ $\dfrac{16t^4}{81}$

123. $\dfrac{(a^2b)^{15}}{(a^2b)^9}$ $a^{12}b^6$

124. $\dfrac{(s^2t^3)^4}{(s^2t^3)^2}$ s^4t^6

125. $\dfrac{(ab^2)^3}{(ab)^2}$ ab^4

126. $\dfrac{(m^3n^4)^3}{(mn^2)^3}$ m^6n^6

127. $\dfrac{(r^4s^3)^4}{(rs^3)^3}$ $r^{13}s^3$

128. $\dfrac{(x^2y^5)^5}{(x^3y)^2}$ x^4y^{23}

129. $\left(\dfrac{y^3y}{2yy^2}\right)^3$ $\dfrac{y^3}{8}$

130. $\left(\dfrac{2y^3y}{yy^2}\right)^3$ $8y^3$

131. $\left(\dfrac{3t^3t^4t^5}{4t^2t^6}\right)^3$ $\dfrac{27t^{12}}{64}$

132. $\left(\dfrac{4t^3t^4t^5}{3t^2t^6}\right)^3$ $\dfrac{64t^{12}}{27}$

133. $\left(\dfrac{t^2}{2}\right)\left(\dfrac{t^2}{2}\right)\left(\dfrac{t^2}{2}\right)$ $\dfrac{t^6}{8}$

134. $c \cdot c \cdot c \cdot d \cdot d$ c^3d^2

135. $(cd^4)(cd)$ c^2d^5

136. $ab^3c^4 \cdot ab^4c^2$ $a^2b^7c^6$

137. $\dfrac{y^3y^4}{yy^2}$ y^4

138. $\dfrac{b^4b^5}{b^2b^3}$ b^4

APPLICATIONS

Find each area or volume. You may leave π in your answer.

139. a^{10} mi^2

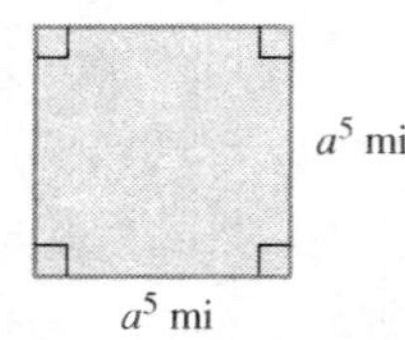

140. $16y^6\pi$ yd^2

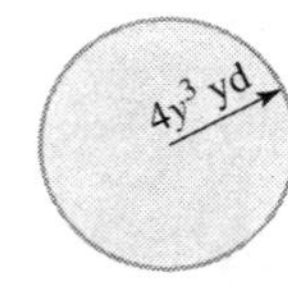

141. x^9 m^3

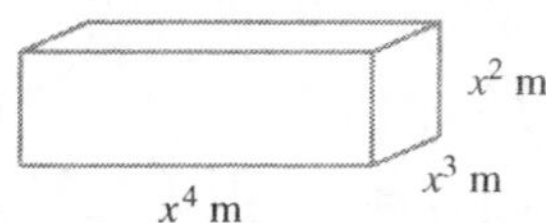

142. x^{21} cm^3

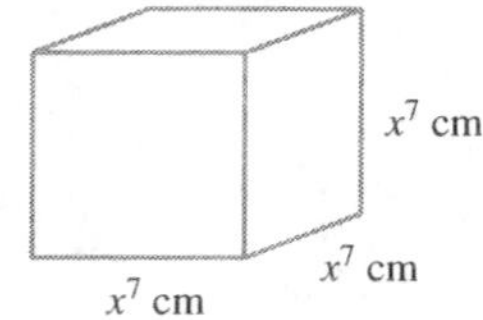

143. ART HISTORY Leonardo da Vinci's drawing relating a human figure to a square and a circle is shown.

a. Find an expression that represents the area of the square if the man's height is $5x$ feet. $25x^2$ ft^2

b. Find an expression that represents the area of the circle if the distance from his waist to his feet is $3x$ feet. Leave π in your answer. $9\pi x^2$ ft^2

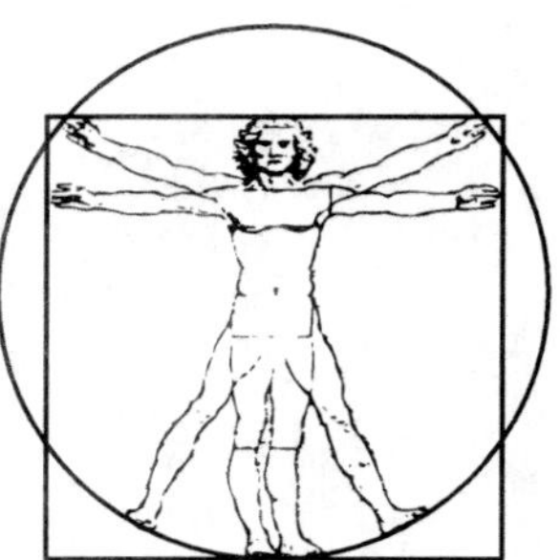

144. PACKAGING Use the illustration to find the volume of the bowling ball and the cardboard box it is packaged in. You may leave π in your answer. $36\pi x^3$ in.^{3}, $216x^3$ in.^{3}

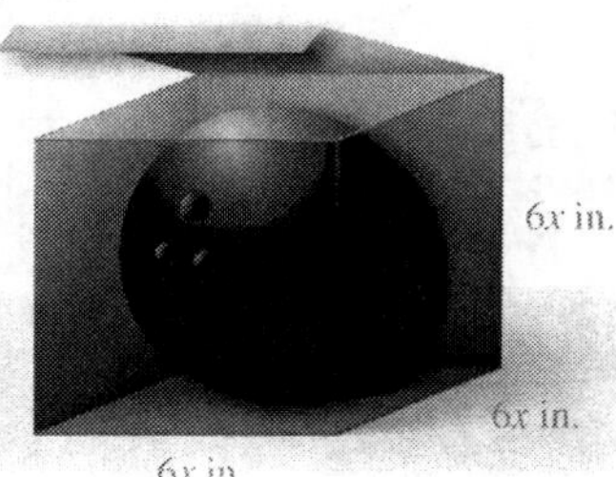

145. BOUNCING BALLS A ball is dropped from a height of 32 feet. Each rebound is one-half of its previous height.

a. Draw a diagram of the path of the ball, showing four bounces.

b. Explain why the expressions $32\left(\frac{1}{2}\right)$, $32\left(\frac{1}{2}\right)^2$, $32\left(\frac{1}{2}\right)^3$, and $32\left(\frac{1}{2}\right)^4$ represent the height of the ball on the first, second, third, and fourth bounces, respectively. Find the heights of the first four bounces. 16 ft, 8 ft, 4 ft, 2 ft

146. HAVING BABIES The probability that a couple will have n baby boys in a row is given by the formula $\left(\frac{1}{2}\right)^n$ Find the probability that a couple will have four baby boys in a row. $\frac{1}{16}$

147. COMPUTERS Text is stored by computers using a sequence of eight 0's and 1's. Such a sequence is called a **byte.** An example of a byte is 10101110.

a. Write four other bytes, all ending in 1. 11000001, 11010001, 11001101, 11000011 (answers may vary)

b. Each of the eight digits of a byte can be chosen in *two* ways (either 0 or 1). The total number of different bytes can be represented by an exponential expression with base 2. What is it? 2^8

148. INVESTING Guess the answer to the following problem. Then use a calculator to find the correct answer. Were you close?

If the value of 1¢ is to double every day, what will the penny be worth after 31 days? $21,474,836.48

WRITING

149. Explain the mistake.

$$2^3 \cdot 2^2 = 4^5$$
$$= 1{,}024$$

150. Are the expressions $2x^3$ and $(2x)^3$ equivalent? Explain.

151. Is the operation of raising to a power commutative? That is, is $a^b = b^a$? Explain.

152. When a number is raised to a power, is the result always larger than the original number? Support your answer with some examples.

REVIEW

Match each equation with its graph below.

153. $y = 2x - 1$ c

154. $y = 3x - 1$ a

155. $y = 3$ d

156. $x = 3$ b

a.

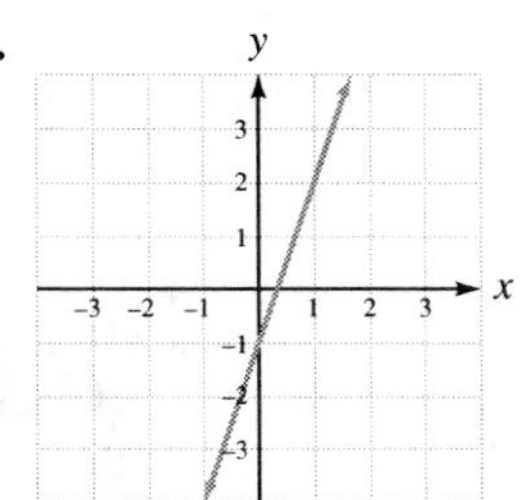

b.

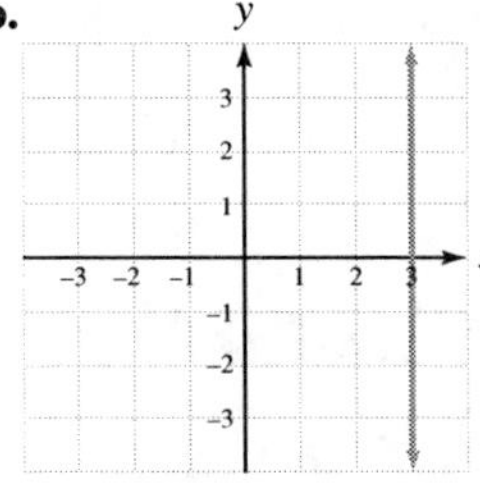

c.

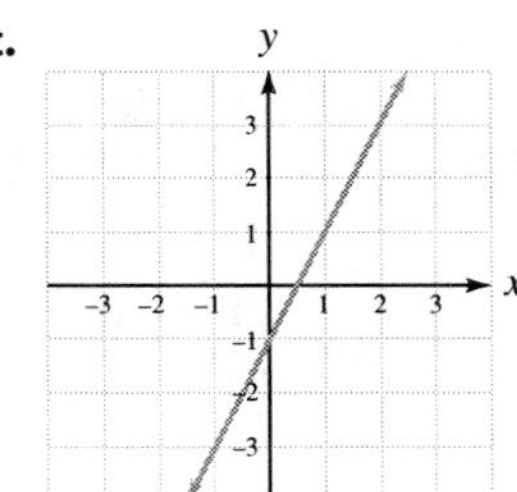

d.

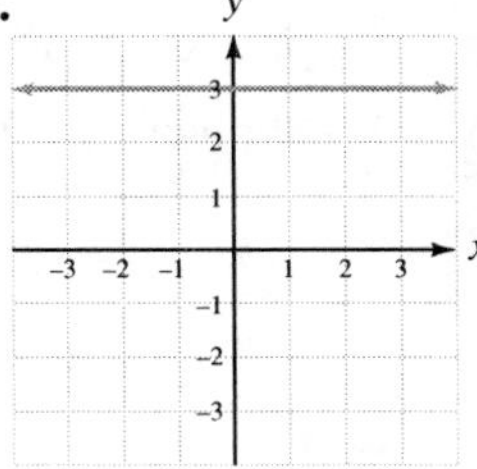

SECTION 6.2
Negative and Zero Exponents

Objectives

1. Use the zero exponent rule.
2. Use the negative integer exponent rule.
3. Use exponent rules to write equivalent expressions with positive exponents.
4. Use all exponent rules to simplify expressions.
5. Use exponent rules with variable exponents.

In the previous section, we discussed natural-number exponents. We now extend the discussion to include exponents that are zero and exponents that are negative integers.

1 Use the zero exponent rule.

When we discussed the quotient rule for exponents in the previous section, the exponent in the numerator was always greater than the exponent in the denominator. We now consider what happens when the exponents are equal. To develop the definition of a zero exponent, we will simplify the expression $\frac{5^3}{5^3}$ in two ways and compare the results. If we use the quotient rule for exponents, where the exponents in the numerator and denominator are equal, we obtain 5^0. However, by removing the common factors of 5, we obtain 1.

$$\frac{5^3}{5^3} = 5^{3-3} = 5^0 \qquad \frac{5^3}{5^3} = \frac{\overset{1}{\cancel{5}} \cdot \overset{1}{\cancel{5}} \cdot \overset{1}{\cancel{5}}}{\underset{1}{\cancel{5}} \cdot \underset{1}{\cancel{5}} \cdot \underset{1}{\cancel{5}}} = 1$$

These must be equal.

For this reason, we conclude that $5^0 = 1$. This example suggests the following rule.

Zero Exponents

Any nonzero real number raised to the 0 power is 1. For any nonzero real number x,

$$x^0 = 1$$

Self Check 1

Write each expression without using exponents:

a. $(-0.115)^0$ 1

b. $-5a^0b$ $-5b$

Now Try **Problems 21, 23, and 24**

Teaching Example 1 Write each expression without using exponents:
a. 30^0 b. $5y^0$ c. $(5y)^0$
Answers:
a. 1 b. 5 c. 1

EXAMPLE 1 Write each expression without using exponents:

a. $\left(\frac{1}{13}\right)^0$ **b.** $3x^0$ **c.** $(3x)^0$

Strategy We will note the base and exponent in each case. Since each expression has an exponent that is zero, we will use the zero-exponent rule.

WHY If an expression contains a nonzero base raised to the 0 power, we can replace it with 1.

Solution

a. $\left(\frac{1}{13}\right)^0 = 1$ The base is $\frac{1}{13}$; the exponent is 0.

b. $3x^0 = 3(1)$ The base is x; the exponent is 0.

$= 3$

c. $(3x)^0 = 1$ The base is $3x$; the exponent is 0.

Parts b and c point out that $3x^0 \neq (3x)^0$.

Caution! Remember, the base is only that which is directly in front of the exponent unless there are parentheses. For $3x^0$, the base is x and the exponent is 0. For $(3x)^0$, the base is $3x$ and the exponent 0.

2 Use the negative integer exponent rule.

To develop the definition of a negative exponent, we will simplify the expression $\frac{6^2}{6^5}$ in two ways. If we use the quotient rule for exponents, where the exponent in the numerator is less than the exponent in the denominator, we obtain 6^{-3}. However, by removing the common factors of 6, we obtain $\frac{1}{6^3}$.

$$\frac{6^2}{6^5} = 6^{2-5} = 6^{-3} \qquad \frac{6^2}{6^5} = \frac{\overset{1}{\cancel{6}} \cdot \overset{1}{\cancel{6}}}{\underset{1}{\cancel{6}} \cdot \underset{1}{\cancel{6}} \cdot 6 \cdot 6 \cdot 6} = \frac{1}{6^3}$$

These must be equal.

For this reason, we conclude that $6^{-3} = \frac{1}{6^3}$. In general, we have the following rule.

Negative Exponents

If x represents any nonzero number and n represents a natural number, then

$$x^{-n} = \frac{1}{x^n}$$

In words, x^{-n} is the reciprocal of x^n.

The definition of a negative exponent states that another way to write x^{-n} is to write its reciprocal, changing the sign of the exponent. We can use this definition to write expressions that contain negative exponents as expressions without negative exponents.

The Language of Algebra The *negative integers* are: $-1, -2, -3, -4, -5, \ldots$

EXAMPLE 2 Simplify by using the definition of negative exponents:
a. 3^{-5} **b.** $(-2)^{-3}$

Strategy Since each expression has an exponent that is negative, we will use the negative exponent rule.

WHY This rule enables us to write an exponential expression that has a negative exponent in an equivalent form using a positive exponent.

Solution

a. $3^{-5} = \frac{1}{3^5}$ Write the reciprocal of 3^{-5} and change the exponent from -5 to 5.

$= \frac{1}{243}$ Evaluate 3^5.

b. $(-2)^{-3} = \frac{1}{(-2)^3}$ Write the reciprocal of $(-2)^{-3}$ and change the exponent from -3 to 3.

$= -\frac{1}{8}$ Evaluate $(-2)^3$.

Self Check 2

Simplify by using the definition of negative exponents:
a. 4^{-4} $\frac{1}{256}$
b. $(-5)^{-3}$ $-\frac{1}{125}$

Now Try **Problems 28 and 30**

Teaching Example 2 Simplify by using the definition of negative exponents:
a. 5^{-2} b. $(-3)^{-4}$
Answers:
a. $\frac{1}{25}$ b. $\frac{1}{81}$

Caution! A negative exponent does not indicate a negative number. It indicates a reciprocal. For example:

$$4^{-2} = \frac{1}{4^2} = \frac{1}{16} \qquad 4^{-2} \neq -16 \qquad 4^{-2} \neq -\frac{1}{4^2}$$

3 Use exponent rules to write equivalent expressions with positive exponents.

Negative exponents can appear in the numerator and/or the denominator of a fraction. To develop rules for such situations, we consider the following example.

$$\frac{a^{-4}}{b^{-3}} = \frac{\frac{1}{a^4}}{\frac{1}{b^3}} = \frac{1}{a^4} \div \frac{1}{b^3} = \frac{1}{a^4} \cdot \frac{b^3}{1} = \frac{b^3}{a^4}$$

We can obtain this result in a simpler way. In $\frac{a^{-4}}{b^{-3}}$, we can move a^{-4} from the numerator to the denominator and change the sign of the exponent, and we can move b^{-3} from the denominator to the numerator and change the sign of the exponent.

$$\frac{a^{-4}}{b^{-3}} = \frac{b^3}{a^4}$$

The Language of Algebra *Factors* of a numerator or denominator may be moved *across the fraction bar* if we change the sign of their exponent.

This example suggests the following rules.

Changing from Negative to Positive Exponents

A factor can be moved from the denominator to the numerator or from the numerator to the denominator of a fraction if the sign of its exponent is changed.

For any nonzero real numbers x and y, and any integers m and n,

$$\frac{1}{x^{-n}} = x^n \qquad \text{and} \qquad \frac{x^{-m}}{y^{-n}} = \frac{y^n}{x^m}$$

These rules streamline the process when simplifying fractions involving negative exponents.

Self Check 3

Simplify by using the definition of negative exponents:

a. $\frac{1}{9^{-1}}$ 9

b. $\frac{8^{-2}}{7^{-1}}$ $\frac{7}{64}$

Now Try **Problems 32 and 34**

Teaching Example 3 Simplify by using the definition of negative exponents:

a. $\frac{1}{7^{-2}}$ b. $\frac{4^{-2}}{11^{-1}}$

Answers:

a. 49 b. $\frac{11}{16}$

EXAMPLE 3 Simplify by using the definition of negative exponents:

a. $\frac{1}{5^{-2}}$ **b.** $\frac{2^{-3}}{3^{-4}}$

Strategy Since the exponents are negative numbers, we will use the negative exponent rule.

WHY It is usually easier to simplify exponential expressions if the exponents are positive.

Solution

a. $\frac{1}{5^{-2}} = 5^2$ Move 5^{-2} to the numerator and change the sign of the exponent.

$= 25$ Evaluate 5^2.

b. $\frac{2^{-3}}{3^{-4}} = \frac{3^4}{2^3}$ Move 2^{-3} to the denominator and change the sign of the exponent. Move 3^{-4} to the numerator and change the sign of the exponent.

$= \frac{81}{8}$ Evaluate $3^4 = 81$ and $2^3 = 8$.

EXAMPLE 4 Simplify by using the definition of negative exponents. Assume that no denominators are zero.

a. x^{-4} **b.** $\frac{x^{-3}}{y^{-7}}$ **c.** $(-2x)^{-2}$ **d.** $-2x^{-2}$

Strategy We will note the base and exponent in each case. Since each expression has exponents that are negative numbers, we will use the negative exponent rule.

WHY The negative exponent rule enables us to write an exponential expression that has negative exponents in an equivalent form using positive exponents.

Solution

a. $x^{-4} = \dfrac{1}{x^4}$

b. $\dfrac{x^{-3}}{y^{-7}} = \dfrac{y^7}{x^3}$

c. $(-2x)^{-2} = \dfrac{1}{(-2x)^2} = \dfrac{1}{4x^2}$

d. $-2x^{-2} = -2\left(\dfrac{1}{x^2}\right) = -\dfrac{2}{x^2}$

Self Check 4

Simplify by using the definition of negative exponents:

a. a^{-5} **b.** $\dfrac{r^{-4}}{s^{-5}}$ **c.** $3y^{-3}$

Now Try **Problems 36, 38, 40, and 42**

Self Check 4 Answers

a. $\dfrac{1}{a^5}$ b. $\dfrac{s^5}{r^4}$ c. $\dfrac{3}{y^3}$

Teaching Example 4 Simplify by using the definition of negative exponents:

a. b^{-1} b. $\dfrac{a^{-3}}{b^{-4}}$

c. $(-3b)^{-2}$ d. $-3b^{-2}$

Answers:

a. $\dfrac{1}{b}$ b. $\dfrac{b^4}{a^3}$ c. $\dfrac{1}{9b^2}$ d. $\dfrac{-3}{b^2}$

When a fraction base is raised to a negative power, we can use rules for exponents to change the sign of the exponent. For example,

$$\left(\frac{x}{y}\right)^{-2} = \frac{x^{-2}}{y^{-2}} = \frac{y^2}{x^2} = \left(\frac{y}{x}\right)^2$$

The exponent is the opposite of −2.
The base is the reciprocal of $\frac{x}{y}$.

This example suggests the following rule.

Negative Exponents and Reciprocals

A fraction raised to a power is equal to the reciprocal of the fraction raised to the opposite power.

For any nonzero real numbers x and y, and any integer n,

$$\left(\frac{x}{y}\right)^{-n} = \left(\frac{y}{x}\right)^n$$

EXAMPLE 5 Write $\left(\dfrac{5}{16}\right)^{-1}$ without using exponents.

Strategy We will use the negative exponent and reciprocal rule.

WHY The expression involves a fraction base to a negative exponent. It is often easier to simplify exponential expressions if the exponents are positive.

Solution

$\left(\dfrac{5}{16}\right)^{-1} = \left(\dfrac{16}{5}\right)^1$ The base is $\frac{5}{16}$ and the exponent is −1. Write the reciprocal of the base and change the sign of the exponent.

$= \dfrac{16^1}{5^1}$ To raise a fraction to a power, we raise both the numerator and the denominator to that power.

$= \dfrac{16}{5}$

Self Check 5

Write $\left(\dfrac{3}{7}\right)^{-2}$ without using exponents. $\frac{49}{9}$

Now Try **Problem 44**

Teaching Example 5 Write $\left(\frac{2}{3}\right)^{-3}$ without using exponents.

Answer:

$\frac{27}{8}$

4 Use all exponent rules to simplify expressions.

The rules for exponents involving products, powers, and quotients are also true for zero and negative exponents.

Summary of Exponent Rules

If m and n represent integers and there are no divisions by zero, then

Product rule	***Power rule***	***Power of a product***
$x^m \cdot x^n = x^{m+n}$	$(x^m)^n = x^{mn}$	$(xy)^n = x^n y^n$
Quotient rule	***Power of a quotient***	***Exponents of 0 and 1***
$\frac{x^m}{x^n} = x^{m-n}$	$\left(\frac{x}{y}\right)^n = \frac{x^n}{y^n}$	$x^0 = 1$ and $x^1 = x$

Negative exponent

$$x^{-n} = \frac{1}{x^n}$$

Negative exponents appearing in fractions

$$\frac{1}{x^{-n}} = x^n \qquad \frac{x^{-m}}{y^{-n}} = \frac{y^n}{x^m} \qquad \left(\frac{x}{y}\right)^{-n} = \left(\frac{y}{x}\right)^n$$

The rules for exponents are used to simplify expressions involving products, quotients, and powers. In general, an expression involving exponents is simplified when

- Each base occurs only once
- There are no parentheses
- There are no negative or zero exponents

Self Check 6

Simplify and write the result without using negative exponents:

a. $(x^4)^{-3}$ $\frac{1}{x^{12}}$

b. $\frac{a^4}{a^8}$ $\frac{1}{a^4}$

c. $\frac{a^{-4}a^{-5}}{a^{-3}}$ $\frac{1}{a^6}$

Now Try **Problems 48, 50, 52, and 54**

Teaching Example 6 Simplify and write the result without using negative exponents:

a. $(x^{-2})^4$ b. $\frac{x^4}{x^6}$ c. $(x^5x^2)^{-2}$ d. $\frac{a^{-3}a^{-6}}{a^{-7}}$

Answers:

a. $\frac{1}{x^8}$ b. $\frac{1}{x^2}$ c. $\frac{1}{x^{14}}$ d. $\frac{1}{a^2}$

EXAMPLE 6 Simplify and write the result without using negative exponents. Assume that no denominators are zero.

a. $(x^{-3})^2$ **b.** $\frac{x^3}{x^7}$ **c.** $(x^3x^2)^{-3}$ **d.** $\frac{y^{-4}y^{-3}}{y^{-20}}$

Strategy In each case, we want to use the exponent rules to write an equivalent expression that uses each base with a positive exponent only once.

WHY The expressions are not in simplest form. In each case either the bases occur as a factor more than once, there are parentheses, or there are negative exponents.

Solution

a. $(x^{-3})^2 = x^{-6}$ Use the power rule. Keep the base and multiply the exponents.

$= \frac{1}{x^6}$ Write the reciprocal of x^{-6} and change the sign of the exponent.

b. $\frac{x^3}{x^7} = x^{3-7}$ Use the quotient rule. Keep the base and subtract the exponents.

$= x^{-4}$ Do the subtraction: $3 - 7 = -4$.

$= \frac{1}{x^4}$ Write the reciprocal of x^{-4} and change the sign of the exponent.

c. $(x^3x^2)^{-3} = (x^5)^{-3}$ Use the product rule. Keep the base and add the exponents.

$= x^{-15}$ Use the power rule. Keep the base and multiply the exponents.

$= \frac{1}{x^{15}}$ Write the reciprocal of x^{-15} and change the sign of the exponent.

d. $\frac{y^{-4}y^{-3}}{y^{-20}} = \frac{y^{-7}}{y^{-20}}$ Use the product rule in the numerator.

$= y^{-7-(-20)}$ Use the quotient rule.

$= y^{13}$ Do the subtraction: $-7 - (-20) = -7 + 20 = 13$.

EXAMPLE 7 Simplify and write the answer without negative exponents. Assume no denominators are zero.

a. $\dfrac{12a^3b^4}{4a^5b^2}$ **b.** $\left(-\dfrac{x^3y^2}{xy^{-3}}\right)^{-2}$

Strategy In each case, we want to use the exponent rules to write an equivalent expression that uses each base with a positive exponent only once.

WHY The expressions are not in simplest form. In each case, either the bases occur as factors more than once, there are parentheses, or there are negative exponents.

Solution

a. $\dfrac{12a^3b^4}{4a^5b^2} = 3a^{3-5}b^{4-2}$ Simplify the numerical coefficients. Use the quotient rule twice.

$= 3a^{-2}b^2$ Do the subtractions.

$= \dfrac{3b^2}{a^2}$ Move a^{-2} to the denominator and change the sign of the exponent.

b. $\left(-\dfrac{x^3y^2}{xy^{-3}}\right)^{-2} = \left(-\dfrac{xy^{-3}}{x^3y^2}\right)^2$ Write the reciprocal of the base and change the sign of the exponent.

$= (-x^{1-3}y^{-3-2})^2$ Use the quotient rule for exponents twice.

$= (-x^{-2}y^{-5})^2$ Do the subtractions.

$= x^{-4}y^{-10}$ Raise each factor to the second power.

$= \dfrac{1}{x^4y^{10}}$ Move x^{-4} and y^{-10} to the denominator and change the sign of the exponents.

Self Check 7

Simplify and write the result without using negative exponents:

a. $\dfrac{20x^5y^3}{15x^2y^8}$ $\dfrac{4x^3}{3y^5}$

b. $\left(\dfrac{x^5y^3}{xy^{-3}}\right)^{-3}$ $\dfrac{1}{x^{12}y^{18}}$

Now Try **Problems 56 and 58**

Teaching Example 7
a. $\dfrac{15a^7b^3}{25ab^{10}}$ b. $\left(\dfrac{a^3b^{-2}}{a^2b^2}\right)^{-4}$
Answers:
a. $\dfrac{3a^6}{5b^7}$ b. $\dfrac{b^{16}}{a^4}$

5 Use exponent rules with variable exponents.

We can apply the rules for exponents to simplify expressions involving variable exponents.

EXAMPLE 8 Simplify. Assume that there are no divisions by 0.

a. $\dfrac{6^n}{6^n}$ **b.** $x^{2m}x^{3m}$ **c.** $\dfrac{y^{2m}}{y^{4m}}$

Strategy We will use the rules for exponents and the rules for adding, subtracting, and multiplying variable expressions.

WHY The exponents are variables.

Solution

a. $\dfrac{6^n}{6^n} = 6^{n-n}$ Keep the common base and subtract the exponents.

$= 6^0$ Combine like terms: $n - n = 0$.

$= 1$ Evaluate: $6^0 = 1$.

b. $x^{2m}x^{3m} = x^{2m+3m}$ Keep the common base and add the exponents.

$= x^{5m}$ Combine like terms: $2m + 3m = 5m$.

c. $\dfrac{y^{2m}}{y^{4m}} = y^{2m-4m}$ Keep the base and subtract the exponents.

$= y^{-2m}$ Combine like terms: $2m - 4m = -2m$.

$= \dfrac{1}{y^{2m}}$ Write the reciprocal of y^{-2m} and change the exponent to $2m$.

Self Check 8

Simplify each expression:

a. $\dfrac{7^m}{7^m}$ 1

b. $z^{3n}z^{2n}$ z^{5n}

c. $\dfrac{z^{3n}}{z^{5n}}$ $\dfrac{1}{z^{2n}}$

Now Try **Problems 60, 62, 66, and 68**

Teaching Example 8 Simplify each expression:
a. $\dfrac{5^{2n}}{5^n}$ b. $x^{3b}x^{5b}$ c. $\dfrac{y^{5b}}{y^{2b}}$ d. $\dfrac{x^{4n}}{x^{9n}}$
Answers:
a. 5^n b. x^{8b} c. y^{3b} d. $\dfrac{1}{x^{5n}}$

Using Your CALCULATOR Finding Present Value

As a gift for their newborn grandson, the grandparents want to deposit enough money in the bank now so that when he turns 18, the young man will have a college fund of \$20,000 waiting for him. How much should they deposit now if the money will earn 6% annually?

To find how much money P must be invested at an annual rate i (expressed as a decimal) to have \$$A$ in n years, we use the formula $P = A(1 + i)^{-n}$. If we substitute 20,000 for A, 0.06 (6%) for i, and 18 for n, we have

$$P = A(1 + i)^{-n} \quad \text{P is called the present value.}$$
$$P = 20{,}000(1 + 0.06)^{-18}$$

To find P with a reverse-entry calculator, we enter these numbers and press these keys.

(1 + .06) y^x 18 +/− × 20000 = **7006.875823**

To evaluate the expression with a graphing or a direct-entry calculator, we use the following keystrokes.

20000 × (1 + .06) ^ (−) 18 ENTER

20000 × (1 + .06)^ − 18
7006.875823

They must invest approximately \$7,006.88 to have \$20,000 in 18 years.

ANSWERS TO SELF CHECKS

1. a. 1 **b.** $-5b$ **2. a.** $\frac{1}{256}$ **b.** $-\frac{1}{125}$ **3. a.** 9 **b.** $\frac{7}{64}$ **4. a.** $\frac{1}{a^5}$ **b.** $\frac{s^5}{r^4}$ **c.** $\frac{3}{y^3}$ **5.** $\frac{49}{9}$
6. a. $\frac{1}{x^{12}}$ **b.** $\frac{1}{a^4}$ **c.** $\frac{1}{a^6}$ **7. a.** $\frac{4x^3}{3y^5}$ **b.** $\frac{1}{x^{12}y^{18}}$ **8. a.** 1 **b.** z^{5n} **c.** $\frac{1}{z^{2n}}$

SECTION 6.2 STUDY SET

VOCABULARY

Fill in the blanks.

1. In the exponential expression 8^{-3}, 8 is the base and -3 is the exponent.
2. In the exponential expression 5^{-1}, the exponent is a negative integer.
3. Another way to write 2^{-3} is to write its reciprocal and to change the sign of the exponent: $2^{-3} = \frac{1}{2^3}$.
4. In the expression 6^m, the exponent is a variable.

CONCEPTS

5. In parts a and b, fill in the blanks as you simplify the fraction in two different ways. Then complete the sentence in part c.

a. $\frac{6^4}{6^4} = 6^{4-4} = 6^0$ **b.** $\frac{6^4}{6^4} = \frac{6 \cdot 6 \cdot 6 \cdot 6}{6 \cdot 6 \cdot 6 \cdot 6} = 1$

c. So we define 6^0 to be 1, and, in general, if x is any nonzero real number, then $x^0 = 1$.

6. In parts a and b, fill in the blanks as you simplify the fraction in two different ways. Then complete the sentence in part c.

a. $\frac{8^3}{8^5} = 8^{3-5} = 8^{-2}$ **b.** $\frac{8^3}{8^5} = \frac{8 \cdot 8 \cdot 8}{8 \cdot 8 \cdot 8 \cdot 8 \cdot 8} = \frac{1}{8^2}$

c. We define 8^{-2} to be $\frac{1}{8^2}$, and, in general, if x is any nonzero real number, then $x^{-n} = \frac{1}{x^n}$.

Selected exercises available online at **www.webassign.net/brookscole**

Complete each table.

7.

x	3^x
2	9
1	3
0	1
−1	$\frac{1}{3}$
−2	$\frac{1}{9}$

8.

x	4^x
2	16
1	4
0	1
−1	$\frac{1}{4}$
−2	$\frac{1}{16}$

9.

x	$(-9)^x$
2	81
1	−9
0	1
−1	$-\frac{1}{9}$
−2	$\frac{1}{81}$

10.

x	$(-5)^x$
2	25
1	−5
0	1
−1	$-\frac{1}{5}$
−2	$\frac{1}{25}$

Use the graph to determine the missing y-coordinates in the table and express each y-coordinate as a power of 2.

11.

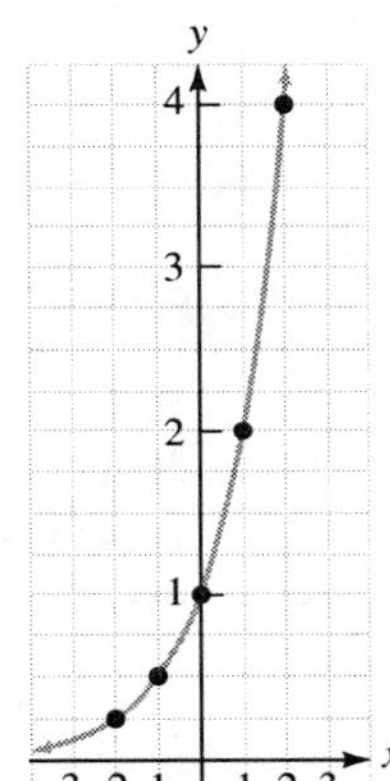

x	y	y as a power of 2
2	4	2^2
1	2	2^1
0	1	2^0
−1	$\frac{1}{2}$	2^{-1}
−2	$\frac{1}{4}$	2^{-2}

12.

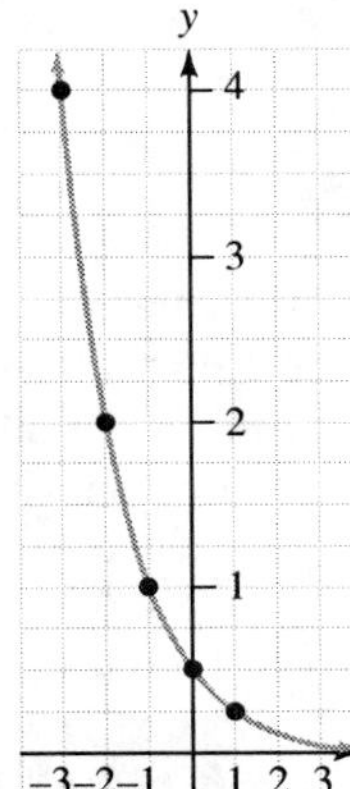

x	y	y as a power of 2
1	$\frac{1}{4}$	2^{-2}
0	$\frac{1}{2}$	2^{-1}
−1	1	2^0
−2	2	2^1
−3	4	2^2

NOTATION

Complete each solution.

13. $(y^5y^3)^{-5} = (y^8)^{-5}$
$= y^{-40}$
$= \frac{1}{y^{40}}$

14. $\left(\frac{a^2b^3}{a^{-3}b}\right)^{-3} = \left(a^{2-(-3)}b^{3-1}\right)^{-3}$
$= \left(a^5b^2\right)^{-3}$
$= \frac{1}{(a^5b^2)^3}$
$= \frac{1}{a^{15}b^6}$

15. In the expression $3x^{-2}$, what is the base and what is the exponent? base x, exponent −2

16. In the expression $-3x^{-2}$, what is the base and what is the exponent? base x, exponent −2

17. Determine the base and the exponent and evaluate each expression.

a. -4^2 4, 2, −16

b. 4^{-2} 4, −2, $\frac{1}{16}$

c. -4^{-2} 4, −2, $-\frac{1}{16}$

18. Determine the base and the exponent and evaluate each expression.

a. $(-7)^2$ −7, 2, 49

b. $(-7)^{-2}$ −7, −2, $\frac{1}{49}$

c. -7^{-2} 7, −2, $-\frac{1}{49}$

GUIDED PRACTICE

Write each expression without using exponents. See Example 1.

19. 7^0 1

20. 9^0 1

21. $\left(\frac{1}{4}\right)^0$ 1

22. $\left(\frac{3}{8}\right)^0$ 1

23. $2x^0$ 2

24. $(2x)^0$ 1

25. $(-x)^0$ 1

26. $-x^0$ −1

Simplify each expression by using the definition of negative exponents. See Example 2.

27. 12^{-2} $\frac{1}{144}$

28. 11^{-2} $\frac{1}{121}$

29. $(-4)^{-1}$ $-\frac{1}{4}$

30. $(-8)^{-2}$ $\frac{1}{64}$

Simplify each expression by using the definition of negative exponents. See Example 3.

31. $\frac{1}{5^{-3}}$ 125

32. $\frac{1}{3^{-3}}$ 27

33. $\frac{2^{-4}}{3^{-1}}$ $\frac{3}{16}$

34. $\frac{7^{-2}}{2^{-3}}$ $\frac{8}{49}$

Write each expression without using negative exponents. See Example 4.

35. x^{-2} $\frac{1}{x^2}$

36. y^{-3} $\frac{1}{y^3}$

37. $\frac{a^{-2}}{b^{-3}}$ $\frac{b^3}{a^2}$

38. $\frac{m^{-7}}{n^{-5}}$ $\frac{n^5}{m^7}$

39. $(-4y)^{-2}$ $\frac{1}{16y^2}$

40. $(-5d)^{-3}$ $-\frac{1}{125d^3}$

41. $-2b^{-5}$ $-\frac{2}{b^5}$

42. $-3c^{-4}$ $-\frac{3}{c^4}$

Write each expression without using exponents. See Example 5.

43. $\left(\frac{7}{8}\right)^{-1}$ $\frac{8}{7}$

44. $\left(\frac{16}{5}\right)^{-1}$ $\frac{5}{16}$

45. $\left(\frac{3}{4}\right)^{-2}$ $\frac{16}{9}$

46. $\left(\frac{2}{3}\right)^{-2}$ $\frac{9}{4}$

Write each expression without using negative exponents. See Example 6.

47. $(a^{-4})^3$ $\frac{1}{a^{12}}$

48. $(b^{-3})^5$ $\frac{1}{b^{15}}$

49. $\frac{a^3}{a^8}$ $\frac{1}{a^5}$

50. $\frac{t^5}{t^{12}}$ $\frac{1}{t^7}$

51. $(ab^2)^{-3}$ $\frac{1}{a^3b^6}$

52. $(m^2n^3)^{-2}$ $\frac{1}{m^4n^6}$

53. $\frac{y^{-4}y^{-3}}{y^{-10}}$ y^3

54. $\frac{x^{-4}x^{-5}}{x^{-8}x^{-4}}$ x^3

Write each expression without using negative exponents. See Example 7.

55. $\frac{15p^2q^3}{5p^3q^2}$ $\frac{3q}{p}$

56. $\frac{27m^3n^5}{6m^5n^3}$ $\frac{9n^2}{2m^2}$

57. $\left(\frac{a^2b^5}{a^2b^{-2}}\right)^{-2}$ $\frac{1}{b^{14}}$

58. $\left(\frac{a^3b^{-2}}{a^2b^3}\right)^{-3}$ $\frac{b^{15}}{a^3}$

Simplify each expression. Assume that there are no divisions by 0. See Example 8.

59. $\frac{7^n}{7^n}$ 1

60. $\frac{8^p}{8^p}$ 1

61. $x^{2m}x^m$ x^{3m}

62. $y^{3m}y^{2m}$ y^{5m}

63. $u^{2m}u^{-3m}$ $\frac{1}{u^m}$

64. $r^{5m}r^{-6m}$ $\frac{1}{r^m}$

65. $\frac{y^{3m}}{y^{2m}}$ y^m

66. $\frac{z^{4m}}{z^{2m}}$ z^{2m}

67. $\frac{x^{3n}}{x^{6n}}$ $\frac{1}{x^{3n}}$

68. $\frac{x^m}{x^{5m}}$ $\frac{1}{x^{4m}}$

TRY IT YOURSELF

Write each answer without using parentheses or negative exponents.

69. $\left(\frac{a^2b^3}{ab^4}\right)^0$ 1

70. $\frac{2}{3}\left(\frac{xyz}{x^2y}\right)^0$ $\frac{2}{3}$

71. $\frac{5}{2x^0}$ $\frac{5}{2}$

72. $\frac{4}{3a^0}$ $\frac{4}{3}$

73. -4^{-3} $-\frac{1}{64}$

74. -6^{-3} $-\frac{1}{216}$

75. $-(-4)^{-3}$ $\frac{1}{64}$

76. $-(-4)^{-2}$ $-\frac{1}{16}$

77. $\frac{y^4y^3}{y^4y^{-2}}$ y^5

78. $\frac{x^{12}x^{-7}}{x^3x^4}$ $\frac{1}{x^2}$

79. $\frac{1}{c^{-5}}$ c^5

80. $\frac{3}{a^{-7}}$ $3a^7$

81. $\frac{3^{-2}}{2^{-3}}$ $\frac{8}{9}$

82. $\frac{5^{-3}}{3^{-4}}$ $\frac{81}{125}$

83. $(2y)^{-4}$ $\frac{1}{16y^4}$

84. $(-3x)^{-1}$ $-\frac{1}{3x}$

85. $2^5 \cdot 2^{-2}$ 8

86. $10^2 \cdot 10^{-4}$ $\frac{1}{100}$

87. $4^{-3} \cdot 4^{-2} \cdot 4^5$ 1

88. $3^{-4} \cdot 3^5 \cdot 3^{-3}$ $\frac{1}{9}$

89. $\frac{3^5 \cdot 3^{-2}}{3^3}$ 1

90. $\frac{6^2 \cdot 6^{-3}}{6^{-2}}$ 6

91. $\frac{y^4}{y^5}$ $\frac{1}{y}$

92. $\frac{t^7}{t^{10}}$ $\frac{1}{t^3}$

93. $\frac{(r^2)^3}{(r^3)^4}$ $\frac{1}{r^6}$

94. $\frac{(b^3)^4}{(b^5)^4}$ $\frac{1}{b^8}$

95. $\frac{10a^4a^{-2}}{5a^2a^0}$ 2

96. $\frac{9b^0b^3}{3b^{-3}b^4}$ $3b^2$

97. $(ab^2)^{-2}$ $\frac{1}{a^2b^4}$

98. $(c^2d^3)^{-2}$ $\frac{1}{c^4d^6}$

99. $(x^2y)^{-3}$ $\frac{1}{x^6y^3}$

100. $(-xy^2)^{-4}$ $\frac{1}{x^4y^8}$

101. $(x^{-4}x^3)^3$ $\frac{1}{x^3}$

102. $(y^{-2}y)^3$ $\frac{1}{y^3}$

103. $(a^{-2}b^3)^{-4}$ $\frac{a^8}{b^{12}}$

104. $(y^{-3}z^5)^{-6}$ $\frac{y^{18}}{z^{30}}$

105. $(-2x^3y^{-2})^{-5}$ $-\frac{y^{10}}{32x^{15}}$

106. $(-3u^{-2}v^3)^{-3}$ $-\frac{u^6}{27v^9}$

107. $\left(\frac{a^3}{a^{-4}}\right)^2$ a^{14}

108. $\left(\frac{a^4}{a^{-3}}\right)^3$ a^{21}

109. $\left(\frac{4x^2}{3x^{-5}}\right)^4$ $\frac{256x^{28}}{81}$

110. $\left(\frac{-3r^4r^{-3}}{r^{-3}r^7}\right)^3$ $-\frac{27}{r^9}$

111. $\left(\frac{12y^3z^{-2}}{3y^{-4}z^3}\right)^2$ $\frac{16y^{14}}{z^{10}}$

112. $\left(\frac{6xy^3}{3x^{-1}y}\right)^3$ $8x^6y^6$

APPLICATIONS

113. THE DECIMAL NUMERATION SYSTEM Decimal numbers are written by putting digits into place-value columns that are separated by a decimal point. Express the place value of each of the columns shown using a power of 10.
$10^2, 10^1, 10^0, 10^{-1}, 10^{-2}, 10^{-3}, 10^{-4}$

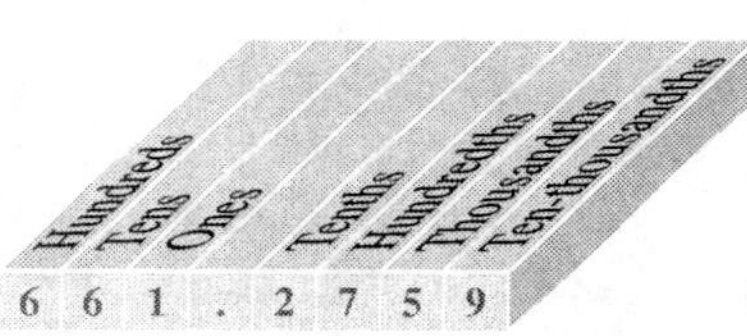

114. UNIT COMPARISONS Consider the relative sizes of the items listed in the table. In the column titled "measurement," write the most appropriate number from the following list. Each number is used only once.

10^0 meter $\quad 10^{-1}$ meter $\quad 10^{-2}$ meter
10^{-3} meter $\quad 10^{-4}$ meter $\quad 10^{-5}$ meter

Item	Measurement (m)
Thickness of a dime	10^{-3}
Height of a bathroom sink	10^0
Length of a pencil eraser	10^{-2}
Thickness of soap bubble film	10^{-5}
Width of a video cassette	10^{-1}
Thickness of a piece of paper	10^{-4}

115. RETIREMENT YEARS How much money should a young married couple invest now at an 8% annual rate if they want to have \$100,000 in the bank when they reach retirement age in 40 years? (See the Using Your Calculator box in this section for the formula.) approximately \$4,603

116. BIOLOGY During bacterial reproduction, the time required for a population to double is called the **generation time.** If b bacteria are introduced into a medium, then after the generation time has elapsed, there will be $2b$ bacteria. After n generations, there will be $b \cdot 2^n$ bacteria. Explain what this expression represents when $n = 0$.
It gives the initial number of bacteria b.

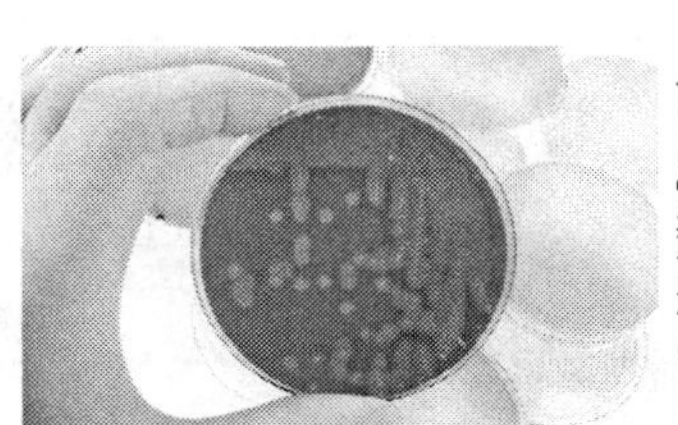

WRITING

117. Explain how you would help a friend understand that 2^{-3} is not equal to -8.

118. Describe how you would verify on a calculator that

$$2^{-3} = \frac{1}{2^3}$$

REVIEW

119. IQ TESTS An IQ (intelligence quotient) is a score derived from the formula

$$\text{IQ} = \frac{\text{mental age}}{\text{chronological age}} \cdot 100$$

Find the mental age of a 10-year-old girl if she has an IQ of 135. 13.5 yr

120. DIVING When you are under water, the pressure in your ears is given by the formula

$$\text{Pressure} = \text{depth} \cdot \text{density of water}$$

Find the density of water (in lb/ft^3) if, at a depth of 9 feet, the pressure on your eardrum is 561.6 lb/ft^2. 62.4 lb/ft^3

121. Write the equation of the line having slope $\frac{3}{4}$ and y-intercept -5. $y = \frac{3}{4}x - 5$

122. Find $f(-6)$ if $f(x) = x^2 - 3x + 1$. 55

SECTION 6.3 Polynomials

Objectives

1 Know the vocabulary for polynomials

2 Evaluate polynomials.

In arithmetic, we learned how to add, subtract, multiply, divide, and find powers of numbers. In algebra, we will learn how to perform these operations on *polynomials.* In this section, we will introduce polynomials, classify them into groups, define their degrees, and show how to evaluate them at specific values of their variables.

1 Know the vocabulary for polynomials.

Recall that a **term** is a number or a product of a number and one or more variables, which may be raised to powers. Examples of terms are

$$3x, \quad -4y^2, \quad \frac{1}{2}a^2b^3, \quad t, \quad \text{and} \quad 25$$

The **numerical coefficients,** or simply **coefficients,** of the first four of these terms are $3, -4, \frac{1}{2}$, and 1, respectively. Because $25 = 25x^0$, 25 is considered to be the numerical coefficient of the term 25.

Polynomials

A **polynomial** is a term or a sum of terms in which all variables have whole-number exponents. No variable appears in a denominator.

Here are some examples of polynomials:

$$3x + 2, \quad 4y^2 - 2y - 3, \quad -8xy^2, \quad \text{and} \quad a^3 + 3a^2b + 3ab^2 + b^3$$

The polynomial $3x + 2$ has two terms, $3x$ and 2, and we say it is a **polynomial in one variable, *x*.** A single number is called a **constant,** and so its last term, 2, is called the **constant term.**

Since $4y^2 - 2y - 3$ can be written as $4y^2 + (-2y) + (-3)$, it is the sum of three terms, $4y^2$, $-2y$, and -3. It is written in **decreasing** or **descending powers** of y, because the powers on y decrease from left to right.

$-8xy^2$ is a polynomial with just one term. We say that it is a **polynomial in two variables, *x* and *y*.**

The four-term polynomial $a^3 + 3a^2b + 3ab^2 + b^3$ is written in descending powers of a and **ascending powers** of b.

Caution! The expression $2x^3 - 3x^{-2} + 5$ is not a polynomial, because the second term contains a variable with an exponent that is not a whole number. Similarly, $y^2 - \frac{7}{y}$ is not a polynomial, because $\frac{7}{y}$ has a variable in the denominator.

Self Check 1

Determine whether each expression is a polynomial:

a. $3x^{-4} + 2x^2 - 3$ no

b. $7.5p^3 - 4p^2 - 3p + 4$ yes

Now Try **Problems 17 and 18**

Teaching Example 1 Determine whether each expression is a polynomial:

a. $\frac{5}{x} + 4x^2 - 3$

b. $\frac{1}{2}x^2 + 2x - 7$

Answers:

a. no b. yes

EXAMPLE 1 Determine whether each expression is a polynomial.

a. $x^2 + 2x + 1$ **b.** $3a^{-1} - 2a - 3$ **c.** $\frac{1}{2}x^3 - 2.3x$ **d.** $\frac{p + 3}{p - 1}$

Strategy We will note the exponents on the variable bases. We will also identify each denominator.

WHY The expression is a polynomial when all the variables have whole number exponents and no variable appears in a denominator of a fraction.

Solution

a. $x^2 + 2x + 1$ is a polynomial.

b. $3a^{-1} - 2a - 3$ is not a polynomial. In the first term, the exponent on the variable is not a whole number.

c. $\frac{1}{2}x^3 - 2.3x$ is a polynomial, because it can be written as the sum $\frac{1}{2}x^3 + (-2.3x)$.

d. $\frac{p + 3}{p - 1}$ is not a polynomial. For a polynomial, variables cannot be in the denominator of a fraction.

A polynomial with one term is called a **monomial.** A polynomial with two terms is called a **binomial.** A polynomial with three terms is called a **trinomial.** Here are some examples.

Monomials	Binomials	Trinomials
$-6x$	$3u^3 - 4u^2$	$-5t^2 + 4t + 3$
$5x^2y$	$18a^2b + 4ab$	$27x^3 - 6x - 2$
29	$-29z^{17} - 1$	$a^2 + 2ab + b^2$

Self Check 2

Classify each polynomial as a monomial, a binomial, or a trinomial:

a. $5x$ monomial

b. $-5x^2 + 2x - 0.5$ trinomial

c. $16x^2 - 9y^2$ binomial

Now Try **Problems 26, 29, and 33**

EXAMPLE 2 Classify each polynomial as a monomial, a binomial, or a trinomial:

a. $5.2x^4 + 3.1x$ **b.** $7g^4 - 5g^3 - 2$ **c.** $-5x^2y^3$

Strategy We will count the number of terms in each polynomial.

WHY The number of terms determines the type of polynomial.

Solution

a. The polynomial $5.2x^4 + 3.1x$ has two terms, $5.2x^4$ and $3.1x$, so it is a binomial.

b. The polynomial $7g^4 - 5g^3 - 2$ has three terms, $7g^4$, $-5g^3$, and -2, so it is a trinomial.

c. The polynomial $-5x^2y^3$ has one term, so it is a monomial.

Teaching Example 2 Classify each polynomial as a monomial, a binomial, or a trinomial:
a. $3x^5 - 2x^2 + 1$ b. $5xy^2$
c. $2x^3 + 3y^4$
Answers:
a. trinomial b. monomial
c. binomial

Success Tip Recall that terms are separated by + or − symbols and the numerical coefficient is the numerical factor of the term.

The monomial $7x^6$ is called a **monomial of sixth degree** or a **monomial of degree 6,** because the variable x occurs as a factor six times. The monomial $3x^3y^4$ is a monomial of seventh degree, because the variables x and y occur as factors a total of seven times. Here are some more examples:

$2.7a$ is a monomial of degree 1.
$-2x^3$ is a monomial of degree 3.
$47x^2y^3$ is a monomial of degree 5.
8 is a monomial of degree 0, because $8 = 8x^0$.

These examples illustrate the following definition.

Degree of a Monomial

If a represents a nonzero constant, the **degree of the monomial** ax^n is n.

The **degree of a monomial** in several variables is the sum of the exponents on those variables.

Caution! Note that the degree of ax^n is not defined when $a = 0$. Since $ax^n = 0$ when $a = 0$, the constant 0 has no defined degree.

Because each term of a polynomial is a monomial, we define the degree of a polynomial by considering the degrees of each of its terms.

Degree of a Polynomial

The **degree of a polynomial** is determined by the term with the largest degree.

Here are some examples:

- $x^2 + 2x$ is a binomial of degree 2, because the degree of its first term is 2 and the degree of its second term is less than 2.
- $1 + d^3 - 3d^2$ is a trinomial of degree 3, because the degree of its second term is 3 and the degree of each of its other terms is less than 3.
- $25y^{13} - 15y^8z^{10} - 32y^{10}z^8 + 4$ is a polynomial of degree 18, because its second and third terms are of degree 18. Its other terms have degree less than 18.

EXAMPLE 3 Find the degree of each polynomial:

a. $-4x^3 - 5x^2 + 3x$ **b.** $1.6w - 1.6$ **c.** $-17a^2b^3 + 12ab^6$

Strategy We will find the degree of each term and compare them.

WHY The degree of the polynomial is the same as the highest-degree term.

Self Check 3

Find the degree of each polynomial:
a. $15p^3 - 15p^2 - 3p + 4$ 3
b. $-14st^4 + 12s^3t$ 5

Now Try **Problems 39 and 44**

Teaching Example 3 Find the degree of each polynomial:
a. $5x^3y + 2xy^7 - 4xy^5z^3$ **b.** $4 + 7x^3$
Answers:
a. 9 **b.** 3

Solution

a. The trinomial $-4x^3 - 5x^2 + 3x$ has terms of degree 3, 2, and 1. Therefore, its degree is 3.

b. The first term of $1.6w - 1.6$ has degree 1 and the second term has degree 0, so the binomial has degree 1.

c. The degree of the first term of $-17a^2b^3 + 12ab^6$ is 5 and the degree of the second term is 7, so the binomial has degree 7.

If written in descending powers of the variable, the **lead term** of a polynomial is the term of highest degree. For example, the leading term of $-4x^3 - 5x^2 + 3x$ is $-4x^3$. The coefficient of the leading term (in this case, -4) is called the **lead coefficient.**

2 Evaluate polynomials.

Each of the equations below defines a function, because each input x-value determines exactly one output value. Since the right-hand side of each equation is a polynomial, these functions are called **polynomial functions.**

$f(x) = 6x + 4$	$g(x) = 3x^2 + 4x - 5$	$h(x) = -x^3 + x^2 - 2x + 3$
This polynomial has two terms. Its degree is 1.	This polynomial has three terms. Its degree is 2.	This polynomial has four terms. Its degree is 3.

To *evaluate a polynomial function* for a specific value, we replace the variable in the defining equation with the input value. Then we simplify the resulting expression to find the output. For example, suppose we wish to evaluate the polynomial function $f(x) = 6x + 4$ for $x = 1$. Then $f(1)$ represents the value of $f(x) = 6x + 4$ when $x = 1$. We find $f(1)$ as follows.

$f(x) = 6x + 4$ This is the given function.
$f(1) = 6(1) + 4$ Substitute 1 for x. The number 1 is the input.
$= 6 + 4$ Perform the multiplication.
$= 10$ Perform the addition. 10 is the output.

Thus, $f(1) = 10$.

Self Check 4
Consider the function $h(x) = -x^3 + x - 2x + 3$
Find:
a. $h(0)$ 3
b. $h(-3)$ 33

Now Try **Problems 52 and 60**

Teaching Example 4 Consider the function $h(x) = -x^2 + 5x - 1$
Find:
a. $h(-3)$ **b.** $h(4)$
Answers:
a. -25
b. 3

EXAMPLE 4

Consider the function $g(x) = 3x^2 + 4x - 5$. Find:
a. $g(0)$ **b.** $g(-2)$

Strategy We will substitute the value in the parentheses on the left-hand side of the equation for the letter on the right-hand side. Then we will follow the rules for the order of operations to simplify the right-hand side.

WHY To *evaluate a polynomial* means to find its numerical value, once we know the value of the variable.

Solution

a.
$g(x) = 3x^2 + 4x - 5$ This is the given function.
$g(0) = 3(0)^2 + 4(0) - 5$ To find g(0), substitute 0 for x.
$= 3(0) + 4(0) - 5$ Evaluate the power.
$= 0 + 0 - 5$ Perform the multiplications.
$g(0) = -5$

b.
$g(x) = 3x^2 + 4x - 5$ This is the given function.
$g(-2) = 3(-2)^2 + 4(-2) - 5$ To find g(−2), substitute −2 for x.
$= 3(4) + 4(-2) - 5$ Evaluate the power.
$= 12 + (-8) - 5$ Perform the multiplications.
$g(-2) = -1$

EXAMPLE 5 *Supermarket Displays* The polynomial function $f(c) = \frac{1}{3}c^3 + \frac{1}{2}c^2 + \frac{1}{6}c$ gives the number of cans used in a display shaped like a square pyramid, having a square base formed by c cans per side. Find the number of cans of soup used in the display shown in the figure.

Strategy We will count the number of cans along one side of the square base of the display. Then we will evaluate the function at that number.

WHY The function gives the number of cans in the display based on the number of cans along one side of the square base.

Solution

Since each side of the square base of the display is formed by 4 cans, $c = 4$. We can find the number of cans used in the display by finding $f(4)$.

$$f(c) = \frac{1}{3}c^3 + \frac{1}{2}c^2 + \frac{1}{6}c \quad \text{This is the given function.}$$

$$f(4) = \frac{1}{3}(4)^3 + \frac{1}{2}(4)^2 + \frac{1}{6}(4) \quad \text{Substitute 4 for } c.$$

$$= \frac{1}{3}(64) + \frac{1}{2}(16) + \frac{1}{6}(4) \quad \text{Find the powers.}$$

$$= \frac{64}{3} + 8 + \frac{2}{3} \quad \text{Multiply, and then simplify: } \frac{4}{6} = \frac{2}{3}.$$

$$= \frac{66}{3} + 8 \quad \text{Add the fractions.}$$

$$= 22 + 8$$

$$= 30$$

30 cans of soup were used in the display.

Self Check 5

Find the number of cans used in a display having a square base formed by 5 cans per side. 55

Now Try **Problem 80**

Teaching Example 5 Find the number of cans used in a display having a square base formed by 7 cans per side. *Answer:* 140

ANSWERS TO SELF CHECKS

1. a. no **b.** yes **2. a.** monomial **b.** trinomial **c.** binomial **3. a.** 3 **b.** 5 **4. a.** 3 **b.** 33 **5.** 55

SECTION 6.3 STUDY SET

VOCABULARY

Fill in the blanks.

1. A polynomial is a term or a sum of terms in which all variables have whole-number exponents.

2. The numerical coefficient of the term $-25x^2y^3$ is -25.

3. The degree of the monomial $3x^7$ is 7.

4. The degree of a polynomial is the same as the degree of its term with the largest degree.

5. A monomial is a polynomial with one term.

6. A binomial is a polynomial with two terms.

7. A trinomial is a polynomial with three terms.

8. For the polynomial $6x^2 + 3x - 1$, the leading term is $6x^2$, and the leading coefficient is 6. The constant term is -1.

9. The notation $f(x)$ is read as f of x.

10. $f(2)$ represents the value of a function when $x = 2$.

Selected exercises available online at **www.webassign.net/brookscole**

CONCEPTS

Fill in the blanks.

11. $4x^3 + 7x^2 - 3x - 15$ is a polynomial in x. It is written in decreasing or descending powers of x.
12. $-7 + 2y + 3y^2 - 8y^3$ is a polynomial in y. It is written in ascending powers of y.
13. Write $x - 9 + 3x^2$ in descending powers of x. $3x^2 + x - 9$
14. Write $-2xy + y^2 + x^2$ in descending powers of x. $x^2 - 2xy + y^2$

NOTATION

Complete each solution.

15. If $f(x) = -2x^2 + 3x - 1$, find $f(2)$.

$$\begin{aligned} f(2) &= -2(2)^2 + 3(2) - 1 \\ &= -2(4) + 6 - 1 \\ &= -8 + 6 - 1 \\ &= -2 - 1 \\ &= -3 \end{aligned}$$

16. If $f(x) = -2x^2 + 3x - 1$, find $f(-2)$.

$$\begin{aligned} f(-2) &= -2(-2)^2 + 3(-2) - 1 \\ &= -2(4) + 3(-2) - 1 \\ &= -8 + (-6) - 1 \\ &= -14 - 1 \\ &= -15 \end{aligned}$$

GUIDED PRACTICE

Determine whether each expression is a polynomial. See Example 1.

17. $x^3 - 5x^2 - 2$ yes
18. $x^{-4} - 5x$ no
19. $\frac{1}{2x} + 3$ no
20. $x^3 - 1$ yes
21. $x^2 - y^2$ yes
22. $a^4 + a^3 + a^2 + a$ yes
23. $a^3 + 2a^2 - a + 2$ yes
24. $\frac{1}{x^2 + x - 7}$ no

Classify each polynomial as a monomial, a binomial, a trinomial, or none of these. See Example 2.

25. $3x + 7$ binomial
26. $3y - 5$ binomial
27. $y^2 + 4y + 3$ trinomial
28. $3xy$ monomial
29. $3z^2$ monomial
30. $3x - 2x^3 + 3x - 1$ none of these
31. $t - 32$ binomial
32. $9x^2y^3z^4$ monomial
33. $s^2 - 23s + 31$ trinomial
34. $2x^3 - 5x^2 + 6x - 3$ none of these
35. $3x^5 - x^4 - 3x^3 + 7$ none of these
36. x^3 monomial

Find the degree of each polynomial. See Example 3.

37. $3x^4$ 4th
38. $3x^5$ 5th
39. $-2x^2 + 3x + 1$ 2nd
40. $-3x + 3x^2 - 5x^4$ 4th
41. $3x - 5$ 1st
42. $y^3 + 4y^2$ 3rd
43. $-5r^2s^2 - r^3s + 3$ 4th
44. $4r^2s^3 - 5r^2s^8$ 10th
45. $x^{12} + 3x^2y^3$ 12th
46. $17ab^5 - 12a^3b$ 6th
47. 38 0th
48. -24 0th

Let $f(x) = 5x - 3$ and find each value. See Example 4.

49. $f(2)$ 7
50. $f(0)$ −3
51. $f(-1)$ −8
52. $f(-2)$ −13
53. $f\left(\frac{1}{5}\right)$ −2
54. $f\left(\frac{4}{5}\right)$ 1
55. $f(-0.9)$ −7.5
56. $f(-1.2)$ −9

Let $g(x) = -x^2 - 4$ and find each value.

57. $g(0)$ −4
58. $g(1)$ −5
59. $g(-1)$ −5
60. $g(-2)$ −8

Let $g(x) = -x^2 - 4$ and find each value.

61. $g(1.3)$ −5.69
62. $g(2.4)$ −9.76
63. $g(-13.6)$ −188.96
64. $g(-25.3)$ −644.09

TRY IT YOURSELF

Let $h(x) = x^3 - 2x + 3$ and find each value.

65. $h(0)$ 3
66. $h(3)$ 24
67. $h(-2)$ −1
68. $h(-1)$ 4
69. $h(0.9)$ 1.929
70. $h(0.4)$ 2.264
71. $h(-8.1)$ −512.241
72. $h(-7.7)$ −438.133

Let $f(x) = -x^4 - x^3 + x^2 + x - 1$ and find each value.

73. $f(1)$ −1
74. $f(-1)$ −1
75. $f(-2)$ −7
76. $f(2)$ −19

APPLICATIONS

77. PACKAGING To make boxes, a manufacturer cuts equal-sized squares from each corner of a 10-inch × 12-inch piece of cardboard, and then folds up the sides. The polynomial function

$$f(x) = 4x^3 - 44x^2 + 120x$$

gives the volume (in cubic inches) of the resulting box when a square with sides x inches long is cut from each corner. Find the volume of a box if 3-inch squares are cut out. 72 in.^{3}

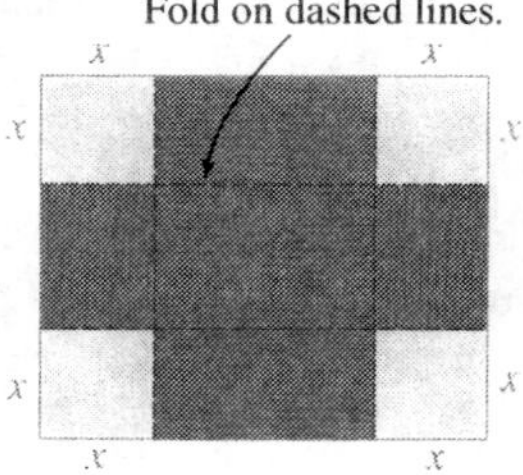

78. MAXIMIZING REVENUE The revenue (in dollars) that a manufacturer of office desks receives is given by the polynomial function

$$f(d) = -0.08d^2 + 100d$$

where d is the number of desks manufactured.

a. Find the total revenue if 625 desks are manufactured. \$31,250

b. Does increasing the number of desks being manufactured to 650 increase the revenue? no

79. WATER BALLOONS Some college students launched water balloons from the balcony of their dormitory on unsuspecting sunbathers. The height in feet of the balloons at a time t seconds after being launched is given by the polynomial function

$$f(t) = -16t^2 + 12t + 20$$

What was the height of the balloons 0.5 second and 1.5 seconds after being launched? 22 ft, 2 ft

80. STOPPING DISTANCE The number of feet that a car travels before stopping depends on the driver's reaction time and the braking distance, as shown below. For one driver, the stopping distance is given by the polynomial function

from Campus to Careers
Police Officer

© Robert E. Daemmrich/Getty Images

$$f(v) = 0.04v^2 + 0.9v$$

where v is the velocity of the car. Find the stopping distance when the driver is traveling at 30 mph. 63 ft

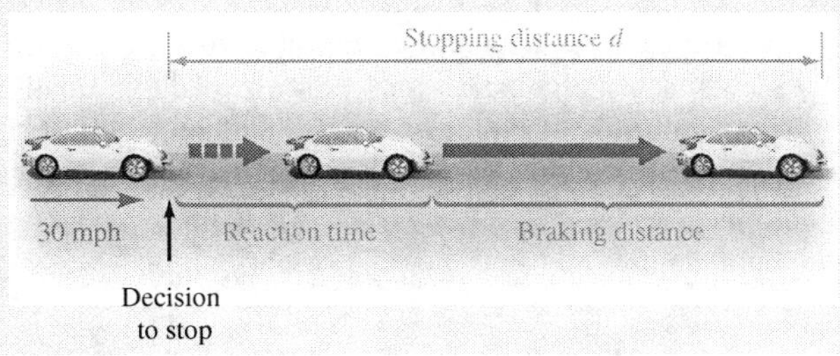

81. SUSPENSION BRIDGES The function

$$f(s) = 400 + 0.0066667s^2 - 0.0000001s^4$$

approximates the length of the cable between the two vertical towers of a suspension bridge, where s is the sag in the cable. Estimate the length of the cable of the bridge in the next column if the sag is 24.6 feet.

about 404 ft

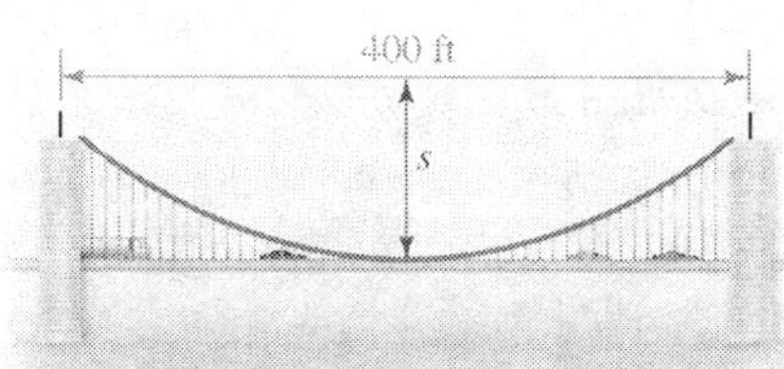

82. PRODUCE DEPARTMENTS Suppose a grocer is going to set up a pyramid-shaped display of cantaloupes like that shown in the figure in Example 5. If each side of the square base of the display is made of six cantaloupes, how many will be used in the display? 91

83. DOLPHINS At a marine park, three trained dolphins jump in unison over an arching stream of water whose path can be described by the polynomial function

$$f(x) = -0.05x^2 + 2x$$

Given the takeoff points for each dolphin, how high must each dolphin jump to clear the stream of water? 18.75 ft, 20 ft, 15 ft

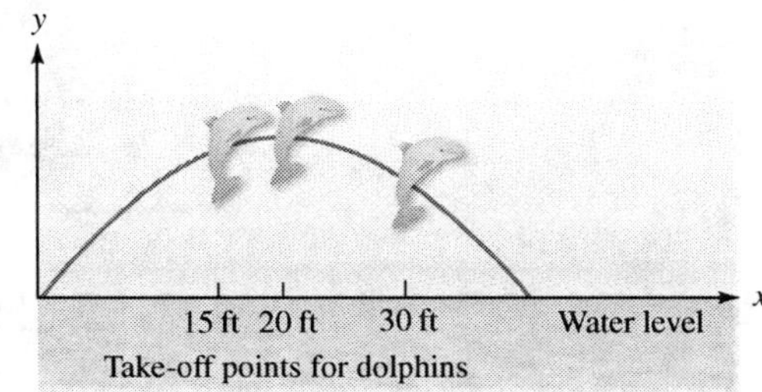

84. TUNNELS The arch at the entrance to a tunnel is described by the polynomial function

$$f(x) = -0.25x^2 + 23$$

What is the height of the arch at the edge of the pavement? 14 ft

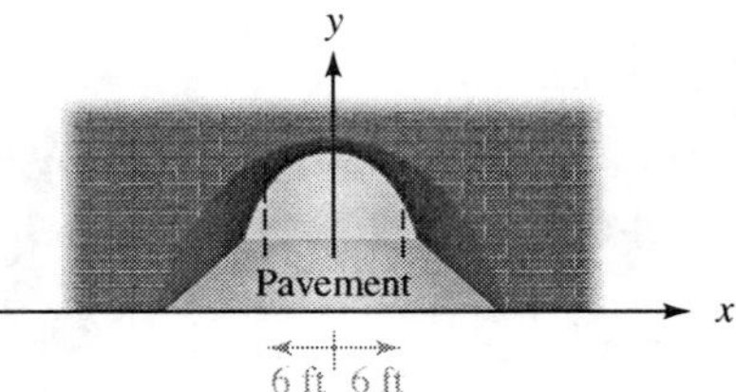

WRITING

85. Describe how to determine the degree of a polynomial.

86. List some words that contain the prefixes *mono, bi,* or *tri.*

REVIEW

Solve each inequality and graph its solution set.

87. $-4(3y + 2) \le 28$

$y \ge -3$ $[-3, \infty)$

88. $-5 < 3t + 4 \le 13$

$-3 < t \le 3$ $(-3, 3]$

Write each expression without using parentheses or negative exponents.

89. $(x^2x^4)^3$ x^{18}

90. $(a^2)^3(a^3)^2$ a^{12}

91. $\left(\dfrac{y^2y^5}{y^4}\right)^3$ y^9

92. $\left(\dfrac{2t^2}{t}\right)^{-4}$ $\dfrac{1}{16t^4}$

Objectives

1. Add monomials.
2. Subtract monomials.
3. Add polynomials.
4. Subtract polynomials.
5. Add and subtract multiples of polynomials.

SECTION 6.4 Adding and Subtracting Polynomials

In figure (a), the heights of the Seattle Space Needle and the Eiffel Tower in Paris are given. Using rules from arithmetic, we can find the difference in the heights of the towers by subtracting two numbers.

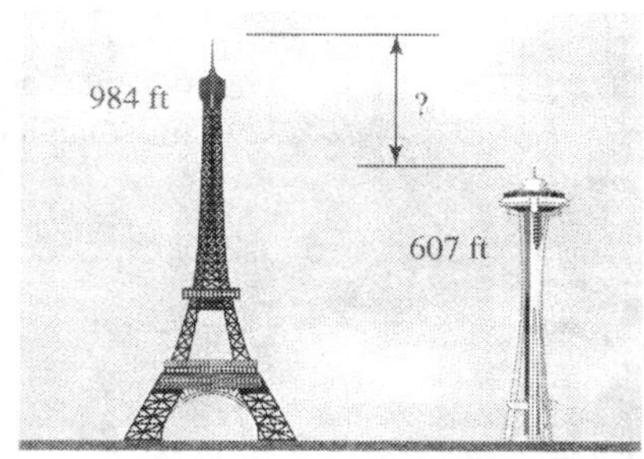

Arithmetic

$984 - 607 = 377$

The difference in height is 377 feet.

(a)

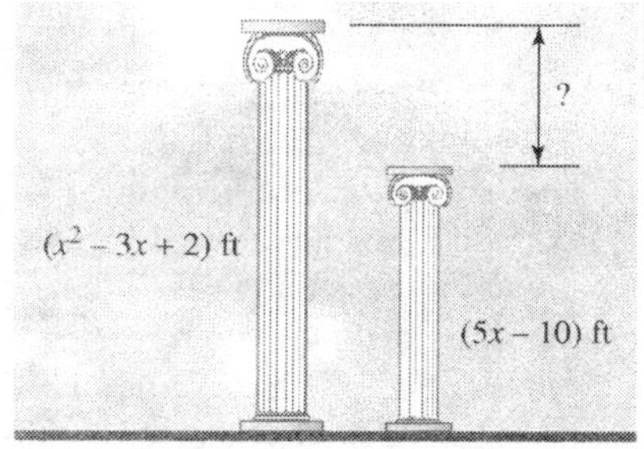

Algebra

$(x^2 - 3x + 2) - (5x - 10) = ?$

(b)

In figure (b), the heights of two types of classical Greek columns are expressed using *polynomials.* To find the difference in their heights, we must subtract the polynomials. In this section, we will discuss the algebraic rules that are used to do this. Since any subtraction can be written in terms of addition, we will consider the procedures used to add polynomials first. We begin with monomials, which are polynomials having just one term.

1 Adding monomials.

Recall that like terms have the same variables with the same exponents:

Like terms	**Unlike terms**
$-7x$ and $15x$	$-7x$ and $15a$
$4y^3$ and $16y^3$	$4y^3$ and $16y^2$
$\frac{1}{2}xy^2$ and $-\frac{1}{3}xy^2$	$\frac{1}{2}xy^2$ and $-\frac{1}{3}x^2y$

Also recall that to combine like terms, we combine their coefficients and keep the same variables with the same exponents. For example,

$$4y + 5y = (4 + 5)y = 9y \quad \text{and} \quad 8x^2 + x^2 = (8 + 1)x^2 = 9x^2$$

Likewise,

$$3a + 4b + 6a + 3b = 9a + 7b \quad \text{and} \quad 4cd^3 + 9cd^3 = 13cd^3$$

These examples suggest that to add like monomials, we simply combine like terms.

> ***The Language of Algebra*** Simplifying the sum or difference of like terms is called *combining like terms.*

EXAMPLE 1 Perform the following additions.

a. $4x^4 + 81x^4$ **b.** $8x^2y^2 + 6x^2y^2 + x^2y^2$ **c.** $32c^2 + 10c + 4c^2$

Strategy We will note the terms that have the same variables with the same exponents. Then we will combine their coefficients and keep the same variables with the same exponents.

WHY Only like terms can be simplified with addition.

Solution

a. $4x^4 + 81x^4 = 85x^4$ Think: $(4 + 81)x^4 = 85x^4$.

b. $8x^2y^2 + 6x^2y^2 + x^2y^2 = 15x^2y^2$ Think: $(8 + 6 + 1)x^2y^2 = 15x^2y^2$.

c. $32c^2 + 10c + 4c^2 = 32c^2 + 4c^2 + 10c$ Write the like terms together.

$= 36c^2 + 10c$ Think: $(32 + 4)c^2 = 36c^2$.

Self Check 1

Perform the following additions:

a. $27x^6 + 8x^6$ $35x^6$

b. $12pq^2 + 5pq^2 + 8pq^2$ $25pq^2$

c. $6a^3 + 15a + a^3$ $7a^3 + 15a$

Now Try **Problem 19**

Teaching Example 1 Perform the following additions:

a. $15x^4 + x^4$

b. $4ab^3 + 2ab^3 + 5ab^3$

c. $4x^2 + 2x + 1 + x^2 + 5x$

Answers:

a. $16x^4$ b. $11ab^3$ c. $5x^2 + 7x + 1$

> ***Caution!*** When combining like terms, the exponents on the variables *stay the same*. Don't incorrectly add the exponents.

> ***Success Tip*** When performing operations on polynomials, we usually write the terms of the solution in decreasing (or descending) powers of one variable. For instance, in Example 1, part c, the solution was written as $36c^2 + 10c$ instead of $10c + 36c^2$.

2 Subtract monomials.

To subtract one monomial from another, we add the opposite of the monomial that is to be subtracted.

EXAMPLE 2 Find each difference.

a. $8x^2 - 3x^2$ **b.** $6xy - 9xy$ **c.** $-3r - 5 - 4r$ **d.** $0.9x^2 - 1.2x - 0.5x^2 - 0.4x$

Strategy We will note the terms that have the same variables with the same exponents. Then we will combine their coefficients and keep the same variables with the same exponents.

WHY Only like terms can be simplified with subtraction.

Solution

a. $8x^2 - 3x^2 = 8x^2 + (-3x^2)$ Add the opposite of $3x^2$, which is $-3x^2$.

$= 5x^2$ Combine like terms.

b. $6xy - 9xy = 6xy + (-9xy)$ Add the opposite of $9xy$, which is $-9xy$.

$= -3xy$ Combine like terms.

Self Check 2

Find each difference:

a. $12m^3 - 7m^3$

b. $-4pq - 27p - 8pq$

c. $-2.5x^3 - 0.3x^3$

Now Try **Problems 25 and 30**

Self Check 2 Answers

a. $5m^3$ b. $-12pq - 27p$ c. $-2.8x^3$

Teaching Example 2 Find each difference:

a. $6x^3 - 10x^3$ b. $2x^2 - 5x^2 - 3x^2$

c. $6.4x - 3.3x$

Answers:

a. $-4x^3$ b. $-6x^2$ c. $3.1x$

c. $-3r - 5 - 4r = -3r + (-5) + (-4r)$ Add the opposite of 5 and 4r.
$= -3r + (-4r) + (-5)$ Write like terms together.
$= -7r - 5$ Combine like terms. Write the addition of −5 as a subtraction of 5.

d. $0.9x^2 - 1.2x - 0.5x^2 - 0.4x = 0.9x^2 + (-1.2x) + (-0.5x^2) + (-0.4x)$
$= 0.9x^2 + (-0.5x^2) + (-1.2x) + (-0.4x)$
$= 0.4x^2 - 1.6x$

3 Add polynomials.

Because of the distributive property, we can remove parentheses enclosing several terms when the sign preceding the parentheses is a + sign. We simply drop the parentheses.

$+(3x^2 + 3x - 2) = +1(3x^2 + 3x - 2)$
$= 1(3x^2) + 1(3x) + 1(-2)$ Distribute the multiplication by 1.
$= 3x^2 + 3x + (-2)$ Multiplicative identity property.
$= 3x^2 + 3x - 2$ Write the addition of −2 as a subtraction of 2.

We can add polynomials by removing parentheses, if necessary, and then combining any like terms that are contained within the polynomials.

Self Check 3
Add: $(2a^2 - a + 4) + (5a^2 + 6a - 5)$ $7a^2 + 5a - 1$
Now Try **Problem 36**

Teaching Example 3 Add: $(3c^2 - 2c - 5) + (4c^2 - 7c + 3)$
Answer:
$7c^2 - 9c - 2$

EXAMPLE 3 Add: $(3x^2 - 3x + 2) + (2x^2 + 7x - 4)$

Strategy We will reorder and write the like terms together. Then we will combine like terms.

WHY To add polynomials means to combine their like terms.

Solution

$(3x^2 - 3x + 2) + (2x^2 + 7x - 4)$
$= 3x^2 - 3x + 2 + 2x^2 + 7x - 4$ Drop the parentheses.
$= 3x^2 + 2x^2 - 3x + 7x + 2 - 4$ Write like terms together.
$= 5x^2 + 4x - 2$ Combine like terms.

Problems such as Example 3 are often written with like terms aligned vertically. We can then add the polynomials column by column.

$$\begin{array}{r} 3x^2 - 3x + 2 \\ + \quad 2x^2 + 7x - 4 \\ \hline 5x^2 + 4x - 2 \end{array}$$

Self Check 4
Add $4q^2 - 7$ and $2q^2 - 8q + 9$ using the vertical form.
Now Try **Problem 40**
Self Check 4 Answer
$6q^2 - 8q + 2$

Teaching Example 4 Add $8c^2 + 2c - 1$ and $4c^2 + 5$ using the vertical form.
Answer:
$12c^2 + 2c + 4$

EXAMPLE 4 Add $4x^2 - 3$ and $3x^2 - 8x + 8$ using the vertical form.

Strategy We will write one polynomial underneath the other, aligning the like terms and drawing a horizontal line beneath them. Then we will add the like terms, column by column, and write each result under the line.

WHY *Vertical form* means to arrange the like terms in columns.

Solution

Since the first polynomial does not have an x-term, we leave a space so that the constant terms can be aligned.

$$\begin{array}{r} 4x^2 \qquad\quad - 3 \\ + \quad 3x^2 - 8x + 8 \\ \hline 7x^2 - 8x + 5 \end{array}$$

4 Subtract polynomials.

Because of the distributive property, we can remove parentheses enclosing several terms when the sign preceding the parentheses is a − sign. We simply drop the minus sign and the parentheses, and *change the sign of every term within the parentheses.*

$$\begin{aligned}-(3x^2 + 3x - 2) &= -1(3x^2 + 3x - 2)\\ &= -1(3x^2) + (-1)(3x) + (-1)(-2)\\ &= -3x^2 + (-3x) + 2\\ &= -3x^2 - 3x + 2\end{aligned}$$

This suggests that the way to subtract polynomials is to remove parentheses, change the sign of each term of the second polynomial, and combine like terms.

EXAMPLE 5 Find each difference.

a. $(3x - 4) - (5x + 7)$ **b.** $(3x^2 - 4x - 6) - (2x^2 - 6x)$

c. $(-t^3 - 2t^2 - 1) - (-t^3 - 2t^2 + 1)$

Strategy We will change the signs of the terms of the polynomial being subtracted, drop the parentheses, and collect like terms.

WHY This is the method for subtracting two polynomials.

Solution

a. $(3x - 4) - (5x + 7) = 3x - 4 - 5x - 7$ Change the sign of each term inside $(5x + 7)$ and drop the parentheses.

$= -2x - 11$ Combine like terms.

b. $(3x^2 - 4x - 6) - (2x^2 - 6x)$

$= 3x^2 - 4x - 6 - 2x^2 + 6x$ Change the sign of each term of $2x^2 - 6x$ and drop the parentheses.

$= x^2 + 2x - 6$ Combine like terms.

c. $(-t^3 - 2t^2 - 1) - (-t^3 - 2t^2 + 1)$

$= -t^3 - 2t^2 - 1 + t^3 + 2t^2 - 1$ Change the sign of each term of $-t^3 - 2t^2 + 1$ and drop the parentheses.

$= -2$ Combine like terms.

Self Check 5

Find the difference: $(-2a^2 + 5) - (-5a^2 - 7)$

Now Try **Problems 41 and 43**

Self Check 5 Answer
$3a^2 + 12$

Teaching Example 5 Find the difference: $(-3x^2 + 5x - 7) - (x^2 - 6)$
Answer:
$-4x^2 + 5x - 1$

To subtract polynomials in vertical form, we add the opposite of the **subtrahend** (the bottom polynomial) to the **minuend** (the top polynomial).

EXAMPLE 6 Subtract $3x^2 - 2x$ from $2x^2 + 4x$.

Strategy Since $3x^2 - 2x$ is to be subtracted from $2x^2 + 4x$, we will write $3x^2 - 2x$ below $2x^2 + 4x$ in vertical form. Then we will change the signs of the terms of $3x^2 - 2x$ and add column by column.

WHY *Vertical Form* means to align the like terms in columns.

Solution

$$\begin{array}{rcr} & \text{Change signs} & \\ 2x^2 + 4x & \longrightarrow & 2x^2 + 4x \\ -\;\underline{3x^2 - 2x} & & +\;\underline{-3x^2 + 2x} \\ & \text{and add} & -x^2 + 6x \end{array}$$

Self Check 6

Subtract $2p^2 + 2p - 8$ from $5p^2 - 6p + 7$. $3p^2 - 8p + 15$

Now Try **Problem 45**

Teaching Example 6 Subtract $-5x^2 + 2x - 1$ from $4x^2 + 6x + 7$.
Answer:
$9x^2 + 4x + 8$

Self Check 7

Subtract $-2q^2 - 2q$ from the sum of $q^2 - 6q$ and $3q^2 + q$. $6q^2 - 3q$

Now Try **Problem 51**

Teaching Example 7 Subtract $5x^3 - x$ from the sum of $x^2 + x$ and $2x^3 + x^2$.
Answer:
$-3x^3 + 2x^2 + 2x$

EXAMPLE 7 Subtract $12a - 7$ from the sum of $6a + 5$ and $4a - 10$.

Strategy We will use brackets to show that $(12a - 7)$ is to be subtracted from the *sum* of $(6a + 5)$ and $(4a - 10)$.

WHY The key words of the problem *subtract from* and *sum* indicate mathematical operations.

Solution

$$[(6a + 5) + (4a - 10)] - (12a - 7)$$

Next, we remove the grouping symbols to obtain

$$= 6a + 5 + 4a - 10 - 12a + 7 \quad \text{Change the sign of each term in } (12a - 7).$$
$$= -2a + 2 \quad \text{Combine like terms.}$$

5 Add and subtract multiples of polynomials.

Because of the distributive property, we can remove parentheses enclosing several terms when a monomial precedes the parentheses. We simply multiply every term within the parentheses by that monomial. For example, to add $3(2x + 5)$ and $2(4x - 3)$, we proceed as follows:

$$3(2x + 5) + 2(4x - 3) = 6x + 15 + 8x - 6 \quad \text{Distribute the multiplication by 3 and by 2.}$$
$$= 6x + 8x + 15 - 6 \quad 15 + 8x = 8x + 15.$$
$$= 14x + 9 \quad \text{Combine like terms.}$$

Self Check 8

Remove parentheses and simplify: $2(a^2 - 3a) + 5(a^2 + 2a)$ $7a^2 + 4a$

Now Try **Problems 53 and 55**

Teaching Example 8 Remove parentheses and simplify: $5(q^2 + 2q) + 3(2q^2 - 4)$
Answer:
$11q^2 + 10q - 12$

EXAMPLE 8 Remove the parentheses and simplify.

a. $3(x^2 + 4x) + 2(x^2 - 4)$ **b.** $-8(y^2 - 2y + 3) - 4(2y^2 + y - 6)$

Strategy We will use the distributive property to remove parentheses. Then we will collect like terms.

WHY This is what it means to simplify a polynomial.

Solution

a. $3(x^2 + 4x) + 2(x^2 - 4) = 3x^2 + 12x + 2x^2 - 8$ Use the distributive property to remove parentheses.
$= 5x^2 + 12x - 8$ Collect like terms.

b. $-8(y^2 - 2y + 3) - 4(2y^2 + y - 6) = -8y^2 + 16y - 24 - 8y^2 - 4y + 24$
$= -16y^2 + 12y$

Self Check 9

Two warning flares are fired upward at the same time from different parts of a ship. The height of the first flare is $(-16t^2 + 115t + 25)$ feet and the height of the higher-traveling second flare is $(-16t^2 + 130t + 30)$ feet, after t seconds. Find a polynomial that represents the difference in the heights. $(15t + 5)$ ft

Now Try **Problem 88**

EXAMPLE 9 *Property Values* A house purchased for \$95,000 is expected to appreciate according to the polynomial function $f(x) = 2{,}500x + 95{,}000$, where $f(x)$ is the value of the house after x years. A second house purchased for \$125,000 is expected to appreciate according to the equation $f(x) = 4{,}500x + 125{,}000$. Find one polynomial function that will give the total value of both properties after x years.

Strategy To find the polynomial function that will give the total value of both properties, we will add the two polynomials.

WHY To *find a total* means to add.

Solution

The value of the first house after x years is given by the polynomial $2{,}500x + 95{,}000$. The value of the second house after x years is given by the polynomial $4{,}500x + 125{,}000$. The value of both houses will be the sum of these two polynomials.

$$(2{,}500x + 95{,}000) + (4{,}500x + 125{,}000) = 7{,}000x + 220{,}000$$

The total value of the properties is given by the polynomial function $f(x) = 7{,}000x + 220{,}000$.

Teaching Example 9 Two firework shells are fired upward at the same time from different platforms. The height, after t seconds, of the first shell is $(-16t^2 + 160t + 3)$ feet. The height, after t seconds, of a higher-flying second shell is $(-16t^2 + 200t + 1)$ feet. Find a polynomial that represents the difference in the heights of the shells.
Answer:
$40t - 2$

ANSWERS TO SELF CHECKS

1. a. $35x^6$ **b.** $25pq^2$ **c.** $7a^3 + 15a$ **2. a.** $5m^3$ **b.** $-12pq - 27p$ **c.** $-2.8x^3$ **3.** $7a^2 + 5a - 1$ **4.** $6q^2 - 8q + 2$ **5.** $3a^2 + 12$ **6.** $3p^2 - 8p + 15$ **7.** $6q^2 - 3q$ **8.** $7a^2 + 4a$ **9.** $(15t + 5)$ ft

SECTION 6.4 STUDY SET

VOCABULARY

Fill in the blanks.

1. The expression $(x^2 - 3x + 2) + (x^2 - 4x)$ is the sum of two polynomials.
2. The expression $(x^2 - 3x + 2) - (x^2 - 4x)$ is the difference of two polynomials.
3. Like terms have the same variables and the same exponents.
4. "To add or subtract like terms" means to combine their coefficients and keep the same variables with the same exponents.

CONCEPTS

Fill in the blanks.

5. To add like monomials, combine like terms.
6. $a - b = a + (-b)$
7. To add two polynomials, combine any like terms contained in the polynomials.
8. To subtract two polynomials, change the sign of each term in the second polynomial, and combine like terms.
9. When the sign preceding parentheses is a − sign, we can remove the parentheses by dropping the sign and the parentheses, and changing the sign of every term within the parentheses.
10. When a monomial precedes parentheses, we can remove the parentheses by multiplying every term within the parentheses by that monomial.
11. $-(-2x^2 - 3x + 4) = 2x^2 + 3x - 4$
12. $-3(-2x^2 - 3x + 4) = 6x^2 + 9x - 12$

13. JETS Find the polynomial representing the length of the passenger jet. $(11x - 12)$ ft

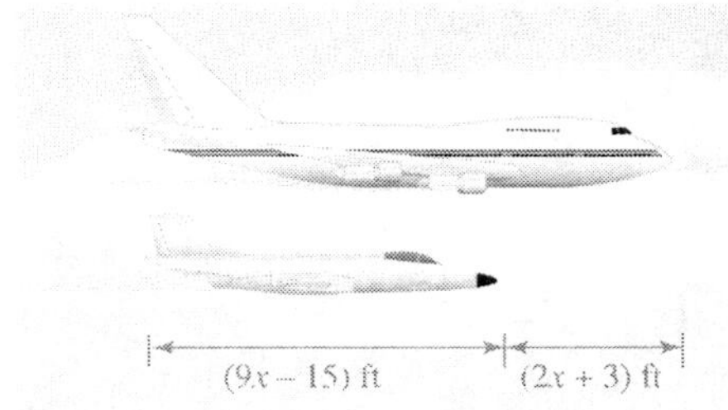

14. WATER SKIING Find the polynomial representing the distance of the water skier from the boat. $(9y - 4)$ m

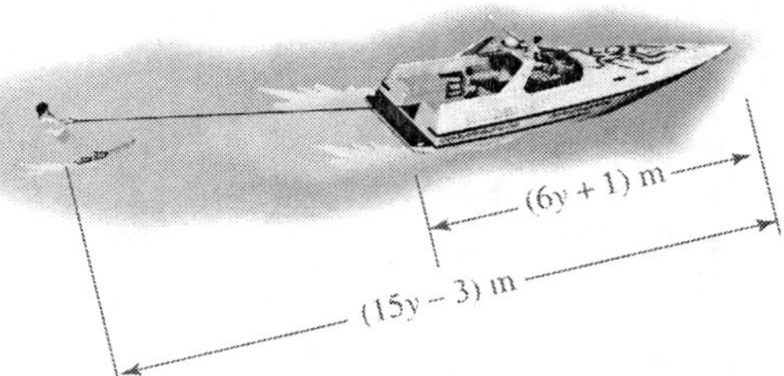

NOTATION

Complete each solution.

15. $(5x^2 + 3x) - (7x^2 - 2x)$
$= 5x^2 + 3x - 7x^2 + 2x$
$= 5x^2 - 7x^2 + 3x + 2x$
$= -2x^2 + 5x$

16. $4(3x^2 - 2x) - (2x + 4)$
$= 12x^2 - 8x - 2x - 4$
$= 12x^2 - 10x - 4$

GUIDED PRACTICE

Perform the following additions. See Example 1.

17. $4y + 5y$ $9y$

18. $2x + 3x$ $5x$

19. $8t^2 + 4t^2$ $12t^2$

20. $15x^2 + 10x^2$ $25x^2$

21. $4r + 3r + 7r$ $14r$

22. $2b + 7b + 3b$ $12b$

23. $4ab + 4ab + ab$ $9ab$

24. $xy + 4xy + 2xy$ $7xy$

Find each difference. See Example 2.

25. $7a^3 - 4a^3$ $3a^3$

26. $12ab - 5ab$ $7ab$

27. $-32u^3 - 16u^3$ $-48u^3$

28. $-25x^3 - 7x^3$ $-32x^3$

29. $-3m - 6 - 4m$ $-7m - 6$

30. $6c - 10 - 3c - 2$ $3c - 12$

31. $0.8p^2 - 3.1p - 2.7p^2 - 1.4p$ $-1.9p^2 - 4.5p$

32. $1.7x - 3.2y - 2.5x - 7.5y$ $-0.8x - 10.7y$

Find each sum. See Examples 3–4.

33. $(3x + 7) + (4x - 3)$ $7x + 4$

34. $(2y - 3) + (4y + 7)$ $6y + 4$

35. $(3x^2 - 3x - 2) + (3x^2 + 4x - 3)$ $6x^2 + x - 5$

36. $(4c^2 + 3c - 2) + (3c^2 + 4c + 2)$ $7c^2 + 7c$

37. $$\begin{array}{r} 3x^2 + 4x + 5 \\ +\underline{2x^2 - 3x + 6} \\ 5x^2 + x + 11 \end{array}$$

38. $$\begin{array}{r} 2x^3 + 2x^2 - 3x + 5 \\ +\underline{3x^3 - 4x^2 - x - 7} \\ 5x^3 - 2x^2 - 4x - 2 \end{array}$$

39. $$\begin{array}{r} 2x^3 - 3x^2 + 4x - 7 \\ +\underline{-9x^3 - 4x^2 - 5x + 6} \\ -7x^3 - 7x^2 - x - 1 \end{array}$$

40. $$\begin{array}{r} -3x^3 + 4x^2 - 4x + 9 \\ +\underline{2x^3 \qquad + 9x - 3} \\ -x^3 + 4x^2 + 5x + 6 \end{array}$$

Find each difference. See Examples 5–6.

41. $(4a + 3) - (2a - 4)$ $2a + 7$

42. $(5b - 7) - (3b - 5)$ $2b - 2$

43. $(3a^2 - 2a + 4) - (a^2 - 3a + 7)$ $2a^2 + a - 3$

44. $(2b^2 + 3b - 5) - (2b^2 - 4b - 9)$ $7b + 4$

45. $$\begin{array}{r} 3x^2 + 4x - 5 \\ -\underline{-2x^2 - 2x + 3} \\ 5x^2 + 6x - 8 \end{array}$$

46. $$\begin{array}{r} 3y^2 - 4y + 7 \\ -\underline{6y^2 - 6y - 13} \\ -3y^2 + 2y + 20 \end{array}$$

47. $$\begin{array}{r} 4x^3 + 4x^2 - 3x + 10 \\ -\underline{5x^3 - 2x^2 - 4x - 4} \\ -x^3 + 6x^2 + x + 14 \end{array}$$

48. $$\begin{array}{r} 3x^3 + 4x^2 + 7x + 12 \\ -\underline{-4x^3 + 6x^2 + 9x - 3} \\ 7x^3 - 2x^2 - 2x + 15 \end{array}$$

Perform the operations. See Example 7.

49. Find the difference when $t^3 - 2t^2 + 2$ is subtracted from the sum of $3t^3 + t^2$ and $-t^3 + 6t - 3$. $t^3 + 3t^2 + 6t - 5$

50. Find the difference when $-3z^3 - 4z + 7$ is subtracted from the sum of $2z^2 + 3z - 7$ and $-4z^3 - 2z - 3$. $-z^3 + 2z^2 + 5z - 17$

51. Find the sum when $3x^2 + 4x - 7$ is added to the sum of $-2x^2 - 7x + 1$ and $-4x^2 + 8x - 1$. $-3x^2 + 5x - 7$

52. Find the difference when $32x^2 - 17x + 45$ is subtracted from the sum of $23x^2 - 12x - 7$ and $-11x^2 + 12x + 7$. $-20x^2 + 17x - 45$

Simplify each expression. See Example 8.

53. $2(x + 3) + 4(x - 2)$
$6x - 2$

54. $3(y - 4) - 5(y + 3)$
$-2y - 27$

55. $-2(x^2 + 7x - 1) - 3(x^2 - 2x + 2)$
$-5x^2 - 8x - 4$

56. $-5(y^2 - 2y - 6) + 6(2y^2 + 2y - 5)$
$7y^2 + 22y$

57. $2(2y^2 - 2y + 2) - 4(3y^2 - 4y - 1) + 4(y^2 - y - 1)$
$-4y^2 + 8y + 4$

58. $-4(z^2 - 5z) - 5(4z^2 - 1) + 6(2z - 3)$
$-24z^2 + 32z - 13$

59. $2(ab^2 - b) - 3(a + 2ab) + (b - a + a^2b)$
$a^2b + 2ab^2 - 6ab - 4a - b$

60. $3(xy + y) - 2(x - 4 + y) + 2(y^3 + y^2)$
$2y^3 + 2y^2 + 3xy - 2x + y + 8$

TRY IT YOURSELF

Perform the operations and simplify.

61. $1.8x - 1.9x$ $-0.1x$

62. $1.7y - 2.2y$ $-0.5y$

63. $\frac{1}{2}st + \frac{3}{2}st$ $2st$

64. $\frac{2}{5}at + \frac{1}{5}at$ $\frac{3}{5}at$

65. $(3x)^2 - 4x^2 + 10x^2$ $15x^2$

66. $(2x)^4 - (3x^2)^2$ $7x^4$

67. $(2x + 3y) + (5x - 10y)$ $7x - 7y$

68. $(5x - 8y) - (-2x + 5y)$ $7x - 13y$

69. $(-8x - 3y) - (-11x + y)$ $3x - 4y$

70. $(-4a + b) + (5a - b)$ a

71. $(2x^2 - 3x + 1) - (4x^2 - 3x + 2) + (2x^2 + 3x + 2)$
$3x + 1$

72. $(-3z^2 - 4z + 7) + (2z^2 + 2z - 1) - (2z^2 - 3z + 7)$
$-3z^2 + z - 1$

73. $(4.52x^2 + 1.13x - 0.89) + (9.02x^2 - 7.68x + 7.04)$ $13.54x^2 - 6.55x + 6.15$

74. $(0.891a^4 - 0.442a^2 + 0.121a) - (-0.160a^4 + 0.249a^2 + 0.789a)$ $1.051a^4 - 0.691a^2 - 0.668a$

75. $2(5a + 3b - c) - 5(-2a + 4b + 4c)$ $20a - 14b - 22c$

76. $-3(4p - 3q + r) + 4(-2p - 3q - 2r)$ $-20p - 3q - 11r$

77.
$$\begin{array}{r} -3x^2 + 4x + 25 \\ + \quad 5x^2 \qquad - 12 \\ \hline 2x^2 + 4x + 13 \end{array}$$

78.
$$\begin{array}{r} -6x^3 - 4x^2 + 7 \\ + \; -7x^3 + 9x^2 \qquad \\ \hline -13x^3 + 5x^2 + 7 \end{array}$$

79.
$$\begin{array}{r} -2x^2y^2 \qquad\qquad + 12y^2 \\ - \; 10x^2y^2 + 9xy - 24y^2 \\ \hline -12x^2y^2 - 9xy + 36y^2 \end{array}$$

80.
$$\begin{array}{r} 25x^3 \qquad\qquad + 31xz^2 \\ - \; 12x^3 + 27x^2z - 17xz^2 \\ \hline 13x^3 - 27x^2z + 48xz^2 \end{array}$$

Find the polynomial that represents the perimeter of each figure.

81. $(3x^2 + 6x - 2)$ yd

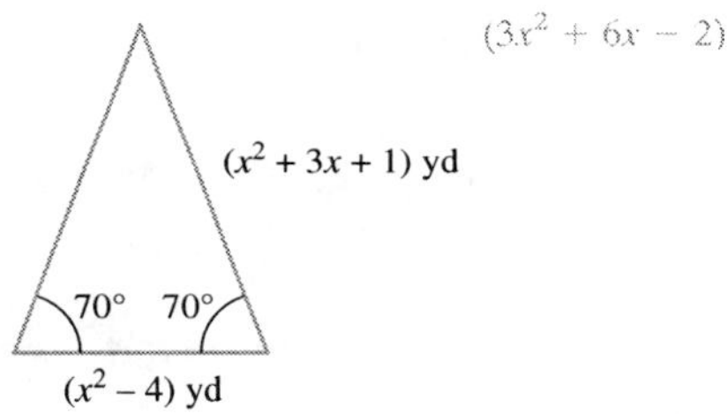

82. $(7x^2 + 5x + 6)$ mi

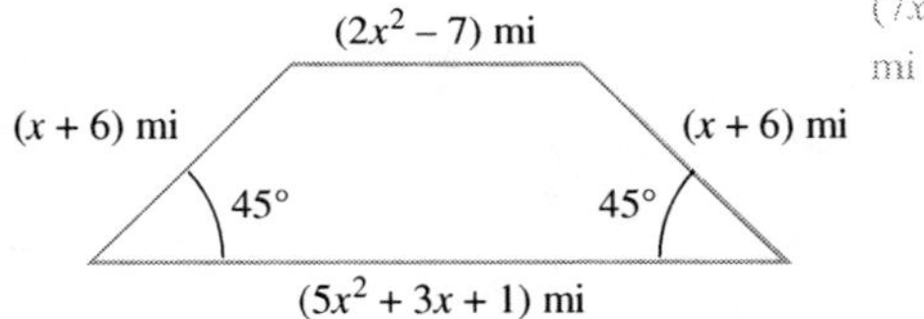

APPLICATIONS

83. GREEK ARCHITECTURE Find the difference in the heights of the columns shown in figure (b) on page 422 at the beginning of this section. $(x^2 - 8x + 12)$ ft

84. CLASSICAL GREEK COLUMNS If the columns shown in figure (b) on page 442 at the beginning of this section were stacked one atop the other, to what height would they reach? $(x^2 + 2x - 8)$ ft

85. AUTO MECHANICS Find the polynomial representing the length of the fan belt shown in the next column. The dimensions are in inches. Your answer will involve π. $(3x^2 + 11x + 4.5\pi)$ in.

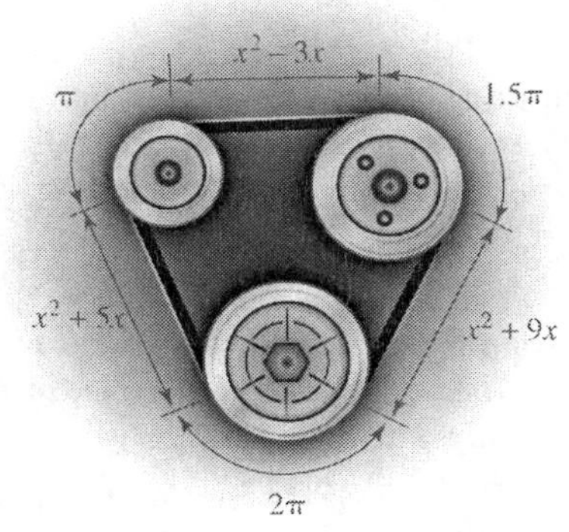

86. READING BLUEPRINTS

a. What is the difference in the length and width of the one-bedroom apartment shown below? $(6x + 5)$ ft

b. Find the perimeter of the apartment. $(4x^2 + 26)$ ft

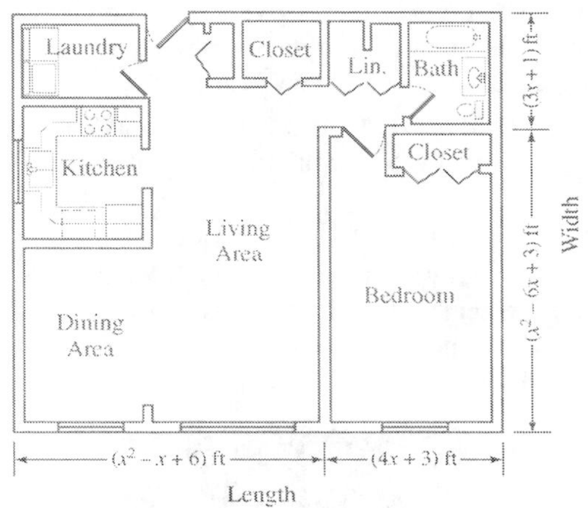

If a house is purchased for \$105,000 and is expected to appreciate \$900 per year, its value y after x years is given by the polynomial function $f(x) = 900x + 105{,}000$.

87. VALUE OF A HOUSE Find the expected value of the house in 10 years. \$114,000

88. VALUE OF A HOUSE A second house is purchased for \$120,000 and is expected to appreciate \$1,000 per year.

a. Find a polynomial function that will give the value y of the house in x years. $f(x) = 1{,}000x + 120{,}000$

b. Find the value of this second house after 12 years. \$132,000

89. VALUE OF TWO HOUSES Find one polynomial function that will give the combined value y of both houses, one from the directions and the other from problem 88, after x years. $f(x) = 1{,}900x + 225{,}000$

90. VALUE OF TWO HOUSES Find the value of the two houses after 20 years by

a. substituting 20 into the polynomial functions $f(x) = 900x + 105{,}000$ and $f(x) = 1{,}000x + 120{,}000$ and adding. \$263,000

b. substituting 20 into the result of Exercise 89. \$263,000

A business purchases two computers, one for \$6,600 and the other for \$9,200. The first computer is expected to depreciate \$1,100 per year and the second \$1,700 per year.

91. VALUE OF A COMPUTER Write a polynomial function that gives the value of the first computer after x years. $f(x) = -1{,}100x + 6{,}600$

92. VALUE OF A COMPUTER Write a polynomial function that gives the value of the second computer after x years. $f(x) = -1{,}700x + 9{,}200$

93. VALUE OF TWO COMPUTERS Find one polynomial function that gives the combined value of both computers whose functions were found in Exercises 91 and 92 after x years. $f(x) = -2{,}800x + 15{,}800$

94. VALUE OF TWO COMPUTERS In two ways, find the combined value of the two computers after 3 years. \$7,400

95. NAVAL OPERATIONS Two warning flares are simultaneously fired upward from different parts of a ship. The height of the first flare is $(-16t^2 + 128t + 20)$ feet and the height of the higher-traveling second flare is $(-16t^2 + 150t + 40)$ feet, after t seconds.

a. Find a polynomial that represents the difference in the heights of the flares. $22t + 20$

b. In 4 seconds, the first flare reaches its peak, explodes, and lights up the sky. How much higher is the second flare at that time? 108 ft

96. PIÑATAS Find the polynomial that represents the length of the rope used to hold up the piñata. $(2a^2 + 6a + 5)$ in.

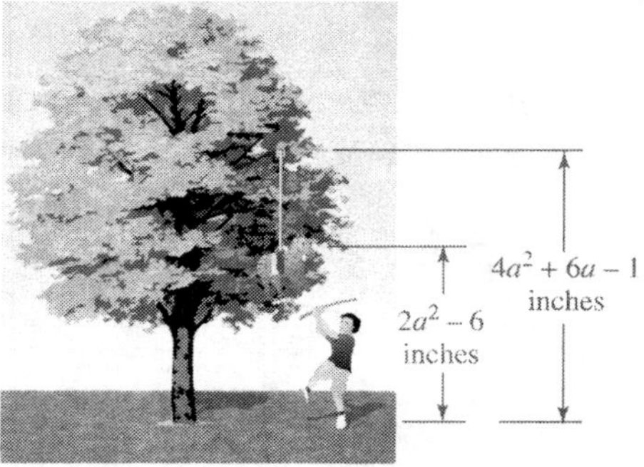

WRITING

97. How do you recognize like terms?

98. How do you add like terms?

99. Explain the concept that is illustrated by the statement

$$-(x^2 + 3x - 1) = -1(x^2 + 3x - 1)$$

100. Explain the mistake made in the following simplification:

$$\begin{aligned}(12x - 4) - (3x - 1) &= 12x - 4 - 3x - 1 \\ &= 9x - 5\end{aligned}$$

REVIEW

101. What is the sum of the measures of the angles of a triangle? 180°

102. What is the sum of the measures of two complementary angles? 90°

103. Solve the inequality $-4(3x - 3) \geq -12$ and graph the solution. $x \leq 2$ $(-\infty, 2]$

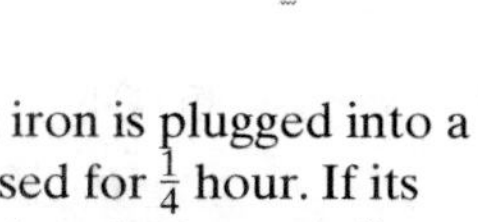

104. CURLING IRONS A curling iron is plugged into a 110-volt electrical outlet and used for $\frac{1}{4}$ hour. If its resistance is 10 ohms, find the electrical power (in kilowatt hours, kwh) used by the curling iron by applying the formula:

$$\text{kwh} = \frac{(\text{volts})^2}{1{,}000 \cdot \text{ohms}} \cdot \text{hours}$$ 0.3025 kwh

SECTION 6.5
Multiplying Polynomials

Objectives

1. Multiply monomials.
2. Multiply a polynomial by a monomial.
3. Multiply binomials.
4. Use special product formulas.
5. Multiply polynomials.
6. Multiply polynomials to solve equations.

We now discuss multiplying polynomials. We will begin with the simplest case—finding the product of two monomials.

1 Multiply monomials.

To multiply two monomials, such as $8x^2$ and $-3x^4$, we use the commutative and associative properties of multiplication to group the numerical factors and the variable factors. Then we multiply the numerical factors and multiply the variable factors.

$$\begin{aligned} 8x^2(-3x^4) &= 8(-3)x^2x^4 \\ &= -24x^6 \end{aligned}$$

This example suggests the following rule.

Multiplying Monomials

To multiply two monomials, multiply the numerical factors (the coefficients) and then multiply the variable factors.

EXAMPLE 1 Multiply:

a. $3x^4(2x^5)$ **b.** $-2a^2b^3(5ab^2)$ **c.** $-4y^5z^2(2y^3z^3)(3yz)$ **d.** $\left(\frac{3}{4}x^2y^3\right)\left(\frac{8}{3}xy^2\right)$

Strategy We will multiply the numerical factors and then multiply the variable factors.

WHY The commutative and associative properties of multiplication enable us to reorder and regroup the factors.

Solution

a. $3x^4(2x^5) = 3(2)\,x^4x^5$ Reorder the factors.

$= 6x^9$ Multiply the numerical factors, 3 and 2. Multiply the variable factors: $x^4x^5 = x^{4+5} = x^9$.

b. $-2a^2b^3(5ab^2) = -10a^3b^5$ Think: $-2(5) = -10$, $a^2 \cdot a = a^3$, and $b^3 \cdot b^2 = b^5$.

c. $-4y^5z^2(2y^3z^3)(3yz) = -24y^9z^6$ Think: $-4(2)(3) = -24$, $y^5 \cdot y^3 \cdot y = y^9$, and $z^2 \cdot z^3 \cdot z = z^6$.

d. $\left(\frac{3}{4}x^2y^3\right)\left(\frac{8}{3}xy^2\right) = 2x^3y^5$ Think: $\frac{3}{4}\left(\frac{8}{3}\right) = 2$, $x^2 \cdot x = x^3$, and $y^3 \cdot y^2 = y^5$.

Self Check 1

Multiply:

a. $(5a^2b^3)(6a^3b^4)$ $30a^5b^7$

b. $(-15p^3q^2)(5p^3q^2)$ $-75p^6q^4$

c. $\left(\frac{2}{3}x^2y\right)(9y^2)$ $6x^2y^3$

Now Try **Problems 13 and 18**

Teaching Example 1 Multiply:
a. $(3t^4)(-2t^5)$ b. $\left(\frac{1}{3}a^2b^4\right)(21ab^8)$
Answers:
a. $-6t^9$ b. $7a^3b^{12}$

Success Tip Notice that we *multiply* the numerical coefficients. To multiply the variable factors with like bases, keep the base and *add* the exponents.

2 Multiply a polynomial by a monomial.

To find the product of a polynomial (with more than one term) and a monomial, we use the distributive property. To multiply $2x + 4$ by $5x$, for example, we proceed as follows:

$5x(2x + 4) = 5x(2x) + 5x(4)$ Distribute the multiplication by 5x.

$= 10x^2 + 20x$ Multiply the monomials: $5x(2x) = 10x^2$ and $5x(4) = 20x$.

This example suggests the following rule.

Multiplying Polynomials by Monomials

To multiply a polynomial with more than one term by a monomial, multiply each term of the polynomial by the monomial and simplify.

Self Check 2

Multiply:

a. $2p^3(3p^2 - 5p)$
b. $-5a^2b(3a + 2b - 4ab)$
c. $(3ab - 4b + 2)(1.5a^4b)$

Now Try **Problems 22 and 30**

Self Check 2 Answers
a. $6p^5 - 10p^4$
b. $-15a^3b - 10a^2b^2 + 20a^3b^2$
c. $4.5a^5b^2 - 6a^4b^2 + 3a^4b$

Teaching Example 2 Multiply:
a. $4x^2(3x^3 - 2x)$ b. $(3x^4 - 2x)(5x^3)$
c. $2.3x^3(2x - 3)$
Answers:
a. $12x^5 - 8x^3$
b. $15x^7 - 10x^4$ c. $4.6x^4 - 6.9x^3$

EXAMPLE 2 Multiply:

a. $3a^2(3a^2 - 5a)$ b. $-2xz^2(2x - 3z + 2z^2)$ c. $(2.1b^2 - 3b)(0.1b^3)$

Strategy We will multiply each term of the polynomial by the monomial.

WHY We use the distributive property to multiply a monomial and a polynomial.

Solution

a. $3a^2(3a^2 - 5a) = 3a^2(3a^2) - 3a^2(5a)$ Distribute the multiplication by $3a^2$.

$= 9a^4 - 15a^3$ Multiply the monomials.

b. $-2xz^2(2x - 3z + 2z^2)$

$= -2xz^2(2x) - (-2xz^2)(3z) + (-2xz^2)(2z^2)$ Use the distributive property.

$= -4x^2z^2 - (-6xz^3) + (-4xz^4)$ Multiply the monomials.

$= -4x^2z^2 + 6xz^3 - 4xz^4$

c. $(2.1b^2 - 3b)(0.1b^3) = 2.1b^2(0.1b^3) - 3b(0.1b^3)$ Distribute the multiplication by $0.1b^3$.

$= 0.21b^5 - 0.3b^4$ Multiply the monomials.

Success Tip $(2.1b^2 - 3b)(0.1b^3)$ could also be rewritten as $(0.1b^3)(2.1b^2 - 3b)$ using the commutative property of multiplication. Then use the distributive property to find the product $0.21b^5 - 0.3b^4$.

3 Multiply binomials.

To multiply two binomials, we must use the distributive property more than once. For example, to multiply $2a - 4$ by $3a + 5$, we proceed as follows.

$(2a - 4)(3a + 5) = (2a - 4)(3a) + (2a - 4)(5)$ Distribute the multiplication by $(2a - 4)$.

$= 3a(2a - 4) + 5(2a - 4)$ Use the commutative property of multiplication.

$= 3a(2a) - 3a(4) + 5(2a) - 5(4)$ Distribute the multiplication by $3a$ and by 5.

$= 6a^2 - 12a + 10a - 20$ Perform the multiplications.

$= 6a^2 - 2a - 20$ Combine like terms.

This example suggests the following rule.

Multiplying Two Binomials

To multiply two binomials, multiply each term of one binomial by each term of the other binomial and combine like terms.

EXAMPLE 3 Multiply: $(2x - y)(3x + 4y)$

Strategy We will multiply each term of $3x + 4y$ by $2x$ and $-y$.

WHY To multiply two binomials, each term of one binomial must be multiplied by each term of the other binomial.

Solution

$(2x - y)(3x + 4y) = 2x(3x + 4y) - y(3x + 4y)$ Multiply $3x + 4y$ by $2x$ and by $-y$.

$= 6x^2 + 8xy - 3xy - 4y^2$ Distribute the multiplication by $2x$. Distribute the multiplication by $-y$.

$= 6x^2 + 5xy - 4y^2$ Collect like terms.

Self Check 3

Multiply: $(7x + 2y)(5x - 2y)$

Now Try **Problem 37**

Self Check 3 Answer
$35x^2 - 4xy - 4y^2$

Teaching Example 3 Multiply: $(9x - 2y)(2x - 3y)$
Answer:
$18x^2 - 31xy + 6y^2$

We can use a shortcut method, called the **FOIL** method, to multiply binomials. FOIL is an acronym for **F**irst terms, **O**uter terms, **I**nner terms, and **L**ast terms. To use the FOIL method to multiply $2a - 4$ by $3a + 5$, we

1. multiply the **F**irst terms $2a$ and $3a$ to obtain $6a^2$,
2. multiply the **O**uter terms $2a$ and 5 to obtain $10a$,
3. multiply the **I**nner terms -4 and $3a$ to obtain $-12a$, and
4. multiply the **L**ast terms -4 and 5 to obtain -20.

Then we simplify the resulting polynomial, if possible.

First terms Last terms

$(2a - 4)(3a + 5) = 2a(3a) + 2a(5) + (-4)(3a) + (-4)(5)$

$= 6a^2 + 10a - 12a - 20$ Perform the multiplications.

Inner terms

Outer terms $= 6a^2 - 2a - 20$ Combine like terms.

EXAMPLE 4 Find each product. **a.** $(x + 5)(x + 7)$ **b.** $(3x + 4)(2x - 3)$ **c.** $(a - 7b)(a - 4b)$ **d.** $\left(\frac{3}{4}r - 3s\right)\left(\frac{1}{2}r + 4t\right)$

Strategy We will use the FOIL method.

WHY In each case we are to find the product of two binomials, and the FOIL method is a shortcut for multiplying two binomials.

Solution

F L

F O I L

a. $(x + 5)(x + 7) = x(x) + x(7) + 5(x) + 5(7)$

$= x^2 + 7x + 5x + 35$ Multiply the monomials.

$= x^2 + 12x + 35$ Combine like terms.

I O

F L

F O I L

b. $(3x + 4)(2x - 3) = 3x(2x) + 3x(-3) + 4(2x) + 4(-3)$

$= 6x^2 - 9x + 8x - 12$ Multiply the monomials.

$= 6x^2 - x - 12$ Combine like terms.

I O

Self Check 4

Find each product:
a. $(y + 3)(y + 1)$
b. $(2a - 1)(3a + 2)$
c. $(5y - 2z)(2y + 3z)$
d. $\left(4r + \frac{1}{2}s\right)\left(2r - \frac{1}{2}s\right)$

Now Try **Problems 40 and 41**

Self Check 4 Answers
a. $y^2 + 4y + 3$
b. $6a^2 + a - 2$
c. $10y^2 + 11yz - 6z^2$
d. $8r^2 - rs - \frac{1}{4}s^2$

Teaching Example 4 Find each product:
a. $(x + 4)(x + 3)$
b. $(4x + 2)(5x - 6)$
c. $\left(3x + \frac{2}{3}\right)\left(6x - \frac{1}{3}\right)$
Answers:
a. $x^2 + 7x + 12$ b. $20x^2 - 14x - 12$
c. $18x^2 + 3x - \frac{2}{9}$

F L

F O I L

c. $(a - 7b)(a - 4b) = a(a) + a(-4b) + (-7b)(a) + (-7b)(-4b)$

$= a^2 - 4ab - 7ab + 28b^2$ Multiply the monomials.

$= a^2 - 11ab + 28b^2$ Combine like terms.

I O

F L

F O I L

d. $\left(\frac{3}{4}r - 3s\right)\left(\frac{1}{2}r + 4t\right) = \frac{3}{4}r\left(\frac{1}{2}r\right) + \frac{3}{4}r(4t) - 3s\left(\frac{1}{2}r\right) - 3s(4t)$

$= \frac{3}{8}r^2 + 3rt - \frac{3}{2}rs - 12st$ There are no like terms.

I O

Self Check 5

Simplify: $(x + 3)(2x - 1) + 2x(x - 1)$. $4x^2 + 3x - 3$

Now Try **Problems 45 and 51**

Teaching Example 5 Simplify: $-3(2x + 5)(x - 4)$

Answer: $-6x^2 + 9x + 60$

EXAMPLE 5 Simplify each expression.

a. $3(2x - 3)(x + 1)$ **b.** $(x + 1)(x - 2) - 3x(x + 3)$

Strategy We will use the FOIL method and the distributive property to remove the parentheses. Then we will combine like terms.

WHY To simplify an expression means to remove parentheses and combine like terms.

Solution

a. $3(2x - 3)(x + 1) = 3(2x^2 + 2x - 3x - 3)$ Multiply the binomials.

$= 3(2x^2 - x - 3)$ Combine like terms.

$= 6x^2 - 3x - 9$ Distribute the multiplication by 3.

b. $(x + 1)(x - 2) - 3x(x + 3) = x^2 - 2x + x - 2 - 3x^2 - 9x$

$= -2x^2 - 10x - 2$ Combine like terms.

4 Use special products formulas.

Certain products of binomials occur so frequently in algebra that it is worthwhile to learn formulas for computing them. To develop a rule to find the *square of a sum,* we consider $(x + y)^2$.

$(x + y)^2 = (x + y)(x + y)$ In $(x + y)^2$, the base is $(x + y)$ and the exponent is 2.

$= x^2 + xy + xy + y^2$ Multiply the binomials.

$= x^2 + 2xy + y^2$ Combine like terms: $xy + xy = 2xy$.

We note that the terms of this result are related to the terms of the original expression. That is, $(x + y)^2$ is equal to the square of its first term (x^2), plus twice the product of both its terms ($2xy$), plus the square of its last term (y^2).

To develop a rule to find the *square of a difference,* we consider $(x - y)^2$.

$(x - y)^2 = (x - y)(x - y)$

$= x^2 - xy - xy + y^2$ Multiply the binomials.

$= x^2 - 2xy + y^2$ Combine like terms: $-xy - xy = -2xy$.

Again, the terms of the result are related to the terms of the original expression. When we find $(x - y)^2$, the product is composed of the square of its first term (x^2), twice the product of both its terms ($-2xy$), and the square of its last term (y^2).

The final special product is the product of two binomials that differ only in the signs of the last terms. To develop a rule to find the product of a *sum and a difference,* we consider $(x + y)(x - y)$.

$$(x + y)(x - y) = x^2 - xy + xy - y^2 \quad \text{Multiply the binomials.}$$
$$= x^2 - y^2 \quad \text{Combine like terms: } -xy + xy = 0.$$

The product is the square of the first term (x^2) minus the square of the second term (y^2). The expression $x^2 - y^2$ is called a **difference of two squares.**

Because these special products occur so often, it is wise to memorize their forms.

Special Products

$(x + y)^2 = x^2 + 2xy + y^2$	The square of a sum
$(x - y)^2 = x^2 - 2xy + y^2$	The square of a difference
$(x + y)(x - y) = x^2 - y^2$	The product of a sum and difference

EXAMPLE 6 Find: **a.** $(t + 9)^2$ **b.** $(8a - 5)^2$ **c.** $(3y + 4z)(3y - 4z)$

Strategy We will identify the special product and apply the appropriate rule.

WHY The rules for special products enables us to compute them quickly.

Solution

a. This is the square of a sum. The terms of the binomial being squared are t and 9.

$$(t + 9)^2 = \underbrace{t^2}_{\text{The square of the first term, } t.} + \underbrace{2(t)(9)}_{\text{Twice the product of both terms.}} + \underbrace{9^2}_{\text{The square of the last term, } 9.}$$
$$= t^2 + 18t + 81$$

b. This is the square of a difference. The terms of the binomial being squared are $8a$ and -5.

$$(8a - 5)^2 = \underbrace{(8a)^2}_{\text{The square of the first term, } 8a.} - \underbrace{2(8a)(5)}_{\text{Twice the product of both terms.}} + \underbrace{5^2}_{\text{The square of the last term, } 5.}$$
$$= 64a^2 - 80a + 25 \quad \text{Use the power rule for products: } (8a)^2 = 8^2a^2 = 64a^2.$$

c. The binomials differ only in the signs of the last terms. This is the product of a sum and a difference.

$$(3y + 4z)(3y - 4z) = (3y)^2 - (4z)^2 \quad \text{This is the square of the first term minus the square of the second term.}$$
$$= 9y^2 - 16z^2 \quad \text{Use the power rule for products twice.}$$

Self Check 6

Find:

a. $(r + 6)^2$

b. $(7g - 2)^2$

c. $(5m - 9n)(5m + 9n)$

Now Try **Problems 53, 56, and 57**

Self Check 6 Answers

a. $r^2 + 12r + 36$

b. $49g^2 - 28g + 4$

c. $25m^2 - 81n^2$

Teaching Example 6 Find:

a. $(x + 5)^2$

b. $(2y - 3)^2$

c. $(4x + 3y)(4x - 3y)$

Answers:

a. $x^2 + 10x + 25$

b. $4y^2 - 12y + 9$

c. $16x^2 - 9y^2$

Caution! A common error when squaring a binomial is to forget the middle term of the product. For example, $(x + 2)^2 \neq x^2 + 4$ and $(x - 2)^2 \neq x^2 - 4$. Applying the special product formulas, we have $(x + 2)^2 = x^2 + 4x + 4$ and $(x - 2)^2 = x^2 - 4x + 4$.

5 Multiply polynomials.

We must use the distributive property more than once to multiply a polynomial by a binomial. For example, to multiply $3x^2 + 3x - 5$ by $2x + 3$, we proceed as follows:

$$\begin{aligned}(2x + 3)(3x^2 + 3x - 5) &= (2x + 3)3x^2 + (2x + 3)3x - (2x + 3)5 \\ &= 3x^2(2x + 3) + 3x(2x + 3) - 5(2x + 3) \\ &= 6x^3 + 9x^2 + 6x^2 + 9x - 10x - 15 \\ &= 6x^3 + 15x^2 - x - 15\end{aligned}$$

This example suggests the following rule.

Multiplying Polynomials

To multiply one polynomial by another, multiply each term of one polynomial by each term of the other polynomial and combine like terms.

It is often convenient to organize the work vertically.

Self Check 7

Multiply using vertical form:

a. $(3x + 2)(2x^2 - 4x + 5)$

b. $(-2x^2 + 3)(2x^2 - 4x - 1)$

Now Try **Problem 63**

Self Check 7 Answers

a. $6x^3 - 8x^2 + 7x + 10$

b. $-4x^4 + 8x^3 + 8x^2 - 12x - 3$

Teaching Example 7 Multiply using vertical form:

a. $(5x - 3)(2x^2 + x - 4)$

b. $(-3x^2 + 4)(4x^2 - 3x + 2)$

Answers:

a. $10x^3 - x^2 - 23x + 12$

b. $-12x^4 + 9x^3 + 10x^2 - 12x + 8$

EXAMPLE 7 Multiply using vertical form:

a. $(3a^2 - 4a + 7)(2a + 5)$ **b.** $(3y^2 - 5y + 4)(-4y^2 - 3)$

Strategy First, we will write one polynomial underneath the other and draw a horizontal line beneath them. Then, we will multiply each term of the upper polynomial by each term of the lower polynomial, making sure to line up like terms.

WHY *Vertical form* means to use an approach similar to that used in arithmetic to multiply two numbers.

Solution

a. Multiply:

$$\begin{array}{rrrrl} & 3a^2 & - 4a & + 7 & \\ & & 2a & + 5 & \\ \hline & 15a^2 & - 20a & + 35 & \text{Multiply } 3a^2 - 4a + 7 \text{ by } 5. \\ 6a^3 & - 8a^2 & + 14a & & \text{Multiply } 3a^2 - 4a + 7 \text{ by } 2a. \\ \hline 6a^3 & + 7a^2 & - 6a & + 35 & \text{In each column, combine like terms.} \end{array}$$

b. Multiply:

$$\begin{array}{rrrrrl} & & 3y^2 & - 5y & + 4 & \\ & & -4y^2 & & - 3 & \\ \hline & & -9y^2 & + 15y & - 12 & \text{Multiply } 3y^2 - 5y + 4 \text{ by } -3. \\ -12y^4 & + 20y^3 & - 16y^2 & & & \text{Multiply } 3y^2 - 5y + 4 \text{ by } -4y^2. \\ \hline -12y^4 & + 20y^3 & - 25y^2 & + 15y & - 12 & \end{array}$$

When finding the product of three polynomials, we begin by multiplying any two of them, and then we multiply that result by the third polynomial.

Self Check 8

Find the product:

$-2y(y + 3)(3y - 2)$

Now Try **Problem 68**

EXAMPLE 8 Find the product: $-3a(4a + 1)(a - 7)$

Strategy We will find the product of $4a + 1$ and $a - 7$ and then multiply that result by $-3a$.

WHY It is better to find the most difficult product first. Save the simpler multiplication by $-3a$ for last.

Solution

$-3a(4a + 1)(a - 7) = -3a(4a^2 - 28a + a - 7)$ Multiply the two binomials.

$= -3a(4a^2 - 27a - 7)$ Combine like terms.

$= -12a^3 + 81a^2 + 21a$ Distribute the multiplication by $-3a$.

Self Check 8 Answer
$-6y^3 - 14y^2 + 12y$

Teaching Example 8 Multiply:
$-3x(x - 5)(2x + 1)$
Answer:
$-6x^3 + 27x^2 + 15x$

6 Multiply polynomials to solve equations.

To solve an equation involving products of polynomials, we can do the multiplication on each side and proceed as follows.

EXAMPLE 9 Solve: $(x + 2)(x + 3) = x(x + 7)$

Strategy We will multiply the binomials on the left side of the equation and use the distributive property on the right side.

WHY The first step in solving equations is to remove parentheses.

Solution

$$(x + 2)(x + 3) = x(x + 7)$$

$x^2 + 3x + 2x + 6 = x^2 + 7x$

$x^2 + 3x + 2x + 6 - x^2 = x^2 + 7x - x^2$ Subtract x^2 from both sides.

$5x + 6 = 7x$ Combine like terms: $x^2 - x^2 = 0$ and $3x + 2x = 5x$.

$6 = 2x$ Subtract $5x$ from both sides.

$3 = x$ Divide both sides by 2.

Check: $(x + 2)(x + 3) = x(x + 7)$

$(3 + 2)(3 + 3) \stackrel{?}{=} 3(3 + 7)$ Replace x with 3.

$5(6) \stackrel{?}{=} 3(10)$ Perform the additions within parentheses.

$30 = 30$

Self Check 9

Solve:
$(x + 5)(x - 4) = x(x + 3)$

Now Try **Problem 71**

Self Check 9 Answer
$x = -10$

Teaching Example 9 Solve:
$x(x - 4) = (x + 2)(x - 7)$
Answer:
-14

EXAMPLE 10 *Dimensions of a Painting* A square painting is surrounded by a border 2 inches wide. If the area of the border is 96 square inches, find the dimensions of the painting.

Analyze Refer to the figure, which shows a square painting surrounded by a border 2 inches wide. We know that the area of this border is 96 square inches, and we are to find the dimensions of the painting.

Form Let x = the length of a side of the square painting. Since the border is 2 inches wide, the length and the width of the outer rectangle are both $(x + 2 + 2)$ inches. Then the outer rectangle is also a square, and its dimensions are $(x + 4)$ by $(x + 4)$ inches. Since the area of a square is the product of its length and width, the area of the larger square is $(x + 4)(x + 4)$, and the area of the painting is $x \cdot x$. If we subtract the area of the painting from the area of the larger square, the difference is 96.

Self Check 10

A square painting is surrounded by a border 1 inch wide. If the area of the border is 84 square inches, find the dimensions of the painting. 20 in. by 20 in.

Now Try **Problem 114**

Teaching Example 10 A square painting is surrounded by a border 3 inches wide. If the area of the border is 216 square inches, find the dimensions of the painting.
Answer:
15 in. by 15 in.

The area of the large square	minus	the area of the square painting	is	the area of the border.
$(x + 4)(x + 4)$	$-$	$x \cdot x$	$=$	96

Solve

$$(x + 4)(x + 4) - x^2 = 96 \quad x \cdot x = x^2.$$
$$x^2 + 8x + 16 - x^2 = 96 \quad (x + 4)(x + 4) = (x + 4)^2 = x^2 + 8x + 16.$$
$$8x + 16 = 96 \quad \text{Combine like terms: } x^2 - x^2 = 0.$$
$$8x = 80 \quad \text{Subtract 16 from both sides.}$$
$$x = 10 \quad \text{Divide both sides by 8.}$$

State The dimensions of the painting are 10 inches by 10 inches.

Check Verify that the 2-inch-wide border of a 10-inch-square painting would have an area of 96 square inches.

ANSWERS TO SELF CHECKS

1. a. $30a^5b^7$ **b.** $-75p^6q^4$ **c.** $6x^2y^3$ **2. a.** $6p^5 - 10p^4$ **b.** $-15a^3b - 10a^2b^2 + 20a^3b^2$ **c.** $4.5a^5b^2 - 6a^4b^2 + 3a^4b$ **3.** $35x^2 - 4xy - 4y^2$ **4. a.** $y^2 + 4y + 3$ **b.** $6a^2 + a - 2$ **c.** $10y^2 + 11yz - 6z^2$ **d.** $8r^2 - rs - \frac{1}{4}s^2$ **5.** $4x^2 + 3x - 3$ **6. a.** $r^2 + 12r + 36$ **b.** $49g^2 - 28g + 4$ **c.** $25m^2 - 81n^2$ **7. a.** $6x^3 - 8x^2 + 7x + 10$ **b.** $-4x^4 + 8x^3 + 8x^2 - 12x - 3$ **8.** $-6y^3 - 14y^2 + 12y$ **9.** $x = -10$ **10.** 20 in. by 20 in.

SECTION 6.5 STUDY SET

VOCABULARY

Fill in the blanks.

1. The expression $(2a - 4)(3a + 5)$ is the product of two binomials.
2. The expression $(2a - 4)(3a^2 + 5a - 1)$ is the product of a binomial and a trinomial.
3. In the acronym FOIL, F stands for first terms, O for outer terms, I for inner terms, and L for last terms.
4. $(x + 5)^2$ is the square of a sum, and $(x - 5)^2$ is the square of a difference.

CONCEPTS

Consider the product $(2x + 5)(3x - 4)$.

5. The product of the first terms is $6x^2$.
6. The product of the outer terms is $-8x$.
7. The product of the inner terms is $15x$.
8. The product of the last terms is -20.

9. STAMPS Find the area of the stamp. $(6x^2 + x - 1)$ cm^2

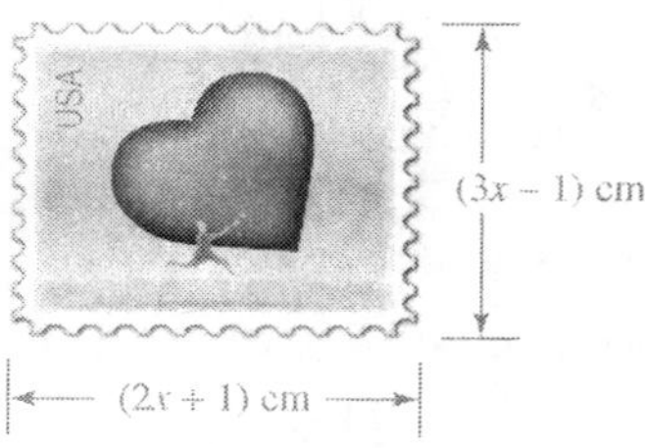

10. LUGGAGE Find the volume of the garment bag shown below. $(2x^3 - 4x^2 - 6x)$ in.^{3}

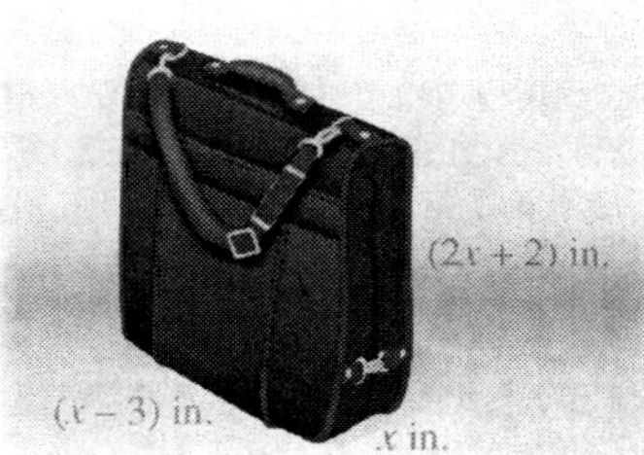

Selected exercises available online at www.webassign.net/brookscole

NOTATION

Complete each solution.

11. $7x(3x^2 - 2x + 5) = 7x(3x^2) - 7x(2x) + 7x(5)$
$= 21x^3 - 14x^2 + 35x$

▶ **12.** $(2x + 5)(3x - 2) = 2x(3x) - 2x(2) + 5(3x) - 5(2)$
$= 6x^2 - 4x + 15x - 10$
$= 6x^2 + 11x - 10$

GUIDED PRACTICE

Multiply. See Example 1.

13. $(3x^2)(4x^3)$ $12x^5$

▶ **14.** $(-2a^3)(3a^2)$ $-6a^5$

▶ **15.** $(-5x^3y^6)(x^2y^2)$ $-5x^5y^8$

16. $(3x^2y)(2xy^2)$ $6x^3y^3$

17. $(x^2y^5)(x^2z^5)(-3z^3)$ $-3x^4y^5z^8$

18. $(3ab^2)(-2ab)(4ab^3)$ $-24a^3b^6$

19. $\left(\frac{1}{2}x^2y^3\right)\left(\frac{2}{3}x^3y^2\right)$ $\frac{1}{3}x^5y^5$

20. $\left(-\frac{3}{4}r^4st^2\right)(2r^2st)\left(-\frac{2}{3}rst\right)$ $r^7s^3t^4$

Multiply. See Example 2.

21. $-4t(t + 7)$ $-4t^2 - 28t$

22. $-8c(2c - 3)$ $-16c^2 + 24c$

▶ **23.** $6s^2(s^2 - 3s)$ $6s^4 - 18s^3$

24. $3a^3(2a^2 + 5a)$ $6a^5 + 15a^4$

25. $3y(x + 4y)$ $3xy + 12y^2$

26. $-3a^2b(a - b)$ $-3a^3b + 3a^2b^2$

▶ **27.** $2x^2(3x^2 + 4x - 7)$ $6x^4 + 8x^3 - 14x^2$

28. $3y^3(2y^2 - 7y - 8)$ $6y^5 - 21y^4 - 24y^3$

29. $2ab^2(2a + 3b - 2a^2)$ $4a^2b^2 + 6ab^3 - 4a^3b^2$

30. $-2p^2q(3p - 2q - 3pq)$ $-6p^3q + 4p^2q^2 + 6p^3q^2$

31. $(3.1p^2 - 4q)(0.2p^2)$ $0.62p^4 - 0.8p^2q$

32. $(1.5m^2 + 5.1n)(1.2m^3)$ $1.8m^5 + 6.12m^3n$

Find each product. See Examples 3–4.

33. $(a + 4)(a + 5)$ $a^2 + 9a + 20$

34. $(y - 3)(y + 5)$ $y^2 + 2y - 15$

▶ **35.** $(3x - 2)(x + 4)$ $3x^2 + 10x - 8$

36. $(t + 4)(2t - 3)$ $2t^2 + 5t - 12$

37. $(2a + 4)(3a - 5)$ $6a^2 + 2a - 20$

38. $(2b - 1)(3b + 4)$ $6b^2 + 5b - 4$

39. $(3x - 5)(2x + 1)$ $6x^2 - 7x - 5$

40. $(2y - 5)(3y + 7)$ $6y^2 - y - 35$

▶ **41.** $(2t + 3s)(3t - s)$ $6t^2 + 7st - 3s^2$

42. $(3a - 2b)(4a + b)$ $12a^2 - 5ab - 2b^2$

43. $\left(\frac{1}{4}t - u\right)\left(-\frac{1}{2}t + u\right)$ $-\frac{1}{8}t^2 + \frac{3}{4}ut - u^2$

44. $\left(-\frac{1}{3}t + 2s\right)\left(\frac{2}{3}t - 3s\right)$ $-\frac{2}{9}t^2 + \frac{7}{3}st - 6s^2$

Simplify each expression. See Example 5.

45. $4(2x + 1)(x - 2)$ $8x^2 - 12x - 8$

46. $-5(3a - 2)(2a + 3)$ $-30a^2 - 25a + 30$

47. $3a(a + b)(a - b)$ $3a^3 - 3ab^2$

▶ **48.** $-2r(r + s)(r + s)$ $-2r^3 - 4r^2s - 2rs^2$

49. $2t(t + 2) + 3t(t - 5)$ $5t^2 - 11t$

50. $3y(y + 2) + (y + 1)(y - 1)$ $4y^2 + 6y - 1$

51. $(x + y)(x - y) + x(x + y)$ $2x^2 + xy - y^2$

▶ **52.** $(3x + 4)(2x - 2) - (2x + 1)(x + 3)$ $4x^2 - 5x - 11$

Find each product. See Example 6.

▶ **53.** $(x + 4)^2$ $x^2 + 8x + 16$

54. $(a + 3)^2$ $a^2 + 6a + 9$

55. $(t - 3)^2$ $t^2 - 6t + 9$

56. $(z - 5)^2$ $z^2 - 10z + 25$

57. $(4x + 5)(4x - 5)$ $16x^2 - 25$

▶ **58.** $(5z + 1)(5z - 1)$ $25z^2 - 1$

59. $(x - 2y)^2$ $x^2 - 4xy + 4y^2$

60. $(3a + 2b)^2$ $9a^2 + 12ab + 4b^2$

Find each product. See Example 7.

61. $$\begin{array}{r} x^2 - 2x + 1 \\ \underline{x + 2} \end{array}$$ $x^3 - 3x + 2$

▶ **62.** $$\begin{array}{r} 5r^2 + r + 6 \\ \underline{2r - 1} \end{array}$$ $10r^3 - 3r^2 + 11r - 6$

63. $$\begin{array}{r} 4x^2 + 3x - 4 \\ \underline{3x + 2} \end{array}$$ $12x^3 + 17x^2 - 6x - 8$

64. $$\begin{array}{r} x^2 - x + 1 \\ \underline{x + 1} \end{array}$$ $x^3 + 1$

Find each product. See Example 8.

65. $3x(-2x^2)(x + 4)$ $-6x^4 - 24x^3$

66. $-2a^2(-3a^3)(3a - 2)$ $18a^6 - 12a^5$

▶ **67.** $-2x(x + 3)(2x - 3)$ $-4x^3 - 6x^2 + 18x$

68. $5x^2(2x + 3)(2x - 5)$ $20x^4 - 20x^3 - 75x^2$

Solve each equation. See Example 9.

69. $(s - 4)(s + 1) = s^2 + 5$ -3

70. $(y - 5)(y - 2) = y^2 - 4$ 2

71. $z(z + 2) = (z + 4)(z - 4)$ -8

▶ **72.** $(z + 3)(z - 3) = z(z - 3)$ 3

73. $(x + 4)(x - 4) = (x - 2)(x + 6)$ -1

74. $(y - 1)(y + 6) = (y - 3)(y - 2) + 8$ 2

75. $(a - 3)^2 = (a + 3)^2$ 0

▶ **76.** $(b + 2)^2 = (b - 1)^2$ $-\frac{1}{2}$

TRY IT YOURSELF

Find each product.

77. $3x(x - 2)$ $3x^2 - 6x$

78. $4y(y + 5)$ $4y^2 + 20y$

79. $-2x^2(3x^2 - x)$ $-6x^4 + 2x^3$

80. $4b^3(2b^2 - 2b)$ $8b^5 - 8b^4$

81. $3xy(x + y)$ $3x^2y + 3xy^2$

82. $-4x^2z(3x^2 - z)$ $-12x^4z + 4x^2z^2$

83. $(r + 4)(r - 4)$ $r^2 - 16$

84. $(b + 2)(b - 2)$ $b^2 - 4$

85. $(2s + 1)(2s + 1)$ $4s^2 + 4s + 1$

86. $(3t - 2)(3t - 2)$ $9t^2 - 12t + 4$

87. $(x + y)(x + z)$ $x^2 + xz + xy + yz$

88. $(a - b)(x + y)$ $ax + ay - bx - by$

89. $(x + 2)(x^2 - 2x + 3)$ $x^3 - x + 6$

▶ **90.** $(x - 5)(x^2 + 2x - 3)$ $x^3 - 3x^2 - 13x + 15$

91. $(4t + 3)(t^2 + 2t + 3)$ $4t^3 + 11t^2 + 18t + 9$

▶ **92.** $(3x + 1)(2x^2 - 3x + 1)$ $6x^3 - 7x^2 + 1$

93. $(-3x + y)(x^2 - 8xy + 16y^2)$ $-3x^3 + 25x^2y - 56xy^2 + 16y^3$

94. $(3x - y)(x^2 + 3xy - y^2)$ $3x^3 + 8x^2y - 6xy^2 + y^3$

95. $(x + 5)^2$ $x^2 + 10x + 25$

96. $(y - 6)^2$ $y^2 - 12y + 36$

97. $(2a - 3b)^2$ $4a^2 - 12ab + 9b^2$

▶ **98.** $(2x + 5y)^2$ $4x^2 + 20xy + 25y^2$

99. $(4x + 5y)^2$ $16x^2 + 40xy + 25y^2$

100. $(6p - 5q)^2$ $36p^2 - 60pq + 25q^2$

101. $2a(a + 2) - 3a(5 - a)$ $5a^2 - 11a$

102. $(3b + 4)(2b - 2) + (2b + 1)(b + 3)$ $8b^2 + 9b - 5$

APPLICATIONS

Find the area of each figure. You may leave π in your answer.

103.

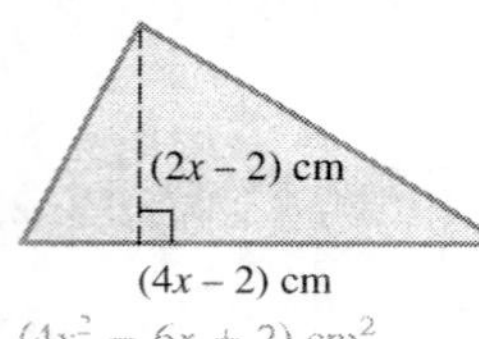

$(4x^2 - 6x + 2)$ cm^2

104.

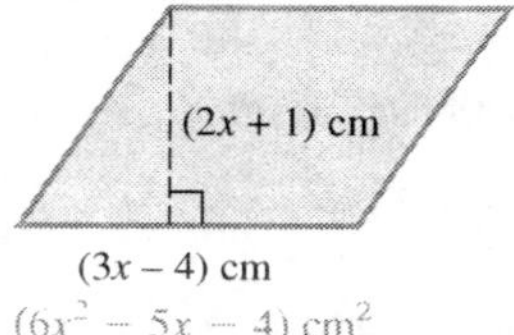

$(6x^2 - 5x - 4)$ cm^2

▶ **105.**

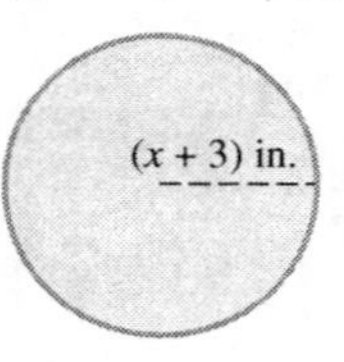

$(x^2 + 6x + 9)\pi$ in.^{2}

▶ **106.**

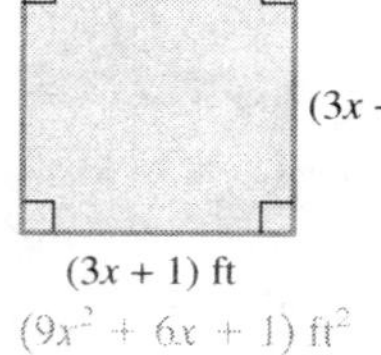

$(9x^2 + 6x + 1)$ ft^2

▶ **107.** TOYS Find the perimeter and the area of the screen of the Etch A Sketch. $(24x + 14)$ cm, $(35x^2 + 43x + 12)$ cm^2

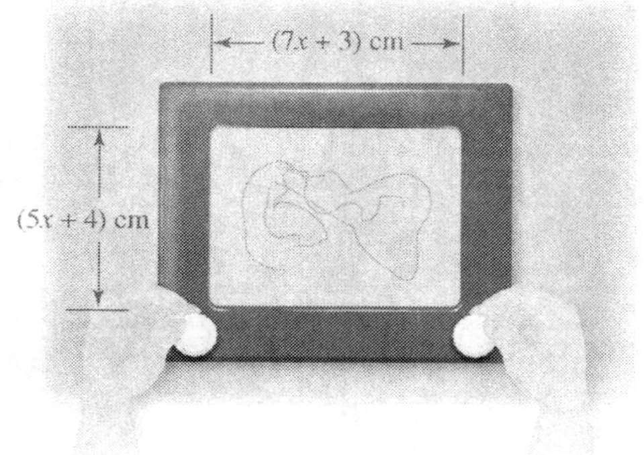

▶ **108.** SUNGLASSES An ellipse is an oval-shaped closed curve. The area of an ellipse is approximately $3.14ab$, where a is its length and b is its width. Find the polynomial that approximates the total area of the elliptical-shaped lenses of the sunglasses shown. $(6.28x^2 - 6.28)$ in.^{2}

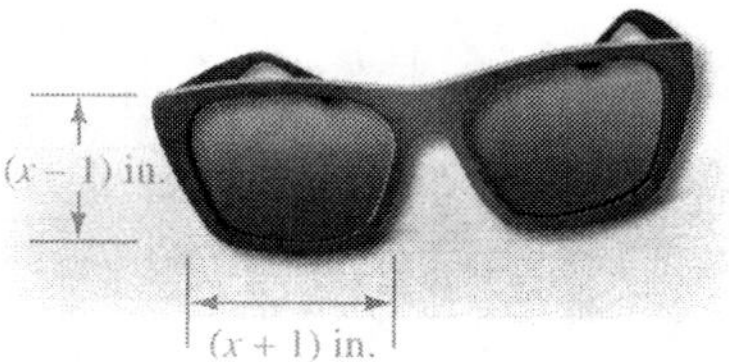

▶ **109.** GARDENING See the following illustration.

a. What is the area of the region planted with corn? tomatoes? beans? carrots? Use your answers to find the total area of the garden. x^2 ft^2, $6x$ ft^2, $5x$ ft^2, 30 ft^2; $(x^2 + 11x + 30)$ ft^2

b. What is the length of the garden? What is its width? Use your answers to find its area. $(x + 6)$ ft, $(x + 5)$ ft; $(x^2 + 11x + 30)$ ft^2

c. How do the answers from parts a and b for the area of the garden compare? They are the same.

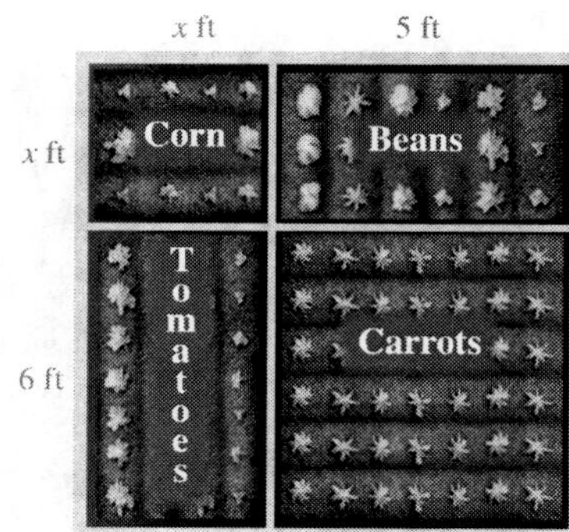

110. PAINTING See the illustration. To purchase the correct amount of enamel to paint these two garage doors, a painter must find their areas. Find a polynomial that gives the number of square feet to be painted. All dimensions are in feet, and the windows are squares with sides of x feet. $(36x^2 + 36x + 6)$ ft^2

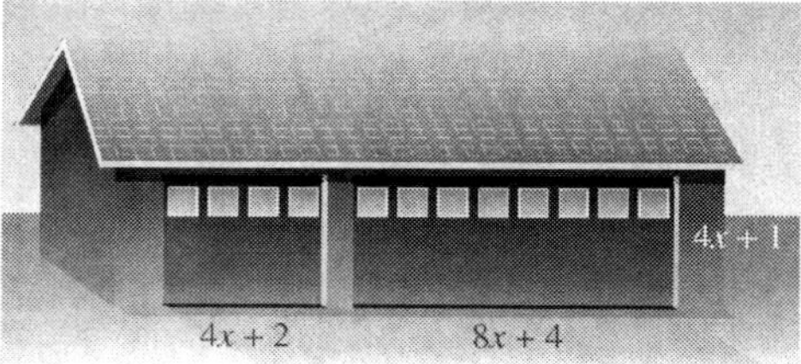

▶ **111.** INTEGER PROBLEM The difference between the squares of two consecutive positive integers is 11. Find the integers. (*Hint:* Let x and $x + 1$ represent the consecutive integers.) 5 and 6

112. INTEGER PROBLEM If 3 less than a certain integer is multiplied by 4 more than the integer, the product is 6 less than the square of the integer. Find the integer. 6

113. STONE-GROUND FLOUR The radius of a millstone is 3 meters greater than the radius of another, and their areas differ by 15π square meters. Find the radius of the larger millstone. 4 m

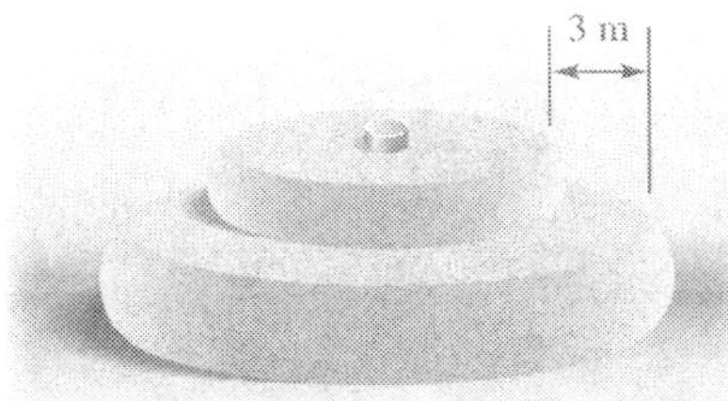

114. BOOKBINDING Two square sheets of cardboard used for making book covers differ in area by 44 square inches. An edge of the larger square is 2 inches greater than an edge of the smaller square. Find the length of an edge of the smaller square. 10 in.

115. BASEBALL In major league baseball, the distance between bases is 30 feet greater than it is in softball. The bases in major league baseball mark the corners of a square that has an area 4,500 square feet greater than for softball. Find the distance between the bases in baseball. 90 ft

116. PULLEY DESIGNS The radius of one pulley in the illustration is 1 inch greater than the radius of the second pulley, and their areas differ by 4π square inches. Find the radius of the smaller pulley. $\frac{3}{2}$ in.

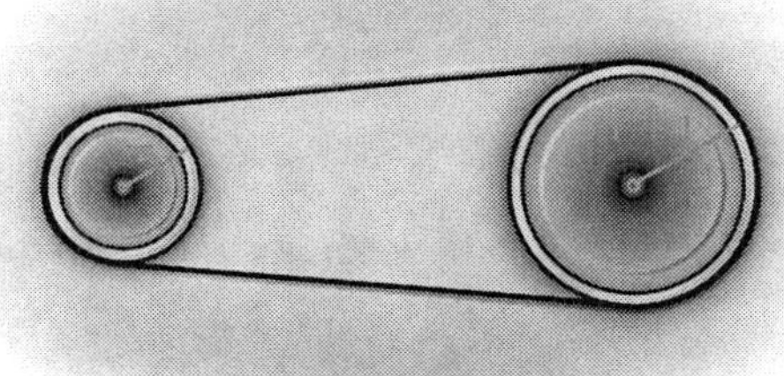

117. SIGNS Find a polynomial that represents the area of the sign. $\left(\frac{1}{2}h^2 - 2h\right)$ in.^{2}

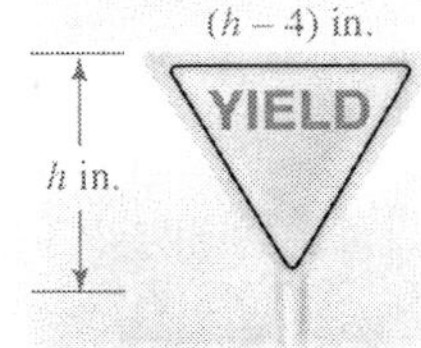

118. BASEBALL Find a polynomial that represents the amount of space within the batting cage. $(45x^3 + 12x^2 - 19x - 6)$ ft^3

WRITING

119. Describe the steps involved in finding the product of $x + 2$ and $x - 2$.

120. Writing $(x + y)^2$ as $x^2 + y^2$ illustrates a common error. Explain.

REVIEW

Refer to the illustration.

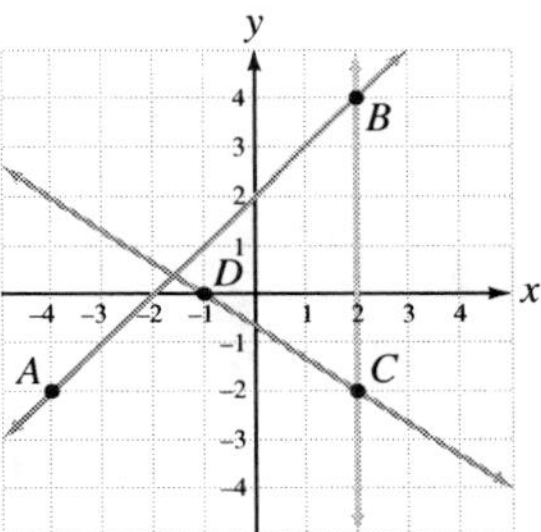

121. Find the slope of line AB. 1

122. Find the slope of line BC. no defined slope

123. Find the slope of line CD. $-\frac{2}{3}$

124. Find the slope of the x-axis. 0

125. Find the y-intercept of line AB. (0, 2)

126. Find the x-intercept of line AB. (−2, 0)

SECTION 6.6
Special Products

Objectives

1. Divide a monomial by a monomial.
2. Divide a polynomial by a monomial.
3. Write equivalent forms of formulas.

In this section, we will discuss how to divide polynomials by monomials. We will first divide monomials by monomials and then divide polynomials with more than one term by monomials.

1 Divide a monomial by a monomial.

Recall that to simplify a fraction, we write both its numerator and denominator as the product of several factors and then divide out all common factors:

$$\frac{4}{6} = \frac{2 \cdot 2}{2 \cdot 3} \quad \text{Factor 4 and 6.}$$

$$= \frac{\overset{1}{\cancel{2}} \cdot 2}{\underset{1}{\cancel{2}} \cdot 3} \quad \text{Divide out the common factor of 2.}$$

$$= \frac{2}{3}$$

$$\frac{20}{25} = \frac{4 \cdot 5}{5 \cdot 5} \quad \text{Factor 20 and 25.}$$

$$= \frac{4 \cdot \overset{1}{\cancel{5}}}{\underset{1}{\cancel{5}} \cdot 5} \quad \text{Divide out the common factor of 5.}$$

$$= \frac{4}{5}$$

We can use the same method to simplify algebraic fractions that contain variables.

$$\frac{3p^2}{6p} = \frac{3 \cdot p \cdot p}{2 \cdot 3 \cdot p} \quad \text{Factor } p^2 \text{ and 6.}$$

$$= \frac{\overset{1}{\cancel{3}} \cdot \overset{1}{\cancel{p}} \cdot p}{2 \cdot \underset{1}{\cancel{3}} \cdot \underset{1}{\cancel{p}}} \quad \text{Divide out the common factors of 3 and } p.$$

$$= \frac{p}{2}$$

To divide monomials, we can use either the preceding method for simplifying arithmetic fractions or the rules for exponents.

Self Check 1

Divide: $\frac{-5p^2q^3}{10pq^4}$ $-\frac{p}{2q}$

Now Try **Problems 27 and 32**

Teaching Example 1 Divide:
a. $\frac{a^3b^2}{ab^6}$ b. $\frac{-12a^3b^5}{2a^7b^9}$
Answers:
a. $\frac{a^2}{b^4}$ b. $\frac{-6}{a^4b^4}$

EXAMPLE 1 Divide: **a.** $\frac{x^2y}{xy^2}$ **b.** $\frac{-8a^3b^2}{4ab^3}$

Strategy We will use the rules for simplifying fractions and/or the quotient rule for exponents.

WHY We need to make sure that the numerator and denominator have no common factors other than 1. If that is the case, then the fraction is in *simplest form.*

Solution

By simplifying fractions

a. $\frac{x^2y}{xy^2} = \frac{x \cdot x \cdot y}{x \cdot y \cdot y}$

$$= \frac{\overset{1}{\cancel{x}} \cdot x \cdot \overset{1}{\cancel{y}}}{\underset{1}{\cancel{x}} \cdot y \cdot \underset{1}{\cancel{y}}}$$

$$= \frac{x}{y}$$

Using the rules for exponents

$$\frac{x^2y}{xy^2} = x^{2-1}y^{1-2}$$

$$= x^1y^{-1}$$

$$= \frac{x}{y}$$

b. $\dfrac{-8a^3b^2}{4ab^3} = \dfrac{-2 \cdot 4 \cdot a \cdot a \cdot a \cdot b \cdot b}{4 \cdot a \cdot b \cdot b \cdot b}$

$= \dfrac{-2 \cdot \overset{1}{\cancel{4}} \cdot \overset{1}{\cancel{a}} \cdot a \cdot a \cdot \overset{1}{\cancel{b}} \cdot \overset{1}{\cancel{b}}}{\underset{1}{\cancel{4}} \cdot \underset{1}{\cancel{a}} \cdot \underset{1}{\cancel{b}} \cdot \underset{1}{\cancel{b}} \cdot b}$

$= -\dfrac{2a^2}{b}$

$\dfrac{-8a^3b^2}{4ab^3} = \dfrac{-2^3a^3b^2}{2^2ab^3}$

$= -2^{3-2}a^{3-1}b^{2-3}$

$= -2^1a^2b^{-1}$

$= -\dfrac{2a^2}{b}$

EXAMPLE 2 Simplify $\dfrac{25(s^2t^3)^2}{15(st^3)^3}$ and write the result using positive exponents only.

Strategy We will use the rules for exponents to remove the parentheses. Then we will simplify the fraction.

WHY We need to make sure that the numerator and denominator have no common factors other than 1. If that is the case, then the fraction is in *simplest form.*

Solution

$\dfrac{25(s^2t^3)^2}{15(st^3)^3} = \dfrac{25s^4t^6}{15s^3t^9}$ Use the power rules for exponents: $(xy)^n = x^ny^n$ and $(x^m)^n = x^{mn}$.

$= \dfrac{5 \cdot 5 \cdot s^{4-3}t^{6-9}}{5 \cdot 3}$ Factor 25 and 15. Use the quotient rule for exponents: $\frac{x^m}{x^n} = x^{m-n}$.

$= \dfrac{5 \cdot \overset{1}{\cancel{5}} \cdot s^1t^{-3}}{\underset{1}{\cancel{5}} \cdot 3}$ Divide out the common factors of 5. Perform the subtractions.

$= \dfrac{5s}{3t^3}$ Use the negative integer exponent rule: $t^{-3} = \frac{1}{t^3}$.

Self Check 2

Simplify: $\dfrac{-24(h^3p)^5}{20(h^2p^2)^3}$ $-\dfrac{6h^9}{5p}$

Now Try **Problems 35 and 40**

Teaching Example 2 Simplify: $\dfrac{3(2x^2y^3)^3}{6(3xy^4)^2}$
Answer: $\dfrac{4x^4y}{9}$

2 Divide a polynomial by a monomial.

Adding and Subtracting Fractions with Like Denominators

To add (or subtract) fractions with like denominators, we add (or subtract) their numerators and keep the common denominator. In symbols, if a, b, and d represent numbers, and d is not 0,

$$\frac{a}{d} + \frac{b}{d} = \frac{a+b}{d} \quad \text{and} \quad \frac{a}{d} - \frac{b}{d} = \frac{a-b}{d}$$

We can use this rule in reverse to divide polynomials by monomials.

Dividing a Polynomial by a Monomial

To divide a polynomial by a monomial, divide each term of the polynomial by the monomial.

If A, B and D represent monomials, where $D \neq 0$, then

$$\frac{A+B}{D} = \frac{A}{D} + \frac{B}{D}$$

Self Check 3

Divide: $\frac{4 - 8b}{4}$ $1 - 2b$

Now Try **Problem 42**

Teaching Example 3 Divide: $\frac{10x - 15}{5}$
Answer: $2x - 3$

EXAMPLE 3

Divide: $9x + 6$ by 3

Strategy We will set up the fraction to represent the division. Then we will divide each term of the numerator by the denominator.

WHY This is the rule for dividing a polynomial by a monomial.

Solution

$$\frac{9x + 6}{3} = \frac{9x}{3} + \frac{6}{3}$$ Divide each term of the numerator by the denominator.

$$= 3x + 2$$ Simplify each fraction.

Self Check 4

Divide: $\frac{9a^2b - 6ab^2 + 3ab}{3ab}$

Now Try **Problem 49**

Self Check 4 Answer
$3a - 2b + 1$

Teaching Example 4 Divide: $\frac{4p^2q^3 + 12p^3q - 6pq}{2pq}$
Answer: $2pq^2 + 6p^2 - 3$

EXAMPLE 4

Divide: $\frac{6x^2y^2 + 4x^2y - 2xy}{2xy}$

Strategy We will divide each term of the polynomial in the numerator by the monomial in the denominator.

WHY This is the rule for dividing a polynomial by a monomial.

Solution

$$\frac{6x^2y^2 + 4x^2y - 2xy}{2xy}$$

$$= \frac{6x^2y^2}{2xy} + \frac{4x^2y}{2xy} - \frac{2xy}{2xy}$$ Divide each term of the numerator by the denominator.

$$= 3xy + 2x - 1$$ Simplify each fraction.

Self Check 5

Divide: $\frac{14p^3q + pq^2 - p}{7p^2q}$

Now Try **Problem 52**

Self Check 5 Answer
$2p + \frac{q}{7p} - \frac{1}{7pq}$

Teaching Example 5 Divide: $\frac{18x^3y^2 - 6x^2y - x}{9x^2y^2}$
Answer: $2x - \frac{2}{3y} - \frac{1}{9xy^2}$

EXAMPLE 5

Divide: $\frac{12a^3b^2 - 4a^2b + a}{6a^2b^2}$

Strategy We will divide each term of the polynomial in the numerator by the monomial in the denominator.

WHY This is the rule for dividing a polynomial by a monomial.

Solution

$$\frac{12a^3b^2 - 4a^2b + a}{6a^2b^2}$$

$$= \frac{12a^3b^2}{6a^2b^2} - \frac{4a^2b}{6a^2b^2} + \frac{a}{6a^2b^2}$$ Divide each term of the numerator by the denominator.

$$= 2a - \frac{2}{3b} + \frac{1}{6ab^2}$$ Simplify each fraction.

Self Check 6

Divide: $\frac{(x + y)^2 - (x - y)^2}{xy}$ 4

Now Try **Problem 55**

EXAMPLE 6

Divide: $\frac{(x - y)^2 - (x + y)^2}{xy}$

Strategy We will remove the parentheses in the numerator and collect like terms. Then we will divide each term of the polynomial in the numerator by the monomial in the denominator.

WHY This is the rule for dividing a polynomial by a monomial.

Solution

$$\frac{(x-y)^2-(x+y)^2}{xy}$$

$$=\frac{x^2-2xy+y^2-(x^2+2xy+y^2)}{xy}$$ Use the special product rules to square the binomials in the numerator.

$$=\frac{x^2-2xy+y^2-x^2-2xy-y^2}{xy}$$ Change the sign of each term within $(x^2+2xy+y^2)$.

$$=\frac{-4xy}{xy}$$ Combine like terms.

$$=-4$$ Divide out the common factors of x and y.

Teaching Example 6 Divide: $\frac{2(x+y)^2-(x+y)(x-y)}{xy}$

Answer: $\frac{x}{y}+4+\frac{3y}{x}$

3 Write equivalent forms of formulas.

The area of the trapezoid shown here is given by the formula $A=\frac{1}{2}h(B+b)$, where B and b are its bases and h is its height. To solve the formula for b, we proceed as follows.

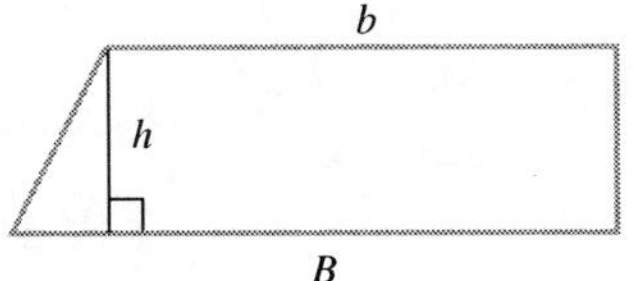

$$A=\frac{1}{2}h(B+b)$$

$$2\cdot A=2\cdot\frac{1}{2}h(B+b)$$ Multiply both sides by 2 to clear the equation of the fraction.

$$2A=h(B+b)$$ Simplify: $2\cdot\frac{1}{2}=\frac{2}{2}=1$

$$2A=hB+hb$$ Distribute the multiplication by h.

$$2A-hB=hB+hb-hB$$ Subtract hB from both sides.

$$2A-hB=hb$$ Combine like terms: $hB-hB=0$.

$$\frac{2A-hB}{h}=\frac{hb}{h}$$ To undo the multiplication by h, divide both sides by h.

$$\frac{2A-hB}{h}=b$$

EXAMPLE 7 Another student worked the previous problem in a different way and got a result of $b=\frac{2A}{h}-B$. Is this result correct?

Strategy We will use the rule for dividing a polynomial by a monomial on the right side of $b=\frac{2A-hB}{h}$.

WHY If the right side of $b=\frac{2A-hB}{h}$ is the same as the right side of $b=\frac{2A}{h}-B$ after applying the rule for dividing a polynomial by a monomial, then the answer is also correct.

Solution

To determine whether this result is correct, we must show that

$$\frac{2A-hB}{h}=\frac{2A}{h}-B$$

We can do this by dividing $2A-hB$ by h.

$$\frac{2A-hB}{h}=\frac{2A}{h}-\frac{hB}{h}$$ Divide each term of $2A-hB$ by the denominator, which is h.

$$=\frac{2A}{h}-B$$ Simplify the second fraction: $\frac{hB}{h}=B$.

The results are the same.

Self Check 7

Suppose another student got $b=2A-\frac{hB}{h}$. Is this result correct? no

Now Try **Problem 77**

Teaching Example 7 Is $w=\frac{P-2L}{2}$ equivalent to $w=\frac{P}{2}-L$?

Answer: yes

ANSWERS TO SELF CHECKS

1. $-\frac{p}{2q}$ **2.** $-\frac{6h^9}{5p}$ **3.** $1 - 2b$ **4.** $3a - 2b + 1$ **5.** $2p + \frac{q}{7p} - \frac{1}{7pq}$ **6.** 4 **7.** no

SECTION 6.6 STUDY SET

VOCABULARY

Fill in the blanks.

1. A polynomial is an algebraic expression that is the sum of one or more terms containing whole-number exponents.
2. A monomial is a polynomial with one term.
3. A binomial is a polynomial with two terms.
4. A trinomial is a polynomial with three terms.
5. $\frac{x^m}{x^n} = x^{m-n}$ is a rule for exponents.
6. To simplify a fraction, we divide out common factors of the numerator and denominator.

CONCEPTS

Fill in the blanks.

7. $\frac{18x + 9}{9} = \frac{18x}{9} + \frac{9x}{9}$
8. $\frac{30x^2 + 12x - 24}{6} = \frac{30x^2}{6} + \frac{12x}{6} - \frac{24}{6}$
9. $\frac{x^m}{x^n} = x^{m-n}$
10. $x^{-n} = \frac{1}{x^n}$
11. **a.** Solve the formula $d = rt$ for t. $t = \frac{d}{r}$
    b. Use your answer from part a to complete the table.

	r	$\cdot\ t$	$= d$
Motorcycle	$2x$	$3x^2$	$6x^3$

12. **a.** Solve the formula $I = Prt$ for r. $r = \frac{I}{Pt}$
    b. Use your answer from part a to complete the table.

	P	$\cdot\ r$	$\cdot\ t$	$= I$
Savings account	$8x^3$	$\frac{3x^2}{2}$	$2x$	$24x^6$

13. How many nickels would have a value of $(10x + 35)$ cents? $2x + 7$
14. How many twenty-dollar bills would have a value of $\$(60x - 100)$? $3x - 5$

NOTATION

Complete each solution.

15. $\frac{a^2b^3}{a^3b^2} = \frac{a \cdot a \cdot b \cdot b \cdot b}{a \cdot a \cdot a \cdot b \cdot b}$

$= \frac{\overset{1}{\cancel{a}} \cdot \overset{1}{\cancel{a}} \cdot \overset{1}{\cancel{b}} \cdot \overset{1}{\cancel{b}} \cdot b}{\underset{1}{\cancel{a}} \cdot \underset{1}{\cancel{a}} \cdot a \cdot \underset{1}{\cancel{b}} \cdot \underset{1}{\cancel{b}}}$

$= \frac{b}{a}$

16. $\frac{6pq^2 - 9p^2q^2 + pq}{3p^2q}$

$= \frac{6pq^2}{3p^2q} - \frac{9p^2q^2}{3p^2q} + \frac{pq}{3p^2q}$

$= \frac{6 \cdot p \cdot q \cdot q}{3 \cdot p \cdot p \cdot q} - \frac{3 \cdot 3 \cdot p \cdot p \cdot q \cdot q}{3 \cdot p \cdot p \cdot q} + \frac{p \cdot q}{3 \cdot p \cdot p \cdot q}$

$= \frac{2q}{p} - 3q + \frac{1}{3p}$

GUIDED PRACTICE

Simplify each fraction. See Objective 1.

17. $\frac{5}{15}$ $\frac{1}{3}$
18. $\frac{64}{128}$ $\frac{1}{2}$
19. $\frac{-125}{75}$ $-\frac{5}{3}$
20. $\frac{-98}{21}$ $-\frac{14}{3}$
21. $\frac{120}{160}$ $\frac{3}{4}$
22. $\frac{70}{420}$ $\frac{1}{6}$
23. $\frac{-3{,}612}{-3{,}612}$ 1
24. $\frac{-288}{-112}$ $\frac{18}{7}$

Perform each division. See Example 1.

25. $\frac{x^5}{x^2}$ x^3
26. $\frac{a^{12}}{a^8}$ a^4
27. $\frac{r^3s^2}{rs^3}$ $\frac{r^2}{s}$
28. $\frac{y^4z^3}{y^2z^2}$ y^2z
29. $\frac{8x^3y^2}{4xy^3}$ $\frac{2x^2}{y}$
30. $\frac{-3y^3z}{6yz^2}$ $-\frac{y^2}{2z}$
31. $\frac{12u^5v}{-4u^2v^3}$ $-\frac{3u^3}{v^2}$
32. $\frac{16rst^2}{-8rst^3}$ $-\frac{2}{t}$

Perform each division. See Example 2.

33. $\frac{(a^3b^4)^3}{ab^4}$ a^8b^8

34. $\frac{(a^2b^3)^3}{a^6b^6}$ b^3

35. $\frac{15(r^2s^3)^2}{-5(rs^5)^3}$ $-\frac{3r}{s^9}$

36. $\frac{-5(a^2b)^3}{10(ab^2)^3}$ $-\frac{a^3}{2b^3}$

37. $\frac{-32(x^3y)^3}{128(x^2y^2)^3}$ $-\frac{x^3}{4y^3}$

38. $\frac{68(a^6b^7)^2}{-96(abc^2)^3}$ $-\frac{17a^9b^{11}}{24c^6}$

39. $\frac{-(4x^3y^3)^2}{(x^2y^4)^3}$ $-\frac{16}{y^6}$

40. $\frac{(2r^3s^2)^2}{-(4r^2s^2)^2}$ $-\frac{r^2}{4}$

Perform each division. See Examples 3–5.

41. $\frac{6x + 9}{3}$ $2x + 3$

42. $\frac{8x + 12y}{4}$ $2x + 3y$

43. $\frac{5x - 10y}{25xy}$ $\frac{1}{5y} - \frac{2}{5x}$

44. $\frac{2x - 32}{16x}$ $\frac{1}{8} - \frac{2}{x}$

45. $\frac{3x^2 + 6y^3}{3x^2y^2}$ $\frac{1}{y^2} + \frac{2y}{x^2}$

46. $\frac{4a^2 - 9b^2}{12ab}$ $\frac{a}{3b} - \frac{3b}{4a}$

47. $\frac{15a^3b^2 - 10a^2b^3}{5a^2b^2}$ $3a - 2b$

48. $\frac{9a^4b^3 - 16a^3b^4}{12a^2b}$ $\frac{3a^2b^2}{4} - \frac{4ab^3}{3}$

49. $\frac{4x - 2y + 8z}{4xy}$ $\frac{1}{y} - \frac{1}{2x} + \frac{2z}{xy}$

50. $\frac{5a^2 + 10b^2 - 15ab}{5ab}$ $\frac{a}{b} + \frac{2b}{a} - 3$

51. $\frac{12x^3y^2 - 8x^2y - 4x}{4xy}$ $3x^2y - 2x - \frac{1}{y}$

52. $\frac{12a^2b^2 - 8a^2b - 4ab}{4ab}$ $3ab - 2a - 1$

Perform each division. See Example 6.

53. $\frac{5x(4x - 2y)}{2y}$ $\frac{10x^2}{y} - 5x$

54. $\frac{9y(x^2 - 3xy)}{3x^2}$ $3y^2 - \frac{9y^2}{x}$

55. $\frac{(x - y)^2 - (x + y)^2}{2xy}$ -2

56. $\frac{(2m - n)(3m - 2n)}{-3m^2n^2}$ $-\frac{2}{n^2} + \frac{7}{3mn} - \frac{2}{3m^2}$

TRY IT YOURSELF

Simplify each expression.

57. $\frac{-16r^3y^2}{-4r^2y^4}$ $\frac{4r}{y^2}$

58. $\frac{35xyz^2}{-7x^2yz}$ $-\frac{5z}{x}$

59. $\frac{-65rs^2t}{15r^2s^3t}$ $-\frac{13}{3rs}$

60. $\frac{112u^3z^6}{-42u^3z^6}$ $-\frac{8}{3}$

61. $\frac{x^2x^3}{xy^6}$ $\frac{x^4}{y^6}$

62. $\frac{x^2y^2}{x^2y^3}$ $\frac{1}{y}$

63. $\frac{(a^2a^3)^4}{(a^4)^3}$ a^8

64. $\frac{(b^3b^4)^5}{(bb^2)^2}$ b^{29}

65. $\frac{-25x^2y + 30xy^2 - 5xy}{-5xy}$ $5x - 6y + 1$

66. $\frac{-30a^2b^2 - 15a^2b - 10ab^2}{-10ab}$ $3ab + \frac{3a}{2} + b$

67. $\frac{(-2x)^3 + (3x^2)^2}{6x^2}$ $-\frac{4x}{3} + \frac{3x^2}{2}$

68. $\frac{(-3x^2y)^3 + (3xy^2)^3}{27x^3y^4}$ $-\frac{x^3}{y} + y^2$

69. $\frac{4x^2y^2 - 2(x^2y^2 + xy)}{2xy}$ $xy - 1$

70. $\frac{-5a^3b - 5a(ab^2 - a^2b)}{10a^2b^2}$ $-\frac{1}{2}$

71. $\frac{(a + b)^2 - (a - b)^2}{2ab}$ 2

72. $\frac{(x - y)^2 + (x + y)^2}{2x^2y^2}$ $\frac{1}{y^2} + \frac{1}{x^2}$

APPLICATIONS

73. POOL The rack shown is used to set up the balls when beginning a game of pool. If the perimeter of the rack, in inches, is given by the polynomial $6x^2 - 3x + 9$, what is the length of one side? $(2x^2 - x + 3)$ in.

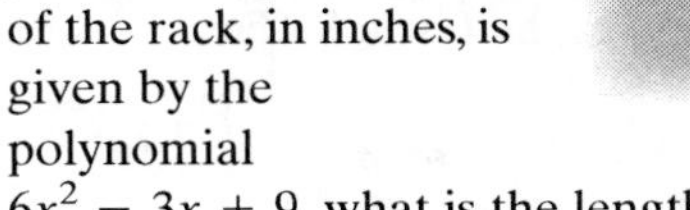

74. CHECKERBOARDS If the perimeter (in inches) of the checkerboard is $12x^2 - 8x + 32$, find an expression that represents the length of one side. $(3x^2 - 2x + 8)$ in.

75. AIR CONDITIONING If the volume occupied by the air conditioning unit shown is $(36x^3 - 24x^2)$ cubic feet, find an expression that represents its height. $(3x - 2)$ ft

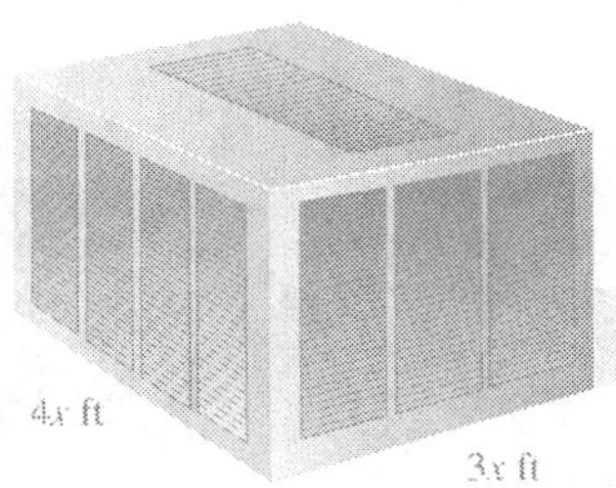

76. MINIBLINDS The area covered by the miniblinds is $(3x^3 - 6x)$ square feet. Find an expression that represents the length of the blinds. $(x^2 - 2)$ ft

77. CONFIRMING FORMULAS Are these formulas the same?

$$l = \frac{P - 2w}{2} \quad \text{and} \quad l = \frac{P}{2} - w$$ yes

78. CONFIRMING FORMULAS Are these formulas the same?

$$r = \frac{G + 2b}{2b} \quad \text{and} \quad r = \frac{G}{2b} + b$$ no

79. ELECTRIC BILLS On an electric bill, the following two formulas are used to compute the average cost of x kwh of electricity. Are the formulas equivalent? no

$$\frac{0.08x + 5}{x} \quad \text{and} \quad 0.08x + \frac{5}{x}$$

80. PHONE BILLS On a phone bill, the following two formulas are used to compute the average cost per minute of x minutes of phone usage. Are the formulas equivalent? yes

$$\frac{0.15x + 12}{x} \quad \text{and} \quad 0.15 + \frac{12}{x}$$

WRITING

81. Explain the error.

$$\frac{3x + 5}{5} = \frac{3x + \overset{1}{\cancel{5}}}{\underset{1}{\cancel{5}}} = 3x$$

82. Explain how to perform this division.

$$\frac{4x^2y + 8xy^2}{4xy}$$

REVIEW

Identify each polynomial as a monomial, a binomial, a trinomial, or none of these.

83. $5a^2b + 2ab^2$ binomial

84. $-3x^3y$ monomial

85. $-2x^3 + 3x^2 - 4x + 12$ none of these

86. $17t^2 - 15t + 27$ trinomial

87. What is the degree of the trinomial $3x^2 - 2x + 4$? 2

88. What is the numerical coefficient of the second term of the trinomial $-7t^2 + 5t + 17$? 5

SECTION 6.7 Dividing Polynomials

Objectives

1. Divide polynomials by polynomials.
2. Write powers in descending order.
3. Divide polynomials that are missing terms.

In this section, we will discuss how to divide one polynomial by another.

1 Divide polynomials by polynomials.

To divide one polynomial by another, we use a method similar to long division in arithmetic. We illustrate the method with several examples.

Self Check 1

Divide $x^2 + 7x + 12$ by $x + 3$.

***Now Try* Problem 20**

Self Check 1 Answer

$x + 4$

EXAMPLE 1 Divide $x^2 + 5x + 6$ by $x + 2$.

Strategy We will use the long division method. The dividend is $x^2 + 5x + 6$ and the divisor is $x + 2$.

WHY Since the divisor has more than one term, we must use the long division method to divide the polynomials.

Solution

We write the division using the symbol $\overline{)\quad}$ and proceed as follows:

Step 1

$$x + 2\overline{)x^2 + 5x + 6}\quad\text{quotient: } x$$

Divide the first term of $x^2 + 5x + 6$ by the first term of $x + 2$. $\frac{x^2}{x} = x$. Write x above the division symbol.

Step 2

$$\begin{array}{r} x \\ x + 2\overline{)x^2 + 5x + 6} \\ \underline{x^2 + 2x} \end{array}$$

Multiply each term in the divisor by x. Write the result, $x^2 + 2x$, under $x^2 + 5x$, and draw a line. Be sure to align like terms.

Step 3

$$\begin{array}{r} x \\ x + 2\overline{)x^2 + 5x\ \ + 6} \\ \underline{-(x^2 + 2x)} \\ 3x\ \ + 6 \end{array}$$

Subtract $x^2 + 2x$ from $x^2 + 5x$. Work vertically, column by column: $x^2 - x^2 = 0$ and $5x - 2x = 3x$.

Bring down the 6.

Step 4

$$\begin{array}{r} x + 3 \\ x + 2\overline{)x^2 + 5x\ \ + 6} \\ \underline{-(x^2 + 2x)} \\ 3x\ \ + 6 \end{array}$$

Divide the first term of $3x + 6$ by the first term of the divisor. $\frac{3x}{x} = +3$. Write $+3$ above the division symbol to form the second term of the quotient.

Step 5

$$\begin{array}{r} x + 3 \\ x + 2\overline{)x^2 + 5x + 6} \\ \underline{x^2 + 2x + 6} \\ 3x + 6 \\ \underline{3x + 6} \\ 0 \end{array}$$

Multiply each term in the divisor by 3. Write the product under $3x + 6$ and draw a line.

Step 6

$$\begin{array}{r} x + 3 \\ x + 2\overline{)x^2 + 5x\ \ + 6} \\ \underline{-(x^2 + 2x)} \\ 3x\ \ + 6 \\ \underline{-(3x\ \ + 6)} \\ 0 \end{array}$$

Subtract $3x + 6$ from $3x + 6$. Work vertically: $3x - 3x = 0$ and $6 - 6 = 0$.

This is the remainder.

The quotient is $x + 3$ and the remainder is 0.

Step 7 Check the work by verifying that $(x + 2)(x + 3)$ is $x^2 + 5x + 6$.

$$\begin{aligned}(x + 2)(x + 3) &= x^2 + 3x + 2x + 6 \\ &= x^2 + 5x + 6\end{aligned}$$

The answer checks.

The answer checks.

Teaching Example 1 Divide $x^2 - 6x - 16$ by $x - 8$.
Answer:
$x + 2$

EXAMPLE 2

Divide: $\dfrac{6x^2 - 7x - 2}{2x - 1}$

Strategy We will use the long division method. The dividend is $6x^2 - 7x - 2$ and the divisor is $2x - 1$.

WHY Since the divisor has more than one term, we must use the long division method to divide the polynomials.

Solution

We write the division using a long division symbol $\overline{)\quad}$ and proceed as follows:

Step 1

$$\begin{array}{r} 3x \\ 2x - 1\overline{)6x^2 - 7x - 2} \end{array}$$

Divide the first term of the dividend by the first term of the divisor. $\frac{6x^2}{2x} = 3x$. Write the $3x$ above the division symbol.

Self Check 2

Divide: $\dfrac{8x^2 + 6x - 3}{2x + 3}$

Now Try **Problems 21 and 26**

Self Check 2 Answer
$4x - 3 + \dfrac{6}{2x + 3}$

Teaching Example 2 Divide: $\dfrac{9x^2 + 9x + 7}{3x - 2}$
Answer:
$3x + 5 + \dfrac{17}{3x - 2}$

Step 2

$$\begin{array}{r} 3x \phantom{{}-2} \\ 2x-1\overline{)6x^2-7x-2} \\ 6x^2-3x \phantom{{}-2} \\ \hline \end{array}$$

Multiply each term in the divisor by $3x$. Write the product under $6x^2 - 7x$ and draw a line.

Step 3

$$\begin{array}{r} 3x \phantom{{}-2} \\ 2x-1\overline{)6x^2-7x-2} \\ -(6x^2-3x) \phantom{{}-2} \\ \hline -4x-2 \end{array}$$

Subtract $6x^2 - 3x$ from $6x^2 - 7x$. Work vertically: $6x^2 - 6x^2 = 0$ and $-7x - (-3x) = -7x + 3x = -4x$.

Bring down the -2.

Step 4

$$\begin{array}{r} 3x-2 \\ 2x-1\overline{)6x^2-7x-2} \\ -(6x^2-3x) \phantom{{}-2} \\ \hline -4x-2 \end{array}$$

Divide the first term of $-4x - 2$ by the first term of the divisor. $\frac{-4x}{2x} = -2$. Write -2 above the division symbol.

Step 5

$$\begin{array}{r} 3x-2 \\ 2x-1\overline{)6x^2-7x-2} \\ -(6x^2-3x) \phantom{{}-2} \\ \hline -4x-2 \\ -(-4x+2) \\ \hline \end{array}$$

Multiply each term in the divisor by -2. Write the product under $-4x - 2$ and draw a line.

Step 6

$$\begin{array}{r} 3x-2 \\ 2x-1\overline{)6x^2-7x-2} \\ -(6x^2-3x) \phantom{{}-2} \\ \hline -4x-2 \\ -(-4x+2) \\ \hline -4 \end{array}$$

Subtract $-4x + 2$ from $-4x - 2$. Work vertically: $-4x - (-4x) = -4x + 4x = 0$ and $-2 - 2 = -4$.

Here the quotient is $3x - 2$ and the remainder is -4. It is common to write the answer as either

$$3x - 2 + \frac{-4}{2x - 1} \quad \text{or} \quad 3x - 2 - \frac{4}{2x - 1}$$

Quotient + $\frac{\text{remainder}}{\text{divisor}}$.

Step 7 To check, we multiply

$$3x - 2 + \frac{-4}{2x - 1} \quad \text{by} \quad 2x - 1$$

The product should be the dividend.

$$\begin{aligned} (2x-1)\left(3x - 2 + \frac{-4}{2x-1}\right) &= (2x-1)(3x-2) + (2x-1)\left(\frac{-4}{2x-1}\right) \\ &= (2x-1)(3x-2) - 4 \\ &= 6x^2 - 4x - 3x + 2 - 4 \\ &= 6x^2 - 7x - 2 \end{aligned}$$

Because the result is the dividend, the answer checks. ■

2 Write powers in descending order.

The division method works best when the terms of the divisor and the dividend are written in descending powers of the variable. This means that the term involving the highest power of x appears first, the term involving the second-highest power of x appears second, and so on. For example, the terms in

$$3x^3 + 2x^2 - 7x + 5$$

have their exponents written in descending order.

If the powers in the dividend or divisor are not in descending order, we use the commutative property of addition to write them that way.

EXAMPLE 3 Divide: $(4x^2 + 2x^3 + 12 - 2x) \div (x + 3)$

Strategy We will write the dividend in descending powers of x and use the long division method to divide the polynomials.

WHY It is easier to carry out the division when the powers of the variables are written in descending order.

Solution

We write the dividend so that the exponents are in descending order.

$$\begin{array}{r|l} & 2x^2 - 2x + 4 \\ x + 3 & \overline{2x^3 + 4x^2 - 2x + 12} \\ & -(2x^3 + 6x^2) \\ & \quad -2x^2 - 2x \\ & \quad -(-2x^2 - 6x) \\ & \qquad 4x + 12 \\ & \qquad -(4x + 12) \\ & \qquad\qquad 0 \end{array}$$

The first division: $\frac{2x^3}{x} = 2x^2$.

The second division: $\frac{-2x^2}{x} = -2x$.

The third division: $\frac{4x}{x} = 4$.

Check: $(x + 3)(2x^2 - 2x + 4) = 2x^3 - 2x^2 + 4x + 6x^2 - 6x + 12$
$= 2x^3 + 4x^2 - 2x + 12$

Self Check 3

Divide:
$(x^2 - 10x + 6x^3 + 4) \div (2x - 1)$

Now Try **Problem 29**

Self Check 3 Answer
$3x^2 + 2x - 4$

Teaching Example 3 Divide:
$(10x^3 + 12 + x^2 + 17x) \div (5x + 3)$
Answer:
$2x^2 - x + 4$

3 Divide polynomials that are missing terms.

When we write the terms of a dividend in descending powers of x, we must determine whether some powers of the variable are missing. When this happens, we should write such terms with a coefficient of 0 or leave a blank space for them.

EXAMPLE 4 Divide: $\frac{x^2 - 4}{x + 2}$

Strategy The dividend $x^2 - 4$ is missing an x-term. We will insert a $0x$ term as a placeholder and use the long division method.

WHY We insert placeholder terms so that like terms will be aligned in the same column when we subtract.

Solution

$$\begin{array}{r|l} & x - 2 \\ x + 2 & \overline{x^2 + 0x - 4} \\ & -(x^2 + 2x) \\ & \quad -2x - 4 \\ & \quad -(-2x - 4) \\ & \qquad\quad 0 \end{array}$$

The first division: $\frac{x^2}{x} = x$.

The second division: $\frac{-2x}{x} = -2$.

Check: $(x + 2)(x - 2) = x^2 - 2x + 2x - 4$
$= x^2 - 4$

Self Check 4

Divide: $\frac{x^2 - 9}{x - 3}$ $x + 3$

Now Try **Problem 34**

Teaching Example 4 Divide:
$\frac{27x^3 - 1}{3x - 1}$
Answer:
$9x^2 + 3x + 1$

ANSWERS TO SELF CHECKS

1. $x + 4$ **2.** $4x - 3 + \frac{6}{2x + 3}$ **3.** $3x^2 + 2x - 4$ **4.** $x + 3$

SECTION 6.7 STUDY SET

VOCABULARY

Fill in the blanks.

1. In the division $x + 1\overline{)x^2 + 2x + 1}$, the expression $x + 1$ is called the divisor and $x^2 + 2x + 1$ is called the dividend.
2. The answer to a division problem is called the quotient.
3. If a division does not come out even, the leftover part is called a remainder.
4. The powers of x in $2x^4 + 3x^3 + 4x^2 - 7x - 2$ are said to be written in descending order.

CONCEPTS

Write each polynomial with the powers in descending order.

5. $4x^3 + 7x - 2x^2 + 6$ $4x^3 - 2x^2 + 7x + 6$
6. $5x^2 + 7x^3 - 3x - 9$ $7x^3 + 5x^2 - 3x - 9$
7. $9x + 2x^2 - x^3 + 6x^4$ $6x^4 - x^3 + 2x^2 + 9x$
8. $7x^5 + x^3 - x^2 + 2x^4$ $7x^5 + 2x^4 + x^3 - x^2$

Identify the missing terms in each polynomial.

9. $5x^4 + 2x^2 - 1$ $0x^3$ and $0x$
10. $-3x^5 - 2x^3 + 4x - 6$ $0x^4$ and $0x^2$
11. a. Solve $d = rt$ for r. $r = \frac{d}{t}$
    b. Use your answer to part a and the long division method to complete the table.

	r	$\cdot\ t =$	d
Subway	$x - 3$	$x + 4$	$x^2 + x - 12$

12. a. Solve $I = Prt$ for P. $P = \frac{I}{rt}$
    b. Use your answer to part a and the long division method to complete the table.

	P	$\cdot\ r$	$\cdot\ t =$	I
Bonds	$x + 3$	$x + 4$	1	$x^2 + 7x + 12$

13. Using long division, a student found that

$$\frac{3x^2 + 8x + 4}{3x + 2} = x + 2$$

Use multiplication to see whether the result is correct. It is correct.

14. Using long division, a student found that

$$\frac{x^2 + 4x - 21}{x - 3} = x + 7$$

Use multiplication to see whether the result is correct. It is incorrect.

NOTATION

Complete each division.

15.
$$\begin{array}{r} x + 2 \\ x + 2\overline{)x^2 + 4x + 4} \\ \underline{x^2 + 2x} \\ 2x + 4 \\ \underline{2x + 4} \\ 0 \end{array}$$

16.
$$\begin{array}{r} x^2 + x - 2 + \frac{7}{2x + 1} \\ 2x + 1\overline{)2x^3 + 3x^2 - 3x + 5} \\ \underline{2x^3 + x^2} \\ 2x^2 - 3x \\ \underline{2x^2 + x} \\ -4x + 5 \\ \underline{-4x - 2} \\ 7 \end{array}$$

GUIDED PRACTICE

Perform each division. See Example 1.

17. Divide $x^2 + 4x - 12$ by $x - 2$. $x + 6$
18. Divide $x^2 - 5x + 6$ by $x - 2$. $x - 3$
19. Divide $y^2 + 13y + 12$ by $y + 1$. $y + 12$
20. Divide $z^2 - 7z + 12$ by $z - 3$. $z - 4$

Perform each division. See Example 2.

21. $\dfrac{6a^2 + 5a - 6}{2a + 3}$ $3a - 2$
22. $\dfrac{8a^2 + 2a - 3}{2a - 1}$ $4a + 3$
23. $\dfrac{3b^2 + 11b + 6}{3b + 2}$ $b + 3$
24. $\dfrac{3b^2 - 5b + 2}{3b - 2}$ $b - 1$
25. $\dfrac{2x^2 + 5x + 2}{2x - 3}$ $x + 4 + \frac{14}{2x - 3}$
26. $\dfrac{3x^2 - 8x + 8}{3x - 2}$ $x - 2 + \frac{4}{3x - 2}$
27. $\dfrac{4x^2 + 6x - 1}{2x + 1}$ $2x + 2 + \frac{-3}{2x + 1}$
28. $\dfrac{6x^2 - 11x + 2}{3x - 1}$ $2x - 3 + \frac{-1}{3x - 1}$

Write the terms so that the powers of x are in descending order. Then perform each division. See Example 3.

29. $5x + 3\overline{)11x + 10x^2 + 3}$ $2x + 1$
30. $2x - 7\overline{)-x - 21 + 2x^2}$ $x + 3$
31. $4 + 2x\overline{)-10x - 28 + 2x^2}$ $x - 7$
32. $1 + 3x\overline{)9x^2 + 1 + 6x}$ $3x + 1$

Perform each division. See Example 4.

33. $\dfrac{x^2 - 1}{x - 1}$ $x + 1$
34. $\dfrac{x^2 - 9}{x + 3}$ $x - 3$
35. $\dfrac{4x^2 - 9}{2x + 3}$ $2x - 3$
36. $\dfrac{25x^2 - 16}{5x - 4}$ $5x + 4$

TRY IT YOURSELF

Perform each division. If there is a remainder, write the answer in quotient + $\frac{\text{remainder}}{\text{divisor}}$ form.

37. $2x - 1\overline{)x - 2 + 6x^2}$ $3x + 2$

▶ **38.** $2 + x\overline{)3x + 2x^2 - 2}$ $2x - 1$

39. $3 + x\overline{)2x^2 - 3 + 5x}$ $2x - 1$

▶ **40.** $x - 3\overline{)2x^2 - 3 - 5x}$ $2x + 1$

41. $2x + 3\overline{)2x^3 + 7x^2 + 4x - 3}$ $x^2 + 2x - 1$

▶ **42.** $2x - 1\overline{)2x^3 - 3x^2 + 5x - 2}$ $x^2 - x + 2$

43. $3x + 2\overline{)6x^3 + 10x^2 + 7x + 2}$ $2x^2 + 2x + 1$

▶ **44.** $4x + 3\overline{)4x^3 - 5x^2 - 2x + 3}$ $x^2 - 2x + 1$

45. $2x + 1\overline{)2x^3 + 3x^2 + 3x + 1}$ $x^2 + x + 1$

▶ **46.** $3x - 2\overline{)6x^3 - x^2 + 4x - 4}$ $2x^2 + x + 2$

47. $\dfrac{x^3 + 3x^2 + 3x + 1}{x + 1}$ $x^2 + 2x + 1$

48. $\dfrac{x^3 + 6x^2 + 12x + 8}{x + 2}$ $x^2 + 4x + 4$

49. $\dfrac{2x^3 + 7x^2 + 4x + 3}{2x + 3}$ $x^2 + 2x - 1 + \frac{6}{2x + 3}$

▶ **50.** $\dfrac{6x^3 + x^2 + 2x + 1}{3x - 1}$ $2x^2 + x + 1 + \frac{2}{3x - 1}$

51. $\dfrac{2x^3 + 4x^2 - 2x + 3}{x - 2}$ $2x^2 + 8x + 14 + \frac{31}{x - 2}$

52. $\dfrac{3y^3 - 4y^2 + 2y + 3}{y + 3}$ $3y^2 - 13y + 41 + \frac{-120}{y + 3}$

53. $\dfrac{x^3 + 1}{x + 1}$ $x^2 - x + 1$

54. $\dfrac{x^3 - 8}{x - 2}$ $x^2 + 2x + 4$

▶ **55.** $\dfrac{a^3 + a}{a + 3}$ $a^2 - 3a + 10 + \frac{-30}{a + 3}$

56. $\dfrac{y^3 - 50}{y - 5}$ $y^2 + 5y + 25 + \frac{75}{y - 5}$

57. $3x - 4\overline{)15x^3 - 23x^2 + 16x}$ $5x^2 - x + 4 + \frac{16}{3x - 4}$

58. $2y + 3\overline{)21y^2 + 6y^3 - 20}$ $3y^2 + 6y - 9 + \frac{7}{2y + 3}$

APPLICATIONS

▶ **59.** FURNACE FILTERS The area of the furnace filter shown is $(x^2 - 2x - 24)$ square inches.

a. Find an expression for its length. $(x - 6)$ in.

b. Find an expression for its perimeter. $(4x - 4)$ in.

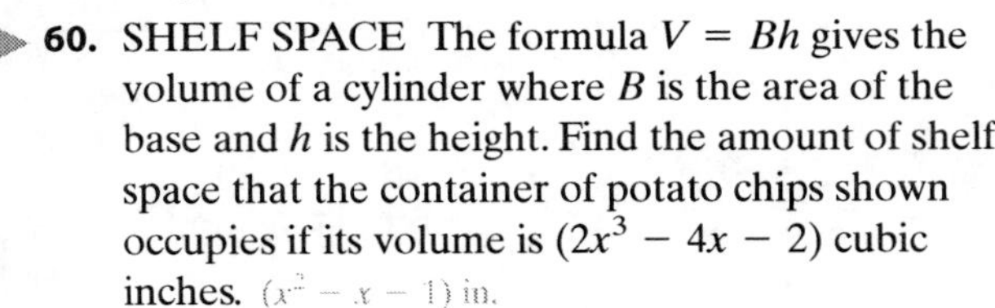

$(x + 4)$ in.

▶ **60.** SHELF SPACE The formula $V = Bh$ gives the volume of a cylinder where B is the area of the base and h is the height. Find the amount of shelf space that the container of potato chips shown occupies if its volume is $(2x^3 - 4x - 2)$ cubic inches. $(x^2 - x - 1)$ in.

▶ **61.** COMMUNICATIONS See the illustration. Telephone poles were installed every $(2x - 3)$ feet along a stretch of railroad track $(8x^3 - 6x^2 + 5x - 21)$ feet long. How many poles were used? $4x^2 + 3x + 7$

▶ **62.** CONSTRUCTION COSTS Find the price per square foot to remodel each of the three rooms listed in the table.

Room	Remodeling cost	Area (ft²)	Cost (per ft²)
Bathroom	$\$(2x^2 + x - 6)$	$2x - 3$	$\$(x + 2)$
Bedroom	$\$(x^2 + 9x + 20)$	$x + 4$	$\$(x + 5)$
Kitchen	$\$(3x^3 - 9x - 6)$	$3x + 3$	$\$(x^2 - x - 2)$

WRITING

63. Explain how the following are related: *dividend, divisor, quotient,* and *remainder.*

▶ **64.** How would you check the results of a division?

REVIEW

Simplify each expression.

65. $(x^5x^6)^2$ x^{22}

▶ **66.** $(a^2)^3(a^3)^4$ a^{18}

67. $3(2x^2 - 4x + 5) + 2(x^2 + 3x - 7)$ $8x^2 - 6x + 1$

68. $-2(y^3 + 2y^2 - y) - 3(3y^3 + y)$ $-11y^3 - 4y^2 - y$

69. What can be said about the slopes of two parallel lines? They are the same.

70. What is the slope of a line perpendicular to a line with a slope of $\frac{3}{4}$? $-\frac{4}{3}$

Objectives

1. Find the greatest common factor of a list of terms.
2. Factor out the greatest common factor.
3. Factor by grouping.

SECTION 6.8
The Greatest Common Factor; Factoring by Grouping

Recall that in Chapter 5 we used the distributive property to multiply a monomial and a binomial. For example,

$$4y(3y + 5) = 4y \cdot 3y + 4y \cdot 5$$
$$= 12y^2 + 20y$$

In this section, we will reverse the operation of multiplication. Given a polynomial such as $12y^2 + 20y$, we will ask, "What factors were multiplied to obtain $12y^2 + 20y$?" The process of finding the factors of a known product is called **factoring.**

Multiplication: Given the factors, we find the polynomial. →

$$4y(3y + 5) = 12y^2 + 20y$$

← Factoring: Given a polynomial, we find the factors.

To **factor a polynomial** means to express it as a product of two (or more) polynomials. The first step when factoring a polynomial is to determine whether its terms have any common factors.

1 Find the greatest common factor of a list of terms.

To determine whether two or more integers have common factors, it is helpful to write them as a product of prime numbers. For example, the prime factorizations of 90 and 42 are given below.

$$90 = 2 \cdot 3 \cdot 3 \cdot 5$$
$$42 = 2 \cdot 3 \cdot 7$$

The color highlighting indicates that 90 and 42 have one prime factor of 2 and one prime factor of 3 in common. We can conclude that $2 \cdot 3 = 6$ is the largest natural number that divides 90 and 42 exactly, and we say that 6 is their *greatest common factor (GCF).*

$$\frac{90}{6} = 15 \quad \text{and} \quad \frac{42}{6} = 7$$

The Greatest Common Factor (GCF)

The **greatest common factor (GCF)** of a list of integers is the largest common factor of those integers.

Self Check 1

Find the GCF of:

a. 45, 60, and 75 15

b. 16, 28, and 35 1

Now Try **Problems 23 and 25**

Teaching Example 1 Find the GCF of:
a. 36, 54, 90 **b.** 12, 15, 28
Answers:
a. 18 **b.** 1

EXAMPLE 1 Find the GCF of each list of numbers:

a. 24, 60, and 96 **b.** 6, 35, and 50

Strategy We will prime factor each number in the list. Then we will identify the common prime factors and find their product.

WHY The product of the common prime factors is the GCF of the numbers in the list.

Solution

a. The prime factors of the three numbers are shown:

$24 = 2 \cdot 2 \cdot 2 \cdot 3$ This can be written as $2^3 \cdot 3$.

$60 = 2 \cdot 2 \cdot 3 \cdot 5$ This can be written as $2^2 \cdot 3 \cdot 5$.

$96 = 2 \cdot 2 \cdot 2 \cdot 2 \cdot 2 \cdot 3$ This can be written as $2^5 \cdot 3$.

The highlighting shows that 24, 60, and 96 each have two factors of 2 and one factor of 3; their greatest common factor is $2 \cdot 2 \cdot 3 = 12$.

b. The prime factorization of each number is shown:

$6 = 2 \cdot 3$

$35 = 5 \cdot 7$

$50 = 2 \cdot 5 \cdot 5$

Since there are no prime factors common to 6, 35, and 50, their GCF is 1.

Success Tip The exponent on any factor in a GCF is the *smallest* exponent that appears on that factor in all of the numbers under consideration.

Strategy for Finding the GCF

1. Write each coefficient as a product of prime factors.
2. Identify the numerical and variable factors common to each term.
3. Multiply the common numerical and variable factors identified in Step 2 to obtain the GCF. If there are no common factors, the GCF is 1.

EXAMPLE 2 Find the GCF of each list of terms:
a. $12x^2$ and $20x$ **b.** $9a^5b^2$, $15a^4b^2$, and $90a^3b^3$

Strategy We will prime factor each coefficient of each term in the list. Then we will identify the numerical and variable factors common to each term and find their product.

WHY The product of the common factors is the GCF of the terms in the list.

Solution

a. ***Step 1*** We write each coefficient, 12 and 20, as a product of prime factors. Recall that an exponent, as in x^2, indicates repeated multiplication.

$12x^2 = 2 \cdot 2 \cdot 3 \cdot x \cdot x$ This can be written as $2^2 \cdot 3 \cdot x^2$.

$20x = 2 \cdot 2 \cdot 5 \cdot x$ This can be written as $2^2 \cdot 5 \cdot x$.

Step 2 There are two common factors of 2 and one common factor of x.

Step 3 We multiply the common factors, 2, 2, and x, to obtain the GCF.

$$GCF = 2 \cdot 2 \cdot x = 2^2 \cdot x = 4x$$

b. ***Step 1*** We write the coefficients, 9, 15, and 90, as products of primes. The exponents on the variables represent repeated multiplication.

$9a^5b^2 = 3 \cdot 3 \cdot a \cdot a \cdot a \cdot a \cdot a \cdot b \cdot b$ This can be written as $3^2 \cdot a^5 \cdot b^2$.

$15a^4b^2 = 3 \cdot 5 \cdot a \cdot a \cdot a \cdot a \cdot b \cdot b$ This can be written as $3 \cdot 5 \cdot a^4 \cdot b^2$.

$90a^3b^3 = 2 \cdot 3 \cdot 3 \cdot 5 \cdot a \cdot a \cdot a \cdot b \cdot b \cdot b$ This can be written as $2 \cdot 3^2 \cdot 5 \cdot a^3 \cdot b^3$.

Self Check 2

Find the GCF of each list of terms:
a. $33c$ and $22c^4$ $11c$
b. $42s^3t^2$, $63s^2t^4$, and $21s^3t^3$ $21s^2t^2$

Now Try **Problems 29 and 31**

Teaching Example 2 Find the GCF of each list of terms:
a. $18y^2$ and $45y$
b. $12x^4y^6$, $18x^5y^4$, and $30x^3y^5$
Answers:
a. $9y$ b. $6x^3y^4$

Step 2 The highlighting shows one common factor of 3, three common factors of a, and two common factors of b.

Step 3 GCF $= 3 \cdot a \cdot a \cdot a \cdot b \cdot b = 3a^3b^2$ ■

2 Factor out the greatest common factor.

To factor $12y^2 + 20y$, we find the GCF of $12y^2$ and $20y$ (which is $4y$) and use the distributive property in reverse: $ab + ac = a(b + c)$

$$12y^2 + 20y = 4y \cdot 3y + 4y \cdot 5$$ Write each term of the polynomial as the product of the GCF, 4y, and one other factor.

$$= 4y(3y + 5)$$ 4y is a common factor of both terms.

This process is called **factoring out the greatest common factor.**

Self Check 3

Factor: $18x - 24$ $6(3x - 4)$

Now Try **Problem 36**

Teaching Example 3 Factor: $6f + 36$
Answer:
$6(f + 6)$

EXAMPLE 3 Factor: $25 - 5m$

Strategy We will prime factor each coefficient of each term in the polynomial. Then we will write each term of the polynomial as a product of the GCF and one other factor.

WHY We can then use the distributive property to factor out the GCF.

Solution

The prime factorizations are shown:

$$\left.\begin{aligned} 25 &= 5 \cdot 5 \\ 5m &= 5 \cdot m \end{aligned}\right\} \quad \text{GCF} = 5$$

We can use the distributive property in reverse to factor out the GCF.

$$25 - 5m = 5 \cdot 5 - 5 \cdot m$$ Factor each monomial using 5 and one other factor.

$$= 5(5 - m)$$ Factor out the common factor of 5.

To check, we multiply: $5(5 - m) = 5 \cdot 5 - 5 \cdot m = 25 - 5m$. ■

Self Check 4

Factor: $32x^2y^4 + 12x^3y^3$

Now Try **Problem 45**

Self Check 4 Answer
$4x^2y^3(8y + 3x)$

Teaching Example 4 Factor: $48s^2t^2 - 84s^3t$
Answer:
$12s^2t(4t - 7s)$

EXAMPLE 4 Factor: $35a^3b^2 + 14a^2b^3$

Strategy We will prime factor each coefficient of each term in the polynomial. Then we will write each term of the polynomial as a product of the GCF and one other factor.

WHY We can then use the distributive property to factor out the GCF.

Solution

The prime factorizations of $35a^3b^2$ and $14a^2b^3$ are shown:

$$\left.\begin{aligned} 35a^3b^2 &= 5 \cdot 7 \cdot a \cdot a \cdot a \cdot b \cdot b \\ 14a^2b^3 &= 2 \cdot 7 \cdot a \cdot a \cdot b \cdot b \cdot b \end{aligned}\right\} \quad \text{GCF} = 7 \cdot a \cdot a \cdot b \cdot b = 7a^2b^2$$

We factor out the GCF, $7a^2b^2$.

$$35a^3b^2 + 14a^2b^3 = 7a^2b^2 \cdot 5a + 7a^2b^2 \cdot 2b$$

$$= 7a^2b^2(5a + 2b)$$ Factor out the GCF $7a^2b^2$.

To check, we multiply: $7a^2b^2(5a + 2b) = 35a^3b^2 + 14a^2b^3$. ■

Caution! If the GCF of the terms of a polynomial is the same as one of the terms, leave a 1 in place of that term when factoring out the GCF.

EXAMPLE 5 Factor: $4x^3y^2z - 2x^2yz + xz$

Strategy We will prime factor each coefficient of each term in the polynomial. Then we will write each term of the polynomial as a product of the GCF and one other factor.

WHY We can then use the distributive property to factor out the GCF.

Solution

The expression has three terms. We factor out the GCF, which is xz.

$$4x^3y^2z - 2x^2yz + xz = xz \cdot 4x^2y^2 - xz \cdot 2xy + xz \cdot 1$$

$$= xz(4x^2y^2 - 2xy + 1) \quad \text{Factor out the GCF } xz.$$

The last term of $4x^3y^2z - 2x^2yz + xz$ has an implied coefficient of 1. When xz is factored out, we must write this coefficient of 1, as shown in blue. To check, we multiply: $xz(4x^2y^2 - 2xy + 1) = 4x^3y^2z - 2x^2yz + xz$.

Self Check 5

Factor: $2ab^2c + 4a^2bc - ab$

Now Try **Problem 51**

Self Check 5 Answer
$ab(2bc + 4ac - 1)$

Teaching Example 5 Factor: $14x^2y^2 - 7xy + 21x^3y$
Answer:
$7xy(2xy - 1) + 3x^2$

EXAMPLE 6 Factor: $x(x + 4) + 3(x + 4)$

Strategy We will identify the terms of the expression and find their GCF.

WHY We can then use the distributive property in reverse to factor out the GCF.

Solution

The given expression has two terms:

$$\underbrace{x(x + 4)}_{\text{The first term}} + \underbrace{3(x + 4)}_{\text{The second term}}$$

The GCF of the terms is $x + 4$, which can be factored out.

$$x(x + 4) + 3(x + 4) = x(x + 4) + 3(x + 4)$$

$$= (x + 4)(x + 3) \quad \text{Factor out the GCF } (x + 4).$$

Self Check 6

Factor: $2y(y - 1) - 7(y - 1)$

Now Try **Problem 56**

Self Check 6 Answer
$(y - 1)(2y - 7)$

Teaching Example 6 Factor: $6a(a + 7) - 5(a + 7)$
Answer:
$(a + 7)(6a - 5)$

It is often useful to factor out a common factor having a negative coefficient.

EXAMPLE 7 Factor -1 out of $-a^3 + 2a^2 - 4$.

Strategy We will write each term of the polynomial as the product of -1 and one other factor.

WHY We can then use the distributive property in reverse to factor out the -1.

Solution

$$-a^3 + 2a^2 - 4 = (-1)a^3 + (-1)(-2a^2) + (-1)4$$

$$= -1(a^3 - 2a^2 + 4) \quad \text{Factor out } -1.$$

$$= -(a^3 - 2a^2 + 4) \quad \text{The coefficient of 1 need not be written.}$$

We check by multiplying: $-(a^3 - 2a^2 + 4) = -a^3 + 2a^2 - 4$.

Self Check 7

Factor -1 out of $-b^4 - 3b^2 + 2$.

Now Try **Problem 61**

Self Check 7 Answer
$-(b^4 + 3b^2 - 2)$

Teaching Example 7 Factor -1 out of $-x^4 - 3x^2 + 5$.
Answer:
$-(x^4 + 3x^2 - 5)$

Self Check 8

Factor out the opposite of the GCF in $-27xy^2 - 18x^2y + 36x^2y^2$.

Now Try **Problem 66**

Self Check 8 Answer
$-9xy(3y + 2x - 4xy)$

Teaching Example 8 Factor out the opposite of the GCF in $-24a^3b^5 + 6a^2b - 12ab$.
Answer:
$-6ab(4a^2b^4 - a + 2)$

EXAMPLE 8 Factor out the opposite of the GCF in $-18a^2b + 6ab^2 - 12a^2b^2$.

Strategy First we will determine the GCF of the terms of the polynomial. Then we will write each term of the polynomial as the product of the opposite of the GCF and one other factor.

WHY We can then use the distributive property to factor out the opposite of the GCF.

Solution
The GCF is $6ab$, the opposite of $6ab$ is $-6ab$. We write each term of the polynomial as the product of $-6ab$ and another factor. Then we factor out $-6ab$.

$$-18a^2b + 6ab^2 - 12a^2b^2 = (-6ab)3a - (-6ab)b + (-6ab)2ab$$
$$= -6ab(3a - b + 2ab) \quad \text{Factor out } -6ab.$$

We check by multiplying: $-6ab(3a - b + 2ab) = -18a^2b + 6ab^2 - 12a^2b^2$.

> ***Success Tip*** When the first coefficient of a polynomial is negative, factor out the opposite of the GCF.

3 Factoring by grouping.

When a polynomial has 4 or more terms, we see if we can factor it by arranging the terms in groups that have common factors. This method is called **factoring by grouping.**

Factoring by Grouping

1. Group the terms of the polynomial so that the first two terms have a common factor and the last two terms have a common factor.
2. Factor out the common factor from each group.
3. Factor out the resulting common binomial factor. If there is no common binomial factor, regroup the terms of the polynomial and repeat steps 2 and 3.

Self Check 9

Factor: $7x - 7y + xy - y^2$

Now Try **Problem 70**

Self Check 9 Answer
$(x - y)(7 + y)$

Teaching Example 9 Factor: $9x + 9y + xy + y^2$
Answer:
$(x + y)(9 + y)$

EXAMPLE 9 Factor: $2c - 2d + cd - d^2$

Strategy We note that there is no common factor of all four terms. Then we will factor out a common factor from the first two terms and a common factor from the last two terms.

WHY Often this will produce a common binomial factor that can be factored out.

Solution
Since 2 is a common factor of the first two terms and d is a common factor of the last two terms, we have

$$2c - 2d + cd - d^2 = 2(c - d) + d(c - d) \quad \text{Factor out 2 from } 2c - 2d \text{ and } d \text{ from } cd - d^2.$$
$$= (c - d)(2 + d) \quad \text{Factor out } c - d.$$

We check by multiplying:

$$(c - d)(2 + d) = 2c + cd - 2d - d^2$$
$$= 2c - 2d + cd - d^2 \quad \text{Rearrange the terms.}$$

EXAMPLE 10 Factor: $x^2y - ax - xy + a$

Strategy We note that there is no common factor of all four terms. Then we will factor out a common factor from the first two terms and a common factor from the last two terms.

WHY Often this will produce a common binomial factor that can be factored out.

Solution

Since x is a common factor of the first two terms, we can factor it out and proceed as follows.

$$x^2y - ax - xy + a = x(xy - a) - xy + a \quad \text{Factor out } x \text{ from } x^2y - ax.$$

If we factor -1 from $-xy + a$, a common binomial factor $(xy - a)$ appears, which we can factor out.

$$\begin{aligned} x^2y - ax - xy + a &= x(xy - a) - 1(xy - a) \\ &= (xy - a)(x - 1) \quad \text{Factor out } (xy - a). \end{aligned}$$

Check by multiplication.

Self Check 10

Factor: $7bt + 3ct - 7b - 3c$

Now Try **Problem 76**

Self Check 10 Answer
$(7b + 3c)(t - 1)$

Teaching Example 10 Factor:
$a^2b - ax - ab + x$
Answer:
$(ab - x)(a - 1)$

> ***Caution!*** When factoring the expressions in the previous two examples, don't think that $2(c - d) + d(c - d)$ or $x(xy - a) - 1(xy - a)$ are in factored form. For an expression to be in factored form, the result must be a product.

The next example illustrates that when factoring a polynomial, we should always look for a common factor first.

EXAMPLE 11 Factor: $10k + 10m - 2km - 2m^2$

Strategy Since all four terms have a common factor of 2, we factor it out first. Then we will factor the resulting polynomial by grouping.

WHY Factoring out the GCF first makes the factoring process easier.

Solution

$$\begin{aligned} 10k + 10m - 2km - 2m^2 &= 2(5k + 5m - km - m^2) \quad \text{Factor out the GCF 2.} \\ &= 2[5(k + m) - m(k + m)] \quad \text{Factor out 5 from } 5k + 5m. \text{ Factor out } -m \text{ from } -km - m^2. \\ &= 2[(k + m)(5 - m)] \quad \text{Factor out } (k + m). \\ &= 2(k + m)(5 - m) \end{aligned}$$

Use multiplication to check the result.

Self Check 11

Factor: $-4t - 4s - 4tz - 4sz$

Now Try **Problem 78**

Self Check 11 Answer
$-4(t + s)(1 + z)$

Teaching Example 11 Factor:
$-6x - 6y - 12ax - 12ay$
Answer:
$-6(x + y)(1 + 2a)$

ANSWERS TO SELF CHECKS

1. a. 15 **b.** 1 **2. a.** $11c$ **b.** $21s^2t^2$ **3.** $6(3x - 4)$ **4.** $4x^2y^3(8y + 3x)$ **5.** $ab(2bc + 4ac - 1)$ **6.** $(y - 1)(2y - 7)$ **7.** $-(b^4 + 3b^2 - 2)$ **8.** $-9xy(3y + 2x - 4xy)$ **9.** $(x - y)(7 + y)$ **10.** $(7b + 3c)(t - 1)$ **11.** $-4(t + s)(1 + z)$

SECTION 6.8 STUDY SET

VOCABULARY

Fill in the blanks.

1. The process of finding the individual factors of a known product is called factoring.
2. To factor a polynomial means to express the polynomial as a product of two (or more) polynomials.
3. The prime factorization of 12 is $2 \cdot 2 \cdot 3$.
4. The GCF of several integers is the largest common factor of those integers.
5. When we write $15x^2 - 25x$ as $5x(3x - 5)$, we say that we have factored out the greatest common factor.
6. When a polynomial has four or more terms, we can attempt to factor it by rearranging its terms in groups that have common factors. This process is called factoring by grouping.

CONCEPTS

Explain what is wrong with each solution.

7. Factor: $6a + 9b + 3$

$$6a + 9b + 3 = 3(2a + 3b + 0)$$
$$= 3(2a + 3b)$$
The 0 in the first line should be 1.

8. Factor out the GCF: $30a^3 - 12a^2$

$$30a^3 - 12a^2 = 6a(5a^2 - 2a)$$
The GCF is $6a^2$, not $6a$.

9. Factor: $ab + b + a + 1$.

$$ab + b + a + 1 = b(a + 1) + (a + 1)$$
$$= (a + 1)b$$
The answer should be $(a + 1)(b + 1)$.

10. What algebraic concept is illustrated in the work shown below? factoring out the GCF

$$4 \cdot 5x + 4 \cdot 3 = 4(5x + 3)$$

11. The prime factorizations of three monomials are shown here. Find their GCF. $3x$

$$3 \cdot 3 \cdot 5 \cdot x \cdot x$$
$$2 \cdot 3 \cdot 5 \cdot x \cdot y$$
$$2 \cdot 2 \cdot 3 \cdot x \cdot y \cdot y$$

Consider the polynomial: $2k - 8 + hk - 4h$

12. Is there a common factor of all the terms? no
13. What is the common factor of the first two terms? 2
14. What is the common factor of the last two terms? h

Complete each factorization.

15. $4a + 12 = 4(a + 3)$
16. $r^4 + r^2 = r^2(r^2 + 1)$
17. $4y^2 + 8y - 2xy = 2y(2y + 4 - x)$
18. $3x^2 - 6xy + 9xy^2 = 3x(x - 2y + 3y^2)$

NOTATION

Complete each factorization.

19. Factor: $b^3 - 6b^2 + 2b - 12$

$$b^3 - 6b^2 + 2b - 12 = b^2(b - 6) + 2(b - 6)$$
$$= (b - 6)(b^2 + 2)$$

▶ 20. Factor: $12b^3 - 6b^2 + 2b - 2$

$$12b^3 - 6b^2 + 2b - 2 = 2(6b^3 - 3b^2 + b - 1)$$

21. In the expression $4x^2y + xy$, what is the coefficient of the last term? 1
22. Is the following statement true?

$$-(x^2 - 3x + 1) = -1(x^2 - 3x + 1)$$ yes

GUIDED PRACTICE

Find the GCF of each list of numbers. See Example 1.

23. 6, 8, 10 2
24. 10, 15, 25 5
25. 30, 45, 60 15
▶ 26. 78, 104, 156 26

Find the GCF of each list of terms. See Example 2.

27. $25y^3$, $35y$ $5y$
28. $36a^2$, $48a$ $12a$
29. $20p^2q$, $40pq^2$ $20pq$
▶ 30. $36m^2n^2$, $54mn$ $18mn$
31. $6t^3$, $12t^2$, $18t$ $6t$
32. $28r^3$, $14r^2$, $35r^4$ $7r^2$
33. $30a^3b^3$, $45a^2b^2$, $60ab$ $15ab$
34. $28u^4v^3$, $35u^3v^2$, $49u^2v$ $7u^2v$

Factor each expression. See Example 3.

35. $3x + 6$ $3(x + 2)$
▶ 36. $2y - 10$ $2(y - 5)$
37. $36 - 6x$ $6(6 - x)$
38. $48 + 12y$ $12(4 + y)$

Factor each expression. See Example 4.

39. $t^3 + 2t^2$ $t^2(t + 2)$
▶ 40. $b^3 - 3b^2$ $b^2(b - 3)$
41. $a^3 - a^2$ $a^2(a - 1)$
42. $r^3 + r^2$ $r^2(r + 1)$
43. $24x^2y^3 + 8xy^2$ $8xy^2(3xy + 1)$
44. $3x^2y^3 - 9x^4y^3$ $3x^2y^3(1 - 3x^2)$
45. $12uv - 18uv^2$ $6uv(2 - 3v)$
46. $14xy - 16x^2y^2$ $2xy(7 - 8xy)$

Factor each expression. See Example 5.

47. $12x^2 - 6 - 24a$ $6(2x^2 - 1 - 4a)$

48. $27a^2 - 9 + 45b$ $9(3a^2 - 1 + 5b)$

49. $3 + 3y - 6z$ $3(1 + y - 2z)$

50. $2 - 4y + 8z$ $2(1 - 2y + 4z)$

51. $ab + ac - a$ $a(b + c - 1)$

52. $rs - rt + r$ $r(s - t + 1)$

53. $12r^2 - 3r + 9r^2s^2$ $3r(4r - 1 + 3rs^2)$

54. $6a - 12a^3b + 36ab$ $6a(1 - 2a^2b + 6b)$

Factor each expression. See Example 6.

55. $3(x + 2) - x(x + 2)$ $(x + 2)(3 - x)$

56. $t(5 - s) + 4(5 - s)$ $(5 - s)(t + 4)$

57. $h^2(14 + r) + 2(14 + r)$ $(14 + r)(h^2 + 2)$

58. $k^2(14 + v) - 7(14 + v)$ $(14 + v)(k^2 - 7)$

Factor −1 out of each expression. See Example 7.

59. $-a - b$ $-(a + b)$

60. $-x - 2y$ $-(x + 2y)$

61. $-3m - 4n + 1$ $-(3m + 4n - 1)$

62. $-3r + 2s - 3$ $-(3r - 2s + 3)$

In each expression, factor out the negative of the GCF. See Example 8.

63. $-3x^2 - 6x$ $-3x(x + 2)$

64. $-4a^2 + 6a$ $-2a(2a - 3)$

65. $-4a^2b^3 + 12a^3b^2 + 4a^2b^2$ $-4a^2b^2(b - 3a - 1)$

66. $-25x^4y^3 + 10x^3y^3 + 30x^2y^3$ $-5x^2y^3(5x^2 - 2x - 6)$

Factor each expression. See Example 9.

67. $2x + 2y + ax + ay$ $(x + y)(2 + a)$

68. $bx + bz + 5x + 5z$ $(x + z)(b + 5)$

69. $7r + 7s - kr - ks$ $(r + s)(7 - k)$

70. $9p - 9q + mp - mq$ $(p - q)(9 + m)$

71. $xr + xs + yr + ys$ $(r + s)(x + y)$

72. $pm - pn + qm - qn$ $(m - n)(p + q)$

73. $2ax + 2bx + 3a + 3b$ $(a + b)(2x + 3)$

74. $3xy + 3xz - 5y - 5z$ $(y + z)(3x - 5)$

Factor each expression completely. See Examples 10–11.

75. $ax^3 + bx^3 + 2ax^2y + 2bx^2y$ $x^2(a + b)(x + 2y)$

76. $x^3y^2 - 2x^2y^2 + 3xy^2 - 6y^2$ $y^2(x - 2)(x^2 + 3)$

77. $4a^2b + 12a^2 - 8ab - 24a$ $4a(b + 3)(a - 2)$

78. $-4abc - 4ac^2 + 2bc + 2c^2$ $-2c(b + c)(2a - 1)$

TRY IT YOURSELF

Completely factor each expression (including −1, if necessary).

79. $\pi R^2 - \pi ab$ $\pi(R^2 - ab)$

80. $\frac{1}{3}\pi R^2h - \frac{1}{3}\pi rh$ $\frac{1}{3}\pi h(R^2 - r)$

81. $-2x + 5y$ $-(2x - 5y)$

82. $-3x + 8z$ $-(3x - 8z)$

83. $-3ab - 5ac + 9bc$ $-(3ab + 5ac - 9bc)$

84. $-6yz + 12xz - 5xy$ $-(6yz - 12xz + 5xy)$

85. $-4a^2b^2c^2 + 14a^2b^2c - 10ab^2c^2$ $-2ab^2c(2ac - 7a + 5c)$

86. $-10x^4y^3z^2 + 8x^3y^2z - 20x^2y$ $-2x^2y(5x^2y^2z^2 - 4xyz + 10)$

87. $2ab + 2ac + 3b + 3c$ $(b + c)(2a + 3)$

88. $3ac + a + 3bc + b$ $(3c + 1)(a + b)$

89. $6x^2 - 2x - 15x + 5$ $(3x - 1)(2x - 5)$

90. $6x^2 + 2x + 9x + 3$ $(3x + 1)(2x + 3)$

91. $9mp + 3mq - 3np - nq$ $(3p + q)(3m - n)$

92. $ax + bx - a - b$ $(a + b)(x - 1)$

93. $2xy + y^2 - 2x - y$ $(2x + y)(y - 1)$

94. $2xy - 3y^2 + 2x - 3y$ $(2x - 3y)(y + 1)$

95. $8z^5 + 12z^2 - 10z^3 - 15$ $(2z^3 + 3)(4z^2 - 5)$

96. $2a^4 + 2a^3 - 4a - 4$ $(a + 1)(2a^3 - 4)$

97. $x^3y - x^2y - xy^2 + y^2$ $y(x^2 - y)(x - 1)$

98. $2x^3z - 4x^2z + 32xz - 64z$ $2z(x - 2)(x^2 + 16)$

APPLICATIONS

99. PICTURE FRAMING The dimensions of a family portrait and the frame in which it is mounted are shown. Write an algebraic expression that describes

a. the area of the picture frame. $12x^3$ in.^{2}

b. the area of the portrait. $20x^2$ in.^{2}

c. the area of the mat used in the framing. Express the result in factored form. $4x^2(3x - 5)$ in.^{2}

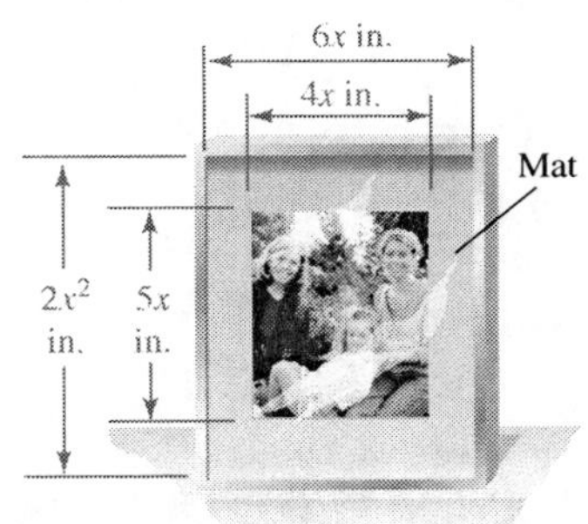

100. REARVIEW MIRRORS The dimensions of the three rearview mirrors on an automobile are given in the illustration below. Write an algebraic expression that gives

a. the area of the rearview mirror mounted on the windshield. $6x^3$ cm^2

b. the total area of the two side mirrors. $24x^2$ cm^2

c. the total area of all three mirrors. Express the result in factored form. $6x^2(x + 4)$ cm^2

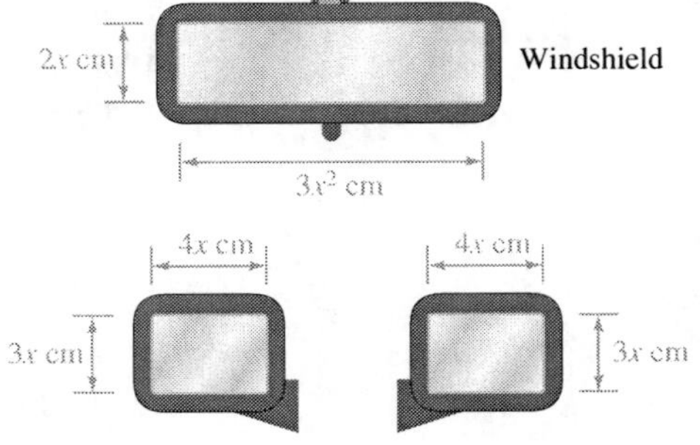

101. COOKING See the following illustration.

a. What is the length of a side of the square griddle, in terms of r? What is the area of the cooking surface of the griddle, in terms of r? $4r$ in., $16r^2$ in.^{2}

b. How many square inches of the cooking surface do the pancakes cover, in terms of r? $4\pi r^2$ in.^{2}

c. Find the amount of cooking surface that is not covered by the pancakes. Express the result in factored form. $16r^2 - 4\pi r^2 = 4r^2(4 - \pi)$ in.^{2}

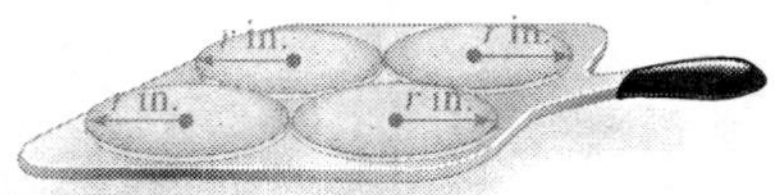

102. AIRCRAFT CARRIERS The rectangular-shaped landing area of $(x^3 + 4x^2 + 5x + 20)$ ft^2 is shaded. The dimensions of the landing area can be found by factoring. What are the length and width of the landing area? $(x^2 + 5)$ ft, $(x + 4)$ ft.

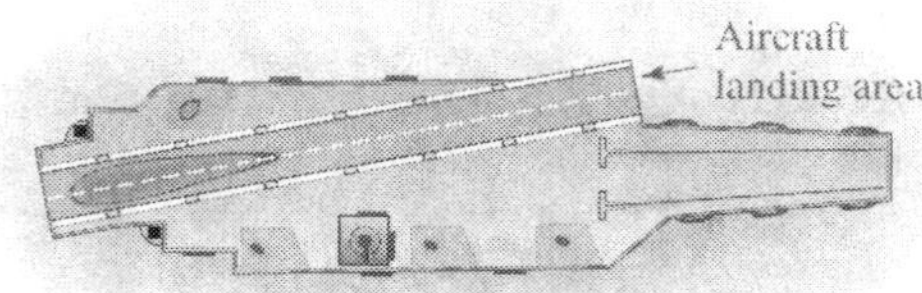

WRITING

103. To add $5x$ and $7x$, we combine like terms: $5x + 7x = 12x$. Explain how this is related to factoring out a common factor.

104. One student commented, "Factoring undoes the distributive property." What do you think she meant? Give an example.

105. If asked to write $ax + ay - bx - by$ in factored form, explain why $a(x + y) - b(x + y)$ is not an acceptable answer.

106. When asked to factor $rx - sy + ry - sx$, a student wrote the expression as $rx + ry - sx - sy$. Then she factored it by grouping. Can the terms be rearranged in this manner? Explain your answer.

REVIEW

107. Simplify: $\left(\frac{y^3y}{2yy^2}\right)^3$ $\frac{y^3}{8}$

108. Find the slope of the line passing through the points $(3, 5)$ and $(-2, -7)$. $\frac{12}{5}$

109. Does the point $(3, 5)$ lie on the graph of the line $4x - y = 7$? yes

110. Simplify: $-5(3a - 2)(2a + 3)$ $-30a^2 - 25a + 30$

Objectives

1. Factor trinomials of the form $x^2 + bx + c$
2. Factor trinomials of the form $x^2 + bx + c$ after factoring out the GCF.
3. Factor trinomials of the form $x^2 + bx + c$ using the grouping method.

SECTION 6.9 Factoring Trinomials of the Form $x^2 + bx + c$

In Chapter 5, we learned how to multiply binomials. For example, to multiply $x + 2$ and $x + 3$, we proceed as follows:

$$(x + 2)(x + 3) = x^2 + 3x + 2x + 6$$
$$= x^2 + 5x + 6$$

To *factor the trinomial* $x^2 + 5x + 6$, we will reverse the multiplication process and determine what factors were multiplied to obtain $x^2 + 5x + 6$. Since the product of two binomials is often a trinomial, many trinomials factor into the product of two binomials.

Multiplication: Given the binomial factors, we find the trinomial. →

$$(x + 2)(x + 3) = x^2 + 5x + 6$$

← Factoring: Given the trinomial, we find the binomial factors.

We will now consider how to factor trinomials of the form $ax^2 + bx + c$, where a (called the **leading coefficient**) is 1.

1 Factor trinomials of the form $x^2 + bx + c$.

To develop a method for factoring trinomials, we multiply $(x + 4)$ and $(x + 5)$.

$$(x + 4)(x + 5) = x \cdot x + x \cdot 5 + 4 \cdot x + 4 \cdot 5 \quad \text{Use the FOIL method.}$$
$$= x^2 + 5x + 4x + 20$$
$$= x^2 + 9x + 20$$

First term, Middle term, Last term

The result has three terms. We can see that

- the first term, x^2, is the product of x and x,
- the last term, 20, is the product of 4 and 5, and
- the coefficient of the middle term, 9, is the sum of 4 and 5.

We can use these facts to factor trinomials with lead coefficients of 1.

EXAMPLE 1 Factor: $x^2 + 5x + 6$

Strategy We will assume that $x^2 + 5x + 6$ is the product of two binomials and we will use a systematic method to find their terms.

WHY Since the terms of $x^2 + 5x + 6$ do not have a common factor (other than 1), the only option available is to try to factor it as the product of two binomials.

Solution
Since the first term of the trinomial is x^2, the first term of each binomial factor must be x. To fill in the blanks, we must find two integers whose product is +6 and whose sum is +5.

$$x^2 + 5x + 6 = (x \quad)(x \quad) \quad \text{Because } x \cdot x \text{ will give } x^2.$$

The positive factorizations of 6 and the sum of the factors are shown in the table.

Factors of 6	Sum of the factors of 6
1(6)	1 + 6 = 7
2(3)	2 + 3 = 5

The last row contains the integers 2 and 3, whose product is 6 and whose sum is 5. To complete the factorization, we enter 2 and 3 as the second terms of the binomial factors.

$$x^2 + 5x + 6 = (x + 2)(x + 3)$$

To check the result, we verify that $(x + 2)(x + 3)$ is $x^2 + 5x + 6$.

$$(x + 2)(x + 3) = x^2 + 3x + 2x + 6 \quad \text{Use the FOIL method.}$$
$$= x^2 + 5x + 6 \quad \text{This is the original trinomial.}$$

Self Check 1

Factor: $y^2 + 7y + 6$

Now Try **Problem 25**

Self Check 1 Answer
$(y + 1)(y + 6)$

Teaching Example 1 Factor: $a^2 + 6a + 8$
Answer:
$(a + 2)(a + 4)$

Success Tip When factoring trinomials, the binomial factors can be written in either order. In Example 1, an equivalent factorization is $x^2 + 5x + 6 = (x + 3)(x + 2)$.

Self Check 2

Factor: $p^2 - 5p + 6$

Now Try **Problem 29**

Self Check 2 Answer
$(p - 3)(p - 2)$

Teaching Example 2 Factor:
$x^2 - 13x + 12$
Answer:
$(x - 12)(x - 1)$

EXAMPLE 2 Factor: $y^2 - 7y + 12$

Strategy We will assume that $y^2 - 7y + 12$ is the product of two binomials and we will use a systematic method to find their terms.

WHY Since the terms of $y^2 - 7y + 12$ do not have a common factor (other than 1), the only option available is to try to factor it as the product of two binomials.

Solution

Since the first term of the trinomial is y^2, the first term of each binomial factor must be y. To fill in the blanks, we must find two integers whose product is 12 and whose sum is -7.

$$y^2 - 7y + 12 = (y \quad)(y \quad)$$ Because $y \cdot y$ will give y^2.

The two-integer factorizations of 12 and the sums of the factors are shown in the following table.

Factors of 12	Sum of the factors of 12
1(12)	$1 + 12 = 13$
2(6)	$2 + 6 = 8$
3(4)	$3 + 4 = 7$
$-1(-12)$	$-1 + (-12) = -13$
$-2(-6)$	$-2 + (-6) = -8$
$-3(-4)$	$-3 + (-4) = -7$

The last row contains the integers -3 and -4, whose product is 12 and whose sum is -7. To complete the factorization, we enter -3 and -4 as the second terms of the binomial factors.

$$y^2 - 7y + 12 = (y - 3)(y - 4)$$

To check the result, we verify that $(y - 3)(y - 4)$ is $y^2 - 7y + 12$.

$$(y - 3)(y - 4) = y^2 - 4y - 3y + 12$$ Use the FOIL method.
$$= y^2 - 7y + 12$$ This is the original trinomial.

Self Check 3

Factor: $p^2 + 3p - 18$

Now Try **Problem 34**

Self Check 3 Answer
$(p + 6)(p - 3)$

Teaching Example 3 Factor:
$x^2 + 5x - 14$
Answer:
$(x + 7)(x - 2)$

EXAMPLE 3 Factor: $a^2 + 2a - 15$

Strategy We will assume that $a^2 + 2a - 15$ is the product of two binomials and we will use a systematic method to find their terms.

WHY Since the terms of $a^2 + 2a - 15$ do not have a common factor (other than 1), the only option available is to try to factor it as the product of two binomials.

Solution

Since the first term of the trinomial is a^2, the first term of each binomial factor must be a. To fill in the blanks, we must find two integers whose product is -15 and whose sum is 2.

$$a^2 + 2a - 15 = (a \quad)(a \quad)$$ Because $a \cdot a$ will give a^2.

The possible factorizations of −15 and the sum of the factors are shown in the following table.

Factors of −15	Sum of the factors of −15
1(−15)	1 + (−15) = −14
3(−5)	3 + (−5) = −2
5(−3)	5 + (−3) = 2
15(−1)	15 + (−1) = 14

The third row contains the integers 5 and −3, whose product is −15 and whose sum is 2. To complete the factorization, we enter 5 and −3 as the second binomial factors.

$$a^2 + 2a - 15 = (a + 5)(a - 3)$$

We can check by multiplying.

$$(a + 5)(a - 3) = a^2 - 3a + 5a - 15$$ Use the FOIL method.

$$= a^2 + 2a - 15$$ This is the original trinomial.

EXAMPLE 4 Factor: $z^2 - 4z - 21$

Strategy We will assume that $z^2 - 4z - 21$ is the product of two binomials and we will use a systematic method to find their terms.

WHY Since the terms of $z^2 - 4z - 21$ do not have a common factor (other than 1), the only option available is to try to factor it as the product of two binomials.

Solution

Since the first term of the trinomial is z^2, the first term of each binomial factor must be z. To fill in the blanks, we must find two integers whose product is −21 and whose sum is −4.

$$z^2 - 4y - 21 = (z \quad)(z \quad)$$ Because $z \cdot z$ will give z^2.

The factorizations of −21 and the sums of the factors are shown in the following table.

Factors of −21	Sum of the factors of −21
1(−21)	1 + (−21) = −20
3(−7)	3 + (−7) = −4
7(−3)	7 + (−3) = 4
21(−1)	21 + (−1) = 20

The second row contains the integers 3 and −7, whose product is −21 and whose sum is −4. To complete the factorization, we enter 3 and −7 as the second terms of the binomial factors.

$$z^2 - 4z - 21 = (z + 3)(z - 7)$$

We can check by multiplying.

$$(z + 3)(z - 7) = z^2 - 7z + 3z - 21$$ Use the FOIL method.

$$= z^2 - 4z - 21$$ This is the original trinomial.

Self Check 4

Factor: $q^2 - 2q - 24$

Now Try **Problem 37**

Self Check 4 Answer

$(q - 6)(q + 4)$

Teaching Example 4 Factor: $x^2 - 3x - 10$

Answer:

$(x - 5)(x + 2)$

The following sign patterns can be helpful when factoring trinomials.

Factoring Trinomials Whose Leading Coefficient Is 1

To factor $x^2 + bx + c$, find two integers whose product is c and whose sum is b.

1. If c is positive, the integers have the same sign.
2. If c is negative, the integers have opposite signs.

When factoring out trinomials of the form $ax^2 + bx + c$, where $a = -1$, we begin by factoring out -1.

Self Check 5

Factor: $-x^2 + 11x - 28$

Now Try **Problem 41**

Self Check 5 Answer
$-(x - 4)(x - 7)$

Teaching Example 5 Factor:
$-x^2 - 5x + 6$
Answer:
$-(x + 6)(x - 1)$

EXAMPLE 5 Factor: $-h^2 + 2h + 15$

Strategy We will factor out -1 and then factor the resulting trinomial.

WHY It is easier to factor trinomials whose leading coefficient is positive.

Solution

We factor out -1 and then factor $h^2 - 2h - 15$.

$$\begin{aligned} -h^2 + 2h + 15 &= -1(h^2 - 2h - 15) && \text{Factor out } -1. \\ &= -(h^2 - 2h - 15) && \text{The 1 need not be written.} \\ &= -(h - 5)(h + 3) && \text{Use the integers } -5 \text{ and } 3, \text{ because their product is } -15 \text{ and their sum is } -2. \end{aligned}$$

We can check by multiplying.

$$\begin{aligned} -(h - 5)(h + 3) &= -(h^2 + 3h - 5h - 15) && \text{Multiply the binomials first.} \\ &= -(h^2 - 2h - 15) && \text{Combine like terms.} \\ &= -h^2 + 2h + 15 && \text{This is the original trinomial.} \end{aligned}$$

The trinomials in the next two examples are of a form similar to $x^2 + bx + c$, and we can use the methods of this section to factor them.

Self Check 6

Factor: $s^2 + 6st - 7t^2$

Now Try **Problem 45**

Self Check 6 Answer
$(s + 7t)(s - t)$

Teaching Example 6 Factor:
$x^2 - 7xy + 12y^2$
Answer:
$(x - 4y)(x - 3y)$

EXAMPLE 6 Factor: $x^2 - 4xy - 5y^2$

Strategy We will assume that $x^2 - 4xy - 5y^2$ is the product of two binomials and we will use a systematic method to find their terms.

WHY Since the terms of $x^2 - 4xy - 5y^2$ do not have a common factor (other than 1), the only option available is to try to factor it as the product of two binomials.

Solution

The trinomial has two variables, x and y. Since the first term is x^2, the first term of each factor must be x.

$$x^2 - 4xy - 5y^2 = (x \quad)(x \quad) \quad \text{Because } x \cdot x \text{ will give } x^2.$$

To fill in the blanks, we must find two *expressions* whose product is the last term, $-5y^2$, and that will give a middle term of $-4xy$. Two such expressions are $-5y$ and y.

$$x^2 - 4xy - 5y^2 = (x - 5y)(x + y)$$

Check:

$$\begin{aligned} (x - 5y)(x + y) &= x^2 + xy - 5xy - 5y^2 && \text{Use the FOIL method.} \\ &= x^2 - 4xy - 5y^2 && \text{This is the original trinomial.} \end{aligned}$$

2 Factor trinomials of the form $x^2 + bx + c$ after factoring out the GCF.

If the terms of a trinomial have a common factor, the GCF should always be factored out before any of the factoring techniques of this section are used. A trinomial is **factored completely** when no factor can be factored further. Always factor completely when you are asked to factor.

EXAMPLE 7 Factor: $2x^4 + 26x^3 + 80x^2$

Strategy We will factor out the GCF, $2x^2$, first. Then we will factor the resulting trinomial.

WHY The first step in factoring any polynomial is to factor out the GCF. Factoring out the GCF first makes factoring by any method easier.

Solution
We begin by factoring out the GCF, $2x^2$.

$$2x^4 + 26x^3 + 80x^2 = 2x^2(x^2 + 13x + 40)$$

Next, we factor $x^2 + 13x + 40$. The integers 8 and 5 have a product of 40 and a sum of 13, so the completely factored form of the given trinomial is

$$2x^4 + 26x^3 + 80x^2 = 2x^2(x + 8)(x + 5)$$ The complete factorization must include $2x^2$.

Check by multiplying $2x^2$, $x + 8$, and $x + 5$.

Self Check 7
Factor: $4m^5 + 8m^4 - 32m^3$
Now Try **Problem 51**
Self Check 7 Answer
$4m^3(m + 4)(m - 2)$

Teaching Example 7 Factor: $3x^4 - 12x^3 + 9x^2$
Answer: $3x^2(x - 1)(x - 3)$

EXAMPLE 8 Factor completely: $-13g^2 + 36g + g^3$

Strategy We will write the terms of the trinomial in descending powers of g.

WHY It is easier to factor a trinomial if its terms are written in descending powers of one variable.

Solution
Before factoring the trinomial, we write its terms in descending powers of g.

$$-13g^2 + 36g + g^3 = g^3 - 13g^2 + 36g$$ Rearrange the terms.
$$= g(g^2 - 13g + 36)$$ Factor out g, which is the GCF.
$$= g(g - 9)(g - 4)$$ Factor the trinomial.

Check by multiplying.

Self Check 8
Factor: $-12t + t^3 + 4t^2$
Now Try **Problem 55**
Self Check 8 Answer
$t(t - 2)(t + 6)$

Teaching Example 8 Factor: $2x^3 - 12x^2 + 10x$
Answer: $2x(x - 1)(x - 5)$

If a trinomial cannot be factored using only integers, it is called a **prime polynomial,** or more specifically, a **prime trinomial.**

EXAMPLE 9 Factor, if possible: $x^2 + 2x + 3$

Strategy We will assume that $x^2 + 2x + 3$ is the product of two binomials and we will use a systematic method to find their terms.

WHY Since the terms of $x^2 + 2x + 3$ do not have a common factor (other than 1), the only option available is to try to factor it as the product of two binomials.

Self Check 9
Factor, if possible: $x^2 - 4x + 6$
Now Try **Problem 58**
Self Check 9 Answer
not possible: prime trinomial

Teaching Example 9 Factor: $x^2 - 6x - 8$, if possible
Answer:
not possible; prime trinomial

Solution

To factor the trinomial, we must find two integers whose product is 3 and whose sum is 2. The possible factorizations of 3 and the sums of the factors are shown in the following table.

Factors of 3	Sum of the factors of 3
1(3)	$1 + 3 = 4$
$-1(-3)$	$-1 + (-3) = -4$

Since two integers whose product is 3 and whose sum is 2 do not exist, $x^2 + 2x + 3$ cannot be factored. It is a *prime trinomial.*

3 Factor trinomials of the form $x^2 + bx + c$ using the grouping method.

Another way to factor trinomials of the form $x^2 + bx + c$ is to write them as equivalent four-termed polynomials and factor by grouping. To factor $x^2 + 8x + 15$ using this method, we proceed as follows.

1. First, identify b as the coefficient of the x-term, and c as the last term. For trinomials of the form $x^2 + bx + c$, we call c the **key number.**

$$\left.\begin{array}{l} x^2 + bx + c \\ \quad\;\;\downarrow \quad\;\; \downarrow \\ x^2 + 8x + 15 \end{array}\right\} b = 8 \text{ and } c = 15$$

2. Now find two integers whose product is the key number, 15, and whose sum is $b = 8$. Since the integers must have a positive product and a positive sum, we consider only positive factors of 15.

Key number = 15	$b = 8$
Positive factors of 15	**Sum of the positive factors of 15**
$1 \cdot 15 = 15$	$1 + 15 = 16$
$3 \cdot 5 = 15$	$3 + 5 = 8$

The second row of the table contains the correct pair of integers 3 and 5, whose product is the key number 15 and whose sum is $b = 8$.

3. Express the middle term, $8x$, of the trinomial as the *sum of two terms,* using the integers 3 and 5 found in step 2 as coefficients of the two terms.

$$x^2 + 8x + 15 = x^2 + 3x + 5x + 15 \quad \text{Express } 8x \text{ as } 3x + 5x.$$

4. Factor the equivalent four-term polynomial by grouping:

$$x^2 + 3x + 5x + 15 = x(x + 3) + 5(x + 3) \quad \text{Factor } x \text{ out of } x^2 + 3x \text{ and 5 out of } 5x + 15.$$

$$= (x + 3)(x + 5) \quad \text{Factor out } x + 3.$$

Check the factorization by multiplying.

The grouping method is an alternative to the method for factoring trinomials discussed earlier in this section. It is especially useful when the constant term, c, has many factors.

Factoring Trinomials of the Form $x^2 + bx + c$ Using Grouping

To factor a trinomial that has a leading coefficient of 1:

1. Identify b and the key number, c.
2. Find two integers whose product is the key number and whose sum is b.
3. Express the middle term, bx, as the sum (or difference) of two terms. Enter the two numbers found in step 2 as coefficients of x in the form shown below. Then factor the equivalent four-term polynomial by grouping.

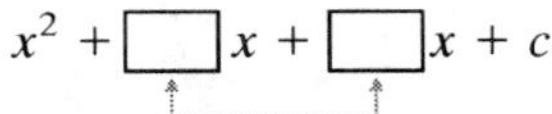

The product of these numbers must be c, and their sum must be b.

4. Check the factorization using multiplication.

EXAMPLE 10 Factor by grouping: $a^2 + a - 20$

Strategy We will express the middle term, a, of the trinomial as the difference of two carefully chosen terms.

WHY We want to produce an equivalent four-term polynomial that can be factored by grouping.

Solution

Since $a^2 + a - 20 = a^2 + 1a - 20$, we identify b as 1 and the key number c as -20. We must find two integers whose product is -20 and whose sum is 1. Since the integers must have a negative product, their signs must be different.

Key number = −20 **b = 1**

Factors of −20	Sum of the factors of −20
$1(-20) = -20$	$1 + (-20) = -19$
$2(-10) = -20$	$2 + (-10) = -8$
$4(-5) = -20$	$4 + (-5) = -1$
$5(-4) = -20$	$5 + (-4) = 1$
$10(-2) = -20$	$10 + (-2) = 8$
$20(-1) = -20$	$20 + (-1) = 19$

The fourth row of the table contains the correct pair of integers 5 and -4, whose product is -20 and whose sum is 1. They serve as the coefficients of $5a$ and $-4a$, the two terms that we use to represent the middle term, a, of the trinomial.

$$a^2 + a - 20 = a^2 + 5a - 4a - 20$$ Express the middle term, a, as $5a - 4a$.

$$= a(a + 5) - 4(a + 5)$$ Factor a out of $a^2 + 5a$ and -4 out of $-4a - 20$.

$$= (a + 5)(a - 4)$$ Factor out $a + 5$.

Check the factorization by multiplying.

Self Check 10

Factor by grouping: $m^2 + m - 42$

Now Try **Problem 61**

Self Check 10 Answer
$(m + 7)(m - 6)$

Teaching Example 10 Factor by grouping: $x^2 - 15x + 14$
Answer:
$(x - 1)(x - 14)$

Success Tip We could also express the middle term as $-4a + 5a$. We obtain the same binomial factors, but in reverse order.

$$a^2 - 4a + 5a - 20$$
$$= a(a - 4) + 5(a - 4)$$
$$= (a - 4)(a + 5)$$

Self Check 11

Factor by grouping: $q^2 - 2qt - 24t^2$

Now Try **Problem 63**

Self Check 11 Answer
$(q + 4t)(q - 6t)$

Teaching Example 11 Factor by grouping: $x^2 + 7xy + 12y^2$
Answer:
$(x + 3y)(x + 4y)$

EXAMPLE 11 Factor by grouping: $x^2 - 4xy - 5y^2$

Strategy We will express the middle term, $-4xy$, of the trinomial as the sum of two carefully chosen terms.

WHY We want to produce an equivalent four-term polynomial that can be factored by grouping.

Key number = −5 $b = -4$

Factors	Sum
$-5(1) = -5$	$-5 + 1 = -4$

Solution

In $x^2 - 4xy - 5y^2$, we identify b as -4 and the key number c as -5. We must find two integers whose product is -5 and whose sum is -4. Such a pair is -5 and 1. They serve as the coefficients of $-5xy$ and $1xy$, the two terms that we use to represent the middle term, $-4xy$, of the trinomial.

$x^2 - 4xy - 5y^2 = x^2 - 5xy + 1xy - 5y^2$ Express the middle term, $-4xy$, as $-5xy + 1xy$. ($1xy - 5xy$ could also be used.)

$= x(x - 5y) + y(x - 5y)$ Factor x out of $x^2 - 5xy$ and y out of $1xy - 5y^2$.

$= (x - 5y)(x + y)$ Factor out $x - 5y$.

Check the factorization by multiplying.

Self Check 12

Factor completely: $3m^3 - 27m^2 + 24m$

Now Try **Problem 66**

Self Check 12 Answer
$3m(m - 8)(m - 1)$

Teaching Example 12 Factor completely: $5x^3 + 5x^2 - 100x$
Answer:
$5x(x + 5)(x - 4)$

EXAMPLE 12 Factor completely: $2x^3 - 20x^2 + 18x$

Strategy We will factor out the GCF, $2x$, first. Then we will factor the resulting trinomial using the grouping method.

WHY The first step in factoring any polynomial is to factor out the GCF.

Solution

We begin by factoring out the GCF, $2x$, from $2x^3 - 20x^2 + 18x$.

$$2x^3 - 20x^2 + 18x = 2x(x^2 - 10x + 9)$$

Key number = 9 $b = -10$

Factors	Sum
$-9(-1) = 9$	$-9 + (-1) = -10$

To factor $x^2 - 10x + 9$ by grouping, we must find two integers whose product is the key number 9 and whose sum is $b = -10$. Such a pair is -9 and -1.

$x^2 - 10x + 9 = x^2 - 9x - 1x + 9$ Express $-10x$ as $-9x - 1x$. ($-1x - 9x$ could also be used.)

$= x(x - 9) - 1(x - 9)$ Factor x out of $x^2 - 9x$ and -1 out of $-1x + 9$.

$= (x - 9)(x - 1)$ Factor out $x - 9$.

The complete factorization of the original trinomial is

$$2x^3 - 20x^2 + 18x = 2x(x - 9)(x - 1)$$ Don't forget to write the GCF, 2x.

Check the factorization by multiplying.

ANSWERS TO SELF CHECKS

1. $(y + 1)(y + 6)$ **2.** $(p - 3)(p - 2)$ **3.** $(p + 6)(p - 3)$ **4.** $(q - 6)(q + 4)$ **5.** $-(x - 4)(x - 7)$ **6.** $(s + 7t)(s - t)$ **7.** $4m^3(m + 4)(m - 2)$ **8.** $t(t - 2)(t + 6)$ **9.** not possible; prime trinomial **10.** $(m + 7)(m - 6)$ **11.** $(q + 4t)(q - 6t)$ **12.** $3m(m - 8)(m - 1)$

SECTION 6.9 STUDY SET

VOCABULARY

Fill in the blanks.

1. A polynomial with three terms is called a trinomial.
2. In the polynomial $x^2 - x - 6$, x^2 is the first term, $-x$ is the middle term, and -6 is the last term.
3. The statement $x^2 - x - 12 = (x - 4)(x + 3)$ shows that $x^2 - x - 12$ factors into the product of two binomials.
4. A trinomial is said to be factored completely when no factor can be factored further.
5. A prime polynomial cannot be factored by using only integer coefficients.
6. When factoring trinomials of the form $x^2 + bx + c$ by the grouping method, the number c is called the key number.

CONCEPTS

Fill in the blanks.

7. Two factorizations of 4 that involve only positive numbers are $4 \cdot 1$ and $2 \cdot 2$. Two factorizations of 4 that involve only negative numbers are $-4(-1)$ and $-2(-2)$.
8. Before attempting to factor a trinomial, be sure that the exponents are written in descending order.
9. Before attempting to factor a trinomial into two binomials, always factor out any common factors first.
10. To factor $x^2 + x - 56$, we must find two integers whose product is -56 and whose sum is 1.
11. Two factors of 18 whose sum is -9 are -6 and -3.

12. Complete the table.

Factors of 8	Sum of the factors of 8
1(8)	$1 + 8 = 9$
2(4)	$2 + 4 = 6$
$-1(-8)$	$-1 + (-8) = -9$
$-2(-4)$	$-2 + (-4) = -6$

13. Complete the table.

Factors of -9	Sum of the factors of -9
$1(-9)$	$1 + (-9) = -8$
$3(-3)$	$3 + (-3) = 0$
$-1(9)$	$-1 + 9 = 8$

14. Find two integers whose:
    a. product is 10 and whose sum is 7. 5, 2
    b. product is 8 and whose sum is -6. $-2, -4$
    c. product is -6 and whose sum is 1. $3, -2$
    d. product is -9 and whose sum is -8. $1, -9$
15. Given: $x^2 + 8x + 15$
    a. What is the coefficient of the x^2 term? 1
    b. What is the last term? What is the coefficient of the middle term? 15, 8
    c. What two integers have a product of 15 and a sum of 8? 5, 3
16. What trinomial has the factorization of $(x + 8)(x - 2)$? $x^2 + 6x - 16$

Selected exercises available online at www.webassign.net/brookscole

Complete each factorization.

17. $x^2 + 3x + 2 = (x + 2)(x + 1)$

18. $y^2 + 4y + 3 = (y + 3)(y + 1)$

19. $t^2 - 9t + 14 = (t - 7)(t - 2)$

20. $c^2 - 9c + 8 = (c - 8)(c - 1)$

21. $a^2 + 6a - 16 = (a + 8)(a - 2)$

22. $x^2 - 3x - 40 = (x - 8)(x + 5)$

NOTATION

Complete each factorization.

23. $6 + 5x + x^2 = x^2 + 5x + 6$
$= (x + 3)(x + 2)$

▶ **24.** $-a^2 - a + 20 = -(a^2 + a - 20)$
$= -(a + 5)(a - 4)$

GUIDED PRACTICE

Factor each trinomial. See Example 1.

25. $z^2 + 12z + 11$ $(z + 11)(z + 1)$

▶ **26.** $x^2 + 7x + 10$ $(x + 5)(x + 2)$

27. $p^2 + 9p + 14$ $(p + 2)(p + 7)$

28. $q^2 + 11q + 24$ $(q + 3)(q + 8)$

Factor each trinomial. See Example 2.

29. $m^2 - 5m + 6$ $(m - 3)(m - 2)$

30. $n^2 - 7n + 10$ $(n - 5)(n - 2)$

31. $y^2 - 13y + 30$ $(y - 3)(y - 10)$

▶ **32.** $r^2 - 10r + 24$ $(r - 4)(r - 6)$

Factor each trinomial. See Example 3.

▶ **33.** $b^2 + 6b - 7$ $(b + 7)(b - 1)$

34. $x^2 + 5x - 24$ $(x + 8)(x - 3)$

35. $a^2 + 6a - 16$ $(a + 8)(a - 2)$

36. $b^2 + 2b - 99$ $(b + 11)(b - 9)$

Factor each trinomial. See Example 4.

▶ **37.** $a^2 - 4a - 5$ $(a - 5)(a + 1)$

▶ **38.** $t^2 - 5t - 50$ $(t - 10)(t + 5)$

39. $z^2 - 3z - 18$ $(z - 6)(z + 3)$

40. $s^2 - 2s - 120$ $(s - 12)(s + 10)$

Factor each trinomial. See Example 5.

41. $-x^2 - 7x - 10$ $-(x + 5)(x + 2)$

42. $-x^2 + 9x - 20$ $-(x - 5)(x - 4)$

43. $-t^2 - 15t + 34$ $-(t + 17)(t - 2)$

▶ **44.** $-t^2 - t + 30$ $-(t + 6)(t - 5)$

Factor each trinomial. See Example 6.

45. $x^2 + 4xy + 4y^2$ $(x + 2y)(x + 2y)$

▶ **46.** $a^2 + 10ab + 9b^2$ $(a + 9b)(a + b)$

47. $m^2 + 3mn - 10n^2$ $(m + 5n)(m - 2n)$

▶ **48.** $m^2 - mn - 12n^2$ $(m - 4n)(m + 3n)$

Factor each trinomial. See Example 7.

49. $2x^2 + 10x + 12$ $2(x + 3)(x + 2)$

▶ **50.** $3y^2 - 21y + 18$ $3(y - 6)(y - 1)$

51. $5p^3 + 25p^2 - 70p$ $5p(p + 7)(p - 2)$

52. $3m^4 - 9m^3 - 54m^2$ $3m^2(m + 3)(m - 6)$

Factor each trinomial. See Example 8.

53. $4rx + r^2 + 3x^2$ $(r + 3x)(r + x)$

54. $a^2 + 5b^2 + 6ab$ $(a + b)(a + 5b)$

▶ **55.** $-3a^2b + a^3 + 2ab^2$ $a(a - 2b)(a - b)$

56. $-13yz^2 + y^2z - 14z^3$ $z(y - 14z)(y + z)$

Factor each trinomial, if possible. See Example 9.

▶ **57.** $r^2 - 9r - 12$ prime

58. $u^2 + 10u + 15$ prime

59. $r^2 - 2rs + 4s^2$ prime

60. $m^2 + 3mn - 20n^2$ prime

Factor each trinomial by grouping. See Examples 10–12.

61. $p^2 + p - 30$ $(p + 6)(p - 5)$

62. $q^2 - 10q + 24$ $(q - 4)(q - 6)$

63. $m^2 - 3mn - 4n^2$ $(m - 4n)(m + n)$

▶ **64.** $r^2 - 2rs - 15s^2$ $(r + 3s)(r - 5s)$

65. $3x^3 - 27x^2 + 60x$ $3x(x - 4)(x - 5)$

66. $2x^3 + 4x^2 - 70x$ $2x(x + 7)(x - 5)$

67. $4y^3 - 28y^2 + 40y$ $4y(y - 5)(y - 2)$

68. $5y^3 + 45y^2 + 100y$ $5y(y + 5)(y + 4)$

TRY IT YOURSELF

Completely factor each of the following expressions. If an expression is prime, so indicate.

69. $a^2 - 10a - 39$ $(a - 13)(a + 3)$

▶ **70.** $v^2 + 9v + 15$ prime

71. $s^2 + 11s - 26$ $(s + 13)(s - 2)$

▶ **72.** $y^2 + 8y + 12$ $(y + 6)(y + 2)$

73. $r^2 - 2r + 4$ prime

74. $m^2 + 3m - 10$ $(m + 5)(m - 2)$

75. $a^2 - 4ab - 12b^2$ $(a - 6b)(a + 2b)$

▶ **76.** $p^2 + pq - 6q^2$ $(p + 3q)(p - 2q)$

77. $-r^2 + 14r - 40$ $-(r - 10)(r - 4)$

78. $-r^2 + 14r - 45$ $-(r - 9)(r - 5)$

79. $-a^2 - 4ab - 3b^2$ $-(a + 3b)(a + b)$

80. $-a^2 - 6ab - 5b^2$ $-(a + b)(a + 5b)$

81. $4 - 5x + x^2$ $(x - 4)(x - 1)$

82. $y^2 + 5 + 6y$ $(y + 5)(y + 1)$

83. $10y + 9 + y^2$ $(y + 9)(y + 1)$

▶ **84.** $x^2 - 13 - 12x$ $(x - 13)(x + 1)$

85. $-r^2 + 2 + r$ $-(r - 2)(r + 1)$

86. $u^2 - 3 + 2u$ $(u + 3)(u - 1)$

87. $-5a^2 + 25a - 30$ $-5(a - 3)(a - 2)$

▶ **88.** $-2b^2 + 20b - 18$ $-2(b - 9)(b - 1)$

89. $-4x^2y - 4x^3 + 24xy^2$ $-4x(x + 3y)(x - 2y)$

▶ **90.** $3x^2y^3 + 3x^3y^2 - 6xy^4$ $3xy^2(x + 2y)(x - y)$

Choose the correct method from Section 6.8 or 6.9 to factor completely each expression. If an expression is prime, so indicate.

91. $m^2 - m - 12$
$(m - 4)(m + 3)$

92. $u^2 + u - 42$
$(u + 7)(u - 6)$

93. $3a^2b + 3ab^2$
$3ab(a + b)$

94. $3p^2 - 12p + 6$
$3(p^2 - 4p + 2)$

95. $-4a^2 - 8a$
$-4a(a + 2)$

96. $3p + p^2 + 3q + pq$
$(p + q)(3 + p)$

97. $-x^2 + 6xy + 7y^2$
$-(x - 7y)(x + y)$

98. $-x^2 - 10xy + 11y^2$
$-(x + 11y)(x - y)$

99. $12xy + 4x^2y - 72y$
$4y(x + 6)(x - 3)$

100. $48xy + 6xy^2 + 96x$
$6x(y + 4)(y + 4)$

101. $3ap + 2p + 3aq + 2q$
$(3a + 2)(p + q)$

102. $-9abc - 9ac^2 + 3bc + 3c^2$
$-3c(b + c)(3a - 1)$

103. $3z^2 - 15z + 12$
$3(z - 4)(z - 1)$

104. $5m^2 + 45m - 50$
$5(m + 10)(m - 1)$

APPLICATIONS

105. PETS The cage shown is used for transporting dogs. Its volume is $(x^3 + 12x^2 + 27x)$ in.^{3}. The dimensions of the cage can be found by factoring this expression. If the cage is longer than it is tall and taller than it is wide, write expressions that represent its length, height, and width.

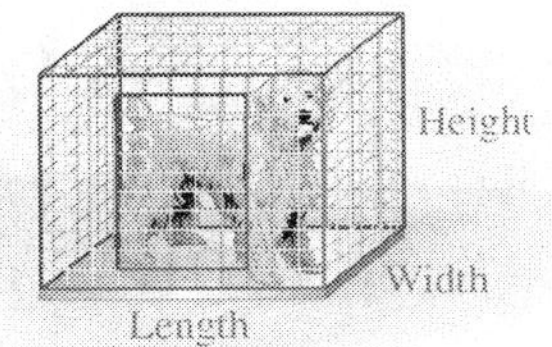

$(x + 9)$ in., $(x + 3)$ in., x in.

106. CARPOOLING The average rate at which a carpool van travels and the distance it covers are given in the table in terms of t. Factor the expression representing the distance traveled and then complete the table.

Rate (mi/hr)	Time (hr)	Distance traveled (mi)
$t + 11$	$t + 5$	$t^2 + 16t + 55$

WRITING

107. Explain what it means when we say that a trinomial is the product of two binomials. Give an example.

108. Are $2x^2 - 12x + 16$ and $x^2 - 6x + 8$ factored in the same way? Explain why or why not.

109. When factoring $x^2 - 2x - 3$, one student got $(x - 3)(x + 1)$, and another got $(x + 1)(x - 3)$. Are both answers acceptable? Explain.

110. Explain how to use multiplication to check the factorization of a trinomial.

111. A student begins to factor a trinomial as shown below. Explain why the student is off to a bad start.

$$x^2 - 2x - 63 = (x - \quad)(x - \quad)$$

112. Explain why the given trinomial is not factored completely.

$$3x^2 - 3x - 60 = 3(x^2 - x - 20)$$

REVIEW

Graph the solution of each inequality on the number line.

113. $x - 3 > 5$

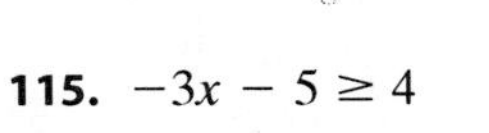

114. $x + 4 \le 3$

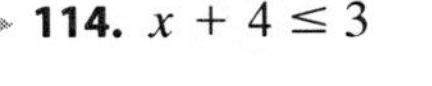
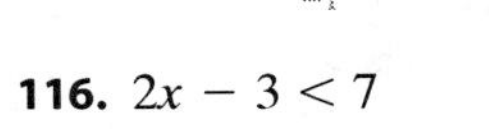

115. $-3x - 5 \ge 4$

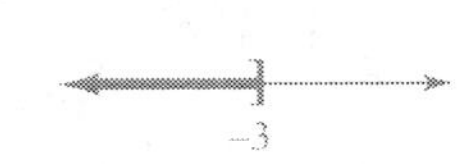

116. $2x - 3 < 7$

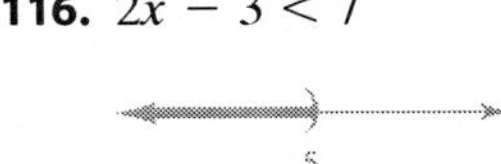

SECTION 6.10
Factoring Trinomials of the Form $ax^2 + bx + c$

Objectives

1. Factor trinomials using the trial-and-check method.
2. Factor trinomials after factoring out the GCF.
3. Factor trinomials using the grouping method.

In this section, we will factor trinomials with leading coefficients other than 1, such as $2x^2 + 5x + 3$ and $6a^2 - 17a + 5$. Two methods are used to factor these trinomials. With the first method, educated guesses are made. These guesses are checked by multiplication. The correct factorization is determined by a process of elimination. The second method is an extension of factoring by grouping.

1 Factor trinomials using the trial-and-check method.

In the work below, we find the products $(2x + 1)(x + 3)$ and $(2x + 3)(x + 1)$. There are several observations that can be made when we compare the results.

$$(2x + 1)(x + 3) = 2x^2 + 6x + x + 3 = 2x^2 + 7x + 3 \qquad (2x + 3)(x + 1) = 2x^2 + 2x + 3x + 3 = 2x^2 + 5x + 3$$

In each case, the result is a trinomial, and

- the first terms are the same $(2x^2)$,
- the last terms are the same (3), and
- the middle terms are different ($7x$ and $5x$).

These observations indicate that when the last terms in $(2x + 1)(x + 3)$ are interchanged to form $(2x + 3)(x + 1)$, only the middle terms of the products are different. This fact is helpful when factoring trinomials using the *trial-and-check method.*

Self Check 1

Factor: $3x^2 + 7x + 2$

Now Try **Problem 27**

Self Check 1 Answer
$(3x + 1)(x + 2)$

Teaching Example 1 Factor: $3x^2 + 8x + 5$
Answer:
$(3x + 5)(x + 1)$

EXAMPLE 1 Factor: $2x^2 + 5x + 3$

Strategy We will assume that $2x^2 + 5x + 3$ is the product of two binomials and we will use a systematic method to find their terms.

WHY Since the terms of $2x^2 + 5x + 3$ do not have a common factor (other than 1), the only option available is to try to factor it as the product of two binomials.

Solution

Since the first term is $2x^2$, the first terms of the binomial factors must be $2x$ and x. To fill in the blanks, we must find two factors of 3 that will give a middle term of $5x$.

$(2x \quad)(x \quad)$ Because $2x \cdot x$ will give $2x^2$.

Because each term of the trinomial is positive, we need only consider positive factors of the last term. Since the positive factors of 3 are 1 and 3, there are two possible factorizations.

$$(2x + 1)(x + 3) \quad \text{or} \quad (2x + 3)(x + 1)$$

The first possibility is incorrect: When we find the outer and inner products and combine like terms, we obtain an incorrect middle term of $7x$.

Outer: $6x$

$(2x + 1)(x + 3)$ Multiply and add to find the middle term: $6x + x = 7x$.

Inner: x

The second possibility is correct, because it gives a middle term of $5x$.

Outer: $2x$

$(2x + 3)(x + 1)$ Multiply and add to find the middle term: $2x + 3x = 5x$.

Inner: $3x$

Thus,

$$2x^2 + 5x + 3 = (2x + 3)(x + 1)$$

EXAMPLE 2 Factor: $6a^2 - 17a + 5$

Strategy We will assume that $6a^2 - 17a + 5$ is the product of two binomials and we will use a systematic method to find their terms.

WHY Since the terms of $6a^2 - 17a + 5$ do not have a common factor (other than 1), the only option available is to try to factor it as the product of two binomials.

Solution

Since the first term is $6a^2$, the first terms of the binomial factors must be $6a$ and a or $3a$ and $2a$. To fill in the blanks, we must find two factors of 5 that will give a middle term of $-17a$.

$$(6a \quad)(a \quad) \quad \text{or} \quad (3a \quad)(2a \quad)$$

Because the sign of the last term is positive and the sign of the middle term is negative, we need only consider negative factors of the last term. Since the negative factors of 5 are -1 and -5, there are four possible factorizations.

$(6a - 1)(a - 5)$ (outer: $-30a$, inner: $-a$) $-30a - a = -31a$.

$(6a - 5)(a - 1)$ (outer: $-6a$, inner: $-5a$) $-6a - 5a = -11a$.

$(3a - 1)(2a - 5)$ (outer: $-15a$, inner: $-2a$) $-15a - 2a = -17a$.

$(3a - 5)(2a - 1)$ (outer: $-3a$, inner: $-10a$) $-3a - 10a = -13a$.

Only the possibility shown in blue gives the correct middle term of $-17a$. Thus,

$$6a^2 - 17a + 5 = (3a - 1)(2a - 5)$$

Self Check 2

Factor: $6x^2 - 7x + 2$

Now Try **Problem 32**

Self Check 2 Answer
$(3x - 2)(2x - 1)$

Teaching Example 2 Factor: $3x^2 - 10x + 8$
Answer:
$(3x - 4)(x - 2)$

EXAMPLE 3 Factor: $3y^2 - 7y - 6$

Strategy We will assume that $3y^2 - 7y - 6$ is the product of two binomials and we will use a systematic method to find their terms.

WHY Since the terms of $3y^2 - 7y - 6$ do not have a common factor (other than 1), the only option available is to try to factor it as the product of two binomials.

Solution

Since the first term is $3y^2$, the first terms of the binomial factors must be $3y$ and y.

$(3y \quad)(y \quad)$ Because $3y \cdot y$ will give $3y^2$.

The second terms of the binomials must be two integers whose product is -6. There are four such pairs: $1(-6)$, $-1(6)$, $2(-3)$, and $-2(3)$. When these pairs are entered, and then reversed, as second terms of the binomials, there are eight possibilities to consider. Four of them can be discarded because they include a binomial whose terms have a common factor. If $3y^2 - 7y - 6$ does not have a common factor, neither can any of its binomial factors.

For the factors −1 and 6: $(3y - 1)(y + 6)$ (outer: $18y$, inner: $-y$; $18y - y = 17y$) or $(3y + 6)(y - 1)$ (A common factor of 3)

Self Check 3

Factor: $5a^2 - 23a - 10$

Now Try **Problem 36**

Self Check 3 Answer
$(5a + 2)(a - 5)$

Teaching Example 3 Factor: $7x^2 - 5x - 2$
Answer:
$(7x + 2)(x - 1)$

$-18y$

For the factors 1 and −6: $(3y + 1)(y - 6)$ or $(3y - 6)(y + 1)$

y A common factor of 3

$-18y + y = -17y$

$9y$

For the factors −2 and 3: $(3y - 2)(y + 3)$ or $(3y + 3)(y - 2)$

$-2y$ A common factor of 3

$9y - 2y = 7y$

$-9y$

For the factors 2 and −3: $(3y + 2)(y - 3)$ or $(3y - 3)(y + 2)$

$2y$ A common factor of 3

$-9y + 2y = -7y$

Only the possibility shown in blue gives the correct middle term of $-7y$. Thus,

$$3y^2 - 7y - 6 = (3y + 2)(y - 3)$$

Check the factorization by multiplication.

> ***Success Tip*** If a trinomial does not have a common factor, the terms of each of its binomial factors will not have a common factor.

Self Check 4

Factor: $4x^2 + 4xy - 3y^2$

Now Try **Problem 39**

Self Check 4 Answer

$(2x + 3y)(2x - y)$

Teaching Example 4 Factor: $6x^2 + 7xy - 20y^2$

Answer:

$(3x - 4y)(2x + 5y)$

EXAMPLE 4 Factor: $4b^2 + 8bc - 45c^2$

Strategy We will assume that $4b^2 + 8bc - 45c^2$ is the product of two binomials and we will use a systematic method to find their terms.

WHY Since the terms of $4b^2 + 8bc - 45c^2$ do not have a common factor (other than 1), the only option available is to try to factor it as the product of two binomials.

Solution

Since the first term is $4b^2$, the first terms of the factors must be $4b$ and b or $2b$ and $2b$.

$$(4b \quad)(b \quad) \quad \text{or} \quad (2b \quad)(2b \quad)$$ Because $4b \cdot b$ or $2b \cdot 2b$ give $4b^2$.

To fill in the blanks, we must find two factors of $-45c^2$ that will give a middle term of $8bc$.

Since $-45c^2$ has many factors, there are many possible combinations for the last terms of the binomial factors. The signs of the factors must be different, because the last term of the trinomial is negative.

If we pick factors of $4b$ and b for the first terms, and $-c$ and $45c$ for the last terms, the multiplication gives an incorrect middle term of $179bc$. So the factorization is incorrect.

$180bc$

$(4b - c)(b + 45c)$ $180bc - bc = 179bc$

$-bc$

If we pick factors of $4b$ and b for the first terms and $15c$ and $-3c$ for the last terms, the multiplication gives an incorrect middle term of $3bc$.

$-12bc$

$(4b + 15c)(b - 3c)$ $-12bc + 15bc = 3bc$

$15bc$

If we pick factors of $2b$ and $2b$ for the first terms and $-5c$ and $9c$ for the last terms, we have

$18bc$

$(2b - 5c)(2b + 9c)$ $18bc - 10bc = 8bc$

$-10bc$

which gives the correct middle term of $8bc$. Thus,

$$4b^2 + 8bc - 45c^2 = (2b - 5c)(2b + 9c)$$

Check by multiplication.

Because some guesswork is often necessary, it is difficult to give specific rules for factoring trinomials with a lead coefficient other than 1. However, the following hints are helpful.

Factoring $ax^2 + bx + c$ $(a \neq 1)$

1. Write the trinomial in descending powers of the variable and factor out any GCF (including -1 if that is necessary to make the leading coefficient positive).
2. Attempt to write the trinomial as *the product of two binomials*. The coefficients of the first terms of each binomial factor must be factors of a, and the last terms must be factors of c.

Factors of a

$(\square x + \square)(\square x + \square)$

Factors of c

3. If the sign of the last term of the trinomial is positive, the signs between the terms of the binomial factors are the same as the sign of the middle term. If the sign of the last term is negative, the signs between the terms of the binomial factors are opposite.
4. Try combinations of coefficients of the first terms and last terms until you find one that gives the middle term of the trinomial. If no combination works, the trinomial is prime.
5. Check the factorization by multiplying.

2 Factor trinomials after factoring out the GCF.

Self Check 5

Factor: $12y - 2y^3 - 2y^2$

Now Try **Problem 43**

Self Check 5 Answer

$-2y(y + 3)(y - 2)$

Teaching Example 5 Factor: $12x - 10x^3 - 26x^2$

Answer:

$-2x(5x - 2)(x + 3)$

EXAMPLE 5 Factor: $2x^2 - 8x^3 + 3x$

Strategy We will write the trinomial in descending powers of x and factor out the common factor, $-x$.

WHY It is easier to factor trinomials that have a positive leading coefficient.

Solution

We write the trinomial in descending powers of x

$$-8x^3 + 2x^2 + 3x$$

and we factor out the negative of the GCF, which is $-x$.

$$-8x^3 + 2x^2 + 3x = -x(8x^2 - 2x - 3)$$

We must now factor $8x^2 - 2x - 3$. Its factorization has the form

$$(x \quad)(8x \quad) \quad \text{or} \quad (2x \quad)(4x \quad)$$ Because $x \cdot 8x$ or $2x \cdot 4x$ will give $8x^2$.

To fill in the blanks, we find two factors of the last term of the trinomial (-3) that will give a middle term of $-2x$. Because the sign of the last term is negative, the signs within its binomial factors will be different. If we pick factors of $2x$ and $4x$ for the first terms and 1 and -3 for the last terms, we have

$-6x$

$$(2x + 1)(4x - 3)$$ $-6x + 4x = -2x$.

$4x$

which gives the correct middle term of $-2x$, so it is correct.

$$8x^2 - 2x - 3 = (2x + 1)(4x - 3)$$

We can now give the complete factorization.

$$-8x^3 + 2x^2 + 3x = -x(8x^2 - 2x - 3)$$
$$= -x(2x + 1)(4x - 3)$$

Check by multiplication.

3 Factor trinomials using the grouping method.

The method of factoring by grouping can be used to help factor trinomials of the form $ax^2 + bx + c$. For example, to factor $2x^2 + 5x + 3$, we proceed as follows.

1. We find the product ac: In $2x^2 + 5x + 3$, $a = 2$, $b = 5$, and $c = 3$, so $ac = 2(3) = 6$. This number is called the **key number.**
2. Next, find two numbers whose product is $ac = 6$ and whose sum is $b = 5$. Since the numbers must have a positive product and a positive sum, we consider only positive factors of 6. The correct factors are 2 and 3.

Positive factors of 6	Sum of the factors of 6
$1 \cdot 6 = 6$	$1 + 6 = 7$
$2 \cdot 3 = 6$	$2 + 3 = 5$

3. Use the factors 2 and 3 as coefficients of two terms to be placed between $2x^2$ and 3:

$$2x^2 + 5x + 3 = 2x^2 + 2x + 3x + 3$$ Express $5x$ as $2x + 3x$.

4. Factor by grouping:

$$2x^2 + 2x + 3x + 3 = 2x(x + 1) + 3(x + 1)$$ Factor $2x$ out of $2x^2 + 2x$ and 3 out of $3x + 3$.

$$= (x + 1)(2x + 3)$$ Factor out $x + 1$.

So $2x^2 + 5x + 3 = (x + 1)(2x + 3)$. Verify this factorization by multiplication.

Factoring $ax^2 + bx + c$ by Grouping

1. Write the trinomial in descending powers of the variable and factor out any GCF (including -1 if that is necessary to make the leading coefficient positive).
2. Calculate the key number ac.
3. Find two numbers whose product is the key number found in step 2 and whose sum is the coefficient of the middle term of the trinomial.
4. Write the numbers in the blanks of the form shown below, and then factor the polynomial by grouping.

$$ax^2 + \square x + \square x + c$$

The product of these numbers must be ac and their sum must be b.

5. Check the factorization using multiplication.

EXAMPLE 6 Factor: $10x^2 + 13x - 3$

Strategy We will express the middle term, $13x$, of the trinomial as the sum of two carefully chosen terms.

WHY We want to produce an equivalent four-term polynomial that can be factored by grouping.

Solution

Since $a = 10$ and $c = -3$ in the trinomial, $ac = -30$. We now find two factors of -30 whose sum is 13. Two such factors are 15 and -2. We use these factors as coefficients of two terms to be placed between $10x^2$ and -3.

$$10x^2 + 13x - 3 = 10x^2 + 15x - 2x - 3$$ Express $13x$ as $15x - 2x$.

Finally, we factor by grouping.

$$10x^2 + 15x - 2x - 3 = 5x(2x + 3) - 1(2x + 3)$$ Factor out $5x$ from $10x^2 + 15x$. Factor out -1 from $-2x - 3$.

$$= (2x + 3)(5x - 1)$$ Factor out $(2x + 3)$.

So $10x^2 + 13x - 3 = (2x + 3)(5x - 1)$. Check the result.

Self Check 6

Factor: $15a^2 + 17a - 4$

Now Try **Problem 51**

Self Check 6 Answer
$(3a + 4)(5a - 1)$

Teaching Example 6 Factor: $6x^2 + 7x - 24$
Answer:
$(3x + 8)(2x - 3)$

EXAMPLE 7 Factor: $12x^5 - 17x^4 + 6x^3$

Strategy We will factor out the GCF, x^3, first. Then we will factor the resulting trinomial using the grouping method.

WHY The first step in factoring any polynomial is to factor out the GCF.

Solution

First, we factor out the GCF, which is x^3.

$$12x^5 - 17x^4 + 6x^3 = x^3(12x^2 - 17x + 6)$$

Self Check 7

Factor: $21a^4 - 13a^3 + 2a^2$

Now Try **Problem 56**

Self Check 7 Answer
$a^2(7a - 2)(3a - 1)$

Teaching Example 7 Factor: $10x^4 - 17x^3 + 3x^2$
Answer:
$x^2(5x - 1)(2x - 3)$

To factor $12x^2 - 17x + 6$, we need to find two integers whose product is $12(6) = 72$ and whose sum is -17. Two such numbers are -8 and -9.

$$\begin{aligned} 12x^2 - 17x + 6 &= 12x^2 - 8x - 9x + 6 && \text{Express } -17x \text{ as } -8x - 9x. \\ &= 4x(3x - 2) - 3(3x - 2) && \text{Factor out } 4x \text{ and factor out } -3. \\ &= (3x - 2)(4x - 3) && \text{Factor out } 3x - 2. \end{aligned}$$

The complete factorization is

$$12x^5 - 17x^4 + 6x^3 = x^3(3x - 2)(4x - 3) \quad \text{Do not forget to write the GCF, } x^3.$$

Check the result.

ANSWERS TO SELF CHECKS

1. $(3x + 1)(x + 2)$ **2.** $(3x - 2)(2x - 1)$ **3.** $(5a + 2)(a - 5)$ **4.** $(2x + 3y)(2x - y)$ **5.** $-2y(y + 3)(y - 2)$ **6.** $(3a + 4)(5a - 1)$ **7.** $a^2(7a - 2)(3a - 1)$

SECTION 6.10 STUDY SET

VOCABULARY

Fill in the blanks.

1. The trinomial $3x^2 - x - 12$ has a leading coefficient of 3. The last term is -12.
2. The numbers 3 and 2 are factors of the first term of the trinomial $6x^2 + x - 12$.
3. Consider $(x - 2)(5x - 1)$. The product of the outer terms is $-x$ and the product of the inner terms is $-10x$.
4. When we write $2x^2 + 7x + 3$ as $(2x + 1)(x + 3)$, we say that we have factored the trinomial—it has been expressed as the product of two binomials.
5. The middle term of $4x^2 - 7x + 13$ is $-7x$.
6. The sum of the middle terms of the polynomial $4a^2 - 12a - a + 3$ is $-13a$.
7. The GCF of the terms of the trinomial $6b^3 - 3b^2 - 12b$ is $3b$.
8. When factoring the trinomial $ax^2 + bx + c$ by grouping, the product ac is called the key number.

CONCEPTS

Complete each sentence.

9. These coefficients must be factors of 5.

$$5x^2 + 6x - 8 = (\quad x + \quad)(\quad x + \quad)$$

These numbers must be factors of -8.

10. The product of these coefficients must be 15.

$$3x^2 + 16x + 5 = 3x^2 + \quad x + \quad x + 5$$

The sum of these coefficients must be 16.

A trinomial has been partially factored. Complete each statement that describes the type of integers we should consider for the blanks.

11. $5y^2 - 13y + 6 = (5y \square)(y \square)$
Since the last term of the trinomial is positive and the middle term is negative, the integers must be negative factors of 6.
12. $5y^2 + 13y + 6 = (5y \square)(y \square)$
Since the last term of the trinomial is positive and the middle term is positive, the integers must be positive factors of 6.
13. $5y^2 + 7y - 6 = (5y \square)(y \square)$
Since the last term of the trinomial is negative, the signs of the integers will be different.
14. $5y^2 - 7y - 6 = (5y \square)(y \square)$
Since the last term of the trinomial is negative, the signs of the integers will be different.

Complete each factorization.

15. $3a^2 + 13a + 4 = (3a + 1)(a + 4)$
16. $2b^2 + 7b + 6 = (2b + 3)(b + 2)$

17. $4z^2 - 13z + 3 = (z - 3)(4z - 1)$

18. $4t^2 - 4t + 1 = (2t - 1)(2t - 1)$

19. $2m^2 + 5m - 12 = (2m - 3)(m + 4)$

20. $10u^2 - 13u - 3 = (2u - 3)(5u + 1)$

A trinomial is to be factored by the grouping method. Complete each statement that describes the type of integers we should consider for the blanks.

21. $8c^2 - 11c + 3 = 8c^2 + \square c + \square c + 3$

We need to find two integers whose product is 24 and whose sum is −11.

22. $15c^2 + 4c - 4 = 15c^2 + \square c + \square c - 4$

We need to find two integers whose product is −60 and whose sum is 4.

Complete each step of the factorization by grouping.

23. $12t^2 + 17t + 6 = 12t^2 + 9t + 8t + 6$

$= 3t(4t + 3) + 2(4t + 3)$

$= (4t + 3)(3t + 2)$

24. $35t^2 - 11t - 6 = 35t^2 + 10t - 21t - 6$

$= 5t(7t + 2) - 3(7t + 2)$

$= (7t + 2)(5t - 3)$

NOTATION

25. Write a trinomial of the form: $ax^2 + bx + c$

a. where $a = 1$ $x^2 + 2x + 3$ (answers may vary)

b. where $a \neq 1$ $2x^2 + 2x + 3$ (answers may vary)

26. Write the terms of the trinomial $40 - t - 4t^2$ in descending powers of the variable. $-4t^2 - t + 40$

GUIDED PRACTICE

Factor each trinomial. See Example 1.

27. $3a^2 + 13a + 4$
$(3a + 1)(a + 4)$

28. $2b^2 + 7b + 6$
$(2b + 3)(b + 2)$

29. $4z^2 + 13z + 3$
$(z + 3)(4z + 1)$

30. $6y^2 + 7y + 2$
$(3y + 2)(2y + 1)$

Factor each trinomial. See Example 2.

31. $4t^2 - 4t + 1$
$(2t - 1)(2t - 1)$

32. $6x^2 - 7x + 2$
$(3x - 2)(2x - 1)$

33. $2x^2 - 3x + 1$
$(2x - 1)(x - 1)$

34. $2y^2 - 7y + 3$
$(2y - 1)(y - 3)$

Factor each trinomial. See Example 3.

35. $8u^2 - 2u - 15$
$(2u - 3)(4u + 5)$

36. $2x^2 - 3x - 2$
$(2x + 1)(x - 2)$

37. $12y^2 - y - 1$
$(4y + 1)(3y - 1)$

38. $10a^2 - 3a - 4$
$(5a - 4)(2a + 1)$

Factor each trinomial. See Example 4.

39. $6r^2 + rs - 2s^2$
$(3r + 2s)(2r - s)$

40. $4a^2 - 4ab + b^2$
$(2a - b)(2a - b)$

41. $2b^2 - 5bc + 2c^2$
$(2b - c)(b - 2c)$

42. $3m^2 + 5mn + 2n^2$
$(3m + 2n)(m + n)$

Factor each trinomial. See Example 5.

43. $4x^2 + 10x - 6$
$2(2x - 1)(x + 3)$

44. $9x^2 + 21x - 18$
$3(3x - 2)(x + 3)$

45. $-y^3 - 13y^2 - 12y$
$-y(y + 12)(y + 1)$

46. $-2xy^2 - 8xy + 24x$
$-2x(y + 6)(y - 2)$

47. $6x^3 - 15x^2 - 9x$
$3x(2x + 1)(x - 3)$

48. $9y^3 + 3y^2 - 6y$
$3y(3y - 2)(y + 1)$

49. $30r^5 + 63r^4 - 30r^3$
$3r^3(5r - 2)(2r + 5)$

50. $6s^5 - 26s^4 - 20s^3$
$2s^3(3s + 2)(s - 5)$

Factor each trinomial by grouping. See Example 6.

51. $10y^2 - 3y - 1$
$(5y + 1)(2y - 1)$

52. $6m^2 + 19m + 3$
$(6m + 1)(m + 3)$

53. $12y^2 - 5y - 2$
$(3y - 2)(4y + 1)$

54. $10x^2 + 21x - 10$
$(2x + 5)(5x - 2)$

Factor each trinomial by grouping. See Example 7.

55. $12y^4 + y^3 - y^2$
$y^2(3y + 1)(4y - 1)$

56. $36p^3 - 3p^2 - 18p$
$3p(4p - 3)(3p + 2)$

57. $-16m^3n - 20m^2n^2 - 6mn^3$
$-2mn(4m + 3n)(2m + n)$

58. $-84x^4 - 100x^3y - 24x^2y^2$
$-4x^2(3x + y)(7x + 6y)$

TRY IT YOURSELF

Completely factor each of the following expressions. If an expression is prime, so indicate.

59. $4x^2 + 8x + 3$
$(2x + 3)(2x + 1)$

60. $15t^2 - 34t + 8$
$(15t - 4)(t - 2)$

61. $7x^2 - 9x + 2$
$(7x - 2)(x - 1)$

62. $2m^2 + 5m - 10$
prime

63. $10u^2 - 13u - 6$
prime

64. $-5t^2 - 13t - 6$
$-(5t + 3)(t + 2)$

65. $-16y^2 - 10y - 1$
$-(8y + 1)(2y + 1)$

66. $-16m^2 + 14m - 3$
$-(8m - 3)(2m - 1)$

67. $-16x^2 - 16x - 3$
$-(4x + 1)(4x + 3)$

68. $13x^2 + 24xy + 11y^2$
$(13x + 11y)(x + y)$

69. $4b^2 + 15bc - 4c^2$
$(4b - c)(b + 4c)$

70. $18a^2 + 31ab - 10b^2$
$(18a - 5b)(a + 2b)$

71. $12x^2 + 5xy - 3y^2$
$(4x + 3y)(3x - y)$

72. $-13x + 3x^2 - 10$
$(3x + 2)(x - 5)$

73. $-14 + 3a^2 - a$
$(3a - 7)(a + 2)$

74. $15 + 8a^2 - 26a$
$(2a - 5)(4a - 3)$

75. $16 - 40a + 25a^2$
$(5a - 4)(5a - 4)$

76. $2a^2 + 3b^2 + 5ab$
$(2a + 3b)(a + b)$

77. $11uv + 3u^2 + 6v^2$
$(3u + 2v)(u + 3v)$

78. $pq + 6p^2 - q^2$
$(3p - q)(2p + q)$

Choose the correct method from sections 6.8, 6.9, or 6.10 to factor completely each of the following expressions. If an expression is prime, so indicate.

79. $12y^2 + 12 - 25y$ $(4y - 3)(3y - 4)$

80. $18t^3 - 30t^2$ $6t^2(3t - 5)$

81. $6x^2 - 15x + 2xy - 5y$ $(3x + y)(2x - 5)$

82. $12t^2 - 1 - 4t$ $(6t + 1)(2t - 1)$

83. $6a^2 - 10 - 11a$ $(3a + 2)(2a - 5)$

84. $3x^2 + 6 + x$ prime

85. $12p^2 + 5pq - 2q^2$ $(3p + 2q)(4p - q)$

86. $25 + 2u^2 + 3u$ prime

87. $-3a^3 - 6a^2 + 9a$ $-3a(a + 3)(a - 1)$

88. $3m^2 + 4m - 6mn - 8n$ $(m - 2n)(3m + 4)$

89. $-28u^3v^3 + 26u^2v^4 - 6uv^5$ $-2uv^3(7u - 3v)(2u - v)$

90. $9t^3 + 33t^2 - 12t$ $3t(t + 4)(3t - 1)$

91. $-16x^4y^3 + 30x^3y^4 + 4x^2y^5$ $-2x^2y^3(8x + y)(x - 2y)$

92. $22pq + 6p^2 + 12q^2$ $2(3p + 2q)(p + 3q)$

93. $-11mn + 12m^2 + 2n^2$ $(3m - 2n)(4m - n)$

94. $-18b + 36b^3 - 3b^2$ $3b(4b - 3)(3b + 2)$

APPLICATIONS

95. OFFICE FURNITURE The area of the desktop shown below is given by the expression $(4x^2 + 20x - 11)$ in.^{2}. Factor this expression to find the expressions that represent its length and width. Then determine the difference in the length and width of the desktop. $(2x + 11)$ in., $(2x - 1)$ in.; 12 in.

96. STORAGE The volume of the 8-foot-wide portable storage container shown below is given by the expression $(72x^2 + 120x - 400)$ ft^3. If its dimensions can be determined by factoring the expression, find the height and the length of the container. $(3x - 5)$ ft, $(3x + 10)$ ft

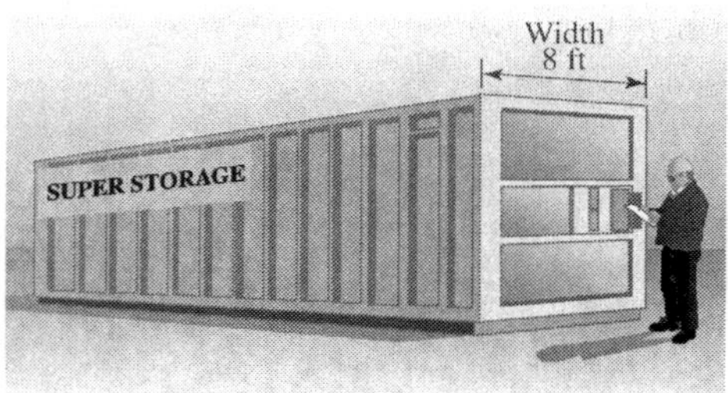

WRITING

97. A student begins to factor a trinomial as shown below. Explain why the student is off to a bad start.

$$3x^2 - 5x - 2 = (3x - \square)(x - \square)$$

98. Two students factor $2x^2 + 20x + 42$ and get two different answers:

$$(2x + 6)(x + 7) \quad \text{and} \quad (x + 3)(2x + 14)$$

Do both answers check? Why don't they agree? Is either answer completely correct? Explain.

99. Why is the process of factoring $6x^2 - 5x - 6$ more complicated than the process of factoring $x^2 - 5x - 6$?

100. How can the factorization shown below be checked?

$$6x^2 - 5x - 6 = (3x + 2)(2x - 3)$$

REVIEW

101. Simplify: $(x^2x^5)^2$ x^{14}

102. Simplify: $\dfrac{(a^3b^4)^2}{ab^5}$ a^5b^3

103. Evaluate: $\dfrac{1}{2^{-3}}$ 8

104. Evaluate: 7^0 1

Objectives

1. Recognize perfect-square trinomials.
2. Factor perfect-square trinomials.
3. Factor the difference of two squares.

SECTION 6.11 Factoring Perfect-Square Trinomials and the Difference of Two Squares

In this section, we will discuss a method that can be used to factor two types of trinomials, called *perfect-square trinomials.* We also develop techniques for factoring a type of binomial called the *difference of two squares.*

1 Recognize perfect-square trinomials.

We have seen that the square of a binomial is a trinomial. We have also seen that the special-product rules shown below can be used to quickly find the square of a sum and the square of a difference. The terms of the resulting trinomial are related to the terms of the binomial that was squared.

$$(A + B)^2 = A^2 + 2AB + B^2$$

This is the square of the first term of the binomial. This is twice the product of the terms of the binomial. This is the square of the last term of the binomial.

$$(A - B)^2 = A^2 - 2AB + B^2$$

Trinomials that are squares of a binomial are called **perfect-square trinomials.** Some examples are

$y^2 + 6y + 9$ Because it is the square of $(y + 3)$: $(y + 3)^2 = y^2 + 6y + 9$

$t^2 - 14t + 49$ Because it is the square of $(t - 7)$: $(t - 7)^2 = t^2 - 14t + 49$

$4m^2 - 20m + 25$ Because it is the square of $(2m - 5)$: $(2m - 5)^2 = 4m^2 - 20m + 25$

EXAMPLE 1 Determine whether the following are perfect-square trinomials: **a.** $x^2 + 10x + 25$ **b.** $c^2 - 12c - 36$ **c.** $25y^2 - 30y + 9$ **d.** $4t^2 + 18t + 81$

Strategy We will compare each trinomial, term-by-term, to one of the special-product forms discussed above.

WHY If a trinomial matches one of these forms, it is a perfect-square trinomial.

Solution

a. To determine whether this is a perfect-square trinomial, we note that

$$x^2 + 10x + 25$$

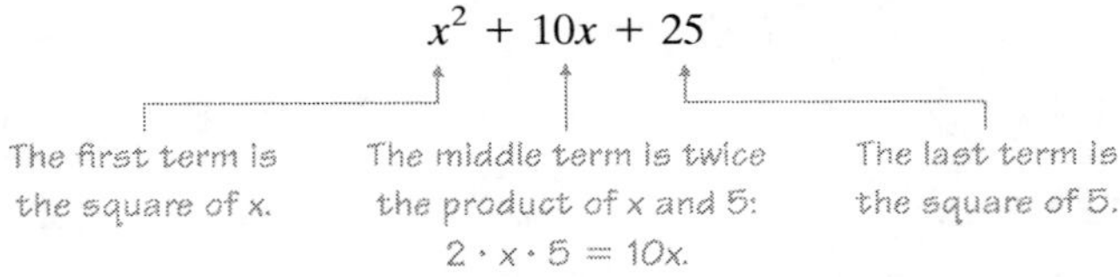

Thus, $x^2 + 10x + 25$ is a perfect-square trinomial.

b. To determine whether this is a perfect-square trinomial, we note that

$$c^2 - 12c - 36$$

The last term, −36, is not the square of a real number.

Since the last term is negative, $c^2 - 12c - 36$ is not a perfect-square trinomial.

c. To determine whether this is a perfect-square trinomial, we note that

$$25y^2 - 30y + 9$$

The first term is the square of 5y. The middle term is twice the product of 5y and −3: $2(5y)(-3) = -30y$. The last term is the square of −3.

Thus, $25y^2 - 30y + 9$ is a perfect-square trinomial.

Self Check 1

Determine whether the following are perfect-square trinomials:

a. $y^2 + 4y + 4$ yes
b. $b^2 - 6b - 9$ no
c. $4z^2 + 4z + 4$ no
d. $49x^2 - 28x + 16$ no

Now Try **Problems 25, 29, and 32**

Teaching Example 1 Determine whether the following are perfect-square trinomials:
a. $x^2 + 14x + 49$
b. $4x^2 - 20x + 25$
c. $x^2 - 10x - 25$
Answers:
a. yes b. yes c. no

The Language of Algebra The expressions $25y^2$ and 9 are called *perfect squares* because $25y^2 = (5y)^2$ and $9 = 3^2$.

d. To determine whether this is a perfect-square trinomial, we note that

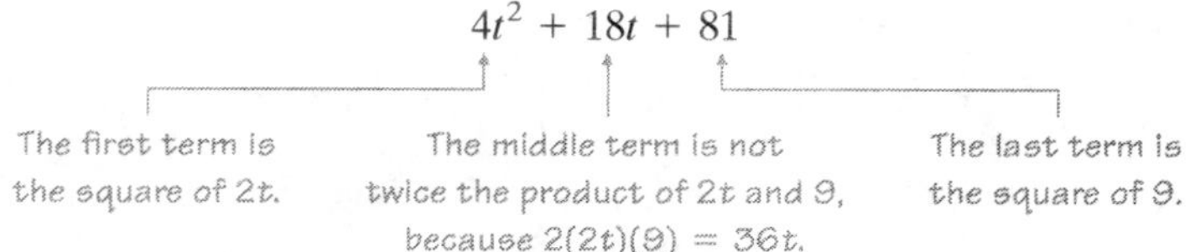

Thus, $4t^2 + 18t + 81$ is not a perfect-square trinomial.

2 Factor perfect-square trinomials.

We can factor perfect-square trinomials using the methods previously discussed in Sections 6.9 and 6.10. However, in many cases, we can factor them more quickly by inspecting their terms and applying the special-product rules in reverse.

Factoring Perfect-Square Trinomials

$$A^2 + 2AB + B^2 = (A + B)^2$$

$$A^2 - 2AB + B^2 = (A - B)^2$$

Each of these trinomials factors as the square of a binomial.

When factoring perfect-square trinomials, it is helpful to know the integers that are perfect squares. The number 400, for example, is a perfect-integer square, because $400 = 20^2$.

$1 = 1^2$	$25 = 5^2$	$81 = 9^2$	$169 = 13^2$	$289 = 17^2$
$4 = 2^2$	$36 = 6^2$	$100 = 10^2$	$196 = 14^2$	$324 = 18^2$
$9 = 3^2$	$49 = 7^2$	$121 = 11^2$	$225 = 15^2$	$361 = 19^2$
$16 = 4^2$	$64 = 8^2$	$144 = 12^2$	$256 = 16^2$	$400 = 20^2$

Self Check 2

Factor:

a. $x^2 + 18x + 81$ $(x + 9)^2$

b. $16x^2 - 8xy + y^2$ $(4x - y)^2$

Now Try **Problems 33 and 35**

Teaching Example 2 Factor:
a. $x^2 - 22x + 121$
b. $x^2 + 16x + 64$
c. $4x^2 - 20xy + 25y^2$
Answers:
a. $(x - 11)^2$ b. $(x + 8)^2$
c. $(2x - 5y)^2$

EXAMPLE 2 Factor: **a.** $x^2 + 20x + 100$ **b.** $9x^2 - 30xy + 25y^2$

Strategy The terms of each trinomial do not have a common factor (other than 1). We will determine whether each is a perfect-square trinomial.

WHY If it is, we can factor it using a special-product rule in reverse.

Solution

a. $x^2 + 20x + 100$ is a perfect-square trinomial, because:

- The first term x^2 is the square of x.
- The last term 100 is the square of 10.
- The middle term is twice the product of x and 10: $2(x)(10) = 20x$.

To find the factorization, we match $x^2 + 20x + 100$ to the proper rule for factoring a perfect-square trinomial.

$$\begin{array}{ccccccc} A^2 + 2 & A & B & + B^2 = & (A & + & B)^2 \\ \downarrow & \downarrow & \downarrow & \downarrow & \downarrow & & \downarrow \\ x^2 + 20x + 10^2 = x^2 + 2 \cdot & x & \cdot 10 & + 10^2 = & (x & + & 10)^2 \end{array}$$

Therefore, $x^2 + 20x + 10^2 = (x + 10)^2$. Check by finding $(x + 10)^2$.

b. $9x^2 - 30xy + 25y^2$ is a perfect-square trinomial, because:

- The first term $9x^2$ is the square of $3x$: $(3x)^2 = 9x^2$.
- The last term $25y^2$ is the square of $-5y$: $(-5y)^2 = 25y^2$.
- The middle term is twice the product of $3x$ and $-5y$: $2(3x)(-5y) = -30xy$.

We can use these observations to write the trinomial in one of the special-product forms that then leads to its factorization.

$$9x^2 - 30xy + 25y^2 = (3x)^2 - 2(3x)(5y) + (-5y)^2 \quad -2(3x)(5y) = 2(3x)(-5y)$$
$$= (3x - 5y)^2$$

Therefore, $9x^2 - 30xy + 25y^2 = (3x - 5y)^2$. Check by finding $(3x - 5y)^2$.

Success Tip The sign of the middle term of a perfect-square trinomial is the same as the sign of the second term of the squared binomial.

$$A^2 + 2AB + B^2 = (A + B)^2$$
$$A^2 - 2AB + B^2 = (A - B)^2$$

EXAMPLE 3 Factor completely: $4a^3 - 4a^2 + a$

Strategy We will factor out the GCF, a, first. Then we will factor the resulting perfect-square trinomial using a special-product rule in reverse.

WHY The first step in factoring any polynomial is to factor out the GCF.

Solution

The terms of $4a^3 - 4a^2 + a$ have the common factor a, which should be factored out first. Within the parentheses, we recognize $4a^2 - 4a + 1$ as a perfect square trinomial of the form $A^2 - 2AB + B^2$, and factor it as such.

$$4a^3 - 4a^2 + a = a(4a^2 - 4a + 1) \quad \text{Factor out } a.$$
$$= a(2a - 1)^2 \quad 4a^2 = (2a)^2, 1 = (-1)^2, \text{ and } -4a = 2(2a)(-1).$$

Self Check 3

Factor completely:
$49x^3 - 14x^2 + x$ $x(7x - 1)^2$

Now Try **Problem 41**

Teaching Example 3 Factor completely: $9x^3 - 6x^2 + x$
Answer:
$x(3x - 1)^2$

3 Factor the difference of two squares.

Recall the special-product rule for multiplying the sum and difference of the same two terms:

$$(A + B)(A - B) = A^2 - B^2$$

The binomial $A^2 - B^2$ is called a **difference of two squares,** because A^2 is the square of A and B^2 is the square of B. If we reverse this rule, we obtain a method for factoring a difference of two squares.

Factoring ⟶

$$A^2 - B^2 = (A + B)(A - B)$$

This pattern is easy to remember if we think of a difference of two squares as the square of a **F**irst quantity minus the square of a **L**ast quantity.

The Language of Algebra The expression $A^2 - B^2$ is a *difference of two squares,* whereas $(A - B)^2$ is the *square of a difference.* They are not equivalent because $(A - B)^2 \neq A^2 - B^2$.

Factoring a Difference of Two Squares

To factor the square of a First quantity minus the square of a Last quantity, multiply the First plus the Last by the First minus the Last.

$$F^2 - L^2 = (F + L)(F - L)$$

Self Check 4

Factor, if possible:

a. $c^2 - 4$ $(c + 2)(c - 2)$
b. $121 - t^2$ $(11 + t)(11 - t)$
c. $x^2 - 24$ prime
d. $s^2 + 36$ prime

Now Try **Problems 45 and 53**

Teaching Example 4 Factor, if possible:
a. $a^2 - 121$ b. $25 - x^2$
c. $x^2 + 36$ d. $x^2 - 8$
Answers:
a. $(a + 11)(a - 11)$
b. $(5 + x)(5 - x)$
c. prime
d. prime

EXAMPLE 4 Factor, if possible:

a. $x^2 - 9$ **b.** $16 - b^2$ **c.** $n^2 - 45$ **d.** $a^2 + 81$

Strategy The terms of each binomial do not have a common factor (other than 1). The only option available is to attempt to factor each as a difference of two squares.

WHY If a binomial is a difference of two squares, we can factor it using a special-product rule in reverse.

Solution

a. $x^2 - 9$ is the difference of two squares because it can be written as $x^2 - 3^2$. We can match it to the rule for factoring a difference of two squares to find the factorization.

$$F^2 - L^2 = (F + L)(F - L)$$
$$\downarrow \quad \downarrow \qquad \downarrow \quad \downarrow \quad \downarrow \quad \downarrow$$
$$x^2 - 3^2 = (x + 3)(x - 3)$$ 9 is a perfect-integer square: $9 = 3^2$.

Therefore, $x^2 - 9 = (x + 3)(x - 3)$.

Check by multiplying: $(x + 3)(x - 3) = x^2 - 9$.

b. $16 - b^2$ is the difference of two squares because $16 - b^2 = 4^2 - b^2$. Therefore,

$$16 - b^2 = (4 + b)(4 - b)$$ 16 is a perfect-integer square: $16 = 4^2$.

Check by multiplying.

c. Since 45 is not a perfect-integer square, $n^2 - 45$ cannot be factored using integers. It is prime.

d. $a^2 + 81$ can be written $a^2 + 9^2$, and is, therefore, the **sum of two squares.** We might attempt to factor $a^2 + 81$ as $(a + 9)(a + 9)$ or $(a - 9)(a - 9)$. However, the following checks show that neither product is $a^2 + 81$.

$$(a + 9)(a + 9) = a^2 + 18a + 81 \qquad (a - 9)(a - 9) = a^2 - 18a + 81$$

In general, the sum of two squares (with no common factor other than 1) cannot be factored using real numbers. Thus, $a^2 + 81$ is prime. ■

Terms containing variables such as $25x^2$ and $4y^4$ are perfect squares, because they can be written as the square of a quantity. For example:

$$25x^2 = (5x)^2 \quad \text{and} \quad 4y^4 = (2y^2)^2$$

Self Check 5

Factor:

a. $16y^2 - 9$ $(4y + 3)(4y - 3)$
b. $9m^2 - 64n^4$ $(3m + 8n^2)(3m - 8n^2)$

Now Try **Problems 57 and 59**

EXAMPLE 5 Factor: **a.** $25x^2 - 49$ **b.** $4y^4 - 121z^2$

Strategy In each case, the terms of the binomial do not have a common factor (other than 1). To factor them, we will write each binomial in a form that clearly shows it is a difference of two squares.

WHY We can then use a special-product rule in reverse to factor it.

Solution

a. We can write $25x^2 - 49$ in the form $(5x)^2 - 7^2$ and match it to the rule for factoring the difference of two squares:

$$F^2 - L^2 = (F + L)(F - L)$$
$$(5x)^2 - 7^2 = (5x + 7)(5x - 7)$$

Therefore, $25x^2 - 49 = (5x + 7)(5x - 7)$. Check by multiplying.

b. We can write $4y^4 - 121z^2$ in the form $(2y^2)^2 - (11z)^2$ and match it to the rule for factoring the difference of two squares:

$$F^2 - L^2 = (F + L)(F - L)$$
$$(2y^2)^2 - (11z)^2 = (2y^2 + 11z)(2y^2 - 11z)$$

Therefore, $4y^4 - 121z^2 = (2y^2 + 11z)(2y^2 - 11z)$. Check by multiplying.

Teaching Example 5 Factor:
a. $36a^2 - 25$
b. $9x^4 - 49y^2$
Answers:
a. $(6a + 5)(6a - 5)$
b. $(3x^2 + 7y)(3x^2 - 7y)$

Success Tip Remember that a *difference of two squares* is a binomial. Each term is a square and the terms have different signs. The powers of the variables in the terms must be even.

EXAMPLE 6 Factor completely: $8x^2 - 8$

Strategy We will factor out the GCF, 8, first. Then we will factor the resulting difference of two squares.

WHY The first step in factoring any polynomial is to factor out the GCF.

Solution

$8x^2 - 8 = 8(x^2 - 1)$ The GCF is 8.

$= 8(x + 1)(x - 1)$ Think of $x^2 - 1$ as $x^2 - 1^2$ and factor the difference of two squares.

Check: $8(x + 1)(x - 1) = 8(x^2 - 1)$ Multiply the binomials first.

$= 8x^2 - 8$ Distribute the multiplication by 8.

Self Check 6

Factor completely: $4x^2 - 400$

***Now Try* Problem 65**

Self Check 6 Answer
$4(x + 10)(x - 10)$

Teaching Example 6 Factor completely: $18x^2 - 32$
Answer:
$2(3x + 4)(3x - 4)$

ANSWERS TO SELF CHECKS

1. a. yes **b.** no **c.** no **d.** no **2. a.** $(x + 9)^2$ **b.** $(4x - y)^2$ **3.** $x(7x - 1)^2$ **4. a.** $(c + 2)(c - 2)$ **b.** $(11 + t)(11 - t)$ **c.** prime **d.** prime **5. a.** $(4y + 3)(4y - 3)$ **b.** $(3m + 8n^2)(3m - 8n^2)$ **6.** $4(x + 10)(x - 10)$

SECTION 6.11 STUDY SET

VOCABULARY

Fill in the blanks.

1. $x^2 + 6x + 9$ is a perfect-square trinomial because it is the square of the binomial $x + 3$.

2. The binomial $x^2 - 25$ is called a difference of two squares.

Selected exercises available online at www.webassign.net/brookscole

CONCEPTS

Fill in the blanks.

3. Consider: $25x^2 + 30x + 9$

a. The first term is the square of $5x$.

b. The last term is the square of 3.

c. The middle term is twice the product of $5x$ and 3.

4. Consider: $49x^2 - 28xy + 4y^2$

a. The first term is the square of $7x$.

b. The last term is the square of $-2y$.

c. The middle term is twice the product of $7x$ and $-2y$.

5. If a trinomial is the square of one quantity, plus the square of a second quantity, plus twice the product of the quantities, it factors into the square of the sum of the quantities.

6. Explain why each trinomial is not a perfect-square trinomial.

a. $9h^2 - 6h + 7$ 7 is not a perfect square.

b. $j^2 - 8j - 16$ The sign of the last term must be positive.

c. $25r^2 + 20r + 16$ The middle term is not twice the product of $5r$ and 4.

7. List the first ten perfect integer squares. 1, 4, 9, 16, 25, 36, 49, 64, 81, 100

8. To factor the square of a First quantity minus the square of a Last quantity, we multiply the First plus the Last by the First minus the Last.

9. a. $36x^2 = (6x)^2$ **b.** $100x^4 = (10x^2)^2$

c. $4x^2 - 9 = (2x)^2 - (3)^2$

10. a. Three incorrect factorizations of $x^2 + 36$ are given below. Explain why each one is wrong.

$(x + 6)(x - 6)$ $x^2 - 36$

$(x + 6)(x + 6)$ $x^2 + 12x + 36$

$(x - 6)(x - 6)$ $x^2 - 12x + 36$

b. Can $x^2 + 36$ be factored using only integer coefficients? no

Complete each factorization.

11. $a^2 - 6a + 9 = (a - 3)^2$

12. $t^2 + 2t + 1 = (t + 1)^2$

13. $4x^2 + 4x + 1 = (2x + 1)^2$

14. $9y^2 - 12y + 4 = (3y - 2)^2$

15. $y^2 - 49 = (y + 7)(y - 7)$

16. $p^4 - q^2 = (p^2 + q)(p^2 - q)$

17. $t^2 - w^2 = (t + w)(t - w)$

18. $49u^2 - 64v^2 = (7u + 8v)(7u - 8v)$

NOTATION

Write each expression as a polynomial in simpler form.

19. $(3a)^2 - 2(3a)(5b) + (5b)^2$ $9a^2 - 30ab + 25b^2$

20. $(2s)^2 + 2(2s)(9t) + (9t)^2$ $4s^2 + 36st + 81t^2$

21. $(6x)^2 - (5y)^2$ $36x^2 - 25y^2$

22. $(4x)^2 - (9y)^2$ $16x^2 - 81y^2$

Use an exponent to write each expression in simpler form.

23. $(x + 8)(x + 8)$ $(x + 8)^2$

▶ **24.** $(x - 8)(x - 8)$ $(x - 8)^2$

GUIDED PRACTICE

Determine whether the following expressions are perfect-square trinomials. See Example 1.

25. $x^2 + 18x + 81$ yes

26. $x^2 + 14x + 49$ yes

27. $y^2 + 2y + 4$ no

28. $y^2 + 4y + 16$ no

▶ **29.** $9n^2 - 30n - 25$ no

30. $9a^2 - 48a - 64$ no

31. $4y^2 - 12y + 9$ yes

32. $9x^2 - 30x + 25$ yes

Factor each polynomial. See Example 2.

33. $x^2 + 6x + 9$ $(x + 3)^2$

▶ **34.** $x^2 + 10x + 25$ $(x + 5)^2$

35. $t^2 - 20t + 100$ $(t - 10)^2$

▶ **36.** $r^2 + 24r + 144$ $(r + 12)^2$

37. $a^2 + 2ab + b^2$ $(a + b)^2$

38. $a^2 - 2ab + b^2$ $(a - b)^2$

39. $16x^2 - 8xy + y^2$ $(4x - y)^2$

▶ **40.** $25x^2 + 20xy + 4y^2$ $(5x + 2y)^2$

Factor each polynomial. See Example 3.

41. $y^3 - 8y^2 + 16y$ $y(y - 4)^2$

42. $u^4 - 18u^3 + 81u^2$ $u^2(u - 9)^2$

▶ **43.** $8x^3 + 24x^2 + 18x$ $2x(2x + 3)^2$

44. $108x^3 + 36x^2 + 3x$ $3x(6x + 1)^2$

Factor each polynomial. If a polynomial is prime, so indicate. See Example 4.

45. $x^2 - 16$ $(x + 4)(x - 4)$

▶ **46.** $x^2 - 25$ $(x + 5)(x - 5)$

47. $t^2 - 49$ $(t + 7)(t - 7)$

48. $m^2 - 121$ $(m + 11)(m - 11)$

49. $49 - c^2$ $(7 + c)(7 - c)$

50. $81 - t^2$ $(9 + t)(9 - t)$

51. $144 - 25a^2$ $(12 + 5a)(12 - 5a)$

52. $169 - 9t^2$ $(13 + 3t)(13 - 3t)$

53. $p^2 - 54$ prime

54. $q^2 - 20$ prime

55. $a^2 + b^2$ prime

56. $121a^2 + 144b^2$ prime

Factor each polynomial. See Example 5.

57. $4y^2 - 1$ $(2y + 1)(2y - 1)$
58. $9z^2 - 1$ $(3z + 1)(3z - 1)$
59. $49a^2 - 169$ $(7a + 13)(7a - 13)$
60. $16b^2 - 225$ $(4b + 15)(4b - 15)$
61. $9x^2 - y^2$ $(3x + y)(3x - y)$
62. $4x^2 - z^2$ $(2x + z)(2x - z)$
63. $16a^2 - 25b^2$ $(4a + 5b)(4a - 5b)$
64. $36a^2 - 121b^2$ $(6a + 11b)(6a - 11b)$

Factor each polynomial. See Example 6.

65. $8a^2 - 32$ $8(a + 2)(a - 2)$
66. $2p^2 - 200$ $2(p + 10)(p - 10)$
67. $7 - 7a^2$ $7(1 + a)(1 - a)$
68. $5 - 20x^2$ $5(1 + 2x)(1 - 2x)$

TRY IT YOURSELF

Factor each expression completely.

69. $z^2 - 2z + 1$ $(z - 1)^2$
70. $v^2 - 14v + 49$ $(v - 7)^2$
71. $4x^2 - 4x + 1$ $(2x - 1)^2$
72. $4x^2 - 20x + 25$ $(2x - 5)^2$
73. $a^4 - 144b^2$ $(a^2 + 12b)(a^2 - 12b)$
74. $81y^4 - 100z^2$ $(9y^2 + 10z)(9y^2 - 10z)$
75. $t^2z^2 - 64$ $(tz + 8)(tz - 8)$
76. $900 - B^2C^2$ $(30 + BC)(30 - BC)$
77. $6x^4 - 6x^2y^2$ $6x^2(x + y)(x - y)$
78. $4b^2y - 16c^2y$ $4y(b + 2c)(b - 2c)$
79. $a^2b^2 - 144$ $(ab + 12)(ab - 12)$
80. $20m^2 + 100m + 125$ $5(2m + 5)^2$
81. $16 - 40z + 25z^2$ $(5z - 4)^2$
82. $49p^2 + 28pq + 4q^2$ $(7p + 2q)^2$
83. $16x^2 - 40x^3 + 25x^4$ $x^2(5x - 4)^2$
84. $8a^2x^3y - 2b^2xy$ $2xy(2ax + b)(2ax - b)$

Choose the correct method from Section 6.8, 6.9, 6.10, or 6.11 to factor completely each of the following expressions:

85. $8x^2 - 32y^2$ $8(x + 2y)(x - 2y)$
86. $2a^2 - 200b^2$ $2(a + 10b)(a - 10b)$
87. $8m^2n^3 - 24mn^4$ $8mn^3(m - 3n)$
88. $3rs + 6r^2 - 18s^2$ $3(2r - 3s)(r + 2s)$
89. $x^2 + 7x + 1$ prime
90. $14t^3 - 40t^2 + 6t^4$ $2t^2(3t - 5)(t + 4)$
91. $-9x^2y^2 + 6xy - 1$ $-(3xy - 1)^2$
92. $2c^2 - 5cd - 3d^2$ $(2c + d)(c - 3d)$
93. $2ac + 4ad + bc + 2bd$ $(c + 2d)(2a + b)$
94. $10r^2 - 13r - 4$ prime
95. $6x^2 - x - 16$ prime
96. $4x^2 + 9y^2$ prime
97. $6a^3 + 35a^2 - 6a$ $a(6a - 1)(a + 6)$
98. $21t^3 - 10t^2 + t$ $t(7t - 1)(3t - 1)$
99. $70p^4q^3 - 35p^4q^2 + 49p^5q^2$ $7p^4q^2(10q - 5 + 7p)$
100. $2ab^2 + 8ab - 24a$ $2a(b + 6)(b - 2)$
101. $a^2c + a^2d^2 + bc + bd^2$ $(c + d^2)(a^2 + b)$
102. $-8p^3q^7 - 4p^2q^3$ $-4p^2q^3(2pq^4 + 1)$

APPLICATIONS

103. GENETICS The Hardy–Weinberg equation, one of the fundamental concepts in population genetics, is

$$p^2 + 2pq + q^2 = 1$$

where p represents the frequency of a certain dominant gene and q represents the frequency of a certain recessive gene. Factor the left-hand side of the equation. $(p + q)^2$

104. SPACE TRAVEL The surface area of the spherical part of the spacecraft shown below is given by $(36\pi r^2 - 48\pi r + 16\pi)$ m^2. Factor the expression. $4\pi(3r - 2)^2$ m^2

105. PHYSICS The illustration shows a time-sequence picture of a falling apple. Factor the expression, which gives the distance the apple falls during the time interval from t_1 to t_2 seconds. $0.5g(t_1 + t_2)(t_1 - t_2)$

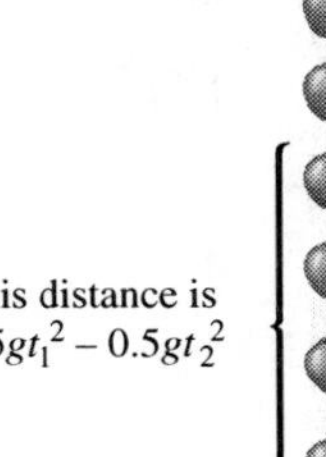

This distance is $0.5gt_1^2 - 0.5gt_2^2$

106. DARTS A circular dart board has a series of rings around a solid center, called the bulls'-eye. To find the area of the outer black ring, we can use the formula

$$A = \pi R^2 - \pi r^2$$

Factor the expression on the right side of the equation. $\pi(R + r)(R - r)$

WRITING

107. When asked to factor $x^2 - 25$, one student wrote $(x + 5)(x - 5)$, and another student wrote $(x - 5)(x + 5)$. Are both answers correct? Explain.

108. Explain the error in the factorization shown below:

$$4x^2 - 16y^2 = (2x + 4y)(2x - 4y)$$

REVIEW

Perform each division.

109. $\dfrac{5x^2 + 10y^2 - 15xy}{5xy}$ $\quad \frac{x}{y} + \frac{2y}{x} - 3$

110. $\dfrac{-30c^2d^2 - 15c^2d - 10cd^2}{-10cd}$ $\quad 3cd + \frac{3c}{2} + d$

111. $2a - 1\overline{)a - 2 + 6a^2}$ $\quad 3a + 2$

112. $4b + 3\overline{)4b^3 - 5b^2 - 2b + 3}$ $\quad b^2 - 2b + 1$

Objectives

1. Define quadratic equations.
2. Solve quadratic equations using the zero-factor property.
3. Solve quadratic equations by factoring.
4. Solve third-degree equations by factoring.

SECTION 6.12 Solving Quadratic Equations by Factoring

Equations that involve first-degree polynomials, such as $9x - 6 = 0$, are called *linear equations.* Equations that involve second-degree polynomials, such as $9x^2 - 6x = 0$, are called **quadratic equations.** In this section, we will define quadratic equations and learn how to solve many of them by factoring.

1 Define quadratic equations.

If a polynomial contains one variable with an exponent to the second (but no higher) power, it is called a **second-degree polynomial.** A quadratic, or second-degree equation, has a term in which the exponent on the variable is 2, and has no other terms of higher degree. Some examples are

$$9x^2 - 6x = 0, \qquad x^2 - 2x - 63 = 0, \qquad \text{and} \qquad 2x^2 + 3x - 2 = 0$$

Quadratic Equation

A **quadratic equation** is an equation that can be written in the **standard form**

$$ax^2 + bx + c = 0$$

where a, b, and c represent real numbers, and a is not 0.

To write a quadratic equation such as $21x = 10 - 10x^2$ in $ax^2 + bx + c = 0$ form (called **standard form**), we use the addition and subtraction properties of equality to get 0 on the right-hand side.

$$21x = 10 - 10x^2$$

$$10x^2 + 21x = 10 - 10x^2 + 10x^2 \qquad \text{Add } 10x^2 \text{ to both sides.}$$

$$10x^2 + 21x = 10 \qquad \text{Combine like terms: } -10x^2 + 10x^2 = 0.$$

$$10x^2 + 21x - 10 = 0 \qquad \text{Subtract 10 from both sides.}$$

2 Solve quadratic equations using the zero-factor property.

To **solve a quadratic equation,** we find all the values of the variable that make the equation true.

The method that we have used to solve linear equations cannot be used to solve a quadratic equation, because those techniques cannot isolate the variable on one side of the equation. However, we can often solve quadratic equations using factoring and the following property of real numbers.

The Zero-Factor Property

If a and b represent real numbers, and

if $ab = 0$, then $a = 0$ or $b = 0$.

In words, the zero-factor property states that when the product of two numbers is zero, at least one of them must be zero.

EXAMPLE 1 Solve: $(4y - 1)(y + 6) = 0$

Strategy We will set $4y - 1$ equal to 0 and $y + 6$ equal to 0 and solve each equation.

WHY The product of $4y - 1$ and $y + 6$ is equal to 0. By the zero-factor property, $4y - 1$ must equal 0, or $y + 6$ must equal 0.

Solution

The left-hand side of the equation is $(4y - 1)(y + 6)$. By the zero-factor property, one of these factors must be 0.

$$4y - 1 = 0 \quad \text{or} \quad y + 6 = 0$$

We can solve each of the linear equations.

$$4y - 1 = 0 \quad \text{or} \quad y + 6 = 0 \qquad \textit{Set each factor equal to zero.}$$
$$4y = 1 \qquad\qquad y = -6 \qquad \textit{Solve each equation.}$$
$$y = \frac{1}{4}$$

The equation has two solutions, $\frac{1}{4}$ and -6. To check, we substitute the results for y in the original equation and simplify.

For $y = \frac{1}{4}$

$$(4y - 1)(y + 6) = 0$$
$$\left[4\left(\frac{1}{4}\right) - 1\right]\left(\frac{1}{4} + 6\right) \stackrel{?}{=} 0$$
$$(1 - 1)\left(6\frac{1}{4}\right) \stackrel{?}{=} 0$$
$$0\left(6\frac{1}{4}\right) \stackrel{?}{=} 0$$
$$0 = 0 \quad \text{True}$$

For $y = -6$

$$(4y - 1)(y + 6) = 0$$
$$[4(-6) - 1](-6 + 6) \stackrel{?}{=} 0$$
$$(-24 - 1)(0) \stackrel{?}{=} 0$$
$$-25(0) \stackrel{?}{=} 0$$
$$0 = 0 \quad \text{True}$$

Self Check 1

Solve: $(4x - 3)(5x - 4) = 0$

Now Try **Problem 15**

Self Check 1 Answer

$\frac{3}{4}, \frac{4}{5}$

Teaching Example 1 Solve: $(x + 11)(7x - 4) = 0$

Answer:

$-11, \frac{4}{7}$

3 Solve quadratic equations by factoring.

In Example 1, the right-hand side of the equation was zero, and the left-hand side was in factored form, so we were able to use the zero-factor property immediately. However, to solve many quadratic equations, we must first do the factoring.

Self Check 2

Solve: $5x^2 + 10x = 0$ 0, −2

Now Try **Problem 22**

Teaching Example 2 Solve: $15x^2 - 25x = 0$
Answer:
$0, \frac{5}{3}$

EXAMPLE 2 Solve: $9x^2 - 6x = 0$

Strategy We will factor the binomial on the left side of the equation and use the zero-factor property.

WHY To use the zero-factor property, we need one side of the equation to be factored completely and the other side to be 0.

Solution

We begin by factoring the left-hand side of the equation.

$$9x^2 - 6x = 0 \quad \text{This is the equation to solve.}$$
$$3x(3x - 2) = 0 \quad \text{Factor out the GCF of } 3x.$$

By the zero-factor property, we have

$$3x = 0 \quad \text{or} \quad 3x - 2 = 0$$

We can solve each of the linear equations to get

$$x = 0 \quad \text{or} \quad x = \frac{2}{3}$$

To check, we substitute the results for x in the original equation and simplify.

For $x = 0$

$$9x^2 - 6x = 0$$
$$9(0)^2 - 6(0) \stackrel{?}{=} 0$$
$$0 - 0 \stackrel{?}{=} 0$$
$$0 = 0 \quad \text{True}$$

For $x = \frac{2}{3}$

$$9x^2 - 6x = 0$$
$$9\left(\frac{2}{3}\right)^2 - 6\left(\frac{2}{3}\right) \stackrel{?}{=} 0$$
$$9\left(\frac{4}{9}\right) - 6\left(\frac{2}{3}\right) \stackrel{?}{=} 0$$
$$4 - 4 \stackrel{?}{=} 0$$
$$0 = 0 \quad \text{True}$$

The solutions of $9x^2 - 6x = 0$ are 0 and $\frac{2}{3}$. ■

We can use the following steps to solve a quadratic equation by factoring.

Solving Quadratic Equations by Factoring

1. Write the equation in standard form: $ax^2 + bx + c = 0$ or $0 = ax^2 + bx + c$.
2. Factor completely.
3. Use the zero-factor property to set each factor equal to zero.
4. Solve each resulting linear equation.
5. Check the results in the original equation.

Self Check 3

Solve: $x^2 = 25$ −5, 5

Now Try **Problem 26**

Teaching Example 3 Solve: $x^2 = 16$
Answer:
4, −4

EXAMPLE 3 Solve: $x^2 = 9$

Strategy We will subtract 9 from both sides of the equation to get 0 on the right side. Then we will factor the resulting binomial and use the zero-factor property.

WHY To use the zero-factor property, we need one side of the equation to be factored completely and the other side to be 0.

Solution

Before we can use the zero-factor property, we must subtract 9 from both sides to make the right-hand side zero.

$x^2 = 9$	This is the equation to solve.
$x^2 - 9 = 0$	Subtract 9 from both sides.
$(x + 3)(x - 3) = 0$	Factor the difference of two squares.
$x + 3 = 0$ or $x - 3 = 0$	Set each factor equal to zero.
$x = -3$ | $x = 3$	Solve each linear equation.

Check each possible solution by substituting it into the original equation.

For $x = -3$	**For $x = 3$**
$x^2 = 9$	$x^2 = 9$
$(-3)^2 \stackrel{?}{=} 9$	$(3)^2 \stackrel{?}{=} 9$
$9 = 9$	$9 = 9$

The solutions of $x^2 = 9$ are -3 and 3.

EXAMPLE 4 Solve: $x^2 - 2x - 63 = 0$

Strategy We will factor the trinomial on the left side of the equation and use the zero-factor property.

WHY To use the zero-factor property, we need one side of the equation to be factored completely and the other side to be 0.

Solution

$x^2 - 2x - 63 = 0$	This is the equation to solve.
$(x + 7)(x - 9) = 0$	Factor the trinomial $x^2 - 2x - 63$.
$x + 7 = 0$ or $x - 9 = 0$	Set each factor equal to zero.
$x = -7$ | $x = 9$	Solve each linear equation.

The solutions are -7 and 9. Check each one.

Self Check 4

Solve: $x^2 + 5x + 6 = 0$ $-2, -3$

Now Try **Problem 31**

Teaching Example 4 Solve: $x^2 - 2x - 35 = 0$
Answer: $7, -5$

EXAMPLE 5 Solve: $2x^2 + 3x = 2$

Strategy We will subtract 2 from both sides of the equation to get 0 on the right side. Then we will factor the resulting trinomial and use the zero-factor property.

WHY To use the zero-factor property, we need one side of the equation to be factored completely and the other side to be 0.

Solution
The equation is not in $ax^2 + bx + c = 0$ form. To get 0 on the right side, we proceed as follows:

$2x^2 + 3x = 2$	This is the equation to solve.
$2x^2 + 3x - 2 = 0$	Subtract 2 from both sides so that the right-hand side is zero.
$(2x - 1)(x + 2) = 0$	Factor $2x^2 + 3x - 2$.
$2x - 1 = 0$ or $x + 2 = 0$	Set each factor equal to zero.
$2x = 1$ | $x = -2$	Solve each linear equation.
$x = \frac{1}{2}$	

Use a check to verify that $\frac{1}{2}$ and -2 are solutions.

Self Check 5

Solve: $3x^2 - 6 = -7x$

Now Try **Problem 34**

Self Check 5 Answer
$\frac{2}{3}, -3$

Teaching Example 5 Solve: $8x^2 - 15 = -2x$
Answer: $\frac{5}{4}, \frac{-3}{2}$

Self Check 6

Solve: $x(4x + 12) = -9$

Now Try **Problem 38**

Self Check 6 Answer

$-\frac{3}{2}, -\frac{3}{2}$

Teaching Example 6 Solve:
$3x(3x - 10) = -25$

Answer:
$\frac{5}{3}, \frac{5}{3}$

EXAMPLE 6 Solve: $x(9x - 12) = -4$

Strategy To write the equation in standard form, we will distribute the multiplication by x and add 4 to both sides. Then we will factor the resulting trinomial and use the zero-factor property.

WHY To use the zero-factor property, we need one side of the equation to be factored completely and the other side to be 0.

Solution

First, we need to write the equation in the form $ax^2 + bx + c = 0$.

$$x(9x - 12) = -4 \quad \text{This is the equation to solve.}$$
$$9x^2 - 12x = -4 \quad \text{Distribute the multiplication by } x.$$
$$9x^2 - 12x + 4 = 0 \quad \text{To get 0 on the right side, add 4 to both sides.}$$
$$(3x - 2)(3x - 2) = 0 \quad \text{Factor the trinomial.}$$
$$3x - 2 = 0 \quad \text{or} \quad 3x - 2 = 0 \quad \text{Set each factor equal to zero.}$$
$$3x = 2 \quad\quad 3x = 2 \quad \text{Add 2 to both sides.}$$
$$x = \frac{2}{3} \quad\quad x = \frac{2}{3} \quad \text{Divide both sides by 3.}$$

The equation has two solutions that are the same. We call $\frac{2}{3}$ a *repeated solution.* Check by substituting it into the original equation.

4 Solve third-degree equations by factoring.

Self Check 7

Solve: $10x^3 + x^2 - 2x = 0$

Now Try **Problem 43**

Self Check 7 Answer

$0, \frac{2}{5}, -\frac{1}{2}$

Teaching Example 7 Solve:
$6x^3 - 11x^2 = 7x$

Answer:
$0, -\frac{1}{2}, \frac{7}{3}$

EXAMPLE 7 Solve: $6x^3 + 12x = 17x^2$

Strategy This equation is not quadratic, because it contains a term involving x^3. However, we can solve it by using factoring. First we get 0 on the right side by subtracting $17x^2$ from both sides. Then we factor the polynomial on the left side and use an extension of the zero-factor property.

WHY To use the zero-factor property, we need one side of the equation to be factored completely and the other side to be 0.

Solution

$$6x^3 + 12x = 17x^2 \quad \text{This is the equation to solve.}$$
$$6x^3 - 17x^2 + 12x = 0 \quad \text{Subtract } 17x^2 \text{ from both sides to get 0 on the right-hand side.}$$
$$x(6x^2 - 17x + 12) = 0 \quad \text{Factor out the GCF, } x.$$
$$x(2x - 3)(3x - 4) = 0 \quad \text{Factor } 6x^2 - 17x + 12.$$
$$x = 0 \quad \text{or} \quad 2x - 3 = 0 \quad \text{or} \quad 3x - 4 = 0 \quad \text{Set each factor equal to zero.}$$
$$2x = 3 \quad\quad 3x = 4 \quad \text{Solve the linear equations.}$$
$$x = \frac{3}{2} \quad\quad x = \frac{4}{3}$$

This equation has three solutions, $0, \frac{3}{2}$, and $\frac{4}{3}$.

ANSWERS TO SELF CHECKS

1. $\frac{3}{4}, \frac{4}{5}$ **2.** $0, -2$ **3.** $-5, 5$ **4.** $-2, -3$ **5.** $\frac{2}{3}, -3$ **6.** $-\frac{3}{2}, -\frac{3}{2}$ **7.** $0, \frac{2}{5}, -\frac{1}{2}$

SECTION 6.12 STUDY SET

VOCABULARY

Fill in the blanks.

1. Any equation that can be written in the form $ax^2 + bx + c = 0$ is called a quadratic equation.
2. To factor a binomial or trinomial means to write it as a product.

CONCEPTS

Fill in the blanks.

3. When the product of two numbers is 0, at least one of them is 0. Symbolically, we can state this: If $ab = 0$, then $a = 0$ or $b = 0$.
4. We can often use factoring and the zero-factor property to solve quadratic equations.
5. To write a quadratic equation in standard form means that one side of the equation must be zero and the other side must be in the form $ax^2 + bx + c$.
6. Classify each equation as quadratic or linear.
   a. $3x^2 + 4x + 2 = 0$ quadratic
   b. $3x + 7 = 0$ linear
   c. $2 = -16 - 4x$ linear
   d. $-6x + 2 = x^2$ quadratic
7. Check to see whether the given number is a solution of the given quadratic equation.
   a. $x^2 - 4x = 0; x = 4$ yes
   b. $x^2 + 2x - 4 = 0; x = -2$ no
8. a. Evaluate $x^2 + 6x - 16$ for $x = 0$. -16
   b. Factor: $x^2 + 6x - 16$ $(x - 2)(x + 8)$
9. The equation $3x^2 - 4x + 5 = 0$ is written in $ax^2 + bx + c = 0$ form. What are a, b, and c? $3, -4, 5$
10. a. How many solutions does the linear equation $2a + 3 = 2$ have? 1
    b. How many solutions does the quadratic equation $2a^2 + 3a = 2$ have? 2

NOTATION

Complete each solution to solve the equation.

11. $7y^2 + 14y = 0$

$7y(y + 2) = 0$

$7y = 0$ or $y + 2 = 0$

$y = 0$ | $y = -2$

12. $12p^2 - p - 6 = 0$

$(4p - 3)(3p + 2) = 0$

$4p - 3 = 0$ or $3p + 2 = 0$

$4p = 3$ | $3p = -2$

$p = \frac{3}{4}$ | $p = -\frac{2}{3}$

GUIDED PRACTICE

Solve each equation. See Example 1.

13. $(x - 2)(x + 3) = 0$ $2, -3$
14. $(x - 3)(x - 2) = 0$ $3, 2$
15. $(2s - 5)(s + 6) = 0$ $\frac{5}{2}, -6$
16. $(3h - 4)(h + 1) = 0$ $\frac{4}{3}, -1$
17. $x(x - 3) = 0$ $0, 3$
18. $x(x + 5) = 0$ $0, -5$
19. $(x - 1)(x + 2)(x - 3) = 0$ $1, -2, 3$
20. $(x + 2)(x + 3)(x - 4) = 0$ $-2, -3, 4$

Solve each equation. See Example 2.

21. $w^2 - 7w = 0$ $0, 7$
22. $p^2 + 5p = 0$ $0, -5$
23. $3x^2 + 8x = 0$ $0, -\frac{8}{3}$
24. $5x^2 - x = 0$ $0, \frac{1}{5}$

Solve each equation. See Example 3.

25. $x^2 = 100$ $-10, 10$
26. $z^2 = 25$ $-5, 5$
27. $4x^2 = 81$ $-\frac{9}{2}, \frac{9}{2}$
28. $9y^2 = 64$ $-\frac{8}{3}, \frac{8}{3}$

Solve each equation. See Example 4.

29. $x^2 - 4x - 21 = 0$ $-3, 7$
30. $x^2 + 2x - 15 = 0$ $3, -5$
31. $x^2 - 13x + 12 = 0$ $12, 1$
32. $x^2 + 7x + 6 = 0$ $-1, -6$

Solve each equation. See Example 5.

33. $4r^2 + 4r = -1$ $-\frac{1}{2}, -\frac{1}{2}$
34. $9m^2 + 6m = -1$ $-\frac{1}{3}, -\frac{1}{3}$
35. $-15x^2 + 2 = -7x$ $\frac{2}{3}, -\frac{1}{5}$
36. $-8x^2 - 10x = -3$ $\frac{1}{4}, -\frac{3}{2}$

Solve each equation. See Example 6.

37. $x(2x - 3) = 20$ $-\frac{5}{2}, 4$
38. $x(2x - 3) = 14$ $\frac{7}{2}, -2$
39. $(d + 1)(8d + 1) = 18d$ $\frac{1}{8}, 1$
40. $4h(3h + 2) = h + 12$ $-\frac{4}{3}, \frac{3}{4}$

Solve each equation. See Example 7.

41. $x^3 + 3x^2 + 2x = 0$ $0, -1, -2$
42. $x^3 - 7x^2 + 10x = 0$ $0, 5, 2$
43. $k^3 - 27k - 6k^2 = 0$ $0, 9, -3$
44. $j^3 - 22j - 9j^2 = 0$ $0, 11, -2$

TRY IT YOURSELF

Solve each equation.

45. $x(2x - 5) = 0$ $0, \frac{5}{2}$
46. $x(5x + 7) = 0$ $0, -\frac{7}{5}$
47. $8s^2 - 16s = 0$ $0, 2$
48. $15s^2 - 20s = 0$ $0, \frac{4}{3}$
49. $x^2 - 25 = 0$ $-5, 5$
50. $x^2 - 36 = 0$ $-6, 6$
51. $4x^2 - 1 = 0$ $-\frac{1}{2}, \frac{1}{2}$
52. $9y^2 - 1 = 0$ $-\frac{1}{3}, \frac{1}{3}$
53. $9y^2 - 4 = 0$ $-\frac{2}{3}, \frac{2}{3}$
54. $16z^2 - 25 = 0$ $-\frac{5}{4}, \frac{5}{4}$
55. $x^2 - 9x + 8 = 0$ $8, 1$
56. $x^2 - 14x + 45 = 0$ $9, 5$
57. $a^2 + 8a = -15$ $-3, -5$
58. $a^2 - a = 56$ $8, -7$
59. $2y - 8 = -y^2$ $-4, 2$
60. $-3y + 18 = y^2$ $3, -6$
61. $2x^2 - 5x + 2 = 0$ $\frac{1}{2}, 2$
62. $2x^2 + x - 3 = 0$ $-\frac{3}{2}, 1$
63. $5x^2 - 6x + 1 = 0$ $\frac{1}{5}, 1$
64. $6x^2 - 5x + 1 = 0$ $\frac{1}{3}, \frac{1}{2}$
65. $(x - 1)(x^2 + 5x + 6) = 0$ $1, -2, -3$
66. $(x - 2)(x^2 - 8x + 7) = 0$ $2, 7, 1$
67. $2x(3x^2 + 10x) = -6x$ $0, -3, -\frac{1}{3}$
68. $2x^3 = 2x(x + 2)$ $0, -1, 2$
69. $x^3 + 7x^2 = x^2 - 9x$ $0, -3, -3$
70. $x^2(x + 10) = 2x(x - 8)$ $0, -4, -4$

WRITING

71. Explain the zero-factor property.
72. Find the error in the following solution:

$$x(x + 1) = 6$$
$$x = 6 \quad \text{or} \quad x + 1 = 6$$
$$x = 5$$

The solutions are 6 and 5.

REVIEW

Perform the operations and simplify.

73. $5b(2b - 3) + 2b(b - 5)$ $12b^2 - 25b$
74. $3x(a + x) - 2(x + 3)$ $3ax + 3x^2 - 2x - 6$
75. $(2b - 3)(2b - 5)$ $4b^2 - 16b + 15$
76. $(a + x)(x + 3)$ $ax + 3a + x^2 + 3x$
77. $\frac{a + 1}{2} + \frac{a - 1}{2}$ a
78. $\frac{x + 2}{3} - \frac{2x + 1}{2}$ $\frac{-4x + 1}{6}$
79. $3z - 2\overline{)6z^2 + 5z - 6}$ $2z + 3$
80. $2a - 1\overline{)6a^3 + a^2 + 4a - 2}$ $3a^2 + 2a + 3 + \frac{1}{2a - 1}$

SECTION 6.13 Applications of Quadratic Equations

Objectives

1. Solve problems given the quadratic equation model.
2. Solve problems involving consecutive integers.
3. Solve problems involving geometric figures.
4. Solve problems involving the Pythagorean Theorem.

In Chapter 2, we solved mixture, investment, and uniform motion problems. To model those equations, we used *linear equations* in one variable. We will now consider situations that are modeled by *quadratic equations*.

1 Solve problems given the quadratic equation model.

Self Check 1

A student uses rubber tubing to launch a water balloon from the roof of his dormitory. The height h (in feet) of the balloon, t seconds after being launched, is given by $h = -16t^2 + 48t + 64$. After how many seconds will the balloon hit the ground? 4 sec

***Now Try* Problem 12**

Teaching Example 1 A pitcher can throw a fast ball at 79 feet per second. If she throws the ball into the air with that velocity, its height h in feet, t seconds after being released, is given by $h = -16t^2 + 79t + 5$. After the ball is thrown, in how many seconds will it hit the ground?
Answer:
5 sec

EXAMPLE 1 ***Softball*** A pitcher can throw a fastball underhand at 63 feet per second (about 45 mph). If she throws a ball into the air with that velocity, its height h in feet, t seconds after being released, is given by the formula

$$h = -16t^2 + 63t + 4$$

After the ball is thrown, in how many seconds will it hit the ground?

Solution

When the ball hits the ground, its height will be 0 feet. To find the time that it will take for the ball to hit the ground, we set h equal to 0, and solve the quadratic equation for t.

$h = -16t^2 + 63t + 4$

$0 = -16t^2 + 63t + 4$ Substitute 0 for the height h.

$0 = -(16t^2 - 63t - 4)$ Factor out -1.

$0 = -(16t + 1)(t - 4)$ Factor $16t^2 - 63t - 4$.

$16t + 1 = 0$	or	$t - 4 = 0$	Set each factor that contains a variable equal to 0.
$16t = -1$		$t = 4$	Solve each equation.
$t = -\frac{1}{16}$			

Since time cannot be negative, we discard the solution $-\frac{1}{16}$. The second solution indicates that the ball hits the ground 4 seconds after being released. Check this answer by substituting 4 for t in $h = -16t^2 + 63t + 4$. You should get $h = 0$.

2 Solve problems involving consecutive integers.

Consecutive integers are integers that follow one another, such as 15 and 16. When solving consecutive integer problems, if we let $x =$ the first integer, then:

- two consecutive integers are x and $x + 1$
- two consecutive even integers are x and $x + 2$
- two consecutive odd integers are x and $x + 2$

EXAMPLE 2 *Women's Tennis* In the 1998 Australian Open, sisters Venus and Serena Williams played against each other for the first time as professionals. Venus was victorious over her younger sister. At that time, their ages were consecutive integers whose product was 272. How old were Venus and Serena when they met in this match?

Analyze

- Venus is older than Serena.
- Their ages were consecutive integers.
- The product of their ages was 272.
- Find Venus' and Serena's age when they played this match.

Form Let $x =$ Serena's age when she played in the 1998 Australian Open. Since their ages were consecutive integers, and since Venus is older, we let $x + 1 =$ Venus' age. The word *product* indicates multiplication.

Serena's age	times	Venus' age	was	272.
x	$\cdot$	$(x + 1)$	$=$	272

Solve

$x(x + 1) = 272$			
$x^2 + x = 272$			Distribute the multiplication by x. Note that this is a quadratic equation.
$x^2 + x - 272 = 0$			Subtract 272 from both sides to make the right side 0.
$(x + 17)(x - 16) = 0$			Factor $x^2 + x - 272$. Two numbers whose product is -272 and whose sum is 1 are 17 and -16.
$x + 17 = 0$	or	$x - 16 = 0$	Set each factor equal to 0.
$x = -17$		$x = 16$	Solve each equation.

Self Check 2

The product of two consecutive integers is 552. Find the integers.

Now Try **Problem 19**

ZOU ZHENG/Xinhua/Landov

Self Check 2 Answers
23 and 24

Teaching Example 2 The product of two consecutive odd integers is 255. Find the integers.
Answer:
15 and 17

State The solutions of the equation are -17 and 16. Since x represents Serena's age, and it cannot be negative, we discard -17. Thus, Serena Williams was 16 years old and Venus Williams was $16 + 1 = 17$ years old when they played against each other for the first time as professionals.

> ***Success Tip*** The prime factorization of 272 is helpful in determining that $272 = 17 \cdot 16$.
>
> $$16\begin{cases} 2\underline{|272} \\ \quad 2\underline{|136} \\ \qquad 2\underline{|68} \\ \qquad\quad 2\underline{|34} \end{cases}$$
> $$\qquad\qquad 17$$

3 Solve problems involving geometric figures.

Self Check 3

A rectangle has an area of 55 square meters. Its length is 1 meter more than twice its width. Find the perimeter of the rectangle. 32 m

Now Try **Problem 23**

Teaching Example 3 A rectangular-shaped X-ray film has an area of 80 square inches. The length is 2 inches longer than the width. Find its width and length.
Answer:
8 in., 10 in.

EXAMPLE 3 *Perimeter of a Rectangle*

Assume that the rectangle has an area of 52 square centimeters and that its length is 1 centimeter more than 3 times its width. Find the perimeter of the rectangle.

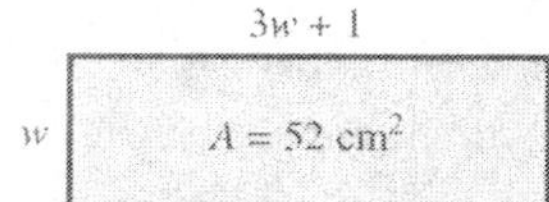

Analyze The area of the rectangle is 52 square centimeters. Recall that the formula that gives the area of a rectangle is $A = lw$. To find the perimeter of the rectangle, we need to know its length and width. We are told that its length is related to its width; the length is 1 centimeter more than 3 times the width.

Form Let w represent the width of the rectangle. Then $3w + 1$ represents its length. Because the area is 52 square centimeters, we substitute 52 for A and $3w + 1$ for l in the formula $A = lw$.

$$A = lw$$
$$52 = (3w + 1)w$$

Solve Now we solve the equation for w.

$52 = (3w + 1)w$ This is the equation to solve.

$52 = 3w^2 + w$ Distribute the multiplication by w.

$0 = 3w^2 + w - 52$ Subtract 52 from both sides to make the left-hand side zero.

$0 = (3w + 13)(w - 4)$ Factor the trinomial.

$3w + 13 = 0$ or $w - 4 = 0$ Set each factor equal to zero.

$3w = -13$ | $w = 4$ Solve each linear equation.

$w = -\frac{13}{3}$

State Since the width cannot be negative, we discard the solution $-\frac{13}{3}$. Thus, the width of the rectangle is 4, and the length is given by

$3w + 1 = 3(4) + 1$ Substitute 4 for w.

$= 12 + 1$

$= 13$

The dimensions of the rectangle are 4 centimeters by 13 centimeters. We find the perimeter by substituting 13 for l and 4 for w in the formula for the perimeter of a rectangle.

$$
\begin{aligned}
P &= 2l + 2w \\
&= 2(13) + 2(4) \\
&= 26 + 8 \\
&= 34
\end{aligned}
$$

The perimeter of the rectangle is 34 centimeters.

Check A rectangle with dimensions of 13 centimeters by 4 centimeters does have an area of 52 square centimeters, and the length is 1 centimeter more than 3 times the width. A rectangle with these dimensions has a perimeter of 34 centimeters.

4 Solve problems involving the Pythagorean Theorem.

The next example involves a right triangle. A **right triangle** is a triangle that contains a 90° angle. The longest side of a right triangle is the **hypotenuse,** which is the side opposite the right angle. The remaining two sides are the **legs** of the triangle. The **Pythagorean theorem** provides a formula relating the lengths of the three sides of a right triangle.

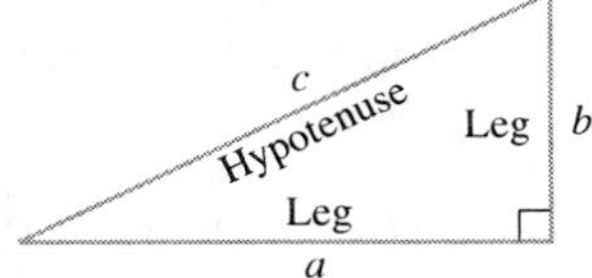

THINK IT THROUGH *Pythagorean Triples*

"Fraternity and sorority membership nationwide is declining, down about 30% in the last decade."

Chronicle of Higher Education, 2003

SEF/Art Resource, NY

The first college social fraternity, Phi Beta Kappa, was founded in 1776 on the campus of The College of William and Mary. However, secret societies have existed since ancient times, and from these roots the essence of today's fraternities and sororities have their foundation. Pythagoras, the Greek mathematician of the 6th century B.C., was the leader of a secret fraternity/sorority called the Pythagoreans. They were a community of men and women that studied mathematics, and in particular, the "magic 3-4-5 triangle." This right triangle is special because the sum of the squares of the lengths of its legs is equal to the square of the length of its hypotenuse: $3^2 + 4^2 = 5^2$ or $9 + 16 = 25$. Today, we call a set of three natural numbers a, b, and c that satisfy $a^2 + b^2 = c^2$ a Pythagorean triple. Show that each list of numbers is a Pythagorean triple.

1. 5, 12, 13 **2.** 7, 24, 25 **3.** 8, 15, 17

4. 9, 40, 41 **5.** 11, 60, 61 **6.** 12, 35, 37

Pythagorean Theorem

If the length of the hypotenuse of a right triangle is c and the lengths of the two legs are a and b, then

$$c^2 = a^2 + b^2$$

Self Check 4

The longer leg of a right triangle is 7 inches longer than the shorter leg. If the hypotenuse is 9 units longer than the shorter leg, find the lengths of the sides of the triangle.

Now Try **Problem 29**

Self Check 4 Answer
8 in., 15 in., and 17 in.

Teaching Example 4 The longer leg of a right triangle is 7 cm longer than the shorter leg. If the hypotenuse is 8 cm longer than the shorter side, find the lengths of the sides of the triangle.
Answer:
5 cm, 12 cm, and 13 cm

EXAMPLE 4 *Right Triangles* The longer leg of a right triangle is 3 units longer than the shorter leg. If the hypotenuse is 6 units longer than the shorter leg, find the lengths of the sides of the triangle.

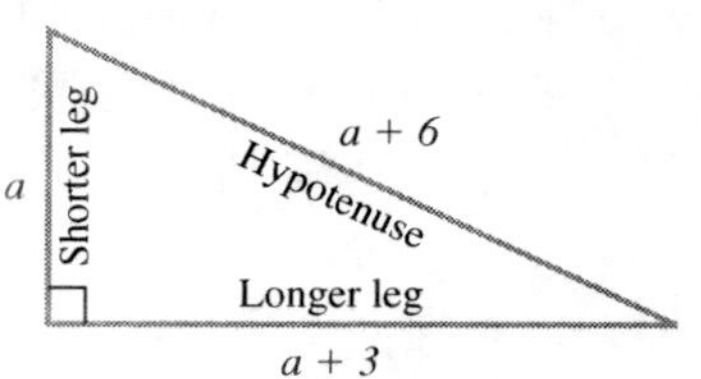

Analyze We begin by drawing a right triangle and labeling the legs and the hypotenuse.

Form We let a = the length of the shorter leg. Then the length of the hypotenuse is $a + 6$ and the length of the longer leg is $a + 3$. By the Pythagorean theorem, we have

(The length of the shorter leg)^2	plus	(The length of the longer leg)^2	equals	(The length of the hypotenuse)^2
a^2	$+$	$(a + 3)^2$	$=$	$(a + 6)^2$

Solve

$$a^2 + (a + 3)^2 = (a + 6)^2$$

$$a^2 + a^2 + 6a + 9 = a^2 + 12a + 36 \quad \text{Find } (a + 3)^2 \text{ and } (a + 6)^2.$$

$$2a^2 + 6a + 9 = a^2 + 12a + 36 \quad \text{Combine like terms on the left-hand side.}$$

$$a^2 - 6a - 27 = 0 \quad \text{Subtract } a^2\text{, } 12a\text{, and 36 from both sides to make the right-hand side 0.}$$

Now solve the quadratic equation for a.

$$a^2 - 6a - 27 = 0$$

$$(a - 9)(a + 3) = 0 \quad \text{Factor.}$$

$$a - 9 = 0 \quad \text{or} \quad a + 3 = 0 \quad \text{Set each factor to zero.}$$

$$a = 9 \quad | \quad a = -3 \quad \text{Solve each equation.}$$

State Since a side cannot have a negative length, we discard the solution -3. Thus, the shorter leg is 9 units long, the hypotenuse is $9 + 6 = 15$ units long, and the longer leg is $9 + 3 = 12$ units long.

Check The longer leg, with length 12, is 3 units longer than the shorter leg, with length 9. The hypotenuse, with length 15, is 6 units longer than the shorter leg. Since these lengths satisfy the Pythagorean theorem, the results check.

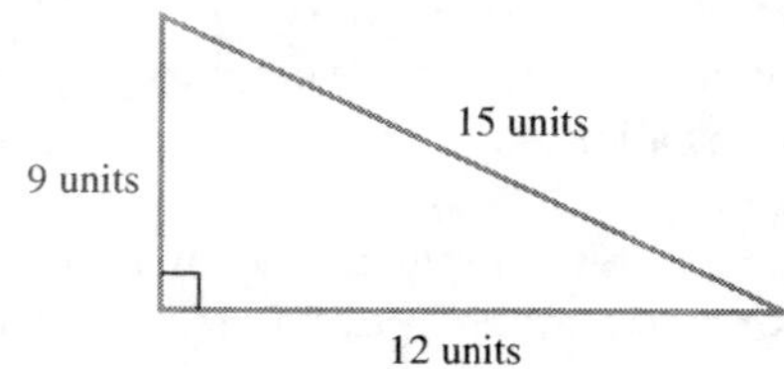

$$9^2 + 12^2 \stackrel{?}{=} 15^2$$

$$81 + 144 \stackrel{?}{=} 225$$

$$225 = 225$$

ANSWERS TO SELF CHECKS

1. 4 sec **2.** 23 and 24 **3.** 32 m **4.** 8 in., 15 in., and 17 in.

SECTION 6.13 STUDY SET

VOCABULARY

Fill in the blanks.

1. Integers that follow one another, such as 6 and 7, are called consecutive integers.
2. A right triangle is a triangle that contains a 90° angle.
3. The longest side of a right triangle is called the hypotenuse.
4. The Pythagorean theorem is a formula that relates the lengths of the three sides of a right triangle.

CONCEPTS

Fill in the blanks.

5. The formula for the area of a rectangle is $A = lw$.
6. If a and b are legs of a right triangle and c is the hypotenuse, then $a^2 + b^2 = c^2$

NOTATION

Complete each solution.

7. $0 = -16t^2 + 32t + 48$
   $0 = -16(t^2 - 2t - 3)$
   $0 = -16(t - 3)(t + 1)$
   $t - 3 = 0$ or $t + 1 = 0$
   $t = 3$ | $t = -1$

8. $6 = w(w + 1)$
   $6 = w^2 + w$
   $0 = w^2 + w - 6$
   $0 = (w + 3)(w - 2)$
   $w + 3 = 0$ or $w - 2 = 0$
   $w = -3$ | $w = 2$

APPLICATIONS

An object has been thrown straight up into the air. The formula $h = vt - 16t^2$ gives the height h of the object above the ground after t seconds, when it is thrown upward with an initial velocity v. See Example 1.

9. TIME OF FLIGHT After how many seconds will the object hit the ground if it is thrown with a velocity of 144 feet per second? 9 sec

10. TIME OF FLIGHT After how many seconds will the object hit the ground if it is thrown with a velocity of 160 feet per second? 10 sec

11. OFFICIATING Before a football game, a coin toss is used to determine which team will kick off. The height h (in feet) of a coin above the ground t seconds after being flipped up into the air is given by

$$h = -16t^2 + 22t + 3$$

How long will the coin be in the air? $\frac{3}{2} = 1.5$ sec

12. DOLPHINS The height h in feet reached by a dolphin t seconds after breaking the surface of the water is given by

$$h = -16t^2 + 32t$$

How long will it take the dolphin to jump out of the water and touch the trainer's hand? 1 sec

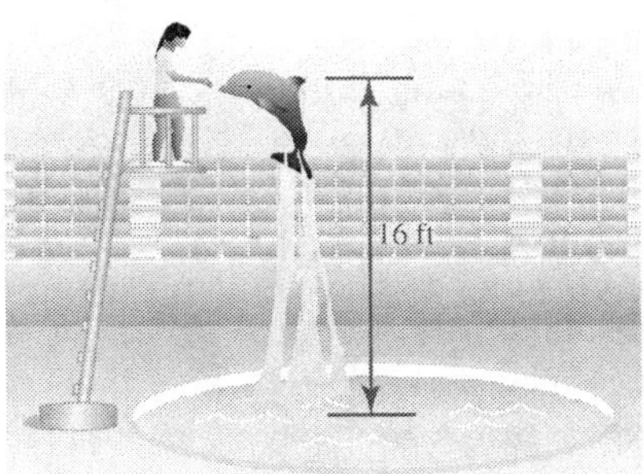

13. EXHIBITION DIVING In Acapulco, Mexico, men diving from a cliff to the water 64 feet below are a tourist attraction. A diver's height h above the water t seconds after diving is given by $h = -16t^2 + 64$. How long does a dive last? 2 sec

14. FORENSIC MEDICINE The kinetic energy E of a moving object is given by $E = \frac{1}{2}mv^2$, where m is the mass of the object (in kilograms) and v is the object's velocity (in meters per second). Kinetic energy is measured in joules. Examining the damage done to a victim, a police pathologist determines that the energy of a 3-kilogram mass at impact was 54 joules. Find the velocity at impact. (*Hint:* Multiply both sides of the equation by 2.) 6 m/s

15. CHOREOGRAPHY For the finale of a musical, 36 dancers are to assemble in a triangular-shaped series of rows, where each successive row has one more dancer than the previous row. The illustration shows the beginning of such a formation. The relationship between the number of rows r and the number of dancers d is given by

$$d = \frac{1}{2}r(r + 1)$$

Determine the number of rows in the formation. (*Hint:* Multiply both sides of the equation by 2.) 8

16. CRAFTS The illustration shows how a geometric wall hanging can be created by stretching yarn from peg to peg across a wooden ring. The relationship between the number of pegs p placed evenly around the ring and the number of yarn segments s that crisscross the ring is given by the formula

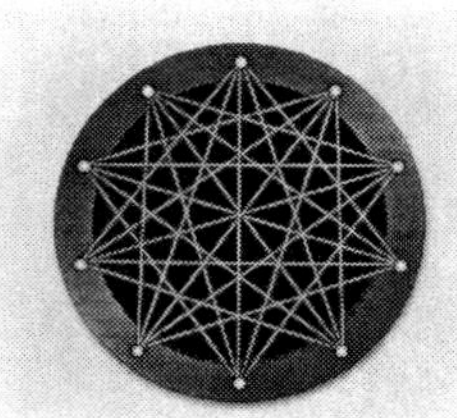

$$s = \frac{p(p - 3)}{2}$$

How many pegs are needed if the designer wants 27 segments to crisscross the ring? (*Hint:* Multiply both sides of the equation by 2.) 9

See Example 2.

17. NASCAR The car numbers of drivers Kasey Kahne and Scott Riggs are consecutive positive integers whose product is 90. If Kahne's car number is the smaller, find the number of each car. Kahne: 9, Riggs: 10

18. BASEBALL Catcher Thurman Munson and pitcher Whitey Ford are two of the sixteen New York Yankees who have had their uniform numbers retired. These numbers are consecutive integers whose product is 240. If Munson's was the smaller number, determine the uniform number of each player. Munson: 15, Ford: 16

19. CUSTOMER SERVICE At a pharmacy, customers take a number to reserve their place in line. If the product of the ticket number now being served and the next ticket number to be served is 156, what number is now being served? 12

20. HISTORY Delaware was the first state to enter the Union and Hawaii was the 50th. If we order the positions of entry for the rest of the states, we find that Kentucky entered the Union right after Vermont, and the product of their order-of-entry numbers is 210. Use the given information to complete each statement:

Kentucky was the 15 th state to enter the Union.

Vermont was the 14 th state to enter the Union.

21. PLOTTING POINTS The x- and y-coordinates of a point in Quadrant I are consecutive odd integers whose product is 143. Find the coordinates of the point. (11, 13)

22. PRESIDENTS George Washington was born on 2-22-1732. He died in 1799 at the age of 67. The month in which he died and the day of the month on which he died are consecutive even integers whose product is 168. When did Washington die? 12-14-1799

See Example 3.

23. INSULATION The area of the rectangular slab of foam insulation in the illustration is 36 square meters. Find the dimensions of the slab. 4 m by 9 m

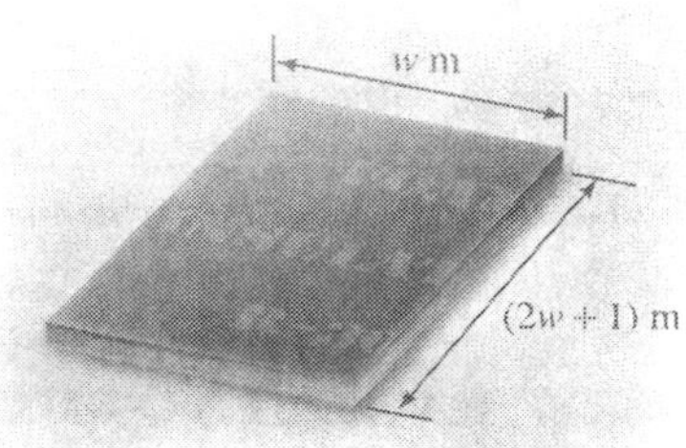

24. FLAGS The length of the flag of Australia is twice as long as it is wide. If the area of an Australian flag is 18 ft^2, find its dimensions. 3 ft by 6 ft

25. SHIPPING PALLETS The length of a rectangular shipping pallet is 2 feet less than 3 times its width. Its area is 21 square feet. Find the dimensions of the pallet. 3 ft by 7 ft

26. BILLIARDS Pool tables are rectangular and their length is twice their width. Find the dimensions of a pool table if it occupies 50 ft^2 of floor space. 5 ft by 10 ft

27. FURNITURE A rectangular kitchen table has an area of 15 square feet. Find the dimensions of the table if its length is 2 ft longer than its width. 3 ft by 5 ft

28. Suppose you are an elementary school teacher. You want to order a rectangular bulletin board to mount on a classroom wall that has an area of 90 square feet. Fire code requirements allow for no more than 30% of a classroom wall to be covered by a bulletin board. If the length of the board to be three times as long as the width, what are the dimensions of the largest bulletin board that meets fire code? 3 ft by 9 ft

from Campus to Careers
Bulletin Boards

See Example 4.

29. BOATING The inclined ramp of the boat launch shown is 8 meters longer than the rise of the ramp. The run is 7 meters longer than the rise. How long are the three sides of the ramp? 5 m, 12 m, 13 m

30. CAR REPAIRS To create some space to work under the front end of a car, a mechanic drives it up steel ramps. The ramp in the illustration is 1 foot longer than the back, and the base is 2 feet longer than the back of the ramp. Find the length of each side of the ramp. 3 ft, 4 ft, 5 ft

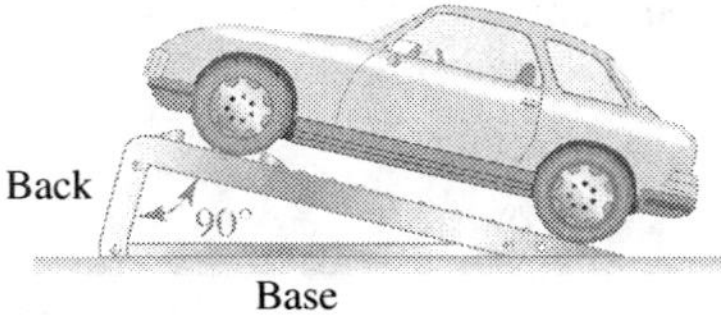

31. GARDENING TOOLS The dimensions (in millimeters) of the teeth of a pruning saw blade are given in the illustration. Find each length. 3 mm, 4 mm, 5 mm

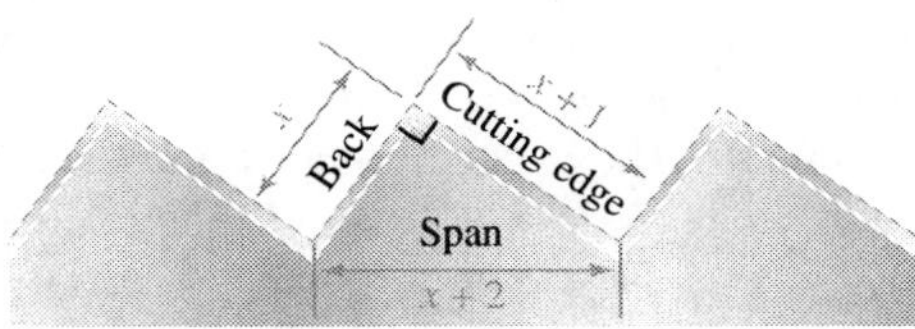

32. HARDWARE An aluminum brace used to support a wooden shelf has a length that is 2 inches less than twice the width of the shelf. The brace is anchored to the wall 8 inches below the shelf. Find the width of the shelf and the length of the brace. 6 in., 10 in.

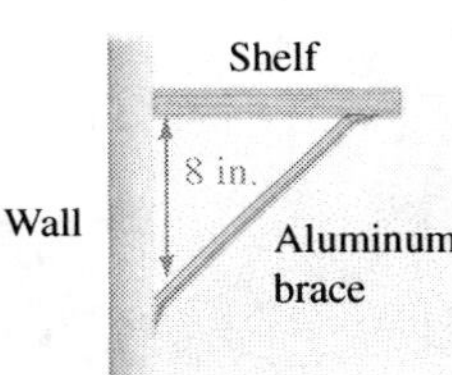

33. DESIGNING A TENT The length of the base of the triangular sheet of canvas above the door of a tent is 2 feet more than twice its height. The area is 30 square feet. Find the height and the length of the base of the triangle. $h = 5$ ft, $b = 12$ ft

34. DIMENSIONS OF A TRIANGLE The height of a triangle is 2 inches less than 5 times the length of its base. The area is 36 square inches. Find the length of the base and the height of the triangle. 4 in., 18 in.

More problems that are modeled by quadratic equations.

35. TUBING A piece of cardboard in the shape of a parallelogram is twisted to form the tube for a roll of paper towels. The parallelogram has an area of 60 square inches. If its height h is 7 inches more than the length of the base b, what is the length of the base? (*Hint:* The formula for the area of a parallelogram is $A = bh$.) 5 in.

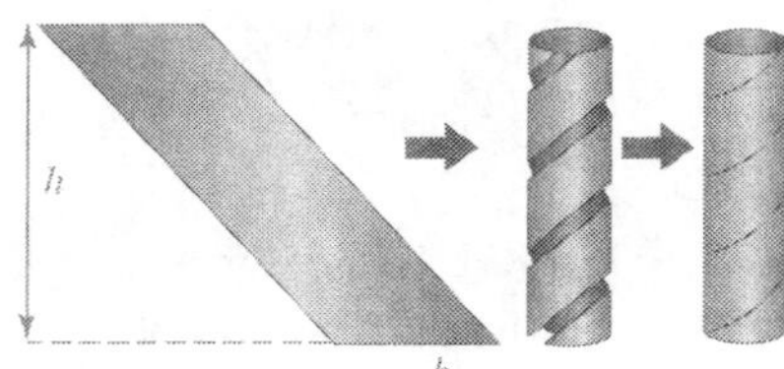

36. SWIMMING POOL BORDERS The owners of the rectangular swimming pool in the illustration want to surround the pool with a crushed-stone border of uniform width. They have enough stone to cover 74 square meters. How wide should they make the border? (*Hint:* The area of the larger rectangle minus the area of the smaller is the area of the border.) 1 m

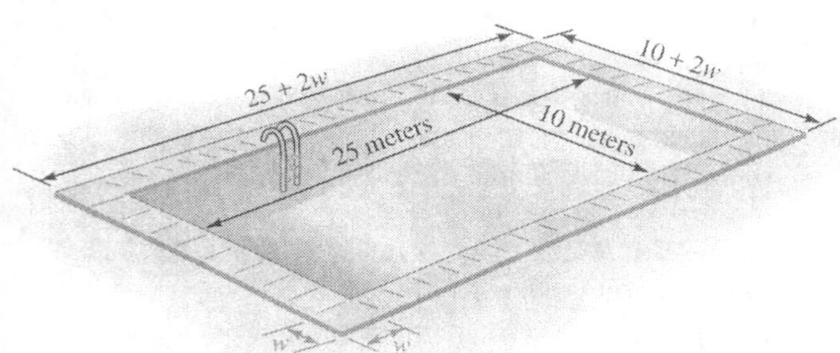

37. HOUSE CONSTRUCTION The formula for the area of a trapezoid is

$$A = \frac{h(B + b)}{2}$$

The area of the trapezoidal truss in the illustration is 24 square meters. Find the height of the trapezoid if one base is 8 meters and the other base is the same as the height. (*Hint:* Multiply both sides of the equation by 2.) 4 m

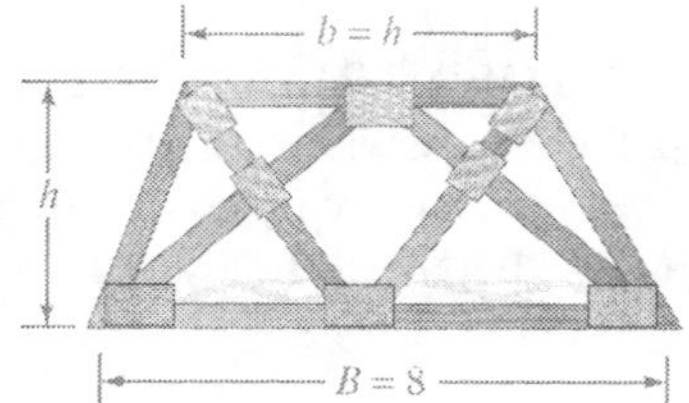

38. VOLUME OF A PYRAMID The volume of a pyramid is given by the formula

$$V = \frac{Bh}{3}$$

where B is the area of its base and h is its height. The volume of the following pyramid is 192 cubic centimeters. Find the dimensions of its rectangular base if one edge of the base is 2 centimeters longer than the other and the height of the pyramid is 12 centimeters. 6 cm by 8 cm

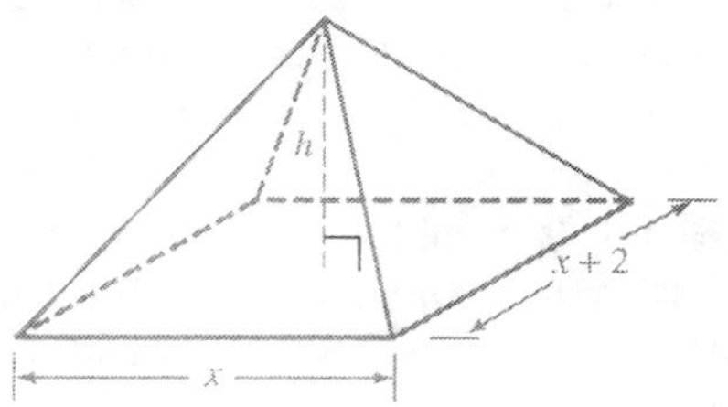

39. THRILL RIDES At the peak of a roller coaster ride, a rider's wristwatch flew off his wrist. The height h (in feet) of the watch, t seconds after he lost it, is given by $h = -16t^2 + 64t + 80$. After how many seconds will the watch hit the ground? 5 sec

40. PARADES A celebrity on the top of a parade float is tossing pieces of candy to children on the street below. The height h (in feet) of a piece of candy, t seconds after being thrown, is given by $h = -16t^2 + 16t + 32$. After how many seconds will the candy hit the ground? 2 sec

WRITING

41. Suppose that to find the length of the base of a triangle, you write a quadratic equation and solve it to find $b = 6$ or $b = -8$. Explain why one solution should be discarded.

42. What error is apparent in the following illustration?

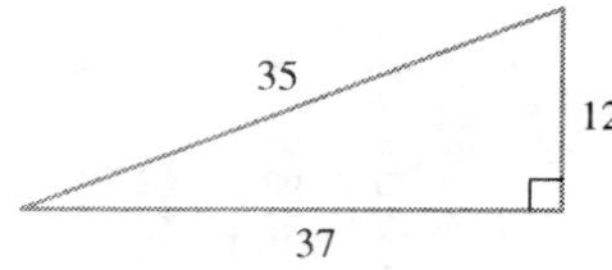

REVIEW

Find each special product.

43. $(5b - 2)^2$ $25b^2 - 20b + 4$

44. $(2a + 3)^2$ $4a^2 + 12a + 9$

45. $(s^2 + 4)^2$ $s^4 + 8s^2 + 16$

46. $(m^2 - 1)^2$ $m^4 - 2m^2 + 1$

47. $(9x + 6)(9x - 6)$ $81x^2 - 36$

48. $(5b + 2c)(5b - 2c)$ $25b^2 - 4c^2$

SECTION 6.14

Determine Minimum and Maximum Values

Objectives

1. Evaluate quadratic functions at a value.
2. Graph functions of the form $f(x) = ax^2$.
3. Graph functions of the form $f(x) = ax^2 + k$.
4. Graph functions of the form $f(x) = a(x - h)^2$.
5. Graph functions of the form $f(x) = a(x - h)^2 + k$.
6. Graph functions of the form $f(x) = ax^2 + bx + c$ by completing the square.
7. Find the vertex using $\frac{-b}{2a}$.
8. Determine minimum and maximum values.
9. Solve quadratic equations graphically.

The graph in the figure below shows a trampolinist's distance from the ground (in relation to time) as she bounds into the air and then falls back down to the trampoline.

From the graph, we can see that the trampolinist is 14 feet above the ground 0.5 second after bounding upward and that her height above the ground after 1.75 seconds is 9 feet.

The parabola shown is the graph of the *quadratic function* $s(t) = -16t^2 + 32t + 2$. In this section, we will discuss two forms in which quadratic functions are written and how to graph them.

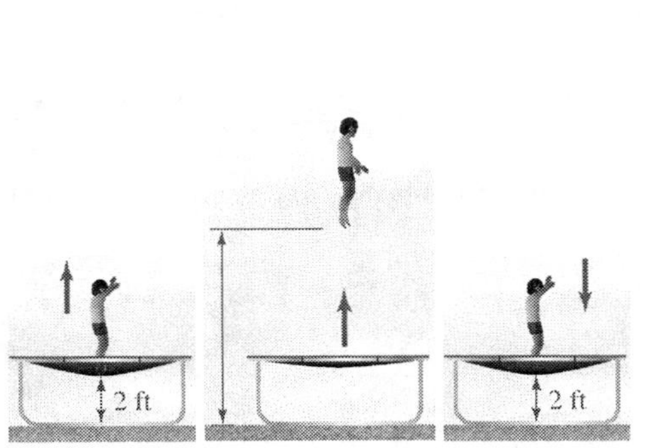

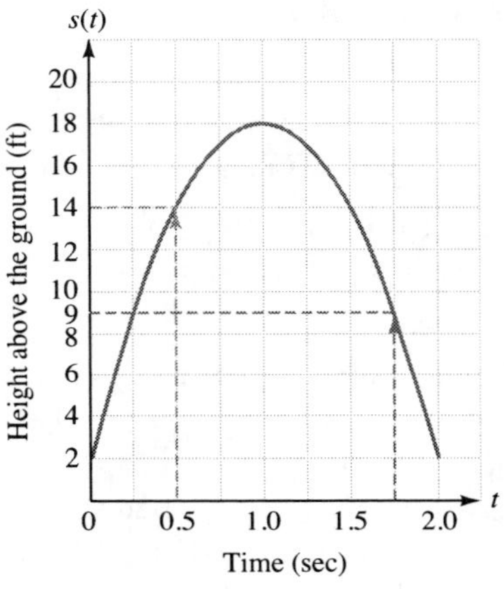

1 Evaluate quadratic functions at a value.

Quadratic Functions

A quadratic function is a second-degree polynomial function of the form

$$f(x) = ax^2 + bx + c$$

where a, b, and c represent real numbers and $a \neq 0$.

EXAMPLE 1 **Trampolines** The quadratic function $s(t) = -16t^2 + 32t + 2$ gives the distance (in feet) that the trampolinist shown in the figure above is from the ground, t seconds after bounding upward. How far is she from the ground after being in the air for $\frac{3}{4}$ second?

Strategy We will substitute 0.75 for the time t in $s(t)$ and simplify.

WHY To find her distance from the ground, we find the value of the function for $t = \frac{3}{4} = 0.75$.

Self Check 1

TRAMPOLINES Find the distance the trampolinist is from the ground after being in the air for $1\frac{1}{2}$ seconds. 14 ft

Now Try **Problem 17**

Teaching Example 1 TRAMPOLINES Find the distance the trampolinist is from the ground after being in the air for $1\frac{3}{4}$ seconds.
Use $s(t) = -16t^2 + 32t + 2$.
Answer:
9 ft

Solution

$$s(t) = -16t^2 + 32t + 2$$
$$s(0.75) = -16(0.75)^2 + 32(0.75) + 2 \quad \text{Replace } t \text{ with } 0.75.$$
$$= -9 + 24 + 2$$
$$= 17$$

The trampolinist is 17 feet off the ground $\frac{3}{4}$ second after bounding upward.

We have seen that important information can be gained from the graph of a quadratic function. We now begin a discussion of how to graph such a function by considering the simplest case, quadratic functions of the form $f(x) = ax^2$.

2 Graph functions of the form $f(x) = ax^2$.

Self Check 2

Graph: $g(x) = \frac{2}{3}x^2$

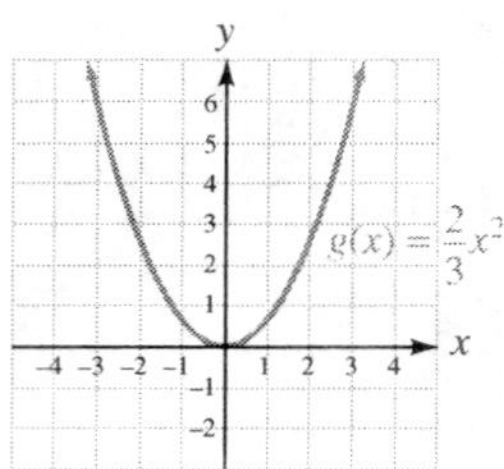

Now Try **Problem 19**

Teaching Example 2 Graph:
$g(x) = \frac{3}{2}x^2$
Answer:

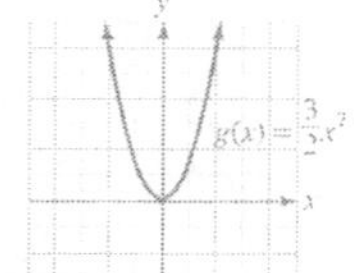

EXAMPLE 2 Graph: **a.** $f(x) = x^2$ **b.** $g(x) = 3x^2$ **c.** $h(x) = \frac{1}{3}x^2$

Strategy We can make a table of values for each function, plot each point, and connect them with a smooth curve.

WHY To graph an equation in two variables means to make a drawing that represents all of its solutions.

Solution

After graphing each curve, we note that the graph of $h(x) = \frac{1}{3}x^2$ is wider than the graph of $f(x) = x^2$, and that the graph of $g(x) = 3x^2$ is narrower than the graph of $f(x) = x^2$. In the function $f(x) = ax^2$, the smaller the value of $|a|$, the wider the graph.

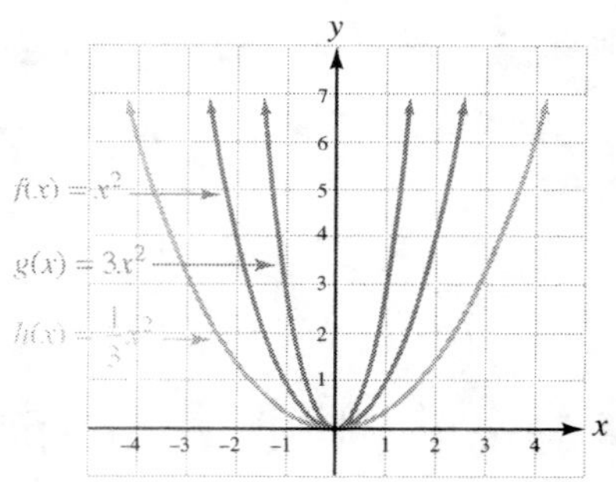

$f(x) = x^2$		
x	$f(x)$	$(x, f(x))$
−2	4	(−2, 4)
−1	1	(−1, 1)
0	0	(0, 0)
1	1	(1, 1)
2	4	(2, 4)

$g(x) = 3x^2$		
x	$g(x)$	$(x, g(x))$
−2	12	(−2, 12)
−1	3	(−1, 3)
0	0	(0, 0)
1	3	(1, 3)
2	12	(2, 12)

$h(x) = \frac{1}{3}x^2$		
x	$h(x)$	$(x, h(x))$
−2	$\frac{4}{3}$	$\left(-2, \frac{4}{3}\right)$
−1	$\frac{1}{3}$	$\left(-1, \frac{1}{3}\right)$
0	0	(0, 0)
1	$\frac{1}{3}$	$\left(1, \frac{1}{3}\right)$
2	$\frac{4}{3}$	$\left(2, \frac{4}{3}\right)$

EXAMPLE 3 Graph: $f(x) = -3x^2$

Strategy We can make a table of values for the function, plot each point, and connect them with a smooth curve.

WHY To graph an equation in two variables means to make a drawing that represents all of its solutions.

Solution

After graphing the curve, we see that the parabola opens downward and has the same shape as the graph of $g(x) = 3x^2$ in Example 2.

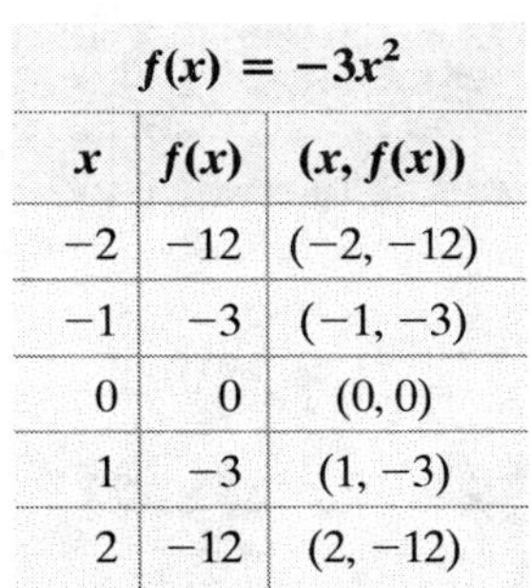

$f(x) = -3x^2$		
x	$f(x)$	$(x, f(x))$
−2	−12	(−2, −12)
−1	−3	(−1, −3)
0	0	(0, 0)
1	−3	(1, −3)
2	−12	(2, −12)

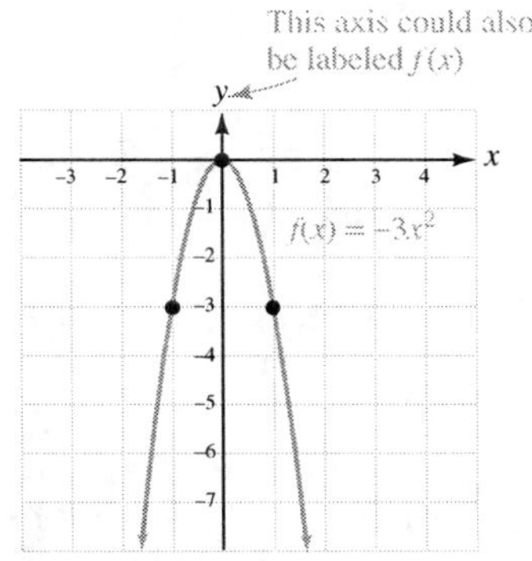

Self Check 3

Graph: $f(x) = -\frac{1}{3}x^2$

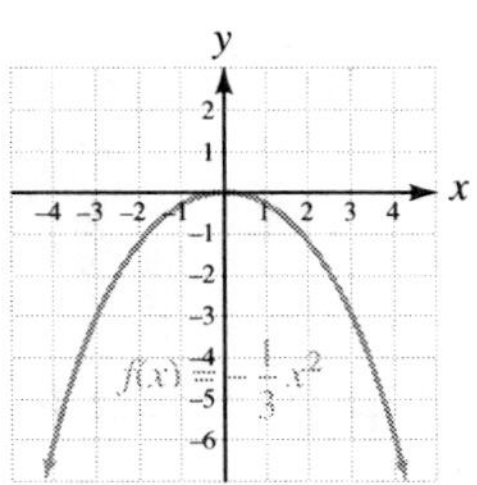

Now Try **Problem 22**

Teaching Example 3 Graph: $f(x) = -\frac{3}{2}x^2$

Answer:

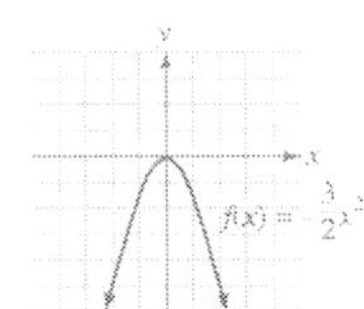

The graphs of quadratic functions of the form $f(x) = ax^2$ are **parabolas.** The lowest point of a parabola that opens upward, or the highest point of a parabola that opens downward, is called the **vertex** of the parabola. The vertical line, called an **axis of symmetry,** that passes through the vertex divides the parabola into two congruent halves. If we fold the paper along the axis of symmetry, the two sides of the parabola will match.

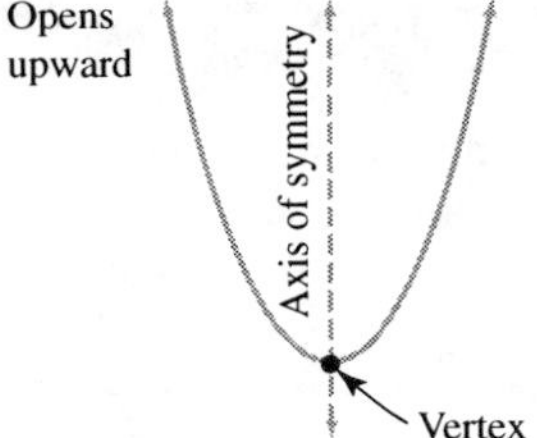

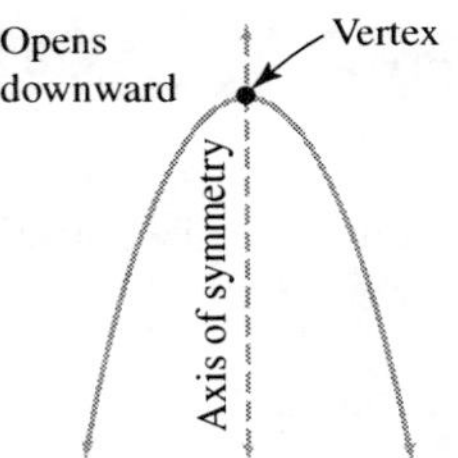

The results of Examples 2 and 3 confirm the following facts.

The Graph of $f(x) = ax^2$

The graph of $f(x) = ax^2$ is a parabola opening upward when $a > 0$ and downward when $a < 0$, with vertex at the point (0, 0) and axis of symmetry the line $x = 0$.

3 Graph functions of the form $f(x) = ax^2 + k$.

EXAMPLE 4 Graph: **a.** $f(x) = 2x^2$ **b.** $g(x) = 2x^2 + 3$ **c.** $h(x) = 2x^2 - 3$

Strategy We can make a table of values for each function, plot each point, and connect them with a smooth curve.

WHY To graph an equation in two variables means to make a drawing that represents all of its solutions.

Self Check 4

Graph: $f(x) = 2x^2 + 1$

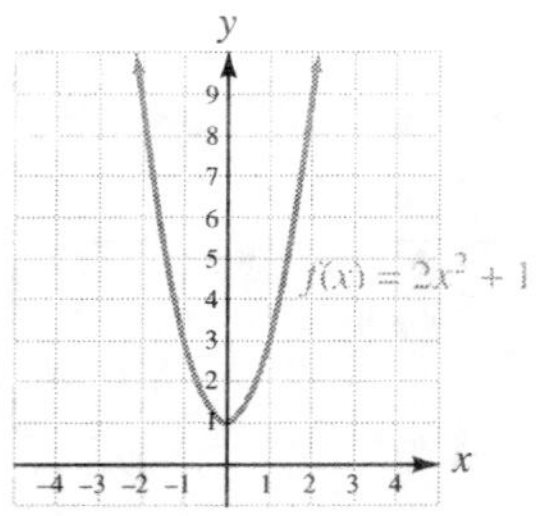

Now Try **Problem 24**

Teaching Example 4 Graph: $f(x) = 2x^2 - 1$

Answer:

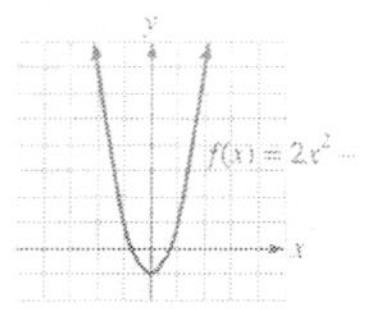

Solution

After graphing the curves, we note that the graph of $g(x) = 2x^2 + 3$ is identical to the graph of $f(x) = 2x^2$, except that it has been translated 3 units upward. The graph of $h(x) = 2x^2 - 3$ is identical to the graph of $f(x) = 2x^2$, except that it has been translated 3 units downward. In each case, the axis of symmetry is the line $x = 0$.

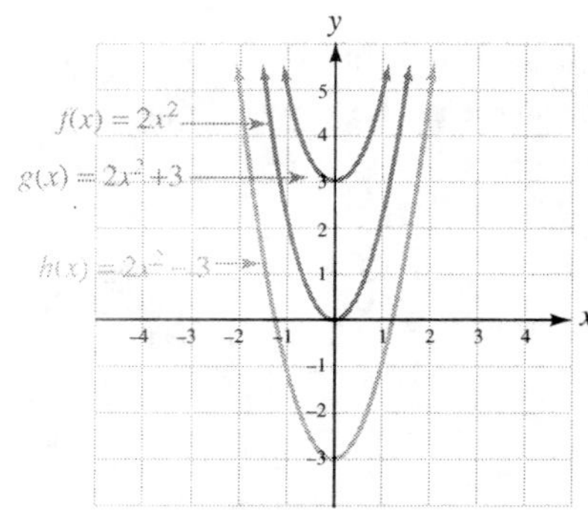

$f(x) = 2x^2$		
x	$f(x)$	$(x, f(x))$
−2	8	(−2, 8)
−1	2	(−1, 2)
0	0	(0, 0)
1	2	(1, 2)
2	8	(2, 8)

$g(x) = 2x^2 + 3$		
x	$g(x)$	$(x, g(x))$
−2	11	(−2, 11)
−1	5	(−1, 5)
0	3	(0, 3)
1	5	(1, 5)
2	11	(2, 11)

$h(x) = 2x^2 - 3$		
x	$h(x)$	$(x, h(x))$
−2	5	(−2, 5)
−1	−1	(−1, −1)
0	−3	(0, −3)
1	−1	(1, −1)
2	5	(2, 5)

The results of Example 4 confirm the following facts.

The Graph of $f(x) = ax^2 + k$

The graph of $f(x) = ax^2 + k$ is a parabola having the same shape as $f(x) = ax^2$ but translated upward k units if k is positive and downward $|k|$ units if k is negative. The vertex is at the point $(0, k)$, and the axis of symmetry is the line $x = 0$.

4 Graph functions of the form $f(x) = a(x - h)^2$.

Self Check 5

Graph: $g(x) = 2(x + 1)^2$

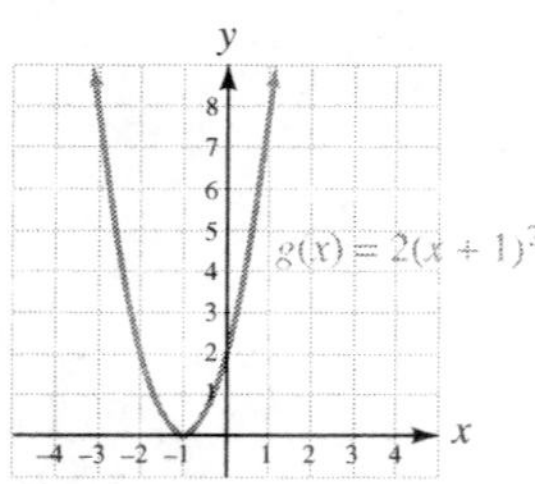

Now Try **Problem 26**

Teaching Example 5 Graph: $g(x) = 2(x - 1)^2$

Answer:

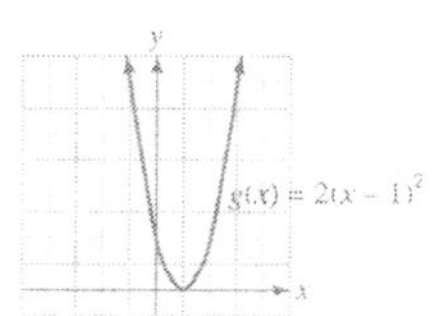

EXAMPLE 5 Graph: **a.** $f(x) = 2x^2$ **b.** $g(x) = 2(x - 3)^2$ **c.** $h(x) = 2(x + 3)^2$

Strategy We can make a table of values for each function, plot each point, and connect them with a smooth curve.

WHY To graph an equation in two variables means to make a drawing that represents all of its solutions.

Solution

After graphing the curves, we note that the graph of $g(x) = 2(x - 3)^2$ is identical to the graph of $f(x) = 2x^2$, except that it has been translated 3 units to the right. The graph of $h(x) = 2(x + 3)^2$ is identical to the graph of $f(x) = 2x^2$, except that it has been translated 3 units to the left.

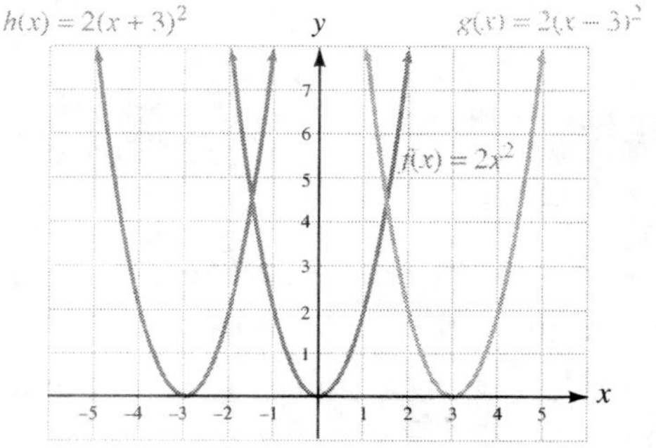

$f(x) = 2x^2$		
x	$f(x)$	$(x, f(x))$
−2	8	(−2, 8)
−1	2	(−1, 2)
0	0	(0, 0)
1	2	(1, 2)
2	8	(2, 8)

$g(x) = 2(x - 3)^2$		
x	$g(x)$	$(x, g(x))$
1	8	(1, 8)
2	2	(2, 2)
3	0	(3, 0)
4	2	(4, 2)
5	8	(5, 8)

$h(x) = 2(x + 3)^2$		
x	$h(x)$	$(x, h(x))$
−5	8	(−5, 8)
−4	2	(−4, 2)
−3	0	(−3, 0)
−2	2	(−2, 2)
−1	8	(−1, 8)

The results of Example 5 confirm the following facts.

The Graph of $f(x) = a(x - h)^2$

The graph of $f(x) = a(x - h)^2$ is a parabola having the same shape as $f(x) = ax^2$ but translated h units to the right if h is positive and $|h|$ units to the left if h is negative. The vertex is at the point $(h, 0)$, and the axis of symmetry is the line $x = h$.

5 Graph functions of the form $f(x) = a(x - h)^2 + k$.

EXAMPLE 6 Graph: $f(x) = 2(x - 3)^2 - 4$

Strategy We will determine whether the graph opens upward or downward and find its vertex and axis of symmetry. Then we will plot some points and complete the graph.

WHY This method will be more efficient than plotting many points.

Solution

The graph of $f(x) = 2(x - 3)^2 - 4$ is identical to the graph of $g(x) = 2(x - 3)^2$, except that it has been translated 4 units downward. The graph of $g(x) = 2(x - 3)^2$ is identical to the graph of $h(x) = 2x^2$, except that it has been translated 3 units to the right. Thus, to graph $f(x) = 2(x - 3)^2 - 4$, we can graph $h(x) = 2x^2$ and shift it 3 units to the right and then 4 units downward, as shown.

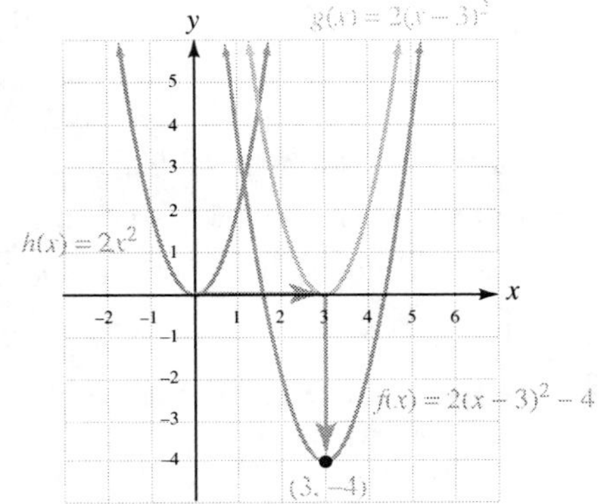

The vertex of the graph is the point $(3, -4)$, and the axis of symmetry is the line $x = 3$.

Self Check 6

Graph: $f(x) = 2(x - 1)^2 - 2$
Label the vertex and draw the axis of symmetry.

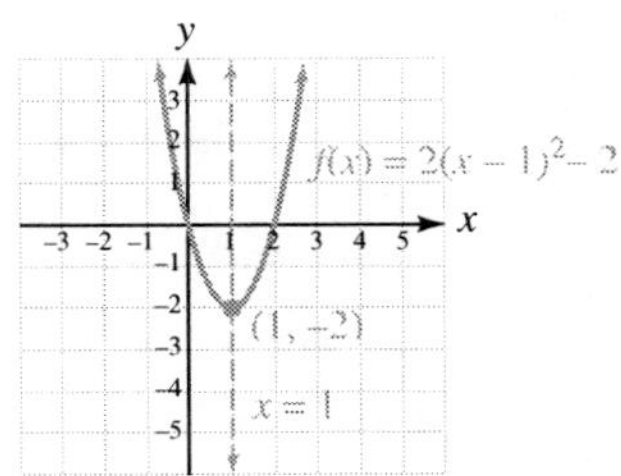

Now Try **Problem 28**

Teaching Example 6 Graph $f(x) = 2(x + 1)^2 - 3$. Label the vertex and draw the axis of symmetry.
Answer:

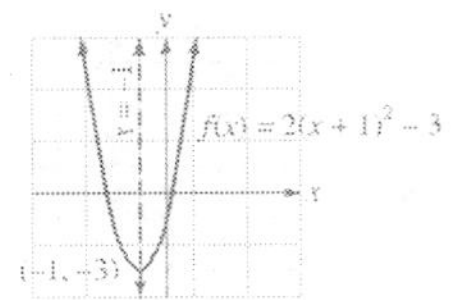

The results of Example 6 confirm the following facts.

Graphing a Quadratic Function in Standard Form

The graph of the quadratic function

$$f(x) = a(x - h)^2 + k \quad \text{where } a \neq 0$$

is a parabola with vertex at (h, k). The axis of symmetry is the line $x = h$. The parabola opens upward when $a > 0$ and downward when $a < 0$.

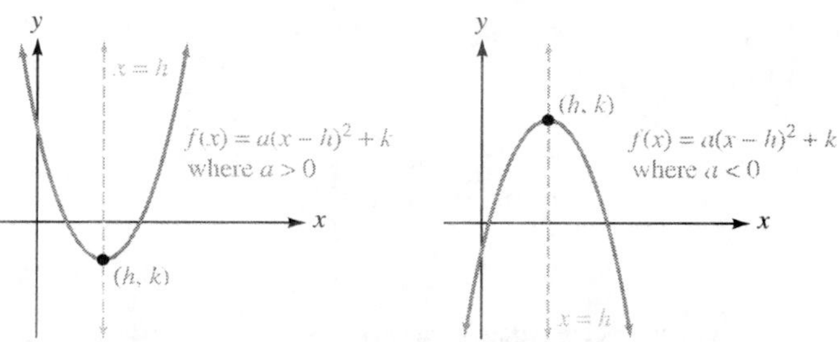

Self Check 7

Answer parts a, b, and c of Example 7 for the graph of: $f(x) = 6(x - 5)^2 + 1$

Now Try **Problem 31**

Self Check 7 Answers

a. upward

b. $(5, 1)$

c. $x = 5$

Teaching Example 7 Answer parts a, b, and c of Example 7 for the graph of: $f(x) = -2(x - 4)^2 + 5$

Answers:

a. downward

b. $(4, 5)$

c. $x = 4$

EXAMPLE 7 Consider the graph of: $f(x) = -3(x + 1)^2 - 4$

a. Does the graph open upward or downward?

b. What are the coordinates of the vertex?

c. What is the axis of symmetry?

Strategy We will compare the given equation with the standard form of a quadratic function to determine the values of a, h, and k.

WHY The coordinates of the vertex will be (h, k) and the equation of the axis of symmetry will be $x = h$. The graph will open upward if $a > 0$ or open downward if $a < 0$.

Solution

Rewriting the given function in $f(x) = a(x - h)^2 + k$ form, we have

Standard form requires a minus sign here. Standard form requires a plus sign here.

$$f(x) = \underset{a}{-3}[x - (\underset{h}{-1})]^2 + (\underset{k}{-4})$$

a. Since $a = -3 < 0$, the parabola opens downward.

b. The vertex is $(h, k) = (-1, -4)$.

c. The axis of symmetry is the line $x = h$. In this case, $x = -1$.

6 Graph functions of the form $f(x) = ax^2 + bx + c$ by completing the square.

To graph functions of the form $f(x) = ax^2 + bx + c$, we complete the square to write the function in the form $f(x) = a(x - h)^2 + k$.

EXAMPLE 8 Graph: $f(x) = 2x^2 - 4x - 1$

Strategy We will complete the square on x and write the equation of the function in standard form, $f(x) = a(x - h)^2 + k$.

WHY When the equation is in standard form we can identify a, h, and k from the equation. This information helps us sketch the graph.

Solution

Step 1 We complete the square on x to write the given function in the form $f(x) = a(x - h)^2 + k$.

$f(x) = 2x^2 - 4x - 1$

$f(x) = 2(x^2 - 2x) - 1$ Factor 2 from $2x^2 - 4x$.

Now we complete the square on x by adding 1 within the parentheses. Since this adds 2 to the right-hand side, we also subtract 2 from the right-hand side.

By the distributive property, when 1 is added to the expression within the parentheses, $2 \cdot 1 = 2$ is added to the right-hand side.

Subtract 2 to counteract the addition of 2.

$f(x) = 2(x^2 - 2x + 1) - 1 - 2$ To complete the square within the parentheses, one-half of $-2 = -1$ and $(-1)^2 = 1$.

(1) $f(x) = 2(x - 1)^2 - 3$ Factor $x^2 - 2x + 1$ and combine like terms.

Step 2 From Equation 1, we can see that $h = 1$ and $k = -3$, so the vertex will be at the point $(1, -3)$, and the axis of symmetry is $x = 1$. We plot the vertex and axis of symmetry on the coordinate system shown below.

Step 3 Finally, we construct a table of values to determine several points on the parabola. Since the x-coordinate of the vertex is 1, we choose values for x close to 1 and on the same side of the axis of symmetry. After plotting $(2, -1)$ and $(3, 5)$, we use symmetry to locate two other points on the parabola: $(-1, 5)$ and $(0, -1)$. Then we draw the graph.

$f(x) = 2x^2 - 4x - 1$

x	$f(x)$	$(x, f(x))$
2	−1	(2, −1)
3	5	(3, 5)

The x-coordinate of the vertex is 1. Choose values for x close to 1 and on the same side of the axis of symmetry.

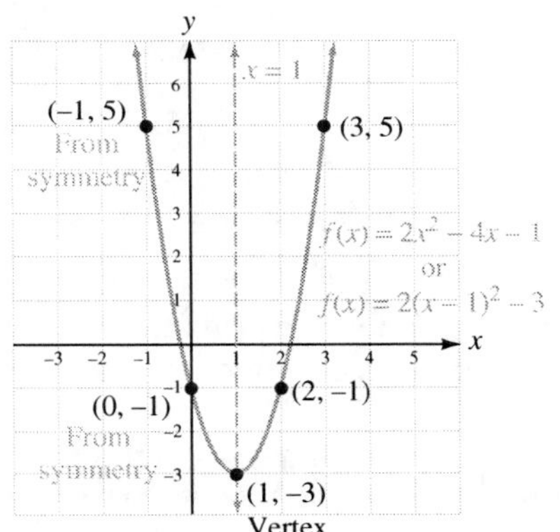

Self Check 8

Graph: $f(x) = 3x^2 - 12x + 8$

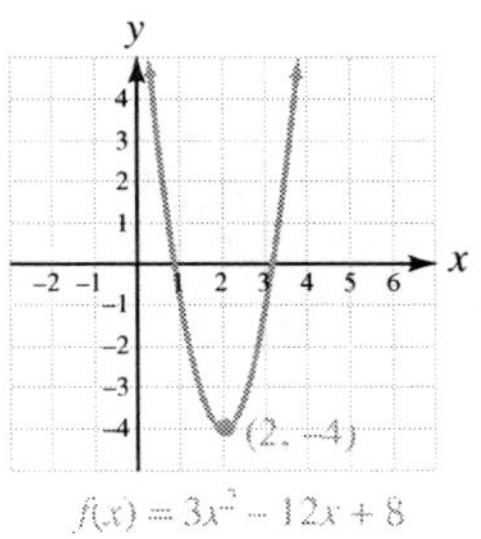

Now Try **Problem 34**

Teaching Example 8 Graph: $f(x) = -2x^2 - 12x - 17$

Answer:

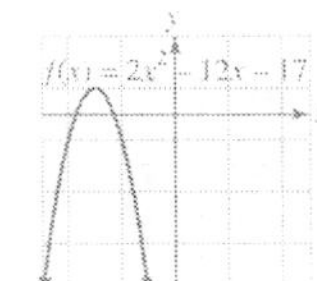

7 Find the vertex using $\frac{-b}{2a}$.

We can derive a formula for the vertex of the graph of $f(x) = ax^2 + bx + c$ by completing the square in the same manner as we did in Example 8. After using similar steps, the result is

$$f(x) = a\left[x - \left(-\frac{b}{2a}\right)\right]^2 + \frac{4ac - b^2}{4a}$$

($-\frac{b}{2a}$ is h; $\frac{4ac - b^2}{4a}$ is k)

The x-coordinate of the vertex is $-\frac{b}{2a}$. The y-coordinate of the vertex is $\frac{4ac - b^2}{4a}$. However, we can also find the y-coordinate of the vertex by substituting the x-coordinate, $-\frac{b}{2a}$, for x in the quadratic function.

Formula for the Vertex of a Parabola

The vertex of the graph of the quadratic function $f(x) = ax^2 + bx + c$ is

$$\left(-\frac{b}{2a}, f\left(-\frac{b}{2a}\right)\right)$$

and the axis of symmetry of the parabola is the line $x = -\frac{b}{2a}$.

In Example 8, for the function $f(x) = 2x^2 - 4x - 1$, $a = 2$ and $b = -4$. To find the vertex of its graph, we compute

$$\begin{aligned} -\frac{b}{2a} &= -\frac{-4}{2(2)} \\ &= -\frac{-4}{4} \\ &= 1 \end{aligned} \qquad \begin{aligned} f\left(-\frac{b}{2a}\right) &= f(1) \\ &= 2(1)^2 - 4(1) - 1 \\ &= -3 \end{aligned}$$

The vertex is the point $(1, -3)$. This agrees with the result we obtained in Example 8 by completing the square.

Using Your CALCULATOR Finding the Vertex

To graph the function $f(x) = 2x^2 + 6x - 3$ and find the coordinates of the vertex and the axis of symmetry of the parabola, we can use a graphing calculator with window settings of $[-10, 10]$ for x and $[-10, 10]$ for y. If we enter the function, we will obtain the graph shown in figure (a).

We then trace to move the cursor to the lowest point on the graph, as shown in figure (b). By zooming in, we can see that the vertex is the point $(-1.5, -7.5)$, or $\left(-\frac{3}{2}, -\frac{15}{2}\right)$, and that the line $x = -\frac{3}{2}$ is the axis of symmetry.

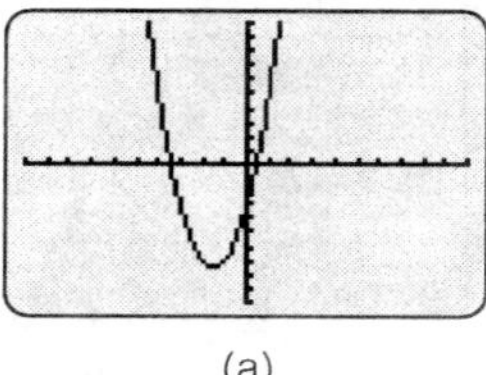

(a)

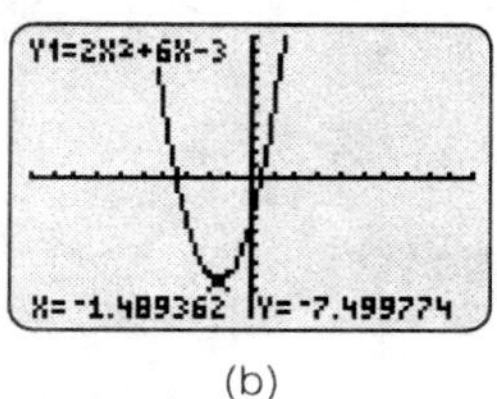

(b)

Some calculators have an fmin or fmax feature that can also be used to find the vertex. Consult your owner's manual for details.

Graphing a Quadratic Function $f(x) = ax^2 + bx + c$

We can determine much about the graph of $f(x) = ax^2 + bx + c$ from the coefficients a, b, and c. This information is summarized as follows:

- Determine whether the parabola opens upward or downward by finding the value of a.
- The x-coordinate of the vertex of the parabola is $x = -\frac{b}{2a}$.
- To find the y-coordinate of the vertex, substitute $-\frac{b}{2a}$ for x and find $f\left(-\frac{b}{2a}\right)$.
- The axis of symmetry is the vertical line passing through the vertex.
- The y-intercept is determined by the value of $f(x)$ when $x = 0$: the y-intercept is $(0, c)$.
- The x-intercepts (if any) are determined by the values of x that make $f(x) = 0$. To find them, solve the quadratic equation $ax^2 + bx + c = 0$.

8 Determine minimum and maximum values.

It is often useful to know the smallest or largest possible value a quantity can assume. For example, companies try to minimize their costs and maximize their profits. If the quantity is expressed by a quadratic function, the vertex of the graph of the function gives its minimum or maximum value.

EXAMPLE 9 *Minimizing Costs* A glassworks that makes lead crystal vases has daily production costs given by the function $C(x) = 0.2x^2 - 10x + 650$, where x is the number of vases made each day. How many vases should be produced to minimize the per-day costs? What will the costs be?

Strategy We will find the vertex of the graph of the quadratic function.

WHY The x-coordinate of the vertex indicates the number of vases to make to keep costs at a minimum, and the y-coordinate indicates the minimum cost.

Solution

The graph of $C(x) = 0.2x^2 - 10x + 650$ is a parabola opening upward. The vertex is the lowest point on the graph. To find the vertex, we compute

$$-\frac{b}{2a} = -\frac{-10}{2(0.2)} \quad b = -10 \text{ and}$$
$$= -\frac{-10}{0.4}$$
$$= 25$$

$$f\left(-\frac{b}{2a}\right) = f(25)$$
$$= 0.2(25)^2 - 10(25) + 650$$
$$= 525$$

The vertex is the point (25, 525), and it indicates that the costs are a minimum of \$525 when 25 vases are made daily.

To solve this problem with a graphing calculator with window settings of [0, 50] for x and [0, 1,000] for y, we graph the function $C(x) = 0.2x^2 - 10x + 650$. By using TRACE and ZOOM, we can locate the vertex of the graph. See the figure to the right. The coordinates of the vertex indicate that the minimum cost is \$525 when the number of vases produced is 25.

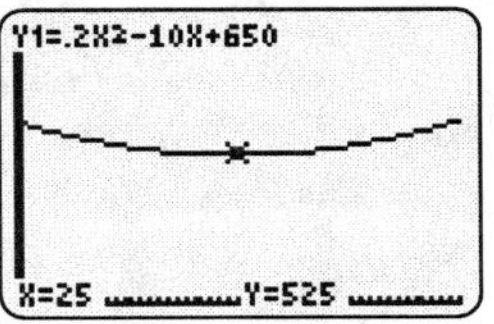

Self Check 9

MINIMIZING COSTS A manufacturing company has a daily production cost of $C(x) = 0.25x^2 - 10x + 800$, where x is the number of items produced and c is the cost. How many items should be produced to minimize the per day cost? What is the minimum cost?

Now Try **Problem 69**

Self Check 9 Answer
20, \$700

Teaching Example 9 PROFITS The profit function for a company is $P = -0.0025x^2 + 120x - 275{,}000$, where x is the number of units sold. What sales level will give a maximum profit?
Answer:
24,000 units

EXAMPLE 10 *Maximizing Area* A kennel owner wants to build the rectangular pen shown in the figure on the next page to house his dog. If he uses one side of his barn, find the maximum area that he can enclose with 80 feet of fencing.

Strategy We will find the vertex of the graph of the quadratic function.

WHY The w-coordinate of the vertex indicates the width of the pen, and the A-coordinate indicates maximum area.

Solution

We can let the width of the area be represented by w. Then the length is represented by $80 - 2w$. The function that gives the area the pen encloses is

$$A(w) = (80 - 2w)w \quad \text{To find the area of a rectangle, multiply its length and width.}$$

We can find the maximum value of A by determining the vertex of the graph of the function. This time, we will find the vertex by completing the square.

$$A(w) = 80w - 2w^2 \quad \text{Distribute the multiplication by } w.$$
$$= -2(w^2 - 40w) \quad \text{Factor out } -2.$$

Self Check 10

FENCES A farmer wants to fence in three sides of a rectangular field with 800 feet of fencing. The other side of the rectangle will be a river. If the enclosed area is to be maximum, find the dimensions of the field. 200 ft by 400 ft

Now Try **Problem 74**

Teaching Example 10 FENCES A farmer wants to fence in three sides of a rectangular field with 1,200 feet of fence. The other side of the rectangle will be a river. If the enclosed area is to be maximum, find the dimensions of the field.
Answer:
300 ft by 600 ft

$= -2(w^2 - 40w + 400) + 800$ Complete the square on w. Within the parentheses, add $\left(\frac{-40}{2}\right)^2 = 400$. Since this subtracts 800 from the right-hand side, add 800 to the right-hand side.

$= -2(w - 20)^2 + 800$ Factor $w^2 - 40w + 400$.

Thus, the coordinates of the vertex of the graph of the quadratic function are (20, 800), and the maximum area is 800 square feet.

To solve this problem with a graphing calculator with window settings of [0, 50] for x and [0, 1,000] for y, we graph the function $A(w) = -2w^2 + 80w$ to get the graph in figure (b). By using TRACE and ZOOM, we can determine the vertex of the graph, which shows that the maximum area is 800 square feet when the width is 20 feet.

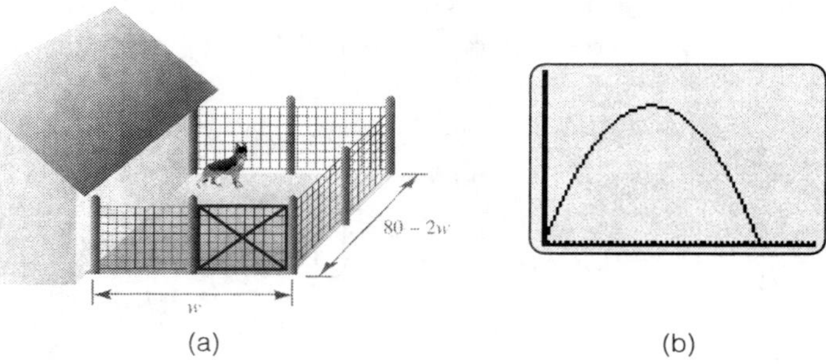

(a) (b)

THINK IT THROUGH *Automobile Accidents*

"Motor vehicle accidents can have many causes, but they can usually be divided into negligence, intentional misconduct, or product liability."

Allen L. Rothenberg, InjuryLawyer.com

The graph below shows the results of a study that explored the relationship between the age of drivers and the number of traffic accidents in which they were involved. For example, we see that drivers 16–20 years old were involved in 28 reported accidents for every one million miles driven. On the graph, sketch a parabola that could be used to model the data and locate its vertex. What information about age of the driver and traffic accidents do the coordinates of the vertex give?

We estimate that 50-year-old drivers are involved in the least number of accidents, 12 per million miles driven.

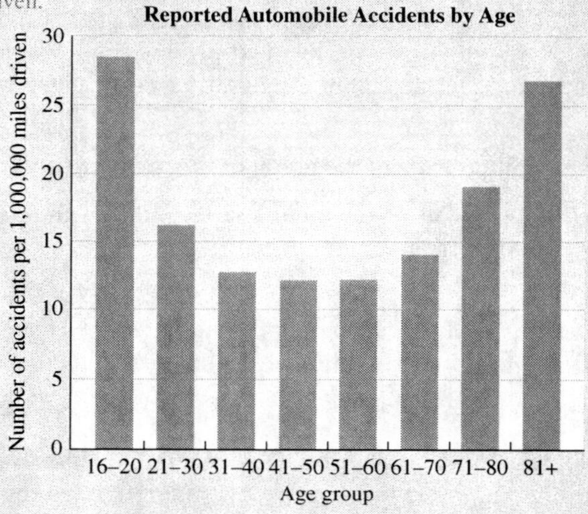

Source: Quality Planning Corporation

9 Solve quadratic equations graphically.

We can solve quadratic equations graphically. For example, the solutions of $x^2 - 6x + 8 = 0$ are the numbers x that will make y equal to 0 in the quadratic function $f(x) = x^2 - 6x + 8$. To find these numbers, we carefully inspect the graph of $f(x) = x^2 - 6x + 8$ and locate the points on the graph with a y-coordinate of 0. In the figure below, these points are (2, 0) and (4, 0), the x-intercepts of the graph. We can conclude that the x-coordinates of the x-intercepts, $x = 2$ and $x = 4$, are the solutions of $x^2 - 6x + 8 = 0$.

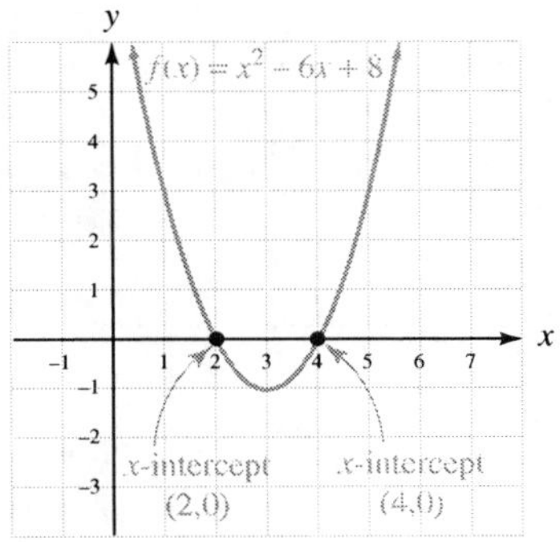

Using Your CALCULATOR **Solving Quadratic Equations Graphically**

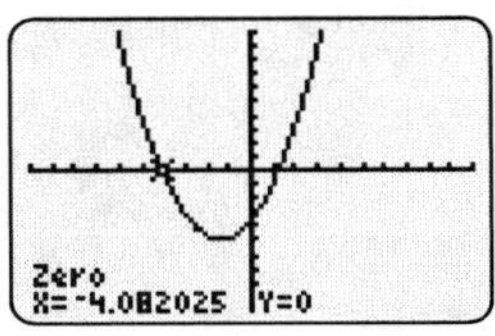

We can use a graphing calculator to find approximate solutions of quadratic equations. For example, the solutions of $0.7x^2 + 2x - 3.5 = 0$ are the numbers x that will make $y = 0$ in the quadratic function $f(x) = 0.7x^2 + 2x - 3.5$. To approximate these numbers, we graph the quadratic function and read the x-intercepts from the graph using the ZERO feature. In the figure, we see that the x-coordinate of the left-most x-intercept of the graph is given as -4.082025. This means that an approximate solution of the equation is -4.08. To find the positive x-intercept, we use similar steps.

When solving quadratic equations graphically, we must consider three possibilities. If the graph of the associated quadratic function has two x-intercepts, the quadratic equation has two real-number solutions. Figure (a) shows an example of this. If the graph has one x-intercept, as shown in figure (b), the equation has one real-number solution. Finally, if the graph does not have an x-intercept, as shown in figure (c), the equation does not have any real-number solutions.

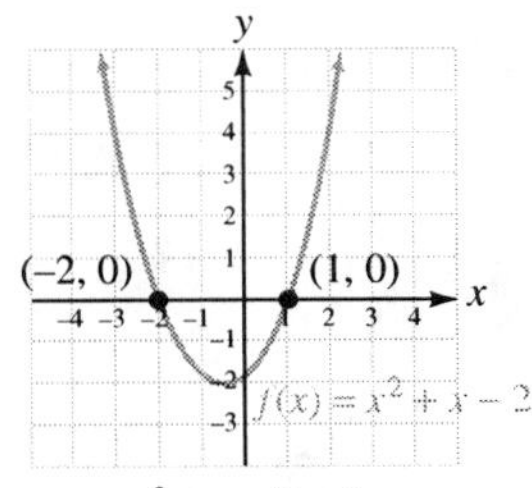

$x^2 + x - 2 = 0$ has two solutions, −2 and 1.

(a)

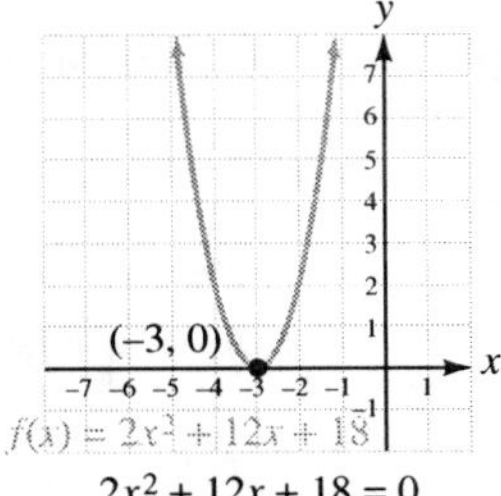

$2x^2 + 12x + 18 = 0$ has one solution, −3.

(b)

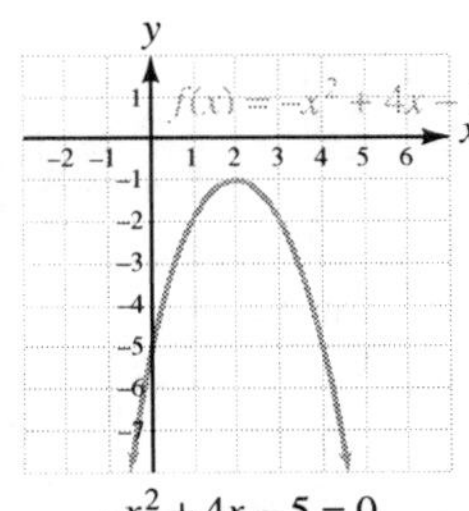

$-x^2 + 4x - 5 = 0$ has no real-number solutions.

(c)

ANSWERS TO SELF CHECKS

1. 14 ft **2.**

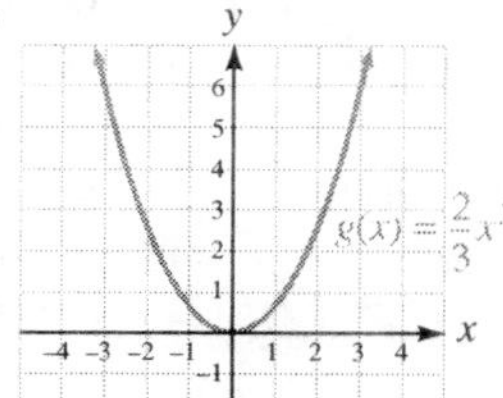

3.

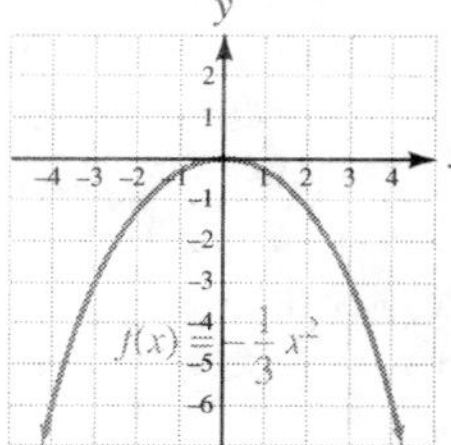

4.

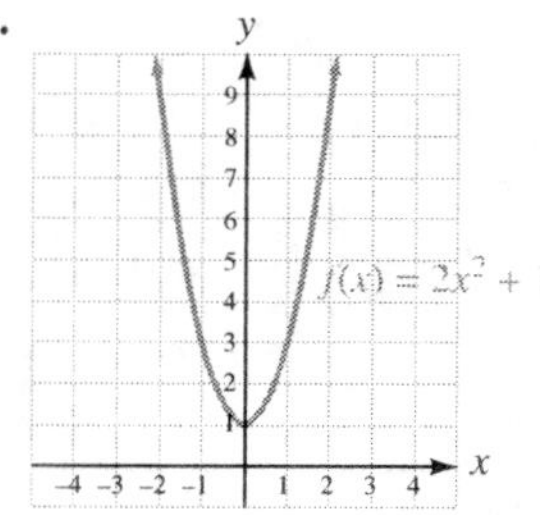

5.

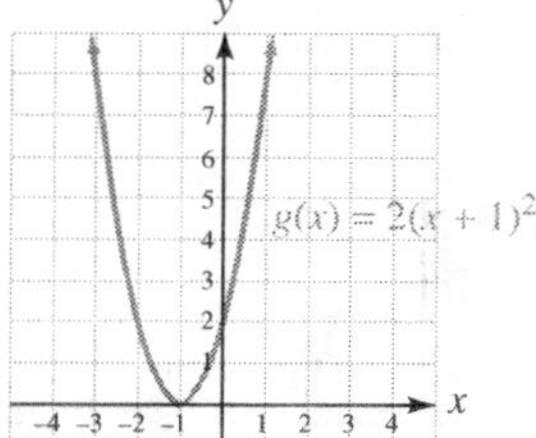

6.

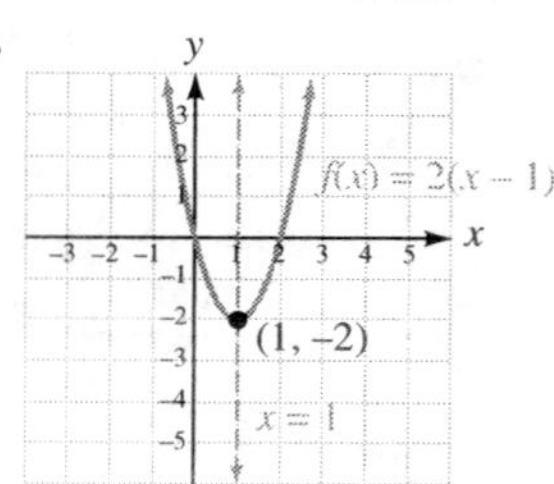

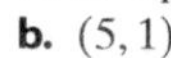

7. a. upward **b.** (5, 1) **c.** $x = 5$ **8.**

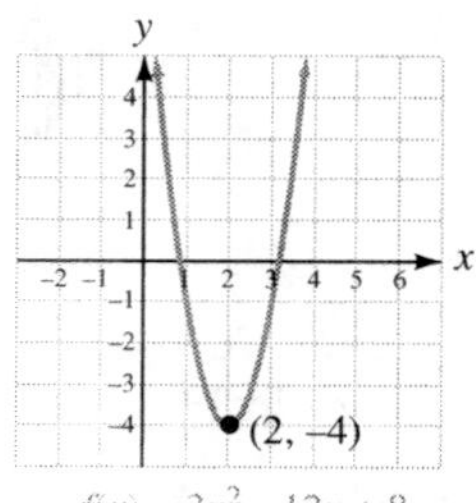

9. 20, $700 **10.** 200 ft by 400 ft

SECTION 6.14 STUDY SET

VOCABULARY

Refer to the illustration and fill in the blanks.

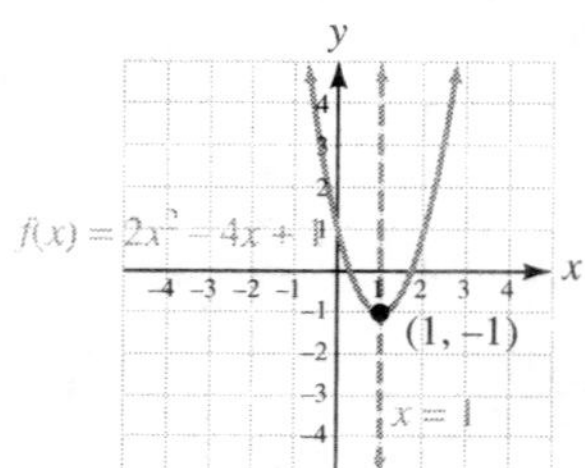

1. The function graphed in the illustration is called a quadratic function.

2. The graph is called a parabola.

3. The lowest point on the graph, $(1, -1)$, is called the vertex of the parabola.

4. The vertical line $x = 1$ divides the parabola into two halves. This line is called the axis of symmetry.

CONCEPTS

Refer to the graph below.

5. What do we call the curve? a parabola

6. Find the x-intercepts of the graph. (1, 0), (3, 0)

7. Find the y-intercept of the graph. (0, −3)

8. Find the vertex. (2, 1)

9. Find the axis of symmetry. $x = 2$

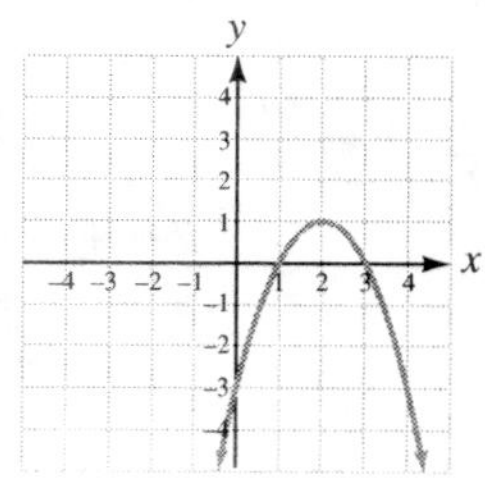

10. The vertex of a parabola is at $(1, -3)$, its y-intercept is at $(0, -2)$, and it passes through the point $(3, 1)$, as shown. Draw the axis of symmetry and use it to help determine two other points on the line.

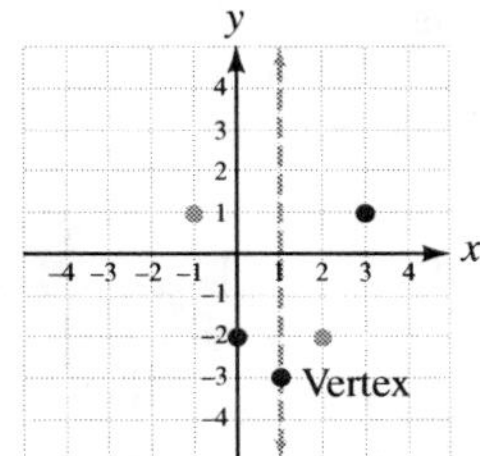

11. Use the graph of $f(x) = \frac{x^2}{10} - \frac{x}{5} - \frac{3}{2}$, shown, to estimate the solutions of the quadratic equation $\frac{x^2}{10} - \frac{x}{5} - \frac{3}{2} = 0$. $-3, 5$

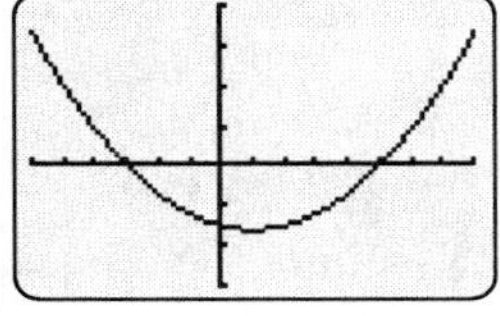

12. Three quadratic equations are to be solved graphically. The graphs of their associated quadratic functions are shown below. Determine which graph indicates that the equation has

a. two real solutions. ii

b. one real solution. iii

c. no real solutions. i

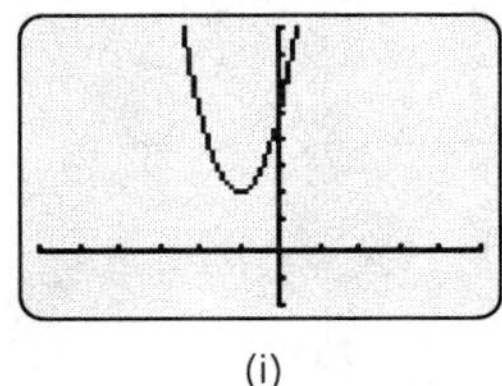
(i)

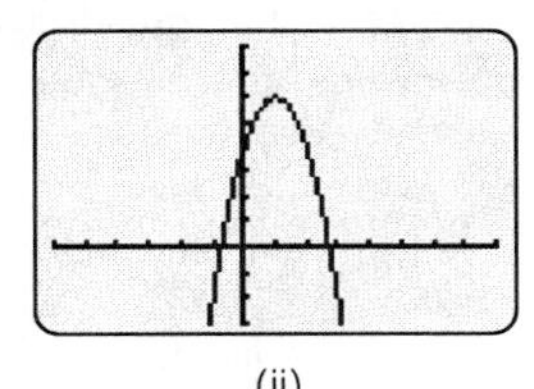
(ii)

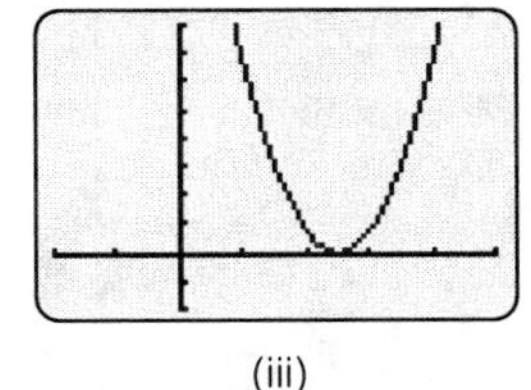
(iii)

NOTATION

13. The function $f(x) = 2(x + 1)^2 + 6$ is written in the form $f(x) = a(x - h)^2 + k$. Is $h = -1$ or is $h = 1$? Explain.
$h = -1$; $f(x) = 2[x - (-1)]^2 + 6$

14. The vertex of a quadratic function $f(x) = ax^2 + bx + c$ is given by the formula $\left(-\frac{b}{2a}, f\left(-\frac{b}{2a}\right)\right)$. Explain what is meant by the notation $f\left(-\frac{b}{2a}\right)$.
Substitute the value $-\frac{b}{2a}$ into the quadratic function for x.

GUIDED PRACTICE

Evaluate the function $s(t) = -16t^2 + 32t + 256$ for the following values of t. See Example 1.

15. $t = 0$ 256

16. $t = 3$ 208

17. $t = 3.5$ 172

18. $t = 4.5$ 76

Make a table of values for each function and graph them on the same coordinate system. See Example 2.

19. $f(x) = x^2, g(x) = 2x^2, s(x) = \frac{1}{2}x^2$

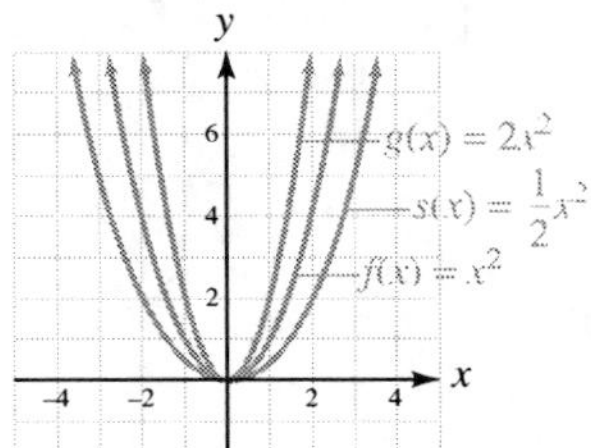

20. $f(x) = x^2, g(x) = 4x^2, s(x) = \frac{1}{4}x^2$

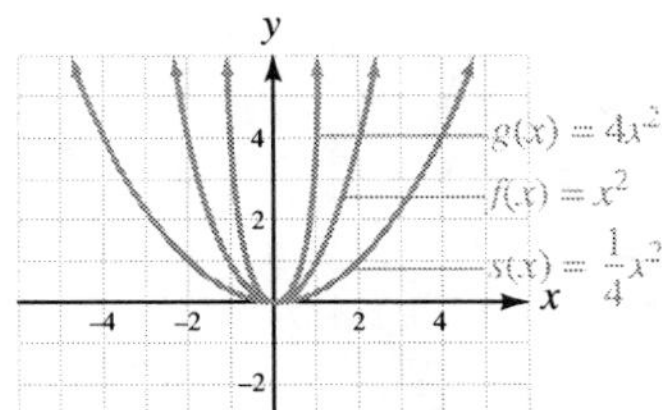

Graph each pair of functions on the same coordinate system. See Example 3.

21. $f(x) = 2x^2, g(x) = -2x^2$

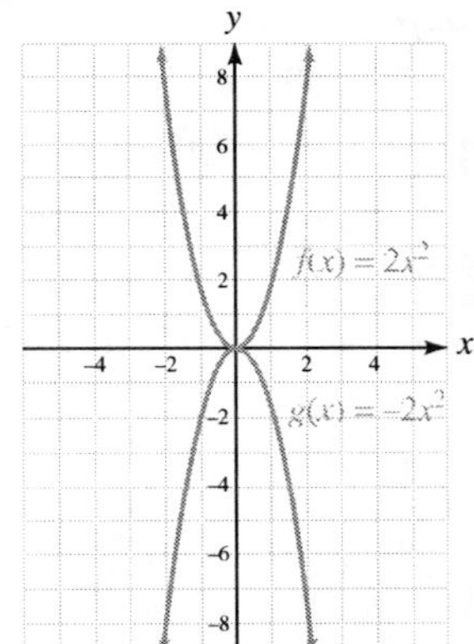

22. $f(x) = \frac{1}{2}x^2, g(x) = -\frac{1}{2}x^2$

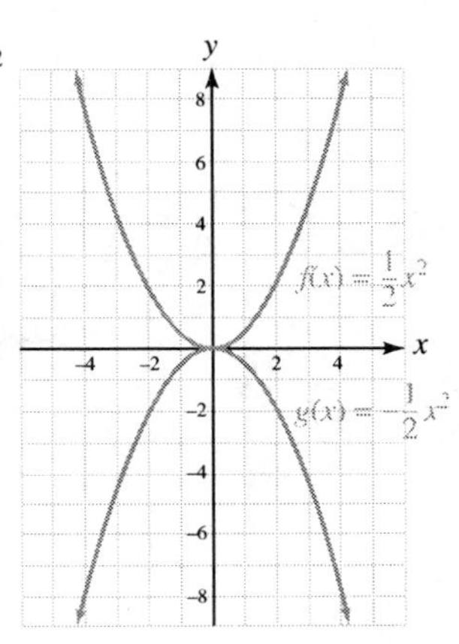

Graph each group of functions on the same coordinate system. See Example 4.

23. $f(x) = 4x^2, g(x) = 4x^2 + 3, s(x) = 4x^2 - 2$

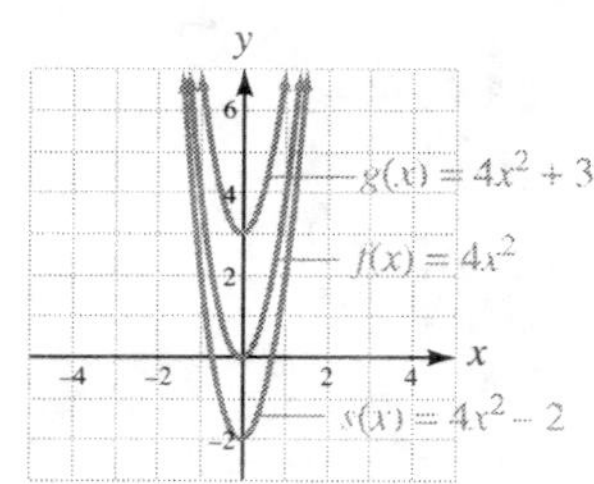

▶ **24.** $f(x) = \frac{1}{3}x^2, g(x) = \frac{1}{3}x^2 + 4, s(x) = \frac{1}{3}x^2 - 3$

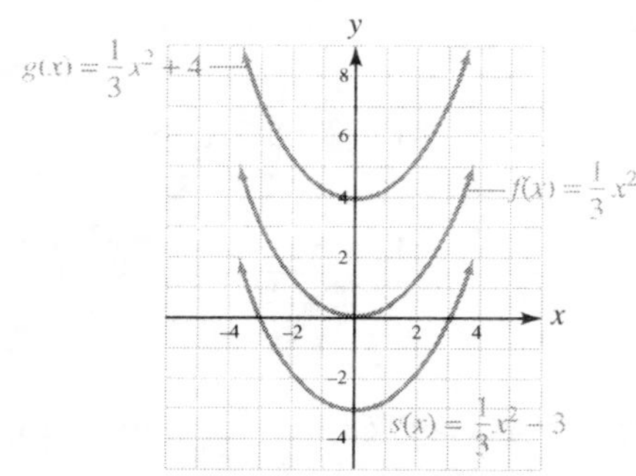

Graph each group of functions on the same coordinate system. See Example 5.

▶ **25.** $f(x) = 3x^2, g(x) = 3(x + 2)^2, s(x) = 3(x - 3)^2$

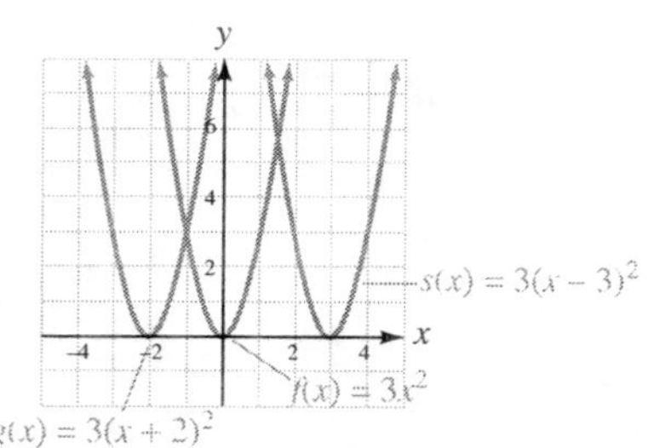

▶ **26.** $f(x) = \frac{1}{2}x^2, g(x) = \frac{1}{2}(x + 3)^2, s(x) = \frac{1}{2}(x - 2)^2$

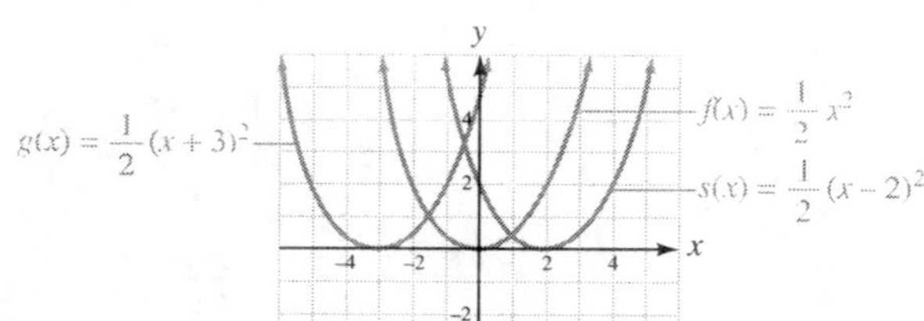

Use translations to graph each function. See Example 6.

27. $f(x) = (x - 3)^2 + 2$ ▶ **28.** $f(x) = (x + 1)^2 - 2$

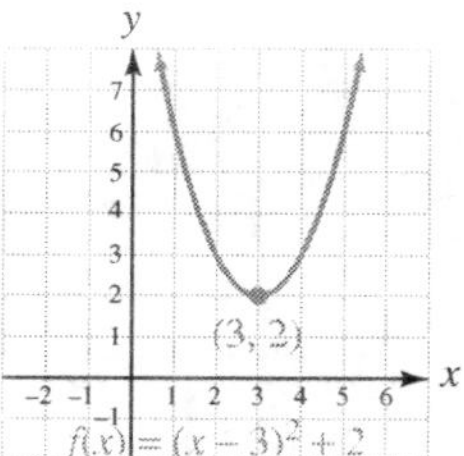

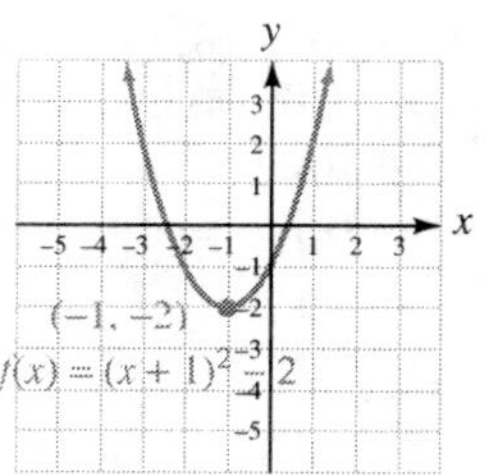

Consider the graph of each function. See Example 7.

a. ***Find the coordinates of the vertex.***

b. ***Find the axis of symmetry.***

c. ***Determine whether the graph will open upward or downward.***

29. $f(x) = (x - 1)^2 + 2$ (1, 2), $x = 1$, upward

▶ **30.** $f(x) = 2(x - 2)^2 - 1$ (2, −1), $x = 2$, upward

31. $f(x) = 2(x + 3)^2 - 4$ (−3, −4), $x = -3$, upward

▶ **32.** $f(x) = -3(x + 1)^2 + 3$ (−1, 3), $x = -1$, downward

Graph each function and find the axis of symmetry. See Example 8.

33. $f(x) = x^2 + x - 6$ axis: $x = -\frac{1}{2}$

34. $f(x) = x^2 - x - 6$

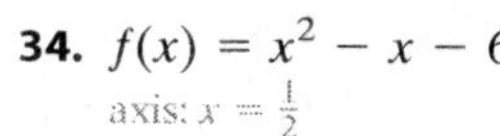

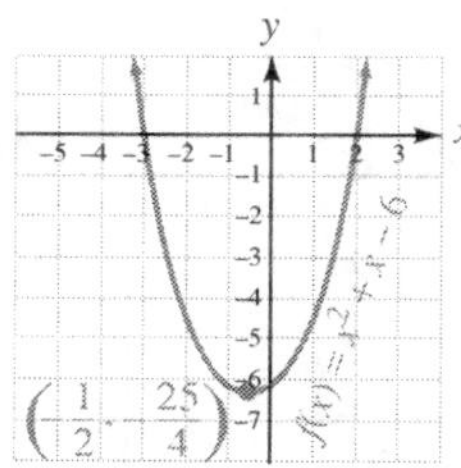

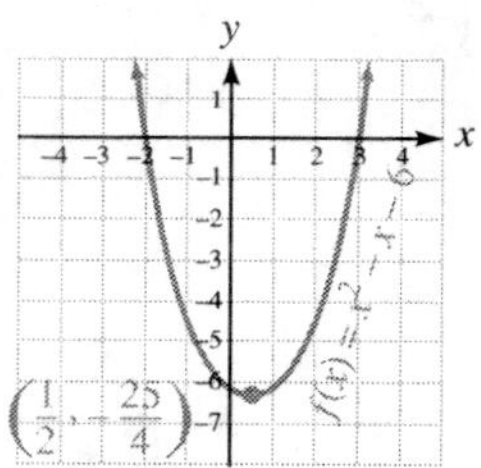

35. $f(x) = 3x^2 - 12x + 10$ axis: $x = 2$

▶ **36.** $f(x) = 4x^2 + 16x + 9$ axis: $x = -2$

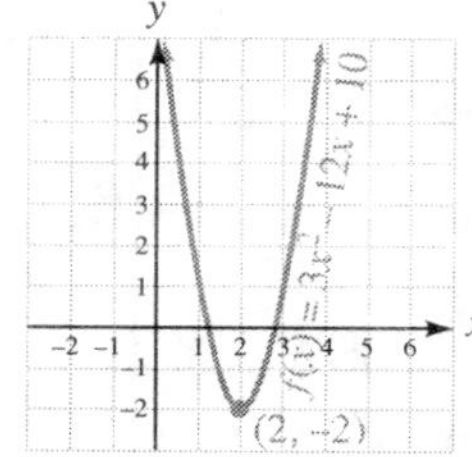

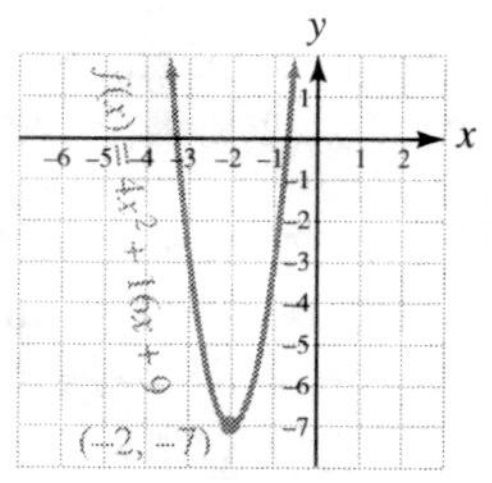

TRY IT YOURSELF

Find the coordinates of the vertex and the axis of symmetry of the graph of each function. If necessary, complete the square on x to write the equation in the form $f(x) = a(x - h)^2 + k$. Do not graph the equation, but determine whether the graph will open upward or downward, and find the axis of symmetry and the coordinates of the vertex.

37. $f(x) = 2x^2 - 4x$ (1, −2), $x = 1$, upward

38. $f(x) = 3x^2 - 3$ (0, −3), $x = 0$, upward

39. $f(x) = -4x^2 + 16x + 5$ $(2, 21)$, $x = 2$, downward

40. $f(x) = 5x^2 + 20x + 25$ $(-2, 5)$, $x = -2$, upward

41. $f(x) = 3x^2 + 4x + 2$ $\left(-\frac{2}{3}, \frac{2}{3}\right)$, $x = -\frac{2}{3}$, upward

42. $f(x) = -6x^2 + 5x - 7$ $\left(\frac{5}{12}, -\frac{143}{24}\right)$, $x = \frac{5}{12}$, downward

First determine the vertex and the axis of symmetry of the graph of the function. Then plot several points and complete the graph.

43. $f(x) = -(x - 2)^2$
$(2, 0)$ axis: $x = 2$

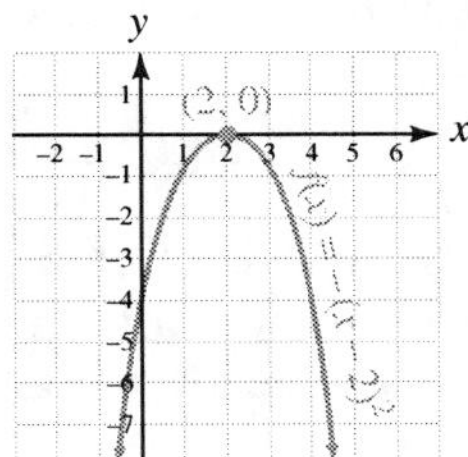

44. $f(x) = -(x + 2)^2$
$(-2, 0)$ axis: $x = -2$

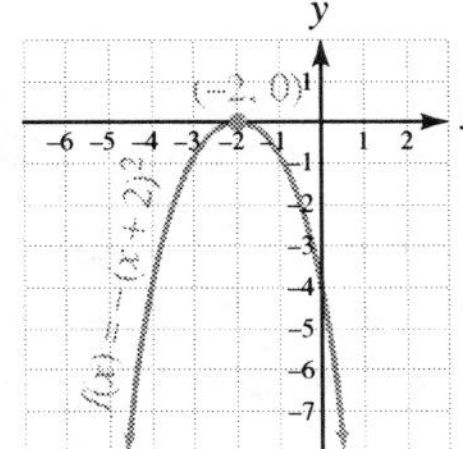

45. $f(x) = -2(x + 3)^2 + 4$
$(-3, 4)$ axis: $x = -3$

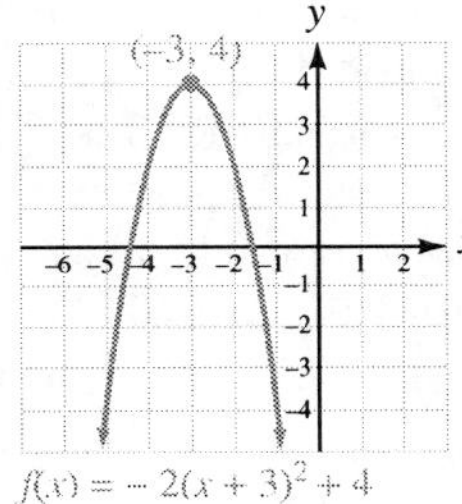

46. $f(x) = 2(x - 2)^2 - 4$
$(2, -4)$ axis: $x = 2$

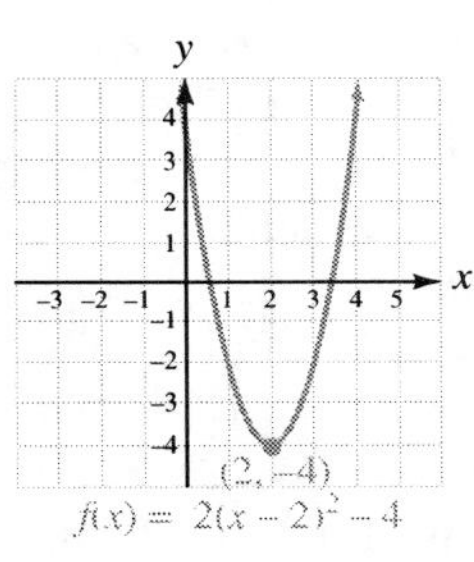

47. $f(x) = -(x + 4)^2 - 1$
$(-4, -1)$ axis: $x = -4$

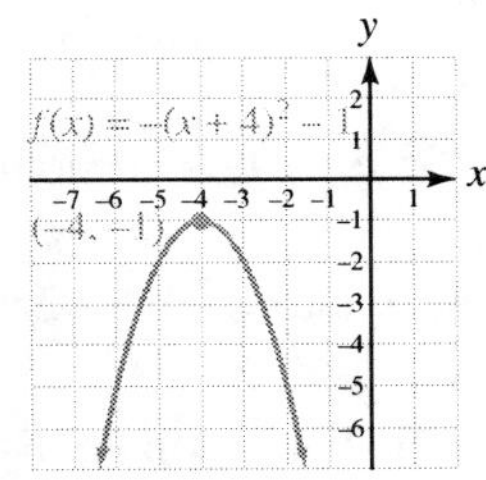

48. $f(x) = -(x - 3)^2 + 1$
$(3, 1)$ axis: $x = 3$

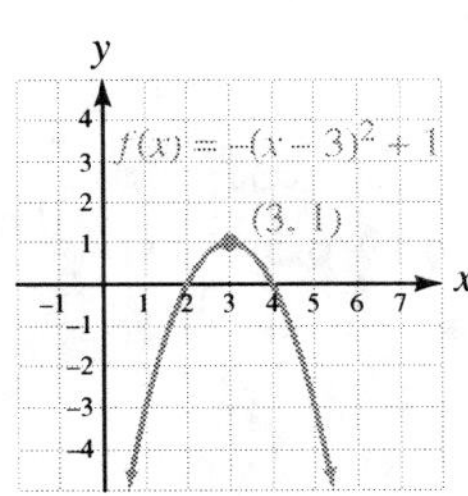

49. $f(x) = 4x^2 + 24x + 37$
$(-3, 1)$ axis: $x = -3$

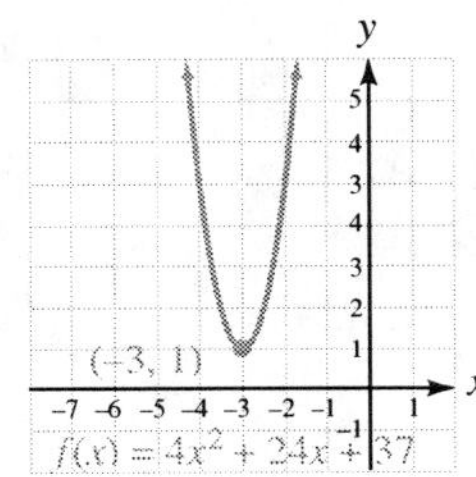

50. $f(x) = 6x^2 + 18x + 16.5$
$\left(-\frac{3}{2}, 3\right)$ axis: $x = -\frac{3}{2}$

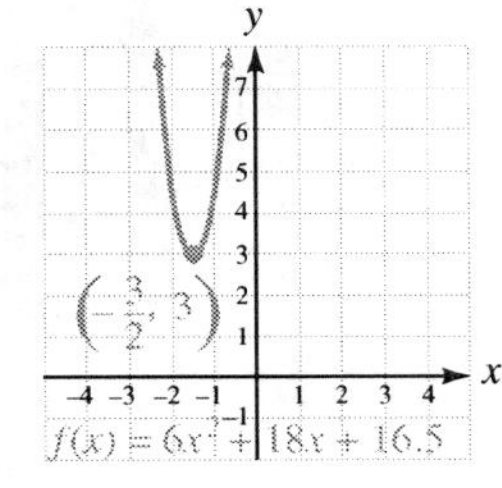

51. $f(x) = -x^2 + 2x + 3$
$(1, 4)$ axis: $x = 1$

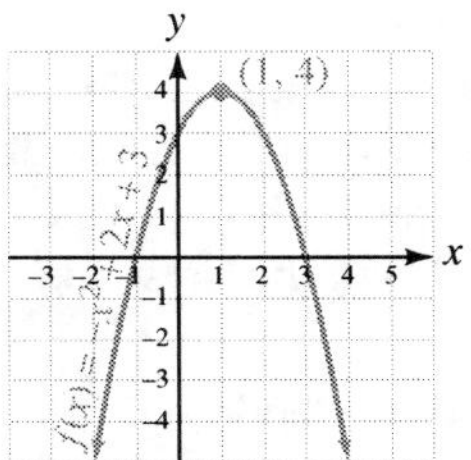

52. $f(x) = -x^2 + x + 2$
$\left(\frac{1}{2}, \frac{9}{4}\right)$ axis: $x = \frac{1}{2}$

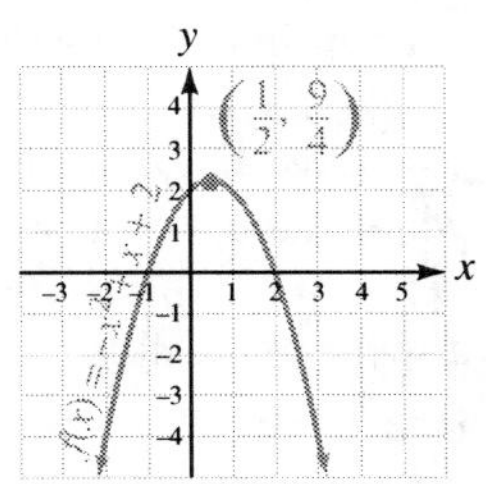

53. $f(x) = -3x^2 + 2x$
$\left(\frac{1}{3}, \frac{1}{3}\right)$ axis: $x = \frac{1}{3}$

54. $f(x) = 5x + x^2$
$\left(-\frac{5}{2}, \frac{-25}{4}\right)$ axis: $x = -\frac{5}{2}$

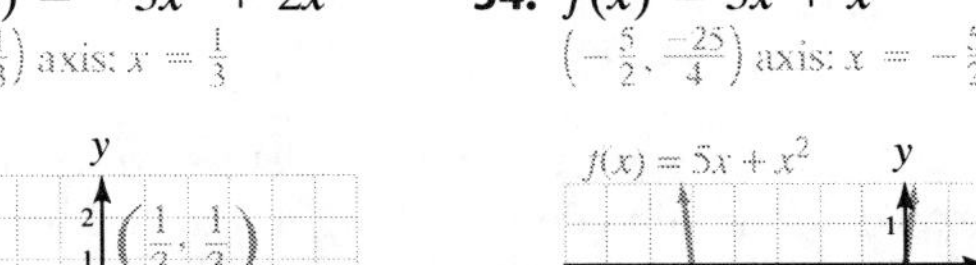

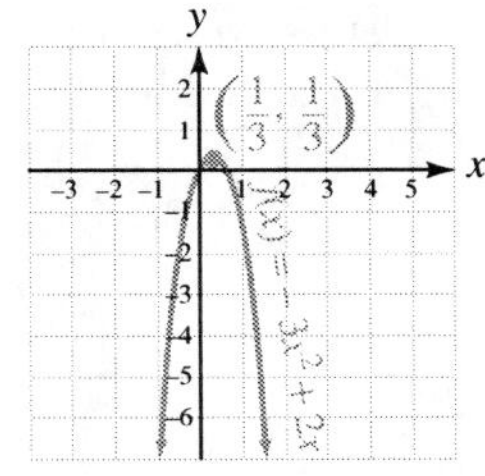

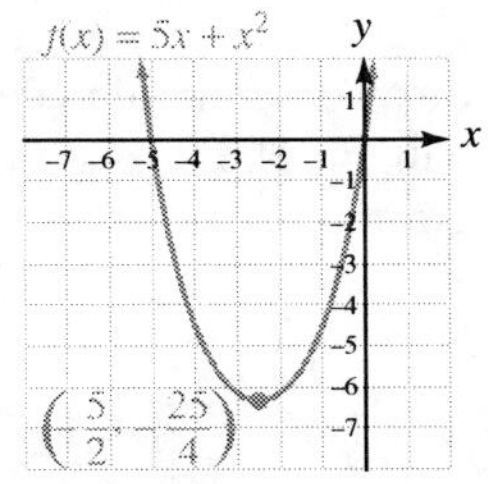

55. $f(x) = -12x^2 - 6x + 6$
$\left(-\frac{1}{4}, \frac{27}{4}\right)$ axis: $x = -\frac{1}{4}$

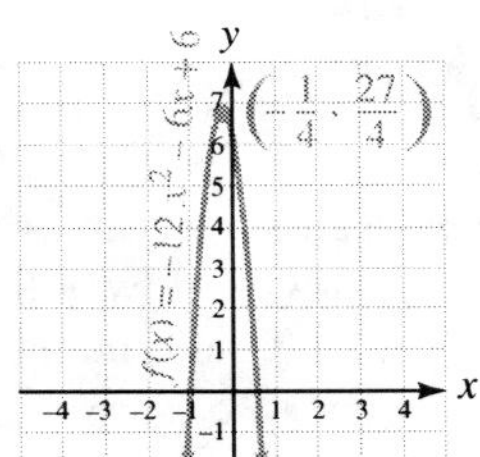

56. $f(x) = -2x^2 + 4x + 3$
$(1, 5)$ axis: $x = 1$

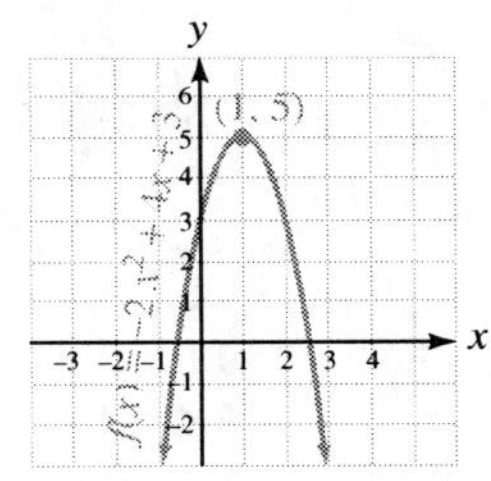

Use a graphing calculator to find the coordinates of the vertex of the graph of each quadratic function. Round to the nearest hundredth.

57. $f(x) = 2x^2 - x + 1$
$(0.25, 0.88)$

58. $f(x) = x^2 + 5x - 6$
$(-2.50, -12.25)$

59. $f(x) = 7 + x - x^2$
$(0.50, 7.25)$

60. $f(x) = 2x^2 - 3x + 2$
$(0.75, 0.88)$

Use a graphing calculator to solve each equation. If an answer is not exact, round to the nearest hundredth.

61. $x^2 + x - 6 = 0$
$2, -3$

62. $2x^2 - 5x - 3 = 0$
$3, -0.5$

63. $0.5x^2 - 0.7x - 3 = 0$
$-1.85, 3.25$

64. $2x^2 - 0.5x - 2 = 0$
$-0.88, 1.13$

APPLICATIONS

65. FIREWORKS A fireworks shell is shot straight up with an initial velocity of 120 feet per second. Its height s after t seconds is given by the equation $s = 120t - 16t^2$. If the shell is designed to explode when it reaches its maximum height, how long after being fired, and at what height, will the fireworks appear in the sky? 3.75 sec, 225 ft

66. BALLISTICS From the top of the building, a ball is thrown straight up with an initial velocity of 32 feet per second. The equation

$$s = -16t^2 + 32t + 48$$

gives the height s of the ball t seconds after it is thrown. Find the maximum height reached by the ball and the time it takes for the ball to hit the ground. 64 ft, 3 sec

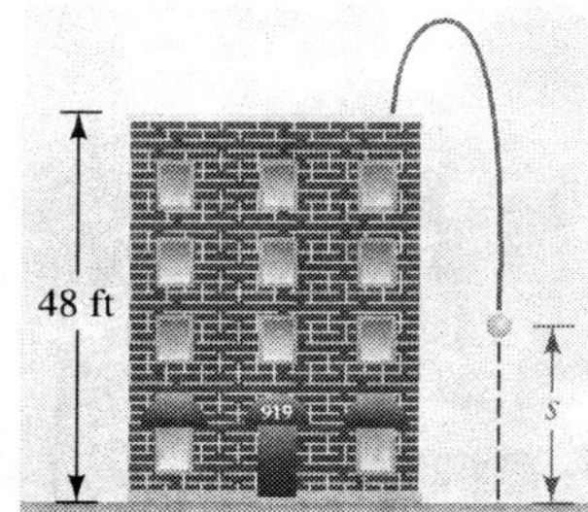

67. FENCING A FIELD A farmer wants to fence in three sides of a rectangular field shown below with 1,000 feet of fencing. The other side of the rectangle will be a river. If the enclosed area is to be maximum, find the dimensions of the field. 250 ft by 500 ft

68. POLICE INVESTIGATIONS A police officer seals off the scene of a car collision using a roll of yellow police tape that is 300 feet long, as shown below. What dimensions should be used to seal off the maximum rectangular area around the collision? What is the maximum area? 75 ft by 75 ft, 5,625 ft^2

69. OPERATING COSTS The cost C in dollars of operating a certain concrete-cutting machine is related to the number of minutes n the machine is run by the function

$$C(n) = 2.2n^2 - 66n + 655$$

For what number of minutes is the cost of running the machine a minimum? What is the minimum cost? 15 min, $160

70. WATER USAGE The height (in feet) of the water level in a reservoir over a 1-year period is modeled by the function

$$H(t) = 3.3(t - 9)^2 + 14$$

where $t = 1$ represents January, $t = 2$ represents February, and so on. How low did the water level get that year, and when did it reach the low mark? 14 ft, September

71. U.S. ARMY The function

$$N(x) = -0.0534x^2 + 0.337x + 0.969$$

gives the number of active-duty military personnel in the United States Army (in millions) for the years 1965–1972, where $x = 0$ corresponds to 1965, $x = 1$ corresponds to 1966, and so on. For this period, when was the army's personnel strength level at its highest, and what was it? Historically, can you explain why? 1968, 1.5 million; the U.S. involvement in the war in Vietnam was at its peak

72. SCHOOL ENROLLMENTS The total annual enrollment (in millions) in U.S. elementary and secondary schools for the years 1975–1996 is given by the model

$$E(x) = 0.058x^2 - 1.162x + 50.604$$

where $x = 0$ corresponds to 1975, $x = 1$ corresponds to 1976, and so on.

a. For this period, when was enrollment the lowest? What was it? 1985, 44.8 million

b. Use the model to complete the bar graph below.

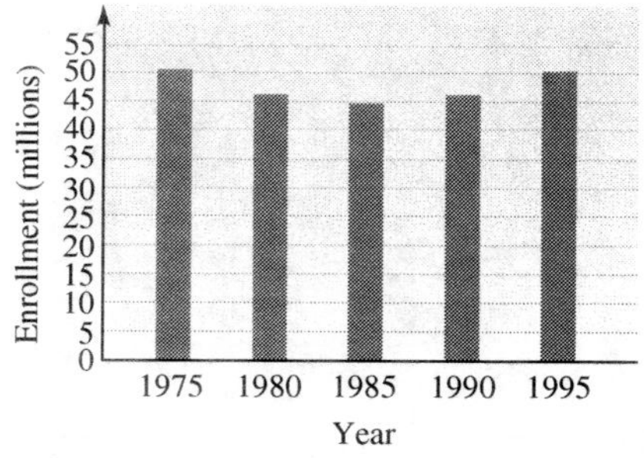

73. MAXIMIZING REVENUE The revenue R received for selling x stereos is given by the formula

$$R = -\frac{x^2}{5} + 80x - 1{,}000$$

How many stereos must be sold to obtain the maximum revenue? Find the maximum revenue. 200, $7,000

74. MAXIMIZING REVENUE When priced at $30 each, a toy has annual sales of 4,000 units. The manufacturer estimates that each $1 increase in cost will decrease sales by 100 units. Find the unit price that will maximize total revenue. (*Hint:* Total revenue = price · the number of units sold.) $35

WRITING

75. Use the example of a stream of water from a drinking fountain to explain the concepts of the vertex and the axis of symmetry of a parabola.

76. What are some quantities that are good to maximize? What are some quantities that are good to minimize?

77. A table of values for $f(x) = 2x^2 - 4x + 3$ is shown on the right. Explain why it appears that the vertex of the graph of f is the point (1, 1).

X	Y1
.25	2.125
.5	1.5
.75	1.125
1	1
1.25	1.125
1.5	1.5
1.75	2.125

X=.25

78. The illustration on the right shows the graph of the quadratic function $f(x) = -4x^2 + 12x$ with domain [0, 3]. Explain how the value of $f(x)$ changes as the value of x increases from 0 to 3.

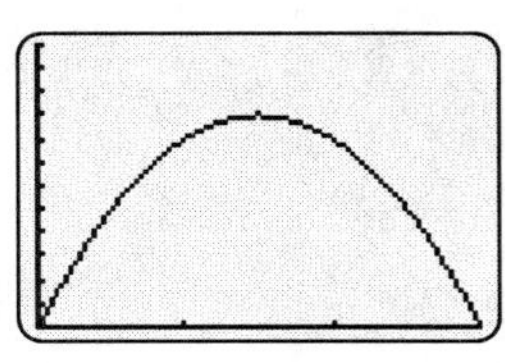

79. A mirror is held against the y-axis of the graph of a quadratic function. What fact about parabolas does this illustrate?

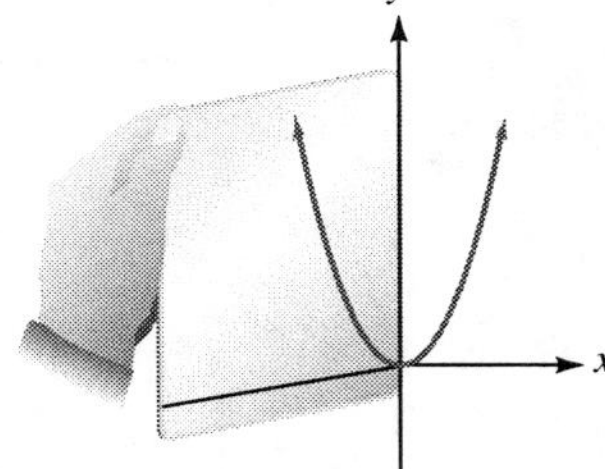

80. Give a definition of the vertex of a parabola that opens upward.

REVIEW

Perform the operations. All variables represent positive numbers.

81. $\sqrt{8a}\sqrt{2a^3b}$ $4a^2\sqrt{b}$

82. $\left(\sqrt{23}\right)^2$ 23

83. $\dfrac{\sqrt{3}}{\sqrt{50}}$ $\dfrac{\sqrt{6}}{10}$

84. $\dfrac{3}{\sqrt[3]{9}}$ $\sqrt[3]{3}$

85. $3\left(\sqrt{5b} - \sqrt{3}\right)^2$ $15b - 6\sqrt{15b} + 9$

86. $-2\sqrt{5b}\left(4\sqrt{2b} - 3\sqrt{3}\right)$ $-8b\sqrt{10} + 6\sqrt{15b}$

Module 7: Rational Expressions and Equations

DMA 070

Reggie Casagrande/Getty Images

Note: A vocation opener will be added here.

Objectives

1. Define rational expressions.
2. Evaluate rational functions.
3. Graph rational functions.
4. Find the domain of a rational function.
5. Simplify rational expressions.
6. Simplify rational expressions that have factors that are opposites.

SECTION 7.1

Rational Functions and Simplifying Rational Expressions

Linear and polynomial functions can be used to model many real-world situations. In this section, we introduce another family of functions known as *rational functions.* Rational functions get their name from the fact that their defining equation contains a *ratio* (fraction) of two polynomials.

1 Define rational expressions.

Fractions that are the quotient of two integers are *rational numbers.* Fractions that are the quotient of two polynomials are called *rational expressions.*

Rational Expressions

A **rational expression** is an expression of the form $\frac{A}{B}$, where A and B are polynomials and B does not equal 0.

Some examples of rational expressions are

$$\frac{3x}{x-7}, \quad \frac{8yz^4}{6y^2z^2}, \quad \frac{5m+n}{8m+16}, \quad \text{and} \quad \frac{6a^2-13a+6}{3a^2+a-2}$$

Caution! Since division by 0 is undefined, the value of a polynomial in the denominator of a rational expression cannot be 0. For example, x cannot be 7 in the rational expression $\frac{3x}{x-7}$, because the value of the denominator would be 0. In $\frac{5m+n}{8m+16}$, m cannot be -2, because the value of the denominator would be 0.

2 Evaluate rational functions.

Rational expressions in one variable often define functions. For example, if the cost of subscribing to an online research network is \$6 per month plus \$1.50 per hour of access time, the average (mean) hourly cost of the service is the total monthly cost, divided by the number of hours of access time used that month:

$$\frac{C}{n} = \frac{1.50n+6}{n}$$ C is the total monthly cost, and n is the number of hours the service is used that month.

The right side of this equation is a rational expression: the quotient of the binomial $1.50n + 6$ and the monomial n.

The rational function that gives the average hourly cost of using the network for n hours per month can be written

$$f(n) = \frac{1.50n+6}{n}$$

We are assuming that at least one access call will be made each month, so the function is defined for $n > 0$.

Rational Functions

A **rational function** is a function whose equation is defined by a rational expression in one variable, where the value of the polynomial in the denominator is never zero.

EXAMPLE 1 Use the function $f(n) = \frac{1.50n + 6}{n}$ to find the average hourly cost when the network described earlier is used for:

a. 1 hour **b.** 9 hours

Strategy We will find $f(1)$ and $f(9)$.

WHY The notation $f(1)$ represents the average hourly cost for 1 hour of use and $f(9)$ represents average hourly cost for 9 hours of use.

Solution

a. To find the average hourly cost for 1 hour of time, we find $f(1)$:

$$f(1) = \frac{1.50(1) + 6}{1} = 7.5$$ Input 1 for n and simplify.

The average hourly cost for 1 hour of access time is \$7.50.

b. To find the average hourly cost for 9 hours of time, we find $f(9)$:

$$f(9) = \frac{1.50(9) + 6}{9} = 2.166666666\ldots$$ Input 9 for n and simplify.

The average hourly cost for 9 hours of access time is approximately \$2.17.

Self Check 1

Find the average hourly cost when the network is used for:

a. 3 hours \$3.50

b. 100 hours \$1.56

Now Try **Problem 91**

Teaching Example 1 Use the function $f(n) = \frac{1.50n + 6}{n}$ to find the average hourly cost when the network is used for

a. 5 hours b. 10 hours

Answers:

a. \$2.70 b. \$2.10

3 Graph rational functions.

To graph the rational function $f(n) = \frac{1.50n + 6}{n}$, we substitute values for n (the inputs) in the function, compute the corresponding values of $f(n)$ (the outputs), and express the results as ordered pairs. From the evaluations in Example 1 and its Self Check, we know four such ordered pairs are: (1, 7.50), (3, 3.50), (9, 2.17), and (100, 1.56). Those pairs and others are listed in the table below. We then plot the points and draw a smooth curve through them to get the graph.

$f(n) = \frac{1.50n + 6}{n}$

n	$f(n)$	
1	7.50	→ (1, 7.50)
2	4.50	→ (2, 4.50)
3	3.50	→ (3, 3.50)
4	3.00	→ (4, 3.00)
5	2.70	→ (5, 2.70)
6	2.50	→ (6, 2.50)
7	2.36	→ (7, 2.36)
8	2.25	→ (8, 2.25)
9	2.17	→ (9, 2.17)
10	2.10	→ (10, 2.10)
100	1.56	→ (100, 1.56)

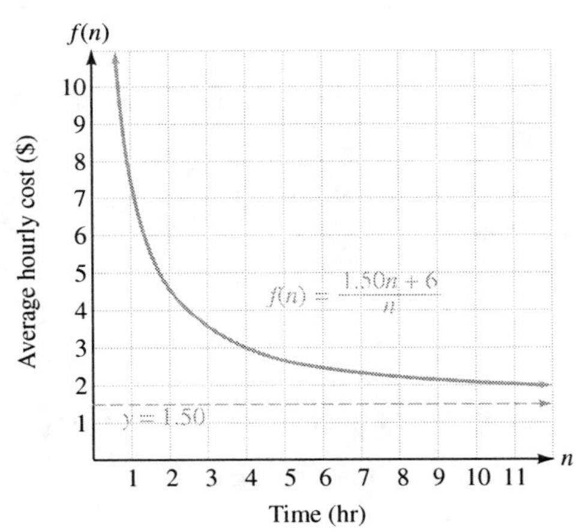

As the access time increases, the graph approaches the line $y = 1.50$, which indicates that the average hourly cost approaches \$1.50 as the hours of use increase.

From the graph, we can see that the average hourly cost decreases as the number of hours of access time increases. Since the cost of each extra hour of access time is \$1.50, the average hourly cost can approach \$1.50 but never drop below it. Thus, the graph of the function approaches the line $y = 1.5$ as n increases. When a graph approaches a line, we call the line an **asymptote.** The line $y = 1.5$ is a **horizontal asymptote** of the graph.

As n gets smaller and approaches 0, the graph approaches the y-axis. The y-axis is a **vertical asymptote** of the graph.

4 Find the domain of a rational function.

Since division by 0 is undefined, any values that make the denominator 0 in a rational function must be excluded from the domain of the function.

Self Check 2

Find the domain of:
$f(x) = \frac{x^2 + 1}{x^2 - 49}$

Now Try **Problem 25**

Self Check 2 Answer
The domain is the set of all real numbers except −7 and 7: $(-\infty, -7) \cup (-7, 7) \cup (7, \infty)$.

Teaching Example 2 Find the domain of: $f(x) = \frac{4x - 8}{x^2 - x - 12}$
Answer:
The set of all real numbers except 4 and −3. $(-\infty, -3) \cup (-3, 4) \cup (4, \infty)$ $\{x \mid x$ is a real number and $x \neq -3, x \neq 4\}$

EXAMPLE 2 Find the domain of: $f(x) = \frac{3x + 2}{x^2 + x - 6}$

Strategy We will set $x^2 + x - 6$ equal to 0 and solve for x.

WHY We don't need to examine the numerator of the rational expression; it can be any value, including 0. The domain of the function includes all real numbers, except those that make the *denominator equal to 0.*

Solution

$x^2 + x - 6 = 0$ Set the denominator equal to 0.

$(x + 3)(x - 2) = 0$ Factor the trinomial.

$x + 3 = 0$ or $x - 2 = 0$ Set each factor equal to 0.

$x = -3$ | $x = 2$ Solve each linear equation.

Thus, the domain of the function is the set of all real numbers except −3 and 2. Using set-builder notation we can describe the domain as $\{x \mid x$ is a real number and $x \neq -3, x \neq 2\}$. In interval notation, the domain is $(-\infty, -3) \cup (-3, 2) \cup (2, \infty)$. ■

The Language of Algebra Another way that Example 2 could be phrased is: *State the restrictions on the variable.* For $\frac{3x + 2}{x^2 + x - 6}$, we can write $x \neq -3$ and $x \neq 2$.

Using Your CALCULATOR **Finding the Domain and Range of a Rational Function**

We can find the domain and range of the function in Example 2 by looking at its graph. If we use window settings of $[-10, 10]$ for x and $[-10, 10]$ for y and graph the function

$$f(x) = \frac{3x + 2}{x^2 + x - 6}$$

we will obtain the graph shown on the next page.

From the figure, we can see that

- As x approaches −3 from the left, the values of y decrease, and the graph approaches the vertical line $x = -3$. As x approaches −3 from the right, the values of y increase, and the graph approaches the vertical line $x = -3$.

From the figure, we can also see that

- As x approaches 2 from the left, the values of y decrease, and the graph approaches the vertical line $x = 2$. As x approaches 2 from the right, the values of y increase, and the graph approaches the vertical line $x = 2$.

The lines $x = -3$ and $x = 2$ are vertical asymptotes. These asymptotes seem to appear in the figure. This is because graphing calculators draw graphs by connecting dots whose x-coordinates are close together. Often when two such points straddle a vertical asymptote and their y-coordinates are far apart, the calculator draws a line between them, producing what appears to be a vertical asymptote. If instead of connected mode, you set your calculator to dot mode by pressing MODE, pressing ▼ five times, pressing ▶ once, and then pressing ENTER, the vertical lines will not appear.

From the figure, we can also see that

- As x increases to the right of 2, the values of y decrease and approach the line $y = 0$.
- As x decreases to the left of -3, the values of y increase and approach the line $y = 0$.

The line $y = 0$ (the x-axis) is a horizontal asymptote. Graphing calculators do not draw lines that appear to be horizontal asymptotes.

From the graph, we can see that every real number x, except -3 and 2, gives a value of y. This observation confirms that the domain of the function is $(-\infty, -3) \cup (-3, 2) \cup (2, \infty)$. We can also see that y can be any value. Thus, the range is $(-\infty, \infty)$.

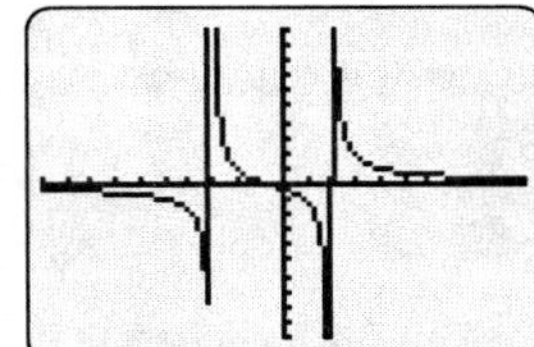

THINK IT THROUGH *Learning and Remembering*

"Most students express a wish to be more efficient in their studies. Knowing how your brain takes in and processes information, and then working with this system, will greatly improve your efficiency."

From the Study Skills Package, University of Waterloo Counseling Services

The graph below is called the *curve of forgetting.* It shows how quickly a typical student forgets the new information presented in a one-hour lecture if he or she does not review the material later. Use the graph to estimate each of the following.

1. What percent of the information is retained by Day 2? about 25%
2. What percent of the information is forgotten by Day 7? about 88%
3. What percent of the information is retained by Day 30? about 10%
4. Do you think the curve of forgetting has an asymptote? Explain why or why not. yes

For ways to improve retention, visit the website www.adm.uwaterloo.ca/infocs/study_skills/curve.html

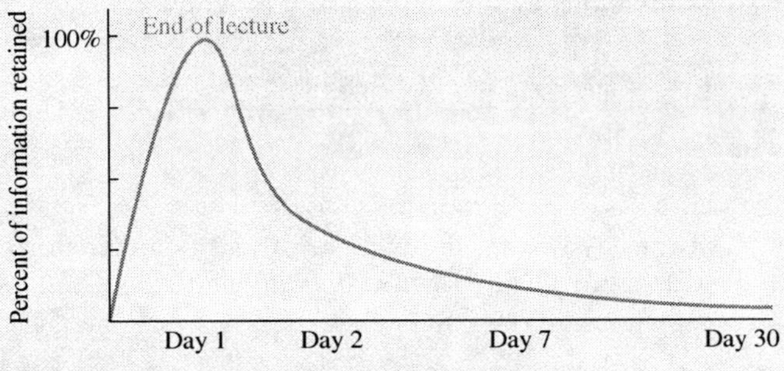

Source: The University of Waterloo, Canada, Counseling Service

5 Simplify rational expressions.

When working with rational expressions, we will use some familiar rules from arithmetic.

Properties of Fractions

If a, b, c, d, and k represent real numbers, and if there are no divisions by 0, then

1. $\frac{a}{b} = \frac{c}{d}$ if and only if $ad = bc$
2. $\frac{a}{1} = a$ and $\frac{a}{a} = 1$
3. $\frac{ak}{bk} = \frac{a}{b} \cdot \frac{k}{k} = \frac{a}{b}$
4. $-\frac{a}{b} = \frac{-a}{b} = \frac{a}{-b}$

Property 3 is true because any number times 1 is that number.

$$\frac{ak}{bk} = \frac{a}{b} \cdot \frac{k}{k} = \frac{a}{b} \cdot 1 = \frac{a}{b} \quad \text{where} \quad b \neq 0 \quad \text{and} \quad k \neq 0$$

To streamline this process, we can replace $\frac{k}{k}$ in $\frac{ak}{bk}$ with the equivalent fraction $\frac{1}{1}$.

$$\frac{ak}{bk} = \frac{a\overset{1}{\cancel{k}}}{b\underset{1}{\cancel{k}}} = \frac{a}{b} \qquad \frac{k}{k} = \frac{1}{1} = 1$$

We say that we have simplified $\frac{ak}{bk}$ by *removing a factor equal to 1.*

The Language of Algebra Property 3 is known as the *fundamental property of fractions.* Stated in another way, it enables us to divide out factors that are common to the numerator and denominator of a fraction.

To **simplify a rational expression** means to write it so that the numerator and denominator have no common factors other than 1.

Simplifying Rational Expressions

1. Factor the numerator and denominator completely to determine their common factors.
2. Remove factors equal to 1 by replacing each pair of factors common to the numerator and denominator with the equivalent fraction $\frac{1}{1}$.
3. Multiply the remaining factors in the numerator and in the denominator.

Self Check 3

Simplify: $\frac{12a^4b^2}{20ab^4}$ $\frac{3a^3}{5b^2}$

Now Try **Problem 33**

Teaching Example 3 Simplify: $\frac{10kr^3}{25k^2r^2}$

Answer:

$\frac{2r}{5k}$

EXAMPLE 3 Simplify: $\frac{8yz^4}{6y^2z^2}$

Strategy We will begin by writing the numerator and denominator in factored form. Then we will remove any factors common to the numerator and denominator.

WHY The rational expression is simplified when the numerator and denominator have no common factors other than 1.

Solution

$$\frac{8yz^4}{6y^2z^2} = \frac{2 \cdot 2 \cdot 2 \cdot y \cdot z \cdot z \cdot z \cdot z}{2 \cdot 3 \cdot y \cdot y \cdot z \cdot z}$$ Factor $8yz^4$ and $6y^2z^2$ completely.

$$= \frac{\overset{1}{\cancel{2}} \cdot 2 \cdot 2 \cdot \overset{1}{\cancel{y}} \cdot \overset{1}{\cancel{z}} \cdot \overset{1}{\cancel{z}} \cdot z \cdot z}{\underset{1}{\cancel{2}} \cdot 3 \cdot \underset{1}{\cancel{y}} \cdot y \cdot \underset{1}{\cancel{z}} \cdot \underset{1}{\cancel{z}}}$$ Replace $\frac{2}{2}$, $\frac{y}{y}$, and $\frac{z}{z}$ with $\frac{1}{1}$. This removes the factor $\frac{2 \cdot y \cdot z \cdot z}{2 \cdot y \cdot z \cdot z} = 1$.

$$= \frac{4z^2}{3y}$$

We say that $\frac{8yz^4}{6y^2z^2}$ simplifies to $\frac{4z^2}{3y}$.

An alternate approach is to use rules for exponents to simplify the rational expression.

$$\frac{8yz^4}{6y^2z^2} = \frac{\overset{1}{\cancel{2}} \cdot 2 \cdot 2 \cdot y^{1-2}z^{4-2}}{\underset{1}{\cancel{2}} \cdot 3} = \frac{4y^{-1}z^2}{3} = \frac{4z^2}{3y}$$ To divide exponential expressions with the same base, keep the base and subtract the exponents.

To simplify rational expressions, we often make use of the factoring methods discussed in Chapter 5.

EXAMPLE 4 Simplify: **a.** $\frac{6x^3}{3x^4 - 9x^3}$ **b.** $\frac{x^2 - 16}{2x^2 + 8x}$

Strategy We will begin by factoring the numerator and denominator. Then we will remove any factors common to the numerator and denominator.

WHY We need to make sure that the numerator and denominator have no common factors other than 1. If that is the case, then the rational expression is simplified.

Solution

a. $$\frac{6x^3}{3x^4 - 9x^3} = \frac{2 \cdot 3 \cdot x^3}{3x^3(x - 3)}$$ Factor the numerator. In the denominator, factor out the GCF, $3x^3$.

$$= \frac{2 \cdot \overset{1}{\cancel{3}} \cdot \overset{1}{\cancel{x^3}}}{\underset{1}{\cancel{3}} \cdot \underset{1}{\cancel{x^3}} \cdot (x - 3)}$$ Remove the factors common to the numerator and denominator.

$$= \frac{2}{x - 3}$$

b. In the numerator, we factor the difference of two squares. In the denominator, we factor out the GCF, $2x$.

$$\frac{x^2 - 16}{2x^2 + 8x} = \frac{\overset{1}{\cancel{(x + 4)}}(x - 4)}{2x\underset{1}{\cancel{(x + 4)}}}$$ Remove the binomial factor $x + 4$ that is common to the numerator and denominator.

$$= \frac{x - 4}{2x}$$ This rational expression does not simplify further.

Self Check 4

Simplify:

a. $\frac{28x^4}{7x^5 - 14x^4}$ $\frac{4}{x - 2}$

b. $\frac{x^2 - 9}{5x^2 - 15x}$ $\frac{x + 3}{5x}$

Now Try **Problems 35 and 39**

Teaching Example 4 Simplify:

a. $\frac{7a^3}{5a^4 - 7a^3}$ b. $\frac{x^2 - 4x - 12}{x^2 - 36}$

Answers:

a. $\frac{7}{5a - 7}$ b. $\frac{x + 2}{x + 6}$

When simplifying rational expressions, we can only remove *factors* common to the entire numerator and denominator. It is incorrect to remove *terms* common to the numerator and denominator.

$$\frac{\overset{1}{\cancel{x}} - 4}{2\underset{1}{\cancel{x}}} \qquad \frac{a^2 - 3a + \overset{1}{\cancel{2}}}{a + \underset{1}{\cancel{2}}} \qquad \frac{\overset{1}{\cancel{y^2}} - 36}{\underset{1}{\cancel{y^2}} - y - 7}$$

x is a term of $x - 4$. 2 is a term of $a^2 - 3a + 2$ and a term of $a + 2$. y^2 is a term of $y^2 - 36$ and a term of $y^2 - y - 7$.

Using Your CALCULATOR **Checking an Algebraic Simplification**

After simplifying an expression, we can use a scientific calculator to check the answer. One way to check whether $\frac{x^2 - 16}{2x^2 + 8x} = \frac{x - 4}{2x}$ is correct in Example 4b is to evaluate $\frac{x^2 - 16}{2x^2 + 8x}$ and $\frac{x - 4}{2x}$ for a value of x (say, 2). The expressions should give identical results.

For $\frac{x^2 - 16}{2x^2 + 8x}$:

[(] 2 [x^2] [−] 16 [)] [÷] [(] 2 [×] 2 [x^2] [+] 8 [×] 2 [)] [=] **−0.5**

For $\frac{x - 4}{2x}$:

[(] 2 [−] 4 [)] [÷] [(] 2 [×] 2 [)] [=] **−0.5**

The results of the evaluations are indeed the same. Evaluate the expressions for several other values of x. If the results differ for any given value, the original expression was not simplified correctly.

We can also use a graphing calculator to show that the simplification in Example 4b is correct. We enter the functions $f(x) = \frac{x^2 - 16}{2x^2 + 8x}$ and $g(x) = \frac{x - 4}{2x}$ as Y_1 and Y_2, respectively. See figure (a). Then select the TABLE feature. Reading across the table, the values of Y_1 and Y_2 should be the same for each value of x as shown in figure (b). Note for $x = -4$ the Y_1 value says error while the Y_2 value is 1. This happens as a result of removing the common factor $x + 4$ in the simplification.

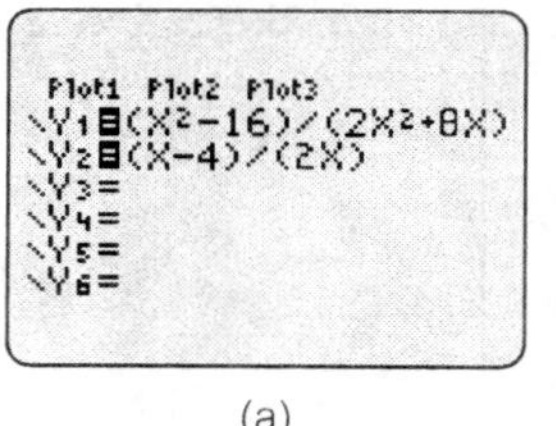

(a)

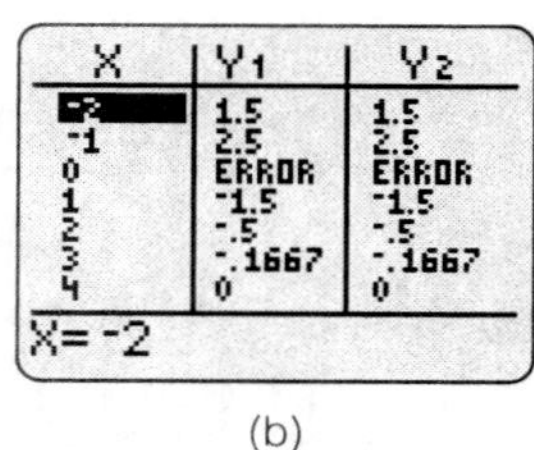

(b)

A third method to informally check the simplification is to compare the graphs of $f(x) = \frac{x^2 - 16}{2x^2 + 8x}$, shown in figure (c), and $g(x) = \frac{x - 4}{2x}$, shown in figure (d). Since the graphs appear to be the same, we can conclude that the simplification is probably correct.

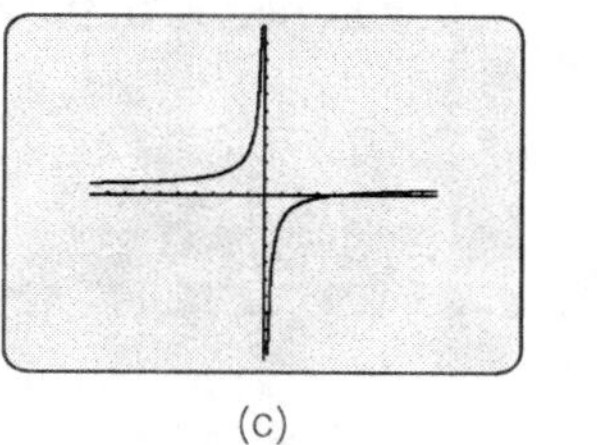
(c)

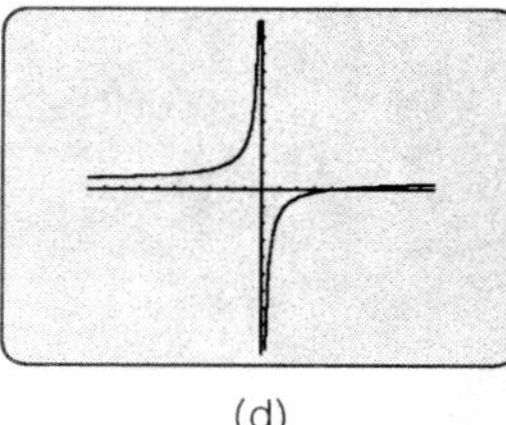
(d)

EXAMPLE 5 Simplify:

a. $\dfrac{x^2 - 10x + 25}{8x - 40}$ **b.** $\dfrac{6a^2 - 13a + 6}{3a^2 + a - 2}$ **c.** $\dfrac{y^3 - 8}{y^3 - 2y^2 + 3y - 6}$

Strategy We will begin by factoring the numerator and denominator completely. Then we will remove any factors common to the numerator and denominator.

WHY We need to make sure that the numerator and denominator have no common factors other than 1. If that is the case, then the rational expression is simplified.

Solution

a. We factor the perfect-square trinomial in the numerator. In the denominator, we factor out the GCF, 8. Then we remove the common factor, $x - 5$.

$$\frac{x^2 - 10x + 25}{8x - 40} = \frac{\overset{1}{\cancel{(x - 5)}}(x - 5)}{8\underset{1}{\cancel{(x - 5)}}}$$ Remove a factor equal to 1: $\frac{x-5}{x-5} = 1$.

$$= \frac{x - 5}{8}$$

b. We factor the trinomials in the numerator and the denominator and then remove the common factor, $3a - 2$.

$$\frac{6a^2 - 13a + 6}{3a^2 + a - 2} = \frac{\overset{1}{\cancel{(3a - 2)}}(2a - 3)}{\underset{1}{\cancel{(3a - 2)}}(a + 1)}$$ Remove a factor equal to 1: $\frac{3a-2}{3a-2} = 1$.

$$= \frac{2a - 3}{a + 1}$$ This expression does not simplify further.

c. $$\frac{y^3 - 8}{y^3 - 2y^2 + 3y - 6} = \frac{(y - 2)(y^2 + 2y + 4)}{y^2(y - 2) + 3(y - 2)}$$ In the numerator, factor the sum of two cubes. In the denominator, begin the process of factoring by grouping.

$$= \frac{(y - 2)(y^2 + 2y + 4)}{(y - 2)(y^2 + 3)}$$ In the denominator, complete the factoring by grouping.

$$= \frac{\overset{1}{\cancel{(y - 2)}}(y^2 + 2y + 4)}{\underset{1}{\cancel{(y - 2)}}(y^2 + 3)}$$ Remove the factor common to the numerator and denominator: $\frac{y-2}{y-2} = 1$.

$$= \frac{y^2 + 2y + 4}{y^2 + 3}$$ This expression does not simplify further.

Self Check 5

Simplify:

a. $\dfrac{x^2 - 6x + 9}{6x - 18}$ $\frac{x-3}{6}$

b. $\dfrac{2b^2 + 7b - 15}{2b^2 + 13b + 15}$ $\frac{2b-3}{2b+3}$

c. $\dfrac{a^3 - 1}{a^3 - a^2 + 6a - 6}$ $\frac{a^2+a+1}{a^2+6}$

Now Try **Problems 43, 47, and 51**

Teaching Example 5 Simplify:
a. $\dfrac{x^2 - 6x + 9}{5x - 15}$ b. $\dfrac{3x^2 + 2x - 8}{3x^2 - x - 4}$
c. $\dfrac{8x^3 + 27}{2x^2 + x - 3}$
Answers:
a. $\dfrac{x - 3}{5}$ b. $\dfrac{x + 2}{x + 1}$ c. $\dfrac{4x^2 - 6x + 9}{x - 1}$

Sometimes we will encounter rational expressions that are already in simplified form. For example, to attempt to simplify

$$\frac{x^2 + xa + 2x + 2a}{x^2 + x - 6}$$

we factor the numerator and denominator:

$$\frac{x^2 + xa + 2x + 2a}{x^2 + x - 6} = \frac{x(x + a) + 2(x + a)}{(x - 2)(x + 3)}$$ In the numerator, begin the process of factoring by grouping. In the denominator, factor the trinomial.

$$= \frac{(x + a)(x + 2)}{(x - 2)(x + 3)}$$ In the numerator, complete the factoring by grouping.

Since there are no common factors in the numerator and denominator, the rational expression is in *lowest terms.* It cannot be simplified.

6 Simplify rational expressions that have factors that are opposites.

If the terms of two polynomials are the same, except that they are opposite in sign, the polynomials are *opposites.* For example, $b - a$ and $a - b$ are opposites.

To simplify $\frac{b-a}{a-b}$, the quotient of opposites, we factor -1 from the numerator and remove any factors common to both the numerator and the denominator:

$$\frac{b-a}{a-b} = \frac{-a+b}{a-b}$$ Rewrite the numerator.

$$= \frac{-\overset{1}{\cancel{(a-b)}}}{\underset{1}{\cancel{(a-b)}}}$$ Factor out -1 from each term in the numerator and remove the common factor $a - b$.

$$= \frac{-1}{1}$$

$$= -1$$

In general, we have the following principle.

The Quotient of Opposites

The quotient of any nonzero polynomial and its opposite is -1.

Self Check 6

Simplify: $\frac{2a^2 - 3ab - 9b^2}{3b^2 - ab}$

Now Try **Problem 55**

Self Check 6 Answer

$-\frac{2a+3b}{b}$ or $\frac{-2a-3b}{b}$

Teaching Example 6 Simplify: $\frac{x^2 - 13xy + 12y^2}{144y^2 - x^2}$

Answer: $-\frac{x-y}{x+12y}$

EXAMPLE 6 Simplify: $\frac{3x^2 - 10xy - 8y^2}{4y^2 - xy}$

Strategy We will begin by factoring the numerator and denominator. Then we look for common factors, or factors that are opposites, and remove them.

WHY We need to make sure that the numerator and denominator have no common factors other than 1. If that is the case, then the rational expression is simplified.

Solution

We factor the numerator and denominator. Because $x - 4y$ and $4y - x$ are opposites, their quotient is -1.

$$\frac{3x^2 - 10xy - 8y^2}{4y^2 - xy} = \frac{(3x+2y)\overset{-1}{\cancel{(x-4y)}}}{y\underset{1}{\cancel{(4y-x)}}}$$ Since $x - 4y$ and $4y - x$ are opposites, simplify by replacing $\frac{x-4y}{4y-x}$ with the equivalent fraction $\frac{-1}{1} = -1$.

$$= \frac{-(3x+2y)}{y}$$

This result can also be written as $-\frac{3x+2y}{y}$ or $\frac{-3x-2y}{y}$.

Caution! A $-$ symbol preceding a fraction may be applied to the numerator or to the denominator, but not to both. For example,

$$-\frac{3x+2y}{y} \neq \frac{-3x-2y}{-y}$$

ANSWERS TO SELF CHECKS

1. a. \$3.50 **b.** \$1.56 **2.** The domain is the set of all real numbers except −7 and 7: $(-\infty, -7) \cup (-7, 7) \cup (7, \infty)$. **3.** $\frac{3a^3}{5b^2}$ **4. a.** $\frac{4}{x-2}$ **b.** $\frac{x+3}{5x}$ **5. a.** $\frac{x-3}{6}$ **b.** $\frac{2b-3}{2b+3}$ **c.** $\frac{a^2+a+1}{a^2+6}$ **6.** $-\frac{2a+3b}{b}$ or $\frac{-2a-3b}{b}$

SECTION 7.1 STUDY SET

VOCABULARY

Fill in the blanks.

1. A quotient of two polynomials, such as $\frac{x^2+x}{x^2-3x}$, is called a _rational_ expression.

2. In the rational expression $\frac{(x+2)(3x-1)}{(x+2)(4x+2)}$, $x+2$ is a common _factor_ of the numerator and the denominator.

3. To _simplify_ a rational expression, we remove factors common to the numerator and denominator.

▶ **4.** Because of the division by 0, the expression $\frac{8}{0}$ is _undefined_.

5. The binomials $x - 15$ and $15 - x$ are called _opposites_, because their terms are the same, except that they are opposite in sign.

6. The graph of the function shown in Problem 7 below approaches the positive x-axis. When a graph approaches a line, we call the line an _asymptote_.

CONCEPTS

7. The graph of rational function f for $x > 0$ is shown in the illustration. Find each of the following.

a. $f(1)$ 1 **b.** $f(2)$ 0.5

c. The value(s) of x for which $f(x) = 4$ 0.25

d. The domain and range of f D: $(0, \infty)$, R: $(0, \infty)$

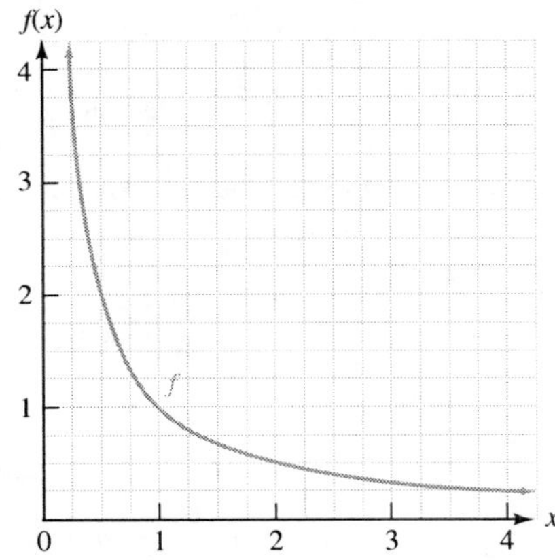

▶ **8.** Fill in the blanks to show that $\frac{x-y}{y-x} = -1$ by factoring out −1 from each term in the numerator.

$$\frac{x-y}{y-x} = \frac{-y+x}{y-x} = \frac{-1(\overset{1}{\cancel{y-x}})}{\underset{1}{\cancel{(y-x)}}} = -1$$

9. Simplify each expression.

a. $\frac{3 \cdot 5 \cdot x \cdot y \cdot y}{5 \cdot 7 \cdot x \cdot x \cdot x \cdot y}$ $\frac{3y}{7x^2}$ **b.** $\frac{(x+8)(x-3)}{(x+2)(x+8)}$ $\frac{x-3}{x+2}$

c. $\frac{a^3(a-9)}{(9-a)(9+a)}$ $-\frac{a^3}{a+9}$

▶ **10.** Simplify each rational expression, if possible.

a. $\frac{x+8}{x}$ does not simplify **b.** $\frac{3a^2+23}{a^2}$ does not simplify

11. MANUFACTURING Each graph shows the average cost to manufacture a certain item for a given number of units produced. Which graph is best described as the graph of a:

a. linear function? iii. **b.** quadratic function? i.

c. rational function? iv. **d.** polynomial function? ii.

i.

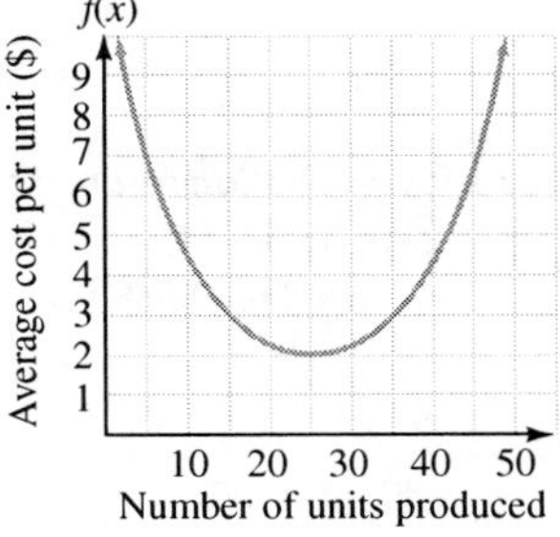

ii.

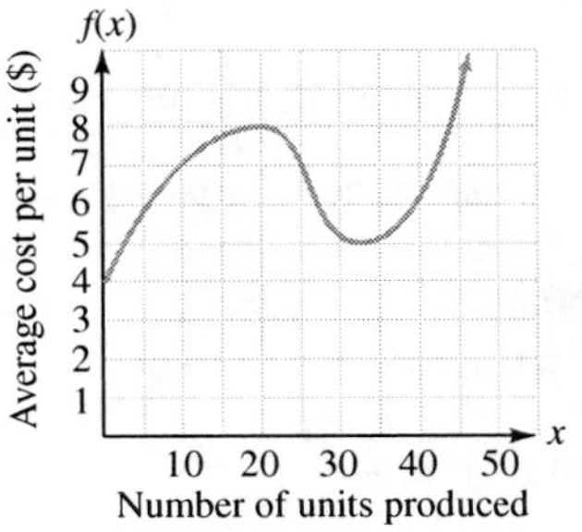

iii.

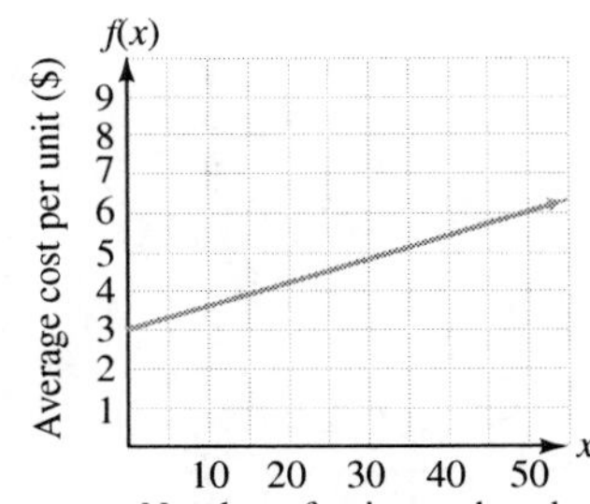

iv.

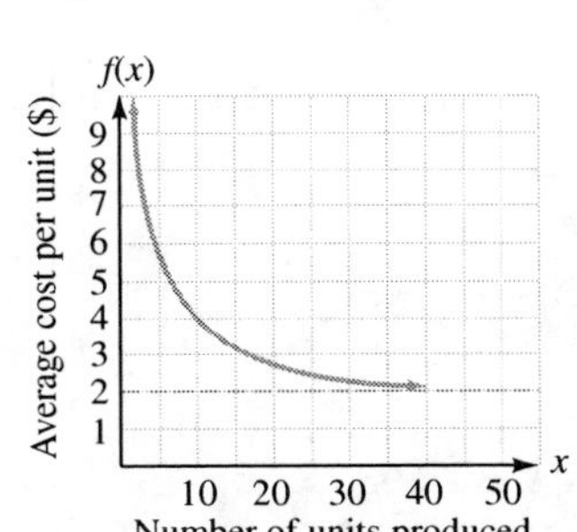

12. Refer to the graphs in Problem 11. Complete the description of the graph by filling in each blank with the word *decreases* or *increases.*

a. Graph **i.** decreases, then steadily increases.

b. Graph **ii.** increases, then decreases, and then steadily increases.

c. Graph **iii.** steadily increases.

d. Graph **iv.** steadily decreases approaching a cost of \$2.00 per unit.

NOTATION

13. A student checks his answers with those in the back of his textbook. Determine whether they are equivalent.

Answer	Book's answer	Equivalent?
$\frac{-3}{x+3}$	$-\frac{3}{x+3}$	yes
$\frac{-x+4}{6x+1}$	$\frac{-(x-4)}{6x+1}$	yes
$\frac{x+7}{(x-4)(x+2)}$	$\frac{x+7}{(x+2)(x-4)}$	yes
$-\frac{x-4}{x+4}$	$\frac{4-x}{x+4}$	yes
$\frac{a-3b}{2b-a}$	$\frac{3b-a}{a-2b}$	yes

14. a. In $\frac{(x+5)\overset{1}{\cancel{(x-5)}}}{x\underset{1}{\cancel{(x-5)}}}$, what do the slashes show?

removing a common factor of the numerator and denominator

b. In $\frac{(x-3)\overset{-1}{\cancel{(x-7)}}}{(x+3)\underset{1}{\cancel{(7-x)}}}$, what do the slashes show?

removing factors that are opposites in the numerator and denominator

GUIDED PRACTICE

Complete the table of values for each rational function (round to the nearest hundredth when appropriate). Then graph the function. Each function is defined for $x > 0$. Label the horizontal asymptote. See Example 1 and Objective 3.

15. $f(x) = \frac{6}{x}$

x	$f(x)$
1	6
2	3
4	1.5
6	1
8	0.75
10	0.6
12	0.5

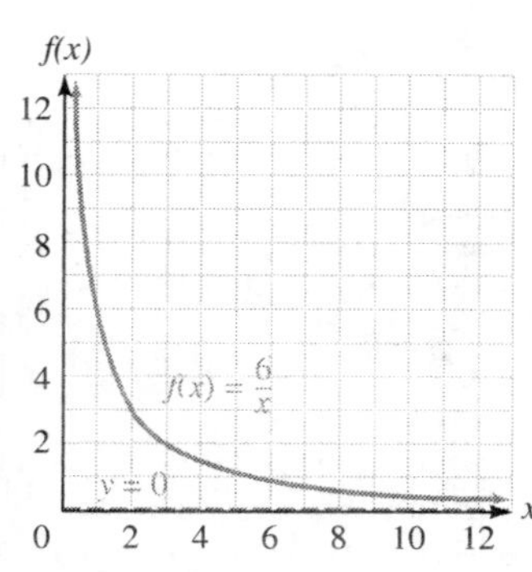

16. $f(x) = \frac{12}{x}$

x	$f(x)$
1	12
4	3
8	1.5
12	1
16	0.75
20	0.6
24	0.5

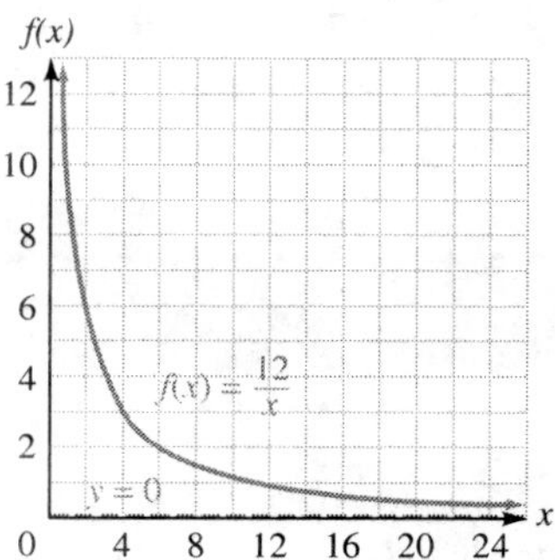

17. $f(x) = \frac{x+2}{x}$

x	$f(x)$
1	3
2	2
4	1.5
6	1.33
8	1.25
10	1.2
12	1.17

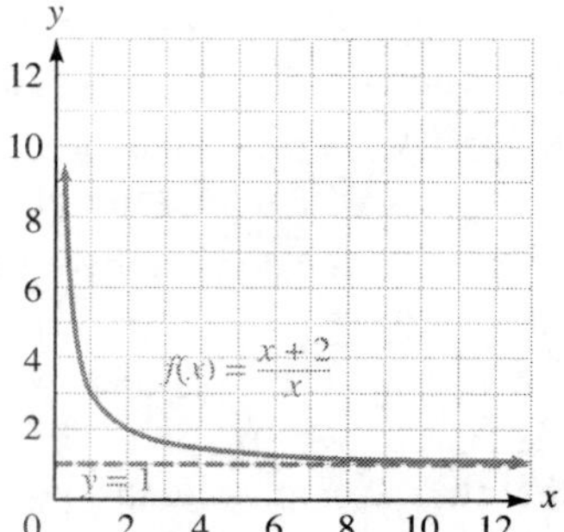

18. $f(x) = \frac{2x+4}{x}$

x	$f(x)$
1	6
4	3
8	2.5
12	2.33
16	2.25
20	2.2
24	2.17

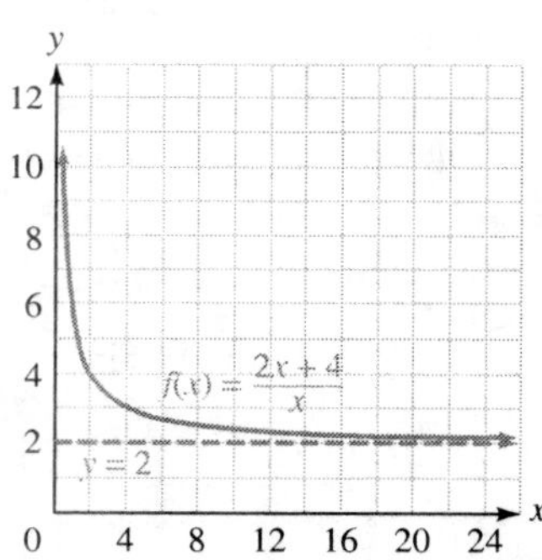

Find the domain of each rational function. Express your answer in words and using interval notation. See Example 2.

19. $f(x) = \frac{2}{x}$

all real numbers except 0, $(-\infty, 0) \cup (0, \infty)$

20. $f(x) = \frac{8}{x-1}$

all real numbers except 1, $(-\infty, 1) \cup (1, \infty)$

21. $f(x) = \frac{2x}{x+2}$

all real numbers except -2, $(-\infty, -2) \cup (-2, \infty)$

22. $f(x) = \frac{2x+1}{x^2-2x}$

all real numbers except 0 and 2, $(-\infty, 0) \cup (0, 2) \cup (2, \infty)$

23. $f(x) = \dfrac{3x - 1}{x - x^2}$ all real numbers except 0 and 1, $(-\infty, 0) \cup (0, 1) \cup (1, \infty)$

24. $f(x) = \dfrac{x^2 + 36}{x^2 - 36}$ all real numbers except −6 and 6, $(-\infty, -6) \cup (-6, 6) \cup (6, \infty)$

25. $f(x) = \dfrac{x^2 + 3x + 2}{x^2 - x - 56}$ all real numbers except −7 and 8, $(-\infty, -7) \cup (-7, 8) \cup (8, \infty)$

▶ **26.** $f(x) = \dfrac{2x^2 - 3x - 2}{x^2 + 2x - 24}$ all real numbers except −6 and 4, $(-\infty, -6) \cup (-6, 4) \cup (4, \infty)$

Simplify each rational expression. See Example 3.

27. $\dfrac{12a^3}{18a}$ $\dfrac{2a^2}{3}$

28. $\dfrac{25b^4}{55b}$ $\dfrac{5b^3}{11}$

29. $\dfrac{15a^2}{25a^8}$ $\dfrac{3}{5a^6}$

30. $\dfrac{12x}{16x^7}$ $\dfrac{3}{4x^6}$

31. $\dfrac{27st}{36st^2}$ $\dfrac{3}{4t}$

32. $\dfrac{49xy^2}{21xy}$ $\dfrac{7y}{3}$

33. $\dfrac{24x^3y^{10}}{18x^4y^3}$ $\dfrac{4y^7}{3x}$

▶ **34.** $\dfrac{15a^5b^4}{21a^8b^3}$ $\dfrac{5b}{7a^3}$

Simplify each rational expression. See Example 4.

35. $\dfrac{4x^2}{2x^3 - 12x^2}$ $\dfrac{2}{x - 6}$

36. $\dfrac{15y^2}{5y^3 + 15y^2}$ $\dfrac{3}{y + 3}$

▶ **37.** $\dfrac{24n^4}{16n^4 + 24n^3}$ $\dfrac{3n}{2n + 3}$

38. $\dfrac{18m^4}{36m^4 - 9m^3}$ $\dfrac{2m}{4m - 1}$

39. $\dfrac{2x + 18}{x^2 - 81}$ $\dfrac{2}{x - 9}$

40. $\dfrac{6x - 12}{x^2 - 4}$ $\dfrac{6}{x + 2}$

41. $\dfrac{4a^2 - 25}{20a - 50}$ $\dfrac{2a + 5}{10}$

42. $\dfrac{9b^2 - 16}{21b + 28}$ $\dfrac{3b - 4}{7}$

Simplify each rational expression. See Example 5.

43. $\dfrac{5x^2 - 10x}{x^2 - 4x + 4}$ $\dfrac{5x}{x - 2}$

44. $\dfrac{x^2 + 6x + 9}{2x^2 + 6x}$ $\dfrac{x + 3}{2x}$

45. $\dfrac{x^2 + 2x + 1}{x^2 + 4x + 3}$ $\dfrac{x + 1}{x + 3}$

46. $\dfrac{y^2 - 4y + 4}{y^2 - 8y + 12}$ $\dfrac{y - 2}{y - 6}$

▶ **47.** $\dfrac{3d^2 + 13d + 4}{3d^2 + 7d + 2}$ $\dfrac{d + 4}{d + 2}$

48. $\dfrac{10r^2 + 17r + 3}{2r^2 + 17r + 21}$ $\dfrac{5r + 1}{r + 7}$

49. $\dfrac{2h^2 + 9h - 5}{4h^2 - 4h + 1}$ $\dfrac{h + 5}{2h - 1}$

50. $\dfrac{6x^2 + x - 2}{8x^2 + 2x - 3}$ $\dfrac{3x + 2}{4x + 3}$

51. $\dfrac{t^3 + 27}{t^3 + 3t^2 + 4t + 12}$ $\dfrac{t^2 - 3t + 9}{t^2 + 4}$

52. $\dfrac{m^3 + 64}{m^3 + 4m^2 + 3m + 12}$ $\dfrac{m^2 - 4m + 16}{m^2 + 3}$

53. $\dfrac{s^3 + s^2 - 6s - 6}{s^3 + 1}$ $\dfrac{s^2 - 6}{s^2 - s + 1}$

▶ **54.** $\dfrac{d^3 + 5d^2 - 5d - 25}{d^3 + 125}$ $\dfrac{d^2 - 5}{d^2 - 5d + 25}$

Simplify each rational expression. See Example 6.

55. $\dfrac{3m^2 - 2mn - n^2}{mn - m^2}$ $-\dfrac{3m + n}{m}$ or $\dfrac{-(3m + n)}{m}$

56. $\dfrac{5s^2 - 4st - t^2}{st - s^2}$ $-\dfrac{5s + t}{s}$ or $\dfrac{-(5s + t)}{s}$

57. $\dfrac{b^2 - a^2}{a - b}$ $-b - a$

58. $\dfrac{d^2 - 16c^2}{4c - d}$ $-d - 4c$

59. $\dfrac{4 - x^2}{x^2 - x - 2}$ $-\dfrac{x + 2}{x + 1}$ or $\dfrac{-(2 + x)}{x + 1}$

▶ **60.** $\dfrac{x^2 - 2x - 15}{25 - x^2}$ $-\dfrac{x + 3}{x + 5}$ or $\dfrac{-(x + 3)}{5 + x}$

61. $\dfrac{20x^3 - 20x^4}{x^2 - 2x + 1}$ $-\dfrac{20x^3}{x - 1}$

▶ **62.** $\dfrac{16m^5 - 2m^6}{m^2 - 16m + 64}$ $-\dfrac{2m^5}{m - 8}$

Use a graphing calculator to graph each rational function. From the graph, determine its domain and range. Answer using interval notation. See Using Your Calculator: Finding the Domain and Range of a Rational Function.

63. $f(x) = \dfrac{x}{x - 2}$ D: $(-\infty, 2) \cup (2, \infty)$, R: $(-\infty, 1) \cup (1, \infty)$

64. $f(x) = \dfrac{x + 2}{x}$ D: $(-\infty, 0) \cup (0, \infty)$, R: $(-\infty, 1) \cup (1, \infty)$

65. $f(x) = \dfrac{x + 1}{x^2 - 4}$ D: $(-\infty, -2) \cup (-2, 2) \cup (2, \infty)$, R: $(-\infty, \infty)$

66. $f(x) = \dfrac{x - 2}{x^2 - 3x - 4}$ D: $(-\infty, -1) \cup (-1, 4) \cup (4, \infty)$, R: $(-\infty, \infty)$

TRY IT YOURSELF

Simplify each expression. If an expression cannot be simplified, write "Does not simplify."

▶ **67.** $\dfrac{x^2 + x - 30}{3x^2 - 3x - 60}$ $\dfrac{x + 6}{3(x + 4)}$

68. $\dfrac{4x^2 + 24x + 32}{16x^2 + 8x - 48}$ $\dfrac{x + 4}{2(2x - 3)}$

▶ **69.** $\dfrac{a^2 - 4}{a^3 - 8}$ $\dfrac{a + 2}{a^2 + 2a + 4}$

70. $\dfrac{x^3 - 27}{3x^2 - 8x - 3}$ $\dfrac{x^2 + 3x + 9}{3x + 1}$

71. $\dfrac{m^3 - mn^2}{mn^2 + m^2n - 2m^3}$ $-\dfrac{m + n}{n + 2m}$ or $\dfrac{-m - n}{n + 2m}$

72. $\dfrac{a^3 - ab^2}{ab^2 - 4a^2b + 3a^3}$ $-\dfrac{a + b}{b - 3a}$ or $\dfrac{a + b}{3a - b}$

73. $\dfrac{sx + 4s - 3x - 12}{sx + 4s + 6x + 24}$ $\dfrac{s - 3}{s + 6}$

74. $\dfrac{ax + by + ay + bx}{a + b}$ $x + y$

75. $\dfrac{2x^2 - 3x - 9}{2x^2 + 3x - 9}$ Does not simplify.

▶ **76.** $\dfrac{6x^2 - 7x - 5}{2x^2 + 5x + 2}$ $\dfrac{3x - 5}{x + 2}$

77. $\dfrac{3x + 6y}{x + 2y}$ 3

78. $\dfrac{y - xy}{xy - x}$ Does not simplify.

79. $\dfrac{x^4 + 3x^3 + 9x^2}{x^3 - 27}$ $\dfrac{x^2}{x - 3}$

80. $\dfrac{x^3 + 8}{x^4 - 2x^3 + 4x^2}$ $\dfrac{x + 2}{x^2}$

81. $\dfrac{2x^2 + 2x - 12}{x^3 + 3x^2 - 4x - 12}$ $\dfrac{2}{x + 2}$

82. $\dfrac{3x^2 - 3y^2}{x^2 + 2y + 2x + yx}$ $\dfrac{3(x - y)}{x + 2}$

83. $\dfrac{4x^2 + 8x + 3}{6 + x - 2x^2}$ $-\dfrac{2x + 1}{x - 2}$ or $\dfrac{2x + 1}{2 - x}$

84. $\dfrac{6x^2 + 13x + 6}{6 - 5x - 6x^2}$ $-\dfrac{3x + 2}{3x - 2}$ or $\dfrac{3x + 2}{2 - 3x}$

85. $\dfrac{x^2 - 6x + 9}{81 - x^4}$ $-\dfrac{x-3}{(9+x^2)(3+x)}$ or $-\dfrac{x-3}{(x^2+9)(x+3)}$

86. $\dfrac{y^2 - 2y + 1}{1 - y^4}$ $-\dfrac{y-1}{(1+y^2)(1+y)}$ or $-\dfrac{y-1}{(y^2+1)(y+1)}$

87. $\dfrac{16p^3q^2}{24pq^8}$ $\dfrac{2p^2}{3q^6}$

88. $\dfrac{30a^3b^{15}}{18a^9b^{10}}$ $\dfrac{5b^5}{3a^6}$

89. $\dfrac{t^3 - 5t^2 + 6t}{9t - t^3}$ $-\dfrac{t-2}{3+t}$ or $-\dfrac{t-2}{t+3}$

90. $\dfrac{a^4 - 27a}{36a - 4a^3}$ $-\dfrac{a^2+3a+9}{4(3+a)}$ or $-\dfrac{a^2+3a+9}{4(a+3)}$

APPLICATIONS

91. ENVIRONMENTAL CLEANUP Suppose the cost (in dollars) of removing $p\%$ of the pollution in a river is given by the rational function

$$f(p) = \frac{50{,}000p}{100 - p} \text{ where } 0 \le p < 100$$

Find the cost of removing each percent of pollution.

a. 50% $50,000 **b.** 80% $200,000

92. DIRECTORY COSTS The average (mean) cost for a service club to publish a directory of its members is given by the rational function

$$f(x) = \frac{1.25x + 700}{x}$$

where x is the number of directories printed. Find the average cost per directory if:

a. 500 directories are printed. $2.65

b. 2,000 directories are printed. $1.60

93. UTILITY COSTS An electric company charges $7.50 per month plus 9¢ for each kilowatt hour (kwh) of electricity used.

a. Find a linear function that gives the total cost of n kwh of electricity. $c(n) = 0.09n + 7.50$

b. Find a rational function that gives the average cost per kwh when using n kwh. $c(n) = \frac{0.09n + 7.50}{n}$

c. Find the average cost per kwh when 775 kwh are used. about 10¢

94. SCHEDULING WORK CREWS The rational function

$$f(t) = \frac{t^2 + 2t}{2t + 2}$$

gives the number of days it would take two construction crews, working together, to frame a house that crew 1 (working alone) could complete in t days and crew 2 (working alone) could complete in $t + 2$ days.

a. If crew 1 could frame a certain house in 15 days, how long would it take both crews working together? almost 8 days

b. If crew 2 could frame a certain house in 20 days, how long would it take both crews working together? about 9.5 days

95. FILLING A POOL The rational function

$$f(t) = \frac{t^2 + 3t}{2t + 3}$$

gives the number of hours it would take two pipes, working together, to fill a pool that the larger pipe (working alone) could fill in t hours and the smaller pipe (working alone) could fill in $t + 3$ hours.

a. If the smaller pipe could fill a pool in 7 hours, how long would it take both pipes to fill the pool? about 2.5 hr

b. If the larger pipe could fill a pool in 8 hours, how long would it take both pipes to fill the pool? about 4.6 hr

96. RETENTION STUDY After learning a list of words, two subjects were tested over a 28-day period to see what percent of the list they remembered. In both cases, their percent recall could be modeled by rational functions, as shown in the illustration.

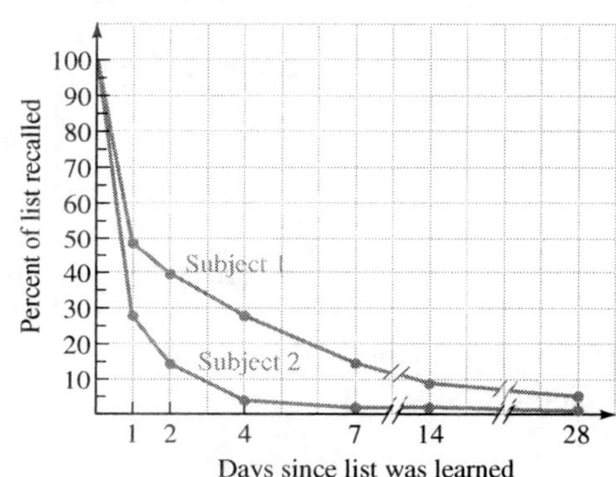

a. Use the graphs to complete the table.

Days since learning	0	1	2	4	7	14	28
% recall—subject 1	100	48	40	28	15	9	5
% recall—subject 2	100	27	15	4	2	2	1

b. After 28 days, which subject had the better recall? subject 1

WRITING

97. A student simplified $\frac{6x^2 - 7x - 5}{2x^2 + 5x + 2}$ and obtained $\frac{3x - 5}{x - 2}$. As a check, she graphed $Y_1 = \frac{6x^2 - 7x - 5}{2x^2 + 5x + 2}$ and $Y_2 = \frac{3x - 5}{x - 2}$. What conclusion can be drawn from the graphs? Explain your answer.

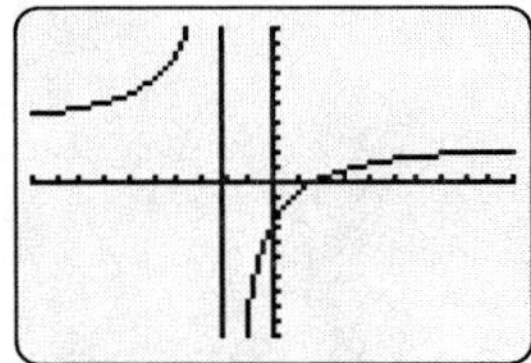

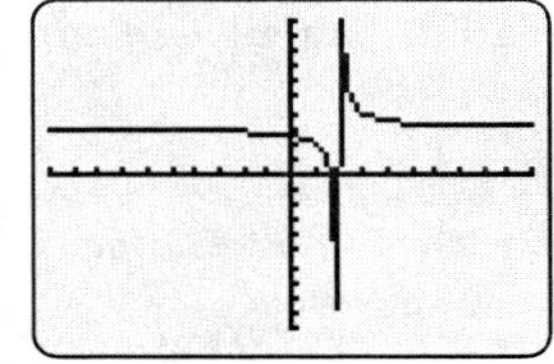

98. Simplify: $\frac{6x^2 + x - 2}{8x^2 + 2x - 3}$. Then explain how the table of values for $Y_1 = \frac{6x^2 + x - 2}{8x^2 + 2x - 3}$ and $Y_2 = \frac{3x + 2}{4x + 3}$ shown in the illustration in the next column can be used to check your result.

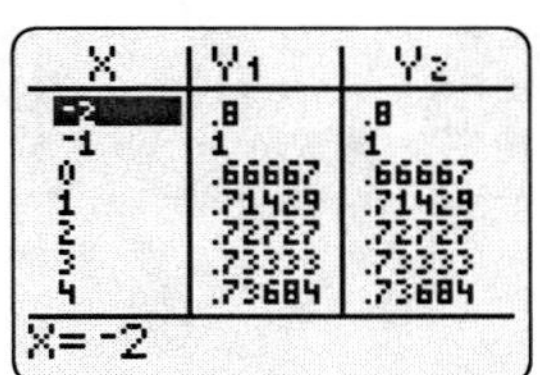

X	Y1	Y2
-2	.8	.8
-1	1	1
0	.66667	.66667
1	.71429	.71429
2	.72727	.72727
3	.73333	.73333
4	.73684	.73684

X= -2

REVIEW

Perform each operation.

99. $(a^2 - 4a - 3)(a - 2)$ $a^3 - 6a^2 + 5a + 6$

100. $(3c^2 + 5c) + (7 - c^2 - 5c)$ $2c^2 + 7$

101. $-3mn^2(m^3 - 7mn - 2m^2)$ $-3m^4n^2 + 21m^2n^3 + 6m^3n^2$

102. $(4u^2 + z^2 - 3u^2z^2) - (u^3 + 3z^2 - 3u^2z^2)$ $-u^3 + 4u^2 - 2z^2$

SECTION 7.2
Multiplying and Dividing Rational Expressions

Objectives

1. Multiply rational expressions.
2. Find powers of rational expressions.
3. Divide rational expressions.
4. Perform mixed operations.

In this section, we review the rules for multiplying and dividing arithmetic fractions—fractions whose numerators and denominators are integers. Then we use these rules, in combination with the simplification skills learned in Section 7.1, to multiply and divide rational expressions.

1 Multiply rational expressions.

Recall that to multiply fractions, we multiply the numerators and multiply the denominators. For example,

$$\frac{3}{5} \cdot \frac{2}{7} = \frac{3 \cdot 2}{5 \cdot 7} = \frac{6}{35}$$

$$\frac{4}{7} \cdot \frac{5}{8} = \frac{4 \cdot 5}{7 \cdot 8} = \frac{\overset{1}{\cancel{2}} \cdot \overset{1}{\cancel{2}} \cdot 5}{7 \cdot \underset{1}{\cancel{2}} \cdot \underset{1}{\cancel{2}} \cdot 2} = \frac{5}{14}$$

Factor 4 as 2 · 2. Factor 8 as 2 · 2 · 2. Then simplify.

We use the same procedure to multiply rational expressions.

Multiplying Rational Expressions

To multiply rational expressions, multiply their numerators and their denominators. Then, if possible, factor and simplify.

For any two rational expressions, $\frac{A}{B}$ and $\frac{C}{D}$,

$$\frac{A}{B} \cdot \frac{C}{D} = \frac{AC}{BD}$$

Self Check 1

Multiply: $\frac{x^7}{16y} \cdot \frac{24y}{17x^3}$ $\frac{3x^4}{34}$

Now Try **Problem 17**

Teaching Example 1 Multiply: $\frac{12x^2}{9y} \cdot \frac{y^3}{x^5}$

Answer: $\frac{4y^2}{3x^3}$

EXAMPLE 1 Multiply: $\frac{25a^3}{11b} \cdot \frac{b}{5a}$

Strategy To find the product, we will use the rule for multiplying rational expressions. In the process, we must be prepared to factor the numerators and denominators so that any common factors can be removed.

WHY We want to give the result in simplified form.

Solution

$$\frac{25a^3}{11b} \cdot \frac{b}{5a} = \frac{25a^3 \cdot b}{11b \cdot 5a}$$ Multiply the numerators. Multiply the denominators.

It is obvious that the numerator and denominator of $\frac{25a^3 \cdot b}{11b \cdot 5a}$ have several common factors, such as 5, a, and b. These common factors become more apparent when we factor the numerator and denominator completely.

$$\frac{25a^3 \cdot b}{11b \cdot 5a} = \frac{5 \cdot 5 \cdot a \cdot a \cdot a \cdot b}{11 \cdot b \cdot 5 \cdot a}$$ Factor $25a^3$.

$$= \frac{\overset{1}{\cancel{5}} \cdot 5 \cdot \overset{1}{\cancel{a}} \cdot a \cdot a \cdot \overset{1}{\cancel{b}}}{11 \cdot \underset{1}{\cancel{b}} \cdot \underset{1}{\cancel{5}} \cdot \underset{1}{\cancel{a}}}$$ Simplify by replacing $\frac{5}{5}$, $\frac{a}{a}$, and $\frac{b}{b}$ with the equivalent fraction $\frac{1}{1}$. This removes the factor $\frac{5 \cdot a \cdot b}{5 \cdot a \cdot b} = 1$.

$$= \frac{5a^2}{11}$$ Multiply the remaining factors in the numerator. Multiply the remaining factors in the denominator.

Success Tip We could also use rules for exponents to simplify the product:

$$\frac{25a^3 \cdot b}{11b \cdot 5a} = \frac{\overset{1}{\cancel{5}} \cdot 5 \cdot a^{3-1} \cdot b^{1-1}}{11 \cdot \underset{1}{\cancel{5}}}$$
$$= \frac{5a^2b^0}{11}$$
$$= \frac{5a^2}{11}$$

Self Check 2

Multiply:

a. $\frac{a^2 + 6a + 9}{18a} \cdot \frac{3a^3}{7a + 21}$

b. $\frac{a^2 + a - 56}{a^2 - 49} \cdot \frac{a^2 - a - 56}{a^2 - 64}$

Now Try **Problems 19 and 23**

Self Check 2 Answers

a. $\frac{a^2(a + 3)}{42}$ b. 1

EXAMPLE 2 Multiply:

a. $\frac{x^2 - 6x + 9}{20x} \cdot \frac{5x^2}{6x - 18}$ **b.** $\frac{x^2 - x - 6}{x^2 - 4} \cdot \frac{x^2 + x - 6}{x^2 - 9}$

Strategy To find the product, we will use the rule for multiplying rational expressions. In the process, we must be prepared to factor the numerators and denominators so that any common factors can be removed.

WHY We want to give the result in simplified form.

Solution

a. $$\frac{x^2 - 6x + 9}{20x} \cdot \frac{5x^2}{6x - 18} = \frac{(x^2 - 6x + 9)5x^2}{20x(6x - 18)}$$ Multiply the numerators. Multiply the denominators.

$$= \frac{(x - 3)(x - 3)5xx}{4 \cdot 5 \cdot x \cdot 6(x - 3)}$$ Factor the numerator. Factor the denominator.

$$= \frac{\overset{1}{\cancel{(x-3)}}(x-3)\overset{1}{\cancel{5}}\overset{1}{\cancel{x}}x}{4 \cdot \underset{1}{\cancel{5}} \cdot \underset{1}{\cancel{x}} \cdot 6\underset{1}{\cancel{(x-3)}}}$$ Simplify by removing common factors of the numerator and denominator.

$$= \frac{x(x-3)}{24}$$ Multiply the remaining monomial factors in the numerator. Multiply the remaining factors in the denominator.

b. $$\frac{x^2 - x - 6}{x^2 - 4} \cdot \frac{x^2 + x - 6}{x^2 - 9} = \frac{(x^2 - x - 6)(x^2 + x - 6)}{(x^2 - 4)(x^2 - 9)}$$ Multiply the numerators. Multiply the denominators.

$$= \frac{(x-3)(x+2)(x+3)(x-2)}{(x+2)(x-2)(x+3)(x-3)}$$ Factor the polynomials.

$$= \frac{\overset{1}{\cancel{(x-3)}}\overset{1}{\cancel{(x+2)}}\overset{1}{\cancel{(x+3)}}\overset{1}{\cancel{(x-2)}}}{\underset{1}{\cancel{(x+2)}}\underset{1}{\cancel{(x-2)}}\underset{1}{\cancel{(x+3)}}\underset{1}{\cancel{(x-3)}}}$$ Simplify by removing common factors of the numerator and denominator.

$$= 1$$

Teaching Example 2 Multiply:

a. $\frac{a^2 + 6a + 9}{a} \cdot \frac{a^3}{a + 3}$

b. $\frac{x^2 - 2x - 15}{x^2 - 25} \cdot \frac{x^2 + 9x + 20}{x^2 + 7x + 12}$

Answers:

a. $a^2(a + 3)$ b. 1

Caution! Note that when all of the factors of the numerator and denominator are removed as shown, the result is 1 and not 0.

Using Your CALCULATOR **Checking an Algebraic Simplification**

We can check the simplification in Example 2a by graphing the functions $f(x) = \left(\frac{x^2 - 6x + 9}{20x}\right)\left(\frac{5x^2}{6x - 18}\right)$, shown in figure (a), and $g(x) = \frac{x(x-3)}{24}$, shown in figure (b), and observing that the graphs are the same, except that 0 and 3 are not included in the domain of the function f.

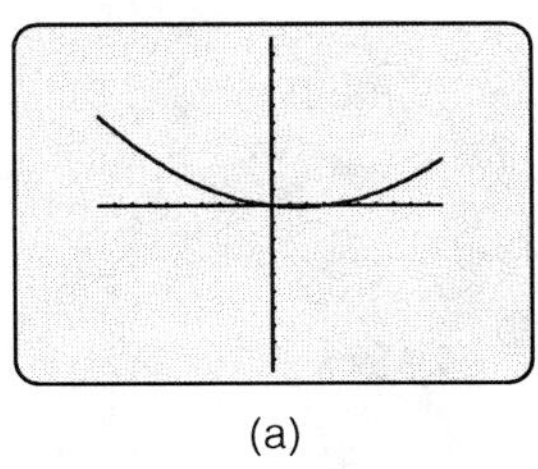
(a)

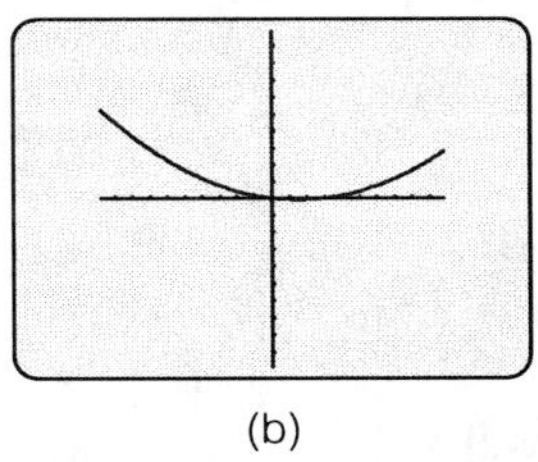
(b)

We can use the split-screen G-T (graph, table) mode to check the result of a multiplication. To set the split-screen feature on a graphing calculator, press MODE, press ▼ seven times, press ▶ twice, then press ENTER. If we enter $Y_3 = Y_1 - Y_2$, use the cursor to highlight the = sign as shown on the next page in figure (c), and then press GRAPH, we get the display shown in figure (d). The zeros under the Y_3 column indicate that the value of $\left(\frac{x^2 - 6x + 9}{20x}\right)\left(\frac{5x^2}{6x - 18}\right)$ and the value of $\frac{x(x-3)}{24}$ are the same for different values of x. (The error message is given because when $x = 0$ and $x = 3$, $\left(\frac{x^2 - 6x + 9}{20x}\right)\left(\frac{5x^2}{6x - 18}\right)$ is undefined.)

The graph of $Y_3 = Y_1 - Y_2$ is difficult to see because it lies on the x-axis. The graph indicates that for all x-values (except those that make the rational expressions undefined), $Y_3 = 0$, or more specifically, $\left(\frac{x^2 - 6x + 9}{20x}\right)\left(\frac{5x^2}{6x - 18}\right) = \frac{x(x-3)}{24}$.

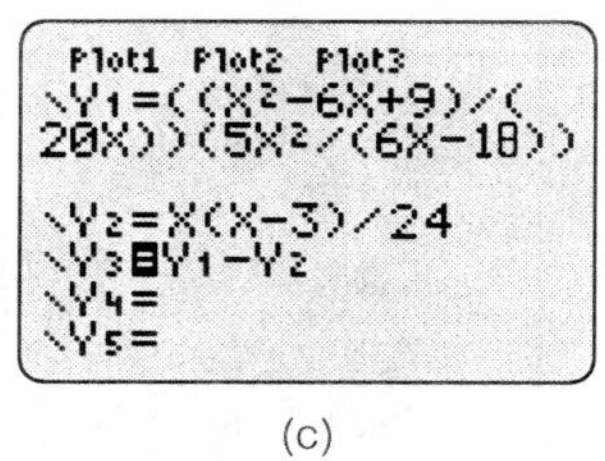

(c)

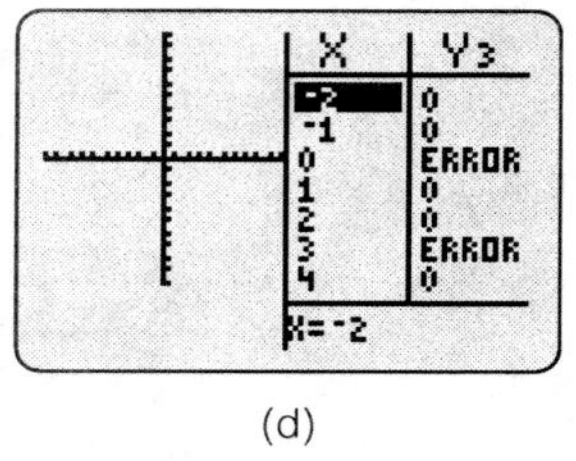

(d)

Self Check 3

Multiply:
$$\frac{2a^2 + 5ab - 12b^2}{2a^2 + 11ab + 12b^2} \cdot \frac{2a^2 - 3ab - 9b^2}{2a^2 - ab - 3b^2}$$

Now Try **Problems 29 and 31**

Self Check 3 Answer

$\frac{a - 3b}{a + b}$

Teaching Example 3 Multiply:
$$\frac{2x^2 + 5xy - 3y^2}{2x^2 + 7xy + 3y^2} \cdot \frac{2x^2 - 9xy - 5y^2}{2x^2 + xy - y^2}$$
Answer:
$\frac{x - 5y}{x + y}$

EXAMPLE 3

Multiply: $\frac{6x^2 + 5xy - 4y^2}{2x^2 + 5xy + 3y^2} \cdot \frac{8x^2 + 6xy - 9y^2}{12x^2 + 7xy - 12y^2}$

Strategy To find the product, we will use the rule for multiplying rational expressions. In the process, we must be prepared to factor the numerators and denominators so that any common factors can be removed.

WHY We want to give the result in simplified form.

Solution

$$\frac{6x^2 + 5xy - 4y^2}{2x^2 + 5xy + 3y^2} \cdot \frac{8x^2 + 6xy - 9y^2}{12x^2 + 7xy - 12y^2}$$

$$= \frac{(6x^2 + 5xy - 4y^2)(8x^2 + 6xy - 9y^2)}{(2x^2 + 5xy + 3y^2)(12x^2 + 7xy - 12y^2)}$$ Multiply the numerators. Multiply the denominators.

$$= \frac{(3x + 4y)(2x - y)(4x - 3y)(2x + 3y)}{(2x + 3y)(x + y)(3x + 4y)(4x - 3y)}$$ Factor the trinomials.

$$= \frac{\overset{1}{\cancel{(3x + 4y)}}(2x - y)\overset{1}{\cancel{(4x - 3y)}}\overset{1}{\cancel{(2x + 3y)}}}{\underset{1}{\cancel{(2x + 3y)}}(x + y)\underset{1}{\cancel{(3x + 4y)}}\underset{1}{\cancel{(4x - 3y)}}}$$ Simplify by removing common factors of the numerator and denominator.

$$= \frac{2x - y}{x + y}$$ Multiply the remaining factors in the numerator. Multiply the remaining factors in the denominator.

Self Check 4

Multiply:
$$\frac{x}{8x^3 - 32x^2 + 8x - 32} \cdot (4x - x^2)$$

Now Try **Problem 39**

Self Check 4 Answer

$-\frac{x^2}{8(x^2 + 1)}$

Teaching Example 4 Multiply:
$$(5x - x^2) \cdot \frac{x}{x^2 - 25}$$
Answer:
$-\frac{x^2}{x + 5}$

EXAMPLE 4

Multiply: $(2x - x^2) \cdot \frac{x}{5x^3 - 10x^2 + 20x - 40}$

Strategy We will write $2x - x^2$ as a rational expression with denominator 1. (Remember, any number divided by 1 remains unchanged.) Then we will use the rule for multiplying rational expressions.

WHY Writing $2x - x^2$ as $\frac{2x - x^2}{1}$ is helpful during the multiplication process when we multiply numerators and multiply denominators.

Solution

$$(2x - x^2) \cdot \frac{x}{5x^3 - 10x^2 + 20x - 40}$$

$$= \frac{2x - x^2}{1} \cdot \frac{x}{5x^3 - 10x^2 + 20x - 40}$$ Write $2x - x^2$ as $\frac{2x - x^2}{1}$.

$$= \frac{(2x - x^2)x}{1(5x^3 - 10x + 20x - 40)}$$ Multiply the numerators. Multiply the denominators.

$$= \frac{x(2 - x)x}{1 \cdot 5(x^3 - 2x^2 + 4x - 8)}$$ Factor out x in the numerator. Factor out 5 in the denominator.

$$= \frac{x(2 - x)x}{1 \cdot 5[x^2(x - 2) + 4(x - 2)]}$$ In the denominator, begin factoring by grouping.

$$= \frac{x(2 - x)x}{1 \cdot 5(x - 2)(x^2 + 4)}$$ In the denominator, complete the factoring by grouping. The brackets [ ] are no longer needed.

$$= \frac{x\overset{-1}{(2 - x)}x}{1 \cdot 5\underset{1}{(x - 2)}(x^2 + 4)}$$ Simplify. Recall that the quotient of any nonzero quantity and its opposite is −1: $\frac{2 - x}{x - 2} = -1$.

$$= \frac{-x^2}{5(x^2 + 4)}$$ Multiply the remaining factors in the numerator. Multiply the remaining factors in the denominator.

Since the − sign can be written in front of the fraction, this result can be expressed as

$$-\frac{x^2}{5(x^2 + 4)}$$

Success Tip In Examples 2–4, we would obtain the same answer if we had factored the numerators and denominators first and simplified before we multiplied.

2 Find powers of rational expressions.

EXAMPLE 5 Find: $\left(\frac{x^2 + x - 1}{2x + 3}\right)^2$

Strategy We will find the product $\left(\frac{x^2 + x - 1}{2x + 3}\right)\left(\frac{x^2 + x - 1}{2x + 3}\right)$ using the rule for multiplying rational expressions.

WHY The exponent 2 means the base, $\frac{x^2 + x - 1}{2x + 3}$, should be written as a factor two times.

Solution

$$\left(\frac{x^2 + x - 1}{2x + 3}\right)^2 = \left(\frac{x^2 + x - 1}{2x + 3}\right)\left(\frac{x^2 + x - 1}{2x + 3}\right)$$

$$= \frac{(x^2 + x - 1)(x^2 + x - 1)}{(2x + 3)(2x + 3)}$$ Multiply the numerators. Multiply the denominators.

$$= \frac{x^4 + 2x^3 - x^2 - 2x + 1}{4x^2 + 12x + 9}$$

Self Check 5

Find: $\left(\frac{x + 5}{x^2 - 6x}\right)^2$

Now Try **Problem 43**

Self Check 5 Answer

$\frac{x^2 + 10x + 25}{x^4 - 12x^3 + 36x^2}$

Teaching Example 5 Find: $\left(\frac{3x + y}{x - 4}\right)^2$

Answer:

$\frac{9x^2 + 6xy + y^2}{x^2 - 8x + 16}$

3 Divide rational expressions.

Recall that one number is called the **reciprocal** of another if their product is 1. To find the reciprocal of a fraction, we invert its numerator and denominator. We have seen that to divide fractions, we multiply the first fraction by the reciprocal of the second fraction.

$$\frac{3}{5} \div \frac{8}{9} = \frac{3}{5} \cdot \frac{9}{8} = \frac{3 \cdot 9}{5 \cdot 8}$$

$$\frac{4}{7} \div \frac{2}{21} = \frac{4}{7} \cdot \frac{21}{2} = \frac{4 \cdot 21}{7 \cdot 2}$$

$$= \frac{27}{40} \qquad\qquad = \frac{\overset{1}{\cancel{2}} \cdot 2 \cdot 3 \cdot \overset{1}{\cancel{7}}}{\underset{1}{\cancel{7}} \cdot \underset{1}{\cancel{2}}}$$

Factor 4 as $2 \cdot 2$. Factor 21 as $3 \cdot 7$. Then simplify.

$$= 6$$

We use the same procedure to divide rational expressions.

Dividing Rational Expressions

To divide two rational expressions, multiply the first by the reciprocal of the second. Then, if possible, factor and simplify.

For any two rational expressions, $\frac{A}{B}$ and $\frac{C}{D}$, where $\frac{C}{D} \neq 0$,

$$\frac{A}{B} \div \frac{C}{D} = \frac{A}{B} \cdot \frac{D}{C} = \frac{AD}{BC}$$

Self Check 6

Divide: $\frac{8a^4}{t^5} \div \frac{28a^3}{t^2}$ $\frac{2a}{7t^3}$

Now Try **Problem 51**

Teaching Example 6 Divide: $\frac{15x}{y^2z^3} \div \frac{25x}{y^3z}$

Answer: $\frac{3y}{5z^2}$

EXAMPLE 6 Divide: $\frac{6}{y^3z^2} \div \frac{20}{yz^3}$

Strategy We will use the rule for dividing rational expressions. After multiplying by the reciprocal, we will use rules for exponents to simplify the result.

WHY We want to give the result in simplified form.

Solution

$$\frac{6}{y^3z^2} \div \frac{20}{yz^3} = \frac{6}{y^3z^2} \cdot \frac{yz^3}{20}$$ Multiply the first rational expression by the reciprocal of the second.

$$= \frac{6yz^3}{20y^3z^2}$$ Multiply the numerators. Multiply the denominators.

$$= \frac{2 \cdot 3 \cdot y^{1-3}z^{3-2}}{2 \cdot 2 \cdot 5}$$ Factor 6 and 20. To divide exponential expressions with the same base, keep the base and subtract the exponents.

$$= \frac{\overset{1}{\cancel{2}} \cdot 3 \cdot y^{-2}z^1}{\underset{1}{\cancel{2}} \cdot 2 \cdot 5}$$ Remove the common factor of 2. Simplify the exponents.

$$= \frac{3z}{10y^2}$$ Write the result without the negative exponent.

Self Check 7

Divide: $\frac{x^3 - 8}{9x - 9} \div \frac{x^2 + 2x + 4}{3x^2 - 3x}$

Now Try **Problem 55**

Self Check 7 Answer $\frac{x(x-2)}{3}$

Teaching Example 7 Divide: $\frac{a^3 - 125}{2a - 10} \div \frac{a^2 + 5a + 25}{12}$

Answer: 6

EXAMPLE 7 Divide: $\frac{x^3 + 8}{4x + 4} \div \frac{x^2 - 2x + 4}{2x^2 - 2}$

Strategy To find the quotient, we will use the rule for dividing rational expressions. After multiplying by the reciprocal, we will factor each polynomial that is not prime and remove any common factors of the numerator and denominator.

WHY We want to give the result in simplified form.

Solution

$$\frac{x^3 + 8}{4x + 4} \div \frac{x^2 - 2x + 4}{2x^2 - 2}$$

$$= \frac{x^3 + 8}{4x + 4} \cdot \frac{2x^2 - 2}{x^2 - 2x + 4}$$ Multiply the first rational expression by the reciprocal of the second.

$$= \frac{(x^3 + 8)(2x^2 - 2)}{(4x + 4)(x^2 - 2x + 4)}$$ Multiply the numerators. Multiply the denominators.

$$= \frac{(x + 2)\overset{1}{\cancel{(x^2 - 2x + 4)}}\overset{1}{\cancel{2}}\overset{1}{\cancel{(x + 1)}}(x - 1)}{2 \cdot \underset{1}{\cancel{2}}\underset{1}{\cancel{(x + 1)}}\underset{1}{\cancel{(x^2 - 2x + 4)}}}$$ Factor completely. $x^2 - 2x + 4$ is prime. Then simplify.

$$= \frac{(x + 2)(x - 1)}{2}$$

Caution! When dividing rational expressions, always write the result in simplest form by removing any factors common to the numerator and denominator.

EXAMPLE 8 Divide: $\frac{b^3 - 4b}{x - 1} \div (b - 2)$

Strategy We will begin by writing $b - 2$ as a rational expression by inserting a denominator 1. Then we will use the rule for dividing rational expressions.

WHY Writing $b - 2$ over 1 is helpful when we invert its numerator and denominator to find its reciprocal.

Solution

$$\frac{b^3 - 4b}{x - 1} \div (b - 2) = \frac{b^3 - 4b}{x - 1} \div \frac{b - 2}{1}$$ Write $b - 2$ as a fraction with a denominator of 1.

$$= \frac{b^3 - 4b}{x - 1} \cdot \frac{1}{b - 2}$$ Multiply the first rational expression by the reciprocal of the second.

$$= \frac{b^3 - 4b}{(x - 1)(b - 2)}$$ Multiply the numerators. Multiply the denominators.

$$= \frac{b(b + 2)\overset{1}{\cancel{(b - 2)}}}{(x - 1)\underset{1}{\cancel{(b - 2)}}}$$ Factor $b^3 - 4b$ and then simplify.

$$= \frac{b(b + 2)}{x - 1}$$ Multiply the remaining factors in the numerator. Multiply the remaining factors in the denominator.

Self Check 8

Divide: $\frac{m^4 - 9m^2}{a^2 - 3a} \div (m^2 + 3m)$

Now Try **Problem 63**

Self Check 8 Answer

$\frac{m(m - 3)}{a(a - 3)}$

Teaching Example 8 Divide: $\frac{a^3 - 16a}{a + 4} \div (a - 4)$

Answer: a

4 Perform mixed operations.

EXAMPLE 9 Simplify: $\frac{x^2 + 2x - 3}{6x^2 + 5x + 1} \div \frac{2x^2 - 2}{2x^2 - 5x - 3} \cdot \frac{6x^2 + 4x - 2}{x^2 - 2x - 3}$

Strategy We will consider the division first by multiplying the first rational expression by the reciprocal of the second. Then we will find the product of the three rational expressions.

WHY By the rules for the order of operations, we must perform division and multiplication in order from left to right.

Solution

Since multiplications and divisions are done in order from left to right, we begin by focusing on the division. We introduce grouping symbols to emphasize this. To divide the expressions within the parentheses, we invert $\frac{2x^2 - 2}{2x^2 - 5x - 3}$ and multiply.

Self Check 9

Simplify:

$\frac{x^2 - 25}{4x^2 + 12x + 9} \div \frac{x^2 - 5x}{3x - 1} \cdot \frac{2x + 3}{3x^2 + 14x - 5}$

Now Try **Problem 67**

Self Check 9 Answer

$\frac{1}{x(2x + 3)}$

Teaching Example 9 Simplify: $\frac{x^2-4}{x^2+4x+4} \div \frac{x^2-x-6}{x^2+8x+12} \cdot \frac{x-3}{x^2+4x-12}$
Answer: $\frac{1}{x+2}$

$$\left(\frac{x^2+2x-3}{6x^2+5x+1} \div \frac{2x^2-2}{2x^2-5x-3}\right)\frac{6x^2+4x-2}{x^2-2x-3}$$
$$= \left(\frac{x^2+2x-3}{6x^2+5x+1} \cdot \frac{2x^2-5x-3}{2x^2-2}\right)\frac{6x^2+4x-2}{x^2-2x-3}$$

Next, we multiply the three rational expressions and simplify the result.

$$= \frac{(x^2+2x-3)(2x^2-5x-3)(6x^2+4x-2)}{(6x^2+5x+1)(2x^2-2)(x^2-2x-3)}$$

$$= \frac{(x+3)\overset{1}{\cancel{(x-1)}}\overset{1}{\cancel{(2x+1)}}\overset{1}{\cancel{(x-3)}}\overset{1}{\cancel{2}}(3x-1)\overset{1}{\cancel{(x+1)}}}{(3x+1)\underset{1}{\cancel{(2x+1)}}\underset{1}{\cancel{2}}(x+1)\underset{1}{\cancel{(x-1)}}\underset{1}{\cancel{(x-3)}}\underset{1}{\cancel{(x+1)}}}$$ Factor each polynomial completely and simplify.

$$= \frac{(x+3)(3x-1)}{(3x+1)(x+1)}$$

ANSWERS TO SELF CHECKS

1. $\frac{3x^4}{34}$ **2. a.** $\frac{a^2(a+3)}{42}$ **b.** 1 **3.** $\frac{a-3b}{a+b}$ **4.** $-\frac{x^2}{8(x^2+1)}$ **5.** $\frac{x^2+10x+25}{x^4-12x^3+36x^2}$ **6.** $\frac{2a}{7t^3}$
7. $\frac{x(x-2)}{3}$ **8.** $\frac{m(m-3)}{a(a-3)}$ **9.** $\frac{1}{x(2x+3)}$

SECTION 7.2 STUDY SET

VOCABULARY

Fill in the blanks.

1. $\frac{a^2-9}{a^2-49} \cdot \frac{a-7}{a+3}$ is the product of two rational expressions.

2. The reciprocal of $\frac{a+3}{a+7}$ is $\frac{a+7}{a+3}$.

3. To find the reciprocal of a rational expression, we invert its numerator and denominator.

▶ **4.** To simplify a rational expression, remove any factors common to the numerator and denominator.

CONCEPTS

Fill in the blanks.

5. To multiply rational expressions, multiply their numerators and multiply their denominators. In symbols,

$$\frac{A}{B} \cdot \frac{C}{D} = \frac{AC}{BD}$$

6. To divide two rational expressions, multiply the first by the reciprocal of the second. In symbols,

$$\frac{A}{B} \div \frac{C}{D} = \frac{A}{B} \cdot \frac{D}{C} = \frac{AD}{BC}$$

NOTATION

Complete each solution.

7. $\frac{x^2+3x}{5x-25} \cdot \frac{x-5}{x+3} = \frac{(x^2+3x)(x-5)}{(5x-25)(x+3)}$
$= \frac{x(x+3)(x-5)}{5(x-5)(x+3)}$
$= \frac{x}{5}$

▶ **8.** $\frac{x^2-x-6}{4x^2+16x} \div \frac{x-3}{x+4} = \frac{x^2-x-6}{4x^2+16x} \cdot \frac{x+4}{x-3}$
$= \frac{(x^2-x-6)(x+4)}{(4x^2+16x)(x-3)}$
$= \frac{(x-3)(x+2)(x+4)}{4x(x+4)(x-3)}$
$= \frac{x+2}{4x}$

▶ Selected exercises available online at www.webassign.net/brookscole

9. A student checks her answers with those in the back of her textbook. Determine whether they are equivalent.

Student's answer	Book's answer	Equivalent?
$\frac{-x^{10}}{y^2}$	$-\frac{x^{10}}{y^2}$	yes
$\frac{x-3}{x+3}$	$\frac{3-x}{x+3}$	no
$\frac{a+b}{(2-x)(c+d)}$	$-\frac{a+b}{(x-2)(c+d)}$	yes

▶ **10. a.** Write $5x^2 + 35x$ as a fraction. → $\frac{5x^2+35x}{1}$

b. What is the reciprocal of $5x^2 + 35x$? → $\frac{1}{5x^2+35x}$

GUIDED PRACTICE

Multiply, and then simplify, if possible. See Objective 1.

11. $\frac{3}{4} \cdot \frac{11}{3}$ → $\frac{11}{4}$

▶ **12.** $\frac{13}{6} \cdot \frac{6}{21}$ → $\frac{13}{21}$

13. $\frac{15}{24} \cdot \frac{16}{25}$ → $\frac{2}{5}$

14. $\frac{49}{36} \cdot \frac{18}{35}$ → $\frac{7}{10}$

Multiply, and then simplify, if possible. See Example 1.

15. $\frac{3a}{10} \cdot \frac{2}{15a^4}$ → $\frac{1}{25a^3}$

16. $\frac{4p}{21} \cdot \frac{7}{12p^6}$ → $\frac{1}{9p^5}$

17. $\frac{12x^6}{7y^4} \cdot \frac{y}{8x^2}$ → $\frac{3x^4}{14y^3}$

▶ **18.** $\frac{b^6}{27a^2} \cdot \frac{18a^4}{5b^9}$ → $\frac{2a^2}{15b^3}$

Multiply, and then simplify, if possible. See Example 2.

19. $\frac{y^2+6y+9}{15y} \cdot \frac{3y^2}{2y+6}$ → $\frac{y(y+3)}{10}$

20. $\frac{3p^2}{6p+24} \cdot \frac{p^2-16}{6p}$ → $\frac{p(p-4)}{12}$

21. $\frac{x^2+x-6}{5x} \cdot \frac{5x-10}{x+3}$ → $\frac{(x-2)^2}{x}$

22. $\frac{z^2+4z-5}{25z-25} \cdot \frac{5z}{z+5}$ → $\frac{z}{5}$

▶ **23.** $\frac{x^2+2x+1}{9x^3} \cdot \frac{2x^2-2x}{2x^2-2}$ → $\frac{x+1}{9x^2}$

24. $\frac{a^4+6a^3}{a^2-16} \cdot \frac{3a-12}{3a+18}$ → $\frac{a^3}{a+4}$

25. $\frac{t^2+t-6}{t^2-6t+9} \cdot \frac{t^2-9}{t^2-4}$ → $\frac{(t+3)^2}{(t-3)(t+2)}$

26. $\frac{s^2-5s+6}{s^2-10s+16} \cdot \frac{s^2-6s-16}{s^2+2s}$ → $\frac{s-3}{s}$

Multiply, and then simplify, if possible. See Example 3.

27. $\frac{2x^2-x-3}{x^2-1} \cdot \frac{x^2+x-2}{2x^2+x-6}$ → 1

28. $\frac{2p^2-5p-3}{p^2-9} \cdot \frac{2p^2+5p-3}{2p^2+5p+2}$ → $\frac{2p-1}{p+2}$

29. $\frac{3t^2-t-2}{6t^2-5t-6} \cdot \frac{4t^2-9}{2t^2+5t+3}$ → $\frac{t-1}{t+1}$

30. $\frac{9x^2+3x-20}{3x^2-7x+4} \cdot \frac{3x^2-5x+2}{9x^2+18x+5}$ → $\frac{3x-2}{3x+1}$

31. $\frac{x^2+4xy+4y^2}{2x^2+4xy} \cdot \frac{3x-6y}{x^2-4y^2}$ → $\frac{3}{2x}$

32. $\frac{x^2-y^2}{xy} \cdot \frac{x^2}{x^2+2xy+y^2}$ → $\frac{x(x-y)}{y(x+y)}$

33. $\frac{3a^2+7ab+2b^2}{a^2+2ab} \cdot \frac{a^2-ab}{3a^2+ab}$ → $\frac{a-b}{a}$

▶ **34.** $\frac{a^2+3ab+2b^2}{a^2-3ab-4b^2} \cdot \frac{a^2-4ab}{ab^2+2b^3}$ → $\frac{a}{b^2}$

Multiply, and then simplify, if possible. See Example 4.

35. $15x\left(\frac{x+1}{15x}\right)$ → $x+1$

36. $30t\left(\frac{t-7}{30t}\right)$ → $t-7$

37. $12y\left(\frac{y+8}{6y}\right)$ → $2y+16$ or $2(y+8)$

▶ **38.** $16x\left(\frac{3x+8}{4x}\right)$ → $12x+32$ or $4(3x+8)$

39. $(6a-a^2) \cdot \frac{a^3}{2a^3-12a^2+6a-36}$ → $-\frac{a^4}{2(a^2+3)}$

40. $(10n-n^2) \cdot \frac{n^6}{n^4-10n^3-2n^2+20n}$ → $-\frac{n^6}{n^2-2}$

41. $(x^2+x-2cx-2c) \cdot \frac{x^2+3x+2}{4c^2-x^2}$ → $-\frac{(x+1)^2(x+2)}{x+2c}$

▶ **42.** $(2ax-10x+a-5) \cdot \frac{x}{2x^2+x}$ → $a-5$

Find each power. See Example 5.

43. $\left(\frac{x-3}{x^2+4}\right)^2$ → $\frac{x^2-6x+9}{x^4+8x^2+16}$

▶ **44.** $\left(\frac{2t^2+t}{t-1}\right)^2$ → $\frac{4t^4+4t^3+t^2}{t^2-2t+1}$

45. $\left(\frac{2m^2-m-3}{x^2-1}\right)^2$ → $\frac{4m^4-4m^3-11m^2+6m+9}{x^4-2x^2+1}$

46. $\left(\frac{k^4+3k}{x^2-x+1}\right)^2$ → $\frac{k^8+6k^5+9k^2}{x^4-2x^3+3x^2-2x+1}$

Divide, and then simplify, if possible. See Objective 3.

47. $\frac{6}{11} \div \frac{36}{55}$ → $\frac{5}{6}$

▶ **48.** $\frac{17}{12} \div \frac{34}{3}$ → $\frac{1}{8}$

49. $\frac{12}{5} \div \frac{24}{45}$ → $\frac{9}{2}$

50. $\frac{18}{7} \div \frac{54}{35}$ → $\frac{5}{3}$

Divide, and then simplify, if possible. See Example 6.

51. $\frac{22x^3}{y^2} \div \frac{33x^9}{y^7}$ $\frac{2y^5}{3x^6}$

▶ 52. $\frac{24a^6}{b} \div \frac{64a^9}{b^2}$ $\frac{3b}{8a^3}$

53. $\frac{pq^2}{50} \div \frac{p^{10}q^2}{15}$ $\frac{3}{10p^9}$

54. $\frac{s^3t^3}{12} \div \frac{s^3t^{11}}{144}$ $\frac{12}{t^8}$

Divide, and then simplify, if possible. See Example 7.

55. $\frac{x^{12}}{x^3 - 8} \div \frac{x^2}{x^2 - 2x}$ $\frac{x^{11}}{x^2 + 2x + 4}$

56. $\frac{x^9}{x^3 + 125} \div \frac{x^4}{x^2 + 5x}$ $\frac{x^6}{x^2 - 5x + 25}$

57. $\frac{x^2 - 16}{x^2 - 25} \div \frac{5x + 20}{10x^2 - 50x}$ $\frac{2x(x - 4)}{x + 5}$

▶ 58. $\frac{a^2 - 9}{a^2 - 49} \div \frac{9a^2 + 27a}{3a + 21}$ $\frac{a - 3}{3a(a - 7)}$

59. $\frac{3n^2 + 5n - 2}{12n^2 - 13n + 3} \div \frac{n^2 + 3n + 2}{4n^2 + 5n - 6}$ $\frac{n + 2}{n + 1}$

▶ 60. $\frac{8y^2 - 14y - 15}{6y^2 - 11y - 10} \div \frac{4y^2 - 9y - 9}{3y^2 - 7y - 6}$ 1

61. $\frac{5cd + d^2}{6d^2} \div \frac{125c^3 + d^3}{6c + 6d}$ $\frac{c + d}{d(25c^2 - 5cd + d^2)}$

62. $\frac{6m - 8n}{9m^3} \div \frac{27m^3 - 64n^3}{9m + 9n}$ $\frac{2(m + n)}{m^3(9m^2 + 12mn + 16n^2)}$

Divide, and then simplify, if possible. See Example 8.

63. $\frac{y^3 - 9y}{y + 2} \div (y - 3)$ $\frac{y(y + 3)}{y + 2}$

64. $\frac{x - 2}{x} \div (x^2 - 4)$ $\frac{1}{x(x + 2)}$

65. $(x + 1) \div \frac{x^2 + 2x + 1}{2}$ $\frac{2}{x + 1}$

▶ 66. $(y + 4) \div \frac{y^2 + 8y + 16}{ab}$ $\frac{ab}{y + 4}$

Perform each operation and simplify, if possible. See Example 9.

67. $\frac{6a^2 - 7a - 3}{a^2 - 1} \div \frac{4a^2 - 12a + 9}{a^2 - 1} \cdot \frac{2a^2 - a - 3}{3a^2 - 2a - 1}$ $\frac{a + 1}{a - 1}$

68. $\frac{x^2 - x - 12}{x^2 + x - 2} \div \frac{x^2 - 6x + 8}{x^2 - 3x - 10} \cdot \frac{x^2 - 3x + 2}{x^2 - 2x - 15}$ 1

69. $\frac{2x^2 - 2x - 4}{x^2 + 2x - 8} \cdot \frac{3x^2 + 15x}{x + 1} \div \frac{4x^2 - 100}{x^2 - x - 20}$ $\frac{3x}{2}$

▶ 70. $\frac{4a^2 - 10a + 6}{a^4 - 3a^3} \div \frac{3 - 2a}{2a^3} \cdot \frac{a - 3}{2a - 2}$ -2

TRY IT YOURSELF

Perform the operations and simplify.

▶ 71. $\frac{x^2 - 6x + 9}{4 - x^2} \div \frac{x^2 - 9}{x^2 - 8x + 12}$ $-\frac{(x - 3)(x - 6)}{(x + 2)(x + 3)}$

▶ 72. $\frac{x^3 + 1}{4} \div \frac{x + 1}{2}$ $\frac{x^2 - x + 1}{2}$

73. $\frac{2x^2 - 2x - 12}{x^2 - 4} \cdot \frac{x^2 - x - 2}{x^3 - 9x}$ $\frac{2(x + 1)}{x(x + 3)}$

74. $\frac{x^2 + 2x - 35}{12x^3} \cdot \frac{x^2 + 4x - 21}{x^2 - 3x}$ $\frac{(x + 7)^2(x - 5)}{12x^4}$

75. $\frac{p^3 - q^3}{p^2 - q^2} \cdot \frac{q^2 + pq}{p^3 + p^2q + pq^2}$ $\frac{q}{p}$

▶ 76. $\frac{x^2 - 4}{2b - bx} \div \frac{x^2 + 4x + 4}{2b + bx}$ -1

77. $\frac{10r^2s}{6rs^2} \cdot \frac{3r^3}{2rs}$ $\frac{5r^3}{2s^2}$

78. $\frac{3a^3b}{25cd^3} \cdot \frac{5cd^2}{6ab}$ $\frac{a^2}{10d}$

79. $10(h - 9)\frac{h - 3}{9 - h}$ $-10h + 30$ or $-10(h - 3)$

▶ 80. $r(r - 25)\frac{r + 4}{r - 25}$ $r^2 + 4r$ or $r(r + 4)$

81. $\frac{2x^2 + 5xy + 3y^2}{3x^2 - 5xy + 2y^2} \div \frac{2x^2 + xy - 3y^2}{3x^2 - 5xy + 2y^2}$ $\frac{x + y}{x - y}$

▶ 82. $\frac{2p^2 - 5pq - 3q^2}{p^2 - 9q^2} \div \frac{2p^2 + 5pq + 2q^2}{2p^2 + 5pq - 3q^2}$ $\frac{2p - q}{p + 2q}$

83. $(4x^2 - 9) \div \frac{2x^2 + 5x + 3}{x + 2} \cdot \frac{1}{2x - 3}$ $\frac{x + 2}{x + 1}$

84. $(4x + 12) \div \frac{2x - 6}{x^2} \cdot \frac{x - 3}{2}$ $x^2(x + 3)$

85. $\frac{x^3 - 3x^2 - 25x + 75}{x^3 - 27} \cdot \frac{2x^3 + 6x^2 + 18x}{x^2 + 10x + 25}$ $\frac{2x(x - 5)}{x + 5}$

86. $\frac{x^2 + 3x + xy + 3y}{x^2 - 9} \cdot \frac{3 - x}{x^3 + 3x^2}$ $-\frac{x + y}{x^2(x + 3)}$

APPLICATIONS

▶ 87. PHYSICS EXPERIMENTS The following table contains data from a physics experiment. Complete the table.

Trial	Rate (m/sec)	Time (sec)	Distance (m)
1	$\frac{k_1^2 + 3k_1 + 2}{k_1 - 3}$	$\frac{k_1^2 - 3k_1}{k_1 + 1}$	$k_1(k_1 + 2)$
2	$\frac{k_2^2 + 6k_2 + 5}{k_2 + 1}$	$k_2 + 6$	$k_2^2 + 11k_2 + 30$

88. GEOMETRY Find a simplified rational expression that represents the volume of the rectangular solid shown here. $\frac{2(x+1)}{x(x+3)}\ \text{ft}^3$

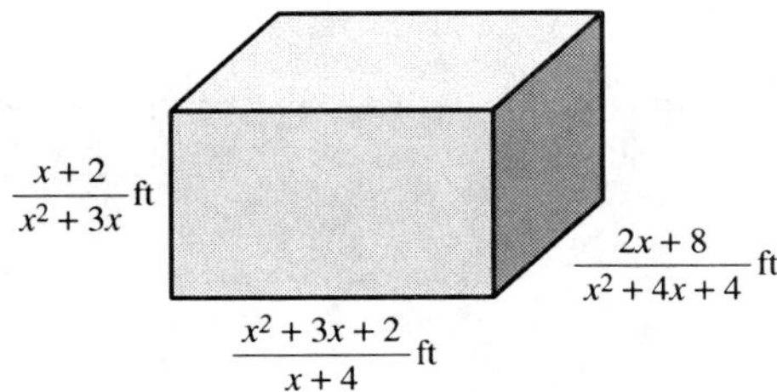

WRITING

89. Explain how to multiply two rational expressions.

90. Write some comments to the student who wrote the following solution, explaining the error.

$$\frac{x^2+x-2}{x^2-4}\cdot\frac{x-2}{x-1}=\frac{(x+2)(x-1)(x-2)}{(x+2)(x-2)(x-1)}$$
$$=0$$

91. The graph of $Y_3 = Y_1 - Y_2$, where

$$Y_1 = \frac{2x^2-5x-3}{x^2-9}\cdot\frac{2x^2+5x-3}{2x^2+5x+2}$$
$$Y_2 = \frac{2x-1}{x+2}$$

is shown. Explain how the graph and table can be used to verify that

$$\frac{2x^2-5x-3}{x^2-9}\cdot\frac{2x^2+5x-3}{2x^2+5x+2}=\frac{2x-1}{x+2}$$

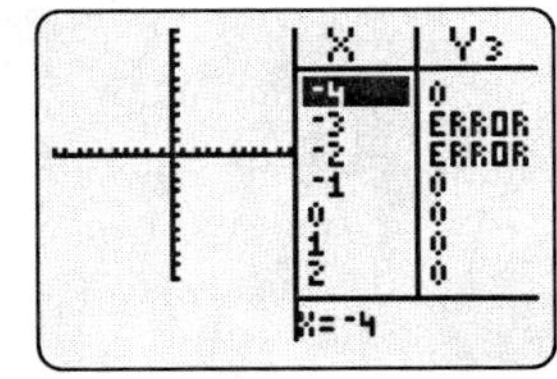

92. A student obtained an answer of $\frac{x+3}{x+7}$ after performing $\frac{x^2-9}{x^2-49} \div \frac{x+3}{x+7}$. As a check, he graphed $Y_3 = Y_1 - Y_2$, where

$$Y_1 = \left(\frac{x^2-9}{x^2-49}\right) \div \left(\frac{x+3}{x+7}\right)$$
$$Y_2 = \frac{x+3}{x+7}$$

The graph is shown. Explain what conclusion can be drawn from the graph and the table.

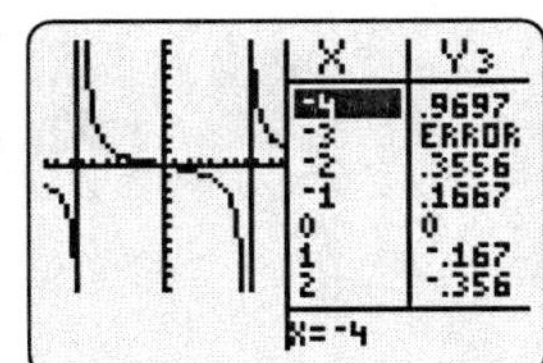

REVIEW

Complete the rules for exponents. Assume that there are no divisions by 0.

93. $x^m x^n = x^{m+n}$

94. $(x^m)^n = x^{mn}$

95. $(xy)^n = x^n y^n$

96. $\left(\frac{x}{y}\right)^n = \frac{x^n}{y^n}$

97. $x^0 = 1$

98. $x^{-n} = \frac{1}{x^n}$

99. $\frac{x^m}{x^n} = x^{m-n}$

100. $\left(\frac{x}{y}\right)^{-n} = \left(\frac{y}{x}\right)^n$

101. $\frac{x^{-m}}{y^{-n}} = \frac{y^n}{x^m}$

102. $x^1 = x$

SECTION 7.3
Adding and Subtracting Rational Expressions

Objectives

1. Add and subtract rational expressions with like denominators.
2. Add and subtract rational expressions with unlike denominators.
3. Find the least common denominator.
4. Perform mixed operations.

The methods used to add and subtract rational expressions are based on the rules for adding and subtracting arithmetic fractions. In this section, we will add and subtract rational expressions with *like* and *unlike* denominators.

1 Add and subtract rational expressions with like denominators.

To add or subtract fractions with a common denominator, we add or subtract their numerators and write the sum or difference over the common denominator. For example,

$$\frac{3}{7}+\frac{2}{7}=\frac{3+2}{7} \qquad \frac{3}{7}-\frac{2}{7}=\frac{3-2}{7}$$
$$=\frac{5}{7} \qquad =\frac{1}{7}$$

We use the same procedure to add and subtract rational expressions with like denominators.

Adding and Subtracting Rational Expressions That Have the Same Denominator

To add (or subtract) rational expressions that have same denominator, add (or subtract) their numerators and write the sum (or difference) over the common denominator. Then, if possible, factor and simplify.

If $\frac{A}{D}$ and $\frac{B}{D}$ are rational expressions,

$$\frac{A}{D}+\frac{B}{D}=\frac{A+B}{D} \quad \text{and} \quad \frac{A}{D}-\frac{B}{D}=\frac{A-B}{D}$$

Self Check 1

Perform the operations:

a. $\frac{17}{22t}+\frac{13}{22t}$ $\frac{15}{11t}$

b. $\frac{a^2}{a^2-2a}-\frac{4}{a^2-2a}$ $\frac{a+2}{a}$

Now Try **Problems 17 and 23**

Teaching Example 1 Perform the operations:

a. $\frac{5}{7x}+\frac{9}{7x}$ b. $\frac{a^2}{a^2+a}-\frac{1}{a^2+a}$

Answers:

a. $\frac{2}{x}$ b. $\frac{a-1}{a}$

EXAMPLE 1 Perform the operations: **a.** $\frac{4}{3x}+\frac{7}{3x}$ **b.** $\frac{a^2}{a^2-1}-\frac{a}{a^2-1}$

Strategy In part a, we will add the numerators and write the sum over the common denominator. In part b, we will subtract the numerators and write the difference over the common denominator. Then, if possible, we will factor and simplify.

WHY These are the rules for adding and subtracting rational expressions that have the *same* denominator.

Solution

a. $\frac{4}{3x}+\frac{7}{3x}=\frac{4+7}{3x}$ Add the numerators. Write the sum over the common denominator, 3x.

$=\frac{11}{3x}$ The result does not simplify.

b. $\frac{a^2}{a^2-1}-\frac{a}{a^2-1}=\frac{a^2-a}{a^2-1}$ Subtract the numerators. Write the difference over the common denominator, a^2-1.

We note that the polynomials in the numerator and the denominator of the result factor.

$$=\frac{a(a-1)}{(a+1)(a-1)}$$

$$=\frac{a(\overset{1}{\cancel{a-1}})}{(a+1)(\underset{1}{\cancel{a-1}})} \quad \text{Simplify.}$$

$$=\frac{a}{a+1}$$

Using Your CALCULATOR Checking Algebra

We can check the subtraction in Example 1b by replacing each a with x and graphing the rational functions $f(x) = \frac{x^2}{x^2 - 1} - \frac{x}{x^2 - 1}$, shown in figure (a), and $g(x) = \frac{x}{x + 1}$, shown in figure (b), and observing that the graphs are the same. Note that -1 and 1 are not in the domain of the first function and that -1 is not in the domain of the second function.

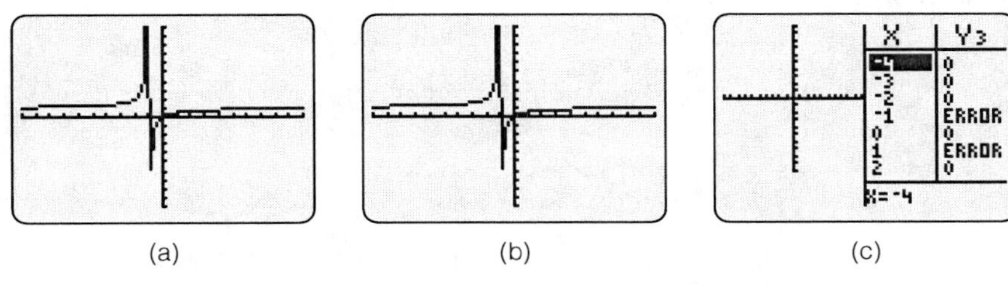

(a) (b) (c)

Figure (c) shows the display when the G-T mode is used to check the simplification. Here, $Y_3 = Y_1 - Y_2$, where $Y_1 = \frac{x^2}{x^2 - 1} - \frac{x}{x^2 - 1}$ and $Y_2 = \frac{x}{x + 1}$.

2 Add and subtract rational expressions with unlike denominators.

Recall that writing a fraction as an equivalent fraction with a larger denominator is called *building the fraction.* For example, to write $\frac{3}{5}$ as an equivalent fraction with a denominator of 35, we multiply it by 1 in the form of $\frac{7}{7}$. When a number is multiplied by 1, its value does not change.

$$\frac{3}{5} = \frac{3}{5} \cdot \frac{7}{7} = \frac{21}{35}$$

To add and subtract rational expressions with different denominators, we write them as equivalent expressions having a common denominator. To do so, we build rational expressions.

Building Rational Expressions

To build a rational expression, multiply it by 1 in the form of $\frac{c}{c}$, where c is any nonzero number or expression.

The following steps summarize how to add or subtract rational expressions with different denominators.

Adding and Subtracting Rational Expressions with Unlike Denominators

1. Find the LCD.
2. Write each rational expression as an equivalent expression with the LCD as the denominator. To do so, build each rational expression using a form of 1 that involves any factor(s) needed to obtain the LCD.
3. Add or subtract the numerators and write the sum or difference over the LCD.
4. Simplify the resulting rational expression, if possible.

Self Check 2

Add: $\frac{5}{a}+\frac{7}{b}$ $\frac{5b+7a}{ab}$

Now Try **Problem 25**

Teaching Example 2 Add: $\frac{9}{a}+\frac{3}{b}$

Answer:
$\frac{9b+3a}{ab}$

EXAMPLE 2

Add: $\frac{3}{x}+\frac{4}{y}$

Strategy The LCD for the rational expressions is xy. We will multiply each one by the appropriate form of 1 to build it into an equivalent rational expression with a denominator of xy.

WHY Since the denominators are different, we cannot add these rational expressions in their present form.

Solution

$$\frac{3}{x}+\frac{4}{y}=\frac{3}{x}\cdot\frac{y}{y}+\frac{4}{y}\cdot\frac{x}{x}$$ Build the rational expressions so that each has a denominator of xy.

$$=\frac{3y}{xy}+\frac{4x}{xy}$$ Multiply the numerators. Multiply the denominators.

$$=\frac{3y+4x}{xy}$$ Add the numerators. Write the sum over the common denominator, xy.

Self Check 3

Subtract: $\frac{3a}{a+3}-\frac{5a}{a-3}$

Now Try **Problems 29 and 31**

Self Check 3 Answer
$-\frac{2a(a+12)}{(a+3)(a-3)}$

Teaching Example 3 Subtract:
$\frac{8x}{x+3}-\frac{2x}{x+1}$

Answer:
$\frac{6x^2+2x}{(x+3)(x+1)}$ or $\frac{2x(3x+1)}{(x+3)(x+1)}$

EXAMPLE 3

Subtract: $\frac{4x}{x+2}-\frac{7x}{x-2}$

Strategy The LCD for the rational expressions is $(x+2)(x-2)$. We will multiply each one by the appropriate form of 1 to build it into an equivalent rational expression with a denominator of $(x+2)(x-2)$.

WHY Since the denominators are different, we cannot subtract these rational expressions in their present form.

Solution

$$\frac{4x}{x+2}-\frac{7x}{x-2}$$

$$=\frac{4x}{x+2}\cdot\frac{x-2}{x-2}-\frac{7x}{x-2}\cdot\frac{x+2}{x+2}$$ Build each rational expression.

$$=\frac{4x^2-8x}{(x+2)(x-2)}-\frac{7x^2+14x}{(x+2)(x-2)}$$ Multiply the numerators. Multiply the denominators. Leave the denominator in factored form. Subtract the numerators. Write the difference over the common denominator.

$$=\frac{(4x^2-8x)-(7x^2+14x)}{(x+2)(x-2)}$$ This numerator is written within parentheses to make sure that we subtract both of its terms.

$$=\frac{4x^2-8x-7x^2-14x}{(x+2)(x-2)}$$ To subtract the polynomials in the numerator, add the first and the opposite of the second.

$$=\frac{-3x^2-22x}{(x+2)(x-2)}$$ Combine like terms in the numerator.

If the common factor of $-x$ is factored out of the terms in the numerator, this result can be written in two other equivalent forms.

$$\frac{-3x^2-22x}{(x+2)(x-2)}=\frac{-x(3x+22)}{(x+2)(x-2)}=-\frac{x(3x+22)}{(x+2)(x-2)}$$

The result does not simplify.

We can use the following fact to add or subtract rational expressions whose denominators are opposites.

Multiplying by −1

When a polynomial is multiplied by −1, the result is its opposite.

EXAMPLE 4 Add: $\dfrac{x}{x-y} + \dfrac{y}{y-x}$

Strategy Since the denominators are opposites, either one can serve as the LCD. If we choose $x - y$, we can multiply $\frac{y}{y-x}$ by $\frac{-1}{-1}$ to build it into an equivalent rational expression with the denominator $x - y$.

WHY When $y - x$ is multiplied by −1, the subtraction is reversed, and the result is $x - y$.

Solution

$$\frac{x}{x-y} + \frac{y}{y-x} = \frac{x}{x-y} + \frac{y}{y-x} \cdot \frac{-1}{-1}$$ Build $\frac{y}{y-x}$ so that it has a denominator of $x - y$.

$$= \frac{x}{x-y} + \frac{-y}{-y+x}$$ Multiply the numerators. Multiply the denominators.

$$= \frac{x}{x-y} + \frac{-y}{x-y}$$ Write the second denominator, $-y + x$, as $x - y$. The rational expressions now have a common denominator.

$$= \frac{x-y}{x-y}$$ Add the numerators. Write the result over the common denominator, $x - y$.

$$= 1$$ Simplify.

Self Check 4

Add: $\dfrac{2a}{a-b} + \dfrac{b}{b-a}$ $\quad \dfrac{2a-b}{a-b}$

Now Try **Problem 33**

Teaching Example 4 Add: $\dfrac{a}{a-7} + \dfrac{7}{7-a}$

Answer: 1

EXAMPLE 5 Subtract: $3 - \dfrac{7}{x-15}$

Strategy We will begin by writing 3 as $\frac{3}{1}$.

WHY Then we can multiply $\frac{3}{1}$ by the appropriate form of 1 to build it into an equivalent rational expression with a denominator of $x - 15$.

Solution

$$3 - \frac{7}{x-15} = \frac{3}{1} - \frac{7}{x-15}$$ $3 = \frac{3}{1}$

$$= \frac{3}{1} \cdot \frac{x-15}{x-15} - \frac{7}{x-15}$$ Build $\frac{3}{1}$ to a rational expression with a denominator of $x - 15$.

$$= \frac{3x-45}{x-15} - \frac{7}{x-15}$$ Distribute the multiplication by 3.

$$= \frac{3x-45-7}{x-15}$$ Subtract the numerators. Write the difference over the common denominator, $x - 15$.

$$= \frac{3x-52}{x-2}$$ Combine like terms in the numerator. The result does not simplify.

Self Check 5

Subtract: $6 - \dfrac{5y}{6-y}$ $\quad \dfrac{-11y+36}{6-y}$

Now Try **Problem 37**

Teaching Example 5 Subtract: $9 - \dfrac{4}{a+3}$

Answer: $\dfrac{9a+23}{a+3}$

3 Find the least common denominator.

When adding or subtracting rational expressions with unlike denominators, it is easiest if we write the rational expressions in terms of the smallest common denominator possible, called the *least* (or lowest) *common denominator (LCD)*. To find the least common denominator of several rational expressions, we follow these steps.

Finding the LCD

1. Factor each denominator completely.
2. The LCD is a product that uses each different factor obtained in step 1 the greatest number of times it appears in any one factorization.

Self Check 6

Find the LCD of:

a. $\frac{5x}{28z^3}$ and $\frac{1}{21z}$

b. $\frac{a-1}{a^2-25}$ and $\frac{3-a^2}{a^2+7a+10}$

Now Try **Problems 41 and 45**

Self Check 6 Answers

a. $84z^3$ b. $(a-5)(a+5)(a+2)$

Teaching Example 6 Find the LCD of:

a. $\frac{13x}{15y^2}$ and $\frac{11x}{25y}$

b. $\frac{x}{x^2-49}$ and $\frac{4}{x^2-14x+49}$

Answers:

a. $75y^2$ b. $(x+7)(x-7)^2$

EXAMPLE 6 Find the LCD of:

a. $\frac{5a}{24b}$ and $\frac{11a}{18b^2}$ **b.** $\frac{1}{x^2-12x+36}$ and $\frac{3-x}{x^2-6x}$

Strategy We begin by factoring completely the denominator of each rational expression.

WHY Since the LCD must contain the factors of each denominator, we need to write each denominator in factored form.

Solution

a. We write each denominator as the product of prime numbers and variables.

$$24b = 2 \cdot 2 \cdot 2 \cdot 3 \cdot b = 2^3 \cdot 3 \cdot b$$
$$18b^2 = 2 \cdot 3 \cdot 3 \cdot b \cdot b = 2 \cdot 3^2 \cdot b^2$$

To find the LCD, we form a product using each of these factors the greatest number of times it appears in any one factorization.

The greatest number of times the factor 2 appears is three times.
The greatest number of times the factor 3 appears is twice.
The greatest number of times the factor b appears is twice.

$$\text{LCD} = 2 \cdot 2 \cdot 2 \cdot 3 \cdot 3 \cdot b \cdot b = 72b^2$$

b. We factor each denominator completely:

$$x^2 - 12x + 36 = (x-6)(x-6) = (x-6)^2$$
$$x^2 - 6x = x(x-6)$$

To find the LCD, we form a product using the highest power of each of the factors:

The greatest number of times the factor x appears is once.
The greatest number of times the factor $x - 6$ appears is twice.

$$\text{LCD} = x(x-6)^2$$

Success Tip Note that the highest power of each factor is used to form the LCD:

$$24b = 2^3 \cdot 3 \cdot b$$
$$18b^2 = 2 \cdot 3^2 \cdot b^2$$
$$\text{LCD} = 2^3 \cdot 3^2 \cdot b^2 = 72b^2$$

Self Check 7

Add: $\frac{5x}{28z^3} + \frac{1}{21z}$ $\frac{15x+4z^2}{84z^3}$

Now Try **Problems 49 and 51**

EXAMPLE 7 Add: $\frac{5a}{24b} + \frac{11a}{18b^2}$

Strategy In Example 6, we saw that the LCD of these rational expressions is $72b^2$. We will multiply each one by the appropriate form of 1 to build it into an equivalent rational expression with a denominator of $72b^2$.

WHY Since the denominators are different, we cannot add these rational expressions in their present form.

Solution

$$\frac{5a}{24b}+\frac{11a}{18b^2}=\frac{5a}{24b}\cdot\frac{3b}{3b}+\frac{11a}{18b^2}\cdot\frac{4}{4}$$ Build the rational expressions so that each has a denominator of $72b^2$.

$$=\frac{15ab}{72b^2}+\frac{44a}{72b^2}$$ Multiply the numerators. Multiply the denominators.

$$=\frac{15ab+44a}{72b^2}$$ Add the numerators. Write the sum over the common denominator. The result does not simplify.

Teaching Example 7 Add: $\frac{7a}{75b^2}+\frac{a}{30b^3}$
Answer: $\frac{14ab+5a}{150b^3}$

EXAMPLE 8

Subtract: $\frac{x}{x^2-2x+1}-\frac{4}{x^2-1}$

Strategy We will factor each denominator, find the LCD, and build the rational expressions so each one has the LCD as its denominator.

WHY Since the denominators are different, we cannot subtract these rational expressions in their present form.

Solution

We factor each denominator to find the LCD:

$$x^2-2x+1=(x-1)(x-1)=(x-1)^2$$ The greatest number of times $x-1$ appears is twice.

$$x^2-1=(x+1)(x-1)$$ The greatest number of times $x+1$ appears is once.

The LCD is $(x-1)^2(x+1)$ or $(x-1)(x-1)(x+1)$.

We now write each rational expression with its denominator in factored form. Then we multiply each numerator and denominator by the missing factor, so that each rational expression has a denominator of $(x-1)(x-1)(x+1)$.

$$\frac{x}{x^2-2x+1}-\frac{4}{x^2-1}$$

$$=\frac{x}{(x-1)(x-1)}-\frac{4}{(x+1)(x-1)}$$ Write each denominator in factored form.

$$=\frac{x}{(x-1)(x-1)}\cdot\frac{x+1}{x+1}-\frac{4}{(x+1)(x-1)}\cdot\frac{x-1}{x-1}$$ Build each rational expression.

$$=\frac{x^2+x}{(x-1)(x-1)(x+1)}-\frac{4x-4}{(x-1)(x-1)(x+1)}$$ Multiply the numerators. Multiply the denominators.

$$=\frac{(x^2+x)-(4x-4)}{(x-1)(x-1)(x+1)}$$ Subtract the numerators. Write the difference over the common denominator.

$$=\frac{x^2+x-4x+4}{(x-1)(x-1)(x+1)}$$ In the numerator, subtract the trinomials.

$$=\frac{x^2-3x+4}{(x-1)(x-1)(x+1)}$$ Combine like terms. The result does not simplify.

Self Check 8

Subtract: $\frac{a+2}{a^2-4a+4}-\frac{a-3}{a^2-4}$

***Now Try* Problem 57**

Self Check 8 Answer
$\frac{9a-2}{(a-2)(a-2)(a+2)}$

Teaching Example 8 Subtract:
a. $\frac{4}{x^2-x-6}-\frac{x}{x^2-9}$
b. $\frac{x+1}{x^2+5x+6}-\frac{x-3}{x^2-4}$
Answers:
a. $\frac{-x^2+2x+12}{(x+3)(x-3)(x+2)}$
b. $\frac{-x+7}{(x+2)(x+3)(x-2)}$

Success Tip To build each rational expression, we use the FOIL method to multiply the numerators. Note that we do not multiply out the denominators. For example, to build the second rational expression, we have:

$$\frac{x-4}{(x+1)(x-1)} \cdot \frac{x-1}{x-1}$$

The result is: $\frac{x^2-5x+4}{(x+1)(x-1)(x-1)}$

4 Perform mixed operations.

Self Check 9

Perform the operations:

$$\frac{5a}{a^2-25} - \frac{7}{a-5} + \frac{2}{a+5}$$

Now Try **Problem 63**

Self Check 9 Answer

$$-\frac{45}{(a+5)(a-5)}$$

Teaching Example 9 Perform the operations:

$$\frac{3a}{a^2-6a+5} - \frac{1}{a^2-1} + \frac{a+2}{a^2-4a-5}$$

Answer:

$$\frac{4a^2+3a+3}{(a-5)(a-1)(a+1)}$$

EXAMPLE 9 Perform the operations: $\frac{2x}{x^2-4} - \frac{1}{x^2-3x+2} + \frac{x+1}{x^2+x-2}$

Strategy We will factor each denominator, find the LCD, and build the rational expressions so each one has the LCD as its denominator.

WHY Since the denominators are different, we cannot add or subtract these rational expressions in their present form.

Solution

We factor each denominator to find the LCD and note that the greatest number of times each factor appears is once.

$$\left.\begin{aligned} x^2-4 &= (x-2)(x+2) \\ x^2-3x+2 &= (x-2)(x-1) \\ x^2+x-2 &= (x-1)(x+2) \end{aligned}\right\} \quad \text{LCD} = (x-2)(x+2)(x-1)$$

We then write each rational expression as an equivalent rational expression with the LCD as its denominator and do the subtraction and addition.

$$\frac{2x}{x^2-4} - \frac{1}{x^2-3x+2} + \frac{x+1}{x^2+x-2}$$

$$= \frac{2x}{(x-2)(x+2)} - \frac{1}{(x-2)(x-1)} + \frac{x+1}{(x-1)(x+2)} \quad \text{Factor the denominators.}$$

$$= \frac{2x}{(x-2)(x+2)} \cdot \frac{x-1}{x-1} - \frac{1}{(x-2)(x-1)} \cdot \frac{x+2}{x+2} + \frac{x+1}{(x-1)(x+2)} \cdot \frac{x-2}{x-2}$$

$$= \frac{2x(x-1) - 1(x+2) + (x+1)(x-2)}{(x+2)(x-2)(x-1)} \quad \text{Write the sum and difference over the common denominator.}$$

$$= \frac{2x^2-2x-x-2+x^2-x-2}{(x+2)(x-2)(x-1)}$$

$$= \frac{3x^2-4x-4}{(x+2)(x-2)(x-1)} \quad \text{Combine like terms.}$$

$$= \frac{(3x+2)\overset{1}{\cancel{(x-2)}}}{(x+2)\underset{1}{\cancel{(x-2)}}(x-1)} \quad \text{Factor the trinomial and simplify.}$$

$$= \frac{3x+2}{(x+2)(x-1)}$$

Caution! Always write the result in simplest form by removing any factors common to the numerator and denominator.

ANSWERS TO SELF CHECKS

1. a. $\frac{15}{11t}$ **b.** $\frac{a+2}{a}$ **2.** $\frac{5b+7a}{ab}$ **3.** $-\frac{2a(a+12)}{(a+3)(a-3)}$ **4.** $\frac{2a-b}{a-b}$ **5.** $\frac{-11y+36}{6-y}$ **6. a.** $84z^3$ **b.** $(a-5)(a+5)(a+2)$ **7.** $\frac{15x+4z^2}{84z^3}$ **8.** $\frac{9a-2}{(a-2)(a-2)(a+2)}$ **9.** $-\frac{45}{(a+5)(a-5)}$

SECTION 7.3 STUDY SET

VOCABULARY

Fill in the blanks.

1. The rational expressions $\frac{7}{6n}$ and $\frac{n+1}{6n}$ have a common denominator of $6n$.
2. The least common denominator of $\frac{x-8}{x+6}$ and $\frac{6-5x}{x}$ is $x(x+6)$.
3. To build a rational expression, we multiply it by a form of 1. For example, $\frac{2}{n^2} \cdot \frac{8}{8} = \frac{16}{8n^2}$.
4. The polynomials $x - y$ and $y - x$ are opposites because their terms are the same but opposite in sign.

CONCEPTS

Fill in the blanks.

5. To add or subtract rational expressions that have the same denominator, add or subtract the numerators, and write the sum or difference over the common denominator.

   In symbols, if $\frac{A}{D}$ and $\frac{B}{D}$ are rational expressions,

$$\frac{A}{D} + \frac{B}{D} = \frac{A+B}{D} \quad \text{and} \quad \frac{A}{D} - \frac{B}{D} = \frac{A-B}{D}$$

6. When a number is multiplied by 1, its value does not change.
7. To find the least common denominator of several rational expressions, factor each denominator completely. The LCD is a product that uses each different factor the greatest number of times it appears in any one factorization.
8. $$\frac{x^2+3x}{x-1} - \frac{2x-1}{x-1} = \frac{x^2+3x-(2x-1)}{x-1}$$
9. Consider the following two procedures.

   i. $$\frac{x^2-2x}{x^2+4x-12} = \frac{x\overset{1}{\cancel{(x-2)}}}{(x+6)\underset{1}{\cancel{(x-2)}}} = \frac{x}{x+6}$$

   ii. $$\frac{x}{x+6} = \frac{x}{x+6} \cdot \frac{x-2}{x-2} = \frac{x^2-2x}{(x+6)(x-2)}$$

   a. In which of these procedures are we *building* a rational expression? ii

   b. For what type of problem is procedure ii often necessary? adding or subtracting rational expressions

   c. What name is used to describe procedure i? simplifying a rational expression

10. The LCD for $\frac{2x+1}{x^2+5x+6}$ and $\frac{3x}{x^2-4}$ is

$$\text{LCD} = (x+2)(x+3)(x-2)$$

   If we want to subtract these rational expressions, what form of 1 should be used:

   a. to build $\frac{2x+1}{x^2+5x+6}$? $\frac{x-2}{x-2}$

   b. to build $\frac{3x}{x^2-4}$? $\frac{x+3}{x+3}$

11. Consider the following factorizations.

$$2 \cdot 3 \cdot 3 \cdot (x-2)$$
$$3(x-2)(x+1)$$

   a. What is the greatest number of times the factor 3 appears in any one factorization? twice

   b. What is the greatest number of times the factor $x - 2$ appears in any one factorization? once

12. The factorizations of the denominators of two rational expressions follow. Find the LCD.

$$2 \cdot 3 \cdot a \cdot a \cdot a \quad 18a^3$$
$$2 \cdot 3 \cdot 3 \cdot a \cdot a$$

13. Factor each denominator completely.

   a. $\frac{17}{40x^2}$ $2 \cdot 2 \cdot 2 \cdot 5 \cdot x \cdot x$

   b. $\frac{x+25}{2x^2-6x}$ $2x(x-3)$

   c. $\frac{n^2+3n-4}{n^2-64}$ $(n+8)(n-8)$

14. By what must $y - 4$ be multiplied to obtain $4 - y$? -1

NOTATION

Complete each solution.

15. $$\frac{6x-1}{3x-1} + \frac{3x-2}{3x-1} = \frac{6x-1+3x-2}{3x-1}$$
$$= \frac{9x-3}{3x-1}$$
$$= \frac{3(3x-1)}{3x-1}$$
$$= 3$$

▶ **16.** $\frac{8}{3v} - \frac{1}{4v^2} = \frac{8}{3v} \cdot \frac{4v}{4v} - \frac{1}{4v^2} \cdot \frac{3}{3}$

$= \frac{32v}{12v^2} - \frac{3}{12v^2}$

$= \frac{32v - 3}{12v^2}$

GUIDED PRACTICE

Add or subtract, and then simplify, if possible. See Example 1.

17. $\frac{8}{3x} + \frac{5}{3x}$ $\frac{13}{3x}$

18. $\frac{3}{4y} + \frac{8}{4y}$ $\frac{11}{4y}$

19. $\frac{t}{4r} + \frac{t}{4r}$ $\frac{t}{2r}$

20. $\frac{16x}{3z^2} - \frac{x}{3z^2}$ $\frac{5x}{z^2}$

21. $\frac{4y}{y-4} - \frac{16}{y-4}$ 4

▶ **22.** $\frac{3x}{2x+2} + \frac{x+4}{2x+2}$ 2

23. $\frac{3x}{x^2-9} - \frac{9}{x^2-9}$ $\frac{3}{x+3}$

▶ **24.** $\frac{9x}{x^2-1} - \frac{9}{x^2-1}$ $\frac{9}{x+1}$

Add or subtract, and then simplify, if possible. See Example 2.

25. $\frac{15}{p} + \frac{2}{q}$ $\frac{15q + 2p}{pq}$

26. $\frac{2}{a} + \frac{19}{b}$ $\frac{2b + 19a}{ab}$

27. $\frac{7}{2b} - \frac{11}{3a}$ $\frac{21a - 22b}{6ab}$

▶ **28.** $\frac{5}{3n} - \frac{7}{4m}$ $\frac{20m - 21n}{12mn}$

Add or subtract, and then simplify, if possible. See Example 3.

29. $\frac{3}{x+2} + \frac{5}{x-4}$ $\frac{8x - 2}{(x+2)(x-4)}$

▶ **30.** $\frac{6}{a+4} - \frac{2}{a+3}$ $\frac{4a + 10}{(a+4)(a+3)}$

31. $\frac{6x}{x+3} - \frac{4x}{x-3}$ $\frac{2x^2 - 30x}{(x+3)(x-3)}$

32. $\frac{t}{t+2} + \frac{8}{t-2}$ $\frac{t^2 + 6t + 16}{(t+2)(t-2)}$

Add or subtract, and then simplify, if possible. See Example 4.

33. $\frac{5x}{x-3} + \frac{4x}{3-x}$ $\frac{x}{x-3}$

▶ **34.** $\frac{8x}{x-4} - \frac{10x}{4-x}$ $\frac{18x}{x-4}$

35. $\frac{9m}{m-n} - \frac{2}{n-m}$ $\frac{9m + 2}{m - n}$

36. $\frac{3s}{s-x} + \frac{1}{x-s}$ $\frac{3s - 1}{s - x}$

Add or subtract, and then simplify, if possible. See Example 5.

37. $4 + \frac{1}{x-2}$ $\frac{4x - 7}{x - 2}$

38. $2 - \frac{1}{x+1}$ $\frac{2x + 1}{x + 1}$

▶ **39.** $x + \frac{4x}{7x-3}$ $\frac{7x^2 + x}{7x - 3}$

40. $x - \frac{3x}{3x-2}$ $\frac{3x^2 - 5x}{3x - 2}$

The denominators of several fractions are given. Find the LCD. See Example 6.

41. $12xy, 18x^2y$ $36x^2y$

▶ **42.** $15ab^2, 27a^2b$ $135a^2b^2$

43. $x^2 + 3x, x^2 - 9$ $x(x+3)(x-3)$

44. $3y^2 - 6y, 3y(y-4)$ $3y(y-2)(y-4)$

45. $x^3 + 27, x^2 + 6x + 9$ $(x+3)^2(x^2 - 3x + 9)$

▶ **46.** $x^3 - 8, x^2 - 4x + 4$ $(x-2)^2(x^2 + 2x + 4)$

47. $2x^2 + 5x + 3, 4x^2 + 12x + 9, x^2 + 2x + 1$ $(2x+3)^2(x+1)^2$

48. $2x^2 + 5x + 3, 4x^2 + 12x + 9, 4x + 6$ $2(2x+3)^2(x+1)$

Perform the operations and simplify the result when possible. See Example 7.

49. $\frac{11}{5m} - \frac{5}{6m}$ $\frac{41}{30m}$

50. $\frac{5}{9s} - \frac{1}{4s}$ $\frac{11}{36s}$

51. $\frac{3}{4ab^2} - \frac{5}{2a^2b}$ $\frac{3a - 10b}{4a^2b^2}$

▶ **52.** $\frac{1}{5xy^3} - \frac{2}{15x^2y}$ $\frac{3x - 2y^2}{15x^2y^3}$

Perform the operations and simplify the result when possible. See Example 8.

53. $\frac{1}{x+3} + \frac{2}{x^2+4x+3}$ $\frac{1}{x+1}$

54. $\frac{4}{y^2+8y+12} + \frac{1}{y+6}$ $\frac{1}{y+2}$

55. $\frac{m}{m^2+9m+20} - \frac{4}{m^2+7m+12}$ $\frac{m - 5}{(m+3)(m+5)}$

56. $\frac{t}{t^2+5t+6} - \frac{2}{t^2+3t+2}$ $\frac{t - 3}{(t+3)(t+1)}$

57. $\frac{x}{x^2+5x+6} + \frac{x}{x^2-4}$ $\frac{2x^2 + x}{(x+3)(x+2)(x-2)}$

▶ **58.** $\frac{2a}{a^2-2a-8} + \frac{3}{a^2-5a+4}$ $\frac{2a^2 + a + 6}{(a-4)(a+2)(a-1)}$

59. $\frac{x+2}{6x-42} - \frac{x-3}{5x-35}$ $\frac{-x + 28}{30(x-7)}$

60. $\frac{x-1}{4x-24} - \frac{3x-2}{5x-30}$ $\frac{-7x + 3}{20(x-6)}$

Perform the operations and simplify the result when possible. See Example 9.

61. $\frac{5x}{x+1} + \frac{3}{x+1} - \frac{2x}{x+1}$ 3

▶ **62.** $\frac{4}{a+4} - \frac{2a}{a+4} + \frac{3a}{a+4}$ 1

63. $\frac{8}{x^2-9} + \frac{2}{x-3} - \frac{6}{x}$ $\frac{-4x^2 + 14x + 54}{x(x+3)(x-3)}$ or $\frac{-2(2x^2 - 7x - 27)}{x(x+3)(x-3)}$

64. $\frac{x}{x^2-4} - \frac{x}{x+2} + \frac{2}{x}$ $\frac{-x^3 + 5x^2 - 8}{x(x+2)(x-2)}$

65. $\dfrac{3x}{2x-1}+\dfrac{x+1}{3x+2}-\dfrac{2x}{6x^3+x^2-2x}$ $\quad\dfrac{11x^2+7x-3}{(2x-1)(3x+2)}$

▶ **66.** $\dfrac{2}{x-2}+\dfrac{3}{x+2}-\dfrac{x-1}{x^2-4}$ $\quad\dfrac{4x-1}{(x+2)(x-2)}$

▶ **67.** $\dfrac{1}{x+y}-\dfrac{1}{x-y}-\dfrac{2y}{y^2-x^2}$ $\quad 0$

68. $\dfrac{a}{a-b}+\dfrac{b}{a+b}+\dfrac{a^2+b^2}{b^2-a^2}$ $\quad\dfrac{2b}{a+b}$

TRY IT YOURSELF

Perform the operations and simplify the result when possible.

69. $\dfrac{s+7}{s+3}-\dfrac{s-3}{s+7}$ $\quad\dfrac{14s+58}{(s+3)(s+7)}$

▶ **70.** $\dfrac{t+5}{t-5}-\dfrac{t-5}{t+5}$ $\quad\dfrac{20t}{(t-5)(t+5)}$

▶ **71.** $\dfrac{x-y}{2}+\dfrac{x+y}{3}$ $\quad\dfrac{5x-y}{6}$

72. $\dfrac{a+b}{3}+\dfrac{a-b}{7}$ $\quad\dfrac{10a+4b}{21}$ or $\dfrac{2(5a+2b)}{21}$

73. $\dfrac{3x^2+3x}{x^2-5x+6}-\dfrac{3x^2-3x+12}{x^2-5x+6}$ $\quad\dfrac{6}{x-3}$

▶ **74.** $\dfrac{2m^2-7}{m^4-9}+\dfrac{4-m^2}{m^4-9}$ $\quad\dfrac{1}{m^2-3}$

75. $\dfrac{a^2+ab}{a^3-b^3}-\dfrac{b^2}{b^3-a^3}$ $\quad\dfrac{1}{a-b}$

▶ **76.** $\dfrac{y^2-3xy}{x^3-y^3}-\dfrac{x^2+4xy}{y^3-x^3}$ $\quad\dfrac{1}{x-y}$

77. $2x+3+\dfrac{1}{x+1}$ $\quad\dfrac{2x^2+5x+4}{x+1}$

78. $x+1+\dfrac{1}{x-1}$ $\quad\dfrac{x^2}{x-1}$

79. $\dfrac{4}{x^2-2x-3}-\dfrac{x}{3x^2-7x-6}$ $\quad\dfrac{-x^2+11x+8}{(3x+2)(x+1)(x-3)}$

80. $\dfrac{x+3}{2x^2-5x+2}-\dfrac{3x-1}{x^2-x-2}$ $\quad-\dfrac{5x+1}{(2x-1)(x+1)}$

81. $\dfrac{3}{x+1}-\dfrac{2}{x-1}+\dfrac{x+3}{x^2-1}$ $\quad\dfrac{2}{x+1}$

82. $\dfrac{7n^2}{m-n}+\dfrac{3m}{n-m}-\dfrac{3m^2-n}{m^2-2mn+n^2}$ $\quad\dfrac{7mn^2-7n^3-6m^2+3mn+n}{(m-n)^2}$

83. $\dfrac{8}{9y^2}+\dfrac{1}{6y^4}$ $\quad\dfrac{16y^2+3}{18y^4}$

84. $\dfrac{5}{6a^3}+\dfrac{7}{8a^2}$ $\quad\dfrac{21a+20}{24a^3}$

Perform the operations and simplify the result when possible. Be careful to apply the correct method, because these problems involve addition, subtraction, multiplication, and division of rational expressions.

85. $\dfrac{6}{b^2-9}\cdot\dfrac{b+3}{2b+4}$ $\quad\dfrac{3}{(b+2)(b-3)}$

86. $\dfrac{3a^2-22a+7}{a-a^2}\cdot\dfrac{8a^2-8a}{a^2+a-56}$ $\quad-\dfrac{24a-8}{a+8}$ or $-\dfrac{8(3a-1)}{a+8}$

87. $\dfrac{4a}{a-5}+a$ $\quad\dfrac{a^2-a}{a-5}$

88. $\dfrac{10z}{z+4}+z$ $\quad\dfrac{z^2+14z}{z+4}$

89. $\dfrac{2a+1}{3a-2}-\dfrac{a-4}{2-3a}$ $\quad\dfrac{3a-3}{3a-2}$ or $\dfrac{3(a-1)}{3a-2}$

90. $\dfrac{2x+1}{x^4-81}+\dfrac{2-x}{x^4-81}$ $\quad\dfrac{1}{(x^2+9)(x-3)}$

91. $\dfrac{x^2+x}{3x-15}\div\dfrac{(x+1)^2}{6x-30}$ $\quad\dfrac{2x}{x+1}$

92. $\dfrac{z^2-9}{z^2+4z+3}\div\dfrac{z^2-3z}{(z+1)^2}$ $\quad\dfrac{z+1}{z}$

93. $\dfrac{m}{m^2+5m+6}-\dfrac{2}{m^2+3m+2}$ $\quad\dfrac{m-3}{(m+3)(m+1)}$

94. $\dfrac{1}{m+1}+\dfrac{1}{m-1}+\dfrac{2}{m^2-1}$ $\quad\dfrac{2}{m-1}$

95. $\dfrac{27p^4}{35q}\div\dfrac{9p}{21q}$ $\quad\dfrac{9p^3}{5}$

96. $\dfrac{12t}{25s^5}\div\dfrac{10t}{15s^2}$ $\quad\dfrac{18}{25s^3}$

97. $\dfrac{6}{5d^2-5d}-\dfrac{3}{5d-5}$ $\quad\dfrac{6-3d}{5d(d-1)}$

▶ **98.** $\dfrac{9}{2r^2-2r}-\dfrac{5}{2r-2}$ $\quad\dfrac{9-5r}{2r(r-1)}$

99. $\dfrac{s^3t}{4s^2-9t^2}\cdot\dfrac{4s^2-12st+9t^2}{s^3t^2}$ $\quad\dfrac{2s-3t}{t(2s+3t)}$

100. $\dfrac{25x^2-40xy+16y^2}{x^2y^4}\cdot\dfrac{xy^4}{25x^2-16y^2}$ $\quad\dfrac{5x-4y}{x(5x+4y)}$

APPLICATIONS

101. DRAFTING Among the tools used in drafting are the 45°–45°–90° and the 30°–60°–90° triangles shown. Find the perimeter of each triangle. Express each result as a single rational expression. $\frac{10r+20}{r}; \frac{3t+9}{t}$

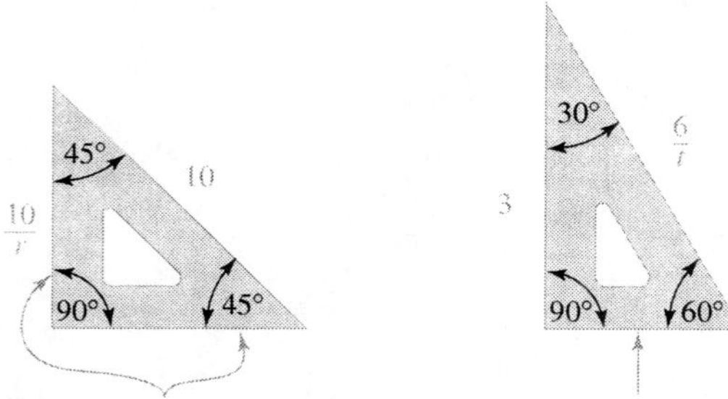

For a 45°–45°–90° triangle, these two sides are the same length.

For a 30°–60°–90° triangle, this side is half as long as the hypotenuse.

102. THE AMAZON The Amazon River flows in an easterly direction to the Atlantic Ocean. In Brazil, when the river is at low stage, the rate of flow is about 5 mph. Suppose that a river guide can canoe in still water at a rate of r mph.

a. Complete the table to find rational expressions that represent the time it would take the guide to canoe 3 miles downriver and to canoe 3 miles upriver on the Amazon.

	Rate (mph)	Time (hr)	Distance (ml)
Downriver	$r + 5$	$\frac{3}{r+5}$	3
Upriver	$r - 5$	$\frac{3}{r-5}$	3

b. Find the difference in the times for the trips upriver and downriver. Express the result as a single rational expression. $\frac{30}{(r+5)(r-5)}$ hr

WRITING

103. Explain how to find the least common denominator of a set of rational expressions.

104. Add the rational expressions by expressing them in terms of a common denominator $24b^3$. (*Note:* This is not the LCD.)

$$\frac{r}{4b^2} + \frac{s}{6b}$$

An extra step had to be performed because the lowest common denominator was not used. What was the step?

105. Write some comments to the student who wrote the following solution, explaining his misunderstanding.

$$\text{Multiply: } \frac{1}{x} \cdot \frac{3}{2} = \frac{1 \cdot 2}{x \cdot 2} \cdot \frac{3 \cdot x}{2 \cdot x}$$
$$= \frac{2}{2x} \cdot \frac{3x}{2x}$$
$$= \frac{6x}{2x}$$

106. Write some comments to the student who wrote the following solution, pointing out where she made an error.

$$\text{Subtract: } \frac{1}{x} - \frac{x+1}{x} = \frac{1 - x + 1}{x}$$
$$= \frac{2 - x}{x}$$

REVIEW

Solve each equation.

107. $a(a - 6) = -9$ a repeated solution of 3

108. $x^2 - \frac{1}{2}(x + 1) = 0$ $1, -\frac{1}{2}$

109. $y^3 + y^2 = 0$ a repeated solution of 0, −1

110. $5x^2 = 6 - 13x$ $\frac{2}{5}, -3$

SECTION 7.4
Solving Rational Equations

Objectives

1. Solve rational equations.
2. Solve rational equations with extraneous solutions.
3. Solve formulas for a specified variable.

In Chapter 1, we solved equations such as $\frac{1}{6}x + \frac{5}{2} = \frac{1}{3}$ by multiplying both sides by the LCD. With this approach, the equation that results is equivalent to the original equation, but easier to solve because it is cleared of fractions.

In this section, we will extend the fraction-clearing strategy to solve another type of equation, called a *rational equation.*

1 Solve rational equations.

If an equation contains one or more rational expressions, it is called a **rational equation.** Rational equations often have a variable in a denominator. Some examples are:

$$\frac{3}{5} + \frac{7}{x+2} = 2, \qquad \frac{x+3}{x-3} = \frac{2}{x^2-4}, \qquad \text{and} \qquad \frac{-x^2+10}{x^2-1} + \frac{3x}{x-1} = \frac{2x}{x+1}$$

To solve a rational equation, we find all the values of the variable that make the equation true. Any value of the variable that makes a denominator in a rational equation equal to 0 cannot be a solution of the equation. Such a number must be rejected, because division by 0 is undefined.

EXAMPLE 1 Solve: $\frac{3}{5} + \frac{7}{x+2} = 2$

Strategy This equation contains a rational expression that has a variable in the denominator. We begin by asking, "What value(s) of x make that denominator 0?"

WHY If a number makes the denominator of a rational expression 0, that number cannot be a solution of the equation because division by 0 is undefined.

Solution

We note that x cannot be -2, because this would produce a 0 in the denominator of $\frac{7}{x+2}$.

Since the denominators of the rational expressions in the equation are 5 and $x + 2$, we multiply both sides by the LCD, $5(x + 2)$, to clear the equation of fractions.

$$\frac{3}{5} + \frac{7}{x+2} = 2$$ This is the equation to solve.

$$5(x+2)\left(\frac{3}{5} + \frac{7}{x+2}\right) = 5(x+2)(2)$$ Write each side of the equation within parentheses and then multiply both sides by the LCD.

$$5(x+2)\left(\frac{3}{5}\right) + 5(x+2)\left(\frac{7}{x+2}\right) = 5(x+2)(2)$$ On the left side, distribute the multiplication by $5(x + 2)$.

$$\overset{1}{\cancel{5}}(x+2)\left(\frac{3}{\underset{1}{\cancel{5}}}\right) + 5\overset{1}{\cancel{(x+2)}}\left(\frac{7}{\underset{1}{\cancel{(x+2)}}}\right) = 5(x+2)(2)$$ On the left side, simplify: $\frac{5}{5} = 1$ and $\frac{x+2}{x+2} = 1$.

$$3(x+2) + 5(7) = 10(x+2)$$ Simplify each side.

Self Check 1

Solve: $\frac{2}{5} + \frac{8}{x-4} = 2$ 9

Now Try **Problem 13**

Teaching Example 1 Solve: $\frac{1}{5} + \frac{2}{x-1} = 3$

Answer: $\frac{12}{7}$

The resulting equation does not contain any fractions. We now solve this linear equation for x.

$$3x + 6 + 35 = 10x + 20 \quad \text{Use the distributive property and simplify.}$$
$$3x + 41 = 10x + 20 \quad \text{Combine like terms.}$$
$$-7x = -21 \quad \text{Subtract 10x and 41 from both sides.}$$
$$x = 3 \quad \text{Divide both sides by } -7.$$

The solution is 3 and the solution set is {3}. To check, we substitute 3 for x in the original equation and simplify:

Check:
$$\frac{3}{5} + \frac{7}{x + 2} = 2$$
$$\frac{3}{5} + \frac{7}{3 + 2} \stackrel{?}{=} 2$$
$$\frac{3}{5} + \frac{7}{5} \stackrel{?}{=} 2$$
$$2 = 2 \quad \text{True}$$

Success Tip To *simplify the expression* $\frac{3}{5} + \frac{7}{x + 2}$, we build each fraction to have the LCD $5(x + 2)$, add the numerators, and write the sum over the LCD.

To *solve the equation* $\frac{3}{5} + \frac{7}{x + 2} = 2$, we multiply both sides by the LCD $5(x + 2)$ to eliminate the denominators.

Using Your CALCULATOR **Solving Rational Equations Graphically**

To use a graphing calculator to solve $\frac{3}{5} + \frac{7}{x + 2} = 2$, we graph the functions $f(x) = \frac{3}{5} + \frac{7}{x + 2}$ and $g(x) = 2$. If we trace and move the cursor closer to the intersection point of the two graphs, we will get the approximate value of x shown in figure (a) on the next page. If we zoom twice and trace again, we get the results shown in figure (b). As we saw in Example 1, the exact solution is 3.

An alternate way of finding the point of intersection of the two graphs is to use the INTERSECT feature. In figure (c), the display shows that the graphs intersect at the point (3, 2). This implies that the solution of the rational equation is 3.

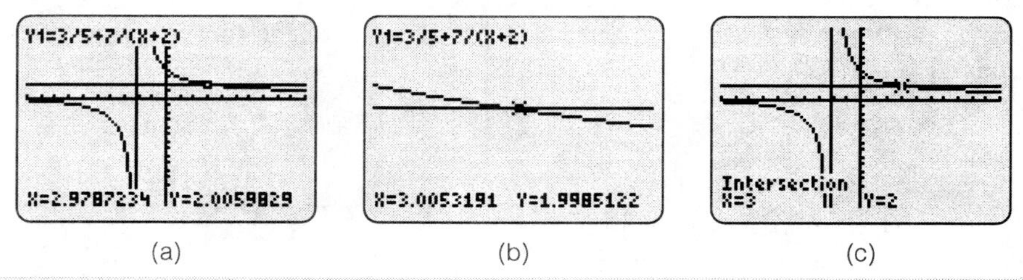

(a) (b) (c)

Self Check 2

Solve: $\frac{2}{x - 3} = \frac{-x}{x^2 - 9} + \frac{4}{x + 3}$

Now Try **Problem 17**

Self Check 2 Answer
18

EXAMPLE 2 Solve: $\frac{-x^2 + 10}{x^2 - 1} + \frac{3x}{x - 1} = \frac{2x}{x + 1}$

Strategy We will begin by factoring the first denominator.

WHY To determine any restrictions on the variable and to find the LCD, we need to write $x^2 - 1$ in factored form.

Teaching Example 2 Solve: $\frac{20}{x^2 - x - 6} + \frac{x}{x - 3} = \frac{x}{x + 2}$
Answer: -4

Solution

Since $x^2 - 1$ factors as $(x + 1)(x - 1)$, we can write the given equation as:

$$\frac{-x^2 + 10}{(x + 1)(x - 1)} + \frac{3x}{x - 1} = \frac{2x}{x + 1} \quad \text{Factor the denominator } x^2 - 1.$$

We see that -1 and 1 cannot be solutions of the equation because they make rational expressions in the equation undefined.

We can clear the equation of fractions by multiplying both sides by $(x + 1)(x - 1)$, which is the LCD of the three rational expressions.

$$(x + 1)(x - 1)\left[\frac{-x^2 + 10}{(x + 1)(x - 1)} + \frac{3x}{x - 1}\right] = (x + 1)(x - 1)\left(\frac{2x}{x + 1}\right)$$

$$(x + 1)(x - 1)\left[\frac{-x^2 + 10}{(x + 1)(x - 1)}\right] + (x + 1)(x - 1)\left(\frac{3x}{x - 1}\right) = (x + 1)(x - 1)\left(\frac{2x}{x + 1}\right)$$

$$\overset{1}{\cancel{(x + 1)}}\overset{1}{\cancel{(x - 1)}}\left[\frac{-x^2 + 10}{\underset{1}{\cancel{(x + 1)}}\underset{1}{\cancel{(x - 1)}}}\right] + (x + 1)\overset{1}{\cancel{(x - 1)}}\left(\frac{3x}{\underset{1}{\cancel{x - 1}}}\right) = \overset{1}{\cancel{(x + 1)}}(x - 1)\left(\frac{2x}{\underset{1}{\cancel{x + 1}}}\right)$$

Simplify. The resulting equation does not contain any fractions. $\quad -x^2 + 10 + 3x(x + 1) = 2x(x - 1)$

Use the distributive property. $\quad -x^2 + 10 + 3x^2 + 3x = 2x^2 - 2x$

Combine like terms on each side. $\quad 2x^2 + 10 + 3x = 2x^2 - 2x$

Subtract $2x^2$ from both sides. $\quad 10 + 3x = -2x$

Add $2x$ to both sides. $\quad 10 + 5x = 0$

Subtract 10 from both sides. $\quad 5x = -10$

Divide both sides by 5. $\quad x = -2$

The solution is -2. Verify that it satisfies the original equation.

> ***Caution!*** After multiplying both sides by the LCD and simplifying, the equation should not contain any fractions. If it does, check for an algebraic error, or perhaps your LCD is incorrect.

We can summarize the procedure used to solve rational equations.

Solving Rational Equations

1. Factor all denominators.
2. Determine which numbers cannot be solutions of the equation.
3. Multiply both sides of the equation by the LCD of all rational expressions in the equation.
4. Use the distributive property to remove parentheses, remove any factors equal to 1, and write the result in simplified form.
5. Solve the resulting equation.
6. Check all possible solutions in the original equation.

Using Your CALCULATOR Checking Apparent Solutions

We can use a scientific calculator to check the solution −2 found in Example 2 by evaluating

$$\frac{-x^2 + 10}{x^2 - 1} + \frac{3x}{x - 1} \quad \text{and} \quad \frac{2x}{x + 1}$$

In each case, the result is 4. Since the results are the same, −2 is a solution of the equation.

We can also check by using a graphing calculator. One way of doing this is to enter

$$Y_1 = \frac{-x^2 + 10}{x^2 - 1} + \frac{3x}{x - 1} \quad \text{and} \quad Y_2 = \frac{2x}{x + 1}$$

and compare the values of the expressions when $x = -2$ in the table mode. See the figure. We know that −2 is a solution of

$$\frac{-x^2 + 10}{x^2 - 1} + \frac{3x}{x - 1} = \frac{2x}{x + 1}$$

because the value of Y1 and Y2 are the same (namely, 4) for $x = -2$.

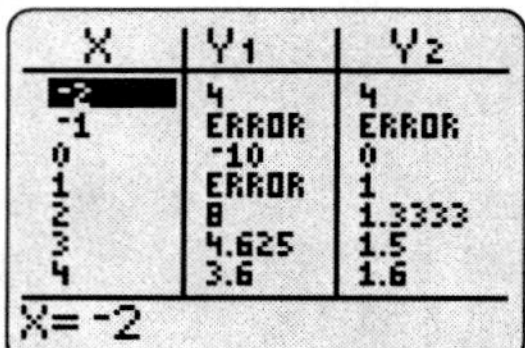

Self Check 3

Solve: $\frac{b}{5} = \frac{b - 14}{2b - 16} - \frac{1}{2}$ 3, 5

Now Try **Problem 25**

Teaching Example 3 Solve: $\frac{x + 1}{5} - 2 = -\frac{4}{x}$

Answer: 4, 5

EXAMPLE 3

Solve: $\frac{a}{2} = \frac{a - 6}{3a - 9} - \frac{1}{3}$

Strategy We will begin by factoring the second denominator.

WHY To determine any restrictions on the variable and to find the LCD, we need to write $3a - 9$ in factored form.

Solution

Since the binomial $3a - 9$ factors as $3(a - 3)$, we can write the given equation as:

$$\frac{a}{2} = \frac{a - 6}{3(a - 3)} - \frac{1}{3} \quad \text{Factor the denominator } 3a - 9.$$

We see that 3 cannot be a solution of the equation, because it makes one of the rational expressions in the equation undefined.

We can clear the equation of fractions by multiplying both sides by $2 \cdot 3 \cdot (a - 3)$, which is the LCD of the three rational expressions.

$$2 \cdot 3 \cdot (a - 3)\left(\frac{a}{2}\right) = 2 \cdot 3 \cdot (a - 3)\left[\frac{a - 6}{3(a - 3)} - \frac{1}{3}\right] \quad \text{Multiply both sides by the LCD, } 2 \cdot 3 \cdot (a - 3).$$

$$2 \cdot 3 \cdot (a - 3)\left(\frac{a}{2}\right) = 2 \cdot 3 \cdot (a - 3)\left[\frac{a - 6}{3(a - 3)}\right] - 2 \cdot 3 \cdot (a - 3)\left(\frac{1}{3}\right) \quad \text{On the right side, distribute } 2 \cdot 3 \cdot (a - 3).$$

$$\overset{1}{\cancel{2}} \cdot 3(a - 3)\left(\frac{a}{\underset{1}{\cancel{2}}}\right) = 2 \cdot \overset{1}{\cancel{3}}\overset{1}{\cancel{(a - 3)}}\left[\frac{a - 6}{\underset{1}{\cancel{3}}\underset{1}{\cancel{(a - 3)}}}\right] - 2 \cdot \overset{1}{\cancel{3}}(a - 3)\left(\frac{1}{\underset{1}{\cancel{3}}}\right) \quad \text{Remove common factors of the numerator and denominator.}$$

$$3a(a - 3) = 2(a - 6) - 2(a - 3)$$

$$3a^2 - 9a = 2a - 12 - 2a + 6 \quad \text{Use the distributive property.}$$

$$3a^2 - 9a = -6 \quad \text{Combine like terms.}$$

To use factoring to solve the resulting quadratic equation, we must write it in standard form $ax^2 + bx + c = 0$.

$3a^2 - 9a + 6 = 0$ To get 0 on the right side, add 6 to both sides.

$a^2 - 3a + 2 = 0$ Divide both sides by 3.

$(a - 1)(a - 2) = 0$ Factor the trinomial.

$a - 1 = 0$ or $a - 2 = 0$ Set each factor equal to 0.

$a = 1$ $\quad$ $a = 2$

Verify that 1 and 2 both satisfy the original equation.

Recall that the quotient of a polynomial and its opposite is -1. For example, $\frac{y-1}{1-y} = -1$. We can use this fact when solving rational equations whose denominators contain factors that are opposites.

EXAMPLE 4 Solve: $\frac{1}{6y - 6} + \frac{1}{1 - y} = \frac{1}{6}$

Strategy We will begin by factoring the first denominator.

WHY To determine any restrictions on the variable and to find the LCD, we need to write $6y - 6$ in factored form.

Solution

Since the binomial $6y - 6$ factors as $6(y - 1)$,we can write the given equation as:

$$\frac{1}{6(y-1)} + \frac{1}{1-y} = \frac{1}{6}$$

We see that 1 cannot be a solution of the equation because it makes two of the rational expressions in the equation undefined.

We note that $y - 1$ and $1 - y$ are opposites. We can clear the equation of fractions by multiplying both sides by $6(y - 1)$.

$$6(y-1)\left[\frac{1}{6(y-1)} + \frac{1}{1-y}\right] = 6(y-1)\left(\frac{1}{6}\right)$$ Multiply both sides by the LCD, $6(y - 1)$.

$$6(y-1)\left[\frac{1}{6(y-1)}\right] + 6(y-1)\left(\frac{1}{1-y}\right) = 6(y-1)\left(\frac{1}{6}\right)$$ On the left side, distribute $6(y - 1)$.

$$\frac{\overset{1}{\cancel{6}}\overset{1}{\cancel{(y-1)}}}{}\left[\frac{1}{\underset{1}{\cancel{6}}\underset{1}{\cancel{(y-1)}}}\right] + 6\overset{-1}{\cancel{(y-1)}}\left(\frac{1}{\underset{1}{\cancel{1-y}}}\right) = \overset{1}{\cancel{6}}(y-1)\left(\frac{1}{\underset{1}{\cancel{6}}}\right)$$ Simplify: $\frac{y-1}{1-y} = -1$.

$$1 - 6 = y - 1$$

$$-5 = y - 1$$ Combine like terms.

$$-4 = y$$ Add 1 to both sides.

The solution is -4. Verify that it satisfies the original equation.

Self Check 4

Solve: $\frac{1}{2h - 8} + \frac{11}{4 - h} = \frac{3}{2}$ -3

Now Try **Problem 33**

Teaching Example 4 Solve: $\frac{3}{2x-2} - \frac{1}{x-1} = \frac{1}{2}$

Answer: 2

2 Solve rational equations with extraneous solutions.

When we multiply both sides of an equation by a quantity that contains a variable, we can get false solutions, called *extraneous solutions.* This happens when we multiply both sides of an equation by 0 and get a solution that gives a 0 in the denominator of a rational expression. Extraneous solutions must be discarded.

Self Check 5

Solve: $2 - \frac{2a}{a-1} = \frac{3a-5}{a-1}$

Now Try **Problem 37**

Self Check 5 Answer
No solution; 1 is extraneous.

Teaching Example 5 Solve:
$\frac{2(x+1)}{x-3} = \frac{x+5}{x-3}$
Answer:
No solution; 3 is extraneous.

EXAMPLE 5 Solve: $3 - \frac{1-2t}{t+2} = \frac{t-3}{t+2}$

Strategy We will clear the equation of fractions by multiplying both sides by the LCD, $t + 2$.

WHY Equations that contain only integers are usually easier to solve than equations that contain fractions.

Solution

We note that t cannot be -2, because this would give a 0 in a denominator.

$$3 - \frac{1-2t}{t+2} = \frac{t-3}{t+2}$$

$$(t+2)\left(3 - \frac{1-2t}{t+2}\right) = (t+2)\left(\frac{t-3}{t+2}\right) \quad \text{Multiply both sides by the LCD.}$$

$$(t+2)(3) - (t+2)\left(\frac{1-2t}{t+2}\right) = (t+2)\left(\frac{t-3}{t+2}\right) \quad \text{On the left side, distribute the multiplication by } t+2.$$

$$(t+2)(3) - \frac{\cancel{(t+2)}}{1}\left(\frac{1-2t}{\cancel{t+2}}\right) = \frac{\cancel{(t+2)}}{1}\left(\frac{t-3}{\cancel{t+2}}\right) \quad \text{Remove common factors of the numerator and denominator.}$$

$$3t + 6 - (1 - 2t) = t - 3 \quad \text{Simplify.}$$

$$3t + 6 - 1 + 2t = t - 3$$

$$5t + 5 = t - 3 \quad \text{Combine like terms.}$$

$$4t = -8$$

$$t = -2$$

Since t cannot be -2, it is an extraneous solution and must be discarded. This equation has no solution.

The Language of Algebra *Extraneous* means not a vital part. Mathematicians speak of *extraneous* solutions. Rock groups don't want any *extraneous* sounds (like humming or feedback) coming from their amplifiers. Artists erase any *extraneous* marks on their sketches.

3 Solve formulas for a specified variable.

Many formulas involve rational expressions. We can use the fraction-clearing method of this section to solve such formulas for a specified variable.

Self Check 6

Solve the law of gravitation formula for r^2. $r^2 = \frac{Gm_1m_2}{F}$

Now Try **Problem 41**

Teaching Example 6 Solve $F = \frac{Gm_1m_2}{r^2}$ for m_1.
Answer:
$m_1 = \frac{Fr^2}{Gm_2}$

EXAMPLE 6 *Physics* The *law of gravitation,* formulated by Sir Isaac Newton in 1684, states that if two masses, m_1 and m_2, are separated by a distance of r, the force F exerted by one mass on the other is

$$F = \frac{Gm_1m_2}{r^2}$$

r
F
m_1
m_2

where G is the gravitational constant. Solve for m_2.

Strategy To solve for m_2, we will treat it as if it were the only variable in the equation. To isolate this variable, we will use the same strategy that we used in previous examples to solve rational equations in one variable.

WHY We can solve a formula as if it were an equation in one variable because all the other variables are treated as if they were numbers (constants).

Solution

$$F = \frac{Gm_1m_2}{r^2}$$

$$r^2(F) = r^2\left(\frac{Gm_1m_2}{r^2}\right)$$ Multiply both sides by the LCD, r^2. Simplify: $\frac{r^2}{r^2} = 1$.

$$\frac{r^2F}{Gm_1} = \frac{Gm_1m_2}{Gm_1}$$ To isolate m_2, divide both sides by Gm_1.

$$\frac{r^2F}{Gm_1} = m_2$$ Simplify the right side by removing the factors G and m_1, which are common to the numerator and denominator.

$$m_2 = \frac{r^2F}{Gm_1}$$ Reverse the sides of the equation so that m_2 is on the left

EXAMPLE 7 *Electronics* In electronic circuits, resistors oppose the flow of an electric current. The total resistance R of a parallel combination of two resistors as shown is given by

$$\frac{1}{R} = \frac{1}{R_1} + \frac{1}{R_2}$$

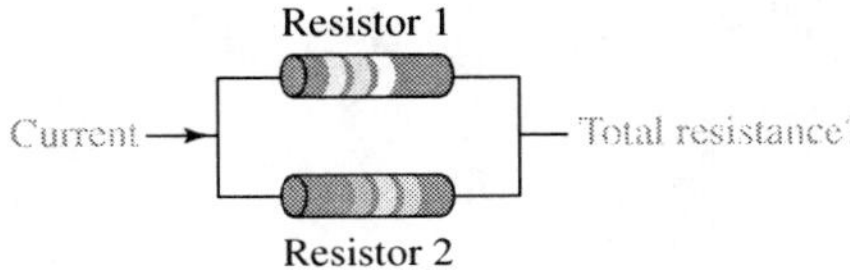

where R_1 is the resistance of the first resistor and R_2 is the resistance of the second resistor. Solve for R.

Strategy To solve for R, we will treat it as if it were the only variable in the equation. To isolate this variable, we will use the same strategy that we used in previous examples to solve rational equations in one variable; we will clear the equation of fractions.

WHY We can solve a formula as if it were an equation in one variable because all the other variables are treated as if they were numbers (constants).

Solution

We begin by clearing the equation of fractions by multiplying both sides by the LCD, which is RR_1R_2.

$$\frac{1}{R} = \frac{1}{R_1} + \frac{1}{R_2}$$

$$RR_1R_2\left(\frac{1}{R}\right) = RR_1R_2\left(\frac{1}{R_1} + \frac{1}{R_2}\right)$$ Multiply both sides by the LCD.

$$RR_1R_2\left(\frac{1}{R}\right) = RR_1R_2\left(\frac{1}{R_1}\right) + RR_1R_2\left(\frac{1}{R_2}\right)$$ On the right side, distribute RR_1R_2.

$$RR_1R_2\left(\frac{1}{R}\right) = RR_1R_2\left(\frac{1}{R_1}\right) + RR_1R_2\left(\frac{1}{R_2}\right)$$ Remove common factors of the numerator and denominator.

$$R_1R_2 = RR_2 + RR_1$$ Simplify.

$$R_1R_2 = R(R_2 + R_1)$$ Factor out R on the right side.

$$\frac{R_1R_2}{R_2 + R_1} = R$$ To isolate R, divide both sides by $R_2 + R_1$.

$$R = \frac{R_1R_2}{R_2 + R_1}$$ Reverse the sides of the equation to write R on the left side.

Self Check 7

Solve $\frac{1}{x} - \frac{1}{y} = \frac{1}{z}$ for z. $z = \frac{xy}{y - x}$

Now Try **Problem 49**

Teaching Example 7 Solve $\frac{1}{R} = \frac{1}{R_1} + \frac{1}{R_2}$ for R_1.
Answer:
$R_1 = \frac{RR_2}{R_2 - R}$

ANSWERS TO SELF CHECKS

1. 9 **2.** 18 **3.** 3, 5 **4.** −3 **5.** No solution; 1 is extraneous **6.** $r^2 = \frac{Gm_1m_2}{F}$ **7.** $z = \frac{xy}{y - x}$

SECTION 7.4 STUDY SET

VOCABULARY

Fill in the blanks.

1. Equations that contain one or more rational expressions, such as $\frac{x}{x+2} = 4 + \frac{10}{x+1}$, are called rational equations.

▶ **2.** When solving a rational equation, if we obtain a number that does not satisfy the original equation, the number is called an extraneous solution.

CONCEPTS

3. Is 2 a solution of the following equations?

a. $\frac{x+2}{x+3} + \frac{1}{x^2+2x-3} = 1$ yes

b. $\frac{x+2}{x-2} + \frac{1}{x^2-4} = 1$ no

4. Consider the rational equation $\frac{x}{x-3} = \frac{1}{x} + \frac{2}{x-3}$.

a. What values of x make a denominator 0? 3, 0

b. What values of x make a rational expression undefined? 3, 0

c. What numbers can't be solutions of the equation? 3, 0

▶ **5.** To clear the following equation of fractions, by what should both sides be multiplied?

$$\frac{4}{10} + y = \frac{4y - 50}{5y - 25}$$ the LCD, $10(y-5)$

6. Perform each multiplication.

a. $4x\left(\frac{3}{4x}\right)$ 3

b. $(x+6)(x-2)\left(\frac{3}{x-2}\right)$ $3(x+6) = 3x + 18$

c. $8(x+4)\left(\frac{7x}{2(x+4)}\right)$ $28x$

d. $6(m-5)\left(\frac{7}{5-m}\right)$ -42

NOTATION

Complete each solution.

7.
$$\frac{10}{3y} - \frac{7}{30} = \frac{9}{2y}$$
$$30y\left(\frac{10}{3y} - \frac{7}{30}\right) = 30y\left(\frac{9}{2y}\right)$$
$$30y\left(\frac{10}{3y}\right) - 30y\left(\frac{7}{30}\right) = 30y\left(\frac{9}{2y}\right)$$
$$100 - 7y = 135$$
$$-7y = 35$$
$$y = -5$$

▶ **8.**
$$\frac{2}{u-1} + \frac{1}{u} = \frac{1}{u^2 - u}$$
$$\frac{2}{u-1} + \frac{1}{u} = \frac{1}{u(u-1)}$$
$$u(u-1)\left(\frac{2}{u-1} + \frac{1}{u}\right) = u(u-1)\left[\frac{1}{u(u-1)}\right]$$
$$u(u-1)\left(\frac{2}{u-1}\right) + u(u-1)\left(\frac{1}{u}\right) = u(u-1)\left[\frac{1}{u(u-1)}\right]$$
$$2u + u - 1 = 1$$
$$3u = 2$$
$$u = \frac{2}{3}$$

GUIDED PRACTICE

Solve each equation. See Example 1.

9. $\frac{1}{4} + \frac{9}{x} = 1$ 12

10. $\frac{1}{3} - \frac{10}{x} = -3$ 3

11. $\frac{1}{a} = \frac{1}{3} - \frac{2}{3a}$ 5

12. $\frac{1}{b} = \frac{1}{8} - \frac{3}{8b}$ 11

13. $\frac{18}{y+1} + \frac{2}{5} = 4$ 4

▶ **14.** $\frac{2}{3} + \frac{10}{a+2} = 4$ 1

15. $\frac{1}{2} + \frac{x}{x-1} = 3$ $\frac{5}{3}$

▶ **16.** $\frac{2}{3} + \frac{a}{a-2} = 5$ $\frac{13}{5}$

Solve each equation. See Example 2.

17. $\frac{4}{t+3}+\frac{8}{t^2-9}=\frac{2}{t-3}$ 5

18. $\frac{5}{x-1}=\frac{1}{x^2-1}+\frac{1}{x-1}$ $-\frac{3}{4}$

19. $\frac{4}{x^2-4}-\frac{5}{x-2}=\frac{1}{x+2}$ $-\frac{2}{3}$

20. $\frac{1}{m+3}-\frac{m}{m^2-9}=\frac{-2}{m-3}$ $-\frac{3}{2}$

21. $\frac{2}{x-2}+\frac{10}{x+5}=\frac{2x}{x^2+3x-10}$ 1

22. $\frac{2}{a+4}+\frac{2a-1}{a^2+2a-8}=\frac{1}{a-2}$ 3

23. $\frac{1}{n+2}-\frac{2}{n-3}=\frac{-2n}{n^2-n-6}$ 7

24. $\frac{2x}{x^2+9x+20}-\frac{3}{x+4}=\frac{2}{x+5}$ $-\frac{23}{3}$

Solve each equation. See Example 3.

25. $\frac{2}{5x-5}+\frac{x-2}{15}=\frac{4}{5x-5}$ 4, −1

26. $\frac{3}{2x+4}=\frac{x-2}{2}+\frac{x-5}{2x+4}$ −4, 3

27. $\frac{p-1}{2}+1=\frac{3}{p}$ 2, −3

28. $\frac{b+1}{2}-\frac{3}{2}=\frac{4}{b}$ 4, −2

29. $\frac{16}{t+3}+\frac{7}{t-2}=3$ $-\frac{1}{3}, 7$

30. $\frac{17}{s-4}-\frac{10}{s+2}=2$ $-\frac{9}{2}, 10$

31. $\frac{5}{x-2}=2-\frac{6}{x+2}$ $-\frac{1}{2}, 6$

32. $\frac{-10}{t+3}=1-\frac{11}{t-3}$ −8, 9

Solve each equation. See Example 4.

33. $\frac{1}{3x-18}+\frac{5}{6-x}=\frac{1}{3}$ −8

34. $\frac{1}{2x-16}+\frac{14}{8-x}=\frac{3}{2}$ −1

35. $\frac{7}{3x-9}+\frac{1}{3-x}=\frac{4}{9}$ 6

36. $\frac{1}{2d-4}-\frac{1}{2-d}=\frac{1}{4}$ 8

Solve each equation. If a solution is extraneous, so indicate. See Example 5.

37. $4-\frac{3x}{x-9}=\frac{5x-72}{x-9}$ No solution; 9 is extraneous.

38. $2-\frac{2x}{x-10}=\frac{4x-60}{x-10}$ No solution; 10 is extraneous.

39. $\frac{6}{x+3}+\frac{48}{x^2-2x-15}-\frac{7}{x-5}=0$ No solution; −3 is extraneous.

40. $\frac{3}{x-4}+\frac{2}{x+5}+\frac{18}{x^2+x-20}=0$ No solution; −5 is extraneous.

Solve each formula for the specified variable. See Examples 6 and 7.

41. $Q=\frac{A-I}{L}$ for A (from banking) $A=LQ+I$

42. $z=\frac{x-\bar{x}}{s}$ for x (from statistics) $x=sz+\bar{x}$

43. $I=\frac{E}{R_L+r}$ for r (from physics) $r=\frac{E-IR_L}{I}$

44. $P=\frac{R-C}{n}$ for C (from business) $C=R-nP$

45. $\mu_R=\frac{n_1(n_1+n_2+1)}{2}$ for n_2 (from statistics) $n_2=\frac{2\mu_R-n_1^2-n_1}{n_1}$

46. $\frac{P_1V_1}{T_1}=\frac{P_2V_2}{T_2}$ for T_2 (from chemistry) $T_2=\frac{P_2T_1V_2}{P_1V_1}$

47. $P=\frac{Q_1}{Q_2-Q_1}$ for Q_1 (from refrigeration/heating) $Q_1=\frac{PQ_2}{1+P}$

48. $S=\frac{a-\ell r}{1-r}$ for r (from mathematics) $r=\frac{S-a}{S-\ell}$

49. $\frac{1}{R}=\frac{1}{R_1}+\frac{1}{R_2}+\frac{1}{R_3}$ for R (from electronics) $R=\frac{R_1R_2R_3}{R_2R_3+R_1R_3+R_1R_2}$

50. $\frac{x}{a}+\frac{y}{b}=1$ for a (from mathematics) $a=\frac{bx}{b-y}$

51. $\frac{E}{e}=\frac{R+r}{r}$ for r (from engineering) $r=\frac{eR}{E-e}$

52. $P+\frac{a}{V^2}=\frac{RT}{V-b}$ for b (from physics) $b=\frac{PV^3+aV-RTV^2}{PV^2+a}$

TRY IT YOURSELF

Solve each equation. If a solution is extraneous, so indicate.

53. $\frac{x+2}{x+3}-1=\frac{-1}{x^2+2x-3}$ 2

54. $\frac{m+6}{3m-12}+\frac{5}{4-m}=\frac{2}{3}$ −1

55. $\frac{3}{y} + \frac{7}{2y} = 13$ $\frac{1}{2}$

56. $\frac{2}{x} + \frac{1}{2} = \frac{7}{2x}$ 3

57. $\frac{3}{r} + \frac{12}{r^2 - 4r} = -\frac{7}{r - 4}$ No solution; 0 is extraneous.

58. $\frac{4t^2 + 36}{t^2 - 9} - \frac{4t}{t + 3} = \frac{-12}{t - 3}$
No solution; −3 is extraneous.

59. $\frac{x + 4}{2x + 14} - \frac{x}{2x + 6} = \frac{3}{16}$
1, −11

60. $\frac{30}{y - 2} + \frac{24}{y - 5} = 13$
8, $\frac{41}{13}$

61. $\frac{3}{m} = 2 - \frac{m}{m - 2}$ 1, 6

62. $\frac{n}{2} = 1 + \frac{12}{n}$ −4, 6

63. $\frac{x + 2}{2x - 6} + \frac{3}{3 - x} = \frac{x}{2}$
a repeated solution of 2

64. $\frac{3}{4x - 8} = \frac{1}{36} - \frac{2}{6 - 3x}$
5

65. $\frac{2}{x} + \frac{1}{2} = \frac{9}{4x} - \frac{1}{2x}$
$-\frac{1}{2}$

66. $\frac{7}{5x} - \frac{1}{2} = \frac{5}{6x} + \frac{1}{3}$
$\frac{17}{25}$

67. $\frac{3 - 5y}{2 + y} = \frac{-5y - 3}{y - 2}$
0

68. $\frac{a - 3}{a + 1} = \frac{a - 6}{a + 5}$
$\frac{9}{7}$

▶ 69. $\frac{21}{x^2 - 4} - \frac{14}{x + 2} = \frac{3}{2 - x}$
5

70. $\frac{-5}{c + 2} = \frac{3}{2 - c} + \frac{2c}{c^2 - 4}$
4

71. $\frac{x - 4}{x - 3} - \frac{x - 2}{3 - x} = x - 3$
5; 3 is extraneous.

72. $\frac{5}{x + 4} + \frac{1}{x + 4} = x - 1$
2, −5

73. $\frac{a + 2}{a + 1} = \frac{a - 4}{a - 3}$ 1

74. $\frac{z + 2}{z + 8} = \frac{z - 3}{z - 2}$ 4

▶ 75. $\frac{5}{y - 1} + \frac{3}{y - 3} = \frac{8}{y - 2}$
6

76. $\frac{3 + 2a}{a^2 + 6 + 5a} + \frac{2 - 5a}{a^2 - 4} = \frac{2 - 3a}{a^2 - 6 + a}$
$-\frac{2}{5}$

77. $\frac{3}{s - 2} + \frac{s - 14}{2s^2 - 3s - 2} - \frac{4}{2s + 1} = 0$
1

78. $\frac{1}{y^2 - 2y - 3} + \frac{1}{y^2 - 4y + 3} - \frac{1}{y^2 - 1} = 0$
−3

79. $\frac{x}{x + 2} = 1 - \frac{3x + 2}{x^2 + 4x + 4}$
2

80. $\frac{a - 1}{a + 3} - \frac{1 - 2a}{3 - a} = \frac{2 - a}{a - 3}$
0

81. $\frac{5}{2z^2 + z - 3} - \frac{2}{2z + 3} = \frac{z + 1}{z - 1} - 1$
$\frac{1}{6}$

82. $\frac{x}{x - 5} + \frac{5}{x} = \frac{11}{6}$ 2, 15

▶ 83. $\frac{5}{3x + 12} - \frac{1}{9} = \frac{x - 1}{3x}$ $-\frac{3}{2}$, 2

84. $\frac{1}{y + 5} = \frac{1}{3y + 6} - \frac{y + 2}{y^2 + 7y + 10}$ $-\frac{7}{5}$

For each expression in part a, perform the indicated operations and then simplify, if possible. Solve each equation in part b and check the result.

▶ 85. **a.** $\frac{11}{12} - \frac{3}{2x} + \frac{4}{x}$
$\frac{11x + 30}{12x}$

b. $\frac{11}{12} - \frac{3}{2x} = \frac{4}{x}$
6

86. **a.** $\frac{1}{6x} - \frac{2}{x - 6}$
$\frac{-11x - 6}{6x(x - 6)}$

b. $\frac{1}{6x} = \frac{2}{x - 6}$
$-\frac{6}{11}$

87. **a.** $\frac{m}{m - 2} - \frac{1}{m - 3}$
$\frac{m^2 - 4m + 2}{(m - 2)(m - 3)}$

b. $\frac{m}{m - 2} - \frac{1}{m - 3} = 1$
4

88. **a.** $\frac{a^2 + 1}{a^2 - a} - \frac{a}{a - 1}$
$\frac{1}{a(a - 1)}$

b. $\frac{a^2 + 1}{a^2 - a} - \frac{a}{a - 1} = \frac{1}{a}$
2

APPLICATIONS

89. PHOTOGRAPHY The illustration shows the relationship between distances when taking a photograph. The design of a camera lens uses the equation

$$\frac{1}{f} = \frac{1}{s_1} + \frac{1}{s_2}$$

which relates the focal length f of a lens to the image distance s_1 and the object distance s_2.

a. Solve the formula for f. $f = \frac{s_1 s_2}{s_1 + s_2}$

b. Find the focal length of the lens in the illustration. (*Hint:* Convert feet to inches.) $4\frac{8}{13}$ in.

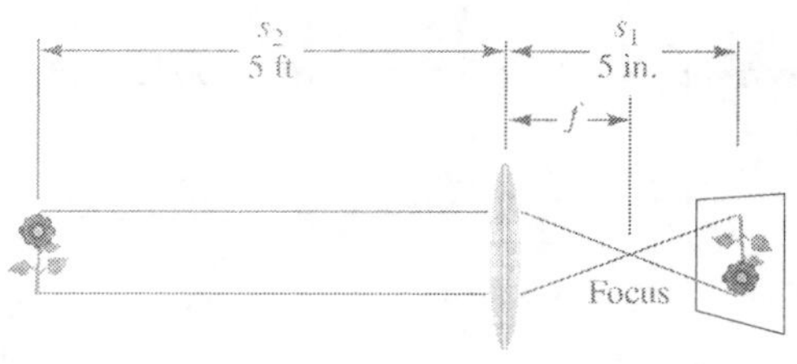

90. OPTICS See the illustration in the next column. The focal length, f, of a lens is given by the lensmaker's formula,

$$\frac{1}{f} = 0.6\left(\frac{1}{r_1} + \frac{1}{r_2}\right)$$

where f is the focal length of the lens and r_1 and r_2 are the radii of the two circular surfaces.

a. Solve the formula for f. $f = \frac{r_1 r_2}{0.6r_1 + 0.6r_2}$

b. Find the focal length of the lens in the illustration. $\frac{20}{3}$ cm

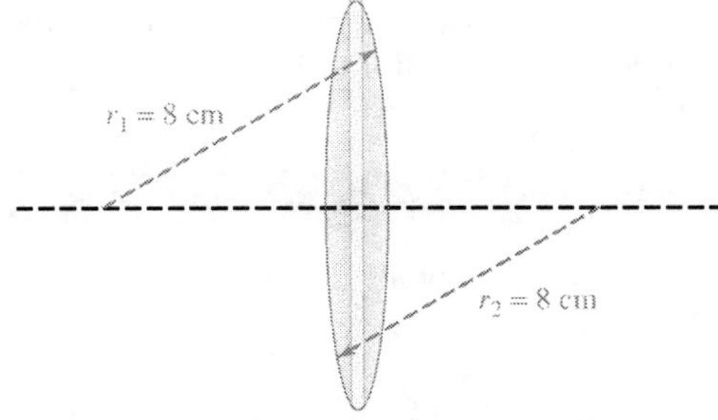

91. ACCOUNTING As a piece of equipment gets older, its value usually lessens. One way to calculate *depreciation* is to use the formula

$$V = C - \left(\frac{C - S}{L}\right)N$$

where V denotes the value of the equipment at the end of year N, L is its useful lifetime (in years), C is its cost new, and S is its salvage value at the end of its useful life.

a. Solve the formula for L. $L = \frac{SN - CN}{V - C}$

b. Determine what an accountant considered the useful lifetime of a forklift that cost \$25,000 new, was worth \$13,000 after 4 years, and has a salvage value of \$1,000. 8 yr

92. ENGINEERING The equation

$$a = \frac{9.8m_2 - f}{m_2 + m_1}$$

models the system shown, where a is the acceleration of the suspended block, m_1 and m_2 are the masses of the blocks, and f is the friction force. Solve for m_2. $m_2 = \frac{am_1 + f}{9.8 - a}$

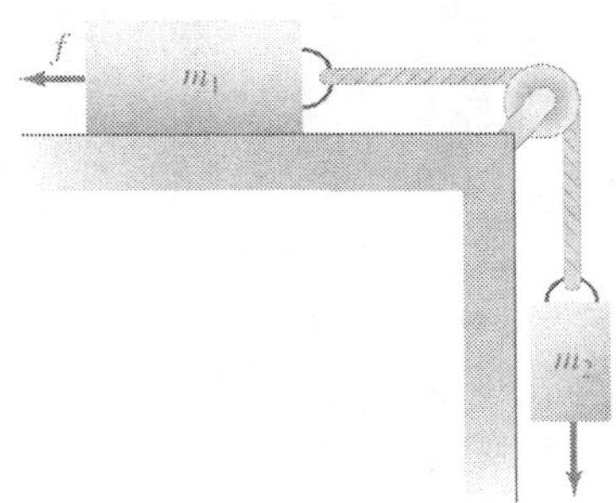

WRITING

93. Why is it necessary to check the solutions of a rational equation?

94. Explain what it means to *clear* a rational equation of fractions. Give an example.

95. Would you use the same approach to answer the following problems? Explain why or why not.

$$\text{Simplify: } \frac{x^2 - 10}{x^2 - 1} - \frac{3x}{x - 1} - \frac{2x}{x + 1}$$

$$\text{Solve: } \frac{x^2 - 10}{x^2 - 1} - \frac{3x}{x - 1} = -\frac{2x}{x + 1}$$

96. Explain how to solve the rational equation graphically:

$$\frac{3x}{x - 2} + \frac{1}{5} = 2$$

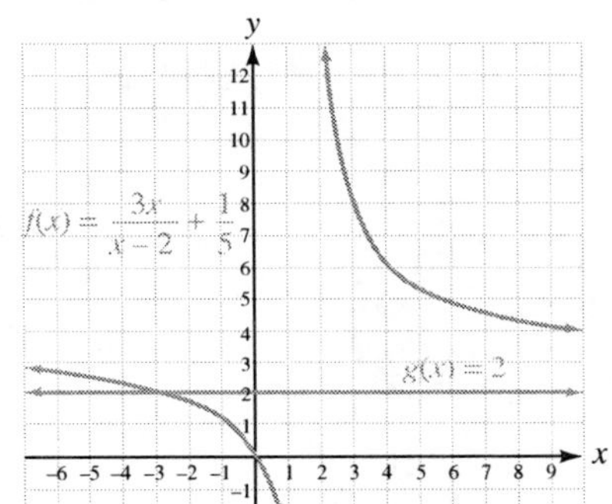

REVIEW

Write each italicized number in scientific notation.

97. OIL The total cost of the Alaskan pipeline, running 800 miles from Prudhoe Bay to Valdez, was *\$9,000,000,000.* 9.0×10^9

98. NATURAL GAS The TransCanada Pipeline transported a record *2,352,000,000,000* cubic feet of gas in 1995. 2.352×10^{12}

99. RADIOACTIVITY The least stable radioactive isotope is lithium 5, which decays in *0.00000000000000000000044* second. 4.4×10^{-22}

100. BALANCES The finest balances in the world are made in Germany. They can weigh objects to an accuracy of *35×10^{-11}* ounce. 3.5×10^{-10}

Objectives

1 Solve shared-work problems.

2 Solve uniform motion problems.

SECTION 7.5 Problem Solving Using Rational Equations

In this section, we will use rational equations to model situations involving work and uniform motion.

1 Solve shared-work problems.

Problems in which two or more people (or machines) work together to complete a job are called **shared-work problems.** To solve such problems, we must determine the **rate of work** for each person or machine involved. For example, suppose it takes you 4 hours to clean your house. Your rate of work can be expressed as $\frac{1}{4}$ of the job is completed per hour. If someone else takes 5 hours to clean the same house, they complete $\frac{1}{5}$ of the job per hour. In general, a rate of work can be determined in the following way.

Rate of Work

If a job can be completed in x hours, the rate of work can be expressed as:

$\frac{1}{x}$ of the job is completed per hour

If a job is completed in some other unit of time, such as x minutes or x days, the rate of work is expressed in that unit.

To solve shared-work problems, we must also determine the *amount of work* completed. To do this, we use a formula similar to the distance formula $d = rt$ used for motion problems.

$$\text{Work completed} = \text{rate of work} \cdot \text{time worked} \quad \text{or} \quad W = rt$$

Self Check 1

PAINTING A HOUSE One crew can paint a house in 3 days and another crew can paint the same house in 4 days. If both crews work together, how long will it take them to paint the house?

Now Try **Problem 11**

Self Check 1 Answer

If both crews work together, it will take $1\frac{5}{7}$ days to paint the house.

Teaching Example 1 LAWN CARE One crew can mow a lawn in 6 hours and another crew can mow the lawn in 4 hours. If both crews work together, how long will it take them to mow the lawn?

Answer:

If both crews work together, it will take $2\frac{2}{5}$ hours to mow the lawn.

EXAMPLE 1 *Home Construction* One crew can drywall a house in 4 days and another crew can drywall the same house in 5 days. If both crews work together, how long will it take to drywall the house?

© Jim Craigmyle/Corbis

Analyze It is helpful to organize the facts of a shared-work problem in a table.

Form Let x = the number of days it will take to drywall the house if both crews work together. Since the crews will be working for the same amount of time, enter x as the time worked for each crew.

If the first crew can drywall the house in 4 days, its rate working alone is $\frac{1}{4}$ of the job per day. If the second crew can drywall the house in 5 days, its rate working alone is $\frac{1}{5}$ of the job per day. To determine the work completed by each crew, multiply the rate by the time.

	Rate	· Time	= Work completed
1st crew	$\frac{1}{4}$	x	$\frac{x}{4}$
2nd crew	$\frac{1}{5}$	x	$\frac{x}{5}$

Enter this information first. (Rate and Time)

Multiply to get each of these entries; $W = rt$. (Work completed)

In shared-work problems, the number 1 represents one whole job completed. So we have

The part of the job done by 1st crew	plus	the part of the job done by 2nd crew	equals	1 job completed.
$\frac{x}{4}$	$+$	$\frac{x}{5}$	$=$	1

Solve

$$\frac{x}{4} + \frac{x}{5} = 1$$

$$20\left(\frac{x}{4} + \frac{x}{5}\right) = 20(1) \quad \text{Clear the equation of fractions by multiplying both sides by the LCD, 20.}$$

$$20\left(\frac{x}{4}\right) + 20\left(\frac{x}{5}\right) = 20 \quad \text{Distribute the multiplication by 20.}$$

$$\overset{1}{\cancel{4}} \cdot 5 \cdot \left(\frac{x}{\underset{1}{\cancel{4}}}\right) + 4 \cdot \overset{1}{\cancel{5}} \cdot \left(\frac{x}{\underset{1}{\cancel{5}}}\right) = 20 \quad \text{Factor 20 as } 4 \cdot 5\text{, and remove common factors.}$$

$$5x + 4x = 20 \quad \text{Simplify.}$$

$$9x = 20 \quad \text{Combine like terms.}$$

$$x = \frac{20}{9} \quad \text{Divide both sides by 9.}$$

State If both crews work together, it will take $\frac{20}{9}$ or $2\frac{2}{9}$ days to drywall the house.

Check In $\frac{20}{9}$ days, the first crew drywalls $\frac{1}{4} \cdot \frac{20}{9} = \frac{5}{9}$ of the house and the second crew drywalls $\frac{1}{5} \cdot \frac{20}{9} = \frac{4}{9}$ of the house. The sum of these efforts, $\frac{4}{9} + \frac{5}{9}$, is $\frac{9}{9}$ or 1 house drywalled. The result checks. ■

Example 1 can be solved in a different way by considering the amount of work done by each crew in 1 day. As before, if we let $x =$ the number of days it will take to drywall the house if both crews work together, then together, in 1 day, they will complete $\frac{1}{x}$ of the job. If we add what the first crew can do in 1 day to what the second crew can do in 1 day, the sum is what they can do together in 1 day.

What 1st crew can do in 1 day	plus	what 2nd crew can do in 1 day	equals	what they can do together in 1 day.
$\frac{1}{4}$	$+$	$\frac{1}{5}$	$=$	$\frac{1}{x}$

To solve the equation, begin by clearing it of fractions.

$$20x\left(\frac{1}{4} + \frac{1}{5}\right) = 20x\left(\frac{1}{x}\right) \quad \text{Multiply both sides by the LCD, 20x.}$$

$$5x + 4x = 20 \quad \text{Distribute the multiplication by 20x and simplify.}$$

$$9x = 20 \quad \text{Combine like terms.}$$

$$x = \frac{20}{9} \quad \text{Divide both sides by 9.}$$

This is the same as the solution obtained in Example 1.

Self Check 2

FILLING A POOL It takes a small garden hose 1 day longer to fill a swimming pool than a larger hose. Working together, they can fill the pool in $1\frac{1}{5}$ days. How long would it take each hose used individually to fill the pool?

***Now Try* Problem 21**

Self Check 2 Answer

The larger hose would take 2 days and the smaller hose would take 3 days to fill the pool.

Teaching Example 2 ROOFING A HOUSE A homeowner estimates that it will take him 3 more days to roof his house than a professional roofer would take. If working together, the homeowner and professional roofer can complete the job in $2\frac{6}{11}$ days, how long would it take the homeowner working alone?

Answer:

It will take the homeowner 7 days to roof his house.

EXAMPLE 2 *Setting up Seating* It takes the head custodian at a school 30 minutes less time than his assistant to set up the chairs for a program in the auditorium. Working together, they can set up the chairs in 20 minutes. How long would it take each person working alone to set up the chairs?

Analyze We will organize the facts of this shared-work problem in a table.

Form Let x = the number of minutes that it takes the assistant to set up the chairs. Then $x - 30$ = the number of minutes that it takes the head custodian to set up the chairs.

If the assistant can set up the chairs in x minutes, his rate working alone is $\frac{1}{x}$ of the job per minute. If the head custodian can set up the chairs in $(x - 30)$ minutes, his rate working alone is $\frac{1}{x-30}$ of the job per minute. Each rate is entered in the table below.

If they work together, it takes them 20 minutes to complete the job. We enter 20 minutes for the time worked for each person. To determine the work completed by each person, we multiply the rate by the time, as shown in the table.

	Rate	· Time	= Work completed
Assistant	$\frac{1}{x}$	20	$\frac{20}{x}$
Head custodian	$\frac{1}{x-30}$	20	$\frac{20}{x-30}$

Enter this information first. *Multiply to get each of these entries; $W = rt$.*

In shared-work problems, the number 1 represents one whole job completed. So we have

The part of the job done by the assistant	plus	the part of the job done by the head custodian	equals	1 job completed.
$\frac{20}{x}$	$+$	$\frac{20}{x-30}$	$=$	1

Solve

$$x(x-30)\left(\frac{20}{x} + \frac{20}{x-30}\right) = x(x-30)(1)$$ *Clear the equation of fractions by multiplying both sides by the LCD, $x(x - 30)$.*

$$\overset{1}{\cancel{x}}(x-30)\left(\frac{20}{\underset{1}{\cancel{x}}}\right) + x\overset{1}{\cancel{(x-30)}}\left(\frac{20}{\underset{1}{\cancel{x-30}}}\right) = x(x-30)(1)$$ *Distribute $x(x - 30)$ and then remove common factors.*

$$(x-30)(20) + x(20) = x(x-30)(1)$$ *Simplify.*

$$20x - 600 + 20x = x^2 - 30x$$ *Perform the multiplication on each side. This is a quadratic equation.*

$$40x - 600 = x^2 - 30x$$ *Combine like terms.*

$$0 = x^2 - 70x + 600$$ *To get 0 on the left side, subtract 40x and add 600 to both sides.*

$$0 = (x - 10)(x - 60)$$ Factor the trinomial.

$$x - 10 = 0 \quad \text{or} \quad x - 60 = 0$$ Set each factor equal to 0.

$$x = 10 \qquad\qquad x = 60$$

State The solutions of the equation are 10 and 60. If it takes them 20 minutes, working together, to set up the chairs, it does not make sense that it would take the assistant 10 minutes working alone. We reject that solution. Thus, we have found that, working alone, it takes the assistant 60 minutes and it takes the head custodian $60 - 30 = 30$ minutes to set up the chairs.

Check In 20 minutes, the assistant completes $\frac{20}{60} = \frac{1}{3}$ of the job while the head custodian completes $\frac{20}{30} = \frac{2}{3}$ of the job. The sum of these efforts, $\frac{1}{3} + \frac{2}{3}$, is $\frac{3}{3}$ or 1 job completed. The results check.

2 Solve uniform motion problems.

In the next two examples, rational equations are used to model situations involving **uniform motion.**

EXAMPLE 3 *Road Trips* A doctor drove 200 miles to attend a national convention. Because of poor weather, her average speed on the return trip was 10 mph less than her average speed going to the convention. If the return trip took 1 hour longer, how fast did she drive in each direction?

Analyze We need to find her rates of speed going to and returning from the convention. They can be represented using a variable. The distance traveled was 200 miles each way. To describe the travel times, we note that

$$rt = d$$ r is the rate of speed, t is the time traveled, and d is the distance.

or

$$t = \frac{d}{r}$$ Divide both sides by r.

Form Let $r =$ the average rate of speed (in mph) going to the meeting. Then $r - 10 =$ the average rate of speed on the return trip. We can organize the facts of the problem in the table.

	Rate	· Time	= Distance
Going	r	$\frac{200}{r}$	200
Returning	$r - 10$	$\frac{200}{r - 10}$	200

Enter this information first.

We obtained these entries by dividing the distance by the rate: $t = \frac{d}{r}$.

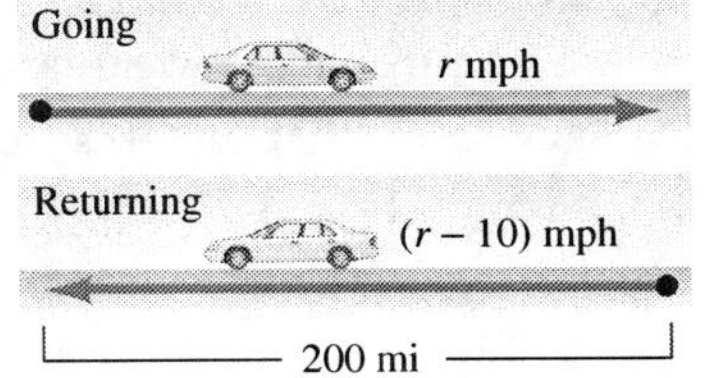

Because the return trip took 1 hour longer, we can form the following equation:

The time it took to travel to the convention	plus	1	equals	the time it took to return.
$\frac{200}{r}$	$+$	1	$=$	$\frac{200}{r - 10}$

Self Check 3

ROAD TRIPS A caravan of students traveled 150 miles to an academic competition. On the return trip, their average speed was 20 mph less than going, due to road construction. If the return trip took 2 hours longer, how fast did they drive in each direction?

Now Try **Problem 31**

Self Check 3 Answer

The caravan of students averaged 50 mph going to the competition and 30 mph returning.

Teaching Example 3 ROAD TRIPS A group of college students traveled 300 miles to spend the weekend at home. Because of traffic conditions, their average speed on the return trip was 10 mph less than their average speed going. If the return trip took 1 hour more, how fast did they drive each direction?

Answer:

They averaged 60 mph going home, and 50 mph returning to college.

Solve We can solve the equation as follows:

$$r(r-10)\left(\frac{200}{r}+1\right) = r(r-10)\left(\frac{200}{r-10}\right)$$ Multiply both sides by the LCD, $r(r-10)$.

$$\overset{1}{\cancel{r}}(r-10)\frac{200}{\underset{1}{\cancel{r}}} + r(r-10)1 = r\overset{1}{\cancel{(r-10)}}\left(\frac{200}{\underset{1}{\cancel{r-10}}}\right)$$ Distribute $r(r-10)$ and then remove common factors.

$$200(r-10) + r(r-10) = 200r$$

$$200r - 2{,}000 + r^2 - 10r = 200r$$ Distribute 200 and r. This is a quadratic equation.

$$190r - 2{,}000 + r^2 = 200r$$ Combine like terms.

$$r^2 - 10r - 2{,}000 = 0$$ To get 0 on the right side, subtract $200r$ from both sides.

$$(r-50)(r+40) = 0$$ Factor $r^2 - 10r - 2{,}000$.

$$r - 50 = 0 \quad \text{or} \quad r + 40 = 0$$ Set each factor equal to 0.

$$r = 50 \quad | \quad r = -40$$

State We must exclude the solution of -40, because a speed cannot be negative. Thus, the doctor averaged 50 mph going to the convention, and she averaged $50 - 10$ or 40 mph returning.

Check At 50 mph, the 200-mile trip took 4 hours. At 40 mph, the return trip took 5 hours, which is 1 hour longer. The results check.

Self Check 4

WATER TRAVEL A motorboat goes 5 miles upstream in the same time it requires to go 7 miles downstream. If the river flows at 2 miles per hour, find the speed of the boat in still water.

***Now Try* Problem 39**

Self Check 4 Answer
The speed of the boat in still water is 12 mph.

Teaching Example 4 DINNER CRUISE A dinner cruise boat can travel 9 miles down the river and return in a total of 3 hours. If the boat can travel 8 mph in still water, find the speed of the river's current.
Answer:
The river's current is 4 mph.

EXAMPLE 4 *Riverboat Cruises* The Forest City Queen can make a 9-mile trip down the Rock River and return in a total of 1.6 hours. If the riverboat travels 12 mph in still water, find the speed of the current in the Rock River.

Analyze We can represent the upstream and downstream rates of speed using a variable. In each case, the distance traveled is 9 miles. To write an expression for the time traveled, divide the distance by the rate of speed.

Form We can let c = the speed of the current (in mph). Since the boat travels 12 mph and a current of c mph pushes the boat while it is going downstream, the speed of the boat going downstream is $(12 + c)$ mph. On the return trip, the current pushes against the boat, and its speed is $(12 - c)$ mph. Since $t = \frac{d}{r}\left(\text{time} = \frac{\text{distance}}{\text{rate}}\right)$, the time required for the downstream leg of the trip is $\frac{9}{12+c}$ hours, and the time required for the upstream leg of the trip is $\frac{9}{12-c}$ hours. We can organize this information in the table.

	Rate	· Time	= Distance
Going downstream	$12 + c$	$\frac{9}{12+c}$	9
Going upstream	$12 - c$	$\frac{9}{12-c}$	9

Enter this information first.

Divide the distance by the rate.

Downstream

$(12 + c)$ mph

current

c mph

Upstream

$(12 - c)$ mph

current

c mph

We also know that the total time required for the round trip is 1.6 or $\frac{8}{5}$ hours.

The time it takes to travel downstream	plus	the time it takes to travel upstream	is	the total time for the round trip.
$\frac{9}{12 + c}$	$+$	$\frac{9}{12 - c}$	$=$	$\frac{8}{5}$

Solve We multiply both sides of the equation by $5(12 + c)(12 - c)$ to clear it of fractions.

$$5(12 + c)(12 - c)\left(\frac{9}{12 + c} + \frac{9}{12 - c}\right) = 5(12 + c)(12 - c)\left(\frac{8}{5}\right)$$

$$5(12 + c)(12 - c)\left(\frac{9}{12 + c}\right) + 5(12 + c)(12 - c)\left(\frac{9}{12 - c}\right) = 5(12 + c)(12 - c)\left(\frac{8}{5}\right)$$

Distribute $5(12 + c)(12 - c)$ and remove common factors.

$$45(12 - c) + 45(12 + c) = 8(12 + c)(12 - c)$$

Simplify.

$$540 - 45c + 540 + 45c = 8(144 - c^2)$$

On the left side, distribute. On the right side, use the FOIL method.

$$1{,}080 = 1{,}152 - 8c^2$$

Combine like terms and multiply. This is a quadratic equation.

$$8c^2 - 72 = 0$$

To get 0 on the right side, add $8c^2$ and subtract 1,152 from both sides.

$$c^2 - 9 = 0$$

Divide both sides by 8.

$$(c + 3)(c - 3) = 0$$

Factor the difference of two squares.

$$c + 3 = 0 \quad \text{or} \quad c - 3 = 0$$

Set each factor equal to 0.

$$c = -3 \quad | \quad c = 3$$

State Since the current cannot be negative, the solution -3 must be discarded. The current in the Rock River is 3 mph.

Check The downstream trip is at $12 + 3 = 15$ mph for $\frac{9}{12 + 3} = \frac{3}{5}$ hr. Thus, the distance traveled is $15 \cdot \frac{3}{5} = 9$ miles. The upstream trip is at $12 - 3 = 9$ mph for $\frac{9}{12 - 3} = 1$ hr. Thus, the distance traveled is $9 \cdot 1 = 9$ miles. Since both distances are 9 miles, the result checks.

ANSWERS TO SELF CHECKS

1. If both crews work together, it will take $1\frac{5}{7}$ days to paint the house.
2. The larger hose would take 2 days and the smaller hose would take 3 days to fill the pool.
3. The caravan of students averaged 50 mph going to the competition and 30 mph returning.
4. The speed of the boat in still water is 12 mph.

SECTION 7.5 STUDY SET

VOCABULARY

Fill in the blanks.

1. In this section, we call problems that involve:
   - people or machines completing jobs, shared-__work__ problems.
   - moving vehicles, uniform __motion__ problems.

2. When a boat travels __downstream__, the speed of the boat is increased by the current. When a boat travels __upstream__, the speed of the boat is decreased by the current.

Selected exercises available online at www.webassign.net/brookscole

CONCEPTS

3. Fill in the blank: If a job can be completed in x hours, then the rate of work can be expressed as $\frac{1}{x}$ of the job is completed per hour.

4. a. It takes a night security officer 35 minutes to check each of the doors in an office building to make sure they are locked. What is the officer's rate of work? $\frac{1}{35}$ of the job per minute

   b. It takes a high school mathematics teacher 4 hours to make out the semester report cards. What part of the job does she complete in x hours? $\frac{x}{4}$

5. Complete the table.

	Rate	· Time	= Work completed
1st crew	$\frac{1}{15}$	x	$\frac{x}{15}$
2nd crew	$\frac{1}{8}$	x	$\frac{x}{8}$

6. Solve $d = rt$ for t. $t = \frac{d}{r}$

7. Complete the table.

	r	· t	$= d$
Running	x	$\frac{12}{x}$	12
Bicycling	$x + 15$	$\frac{12}{x+15}$	12

8. A boat can cruise at 30 mph in still water.

   a. What is its cruising speed upstream against a current of 4 mph? 26 mph

   b. What is its cruising speed downstream with a current of 4 mph? 34 mph

NOTATION

9. Write $\frac{41}{9}$ hours using a mixed number. $4\frac{5}{9}$ hr

10. Fill in the blanks: In the formula $W = rt$, the variable W stands for the work completed, r is the rate, and t is the time.

APPLICATIONS

11. ROOFING A homeowner estimates that it will take him 7 days to roof his house. A professional roofer estimates that he could roof the house in 4 days. How long will it take if the homeowner helps the roofer? $2\frac{6}{11}$ days

12. DECORATING One crew can put up holiday decorations in a department store in 12 hours. A second crew can put up the decorations in 15 hours. How long will it take if both crews work together to decorate the store? $6\frac{2}{3}$ hours

13. HOUSEPAINTING The illustration shows two bids to paint a house.

    a. To get the job done quicker, the homeowner hired both the painters who submitted bids. How long will it take them to paint the house working together? $1\frac{7}{8}$ days

    b. What will the homeowner have to pay each painter? Santos: $412.50, Mays: $375

Santos Painting
Residential Bid:
3 days
@ $220 a day
Total: $660

Mays House Painting
Bid:
$200 per day
5 days work
Total: $1,000

14. GROUNDSKEEPING It takes a groundskeeper 45 minutes to prepare a Little League baseball field for a game. It takes his assistant 55 minutes to prepare the same field. How long will it take if they work together to prepare the field? $24\frac{3}{4}$ min

15. FARMING In 10 minutes, a conveyor belt can move 1,000 bushels of corn into the storage bin shown. A smaller belt can move 1,000 bushels to the storage bin in 14 minutes. If both belts are used, how long will it take to move 1,000 bushels to the storage bin? $5\frac{5}{6}$ min

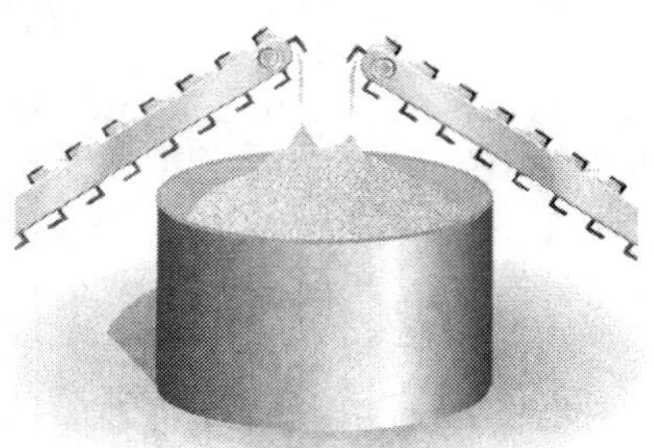

16. BOTTLING At a packaging plant, the older of two machines can fill 5,000 bottles of shampoo in 6 hours. A newer machine can fill 5,000 bottles in 4 hours. If both machines are used, how long will it take to fill 5,000 bottles of shampoo? $2\frac{2}{5}$ hr

17. THRILL RIDES At the end of an amusement park ride, a boat lands in a pool, splashing out a lot of water. Three inlet pipes, each working alone, can fill the pool in 10 seconds, 15 seconds, and 20 seconds, respectively. How would it take to fill the pool if all three inlet pipes are used? $4\frac{8}{13}$ sec

18. SMOKE DAMAGE Three ventilation fans, each working alone, can clear the smoke out of a room in 12 hours, 16 hours, and 24 hours, respectively. How long would it take to clear out the smoke in the room if all three fans are used? $5\frac{1}{3}$ hr

19. FILLING PONDS One pipe can fill a pond in 3 weeks, and a second pipe can fill it in 5 weeks. However, evaporation and seepage can empty the pond in 10 weeks. If both pipes are used, how long will it take to fill the pond? $2\frac{4}{13}$ weeks

▶ **20.** HOUSECLEANING Sally can clean the house in 6 hours, her father can clean the house in 4 hours, and her younger brother, Dennis, can completely mess up the house in 8 hours. If Sally and her father clean and Dennis plays, how long will it take to clean the house? $3\frac{3}{7}$ hr

21. FINE DINING It takes a waiter 5 minutes less time than a busboy to fold the napkins used for the dinner seating in an upscale restaurant. Working together, they can fold the napkins in 6 minutes. How long would it take each person working alone to fold the napkins? waiter: 10 min, busboy: 15 min

▶ **22.** FIRE DRILL If the east and west exit doors of a banquet hall are open, the occupants can clear out in 2 minutes. It takes 3 minutes longer to clear the hall if just the east door is open as it does if just the west door is open. How long does it take to clear the hall if just the west door is open? 3 min

▶ **23.** FUND-RAISING LETTERS Working together, two secretaries can stuff the envelopes for a political fund-raising letter in 4 hours. Working alone, it takes the slower worker 6 hours longer to do the job than the faster worker. How long does it take each to do the job alone? faster worker: 6 hr, slower worker: 12 hr

24. SURVEYS It takes one team 9 days less than another to survey 1,000 people. If the teams work together, it takes them 20 days to complete such a survey. How long will it take each to do the survey alone? faster team: 36 days, slower team: 45 days

25. PLUMBING An experienced plumber can install the plumbing in a new apartment twice as fast as his apprentice. Working together, they can complete the plumbing job in 4 days. How long would it take each, working alone, to complete the plumbing? experienced plumber: 6 days, apprentice: 12 days

▶ **26.** NEWSLETTERS An elementary school teacher can assemble and staple the weekly newsletter three times faster than her student aide. Working together, they can assemble and staple the letters in 12 minutes. How long would it take each, working alone, to complete the job? teacher: 16 min, student aide: 48 min

▶ **27.** DETAILING A CAR It takes a man 3 hours to wash and wax the family car. If his teenage son helps him, it only takes 1 hour. How long would it take the son, working alone, to wash and wax the car? $1\frac{1}{2}$ hours

▶ **28.** CLEANUP CREWS It takes one crew 4 hours to clean an auditorium after an event. If a second crew helps, it only takes 1.5 hours. How long would it take the second crew, working alone, to clean the auditorium? $2\frac{2}{5}$ hours

29. OYSTERS According to the *Guinness Book of World Records,* the record for opening oysters is 100 in 140 seconds by Mike Racz in Invercargill, New Zealand, on July 16, 1990. If it would take a novice $8\frac{1}{2}$ minutes to perform the same task, how long would it take them working together to open 100 oysters? (*Hint:* Work in terms of seconds.) about 110 sec

30. END ZONES One groundskeeper can paint the end zone of a football field in 2 hours. Another can paint it in 1 hour 20 minutes. How many minutes will it take them working together to paint the end zone? 48 min

AP Photo/Brian Garfinkel

▶ **31.** TRUCK DELIVERIES A trucker drove 120 miles to make a delivery and returned home on the same route. Because of foggy conditions, his average speed on the return trip was 10 mph less than his average speed going. If the return trip took 1 hour longer, how fast did he drive in each direction? going: 40 mph, returning: 30 mph

▶ **32.** MOVING HOUSES A house mover towed a historic Victorian home 45 miles to locate it on a new site. On his return, without the heavy house in tow, his average speed was 30 mph faster and the trip was 2 hours shorter. How fast did he drive in each direction? going: 15 mph, returning 45 mph

▶ **33.** TRAIN TRAVEL A train traveled 120 miles from Freeport to Chicago and returned the same distance in a total time of 5 hours. If the train traveled 20 mph slower on the return trip, how fast did the train travel in each direction? going: 60 mph, returning: 40 mph

34. BOXING For his morning workout, a boxer bicycles for 8 miles and then jogs back to camp along the same route. If he bicycles 6 mph faster than he jogs, and the entire workout lasts 2 hours, how fast does he jog? 6 mph

35. RATES OF SPEED Two trains made the same 315-mile run. Since one train traveled 10 mph faster than the other, it arrived 2 hours earlier. Find the speed of each train. 35 mph and 45 mph

36. DELIVERIES A FedEx delivery van traveled from Rockford to Chicago in 3 hours less time than it took a second van to travel from Rockford to St. Louis. If the vans traveled at the same average speed, use the information in the map to help determine how long the first driver was on the road. 2 hr

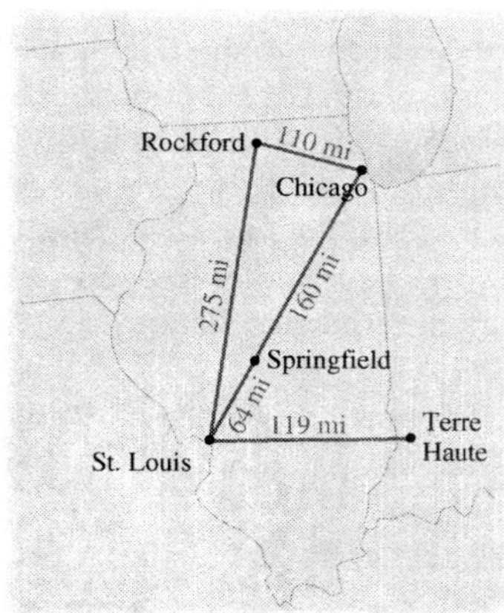

37. COMPARING TRAVEL A plane can fly 600 miles in the same time as it takes a car to go 240 miles. If the car travels 90 mph slower than the plane, find the speed of the plane. 150 mph

38. COMPARING TRAVEL A bicyclist can travel 40 miles in the same time that a motorcyclist can travel 60 miles. If the bicyclist travels 12 mph slower than the motorcyclist, find the speed of the motorcyclist. 36 mph

39. BOATING It takes 6 hours for a boater to travel 16 miles upstream and back. If the speed of the boat in still water is 6 mph, what is the speed of the current? 2 mph

40. RIVER TOURS A wave runner trip begins by going 60 miles upstream against a current. There, the driver turns around and returns with the current. If the still-water speed of the wave runner is set at 25 mph and the entire trip takes 5 hours, what is the speed of the current? 5 mph

41. BOATING A man can drive a motorboat 45 miles down the Colorado River in the same amount of time that he can drive 27 miles upstream. Find the speed of the current if the speed of the boat is 12 mph in still water. 3 mph

42. CROP DUSTING A helicopter spraying fertilizer over a field can fly 0.5 mile downwind in the same time as it can fly 0.4 mile upwind. Find the speed of the wind if the helicopter travels 45 mph in still air when dusting crops. 5 mph

WRITING

43. In Example 1, one crew could drywall a house in 4 days, and another crew could drywall the same house in 5 days. We were asked to find how long it would take them to drywall the house working together. Explain why each of the following approaches is incorrect.

The time it would take to drywall the house

- is the *sum* of the lengths of time it takes each crew to drywall the house:
  4 days + 5 days = 9 day.
- is the *difference* in lengths of time it takes each crew to drywall the house:
  5 days − 4 days = 1 day.
- is the *average* of the lengths of time it takes each crew to drywall the house:
  $\frac{4 \text{ days} + 5 \text{ days}}{2} = \frac{9}{2} \text{ days} = 4\frac{1}{2} \text{ days}$.

44. Write a shared-work problem that can be modeled by the equation

$$\frac{x}{3} + \frac{x}{4} = 1$$

REVIEW

Simplify each expression. Write answers using positive exponents.

45. $\left(\frac{m^{10}}{n}\right)^8$ $\frac{m^{80}}{n^8}$

46. $\left(\frac{g^{20}}{t^{30}}\right)^{-4}$ $\frac{t^{120}}{g^{80}}$

47. $-w^{-2}$ $-\frac{1}{w^2}$

48. $-3s^0t$ $-3t$

49. $-\frac{4x^{-9} \cdot x^{-3}}{x^{-12}}$ -4

50. $\frac{y^{-3}y^{-4}y^0}{(2y^{-2})^3}$ $\frac{1}{8y}$

51. $(-x^2)^5y^7y^3x^{-2}y^0$ $-x^8y^{10}$

52. $5^2r^{-5}(r^6)^3$ $25r^{13}$

Module 8: Radical Expressions and Equations

DMA 080

from Campus to Careers

General Contractor

The growing popularity of remodeling has created a boom for general contractors. If it's an additional bedroom you need or a makeover of a dated kitchen or bathroom, they can provide design and construction expertise, as well as knowledge of local building code requirements. From the planning stages of a project through its completion, general contractors use mathematics every step of the way.

In **Problem 138** of **Study Set 8.2,** you will use concepts from this chapter to examine the movement of construction materials through a tight hallway.

JOB TITLE:
General Contractor

EDUCATION: Courses in mathematics, science, drafting, business math, and English are important. Certificate programs are also available.

JOB OUTLOOK: In general, employment is expected to increase between 9% to 17% through the year 2014.

ANNUAL EARNINGS: Mean annual salary $76,699

FOR MORE INFORMATION:
http://www.bls.gov/oco/ocos005.htm

Objectives

1. Find square roots.
2. Find square roots of expressions containing variables.
3. Graph the square root function.
4. Find cube roots.
5. Graph the cube root function.
6. Find *n*th roots.

SECTION 8.1
Radical Expressions and Functions

In this section, we will reverse the squaring process and learn how to find *square roots* of numbers. We will then generalize the concept of root and consider cube roots, fourth roots, fifth roots, and so on. We will also discuss a new family of functions, called *radical functions.*

1 Find square roots.

When solving problems, we must often find what number must be squared to obtain a second number a. If such a number can be found, it is called a **square root of *a*.** For example,

- 0 is a square root of 0, because $0^2 = 0$.
- 4 is a square root of 16, because $4^2 = 16$.
- -4 is a square root of 16, because $(-4)^2 = 16$.
- $7xy$ is a square root of $49x^2y^2$, because $(7xy)^2 = 49x^2y^2$.
- $-7xy$ is a square root of $49x^2y^2$, because $(-7xy)^2 = 49x^2y^2$.

The preceding examples illustrate the following definition.

Square Root of *a*

The number b is a **square root** of the number a if $b^2 = a$.

All positive numbers have two real-number square roots, one that is positive and one that is negative.

Self Check 1

Find the square roots of 144.

***Now Try* Problem 21**

Self Check 1 Answer
12, −12

Teaching Example 1 Find the two square roots of 49.
Answer:
7, −7

EXAMPLE 1 Find the two square roots of 121.

Strategy We will determine the numbers that, when squared, produce 121.

WHY This is the definition of square root.

Solution
The two square roots of 121 are 11 and −11, because

$$11^2 = 121 \quad \text{and} \quad (-11)^2 = 121$$

In the following definition, the symbol $\sqrt{}$ is called a **radical symbol,** and the number a within the radical symbol is called a **radicand.** An expression containing a radical is called a **radical expression.**

Radical symbol → $\sqrt{a}$ ← radicand
Radical

Square Root Notation

If a is a positive number,

1. $\sqrt{a}$ represents the **positive** or **principal square root** of a. It is the positive number we square to get a.
2. $-\sqrt{a}$ represents the **negative square root** of a. It is the opposite of the principal square root of a: $-\sqrt{a} = -1 \cdot \sqrt{a}$.
3. The principal square root of 0 is 0: $\sqrt{0} = 0$.

To evaluate square root expressions, it is helpful to memorize the natural numbers that are perfect squares.

$1 = 1^2$	$25 = 5^2$	$81 = 9^2$	$169 = 13^2$	$289 = 17^2$
$4 = 2^2$	$36 = 6^2$	$100 = 10^2$	$196 = 14^2$	$324 = 18^2$
$9 = 3^2$	$49 = 7^2$	$121 = 11^2$	$225 = 15^2$	$361 = 19^2$
$16 = 4^2$	$64 = 8^2$	$144 = 12^2$	$256 = 16^2$	$400 = 20^2$

EXAMPLE 2 Evaluate each square root: **a.** $\sqrt{1}$ **b.** $\sqrt{81}$ **c.** $-\sqrt{81}$ **d.** $-\sqrt{225}$ **e.** $\sqrt{\frac{1}{4}}$ **f.** $-\sqrt{\frac{16}{121}}$ **g.** $\sqrt{0.04}$ **h.** $-\sqrt{0.0009}$

Strategy In each case, we will determine what positive number, when squared, produces the radicand. Then we will apply the sign that is in front of the radical.

WHY The symbol $\sqrt{}$ indicates that the positive square root of the number written under it should be found. The symbol $-\sqrt{}$ indicates that the negative square root of the number written under it should be found.

Solution

a. $\sqrt{1} = 1$

b. $\sqrt{81} = 9$

c. $-\sqrt{81} = -9$

d. $-\sqrt{225} = -15$

e. $\sqrt{\frac{1}{4}} = \frac{1}{2}$

f. $-\sqrt{\frac{16}{121}} = -\frac{4}{11}$

g. $\sqrt{0.04} = 0.2$

h. $-\sqrt{0.0009} = -0.03$

Self Check 2

Evaluate each square root:

a. $-\sqrt{49}$ -7

b. $\sqrt{\frac{25}{49}}$ $\frac{5}{7}$

Now Try **Problems 27 and 29**

Teaching Example 2 Evaluate each square root:
a. $\sqrt{121}$ b. $-\sqrt{25}$
c. $\sqrt{\frac{169}{225}}$ d. $-\sqrt{0.36}$

Answers:
a. 11 b. -5 c. $\frac{13}{15}$ d. -0.6

Numbers such as 1, 81, $\frac{1}{4}$, $\frac{16}{121}$, and 0.04 are called **perfect squares,** because each one is the square of a rational number. In Example 2, we saw that the square root of a perfect square is a rational number.

The square roots of many positive numbers are not rational numbers. For example, $\sqrt{11}$ is an *irrational number.* To find an approximate value of $\sqrt{11}$, we enter 11 into a calculator and press the square root key $\boxed{\sqrt{}}$. (On some calculators, the $\boxed{\sqrt{}}$ key must be pressed first.)

$$\sqrt{11} \approx 3.31662479$$

Caution! Square roots of negative numbers are not real numbers. For example, $\sqrt{-9}$ is not a real number, because no real number squared equals -9. Square roots of negative numbers come from a set called the **imaginary numbers**.

2 Find square roots of expressions containing variables.

If $x \neq 0$, the positive number x^2 has x and $-x$ for its two square roots. To denote the positive square root of $\sqrt{x^2}$, we must know whether x is positive or negative.

If x is positive, we can write

$\sqrt{x^2} = x$ $\sqrt{x^2}$ represents the positive square root of x^2, which is x.

If x is negative, then $-x > 0$, and we can write

$\sqrt{x^2} = -x$ $\sqrt{x^2}$ represents the positive square root of x^2, which is $-x$.

If we don't know whether x is positive or negative, we can use absolute value symbols to guarantee that $\sqrt{x^2}$ is positive.

Definition of $\sqrt{x^2}$

For any real number x,

$$\sqrt{x^2} = |x|$$

We use this definition to *simplify* square root radical expressions.

Self Check 3

Simplify:

a. $\sqrt{25a^2}$ $5|a|$

b. $\sqrt{16a^4}$ $4a^2$

Now Try **Problems 34 and 39**

Teaching Example 3 Simplify:
a. $\sqrt{81x^2}$ b. $\sqrt{36a^4}$
c. $\sqrt{x^2 + 14x + 49}$
Answers:
a. $9|x|$ b. $6a^2$ c. $|x + 7|$

EXAMPLE 3 Simplify: **a.** $\sqrt{16x^2}$ **b.** $\sqrt{x^2 + 2x + 1}$ **c.** $\sqrt{m^4}$

Strategy In each case, we will determine what positive expression, when squared, produces the radicand.

WHY The symbol $\sqrt{\ }$ indicates that the positive square root of the expression written under it should be found.

Solution

If x and m can be any real number, we have

a. $\sqrt{16x^2} = \sqrt{(4x)^2}$ Write the radicand $16x^2$ as $(4x)^2$.

$= |4x|$ Because $(|4x|)^2 = 16x^2$. Since x could be negative, absolute value symbols are needed.

$= 4|x|$ Since 4 is a positive constant in the product $4x$, we can write it outside the absolute value symbols.

b. $\sqrt{x^2 + 2x + 1}$

$= \sqrt{(x + 1)^2}$ Factor the radicand: $x^2 + 2x + 1 = (x + 1)^2$.

$= |x + 1|$ Since $x + 1$ can be negative (for example, when $x = -5$, $x + 1$ is -4), absolute value symbols are needed.

c. $\sqrt{m^4} = m^2$ Because $(m^2)^2 = m^4$. Since $m^2 \geq 0$, no absolute value symbols are needed.

If we are told that x represents a *positive* real number in parts a and b of Example 3, we do not need to use absolute value symbols to guarantee that the answers are positive. For example, if $x > 0$, then

$\sqrt{16x^2} = 4x$ If x is positive, $4x$ is positive.

$\sqrt{x^2 + 2x + 1} = x + 1$ If x is positive, $x + 1$ is positive.

3 Graph the square root function.

Since there is one principal square root for every nonnegative real number x, the equation $f(x) = \sqrt{x}$ determines a function, called a **square root function.** Square root functions belong to a larger family of functions known as **radical functions.**

EXAMPLE 4 Graph $f(x) = \sqrt{x}$ and find its domain and range.

Strategy We will graph the function by creating a table of function values and plotting the corresponding ordered pairs.

WHY After drawing a smooth curve through the plotted points, we will have the graph.

Solution

To graph this square root function, we will evaluate it for several values of x. We begin with $x = 0$, since 0 is the smallest input for which $\sqrt{x}$ is defined.

$$f(x) = \sqrt{x}$$

$$f(0) = \sqrt{0} = 0 \quad \text{Substitute 0 for } x.$$

We enter the ordered pair (0, 0) in the table of values below. Then we continue the evaluation process for $x = 1, 4, 9$, and 16 and list the results in the table. After plotting all the ordered pairs, we draw a smooth curve through the points. This is the graph of function f (see figure (a)). Since the equation defines a function, its graph passes the vertical line test.

We can use a graphing calculator with window settings of $[-1, 9]$ for x and $[-1, 9]$ for y to get the graph shown in figure (b). From either graph, we can see that the domain and the range are the set of nonnegative real numbers. Expressed in interval notation, the domain is $[0, \infty)$, and the range is $[0, \infty)$.

$f(x) = \sqrt{x}$		
x	$f(x)$	$(x, f(x))$
0	0	(0, 0)
1	1	(1, 1)
4	2	(4, 2)
9	3	(9, 3)
16	4	(16, 4)

↑ Select values of x that are perfect squares.

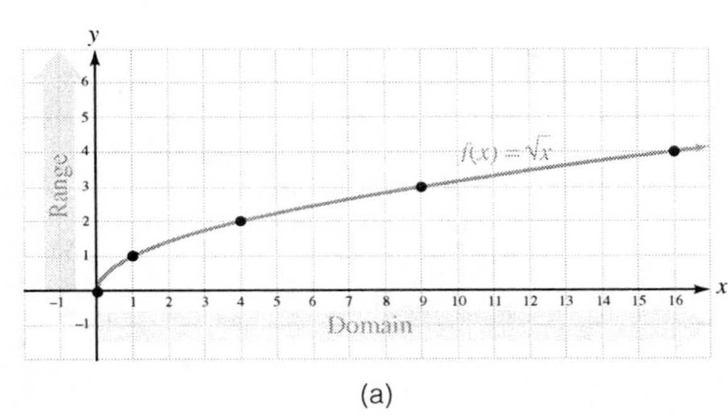

(a)

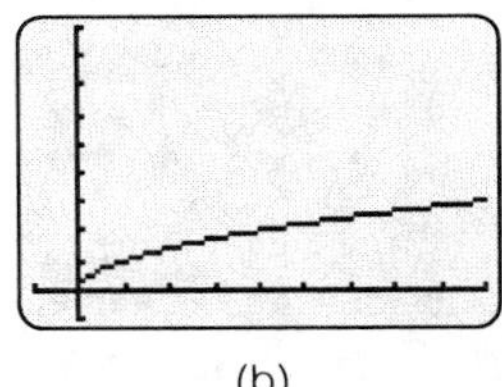

(b)

Self Check 4

Graph $f(x) = \sqrt{x} + 2$ and find its domain and range.

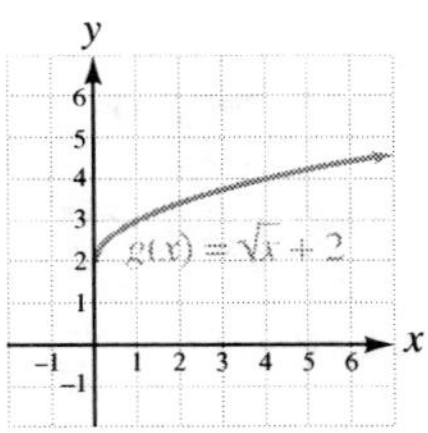

Now Try **Problem 42**

Self Check 4 Answer
D: $[0, \infty)$, R: $[2, \infty)$

Teaching Example 4 Graph $f(x) = \sqrt{x} - 3$ and find its domain and range.
Answer:

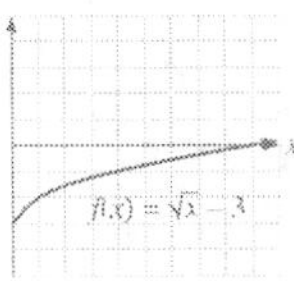

D: $[0, \infty)$, R: $[-3, \infty)$

The graphs of many radical functions are translations or reflections of the square root function, $f(x) = \sqrt{x}$. For example, if $k > 0$,

- The graph of $f(x) = \sqrt{x} + k$ is the graph of $f(x) = \sqrt{x}$ translated k units up.
- The graph of $f(x) = \sqrt{x} - k$ is the graph of $f(x) = \sqrt{x}$ translated k units down.
- The graph of $f(x) = \sqrt{x + k}$ is the graph of $f(x) = \sqrt{x}$ translated k units to the left.
- The graph of $f(x) = \sqrt{x - k}$ is the graph of $f(x) = \sqrt{x}$ translated k units to the right.
- The graph of $f(x) = -\sqrt{x}$ is the graph of $f(x) = \sqrt{x}$ reflected about the x-axis.

Self Check 5

Graph $f(x) = \sqrt{x - 2} - 4$ and find its domain and range.

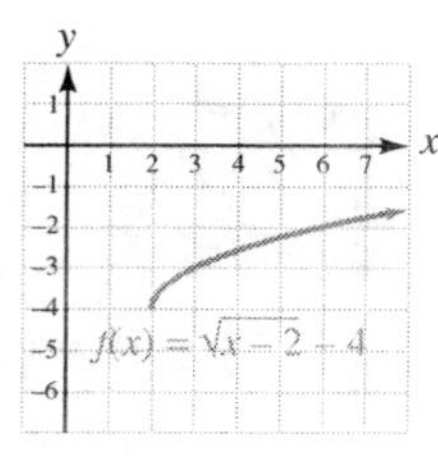

Now Try **Problem 48**

Self Check 5 Answer

D: $[2, \infty)$, R: $[-4, \infty)$

Teaching Example 5 Graph $f(x) = -\sqrt{x - 1} + 2$ and find its domain and range.

Answer:

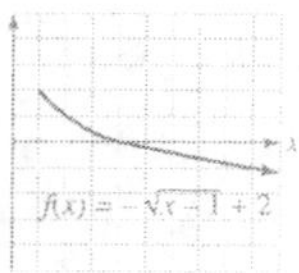

D: $[1, \infty)$, R: $(-\infty, 2]$

EXAMPLE 5 Graph $f(x) = -\sqrt{x + 4} - 2$ and find its domain and range.

Strategy We will graph this function by translating and reflecting the graph $f(x) = \sqrt{x}$.

WHY $f(x) = -\sqrt{x + 4} - 2$ is the reflection of $f(x) = \sqrt{x}$ about the x-axis, translated 4 units left and 2 units down.

Solution

The graph is shown in figure (a). We can confirm this graph by using a graphing calculator with window settings of $[-5, 6]$ for x and $[-6, 2]$ for y to get the graph shown in figure (b).

We can determine the domain of the function algebraically. Since the expression $\sqrt{x + 4}$ is not a real number when $x + 4$ is negative, we must require that

$x + 4 \geq 0$ Because we cannot find the real square root of a negative number.

Solving for x, we have

$x \geq -4$ The x-inputs must be real numbers greater than or equal to -4.

Thus, the domain of $f(x) = -\sqrt{x + 4} - 2$ is the interval $[-4, \infty)$.

From either graph, we can see that the domain is the interval $[-4, \infty)$ and that the range is the interval $(-\infty, -2]$.

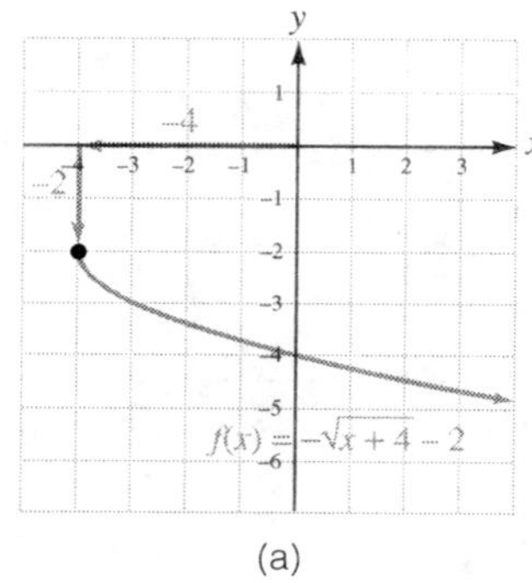

(a)

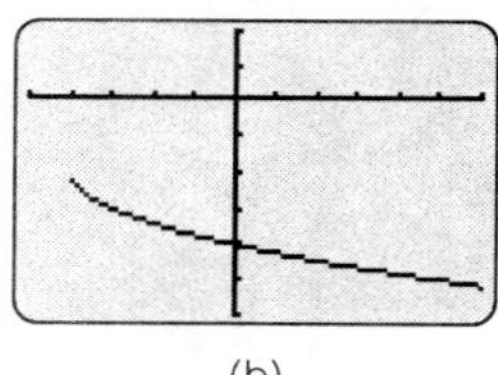

(b)

Self Check 6

PENDULUMS To the nearest hundredth, find the period of a pendulum that is 3 feet long.

Now Try **Problem 108**

Self Check 6 Answer

1.92 sec

Teaching Example 6 PENDULUMS To the nearest tenth, find the period of a pendulum that is 4 feet long.

Answer:

2.2 sec

EXAMPLE 6 *Pendulums* The **period of a pendulum** is the time required for the pendulum to swing back and forth to complete one cycle. The period (in seconds) is a function of the pendulum's length L (in feet) and is given by

$$f(L) = 2\pi\sqrt{\frac{L}{32}}$$

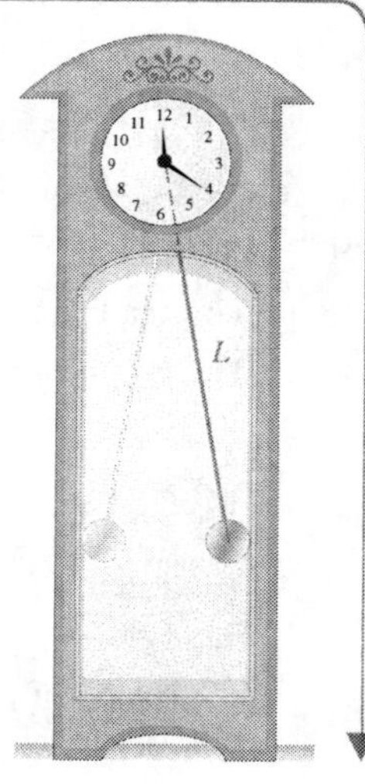

Find the period of the 5-foot-long pendulum of the clock. Round the result to the nearest tenth.

Strategy To find the period of the pendulum we will find $f(5)$.

WHY The notation $f(5)$ represents the period (in seconds) of a pendulum whose length L is 5 feet.

Solution

$$f(L) = 2\pi\sqrt{\frac{L}{32}}$$

$$f(5) = 2\pi\sqrt{\frac{5}{32}} \quad \text{Substitute 5 for } L.$$

$$\approx 2.483647066 \quad \text{Use a calculator to find an approximation.}$$

The period is approximately 2.5 seconds.

Using Your CALCULATOR Evaluating a Square Root Function

To solve Example 6 with a graphing calculator with window settings of $[-2, 10]$ for x and $[-2, 10]$ for y, we graph the function $f(x) = 2\pi\sqrt{\frac{x}{32}}$, as in figure (a). We then trace and move the cursor toward an x-value of 5 until we see the coordinates shown in figure (b). The period is given by the y-value shown on the screen. By zooming in, we can get better results.

After entering $Y_1 = 2\pi\sqrt{\frac{x}{32}}$, we can also use the TABLE mode to evaluate the function. See figure (c).

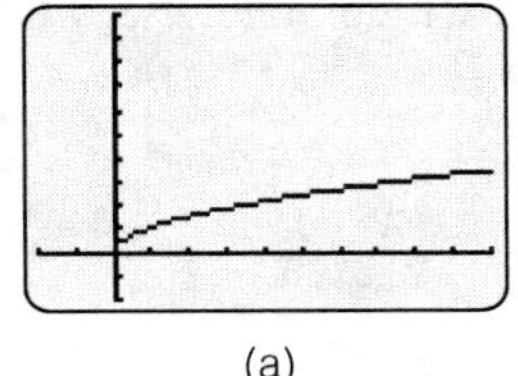

(a)

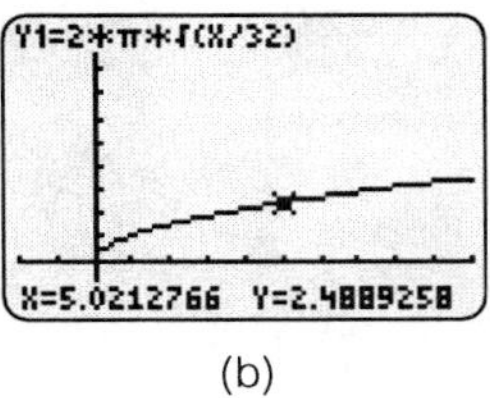

(b)

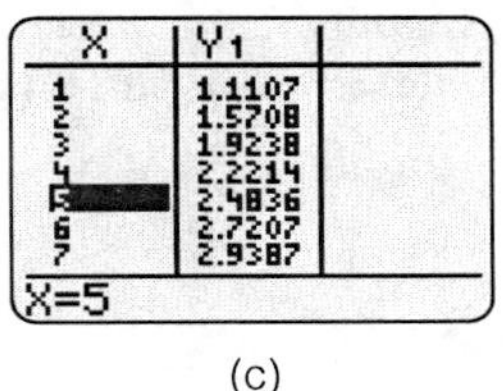

(c)

4 Find cube roots.

When we raise a number to the third power, we are cubing it, or finding its **cube.** We can reverse the cubing process to find **cube roots** of numbers. To find the cube root of 8, we ask "What number, when cubed, is equal to 8?" It follows that 2 is a cube root of 8, because $2^3 = 8$.

In general, we have this definition.

Cube Root of *a*

The number b is a **cube root** of the real number a if $b^3 = a$.

We note that 64 has two real-number square roots, 8 and -8. However, 64 has only one real-number cube root 4, because 4 is the only real number whose cube is 64. All real numbers have one real cube root. A positive number has a positive cube root, a negative number has a negative cube root, and the cube root of 0 is 0.

Cube Root Notation

The **cube root of *a*** is denoted $\sqrt[3]{a}$. By definition

$$\sqrt[3]{a} = b \quad \text{if} \quad b^3 = a$$

Earlier we determined, that the cube root of 8 is 2. In symbols we can write: $\sqrt[3]{8} = 2$. The number 3 is called the **index**

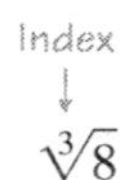

$\sqrt[3]{8}$

> ***Success Tip*** Since every real number has exactly one real cube root, it is unnecessary to use absolute value symbols when simplifying cube roots.

Definition of $\sqrt[3]{x^3}$

For any real number x,

$$\sqrt[3]{x^3} = x$$

To simplify cube root radical expressions, it is helpful to memorize the whole numbers that are perfect cubes.

$1 = 1^3$	$27 = 3^3$	$125 = 5^3$	$343 = 7^3$	$729 = 9^3$
$8 = 2^3$	$64 = 4^3$	$216 = 6^3$	$512 = 8^3$	$1{,}000 = 10^3$

Self Check 7

Simplify:

a. $\sqrt[3]{1{,}000}$ 10

b. $\sqrt[3]{\frac{1}{27}}$ $\frac{1}{3}$

c. $\sqrt[3]{-125a^3}$ $-5a$

Now Try **Problems 50 and 53**

Teaching Example 7 Simplify:

a. $\sqrt[3]{64}$ b. $\sqrt[3]{\frac{8}{27}}$ c. $\sqrt[3]{-216a^3}$

Answers:

a. 4 b. $\frac{2}{3}$ c. $-6a$

EXAMPLE 7

Simplify: **a.** $\sqrt[3]{125}$ **b.** $\sqrt[3]{\frac{1}{8}}$ **c.** $\sqrt[3]{-27x^3}$ **d.** $\sqrt[3]{-\frac{8a^3}{27b^3}}$ **e.** $\sqrt[3]{0.216x^3y^6}$

Strategy In each case, we will determine what number or expression, when cubed, produces the radicand.

WHY The symbol $\sqrt[3]{}$ indicates that the cube root of the number written under it should be found.

Solution

a. $\sqrt[3]{125} = 5$ Because $5^3 = 5 \cdot 5 \cdot 5 = 125$.

b. $\sqrt[3]{\frac{1}{8}} = \frac{1}{2}$ Because $\left(\frac{1}{2}\right)^3 = \frac{1}{2} \cdot \frac{1}{2} \cdot \frac{1}{2} = \frac{1}{8}$.

c. $\sqrt[3]{-27x^3} = -3x$ Because $(-3x)^3 = (-3x)(-3x)(-3x) = -27x^3$.

d. $\sqrt[3]{-\frac{8a^3}{27b^3}} = -\frac{2a}{3b}$ Because $\left(-\frac{2a}{3b}\right)^3 = \left(-\frac{2a}{3b}\right)\left(-\frac{2a}{3b}\right)\left(-\frac{2a}{3b}\right) = -\frac{8a^3}{27b^3}$.

e. $\sqrt[3]{0.216x^3y^6} = 0.6xy^2$ Because $(0.6xy^2)^3 = (0.6xy^2)(0.6xy^2)(0.6xy^2) = 0.216x^3y^6$. ■

5 Graph the cube root function.

Since there is one cube root for every real number x, the equation $f(x) = \sqrt[3]{x}$ defines a function, called the **cube root function.** Like square root functions, cube root functions belong to the family of radical functions.

EXAMPLE 8 Consider $f(x) = \sqrt[3]{x}$. **a.** Graph the function. **b.** Find its domain and range. **c.** Graph: $g(x) = \sqrt[3]{x} - 2$

Strategy We will graph the function by creating a table of function values and plotting the corresponding ordered pairs.

WHY After drawing a smooth curve though the plotted points, we will have the graph. The answers to parts b and c can then be determined from the graph.

Solution

a. To graph the function, we select several values for x and find the corresponding values of $f(x)$. We begin with $x = -8$.

$$f(x) = \sqrt[3]{x}$$

$$f(-8) = \sqrt[3]{-8} \quad \text{Substitute } -8 \text{ for } x.$$

$$f(-8) = -2$$

We enter -8 for x and -2 for $f(x)$ in the table. Then we let $x = -1, 0, 1,$ and 8, and list each corresponding function value in the table. After plotting the ordered pairs, we draw a smooth curve through the points to get the graph shown in figure (a).

$f(x) = \sqrt[3]{x}$

x	$f(x)$	
−8	−2	→ (−8, −2)
−1	−1	→ (−1, −1)
0	0	→ (0, 0)
1	1	→ (1, 1)
8	2	→ (8, 2)

↑ Select values of x that are perfect cubes.

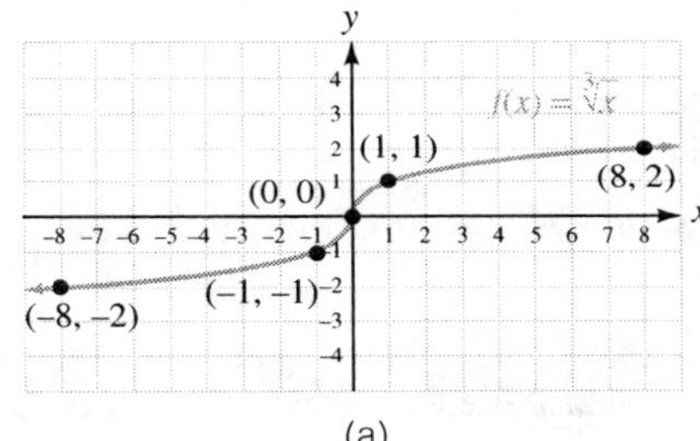

(a)

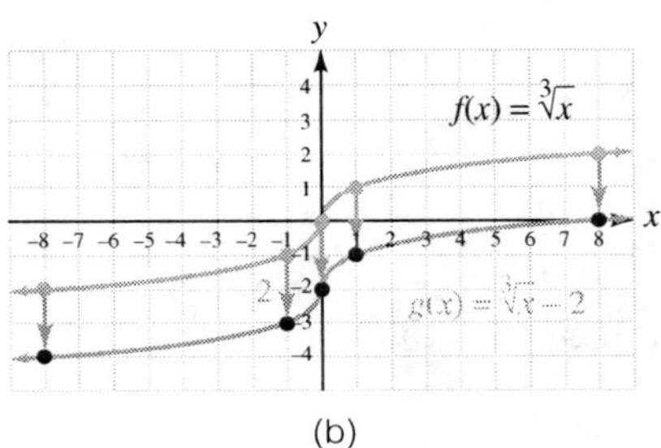

(b)

b. From the graph in figure (a), we see that the domain and the range of function f are the set of real numbers. Thus, the domain is $(-\infty, \infty)$ and the range is $(-\infty, \infty)$.

c. Refer to figure (b). The graph of $g(x) = \sqrt[3]{x} - 2$ is the graph of $f(x) = \sqrt[3]{x}$, translated 2 units downward.

Self Check 8

Consider $f(x) = \sqrt[3]{x} + 1$.

a. Graph the function.

b. Find its domain and range.

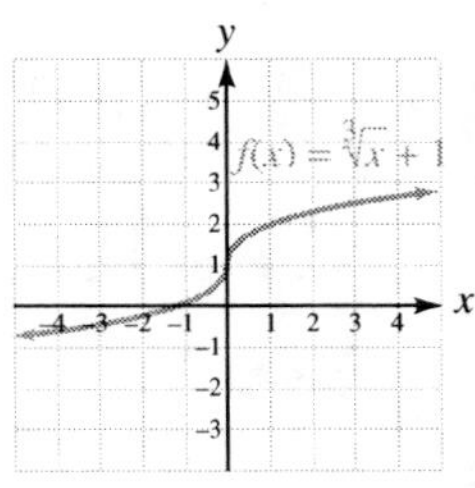

Now Try **Problem 58**

Self Check 8 Answer

D: $(-\infty, \infty)$, R: $(-\infty, \infty)$

Teaching Example 8 Consider $f(x) = \sqrt[3]{x} + 3$.

a. Graph the function.

b. Find its domain and range.

Answers:

a.

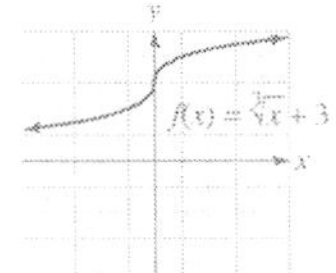

b. D: $(-\infty, \infty)$, R: $(-\infty, \infty)$

6 Find *n*th roots.

Just as there are square roots and cube roots, there are fourth roots, fifth roots, sixth roots, and so on. In general, we have the following definition.

nth Roots of *a*

The ***n*th root of *a*** is denoted by $\sqrt[n]{a}$, and

$$\sqrt[n]{a} = b \quad \text{if} \quad b^n = a$$

The number n is called the **index** (or **order**) of the radical. If n is an even natural number, a must be positive or zero and b must be positive.

When n is an odd natural number, the expression $\sqrt[n]{x}$ where $n > 1$ represents an **odd root.** Since every real number has just one real nth root when n is odd, we don't need to worry about absolute value symbols when finding odd roots. For example,

$\sqrt[5]{243} = \sqrt[5]{3^5} = 3$ Because $3^5 = 243$.

$\sqrt[7]{-128x^7} = \sqrt[7]{(-2x)^7} = -2x$ Because $(-2x)^7 = -128x^7$.

When n is an even natural number, the expression $\sqrt[n]{x}$, where $n > 1$ and $x > 0$, represents an **even root.** In this case, there will be one positive and one negative real nth root. For example, the real sixth roots of 729 are 3 and -3, because $3^6 = 729$ and $(-3)^6 = 729$. When finding even roots, we can use absolute value symbols to guarantee that the nth root is positive.

$\sqrt[4]{(-3)^4} = |-3| = 3$ We could also simplify this as follows: $\sqrt[4]{(-3)^4} = \sqrt[4]{81} = 3$.

$\sqrt[6]{729x^6} = \sqrt[6]{(3x)^6} = |3x| = 3|x|$ The absolute value symbols guarantee that the sixth root is positive.

In general, we have the following rules.

Rules for $\sqrt[n]{x^n}$

If x represents a real number and $n > 1$, then

If n represents an odd natural number, $\sqrt[n]{x^n} = x$.

If n represents an even natural number, $\sqrt[n]{x^n} = |x|$.

In the radical expression $\sqrt[n]{x}$, n is called the **index** (or **order**) of the radical. When the index is 2, the radical is a square root, and we usually do not write the index.

$$\sqrt{x} = \sqrt[2]{x}$$

Caution! When n is even, where $n > 1$ and $x < 0$, $\sqrt[n]{x}$ is not a real number. For example, $\sqrt[4]{-81}$ is not a real number, because no real number raised to the fourth power is -81.

Self Check 9

Evaluate each radical expression, if possible:

a. $\sqrt[4]{\frac{1}{81}}$ $\frac{1}{3}$

b. $\sqrt[5]{10^5}$ 10

c. $\sqrt[6]{-64}$ not a real number

Now Try **Problems 62, 66, and 70**

EXAMPLE 9 Evaluate each radical expression, if possible:

a. $\sqrt[4]{625}$ **b.** $\sqrt[4]{-1}$ **c.** $\sqrt[5]{-32}$ **d.** $\sqrt[6]{\frac{1}{64}}$ **e.** $\sqrt[7]{10^7}$

Strategy In each case, we will determine what number, when raised to the fourth, fifth, sixth, or seventh power, produces the radicand.

WHY The symbols $\sqrt[4]{\ }$, $\sqrt[5]{\ }$, $\sqrt[6]{\ }$, and $\sqrt[7]{\ }$ indicate that the fourth, fifth, sixth, or seventh root of the number written under it should be found.

Solution

a. $\sqrt[4]{625} = 5$, because $5^4 = 625$ — Read $\sqrt[4]{625}$ as "the fourth root of 625."

b. $\sqrt[4]{-1}$ is not a real number. — This is an even root of a negative number.

c. $\sqrt[5]{-32} = -2$, because $(-2)^5 = -32$ — Read $\sqrt[5]{-32}$ as "the fifth root of -32."

d. $\sqrt[6]{\frac{1}{64}} = \frac{1}{2}$, because $\left(\frac{1}{2}\right)^6 = \frac{1}{64}$ — Read $\sqrt[6]{\frac{1}{64}}$ as "the sixth root of $\frac{1}{64}$."

e. $\sqrt[7]{10^7} = 10$, because $10^7 = 10^7$ — Read $\sqrt[7]{10^7}$ as "the seventh root of 10^7."

Teaching Example 9 Evaluate each radical expression, if possible:

a. $\sqrt[5]{\frac{1}{32}}$ b. $\sqrt[4]{-625}$
c. $\sqrt[5]{-243}$ d. $-\sqrt[6]{64}$

Answers:
a. $\frac{1}{2}$ b. not a real number
c. -3 d. -2

Using Your CALCULATOR Finding Roots

The square root key $\sqrt{\ }$ on a reverse entry scientific calculator can be used to evaluate square roots. To evaluate roots with an index greater than 2, we can use the root key $\boxed{\sqrt[x]{y}}$. For example, the function

$$r(V) = \sqrt[3]{\frac{3V}{4\pi}}$$

gives the radius of a sphere with volume V. To find the radius of the spherical propane tank shown in the figure, we substitute 113 for V to get

$$r(V) = \sqrt[3]{\frac{3V}{4\pi}}$$

$$r(113) = \sqrt[3]{\frac{3(113)}{4\pi}}$$

To evaluate a root, we enter the radicand and press the root key $\boxed{\sqrt[x]{y}}$ followed by the index of the radical, which in this case is 3.

3 [×] 113 [÷] [(] 4 [×] [π] [)] [=] [2nd] [$\sqrt[x]{y}$] [3] [=]

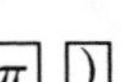 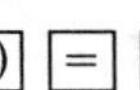 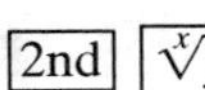 

[2.999139118]

To evaluate the cube root of $\frac{3(113)}{4\pi}$ using a direct entry calculator, we enter these numbers and press these keys.

3 [2nd] [$\sqrt[x]{y}$] [(] 3 [×] 113 [÷] [(] 4 [×] [π] [)] [)] [ENTER]

To evaluate the cube root of $\frac{3(113)}{4\pi}$ using a graphing calculator, we enter these numbers and press these keys.

[MATH] 4 [(] 3 [×] 113 [)] [÷] [(] 4 [×] [2nd] [π] [)] [)] [ENTER]

```
∛((3*113)/(4*π)
)
            2.999139118
```

The radius of the propane tank is about 3 feet.

Self Check 10

Simplify each expression. Assume all variables are unrestricted.

a. $\sqrt[4]{16a^8}$ $2a^2$

b. $\sqrt[5]{(a+5)^5}$ $a+5$

c. $\sqrt{(x^2+4x+4)}$ $|x+2|$

Now Try **Problems 73, 75, and 82**

Teaching Example 10 Simplify each expression. Assume all variables are unrestricted.

a. $\sqrt[7]{x^7}$ b. $\sqrt[4]{x^8}$

c. $\sqrt[6]{64x^6}$ d. $\sqrt[8]{(x+1)^8}$

Answers:

a. x b. x^2 c. $2|x|$ d. $|x+1|$

EXAMPLE 10 Simplify each expression. Assume that x can be any real number.

a. $\sqrt[5]{x^5}$ **b.** $\sqrt[4]{16x^4}$ **c.** $\sqrt[6]{(x+4)^6}$ **d.** $\sqrt[3]{(x+1)^3}$

Strategy When the index n is odd, we will determine what expression, when raised to the nth power, produces the radicand. When the index n is even, we will determine what positive expression, when raised to the nth power produces the radicand.

WHY This is the definition of the nth root.

Solution

a. $\sqrt[5]{x^5} = x$ Since n is odd, absolute value symbols aren't needed.

b. $\sqrt[4]{16x^4} = |2x| = 2|x|$ Since n is even and x can be negative, absolute value symbols are needed to guarantee that the result is positive.

c. $\sqrt[6]{(x+4)^6} = |x+4|$ Absolute value symbols are needed to guarantee that the result is positive.

d. $\sqrt[3]{(x+1)^3} = x+1$ Since n is odd, absolute value symbols aren't needed.

If we know that x represents a positive real number in parts b and c of Example 10, we do not need to use absolute value symbols to guarantee that the results are positive.

$\sqrt[4]{16x^4} = 2x$ If x is positive, $2x$ is positive.

$\sqrt[6]{(x+4)^6} = x+4$ If x is positive, $x+4$ is positive.

We summarize the definitions concerning $\sqrt[n]{x}$ as follows.

Summary of the definitions of $\sqrt[n]{x}$

If n represents a natural number greater than 1 and x represents a real number, then

If $x > 0$, then $\sqrt[n]{x}$ is the positive number such that $\left(\sqrt[n]{x}\right)^n = x$.

If $x = 0$, then $\sqrt[n]{x} = 0$.

If $x < 0$ $\begin{cases} \text{and } n \text{ is odd, then } \sqrt[n]{x} \text{ is the real number such that } \left(\sqrt[n]{x}\right)^n = x. \\ \text{and } n \text{ is even, then } \sqrt[n]{x} \text{ is not a real number.} \end{cases}$

ANSWERS TO SELF CHECKS

1. 12, −12 **2. a.** −7 **b.** $\frac{5}{7}$ **3. a.** $5|a|$ **b.** $4a^2$

4. D: $[0, \infty)$, R: $[2, \infty)$ **5.** D: $[2, \infty)$, R: $[-4, \infty)$ **6.** 1.92 sec **7. a.** 10 **b.** $\frac{1}{3}$ **c.** $-5a$

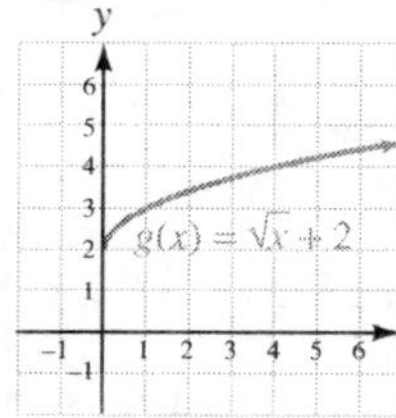

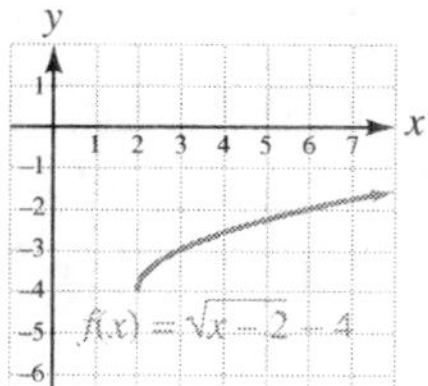

8. a.

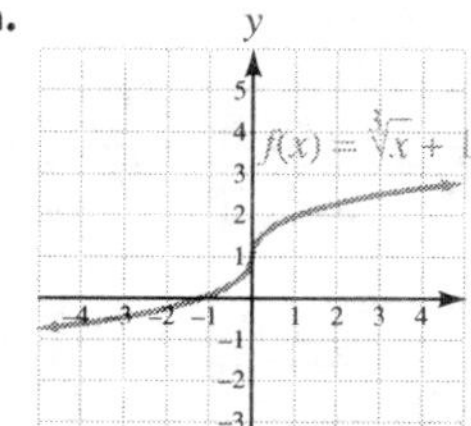

b. D: $(-\infty, \infty)$, R: $(-\infty, \infty)$

9. a. $\frac{1}{3}$ **b.** 10 **c.** not a real number

10. a. $2a^2$ **b.** $a+5$ **c.** $|x+2|$

SECTION 8.1 STUDY SET

VOCABULARY

Fill in the blanks.

1. $5x^2$ is the square root of $25x^4$, because $(5x^2)^2 = 25x^4$.
2. $f(x) = \sqrt{x}$ and $g(t) = \sqrt[3]{t}$ are radical functions.
3. ▶ The symbol $\sqrt{}$ is called a radical symbol.
4. In the expression $\sqrt[3]{27x^6}$, 3 is the index and $27x^6$ is the radicand.
5. When n is an odd number, $\sqrt[n]{x}$ represents an odd root.
6. When n is an even number, $\sqrt[n]{x}$ represents an even root.
7. When we write $\sqrt{b^2 + 6b + 9} = |b + 3|$, we say that we have simplified the radical.
8. 6 is the cube root of 216 because $6^3 = 216$.

CONCEPTS

Fill in the blanks.

9. b is a square root of a if $b^2 = a$.
10. $\sqrt{0} = 0$ and $\sqrt[3]{0} = 0$
11. The number 25 has two square roots. The principal square root of 25 is the positive square root of 25.
12. ▶ $\sqrt{-4}$ is not a real number, because no real number squared equals -4.
13. $\sqrt[3]{x} = y$ if $y^3 = x$
14. $\sqrt{x^2} = |x|$ and $\sqrt[3]{x^3} = x$
15. The graph of $f(x) = \sqrt{x} + 3$ is the graph of $f(x) = \sqrt{x}$ translated 3 units up.
16. ▶ The graph of $f(x) = \sqrt{x + 5}$ is the graph of $f(x) = \sqrt{x}$ translated 5 units to the left.

NOTATION

Translate each sentence into mathematical symbols.

17. The square root of x squared is the absolute value of x. $\sqrt{x^2} = |x|$
18. ▶ The cube root of x cubed is x. $\sqrt[3]{x^3} = x$
19. f of x equals the square root of the quantity x minus five. $f(x) = \sqrt{x - 5}$
20. ▶ The fifth root of negative thirty-two is negative two. $\sqrt[5]{-32} = -2$

GUIDED PRACTICE

Find the two square roots of each number. See Example 1.

21. 81 9, −9
22. ▶ 169 13, −13
23. 256 16, −16
24. 196 14, −14

Evaluate each square root. See Example 2.

25. $\sqrt{121}$ 11
26. $\sqrt{144}$ 12
27. $-\sqrt{64}$ −8
28. $-\sqrt{1}$ −1
29. $\sqrt{\frac{1}{9}}$ $\frac{1}{3}$
30. $-\sqrt{\frac{4}{25}}$ $-\frac{2}{5}$
31. $-\sqrt{0.25}$ −0.5
32. ▶ $\sqrt{0.16}$ 0.4

Find each square root. Assume that all variables are unrestricted, and use absolute value symbols when necessary. See Example 3.

33. $\sqrt{4x^2}$ $2|x|$
34. $\sqrt{16y^4}$ $4y^2$
35. $\sqrt{(t + 5)^2}$ $|t + 5|$
36. $\sqrt{(a + 6)^2}$ $|a + 6|$
37. $\sqrt{(-5b)^2}$ $5|b|$
38. $\sqrt{(-8c)^2}$ $8|c|$
39. $\sqrt{a^2 + 6a + 9}$ $|a + 3|$
40. ▶ $\sqrt{x^2 + 10x + 25}$ $|x + 5|$

Complete each table, graph the function, and determine its domain and range. See Example 4.

41. $f(x) = -\sqrt{x}$

x	$f(x)$
0	0
1	−1
4	−2
9	−3
16	−4

D: $[0, \infty)$, R: $(-\infty, 0]$

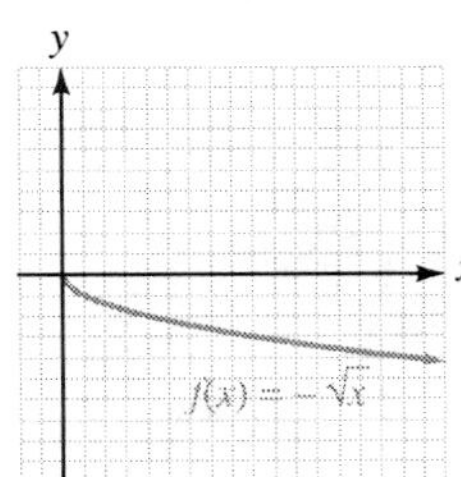

42. ▶ $f(x) = \sqrt{x} - 2$

x	$f(x)$
0	−2
1	−1
4	0
9	1
16	2

D: $[0, \infty)$, R: $[-2, \infty)$

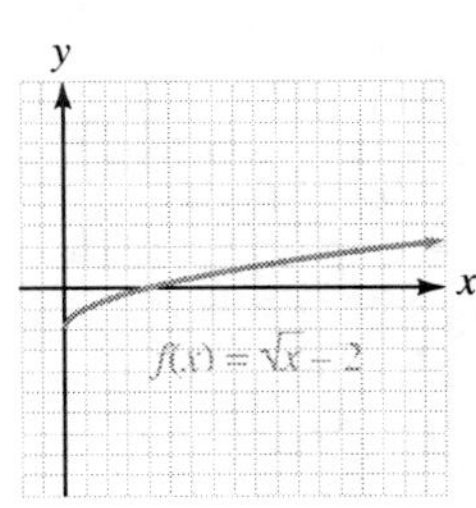

43. $f(x) = \sqrt{x} - 1$

x	$f(x)$
0	−1
1	0
4	1
9	2
16	3

D: $[0, \infty)$, R: $[-1, \infty)$

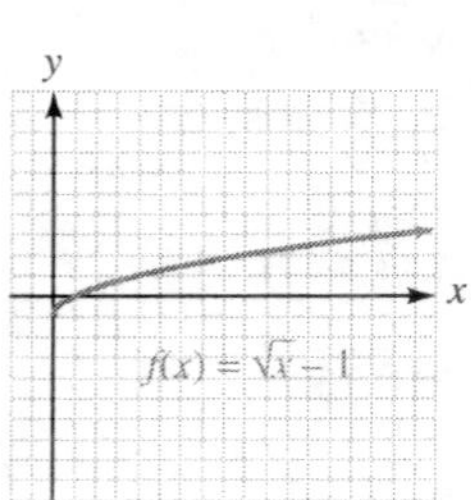

44. $f(x) = -\sqrt{x} + 1$

x	$f(x)$
0	1
1	0
4	−1
9	−2
16	−3

D: $[0, \infty)$, R: $(-\infty, 1]$

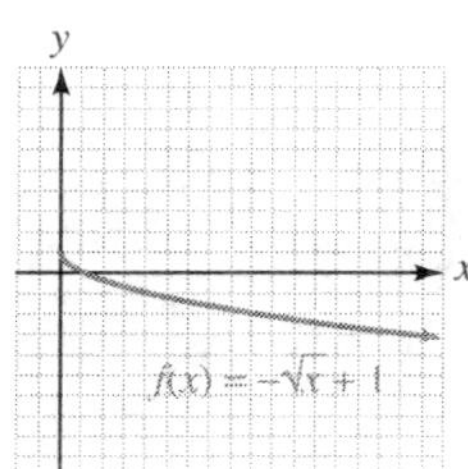

Graph each function and find its domain and range. See Example 5.

45. $f(x) = \sqrt{x + 4}$
D: $[-4, \infty)$, R: $[0, \infty)$

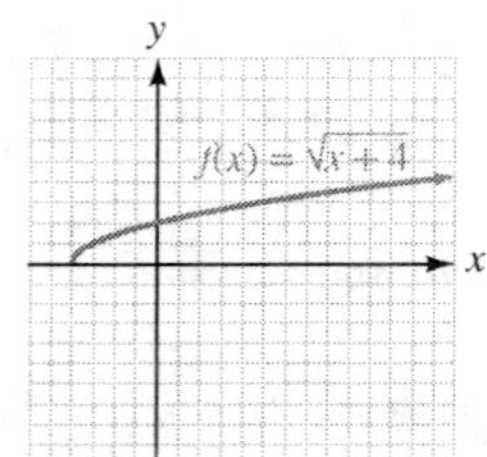

▶ **46.** $f(x) = -\sqrt{x - 1}$
D: $[1, \infty)$, R: $(-\infty, 0]$

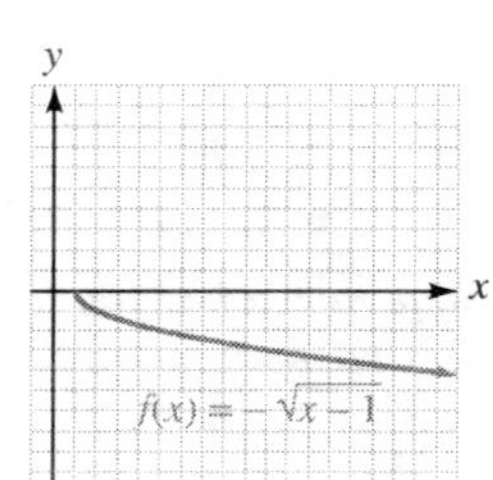

47. $f(x) = \sqrt{x + 2} - 1$
D: $[-2, \infty)$, R: $[-1, \infty)$

48. $f(x) = -\sqrt{x - 3} + 2$
D: $[3, \infty)$, R: $(-\infty, 2]$

Simplify each cube root. See Example 7.

49. $\sqrt[3]{1}$ 1

▶ **50.** $\sqrt[3]{512}$ 8

51. $\sqrt[3]{-125a^3}$ $-5a$

52. $\sqrt[3]{-8y^3}$ $-2y$

53. $\sqrt[3]{-\dfrac{8a^6}{27b^3}}$ $-\dfrac{2a^2}{3b}$

54. $\sqrt[3]{\dfrac{125x^3}{216y^6}}$ $\dfrac{5x}{6y^2}$

55. $\sqrt[3]{0.064a^3b^6}$ $0.4ab^2$

56. $\sqrt[3]{0.001x^6y^6}$ $0.1x^2y^2$

Complete each table, graph the function, and determine its domain and range. See Example 8.

▶ **57.** $f(x) = -\sqrt[3]{x}$

x	$f(x)$
−8	2
−1	1
0	0
1	−1
8	−2

D: $(-\infty, \infty)$, R: $(-\infty, \infty)$

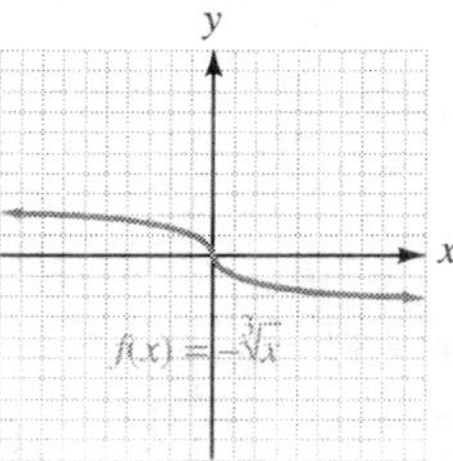

58. $f(x) = \sqrt[3]{x} + 2$

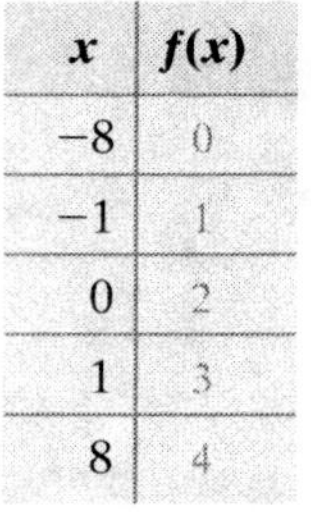

x	$f(x)$
−8	0
−1	1
0	2
1	3
8	4

D: $(-\infty, \infty)$, R: $(-\infty, \infty)$

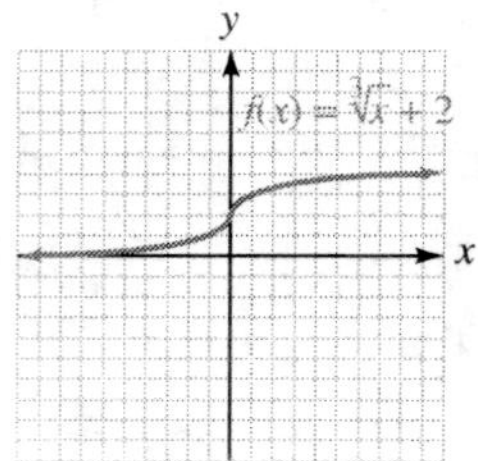

59. $f(x) = \sqrt[3]{x} - 3$

x	$f(x)$
−8	−5
−1	−4
0	−3
1	−2
8	−1

D: $(-\infty, \infty)$, R: $(-\infty, \infty)$

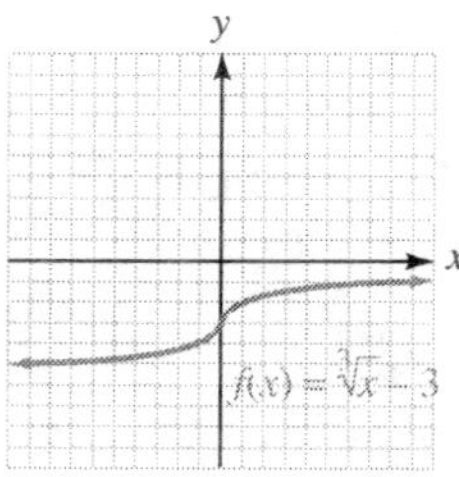

60. $f(x) = -\sqrt[3]{x} + 2$

x	$f(x)$
−8	4
−1	3
0	2
1	1
8	0

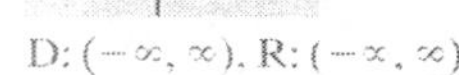
D: $(-\infty, \infty)$, R: $(-\infty, \infty)$

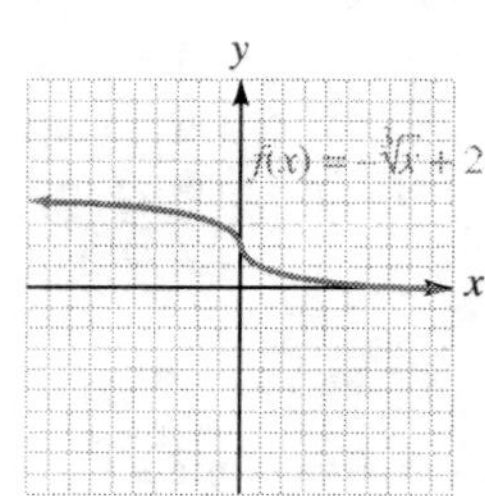

Evaluate each radical, if possible. See Example 9.

61. $\sqrt[4]{81}$ 3

62. $\sqrt[6]{64}$ 2

63. $-\sqrt[5]{243}$ −3

64. $-\sqrt[4]{625}$ −5

65. $\sqrt[4]{-256}$ not real

66. $\sqrt[6]{-729}$ not real

67. $\sqrt[4]{\dfrac{16}{625}}$ $\dfrac{2}{5}$

▶ **68.** $\sqrt[5]{-\dfrac{243}{32}}$ $-\dfrac{3}{2}$

69. $-\sqrt[5]{-\dfrac{1}{32}}$ $\dfrac{1}{2}$

▶ **70.** $-\sqrt[4]{\dfrac{81}{256}}$ $-\dfrac{3}{4}$

71. $\sqrt[8]{10^8}$ 10

72. $\sqrt[11]{-9^{11}}$ −9

Simplify each expression. Assume that all variables represent nonzero numbers. See Example 10.

73. $\sqrt[5]{32a^5}$ $2a$

74. $\sqrt[5]{-32x^5}$ $-2x$

75. $\sqrt[4]{16a^4}$ $2|a|$

76. $\sqrt[8]{x^{24}}$ $|x^3|$

77. $\sqrt[4]{k^{12}}$ $|k^3|$

78. $\sqrt[6]{64b^6}$ $2|b|$

79. $\sqrt[4]{\frac{1}{16}m^4}$ $\frac{1}{2}|m|$

80. $\sqrt[4]{\frac{1}{81}x^8}$ $\frac{1}{3}x^2$

81. $\sqrt[4]{(x+2)^4}$ $|x+2|$

82. $\sqrt[5]{(x+1)^5}$ $x+1$

83. $\sqrt[3]{(x+2)^3}$ $x+2$

84. $\sqrt[4]{(x+4)^4}$ $|x+4|$

TRY IT YOURSELF

Evaluate each radical, if possible.

85. $\sqrt{-25}$ not real

86. $-\sqrt{-49}$ not real

87. $\sqrt{(-4)^2}$ 4

88. $\sqrt{(-9)^2}$ 9

89. $\sqrt[3]{8a^3}$ $2a$

90. $\sqrt[3]{-27x^6}$ $-3x^2$

91. $\sqrt[3]{-1{,}000p^3q^3}$ $-10pq$

92. $\sqrt[3]{343a^6b^3}$ $7a^2b$

93. $\sqrt[3]{-\frac{1}{8}m^6n^3}$ $-\frac{1}{2}m^2n$

94. $\sqrt[3]{0.008z^9}$ $0.2z^3$

95. $\sqrt[3]{-0.064s^6t^6}$ $-0.4s^2t^2$

96. $\sqrt[3]{\frac{27}{1{,}000}a^6b^6}$ $\frac{3}{10}a^2b^2$

Use a calculator to find each square root. Give the answer to four decimal places.

97. $\sqrt{12}$ 3.4641

98. $\sqrt{340}$ 18.4391

99. $\sqrt{679.25}$ 26.0624

100. $\sqrt{0.0063}$ 0.0794

Graph each function and find its domain and range.

101. $f(x) = \sqrt[3]{x} + 1$
D: $(-\infty, \infty)$, R: $(-\infty, \infty)$

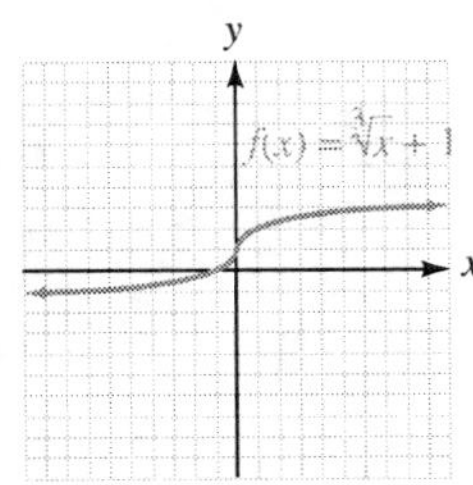

102. $f(x) = -\sqrt[3]{x} + 1$
D: $(-\infty, \infty)$, R: $(-\infty, \infty)$

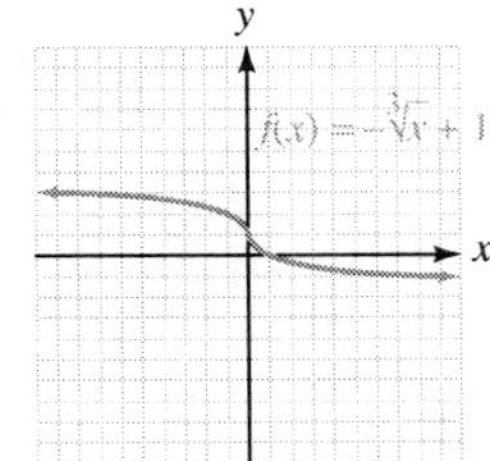

103. $f(x) = -\sqrt[3]{x} - 3$
D: $(-\infty, \infty)$, R: $(-\infty, \infty)$

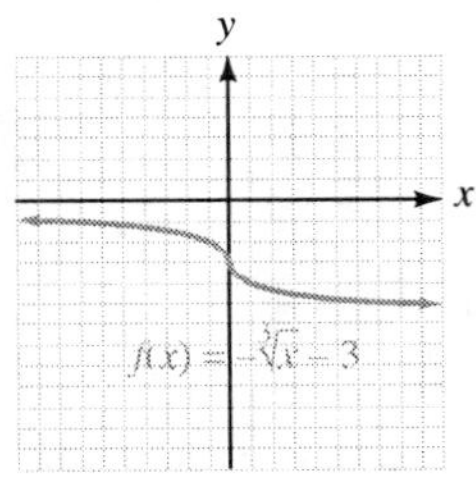

104. $f(x) = \sqrt[3]{x} - 1$
D: $(-\infty, \infty)$, R: $(-\infty, \infty)$

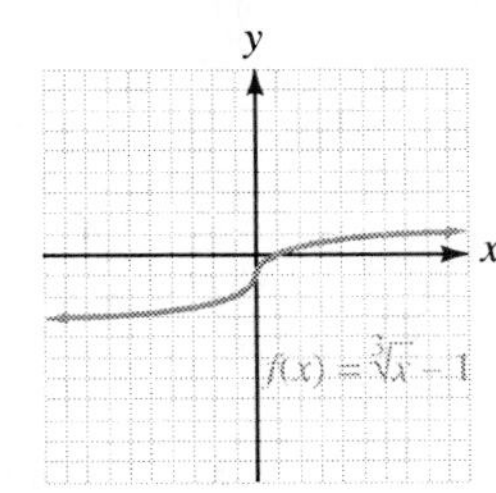

APPLICATIONS

Use a calculator to solve each problem. In each case, round to the nearest tenth.

105. EMBROIDERY The radius r of a circle is given by the formula

$$r = \sqrt{\frac{A}{\pi}}$$

where A is its area. Find the diameter of the embroidery hoop shown on the right if there are 38.5 in.^{2} of stretched fabric on which to embroider. 7.0 in.

106. BASEBALL The length of a diagonal of a square is given by the function $d(s) = \sqrt{2s^2}$, where s is the length of a side of the square. Find the distance from home plate to second base on a softball diamond and on a baseball diamond. The illustration gives the dimensions of each type of infield. 84.9 ft, 127.3 ft

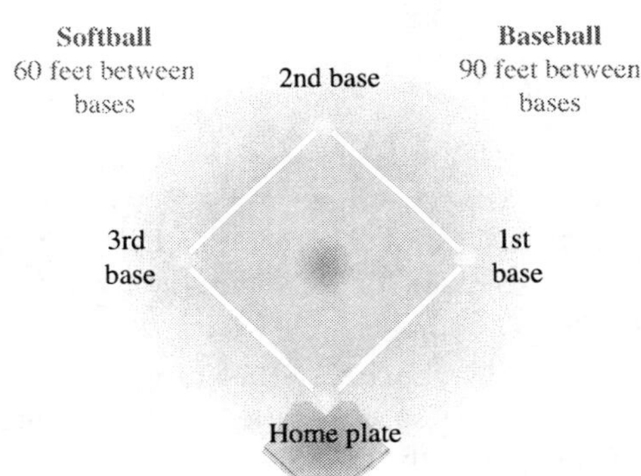

107. PULSE RATES The approximate pulse rate (in beats per minute) of an adult who is t inches tall is given by the function

$$p(t) = \frac{590}{\sqrt{t}}$$

The Guinness Book of World Records 1998 lists Ri Myong-hun of North Korea as the tallest living man, at 7 ft $8\frac{1}{2}$ in. Find his approximate pulse rate as predicted by the function. about 61.3 beats/min

108. THE GRAND CANYON The time t (in seconds) that it takes for an object to fall a distance of s feet is given by the formula

$$t = \frac{\sqrt{s}}{4}$$

In some places, the Grand Canyon is one mile (5,280 feet) deep. How long would it take a stone dropped over the edge of the canyon to hit bottom? 18.2 sec

109. BIOLOGY Scientists will place five rats inside the controlled environment of a sealed hemisphere to study the rats' behavior. The function

$$d(V) = \sqrt[3]{12\left(\frac{V}{\pi}\right)}$$

gives the diameter of a hemisphere with volume V. Use the function to determine the diameter of the base of the hemisphere if each rat requires 125 cubic feet of living space. 13.4 ft

110. AQUARIUMS The function

$$s(g) = \sqrt[3]{\frac{g}{7.5}}$$

determines how long (in feet) an edge of a cube-shaped tank must be if it is to hold g gallons of water. What dimensions should a cube-shaped aquarium have if it is to hold 1,250 gallons of water? 5.5 ft × 5.5 ft × 5.5 ft

111. COLLECTIBLES The *effective rate of interest r* earned by an investment is given by the formula

$$r = \sqrt[n]{\frac{A}{P}} - 1$$

where P is the initial investment that grows to value A after n years. Determine the effective rate of interest earned by a collector on a Lladró porcelain figurine purchased for \$800 and sold for \$950 five years later. 3.5%

112. LAW ENFORCEMENT The graphs of the two radical functions shown in the illustration can be used to estimate the speed (in mph) of a car involved in an accident. Suppose a police accident report listed skid marks to be 220 feet long but failed to give the road conditions. Estimate the possible speeds the car was traveling prior to the brakes being applied. dry: about 72 mph, wet: about 47 mph

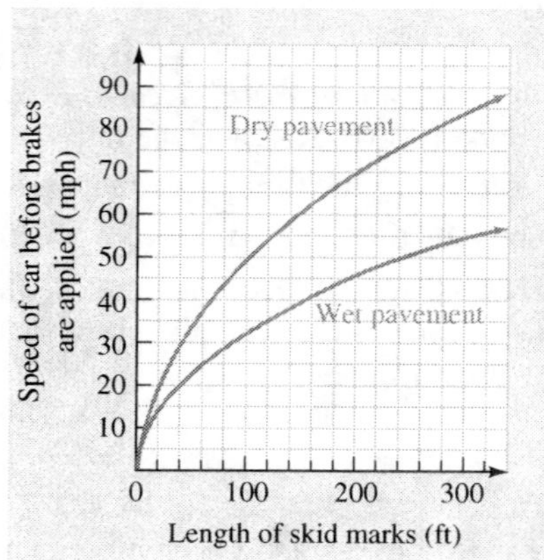

WRITING

113. Explain why 36 has two square roots, but $\sqrt{36}$ is just 6, not −6.

114. If x is any real number, then $\sqrt{x^2} = x$ is not correct. Explain.

115. Explain what is wrong with the graph on the right.

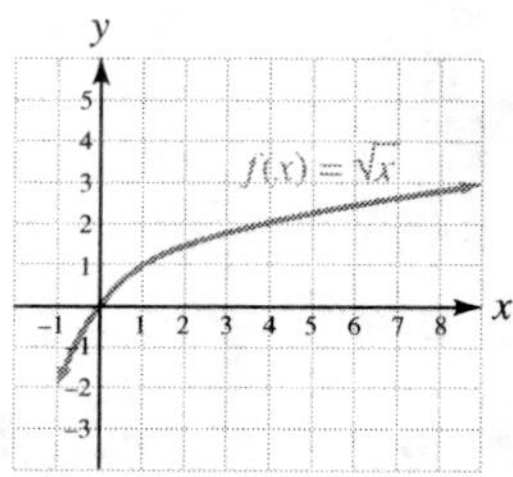

116. Explain how to estimate the domain and range of the radical function that is graphed on the right.

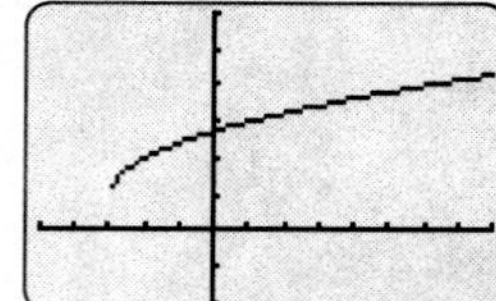

REVIEW

Perform the operations.

117. $\dfrac{x^2 - x - 6}{x^2 - 2x - 3} \cdot \dfrac{x^2 - 1}{x^2 + x - 2}$ 1

118. $\dfrac{x^2 - 3x - 4}{x^2 - 5x + 6} \div \dfrac{x^2 - 2x - 3}{x^2 - x - 2}$ $\dfrac{(x-4)(x+1)}{(x-3)^2}$

119. $\dfrac{3}{m + 1} + \dfrac{3m}{m - 1}$ $\dfrac{3(m^2 + 2m - 1)}{(m + 1)(m - 1)}$

120. $\dfrac{2x + 3}{3x - 1} - \dfrac{x - 4}{2x + 1}$ $\dfrac{x^2 + 21x - 1}{(3x - 1)(2x + 1)}$

SECTION 8.2
Rational Exponents

Objectives

1. Simplify expressions of the form $a^{1/n}$.
2. Convert between radicals and rational exponents.
3. Simplify exponential expressions with variables in their bases.
4. Simplify expressions of the form $a^{m/n}$.
5. Simplify expressions with negative rational exponents.
6. Use rules for exponents to simplify expressions.
7. Simplify radical expressions.

We have worked with exponential expressions containing natural-number exponents, such as 5^3 and x^2. In Chapter 5, the definition of exponent was extended to include zero and negative integers, which gave meaning to expressions such as 8^{-3} and $(-9xy)^0$. In this section, we will again extend the definition of exponent—this time to include rational (fractional) exponents. We will see how expressions such as $9^{1/2}$, $\left(\frac{1}{16}\right)^{3/4}$, and $(-32x^5)^{-2/5}$ can be simplified by writing them in an equivalent radical form or by using the rules for exponents.

1 Simplify expressions of the form $a^{1/n}$.

We have seen that positive-integer exponents indicate the number of times that a base is to be used as a factor in a product. For example, x^5 means that x is to be used as a factor five times.

$$x^5 = \overbrace{x \cdot x \cdot x \cdot x \cdot x}^{\text{5 factors of } x}$$

Furthermore, we recall the following rules for exponents.

Rules for Exponents

If there are no divisions by 0, then for all integers m and n,

1. $x^m x^n = x^{m+n}$ **2.** $(x^m)^n = x^{mn}$ **3.** $(xy)^n = x^n y^n$ **4.** $\left(\frac{x}{y}\right)^n = \frac{x^n}{y^n}$

5. $x^0 = 1 \quad (x \neq 0)$ **6.** $x^{-n} = \frac{1}{x^n}$ **7.** $\frac{x^m}{x^n} = x^{m-n}$ **8.** $\left(\frac{x}{y}\right)^{-n} = \left(\frac{y}{x}\right)^n$

It is possible to raise many bases to fractional powers. Since we want fractional exponents to obey the same rules as integer exponents, the square of $10^{1/2}$ must be 10, because

$(10^{1/2})^2 = 10^{(1/2)\cdot 2}$ Keep the base and multiply the exponents.
$= 10^1$ $\frac{1}{2} \cdot 2 = 1$.
$= 10$ $10^1 = 10$

However, we have seen that

$$\left(\sqrt{10}\right)^2 = 10$$

Since $(10^{1/2})^2$ and $\left(\sqrt{10}\right)^2$ both equal 10, we define $10^{1/2}$ to be $\sqrt{10}$. Likewise, we define

$10^{1/3}$ to be $\sqrt[3]{10}$ and $10^{1/4}$ to be $\sqrt[4]{10}$

Rational Exponents

A **rational exponent** of $\frac{1}{n}$ indicates the nth root of its base.

If n represents a natural number greater than 1 and $\sqrt[n]{x}$ represents a real number, then

$$x^{1/n} = \sqrt[n]{x}$$

We can use this definition to simplify exponential expressions that have rational exponents with a numerator of 1. For example, to simplify $8^{1/3}$, we write it as an equivalent expression in radical form and proceed as follows:

Index

$$8^{1/3} = \sqrt[3]{8} = 2$$

Radicand

The base of the exponential expression, 8, is the radicand. The denominator of the fractional exponent, 3, is the index of the radical.

Thus, $8^{1/3} = 2$.

Self Check 1

Write each expression in radical form and simplify, if possible:

a. $16^{1/2}$ **b.** $\left(-\frac{27}{8}\right)^{1/3}$

c. $-(6x^3)^{1/4}$

Now Try **Problems 20, 22, 23, 27, and 33**

Self Check 1 Answer

a. 4 b. $-\frac{3}{2}$ c. $-\sqrt[4]{6x^3}$

Teaching Example 1 Write each expression in radical form and simplify, if possible:

a. $25^{1/2}$ b. $\left(\frac{81}{16}\right)^{1/4}$ c. $-(3x^4)^{1/5}$

Answers:

a. 5 b. $\frac{3}{2}$ c. $-\sqrt[5]{3x^4}$

EXAMPLE 1 Write each expression in radical form and simplify, if possible.

a. $9^{1/2}$ **b.** $-\left(\frac{16}{9}\right)^{1/2}$ **c.** $(-64)^{1/3}$ **d.** $16^{1/4}$ **e.** $\left(\frac{1}{32}\right)^{1/5}$ **f.** $0^{1/8}$

g. $y^{1/4}$ **h.** $-(2x^2)^{1/5}$

Strategy First, we will identify the base and the exponent of the exponential expression. Then we will write the expression in an equivalent radical form using the rule for rational exponents $x^{1/n} = \sqrt[n]{x}$.

WHY We can use the methods from Section 8.1 to evaluate the resulting square root, cube root, fourth root, and fifth root.

Solution

a. $9^{1/2} = \sqrt{9}$
$= 3$

b. $-\left(\frac{16}{9}\right)^{1/2} = -\sqrt{\frac{16}{9}}$
$= -\frac{4}{3}$

c. $(-64)^{1/3} = \sqrt[3]{-64}$
$= -4$

d. $16^{1/4} = \sqrt[4]{16}$
$= 2$

e. $\left(\frac{1}{32}\right)^{1/5} = \sqrt[5]{\frac{1}{32}}$
$= \frac{1}{2}$

f. $0^{1/8} = \sqrt[8]{0}$
$= 0$

g. $y^{1/4} = \sqrt[4]{y}$

h. $-(2x^2)^{1/5} = -\sqrt[5]{2x^2}$

2 Convert between radicals and rational exponents.

We can use the rules for rational exponents to convert expressions from radical form to exponential form, and visa versa.

Self Check 2

Write the radical with a fractional exponent: $\sqrt[6]{7ab}$

Now Try **Problem 38**

Self Check 2 Answer

$(7ab)^{1/6}$

Teaching Example 2 Write the radical with a fractional exponent: $\sqrt[11]{9xy^2z}$

Answer:

$(9xy^2z)^{1/11}$

EXAMPLE 2 Write $\sqrt{5xyz}$ as an exponential expression with a rational exponent.

Strategy We will use the rule for rational exponents in reverse: $\sqrt[n]{x} = x^{1/n}$.

WHY We are given the radical expression and we want to write an equivalent exponential expression.

Solution

The radicand is $5xyz$, so the base of the exponential expression is $5xyz$. The index of the radical is an understood 2, so the denominator of the fractional exponent is 2.

$$\sqrt{5xyz} = (5xyz)^{1/2}$$

Recall: $\sqrt{5xyz} = \sqrt[2]{5xyz}$

Rational exponents appear in formulas used in many disciplines, such as science and engineering.

EXAMPLE 3 *Satellites* The formula

$$r = \left(\frac{GMP^2}{4\pi^2}\right)^{1/3}$$

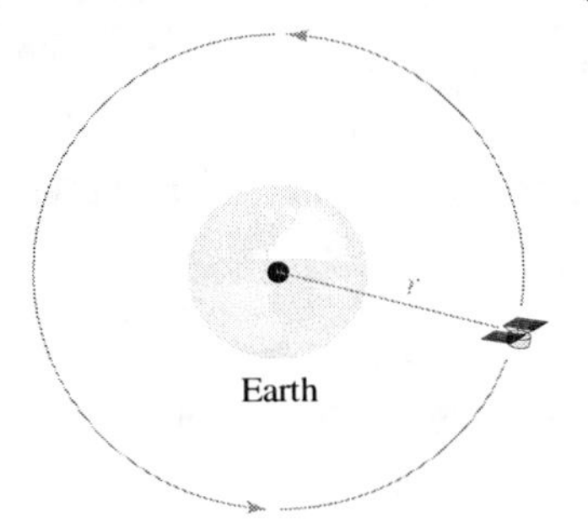

gives the orbital radius (in meters) of a satellite circling Earth, where G and M are constants and P is the time in seconds for the satellite to make one complete revolution. Write the formula using a radical.

Strategy We will write the exponential expression in an equivalent radical form using the rule for rational exponents $x^{1/n} = \sqrt[n]{x}$.

WHY We are given an exponential expression involving a rational exponent with a numerator of 1 and we want to write an equivalent radical expression.

Solution

The fractional exponent $\frac{1}{3}$ has a denominator of 3, which indicates that we are to find the cube root of the base of the exponential expression. So we have

$$r = \sqrt[3]{\frac{GMP^2}{4\pi^2}}$$

Self Check 3

STATISTICS The formula

$$\sigma = \left(\frac{\Sigma(x - \mu)^2}{N}\right)^{1/2}$$

gives the population standard deviation. Write the formula using a radical.

Now Try **Problem 44**

Self Check 3 Answer

$$\sigma = \sqrt{\frac{\Sigma(x - \mu)^2}{N}}$$

Teaching Example 3 STATISTICS

The formula $s = \left(\frac{\Sigma(x - \bar{x})^2}{n - 1}\right)^{1/2}$ gives the sample standard deviation of a set of data. Write the formula using a radical.

Answer:

$$s = \sqrt{\frac{\Sigma(x - \bar{x})^2}{n - 1}}$$

3 Simplify exponential expressions with variables in their bases.

As with radicals, when n represents an *odd natural number* in the expression $x^{1/n}$ where $n > 1$, there is exactly one real nth root, and we don't have to worry about absolute value symbols.

When n represents an *even natural number*, there are two nth roots. Since we want the expression $x^{1/n}$ to represent the positive nth root, we must often use absolute value symbols to guarantee that the simplified result is positive. Thus, if n is even,

$$(x^n)^{1/n} = |x|$$

When n is even and x is negative, the expression $x^{1/n}$ is not a real number.

EXAMPLE 4 Simplify each exponential expression. Assume that the variables can be any real number.

a. $(-8x^3)^{1/3}$ **b.** $(256a^8)^{1/8}$ **c.** $[(y + 4)^2]^{1/2}$ **d.** $(25b^4)^{1/2}$ **e.** $(-256x^4)^{1/4}$

Strategy We will write each exponential expression in an equivalent radical form using the rule for rational exponents $x^{1/n} = \sqrt[n]{x}$.

WHY We can use the methods from Section 8.1 to evaluate the resulting cube root, eighth root, square root, and fourth root.

Solution

a. $(-8x^3)^{1/3} = -2x$ Because $(-2x)^3 = -8x^3$. Since n is odd, no absolute value symbols are needed.

b. $(256a^8)^{1/8} = 2|a|$ Because $(2|a|)^8 = 256a^8$. Since n is even and a can be any real number, $2a$ can be negative. Thus, absolute value symbols are needed.

Self Check 4

Simplify each expression. Assume that the variables can be any real number.

a. $(625a^4)^{1/4}$ $5|a|$

b. $(b^4)^{1/2}$ b^2

Now Try **Problems 48, 49, and 53**

Teaching Example 4 Simplify each exponential expression. Assume that the variables can be any real number.

a. $(-32x^5)^{1/5}$

b. $(81x^4)^{1/4}$

c. $(25x^4)^{1/2}$

d. $(-16x^4)^{1/4}$

Answers:

a. $-2x$ b. $3|x|$ c. $5x^2$

d. not a real number

c. $[(y + 4)^2]^{1/2} = |y + 4|$ — Because $|y + 4|^2 = (y + 4)^2$. Since n is even and y can be any real number, $y + 4$ can be negative. Thus, absolute value symbols are needed.

d. $(25b^4)^{1/2} = 5b^2$ — Because $(5b^2)^2 = 25b^4$. Since $b^2 \geq 0$, no absolute value symbols are needed.

e. $(-256x^4)^{1/4}$ is not a real number. — Because no real number raised to the 4th power is $-256x^4$.

If we are told that the variables represent positive real numbers in parts b and c of Example 4, the absolute value symbols in the answers are not needed.

$(256a^8)^{1/8} = 2a$ — If a represents a positive number, then $2a$ is positive.

$[(y + 4)^2]^{1/2} = y + 4$ — If y represents a positive number, then $y + 4$ is positive.

We summarize the cases as follows.

Summary of the Definitions of $x^{1/n}$

If n represents a natural number greater than 1 and x represents a real number,

If $x > 0$, then $x^{1/n}$ is the positive number such that $(x^{1/n})^n = x$.

If $x = 0$, then $x^{1/n} = 0$.

If $x < 0$ $\begin{cases} \text{and } n \text{ is odd, then } x^{1/n} \text{ is the real number such that } (x^{1/n})^n = x. \\ \text{and } n \text{ is even, then } x^{1/n} \text{ is not a real number.} \end{cases}$

4 Simplify expressions of the form $a^{m/n}$.

We can extend the definition of $x^{1/n}$ to include fractional exponents with numerators other than 1. For example, since $8^{2/3}$ can be written as $(8^{1/3})^2$, we have

$$
\begin{aligned}
8^{2/3} &= (8^{1/3})^2 \\
&= \left(\sqrt[3]{8}\right)^2 && \text{Write } 8^{1/3} \text{ in radical form.} \\
&= 2^2 && \text{Find the cube root first: } \sqrt[3]{8} = 2. \\
&= 4 && \text{Then find the power.}
\end{aligned}
$$

Thus, we can simplify $8^{2/3}$ by finding the second power of the cube root of 8.

The numerator of the rational exponent is the power.

$$8^{2/3} = \left(\sqrt[3]{8}\right)^2$$

The base of the exponential expression is the radicand.

The denominator of the exponent is the index of the radical.

We can also simplify $8^{2/3}$ by taking the cube root of 8 squared.

$$
\begin{aligned}
8^{2/3} &= (8^2)^{1/3} \\
&= 64^{1/3} && \text{Find the power first: } 8^2 = 64. \\
&= \sqrt[3]{64} && \text{Write } 64^{1/3} \text{ in radical form.} \\
&= 4 && \text{Now find the cube root.}
\end{aligned}
$$

In general, we have the following rule.

The Definition of $x^{m/n}$

If m and n represent positive integers ($n \neq 1$) and $\sqrt[n]{x}$ represents a real number,

$$x^{m/n} = \left(\sqrt[n]{x}\right)^m \quad \text{and} \quad x^{m/n} = \sqrt[n]{x^m}$$

Because of the previous definition, we can interpret $x^{m/n}$ in two ways:

1. $x^{m/n}$ means the mth power of the nth root of x.
2. $x^{m/n}$ means the nth root of the mth power of x.

To avoid large numbers, it is usually better to find the root of the base first, and then calculate the power using the rule $x^{m/n} = \left(\sqrt[n]{x}\right)^m$.

EXAMPLE 5

Simplify: **a.** $9^{3/2}$ **b.** $\left(\frac{1}{16}\right)^{3/4}$ **c.** $(-8x^3)^{4/3}$

Strategy First, we will identify the base and the exponent of the exponential expression. Then we will write the expression in an equivalent radical form using the rule for rational exponents $x^{m/n} = \left(\sqrt[n]{x}\right)^m$.

WHY We can use the methods from Section 8.1 to evaluate the resulting square root, fourth root, and cube root.

Solution

Power / Root

a. $9^{3/2} = \left(\sqrt[2]{9}\right)^3$ Because the exponent is 3/2, find the square root of the base, 9, to get 3. Then find the third power of 3.

$= 3^3$

$= 27$

Power / Root

b. $\left(\frac{1}{16}\right)^{3/4} = \left(\sqrt[4]{\frac{1}{16}}\right)^3$ Because the exponent is 3/4, find the fourth root of the base, $\frac{1}{16}$, to get $\frac{1}{2}$. Then find the third power of $\frac{1}{2}$ to get $\frac{1}{8}$.

$= \left(\frac{1}{2}\right)^3$

$= \frac{1}{8}$

Power / Root

c. $(-8x^3)^{4/3} = \left(\sqrt[3]{-8x^3}\right)^4$ Because the exponent is 4/3, find the cube root of the base, $-8x^3$, to get $-2x$. Then find the fourth power of $-2x$ to get $16x^4$.

$= (-2x)^4$

$= 16x^4$

Self Check 5

Simplify:

a. $16^{3/2}$ 64

b. $(-27x^6)^{2/3}$ $9x^4$

Now Try **Problems 57, 62, and 66**

Teaching Example 5 Simplify:

a. $25^{3/2}$ b. $\left(\frac{1}{8}\right)^{4/3}$ c. $(-27x^3)^{4/3}$

Answers:

a. 125 b. $\frac{1}{16}$ c. $81x^4$

Success Tip We can also evaluate $x^{m/n}$ using $\sqrt[n]{x^m}$, however the resulting radicand is often extremely large and more difficult to work with.

$$(-8x^3)^{4/3} = \sqrt[3]{(-8x^3)^4}$$
$$= \sqrt[3]{4{,}096x^{12}}$$
$$= 16x^4$$

Using Your CALCULATOR **Rational Exponents**

We can evaluate exponential expressions containing rational exponents using the exponential key $\boxed{y^x}$ or $\boxed{x^y}$ on a scientific calculator. For example, to evaluate $10^{2/3}$, we enter these numbers and press these keys:

10 $\boxed{y^x}$ $\boxed{(}$ 2 $\boxed{\div}$ 3 $\boxed{)}$ $\boxed{=}$ 4.641588834

Note that parentheses were used when entering the power. Without them, the calculator would interpret the entry as $10^2 \div 3$.

To evaluate the exponential expression using a direct entry or graphing calculator, we use the $\boxed{\wedge}$ key, which raises a base to a power. Again, we use parentheses when entering the power.

10 $\boxed{\wedge}$ $\boxed{(}$ 2 $\boxed{\div}$ 3 $\boxed{)}$ $\boxed{\text{ENTER}}$

```
10^(2/3)
         4.641588834
```

To the nearest hundredth, $10^{2/3} \approx 4.64$.

5 Simplify expressions with negative rational exponents.

To be consistent with the definition of negative-integer exponents, we define $x^{-m/n}$ as follows.

Definition of $x^{-m/n}$

If m and n represent positive integers, $\frac{m}{n}$ is in simplified form, and $x^{1/n}$ represents a real number, then

$$x^{-m/n} = \frac{1}{x^{m/n}} \quad \text{and} \quad \frac{1}{x^{-m/n}} = x^{m/n} \quad \text{where } x \neq 0$$

Self Check 6

Write using positive exponents only and simplify:

a. $16^{-1/4}$ $\frac{1}{2}$

b. $(-27a^3)^{-2/3}$ $\frac{1}{9a^2}$

Now Try **Problems 71, 73, and 75**

EXAMPLE 6 Write each expression using positive exponents only and simplify, if possible: **a.** $64^{-1/2}$ **b.** $(-16)^{-3/4}$ **c.** $(-32x^5)^{-2/5}$ **d.** $\frac{1}{16^{-3/2}}$

Strategy We will use one of the rules $x^{-m/n} = \frac{1}{x^{m/n}}$ or $\frac{1}{x^{-m/n}} = x^{m/n}$ to write the reciprocal of each exponential expression and change the exponent's sign to positive.

WHY If we can produce an equivalent expression having a positive rational exponent, we can use the method of this section to simplify it.

Solution

a. $64^{-1/2} = \dfrac{1}{64^{1/2}} = \dfrac{1}{\sqrt{64}} = \dfrac{1}{8}$

b. $(-16)^{-3/4}$ is not a real number, because $(-16)^{1/4}$ is not a real number.

c. $(-32x^5)^{-2/5} = \dfrac{1}{(-32x^5)^{2/5}} = \dfrac{1}{[(-32x^5)^{1/5}]^2} = \dfrac{1}{\left(\sqrt[5]{-32x^5}\right)^2} = \dfrac{1}{(-2x)^2} = \dfrac{1}{4x^2}$

d. $\dfrac{1}{16^{-3/2}} = 16^{3/2} = (16^{1/2})^3 = \left(\sqrt{16}\right)^3 = 4^3 = 64$

Teaching Example 6 Write each expression using positive exponents only and simplify if possible:
a. $8^{-2/3}$ b. $(-8)^{2/3}$ c. $(-8)^{-2/3}$
d. $-8^{-2/3}$ e. $\dfrac{1}{8^{-2/3}}$
Answers:
a. $\dfrac{1}{4}$ b. 4 c. $\dfrac{1}{4}$ d. $-\dfrac{1}{4}$ e. 4

Caution! By definition, 0^0 is undefined. A base of 0 raised to a negative power is also undefined. For example, 0^{-2} would equal $\frac{1}{0^2}$, which is undefined because we cannot divide by 0.

6 Use rules for exponents to simplify expressions.

We can use the rules for exponents to simplify many expressions with fractional exponents. If all variables represent positive numbers, absolute value symbols are not needed.

EXAMPLE 7 Simplify each expression. All variables represent positive real numbers. Write all answers using positive exponents only.

a. $5^{2/7}5^{3/7}$ b. $(5^{2/7})^3$ c. $(a^{2/3}b^{1/2})^6$ d. $\dfrac{a^{8/3}a^{1/3}}{a^2}$

Strategy We will use the product, power, and quotient rules for exponents to simplify each expression.

WHY The familiar rules for exponents discussed in Chapter 5 are valid for rational exponents.

Solution

a. $5^{2/7}5^{3/7} = 5^{2/7+3/7}$ Use the rule $x^mx^n = x^{m+n}$.
$= 5^{5/7}$ Add: $\frac{2}{7} + \frac{3}{7} = \frac{5}{7}$.

b. $(5^{2/7})^3 = 5^{(2/7)(3)}$ Use the rule $(x^m)^n = x^{mn}$.
$= 5^{6/7}$ Multiply: $\frac{2}{7}(3) = \frac{6}{7}$.

c. $(a^{2/3}b^{1/2})^6 = (a^{2/3})^6(b^{1/2})^6$ Use the rule $(xy)^n = x^ny^n$.
$= a^{12/3}b^{6/2}$ Use the rule $(x^m)^n = x^{mn}$ twice.
$= a^4b^3$ Simplify the exponents.

Self Check 7
Simplify. All variables represent positive numbers.
a. $(x^{1/3}y^{3/2})^6$ x^2y^9
b. $\dfrac{x^{5/3}x^{2/3}}{x^{1/3}}$ x^2

Now Try **Problems 80, 81, 84, and 86**

Teaching Example 7 Simplify. All variables represent positive numbers.
a. $7^{2/9}7^{5/9}$ b. $(7^{1/5})^4$
c. $(x^{1/8}y^{2/3})^{24}$ d. $\dfrac{x^{1/5}x^{7/5}}{x^{3/5}}$
Answers:
a. $7^{7/9}$ b. $7^{4/5}$
c. x^3y^{16} d. x

d. $\dfrac{a^{8/3}a^{1/3}}{a^2} = a^{8/3+1/3-2}$ Use the rules $x^m x^n = x^{m+n}$ and $\frac{x^m}{x^n} = x^{m-n}$.

$= a^{8/3+1/3-6/3}$ $2 = \frac{6}{3}$.

$= a^{3/3}$ $\frac{8}{3} + \frac{1}{3} - \frac{6}{3} = \frac{3}{3}$.

$= a$ $\frac{3}{3} = 1$.

Self Check 8

Simplify. All variables represent positive numbers. Write all answers using positive exponents only.

a. $x^{2/7}(x^{4/7} + x^{5/7})$ $x^{6/7} + x$

b. $x^{1/3}(x^{-1/3} - 2x^{1/3})$ $1 - 2x^{2/3}$

Now Try **Problems 88 and 90**

Teaching Example 8 Simplify. All variables represent positive numbers. Write all answers using positive exponents only.

a. $x^{1/4}(x^{1/4} - x^{3/4})$

b. $x^{5/8}(x^{3/8} + x^{-5/8})$

Answers:

a. $x^{1/2} - x$ b. $x + 1$

EXAMPLE 8 Assume that all variables represent positive numbers, and perform the operations. Write all answers using positive exponents only.

a. $a^{4/5}(a^{1/5} + a^{3/5})$ **b.** $x^{1/2}(x^{-1/2} + x^{1/2})$

Strategy We will use the distributive property and multiply each term within the parentheses by the term outside the parentheses.

WHY Then each expression has the form $a(b + c)$.

Solution

a. $a^{4/5}(a^{1/5} + a^{3/5}) = a^{4/5}a^{1/5} + a^{4/5}a^{3/5}$ Use the distributive property.

$= a^{4/5+1/5} + a^{4/5+3/5}$ Use the rule $x^m x^n = x^{m+n}$.

$= a^{5/5} + a^{7/5}$ Simplify the exponents.

$= a + a^{7/5}$ We cannot add these terms because they are not like terms.

b. $x^{1/2}(x^{-1/2} + x^{1/2}) = x^{1/2}x^{-1/2} + x^{1/2}x^{1/2}$ Use the distributive property.

$= x^{1/2+(-1/2)} + x^{1/2+1/2}$ Use the rule $x^m x^n = x^{m+n}$.

$= x^0 + x^1$ Simplify each exponent.

$= 1 + x$ $x^0 = 1$.

7 Simplify radical expressions.

We can simplify many radical expressions by using the following steps.

Using Rational Exponents to Simplify Radicals

1. Change the radical expression into an exponential expression.
2. Simplify the rational exponents.
3. Change the exponential expression back into a radical.

Self Check 9

Simplify:

a. $\sqrt[6]{3^3}$ $\sqrt{3}$

b. $\sqrt[4]{64x^2y^2}$ $\sqrt{8xy}$

c. $\sqrt[3]{\sqrt[4]{m}}$ $\sqrt[12]{m}$

Now Try **Problems 92 and 94**

Teaching Example 9 Simplify:

a. $\sqrt[15]{2^3}$ b. $\sqrt[21]{x^7y^{14}}$ c. $\sqrt[6]{\sqrt[3]{x}}$

Answers:

a. $\sqrt[5]{2}$ b. $\sqrt[3]{xy^2}$ c. $\sqrt[18]{x}$

EXAMPLE 9 Simplify: **a.** $\sqrt[4]{3^2}$ **b.** $\sqrt[8]{x^6}$ **c.** $\sqrt[9]{27x^6y^3}$ **d.** $\sqrt[5]{\sqrt[3]{t}}$

Strategy We will write each radical expression as an equivalent exponential expression and use rules for exponents to simplify it. Then we will change that result back into a radical.

WHY When the given expression is written in an equivalent exponential form, we can use rules for exponents and our arithmetic skills with fractions to simplify the exponents.

Solution

a. $\sqrt[4]{3^2} = (3^2)^{1/4}$ Change the radical to an exponential expression.

$= 3^{2/4}$ Use the rule $(x^m)^n = x^{mn}$.

$= 3^{1/2}$ Simplify the fractional exponent: $\frac{2}{4} = \frac{1}{2}$.

$= \sqrt{3}$ Change back to radical form.

b. $\sqrt[8]{x^6} = (x^6)^{1/8}$ Change the radical to an exponential expression.
$= x^{6/8}$ Use the rule $(x^m)^n = x^{mn}$.
$= x^{3/4}$ Simplify the fractional exponent: $\frac{6}{8} = \frac{3}{4}$.
$= (x^3)^{1/4}$ Write $\frac{3}{4}$ as $3\left(\frac{1}{4}\right)$.
$= \sqrt[4]{x^3}$ Change back to radical form.

c. $\sqrt[9]{27x^6y^3} = (3^3x^6y^3)^{1/9}$ Write 27 as 3^3 and change the radical to an exponential expression.
$= 3^{3/9}x^{6/9}y^{3/9}$ Raise each factor to the $\frac{1}{9}$ power by multiplying the fractional exponents.
$= 3^{1/3}x^{2/3}y^{1/3}$ Simplify each fractional exponent.
$= (3x^2y)^{1/3}$ Use the rule $(xy)^n = x^ny^n$.
$= \sqrt[3]{3x^2y}$ Change back to radical form.

d. $\sqrt[5]{\sqrt[3]{t}} = \sqrt[5]{t^{1/3}}$ Change the radical $\sqrt[3]{t}$ to exponential notation.
$= (t^{1/3})^{1/5}$ Change the radical $\sqrt[5]{t^{1/3}}$ to exponential notation.
$= t^{1/15}$ Use the rule $(x^m)^n = x^{mn}$. Multiply: $\frac{1}{3} \cdot \frac{1}{5} = \frac{1}{15}$.
$= \sqrt[15]{t}$ Change back to radical form.

ANSWERS TO SELF CHECKS

1. a. 4 **b.** $-\frac{3}{2}$ **c.** $-\sqrt[4]{6x^3}$ **2.** $(7ab)^{1/6}$ **3.** $\sigma = \sqrt{\frac{\Sigma(x-\mu)^2}{N}}$ **4. a.** $5|a|$ **b.** b^2 **5. a.** 64 **b.** $9x^4$ **6. a.** $\frac{1}{2}$ **b.** $\frac{1}{9a^2}$ **7. a.** x^2y^9 **b.** x^2 **8. a.** $x^{6/7} + x$ **b.** $1 - 2x^{2/3}$ **9. a.** $\sqrt{3}$ **b.** $\sqrt{8xy}$ **c.** $\sqrt[12]{m}$

SECTION 8.2 STUDY SET

VOCABULARY

Fill in the blanks.

1. The expressions $4^{1/2}$ and $(-8)^{-2/3}$ have rational (or fractional) exponents.
2. In the exponential expression $27^{4/3}$, 27 is the base, and 4/3 is the exponent.
3. In the radical expression $\sqrt[3]{4{,}096x^{12}}$, 3 is the index, and $4{,}096x^{12}$ is the radicand.
4. $32^{4/5}$ means the fourth power of the fifth root of 32.

CONCEPTS

5. Complete the table by writing the given expression in the alternate form.

Radical form	Exponential form
$\sqrt[5]{25}$	$25^{1/5}$
$(\sqrt[3]{-27})^2$	$(-27)^{2/3}$
$(\sqrt[4]{16})^{-3}$	$16^{-3/4}$
$(\sqrt{81})^3$	$81^{3/2}$
$-\sqrt{\frac{9}{64}}$	$-\left(\frac{9}{64}\right)^{1/2}$

6. Explain the two rules for rational exponents illustrated in the diagrams below.

a. $(-32)^{1/5} = \sqrt[5]{-32}$
The denominator of the rational exponent indicates that we are to find the 5th root of the base.

b. $125^{4/3} = \left(\sqrt[3]{125}\right)^4$
The denominator of the rational exponent indicates that we are to find the cube root of the base. The numerator indicates that we are to find the 4th power of the cube root.

7. Graph each number on the number line.

$$\left\{8^{2/3}, (-125)^{1/3}, -16^{-1/4}, 4^{3/2}, -\left(\frac{9}{100}\right)^{-1/2}\right\}$$

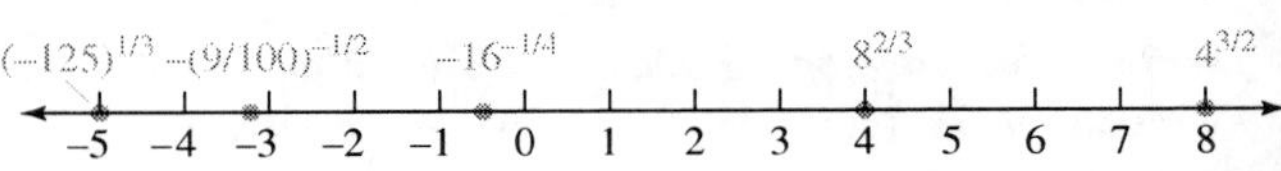

Selected exercises available online at www.webassign.net/brookscole

▶ **8.** Evaluate $25^{3/2}$ in two ways. Which way is easier?
125. The easier way is to compute the root first, and then find the power. We can also find the power first, and then find the root.

Complete each rule for exponents.

9. $x^m x^n = x^{m+n}$ **10.** $(x^m)^n = x^{mn}$

11. $\dfrac{x^m}{x^n} = x^{m-n}$ ▶ **12.** $x^{-n} = \dfrac{1}{x^n}$

13. $x^{1/n} = \sqrt[n]{x}$ **14.** $x^{m/n} = \left(\sqrt[n]{x}\right)^m = \sqrt[n]{x^m}$

Complete each table and graph the function.

15. $f(x) = x^{1/2}$

x	f(x)
0	0
1	1
4	2
9	3
16	4

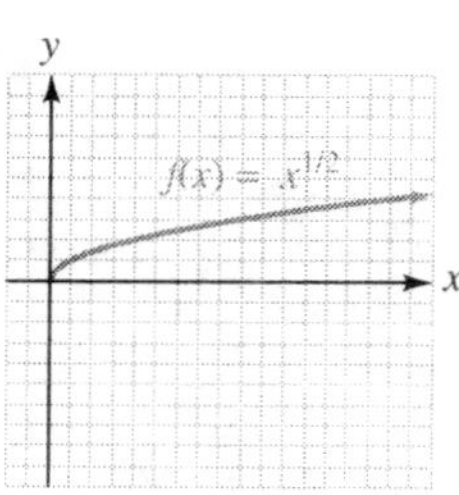

16. $f(x) = x^{1/3}$

x	f(x)
−8	−2
−1	−1
0	0
1	1
8	2

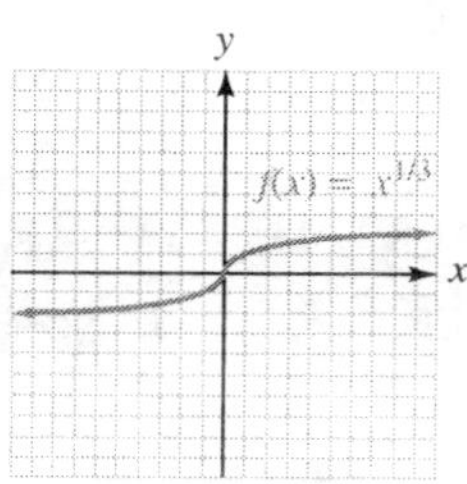

NOTATION

Complete each solution.

17. $(100a^4)^{3/2} = \left(\sqrt{100a^4}\right)^3$
$= \left(10a^2\right)^3$
$= 1{,}000a^6$

▶ **18.** $(m^{1/3}n^{1/2})^6 = (m^{1/3})^6(n^{1/2})^6$
$= m^{6/3}n^{6/2}$
$= m^2n^3$

GUIDED PRACTICE

Write each expression in radical form and simplify. Assume all variables represent positive numbers. See Example 1.

19. $4^{1/2}$ 2 **20.** $25^{1/2}$ 5

21. $\left(\dfrac{1}{16}\right)^{1/2}$ $\frac{1}{4}$ **22.** $-\left(\dfrac{1}{4}\right)^{1/2}$ $-\frac{1}{2}$

23. $(-27)^{1/3}$ −3 **24.** $(-125)^{1/3}$ −5

▶ **25.** $81^{1/4}$ 3 ▶ **26.** $625^{1/4}$ 5

27. $\left(\dfrac{1}{16}\right)^{1/4}$ $\frac{1}{2}$ **28.** $\left(\dfrac{1}{10{,}000}\right)^{1/4}$ $\frac{1}{10}$

29. $32^{1/5}$ 2 **30.** $\left(\dfrac{32}{243}\right)^{1/5}$ $\frac{2}{3}$

31. $0^{1/7}$ 0 ▶ **32.** $b^{1/2}$ $\sqrt{b}$

33. $-(3p^2)^{1/3}$ $-\sqrt[3]{3p^2}$ **34.** $-(5q^3)^{1/4}$ $-\sqrt[4]{5q^3}$

Write each radical as an exponential expression with a rational exponent. See Example 2.

35. $\sqrt{m}$ $m^{1/2}$ **36.** $\sqrt[3]{r}$ $r^{1/3}$

37. $\sqrt[4]{3a}$ $(3a)^{1/4}$ ▶ **38.** $3\sqrt[5]{a}$ $3a^{1/5}$

39. $\sqrt[6]{\dfrac{1}{7}abc}$ $\left(\frac{1}{7}abc\right)^{1/6}$ **40.** $\sqrt[7]{\dfrac{3}{8}p^2q}$ $\left(\frac{3}{8}p^2q\right)^{1/7}$

41. $\sqrt[3]{a^2 - b^2}$ $(a^2 - b^2)^{1/3}$ **42.** $\sqrt{x^2 + y^2}$ $(x^2 + y^2)^{1/2}$

Write each expression using a radical. See Example 3.

43. $c = (a^2 + b^2)^{1/2}$ $c = \sqrt{a^2 + b^2}$ **44.** $v = (2gh)^{1/2}$ $v = \sqrt{2gh}$

45. $d = \left(\dfrac{12V}{\pi}\right)^{1/3}$ $d = \sqrt[3]{\dfrac{12V}{\pi}}$ ▶ **46.** $r = \left(\dfrac{A}{P}\right)^{1/3} - 1$ $r = \sqrt[3]{\dfrac{A}{P}} - 1$

Simplify each expression, if possible. Assume all variables are unrestricted and use absolute value symbols when necessary. See Example 4.

47. $(25y^2)^{1/2}$ $5|y|$ ▶ **48.** $(-27x^3)^{1/3}$ $-3x$

49. $(16x^4)^{1/4}$ $2|x|$ **50.** $(-16x^4)^{1/2}$ not real

51. $(243x^5)^{1/5}$ $3x$ **52.** $[(x + 1)^4]^{1/4}$ $|x + 1|$

53. $(-64x^8)^{1/4}$ not real **54.** $[(x + 5)^3]^{1/3}$ $x + 5$

Simplify each expression. Assume all variables represent positive numbers. See Example 5.

55. $36^{3/2}$ 216 **56.** $27^{2/3}$ 9

57. $81^{3/4}$ 27 **58.** $100^{3/2}$ 1,000

59. $144^{3/2}$ 1,728 **60.** $1{,}000^{2/3}$ 100

61. $\left(\dfrac{1}{8}\right)^{2/3}$ $\frac{1}{4}$ ▶ **62.** $\left(\dfrac{4}{9}\right)^{3/2}$ $\frac{8}{27}$

63. $(25x^4)^{3/2}$ $125x^6$ **64.** $(27a^3b^3)^{2/3}$ $9a^2b^2$

65. $\left(\dfrac{8x^3}{27}\right)^{2/3}$ $\frac{4x^2}{9}$ **66.** $\left(-\dfrac{27}{64y^6}\right)^{2/3}$ $\frac{9}{16y^4}$

Write each expression without using negative exponents, if possible. Assume all variables represent positive numbers. See Example 6.

67. $4^{-1/2}$ $\frac{1}{2}$ **68.** $8^{-1/3}$ $\frac{1}{2}$

69. $(-81)^{-3/4}$ not a real number

70. $(-8x^3)^{-2/3}$ $\frac{1}{4x^2}$

71. $4^{-3/2}$ $\frac{1}{8}$

72. $25^{-5/2}$ $\frac{1}{3{,}125}$

73. $(16x^2)^{-3/2}$ $\frac{1}{64x^3}$

▶ 74. $(81c^4)^{-3/2}$ $\frac{1}{729c^6}$

75. $\frac{1}{8^{-2/3}}$ 4

76. $\frac{1}{32^{-3/5}}$ 8

77. $\frac{1}{(16x^2)^{-3/2}}$ $64x^3$

78. $\frac{1}{(27y^3)^{-2/3}}$ $9y^2$

Perform the operations. Write the answers without negative exponents. Assume all variables represent positive numbers. See Example 7.

79. $5^{3/7}5^{2/7}$ $5^{5/7}$

80. $4^{2/5}4^{2/5}$ $4^{4/5}$

81. $(4^{1/5})^3$ $4^{3/5}$

82. $(3^{1/3})^5$ $3^{5/3}$

83. $(a^{1/2}b^{1/3})^{3/2}$ $a^{3/4}b^{1/2}$

▶ 84. $(mn^{-2/3})^{-3/5}$ $\frac{n^{2/5}}{m^{3/5}}$

85. $\frac{b^{4/3}b^{1/3}}{b^{2/3}}$ b

86. $\frac{c^{5/6}c^{1/3}}{c^{1/2}}$ $c^{2/3}$

Perform the multiplications. Assume all variables represent positive numbers. See Example 8.

87. $y^{1/3}(y^{2/3} + y^{5/3})$ $y + y^2$

▶ 88. $y^{2/5}(y^{-2/5} + y^{3/5})$ $1 + y$

89. $x^{3/5}(x^{7/5} - x^{2/5} + 1)$ $x^2 - x + x^{3/5}$

▶ 90. $x^{4/3}(x^{2/3} + 3x^{5/3} - 4)$ $x^2 + 3x^3 - 4x^{4/3}$

Use rational exponents to simplify each radical. Assume all variables represent positive numbers. See Example 9.

91. $\sqrt[6]{p^3}$ $\sqrt{p}$

92. $\sqrt[8]{q^2}$ $\sqrt[4]{q}$

93. $\sqrt[4]{25b^2}$ $\sqrt{5b}$

▶ 94. $\sqrt[9]{-8x^6}$ $-\sqrt[3]{2x^2}$

TRY IT YOURSELF

Simplify each expression, if possible. Assume all variables represent positive numbers.

95. $125^{1/3}$ 5

96. $8^{1/3}$ 2

97. $32^{1/5}$ 2

98. $0^{1/5}$ 0

99. $-16^{1/4}$ -2

100. $-125^{1/3}$ -5

101. $(-64)^{1/2}$ not real

102. $(-216)^{1/2}$ not real

103. $(-27y^3)^{-2/3}$ $\frac{1}{9y^2}$

▶ 104. $(-8z^9)^{-2/3}$ $\frac{1}{4z^6}$

105. $\left(\frac{27}{8}\right)^{-4/3}$ $\frac{16}{81}$

106. $\left(\frac{25}{49}\right)^{-3/2}$ $\frac{343}{125}$

107. $\left(-\frac{8x^3}{27}\right)^{-1/3}$ $-\frac{3}{2x}$

108. $\left(\frac{16}{81y^4}\right)^{-3/4}$ $\frac{27y^3}{8}$

Write each expression using a radical.

109. $(3x)^{1/4}$ $\sqrt[4]{3x}$

110. $(5ab)^{1/6}$ $\sqrt[6]{5ab}$

111. $(17x^3y)^{1/4}$ $\sqrt[4]{17x^3y}$

112. $(34a^2b^2)^{1/5}$ $\sqrt[5]{34a^2b^2}$

113. $(x^2 + y^2)^{1/2}$ $\sqrt{x^2 + y^2}$

114. $(x^3 + y^3)^{1/3}$ $\sqrt[3]{x^3 + y^3}$

Use a calculator to evaluate each expression. Round to the nearest hundredth.

115. $\sqrt[3]{15}$ 2.47

116. $\sqrt[4]{50.5}$ 2.67

117. $\sqrt[5]{1.045}$ 1.01

118. $\sqrt[5]{-1{,}000}$ -3.98

Simplify each expression. Assume all variables represent positive numbers.

119. $\frac{9^{4/5}}{9^{3/5}}$ $9^{1/5}$

120. $\frac{7^{2/3}}{7^{1/2}}$ $7^{1/6}$

121. $6^{-2/3}6^{-4/3}$ $\frac{1}{36}$

122. $5^{1/3}5^{-5/3}$ $\frac{1}{5^{4/3}}$

123. $a^{2/3}a^{1/3}$ a

▶ 124. $b^{3/5}b^{1/5}$ $b^{4/5}$

125. $(a^{2/3})^{1/3}$ $a^{2/9}$

126. $(t^{4/5})^{10}$ t^8

127. $\frac{(4x^3y)^{1/2}}{(9xy)^{1/2}}$ $\frac{2x}{3}$

128. $\frac{(27x^3y)^{1/3}}{(8xy^2)^{2/3}}$ $\frac{3x^{1/3}}{4y}$

129. $(27x^{-3})^{-1/3}$ $\frac{1}{3}x$

130. $(16a^{-2})^{-1/2}$ $\frac{1}{4}a$

131. $(2x^2y^{-1/4})^3(8y^{-2})^{2/3}$ $\frac{32x^6}{y^{25/12}}$

132. $(27a^3b)^{-1/3}(9a^{-2}b^2)^{-1/2}$ $\frac{1}{9b^{4/3}}$

APPLICATIONS

▶ 133. BALLISTIC PENDULUMS See the illustration in the next column. The formula

$$v = \frac{m + M}{m}(2gh)^{1/2}$$

gives the velocity (in ft/sec) of a bullet with weight m fired into a block with weight M, that raises the height of the block h feet after the collision. The letter g represents the constant, 32. Find the velocity of the bullet to the nearest ft/sec. 736 ft/sec

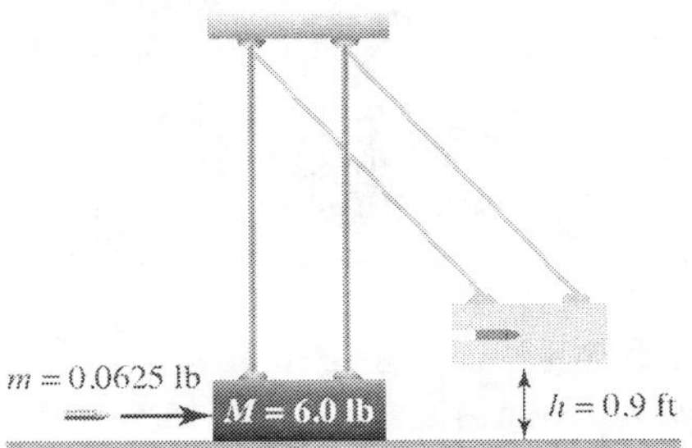

134. GEOGRAPHY The formula

$$A = [s(s - a)(s - b)(s - c)]^{1/2}$$

gives the area of a triangle with sides of length a, b, and c, where s is one-half of the perimeter. Estimate the area of Virginia (to the nearest square mile) using the data given below. 40,700 mi^2

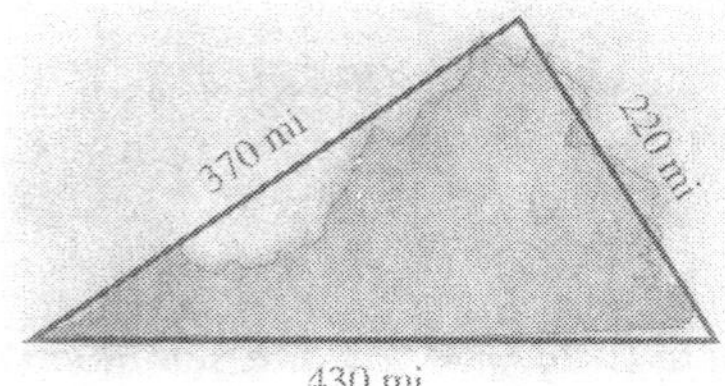

135. RELATIVITY One of the concepts of relativity theory is that an object moving past an observer at a speed near the speed of light appears to have a larger mass because of its motion. If the mass of the object is m_0 when the object is at rest relative to the observer, its mass m will be given by the formula

$$m = m_0\left(1 - \frac{v^2}{c^2}\right)^{-1/2}$$

when it is moving with speed v (in miles per second) past the observer. The letter c is the speed of light, 186,000 mi/sec. If a proton with a rest mass of 1 unit is accelerated by a nuclear accelerator to a speed of 160,000 mi/sec, what mass will the technicians observe it to have? Round to the nearest hundredth. 1.96 units

136. LOGGING The width w and height h of the strongest rectangular beam that can be cut from a cylindrical log of radius a are given by

$$w = \frac{2a}{3}(3^{1/2}) \quad h = a\left(\frac{8}{3}\right)^{1/2}$$

Find the width, height, and cross-sectional area of the strongest beam that can be cut from a log with *diameter* 4 feet. Round to the nearest hundredth. 2.31 ft, 3.27 ft, 7.55 ft²

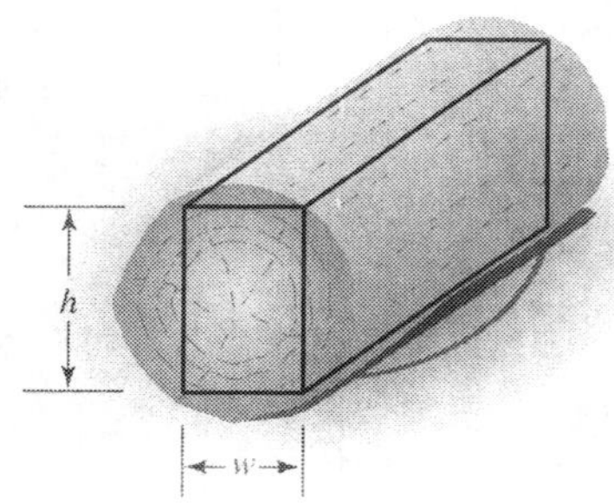

137. CUBICLES The area of the base of a cube is given by the function $A(V) = V^{2/3}$, where V is the volume of the cube. In a preschool room, 18 children's cubicles like that shown are placed on the floor around the room. Estimate how much floor space is lost to the cubicles. Give your answer in square inches and in square feet. 4,608 in.², 32 ft²

138. The length L of the longest board that can be carried horizontally around the right-angle corner of two intersecting hallways is given by the formula

from Campus to Careers
General Contractor

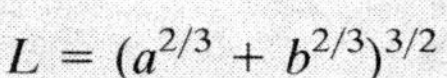

$$L = (a^{2/3} + b^{2/3})^{3/2}$$

where a and b represent the widths of the hallways. Find the longest shelf that a carpenter can carry around the corner if $a = 40$ in. and $b = 64$ in. Give your result in inches and in feet. In each case, round to the nearest tenth. 145.8 in. or 12.1 ft

WRITING

139. What is a rational exponent? Give some examples.

140. Explain how the root key $\boxed{\sqrt[x]{y}}$ on a scientific calculator can be used in combination with other keys to evaluate the expression $16^{3/4}$.

REVIEW

Solve each inequality. Write the solution set using interval notation.

141. $5x - 4 < 11$ $(-\infty, 3)$

142. $-2(3t - 5) \geq 8$ $\left(-\infty, \frac{1}{3}\right]$

143. $\frac{4}{5}(r - 3) > \frac{2}{3}(r + 2)$ $(28, \infty)$

144. $-4 < 2x - 4 \leq 8$ $(0, 6]$

SECTION 8.3

Simplifying and Combining Radical Expressions and Rational Expressions

Objectives

1. Use the product rule to simplify radical expressions.
2. Use prime factorization to simplify radical expressions.
3. Use the quotient rule to simplify radical expressions.
4. Add and subtract radical expressions.

In algebra, it is often helpful to replace an expression with a simpler equivalent expression. This is certainly true when working with radicals. In most cases, radical expressions should be written in simplified form. We use two rules for radicals to do this.

1 Use the product rule to simplify radical expressions.

To introduce the product rule for radicals, we will find $\sqrt{4 \cdot 25}$ and $\sqrt{4}\sqrt{25}$ and compare the results.

Square root of a product	**Product of square roots**	
$\sqrt{4 \cdot 25} = \sqrt{100}$	$\sqrt{4}\sqrt{25} = 2 \cdot 5$	Read as "the square root of 4 times the square root of 25."
$= 10$	$= 10$	

In each case, the answer is 10. Thus, $\sqrt{4 \cdot 25} = \sqrt{4}\sqrt{25}$. Likewise,

$$\sqrt[3]{8 \cdot 27} = \sqrt[3]{216} = 6 \qquad \sqrt[3]{8}\sqrt[3]{27} = 2 \cdot 3 = 6$$

In each case, the answer is 6. Thus, $\sqrt[3]{8 \cdot 27} = \sqrt[3]{8}\sqrt[3]{27}$. These results illustrate the **multiplication property of radicals.**

The Product Rule for Radicals

The nth root of the product of two numbers is equal to the product of their nth roots.

If $\sqrt[n]{a}$ and $\sqrt[n]{b}$ represent real numbers, then

$$\sqrt[n]{ab} = \sqrt[n]{a}\sqrt[n]{b}$$

As long as all radical expressions represent real numbers, *the nth root of the product of two numbers is equal to the product of their nth roots.*

Caution! The multiplication property of radicals applies to the nth root of the product of two numbers. There is no such property for sums or differences. For example,

$$\sqrt{9+4} \neq \sqrt{9} + \sqrt{4} \qquad \sqrt{9-4} \neq \sqrt{9} - \sqrt{4}$$
$$\sqrt{13} \neq 3 + 2 \qquad \sqrt{5} \neq 3 - 2$$
$$\sqrt{13} \neq 5 \qquad \sqrt{5} \neq 1$$

Thus, $\sqrt{a+b} \neq \sqrt{a} + \sqrt{b}$ and $\sqrt{a-b} \neq \sqrt{a} - \sqrt{b}$.

The product rule for radicals can be used to simplify radical expressions. When a radical expression is written in **simplified form,** each of the following is true.

Simplified Form of a Radical Expression

1. Each factor in the radicand is to a power that is less than the index of the radical.
2. The radicand contains no fractions or negative numbers.
3. No radicals appear in the denominator of a fraction.

To simplify radical expressions, we must often factor the radicand using two natural-number factors. To simplify square-root, cube-root, and fourth-root radicals, it is helpful to memorize the following lists.

Perfect squares: 1, 4, 9, 16, 25, 36, 49, 64, 81, 100, 121, 144, 169, 196, 225, ...
Perfect cubes: 1, 8, 27, 64, 125, 216, 343, 512, 729, 1,000, ...
Perfect-fourth powers: 1, 16, 81, 256, 625, ...

Self Check 1

Simplify:

a. $\sqrt{20}$ $2\sqrt{5}$
b. $\sqrt[3]{24}$ $2\sqrt[3]{3}$
c. $\sqrt[5]{128}$ $2\sqrt[5]{4}$

Now Try **Problems 14, 16, and 20**

Teaching Example 1 Simplify:
a. $\sqrt{52}$ b. $\sqrt{75}$
c. $\sqrt[3]{72}$ d. $-\sqrt[4]{80}$
Answers:
a. $2\sqrt{13}$ b. $5\sqrt{3}$
c. $2\sqrt[3]{9}$ d. $-2\sqrt[4]{5}$

EXAMPLE 1 Simplify: **a.** $\sqrt{12}$ **b.** $\sqrt{98}$ **c.** $\sqrt[3]{54}$ **d.** $-\sqrt[4]{48}$

Strategy We will factor each radicand into two factors, one of which is a perfect square, perfect cube, or perfect-fourth power, depending on the index of the radical. Then we can use the product rule for radicals to simplify the expression.

WHY Factoring the radicand in this way leads to a square root, cube root, or fourth root of a perfect square, perfect cube, or perfect-fourth power that we can easily simplify.

Solution

a. To simplify $\sqrt{12}$, we first factor 12 so that one factor is the largest perfect square that divides 12. Since 4 is the largest perfect-square factor of 12, we write 12 as $4 \cdot 3$, use the product rule for radicals, and simplify.

$\sqrt{12} = \sqrt{4 \cdot 3}$ Write 12 as $12 = 4 \cdot 3$.
Write the perfect-square factor first.
$= \sqrt{4}\sqrt{3}$ The square root of a product is equal to the product of the square roots.
$= 2\sqrt{3}$ Evaluate $\sqrt{4}$. Read as "2 times the square root of 3" or as "2 radical 3."

We say that $2\sqrt{3}$ is the simplified form of $\sqrt{12}$.

b. The largest perfect-square factor of 98 is 49. Thus,

$\sqrt{98} = \sqrt{49 \cdot 2}$ Write 98 in factored form: $98 = 49 \cdot 2$.
$= \sqrt{49}\sqrt{2}$ The square root of a product is equal to the product of the square roots: $\sqrt{49 \cdot 2} = \sqrt{49}\sqrt{2}$.
$= 7\sqrt{2}$ Evaluate $\sqrt{49}$.

c. Since the largest perfect-cube factor of 54 is 27, we have

$\sqrt[3]{54} = \sqrt[3]{27 \cdot 2}$ Write 54 as $27 \cdot 2$.
$= \sqrt[3]{27}\sqrt[3]{2}$ The cube root of a product is equal to the product of the cube roots: $\sqrt[3]{27 \cdot 2} = \sqrt[3]{27}\sqrt[3]{2}$.
$= 3\sqrt[3]{2}$ Evaluate $\sqrt[3]{27}$.

d. The largest perfect-fourth power factor of 48 is 16. Thus,

$-\sqrt[4]{48} = -\sqrt[4]{16 \cdot 3}$ Write 48 as 16 · 3.

$= -\sqrt[4]{16}\sqrt[4]{3}$ The fourth root of a product is equal to the product of the fourth roots: $\sqrt[4]{16 \cdot 3} = \sqrt[4]{16} \cdot \sqrt[4]{3}$.

$= -2\sqrt[4]{3}$ Evaluate $\sqrt[4]{16}$.

Variable expressions can also be perfect squares, perfect cubes, perfect-fourth powers, and so on. For example, x^4 is a perfect square because it is the square of x^2.

Perfect squares: $x^2, x^4, x^6, x^8, x^{10}, \ldots$

Perfect cubes: $x^3, x^6, x^9, x^{12}, x^{15}, \ldots$

Perfect-fourth powers: $x^4, x^8, x^{12}, x^{16}, x^{20}, \ldots$

EXAMPLE 2 Simplify:

a. $\sqrt{m^9}$ **b.** $\sqrt{128a^5}$ **c.** $\sqrt[3]{-24x^5}$ **d.** $\sqrt[5]{a^9b^5}$

All variables represent positive real numbers.

Strategy We will factor each radicand into two factors, one of which is a perfect *n*th power.

WHY We can then apply the rule *the nth root of a product is the product of the nth roots* to simplify the radical expression.

Solution

a. The largest perfect-square factor of m^9 is m^8.

$\sqrt{m^9} = \sqrt{m^8 \cdot m}$ Write m^9 in factored form as $m^8 \cdot m$.

$= \sqrt{m^8}\sqrt{m}$ Use the product rule for radicals.

$= m^4\sqrt{m}$ Simplify $\sqrt{m^8}$.

b. Since the largest perfect-square factor of 128 is 64 and the largest perfect-square factor of a^5 is a^4, the largest perfect-square factor of $128a^5$ is $64a^4$. We write $128a^5$ as $64a^4 \cdot 2a$ and proceed as follows:

$\sqrt{128a^5} = \sqrt{64a^4 \cdot 2a}$ Write $128a^5$ in factored form as $64a^4 \cdot 2a$.

$= \sqrt{64a^4}\sqrt{2a}$ Use the product rule for radicals.

$= 8a^2\sqrt{2a}$ Simplify $\sqrt{64a^4}$.

c. We write $-24x^5$ as $-8x^3 \cdot 3x^2$ and proceed as follows:

$\sqrt[3]{-24x^5} = \sqrt[3]{-8x^3 \cdot 3x^2}$ $8x^3$ is the largest perfect-cube factor of $24x^5$. Since the radicand is negative, we factor it using $-8x^3$.

$= \sqrt[3]{-8x^3}\sqrt[3]{3x^2}$ Use the product rule for radicals.

$= -2x\sqrt[3]{3x^2}$ Simplify $\sqrt[3]{-8x^3}$.

d. The largest perfect-fifth power factor of a^9 is a^5, and b^5 is a perfect-fifth power.

$\sqrt[5]{a^9b^5} = \sqrt[5]{a^5b^5 \cdot a^4}$ a^5b^5 is the largest perfect-fifth power factor of a^9b^5.

$= \sqrt[5]{a^5b^5}\sqrt[5]{a^4}$ Use the product rule for radicals.

$= ab\sqrt[5]{a^4}$ Simplify $\sqrt[5]{a^5b^5}$.

Self Check 2

Simplify. All variables represent positive real numbers.

a. $\sqrt{98b^3}$ $7b\sqrt{2b}$

b. $\sqrt[3]{-54y^5}$ $-3y\sqrt[3]{2y^2}$

c. $\sqrt[4]{t^8u^{15}}$ $t^2u^3\sqrt[4]{u^3}$

Now Try **Problems 22, 28, and 32**

Teaching Example 2 Simplify:
a. $\sqrt{b^{11}}$ b. $\sqrt{125x^7}$ c. $\sqrt[3]{-54x^{11}}$
Answers:
a. $b^5\sqrt{b}$ b. $5x^3\sqrt{5x}$ c. $-3x^3\sqrt[3]{2x^2}$

2 Use prime factorization to simplify radical expressions.

When simplifying radical expressions, prime factorization can be helpful in determining how to factor the radicand.

Self Check 3

Simplify:

a. $\sqrt{275}$ $5\sqrt{11}$

b. $\sqrt[3]{189c^4d^3}$ $3cd\sqrt[3]{7c}$

Now Try **Problems 34, 36, and 39**

Teaching Example 3 Simplify. All variables represent positive real numbers.

a. $\sqrt{63}$ b. $\sqrt[3]{-162x^5}$

c. $\sqrt[4]{162x^5y^{11}}$

Answers:

a. $3\sqrt{7}$ b. $-3x\sqrt[3]{6x^2}$

c. $3xy^2\sqrt[4]{2xy^3}$

EXAMPLE 3 Simplify. All variables represent positive real numbers.

a. $\sqrt{150}$ **b.** $\sqrt[3]{297b^4}$ **c.** $\sqrt[4]{224s^8t^7}$

Strategy In each case, the way to factor the radicand is not obvious. Another approach is to prime-factor the coefficient of the radicand and look for groups of like factors.

WHY Identifying groups of like factors of the radicand leads to a factorization of the radicand that can be easily simplified.

Solution

a.

$\sqrt{150} = \sqrt{2 \cdot 3 \cdot 5 \cdot 5}$ Write 150 in prime-factored form.

$= \sqrt{2 \cdot 3}\sqrt{5 \cdot 5}$ Group the pair of like factors together and use the product rule for radicals.

$= \sqrt{2 \cdot 3}\sqrt{5^2}$ Write $5 \cdot 5$ as 5^2.

$= \sqrt{6} \cdot 5$ Evaluate $\sqrt{5^2}$.

$= 5\sqrt{6}$ Write the factor 5 first.

b.

$\sqrt[3]{297b^4} = \sqrt[3]{3 \cdot 3 \cdot 3 \cdot 11 \cdot b^3 \cdot b}$ Write 297 in prime-factored form. The largest perfect-cube factor of b^4 is b^3.

$= \sqrt[3]{3 \cdot 3 \cdot 3 \cdot b^3}\sqrt[3]{11b}$ Group the three like factors of 3 together and use the product rule for radicals.

$= \sqrt[3]{3^3b^3}\sqrt[3]{11b}$ Write $3 \cdot 3 \cdot 3$ as 3^3.

$= 3b\sqrt[3]{11b}$ Simplify $\sqrt[3]{3^3b^3}$.

c.

$\sqrt[4]{224s^8t^7} = \sqrt[4]{2 \cdot 2 \cdot 2 \cdot 2 \cdot 2 \cdot 7 \cdot s^8 \cdot t^4 \cdot t^3}$ Write 224 in prime-factored form. The largest perfect-fourth power factor of t^7 is t^4.

$= \sqrt[4]{2 \cdot 2 \cdot 2 \cdot 2 \cdot s^8 \cdot t^4}\sqrt[4]{2 \cdot 7 \cdot t^3}$ Group the four like factors of 2 together and use the product rule for radicals.

$= \sqrt[4]{2^4s^8t^4}\sqrt[4]{2 \cdot 7 \cdot t^3}$ Write $2 \cdot 2 \cdot 2 \cdot 2$ as 2^4.

$= 2s^2t\sqrt[4]{14t^3}$ Simplify $\sqrt[4]{2^4s^8t^4}$.

3 Use the quotient rule to simplify radical expressions.

To introduce the second property of radicals, we consider these examples.

Square root of a quotient	**Quotient of square roots**
$\sqrt{\frac{100}{4}} = \sqrt{25}$	$\frac{\sqrt{100}}{\sqrt{4}} = \frac{10}{2}$
$= 5$	$= 5$

Since the answer is 5 in each case, $\sqrt{\frac{100}{4}} = \frac{\sqrt{100}}{\sqrt{4}}$. Likewise,

$\sqrt[3]{\frac{64}{8}} = \sqrt[3]{8}$	$\frac{\sqrt[3]{64}}{\sqrt[3]{8}} = \frac{4}{2}$
$= 2$	$= 2$

Since the answer is 2 in each case, $\sqrt[3]{\frac{64}{8}} = \frac{\sqrt[3]{64}}{\sqrt[3]{8}}$. These results illustrate the **division property of radicals.**

Division Property of Radicals

If $\sqrt[n]{a}$ and $\sqrt[n]{b}$ represent real numbers, then

$$\sqrt[n]{\frac{a}{b}} = \frac{\sqrt[n]{a}}{\sqrt[n]{b}} \quad \text{where } b \neq 0$$

As long as all radical expressions represent real numbers, *the nth root of the quotient of two numbers is equal to the quotient of their nth roots.*

EXAMPLE 4 Simplify: **a.** $\sqrt{\frac{7}{64}}$ **b.** $\sqrt{\frac{15}{49x^2}}$ **c.** $\sqrt[3]{\frac{10x^2}{27y^6}}$

Assume that the variables represent positive real numbers.

Strategy In each case, the radical is not in simplified form because the radicand contains a fraction. To write each of these expressions in simplified form, we will use the quotient rule for radicals.

WHY Writing these expressions in $\frac{\sqrt[n]{a}}{\sqrt[n]{b}}$ form leads to square roots of perfect squares and cube roots of perfect cubes that we can easily simplify.

Solution

a. We can write the square root of the quotient as the quotient of two square roots.

$$\sqrt{\frac{7}{64}} = \frac{\sqrt{7}}{\sqrt{64}}$$ The square root of a quotient is equal to the quotient of the square roots.

$$= \frac{\sqrt{7}}{8}$$ Evaluate: $\sqrt{64} = 8$.

b. $$\sqrt{\frac{15}{49x^2}} = \frac{\sqrt{15}}{\sqrt{49x^2}}$$ The square root of a quotient is equal to the quotient of the square roots.

$$= \frac{\sqrt{15}}{7x}$$ Simplify the denominator: $\sqrt{49x^2} = 7x$.

c. We can write the cube root of the quotient as the quotient of two cube roots. Since $y \neq 0$, we have

$$\sqrt[3]{\frac{10x^2}{27y^6}} = \frac{\sqrt[3]{10x^2}}{\sqrt[3]{27y^6}}$$ The cube root of a quotient is equal to the quotient of cube roots.

$$= \frac{\sqrt[3]{10x^2}}{3y^2}$$ Simplify the denominator.

Self Check 4

Simplify:

a. $\sqrt{\frac{11}{36a^2}}$ $\frac{\sqrt{11}}{6a}$

b. $\sqrt[4]{\frac{a^3}{625y^{12}}}$ $\frac{\sqrt[4]{a^3}}{5y^3}$

Assume that all variables represent positive real numbers.

Now Try **Problems 42 and 46**

Teaching Example 4 Simplify:

a. $\sqrt{\frac{13}{36}}$ b. $\sqrt{\frac{22}{81x^2}}$ c. $\sqrt[3]{\frac{5a^2}{8b^9}}$

Assume that the variables represent positive real numbers.

Answers:

a. $\frac{\sqrt{13}}{6}$ b. $\frac{\sqrt{22}}{9x}$ c. $\frac{\sqrt[3]{5a^2}}{2b^3}$

EXAMPLE 5 Simplify each expression. Assume that all variables represent positive numbers. **a.** $\frac{\sqrt{45xy^2}}{\sqrt{5x}}$ **b.** $\frac{\sqrt[3]{-432x^5}}{\sqrt[3]{8x}}$

Strategy We will use the quotient rule in reverse: $\frac{\sqrt[n]{a}}{\sqrt[n]{b}} = \sqrt[n]{\frac{a}{b}}$.

WHY When the radicands are written under a single radical symbol, the result is a rational expression. Our hope is that the rational expression can be simplified.

Self Check 5

Simplify each expression. Assume that all variables represent positive numbers.

a. $\frac{\sqrt{50ab^2}}{\sqrt{2a}}$ $5b$

b. $\frac{\sqrt[3]{-2{,}000x^5y^3}}{\sqrt[3]{2x}}$ $-10xy\sqrt[3]{x}$

Now Try **Problems 49 and 53**

Teaching Example 5 Simplify each expression. Assume that all variables represent positive numbers.

a. $\dfrac{\sqrt{98x^2y}}{\sqrt{2y}}$ b. $\dfrac{\sqrt[3]{-375x^{11}}}{\sqrt[3]{3x^2}}$

Answers:
a. $7x$ b. $-5x^3$

Solution

a. We can write the quotient of the square roots as the square root of a quotient.

$$\frac{\sqrt{45xy^2}}{\sqrt{5x}} = \sqrt{\frac{45xy^2}{5x}} \quad \text{Use the division property of radicals.}$$
$$= \sqrt{9y^2} \quad \text{Simplify } \tfrac{45xy^2}{5x}.$$
$$= 3y \quad \text{Simplify the radical.}$$

b. We can write the quotient of the cube roots as the cube root of a quotient.

$$\frac{\sqrt[3]{-432x^5}}{\sqrt[3]{8x}} = \sqrt[3]{\frac{-432x^5}{8x}} \quad \text{Use the division property of radicals.}$$
$$= \sqrt[3]{-54x^4} \quad \text{Simplify } \tfrac{-432x^5}{8x}.$$
$$= \sqrt[3]{-27x^3 \cdot 2x} \quad -27x^3 \text{ is the largest perfect cube that divides } -54x^4.$$
$$= \sqrt[3]{-27x^3}\sqrt[3]{2x} \quad \text{Use the multiplication property of radicals.}$$
$$= -3x\sqrt[3]{2x} \quad \text{Simplify: } \sqrt[3]{-27x^3} = -3x.$$

4 Add and subtract radical expressions.

Radical expressions with the same index and the same radicand are called **like** or **similar radicals.** For example, $3\sqrt{2}$ and $2\sqrt{2}$ are like radicals. However,

- $3\sqrt{5}$ and $4\sqrt{2}$ are not like radicals, because the radicands are different.
- $3\sqrt[4]{5}$ and $2\sqrt[3]{5}$ are not like radicals, because the indexes are different.

For a given expression containing two or more radical terms, we should attempt to combine like radicals, if possible. For example, to simplify the expression $3\sqrt{2} + 2\sqrt{2}$, we use the distributive property to factor out $\sqrt{2}$ and simplify.

$$3\sqrt{2} + 2\sqrt{2} = (3 + 2)\sqrt{2}$$
$$= 5\sqrt{2}$$

Radicals with the same index but different radicands can often be written as like radicals. For example, to simplify the expression $\sqrt{27} - \sqrt{12}$, we simplify both radicals first, and then we combine the like radicals.

$$\sqrt{27} - \sqrt{12} = \sqrt{9 \cdot 3} - \sqrt{4 \cdot 3} \quad \text{Write 27 and 12 in factored form.}$$
$$= \sqrt{9}\sqrt{3} - \sqrt{4}\sqrt{3} \quad \text{Use the multiplication property of radicals.}$$
$$= 3\sqrt{3} - 2\sqrt{3} \quad \text{Simplify } \sqrt{9} \text{ and } \sqrt{4}.$$
$$= (3 - 2)\sqrt{3} \quad \text{Factor out } \sqrt{3}.$$
$$= \sqrt{3} \quad 1\sqrt{3} = \sqrt{3}.$$

As the previous examples suggest, we can use the following rule to add or subtract radicals.

Adding and Subtracting Radicals

To add or subtract radicals, simplify each radical expression and combine all like radicals. To add or subtract like radicals, combine the coefficients and keep the common radical.

EXAMPLE 6 Simplify: $2\sqrt{12} - 3\sqrt{48} + 3\sqrt{3}$

Strategy Since the radicals are unlike radicals, we cannot add or subtract them in their current form. However, we will simplify the radicals and hope that like radicals result.

WHY Like radicals can be combined.

Solution
We simplify $2\sqrt{12}$ and $3\sqrt{48}$ separately and then combine like radicals.

$$\begin{aligned} 2\sqrt{12} - 3\sqrt{48} + 3\sqrt{3} &= 2\sqrt{4 \cdot 3} - 3\sqrt{16 \cdot 3} + 3\sqrt{3} \\ &= 2\sqrt{4}\sqrt{3} - 3\sqrt{16}\sqrt{3} + 3\sqrt{3} \\ &= 2(2)\sqrt{3} - 3(4)\sqrt{3} + 3\sqrt{3} \\ &= 4\sqrt{3} - 12\sqrt{3} + 3\sqrt{3} \quad \text{All three expressions have the same index and radicand.} \\ &= (4 - 12 + 3)\sqrt{3} \quad \text{Combine the coefficients of these like radicals and keep } \sqrt{3}. \\ &= -5\sqrt{3} \end{aligned}$$

Self Check 6
Simplify:
$3\sqrt{75} - 2\sqrt{12} + 2\sqrt{48}$ $19\sqrt{3}$

Now Try **Problem 59**

Teaching Example 6 Simplify:
$5\sqrt{50} - 3\sqrt{98} - \sqrt{72}$
Answer:
$-2\sqrt{2}$

EXAMPLE 7 Simplify: $\sqrt[3]{16} - \sqrt[3]{54} + \sqrt[3]{24}$

Strategy Since the radicals are unlike radicals, we cannot add or subtract them in their current form. However, we will simplify the radicals and hope that like radicals result.

WHY Like radicals can be combined.

Solution
We begin by simplifying each radical expression separately:

$$\begin{aligned} \sqrt[3]{16} - \sqrt[3]{54} + \sqrt[3]{24} &= \sqrt[3]{8 \cdot 2} - \sqrt[3]{27 \cdot 2} + \sqrt[3]{8 \cdot 3} \\ &= \sqrt[3]{8}\sqrt[3]{2} - \sqrt[3]{27}\sqrt[3]{2} + \sqrt[3]{8}\sqrt[3]{3} \\ &= 2\sqrt[3]{2} - 3\sqrt[3]{2} + 2\sqrt[3]{3} \end{aligned}$$

Now we combine the two radical expressions that have the same index and radicand.

$$\sqrt[3]{16} - \sqrt[3]{54} + \sqrt[3]{24} = -\sqrt[3]{2} + 2\sqrt[3]{3} \quad 2\sqrt[3]{2} - 3\sqrt[3]{2} = -1\sqrt[3]{2} = -\sqrt[3]{2}.$$

Self Check 7
Simplify: $\sqrt[3]{24} - \sqrt[3]{16} + \sqrt[3]{54}$

Now Try **Problem 70**

Self Check 7 Answer
$2\sqrt[3]{3} + \sqrt[3]{2}$

Teaching Example 7 Simplify:
$\sqrt[3]{40} + 2\sqrt[3]{135} - \sqrt[3]{250}$
Answer:
$8\sqrt[3]{5} - 5\sqrt[3]{2}$

Caution! Even though the radical expressions $-\sqrt[3]{2}$ and $2\sqrt[3]{3}$ in the last line of Example 7 have the same index, we cannot combine them, because their radicands are different. Neither can we combine radical expressions having the same radicand but a different index. For example, the expression $\sqrt[3]{2} + \sqrt[4]{2}$ cannot be simplified.

EXAMPLE 8 Simplify: $\sqrt[3]{16x^4} + \sqrt[3]{54x^4} - \sqrt[3]{-128x^4}$

Strategy Since the radicals are unlike radicals, we cannot add or subtract them in their current form. However, we will simplify the radicals and hope that like radicals result.

Self Check 8
Simplify:
$\sqrt{32x^3} + \sqrt{50x^3} - \sqrt{18x^3}$

Now Try **Problem 77**

Self Check 8 Answer
$6x\sqrt{2x}$

Teaching Example 8 Simplify:
$5\sqrt[4]{48x^7} - 2x\sqrt[4]{3x^3} + \sqrt[4]{243x^7}$
Answer:
$11x\sqrt[4]{3x^3}$

WHY Like radicals can be combined.

Solution

We simplify each radical expression separately, factor out $\sqrt[3]{2x}$, and simplify.

$$\sqrt[3]{16x^4} + \sqrt[3]{54x^4} - \sqrt[3]{-128x^4}$$
$$= \sqrt[3]{8x^3 \cdot 2x} + \sqrt[3]{27x^3 \cdot 2x} - \sqrt[3]{-64x^3 \cdot 2x}$$
$$= \sqrt[3]{8x^3}\sqrt[3]{2x} + \sqrt[3]{27x^3}\sqrt[3]{2x} - \sqrt[3]{-64x^3}\sqrt[3]{2x}$$
$$= 2x\sqrt[3]{2x} + 3x\sqrt[3]{2x} + 4x\sqrt[3]{2x}$$ All three radicals have the same index and radicand.
$$= (2x + 3x + 4x)\sqrt[3]{2x}$$ Combine like radicals.
$$= 9x\sqrt[3]{2x}$$ Within the parentheses, combine like terms.

ANSWERS TO SELF CHECKS

1. a. $2\sqrt{5}$ **b.** $2\sqrt[3]{3}$ **c.** $2\sqrt[5]{4}$ **2. a.** $7b\sqrt{2b}$ **b.** $-3y\sqrt[3]{2y^2}$ **c.** $t^2u^3\sqrt[4]{u^3}$
3. a. $5\sqrt{11}$ **b.** $3cd\sqrt[3]{7c}$ **4. a.** $\frac{\sqrt{11}}{6a}$ **b.** $\frac{\sqrt[4]{a^3}}{5y^3}$ **5. a.** $5b$ **b.** $-10xy\sqrt[3]{x}$
6. $19\sqrt{3}$ **7.** $2\sqrt[3]{3} + \sqrt[3]{2}$ **8.** $6x\sqrt{2x}$

SECTION 8.3 STUDY SET

VOCABULARY

Fill in the blanks.

1. Radical expressions such as $\sqrt[3]{4}$ and $6\sqrt[3]{4}$ with the same index and the same radicand are called like radicals.
2. Numbers such as 1, 4, 9, 16, 25, and 36 are called perfect squares. Numbers such as 1, 8, 27, 64, and 125 are called perfect cubes.
3. The largest perfect-square factor of 27 is 9.
4. "To simplify $\sqrt{24}$" means to write it as $2\sqrt{6}$.

CONCEPTS

Fill in the blanks.

5. $\sqrt[n]{ab} = \sqrt[n]{a}\sqrt[n]{b}$

In words, the *n*th root of the product of two numbers is equal to the product of their *n*th roots.

6. $\sqrt[n]{\frac{a}{b}} = \frac{\sqrt[n]{a}}{\sqrt[n]{b}}$

In words, the *n*th root of the quotient of two numbers is equal to the quotient of their *n*th roots.

7. Consider the expressions $\sqrt{4 \cdot 5}$ and $\sqrt{4}\sqrt{5}$. Which expression is
   a. the square root of a product?
   $\sqrt{4 \cdot 5}$
   b. the product of square roots?
   $\sqrt{4}\sqrt{5}$
   c. How are these two expressions related?
   $\sqrt{4 \cdot 5} = \sqrt{4}\sqrt{5}$
8. Consider the expressions $\frac{\sqrt[3]{a}}{\sqrt[3]{x^2}}$ and $\sqrt[3]{\frac{a}{x^2}}$. Which expression is
   a. the cube root of a quotient?
   $\sqrt[3]{\frac{a}{x^2}}$
   b. the quotient of cube roots?
   $\frac{\sqrt[3]{a}}{\sqrt[3]{x^2}}$
   c. How are these two expressions related?
   $\sqrt[3]{\frac{a}{x^2}} = \frac{\sqrt[3]{a}}{\sqrt[3]{x^2}}$
9. a. Write two radical expressions that have the same radicand but a different index. Can the expressions be added?
   $\sqrt{5}$, $\sqrt[3]{5}$ (answers may vary); no
   b. Write two radical expressions that have the same index but a different radicand. Can the expressions be added?
   $\sqrt{5}$, $\sqrt{6}$ (answers may vary); no

▶ **10.** Explain the mistake.

$$\sqrt[3]{54} = \sqrt[3]{27 + 27}$$
$$= \sqrt[3]{27} + \sqrt[3]{27}$$
$$= 3 + 3$$
$$= 6$$

The second step is incorrect. The cube root of a sum is not equal to the sum of the cube roots.

NOTATION

Complete each solution.

▶ **11.** $\sqrt[3]{32k^4} = \sqrt[3]{8k^3 \cdot 4k}$

$= \sqrt[3]{8k^3}\sqrt[3]{4k}$

$= 2k\sqrt[3]{4k}$

▶ **12.** $\dfrac{\sqrt{80s^2t^4}}{\sqrt{5s^2}} = \sqrt{\dfrac{80s^2t^4}{5s^2}}$

$= \sqrt{16t^4}$

$= 4t^2$

GUIDED PRACTICE

Simplify each expression. See Example 1.

13. $\sqrt{20}$ $2\sqrt{5}$

14. $\sqrt{8}$ $2\sqrt{2}$

15. $-\sqrt{200}$ $-10\sqrt{2}$

16. $-\sqrt{250}$ $-5\sqrt{10}$

17. $\sqrt[3]{80}$ $2\sqrt[3]{10}$

▶ **18.** $\sqrt[3]{270}$ $3\sqrt[3]{10}$

19. $-\sqrt[4]{32}$ $-2\sqrt[4]{2}$

20. $\sqrt[4]{768}$ $4\sqrt[4]{3}$

Simplify each expression. Assume that all variables are positive numbers. See Example 2.

21. $\sqrt{a^7}$ $a^3\sqrt{a}$

22. $\sqrt{b^{11}}$ $b^5\sqrt{b}$

23. $\sqrt{50x^2}$ $5x\sqrt{2}$

▶ **24.** $\sqrt{75a^2}$ $5a\sqrt{3}$

25. $\sqrt{32b}$ $4\sqrt{2b}$

26. $\sqrt{80c}$ $4\sqrt{5c}$

27. $\sqrt[3]{-54x^6}$ $-3x^2\sqrt[3]{2}$

▶ **28.** $-\sqrt[3]{-81a^3}$ $3a\sqrt[3]{3}$

29. $\sqrt[5]{\dfrac{3x^{10}}{32}}$ $\dfrac{x^2\sqrt[5]{3}}{2}$

30. $\sqrt[6]{\dfrac{5x^{18}}{64}}$ $\dfrac{x^3\sqrt[6]{5}}{2}$

31. $\sqrt{175a^2b^3}$ $5ab\sqrt{7b}$

32. $\sqrt{128a^3b^5}$ $8ab^2\sqrt{2ab}$

Simplify each expression. Assume that all variables represent positive numbers. See Example 3.

33. $\sqrt{180}$ $6\sqrt{5}$

34. $\sqrt{112}$ $4\sqrt{7}$

35. $\sqrt[3]{16y^4}$ $2y\sqrt[3]{2y}$

36. $\sqrt[3]{40b^7}$ $2b^2\sqrt[3]{5b}$

37. $-\sqrt{300xy}$ $-10\sqrt{3xy}$

▶ **38.** $\sqrt{200x^2y}$ $10x\sqrt{2y}$

39. $\sqrt[4]{32x^{12}y^5}$ $2x^3y\sqrt[4]{2y}$

40. $\sqrt[5]{64x^{10}y^6}$ $2x^2y\sqrt[5]{2y}$

Simplify each expression. Assume that all variables represent positive numbers. See Example 4.

41. $\sqrt{\dfrac{7}{9}}$ $\dfrac{\sqrt{7}}{3}$

▶ **42.** $\sqrt{\dfrac{3}{4}}$ $\dfrac{\sqrt{3}}{2}$

43. $\sqrt[3]{\dfrac{7}{64}}$ $\dfrac{\sqrt[3]{7}}{4}$

44. $\sqrt[3]{\dfrac{4}{125}}$ $\dfrac{\sqrt[3]{4}}{5}$

45. $\sqrt{\dfrac{z^2}{16x^2}}$ $\dfrac{z}{4x}$

46. $\sqrt{\dfrac{b^4}{64a^8}}$ $\dfrac{b^2}{8a^4}$

47. $\sqrt[4]{\dfrac{5x}{16z^4}}$ $\dfrac{\sqrt[4]{5x}}{2z}$

48. $\sqrt[3]{\dfrac{11a^2}{125b^6}}$ $\dfrac{\sqrt[3]{11a^2}}{5b^2}$

Simplify each expression. Assume that all variables represent positive numbers. See Example 5.

49. $\dfrac{\sqrt{98x^3}}{\sqrt{2x}}$ $7x$

50. $\dfrac{\sqrt{75y^5}}{\sqrt{3y}}$ $5y^2$

51. $\dfrac{\sqrt{180ab^4}}{\sqrt{5ab^2}}$ $6b$

52. $\dfrac{\sqrt{112ab^3}}{\sqrt{7ab}}$ $4b$

53. $\dfrac{\sqrt[3]{96a^5}}{\sqrt[3]{6a}}$ $2a\sqrt[3]{2a}$

▶ **54.** $\dfrac{\sqrt[3]{128y^6}}{\sqrt[3]{8y^2}}$ $2y\sqrt[3]{2y}$

55. $\dfrac{\sqrt[3]{567a^4}}{\sqrt[3]{7a}}$ $3a\sqrt[3]{3}$

56. $\dfrac{\sqrt[3]{972x^7}}{\sqrt[3]{9x}}$ $3x^2\sqrt[3]{4}$

Simplify each expression. See Example 6.

57. $\sqrt{98} - \sqrt{50}$ $2\sqrt{2}$

58. $\sqrt{72} - \sqrt{200}$ $-4\sqrt{2}$

59. $3\sqrt{24} + \sqrt{54}$ $9\sqrt{6}$

▶ **60.** $\sqrt{18} + 2\sqrt{50}$ $13\sqrt{2}$

▶ **61.** $\sqrt{20} + \sqrt{125} - \sqrt{80}$ $3\sqrt{5}$

62. $\sqrt{98} - \sqrt{50} - \sqrt{72}$ $-4\sqrt{2}$

63. $\sqrt{63} + \sqrt{72} - \sqrt{28}$ $\sqrt{7} + 6\sqrt{2}$

64. $\sqrt{80} + \sqrt{45} - \sqrt{27}$ $7\sqrt{5} - 3\sqrt{3}$

Simplify each expression. See Example 7.

65. $\sqrt[3]{32} - \sqrt[3]{108}$ $-\sqrt[3]{4}$

66. $\sqrt[3]{80} - \sqrt[3]{10{,}000}$ $-8\sqrt[3]{10}$

67. $2\sqrt[3]{125} - 5\sqrt[3]{64}$ -10

68. $3\sqrt[3]{27} + 12\sqrt[3]{216}$ 81

69. $2\sqrt[3]{16} - \sqrt[3]{54}$ $\sqrt[3]{2}$

▶ **70.** $2\sqrt[3]{250} - 4\sqrt[3]{5} + \sqrt[3]{16}$ $12\sqrt[3]{2} - 4\sqrt[3]{5}$

71. $\sqrt[4]{48} - \sqrt[4]{243} - \sqrt[4]{768}$ $-5\sqrt[4]{3}$

72. $\sqrt[4]{32} + 5\sqrt[4]{2} - \sqrt[4]{162}$ $4\sqrt[4]{2}$

Simplify each expression. Assume all variables represent positive numbers. See Example 8.

73. $4\sqrt{2x} + 6\sqrt{2x}$ $10\sqrt{2x}$

▶ **74.** $16\sqrt[3]{7y} + 3\sqrt[3]{7y}$ $19\sqrt[3]{7y}$

75. $\sqrt{18t} + \sqrt{300t} - \sqrt{243t}$ $3\sqrt{2t} + \sqrt{3t}$

76. $\sqrt{80m} - \sqrt{128m} + \sqrt{288m}$ $4\sqrt{5m} + 4\sqrt{2m}$

77. $\sqrt[3]{24x} + \sqrt[3]{3x}$ $3\sqrt[3]{3x}$

78. $\sqrt[3]{16y} + \sqrt[3]{128y}$ $6\sqrt[3]{2y}$

79. $\sqrt{50a^2} + 2a\sqrt{8} + 2\sqrt{200a^2}$ $29a\sqrt{2}$

80. $\sqrt[3]{54a^6} - 3\sqrt[3]{16a^6} + 4\sqrt[3]{128a^6}$ $13a^2\sqrt[3]{2}$

TRY IT YOURSELF

Simplify each expression. Assume that all variables represent positive numbers.

81. $\sqrt[7]{m^{19}}$ $m^2\sqrt[7]{m^5}$

82. $\sqrt[5]{a^{14}}$ $a^2\sqrt[5]{a^4}$

83. $\sqrt[3]{a^5b^{16}}$ $ab^5\sqrt[3]{a^2b}$

84. $\sqrt[4]{81x^{12}y^9}$ $3x^3y^2\sqrt[4]{y}$

85. $\sqrt[3]{250}$ $5\sqrt[3]{2}$

86. $\sqrt[5]{96x^{12}}$ $2x^2\sqrt[5]{3x^2}$

87. $\dfrac{\sqrt{500}}{\sqrt{5}}$ 10

88. $\dfrac{\sqrt{128}}{\sqrt{2}}$ 8

89. $\sqrt[3]{-81}$ $-3\sqrt[3]{3}$

90. $\sqrt[3]{-72}$ $-2\sqrt[3]{9}$

91. $\sqrt[5]{96}$ $2\sqrt[5]{3}$

92. $\sqrt[7]{256}$ $2\sqrt[7]{2}$

93. $\sqrt[4]{\dfrac{3}{10{,}000}}$ $\dfrac{\sqrt[4]{3}}{10}$

94. $\sqrt[5]{\dfrac{4}{243}}$ $\dfrac{\sqrt[5]{4}}{3}$

95. $-\sqrt{112a^3}$ $-4a\sqrt{7a}$

96. $\sqrt{147a^5}$ $7a^2\sqrt{3a}$

Simplify and combine like radicals. All variables represent positive numbers.

97. $4\sqrt{2x} + 6\sqrt{2x}$ $10\sqrt{2x}$

98. $6\sqrt[3]{5y} + 3\sqrt[3]{5y}$ $9\sqrt[3]{5y}$

99. $8\sqrt[5]{7a^2} - 7\sqrt[5]{7a^2}$ $\sqrt[5]{7a^2}$

100. $10\sqrt[6]{12xyz} - \sqrt[6]{12xyz}$ $9\sqrt[6]{12xyz}$

101. $\sqrt{2} - \sqrt{8}$ $-\sqrt{2}$

102. $\sqrt{20} - \sqrt{125}$ $-3\sqrt{5}$

103. $14\sqrt[4]{32} - 15\sqrt[4]{162}$ $-17\sqrt[4]{2}$

104. $23\sqrt[4]{768} + \sqrt[4]{48}$ $94\sqrt[4]{3}$

105. $3\sqrt[4]{512} + 2\sqrt[4]{32}$ $16\sqrt[4]{2}$

106. $4\sqrt[4]{243} - \sqrt[4]{48}$ $10\sqrt[4]{3}$

107. $\sqrt{25y^2z} - \sqrt{16y^2z}$ $y\sqrt{z}$

108. $\sqrt{25yz^2} + \sqrt{9yz^2}$ $8z\sqrt{y}$

109. $\sqrt{36xy^2} + \sqrt{49xy^2}$ $13y\sqrt{x}$

110. $3\sqrt{2x} - \sqrt{8x}$ $\sqrt{2x}$

111. $2\sqrt[3]{64a} + 2\sqrt[3]{8a}$ $12\sqrt[3]{a}$

112. $3\sqrt[4]{x^4y} - 2\sqrt[4]{x^4y}$ $x\sqrt[4]{y}$

113. $\sqrt{y^5} - \sqrt{9y^5} - \sqrt{25y^5}$ $-7y^2\sqrt{y}$

114. $\sqrt{8y^7} + \sqrt{32y^7} - \sqrt{2y^7}$ $5y^3\sqrt{2y}$

115. $-2\sqrt[5]{x^6y^2} - \sqrt[5]{32x^6y^2} + \sqrt[5]{x^6y^2}$ $-3x\sqrt[5]{xy^2}$

116. $\sqrt[3]{xy^4} + \sqrt[3]{8xy^4} - \sqrt[3]{27xy^4}$ 0

117. $\sqrt{18t} + \sqrt{300t} - \sqrt{243t}$ $3\sqrt{2t} + \sqrt{3t}$

118. $\sqrt{80m} - \sqrt{128m} + \sqrt{288m}$ $4\sqrt{5m} + 4\sqrt{2m}$

APPLICATIONS

First give the exact answer, expressed as a simplified radical expression. Then give an approximation, rounded to the nearest tenth.

119. UMBRELLAS The surface area of a cone is given by the formula $S = \pi r\sqrt{r^2 + h^2}$, where r is the radius of the base and h is its height. Use this formula to find the number of square feet of waterproof cloth used to make the umbrella. $8\pi\sqrt{5}$ ft²; 56.2 ft²

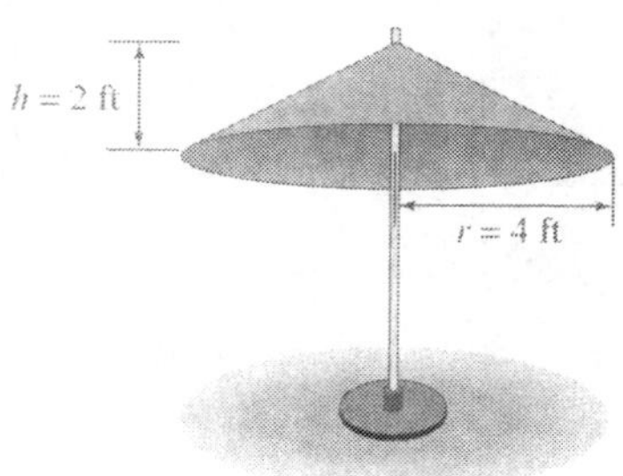

120. STRUCTURAL ENGINEERING Engineers have determined that two additional supports need to be added to strengthen a truss. Find the length L of each new support using the formula

$$L = \sqrt{\frac{b^2}{2} + \frac{c^2}{2} - \frac{a^2}{4}}$$ $3\sqrt{14}$ ft; 11.2 ft

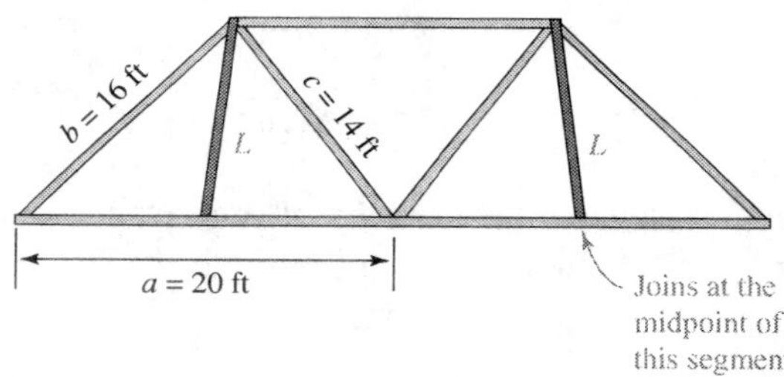

121. BLOW DRYERS The current I (in amps), the power P (in watts), and the resistance R (in ohms) are related by the formula $I = \sqrt{\frac{P}{R}}$. What current is needed for a 1,200-watt hair dryer if the resistance is 16 ohms? $5\sqrt{3}$ amps; 8.7 amps

122. SATELLITES Engineers have determined that a spherical communications satellite needs to have a capacity of 565.2 cubic feet to house all of its operating systems. The volume V of a sphere is related to its radius r by the formula $r = \sqrt[3]{\frac{3V}{4\pi}}$. What radius must the satellite have to meet the engineer's specification? Use 3.14 for π. $3\sqrt[3]{5}$ ft; 5.1 ft

123. DUCTWORK The pattern shown below is laid out on a sheet of galvanized tin. Then it is cut out with snips and bent along the dotted lines to make an air conditioning duct connection. Find the total length of the cut that must be made with the tin snips. (All measurements are in inches.) $(26\sqrt{5} + 10\sqrt{3})$ in.; 75.5 in.

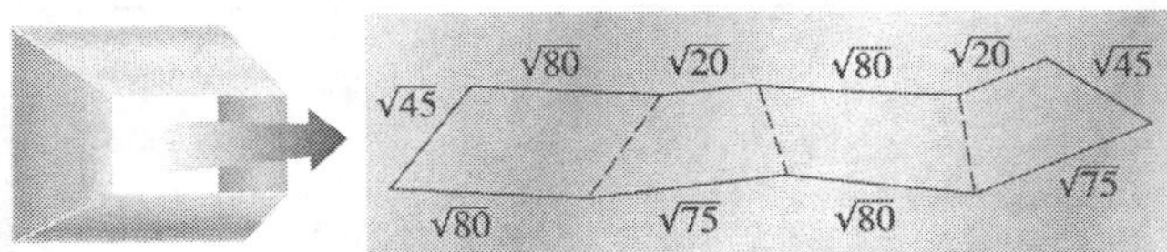

124. OUTDOOR COOKING The diameter of a circle is given by the function $d(A) = 22\sqrt{\frac{A}{\pi}}$, where A is the area of the circle. Find the difference between the diameters of the barbecue grills. $6\sqrt{3}$ in.; 10.4 in.

WRITING

125. Explain why $\sqrt[3]{9x^4}$ is not in simplified form.

126. How are the procedures used to simplify $3x + 4x$ and $3\sqrt{x} + 4\sqrt{x}$ similar?

127. Explain how the graphs of $Y_1 = 3\sqrt{24x} + \sqrt{54x}$ and $Y_2 = 9\sqrt{6x}$ can be used to verify the simplification $3\sqrt{24x} + \sqrt{54x} = 9\sqrt{6x}$. In each graph, settings of $[-5, 20]$ for x and $[-5, 100]$ for y were used.

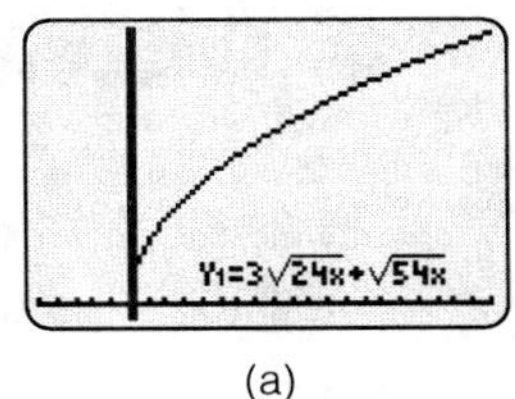

(a)

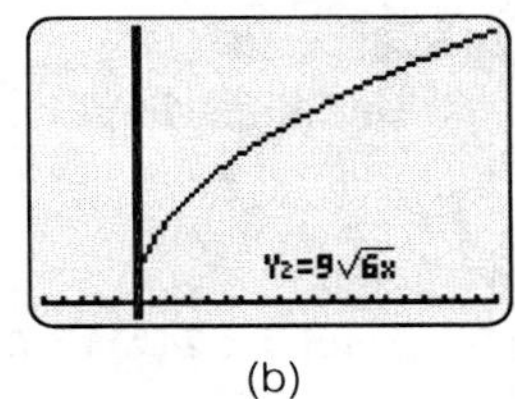

(b)

128. Explain how to verify algebraically that $\sqrt{200x^3y^5} = 10xy^2\sqrt{2xy}$.

REVIEW

Perform each operation.

129. $3x^2y^3(-5x^3y^{-4})$ $\frac{15x^5}{y}$

130. $(2x^2 - 9x - 5) \cdot \frac{x}{2x^2 + x}$ $x - 5$

131. $2p - 5\overline{)6p^2 - 7p - 25}$ $3p + 4 - \frac{5}{2p - 5}$

132. $\dfrac{xy}{\frac{1}{x} - \frac{1}{y}}$ $\frac{x^2y^2}{y - x}$

SECTION 8.4
Multiplying and Dividing Radical Expressions

Objectives

1. Multiply radical expressions.
2. Find powers of radical expressions.
3. Rationalize denominators.
4. Rationalize denominators that have two terms.
5. Rationalize numerators.

In this section, we will discuss how to multiply and divide radical expressions. These problems often require the use of procedures and properties studied earlier, such as simplifying radical expressions, combining like radicals, the FOIL method, and the distributive property.

1 Multiply radical expressions.

We have used the *product rule for radicals* to write radical expressions in simplified form. We can also use this rule to multiply radical expressions that have the same index.

The Product Rule for Radicals

The product of the nth roots of two nonnegative numbers is equal to the nth root of the product of those numbers.

If $\sqrt[n]{a}$ and $\sqrt[n]{b}$ are real numbers,

$$\sqrt[n]{a} \cdot \sqrt[n]{b} = \sqrt[n]{a \cdot b}$$

Self Check 1

Multiply and then simplify:

a. $-2\sqrt{14}\left(5\sqrt{2}\right)$

b. $\sqrt[4]{4x^3} \cdot 9\sqrt[4]{8x^2}$

Now Try **Problems 24 and 28**

Self Check 1 Answers

a. $-20\sqrt{7}$ **b.** $18x\sqrt[4]{2x}$

Teaching Example 1 Multiply and then simplify:

a. $\sqrt{5}\sqrt{10}$

b. $3\sqrt[3]{25x} \cdot \sqrt[3]{15x^2}$

Answers:

a. $5\sqrt{2}$

b. $15x\sqrt[3]{3}$

EXAMPLE 1 Multiply and then simplify:

a. $3\sqrt{6}\left(2\sqrt{3}\right)$ **b.** $-2\sqrt[3]{7x} \cdot 6\sqrt[3]{49x^2}$

Strategy In each case, we will multiply the coefficients and then use the product rule for radicals to multiply the factors of the form $\sqrt[n]{a}$ and $\sqrt[n]{b}$.

WHY The product rule for radicals is used to multiply radicals that have the same index.

Solution

We use the commutative and associative properties of multiplication to multiply the coefficients and the radicals separately. Then we simplify any radicals in the product, if possible.

a.

$3\sqrt{6}\left(2\sqrt{3}\right) = 3(2)\sqrt{6}\sqrt{3}$ Write the coefficients together and multiply the radicals together.

$= 6\sqrt{18}$ $3(2) = 6$ and $\sqrt{6}\sqrt{3} = \sqrt{18}$.

$= 6\sqrt{9}\sqrt{2}$ Simplify: $\sqrt{18} = \sqrt{9 \cdot 2} = \sqrt{9}\sqrt{2}$.

$= 6(3)\sqrt{2}$ Evaluate: $\sqrt{9} = 3$.

$= 18\sqrt{2}$ Multiply.

b.

$-2\sqrt[3]{7x} \cdot 6\sqrt[3]{49x^2} = -2(6)\sqrt[3]{7x}\sqrt[3]{49x^2}$ Write the coefficients together and the radicals together.

$= -12\sqrt[3]{7x \cdot 49x^2}$ Multiply the coefficients and multiply the radicals.

$= -12\sqrt[3]{7x \cdot 7^2x^2}$ Write 49 as 7^2.

$= -12\sqrt[3]{7^3x^3}$ Write $7x \cdot 7^2x^2$ as 7^3x^3.

$= -12(7x)$ Simplify: $\sqrt[3]{7^3x^3} = 7x$.

$= -84x$ Multiply.

Recall that to multiply a polynomial by a monomial, we use the distributive property. We use the same technique to multiply a radical expression that has two or more terms by a radical expression that has only one term.

Self Check 2

Simplify: $4\sqrt{2}\left(3\sqrt{5} - 2\sqrt{8}\right)$

Now Try **Problem 32**

Self Check 2 Answer

$12\sqrt{10} - 32$

EXAMPLE 2 Simplify: $3\sqrt{3}\left(4\sqrt{8} - 5\sqrt{10}\right)$

Strategy We will use the distributive property and multiply each term within the parentheses by the term outside the parentheses.

WHY The given expression has the form $a(b - c)$.

Solution

$3\sqrt{3}(4\sqrt{8} - 5\sqrt{10})$

$= 3\sqrt{3} \cdot 4\sqrt{8} - 3\sqrt{3} \cdot 5\sqrt{10}$ Distribute the multiplication by $3\sqrt{3}$.

$= 12\sqrt{24} - 15\sqrt{30}$ Multiply the coefficients and multiply the radicals.

$= 12\sqrt{4}\sqrt{6} - 15\sqrt{30}$ Simplify: $\sqrt{24} = \sqrt{4 \cdot 6} = \sqrt{4}\sqrt{6}$.

$= 12(2)\sqrt{6} - 15\sqrt{30}$ $\sqrt{4} = 2$.

$= 24\sqrt{6} - 15\sqrt{30}$

Teaching Example 2 Simplify: $2\sqrt{7}(4\sqrt{14} - 5\sqrt{21})$
Answer:
$56\sqrt{2} - 70\sqrt{3}$

Recall that to multiply two binomials, we multiply each term of one binomial by each term of the other binomial and simplify. We multiply two radical expressions, each having two terms, in the same way.

EXAMPLE 3 Multiply: $(\sqrt{7} + \sqrt{2})(\sqrt{7} - 3\sqrt{2})$

Strategy As with binomials, we will multiply each term within the first set of parentheses by each term within the second set of parentheses.

WHY Within each parenthesis there are two terms. This is an application of the FOIL method for multiplying binomials.

Solution

$(\sqrt{7} + \sqrt{2})(\sqrt{7} - 3\sqrt{2})$

$= \sqrt{7}\sqrt{7} - 3\sqrt{7}\sqrt{2} + \sqrt{2}\sqrt{7} - 3\sqrt{2}\sqrt{2}$ Use the FOIL method.

$= 7 - 3\sqrt{14} + \sqrt{14} - 3(2)$ Perform each multiplication: $\sqrt{7}\sqrt{7} = \sqrt{49} = 7$ and $\sqrt{2}\sqrt{2} = \sqrt{4} = 2$.

$= 7 - 2\sqrt{14} - 6$ Combine like radicals: $-3\sqrt{14} + \sqrt{14} = -2\sqrt{14}$.

$= 1 - 2\sqrt{14}$ Combine like terms: $7 - 6 = 1$.

Self Check 3
Multiply:
$(\sqrt{5} + 2\sqrt{3})(\sqrt{5} - \sqrt{3})$

Now Try **Problem 34**

Self Check 3 Answer
$-1 + \sqrt{15}$

Teaching Example 3 Multiply: $(\sqrt{11} - 3\sqrt{2})(4\sqrt{11} - \sqrt{2})$
Answer:
$50 - 13\sqrt{22}$

EXAMPLE 4 Multiply $(\sqrt{3x} - \sqrt{5})(\sqrt{2x} + \sqrt{10})$. Assume that $x > 0$.

Strategy As with binomials, we will multiply each term within the first set of parentheses by each term within the second set of parentheses.

WHY Within each parenthesis there are two terms. This is an application of the FOIL method for multiplying binomials.

Solution

$(\sqrt{3x} - \sqrt{5})(\sqrt{2x} + \sqrt{10})$

$= \sqrt{3x}\sqrt{2x} + \sqrt{3x}\sqrt{10} - \sqrt{5}\sqrt{2x} - \sqrt{5}\sqrt{10}$ Use the FOIL method.

$= \sqrt{6x^2} + \sqrt{30x} - \sqrt{10x} - \sqrt{50}$ Perform each multiplication.

$= \sqrt{6}\sqrt{x^2} + \sqrt{30x} - \sqrt{10x} - \sqrt{25}\sqrt{2}$ Simplify $\sqrt{6x^2}$ and $\sqrt{50}$.

$= \sqrt{6}x + \sqrt{30x} - \sqrt{10x} - 5\sqrt{2}$

Self Check 4
Multiply $(\sqrt{x} + 1)(\sqrt{x} - 3)$. Assume that $x > 0$.

Now Try **Problem 40**

Self Check 4 Answer
$x - 2\sqrt{x} - 3$

Teaching Example 4 Multiply $(\sqrt{7x} + \sqrt{3})(\sqrt{x} - \sqrt{5})$. Assume that $x > 0$.
Answer:
$x\sqrt{7} - \sqrt{35x} + \sqrt{3x} - \sqrt{15}$

> ***Success Tip*** It is important to draw the radical sign carefully so that it completely covers the radicand, but no more than the radicand. To avoid confusion, we often write an expression such as $\sqrt{6}x$ in the form $x\sqrt{6}$.

2 Find powers of radical expressions.

To find the power of a radical expression, such as $\left(\sqrt{5}\right)^2$ or $\left(\sqrt[3]{2}\right)^3$, we can use the definition of exponent and the product rule for radicals.

$$\left(\sqrt{5}\right)^2 = \sqrt{5}\sqrt{5} = \sqrt{25} = 5 \qquad \left(\sqrt[3]{2}\right)^3 = \sqrt[3]{2}\cdot\sqrt[3]{2}\cdot\sqrt[3]{2} = \sqrt[3]{8} = 2$$

These results illustrate the following property of radicals.

> **The *n*th Power of the *n*th Root**
>
> If $\sqrt[n]{a}$ is a real number,
>
> $$\left(\sqrt[n]{a}\right)^n = a$$

Self Check 5

Find:

a. $\left(\sqrt{11}\right)^2$

b. $\left(3\sqrt[3]{4y}\right)^3$

c. $\left(\sqrt{x-8}-5\right)^2$

Now Try **Problems 42, 46, and 48**

Self Check 5 Answers

a. 11 b. $108y$ c. $x - 10\sqrt{x-8} + 17$

Teaching Example 5 Find:
a. $\left(\sqrt{13}\right)^2$ b. $\left(4\sqrt[3]{2x^2}\right)^3$ c. $\left(\sqrt{x}+3\right)^2$

Answers:
a. 13 b. $128x^2$ c. $x + 6\sqrt{x} + 9$

EXAMPLE 5 Find: **a.** $\left(\sqrt{5}\right)^2$ **b.** $\left(2\sqrt[3]{7x^2}\right)^3$ **c.** $\left(\sqrt{m+1}+2\right)^2$

Strategy In part a, we will use the definition of square root. In part b, we will use a power rule for exponents. In part c, we will use the FOIL method.

WHY Part a is the square of a square root, part b has the form $(xy)^n$, and part c has the form $(x + y)^2$.

Solution

a. $\left(\sqrt{5}\right)^2 = 5$ Because the square of the square root of 5 is 5.

b. We can use the power of a product rule for exponents to find $\left(2\sqrt[3]{7x^2}\right)^3$.

$$\begin{aligned}\left(2\sqrt[3]{7x^2}\right)^3 &= 2^3\left(\sqrt[3]{7x^2}\right)^3 && \text{Raise each factor of } 2\sqrt[3]{7x^2} \text{ to the 3rd power.}\\ &= 8(7x^2) && \text{Evaluate: } 2^3 = 8. \text{ Use } \left(\sqrt[n]{a}\right)^n = a.\\ &= 56x^2\end{aligned}$$

c. We can use the FOIL method to find the product.

$$\begin{aligned}\left(\sqrt{m+1}+2\right)^2 &= \left(\sqrt{m+1}+2\right)\left(\sqrt{m+1}+2\right)\\ &= \left(\sqrt{m+1}\right)^2 + 2\sqrt{m+1} + 2\sqrt{m+1} + 2\cdot 2\\ &= m + 1 + 2\sqrt{m+1} + 2\sqrt{m+1} + 4 && \text{Use } \left(\sqrt[n]{a}\right)^n = a.\\ &= m + 4\sqrt{m+1} + 5 && \text{Combine like terms.}\end{aligned}$$

3 Rationalize denominators.

In Section 8.3, we saw that a radical expression is in simplified form when each of the following statements is true.

1. Each factor in the radicand is to a power that is less than the index of the radical.
2. The radicand contains no fractions or negative numbers.
3. No radicals appear in the denominator of a fraction.

We now consider radical expressions that do not satisfy requirement 2 and radical expressions that do not satisfy requirement 3 of this list. We will introduce an algebraic technique, called *rationalizing the denominator,* that is used to write such expressions in an equivalent simplified form.

To divide radical expressions, we **rationalize the denominator** of a fraction to replace the denominator with a rational number. For example, to divide $\sqrt{5}$ by $\sqrt{3}$, we write the division as the fraction

$$\frac{\sqrt{5}}{\sqrt{3}}$$ The denominator is the irrational number $\sqrt{3}$. This radical expression is not in simplified form, because a radical appears in the denominator.

To eliminate the radical in the denominator, we multiply the numerator and the denominator by a number that will give a perfect square *under the radical in the denominator.* Because $3 \cdot 3 = 9$ and 9 is a perfect square, $\sqrt{3}$ is such a number.

$$\frac{\sqrt{5}}{\sqrt{3}} = \frac{\sqrt{5}}{\sqrt{3}} \cdot \frac{\sqrt{3}}{\sqrt{3}}$$ To build an equivalent fraction, multiply by $\frac{\sqrt{3}}{\sqrt{3}} = 1$.

$$= \frac{\sqrt{15}}{\sqrt{9}}$$ Multiply the numerators: $\sqrt{5} \cdot \sqrt{3} = \sqrt{15}$. Multiply the denominators: $\sqrt{3} \cdot \sqrt{3} = \sqrt{9}$.

$$= \frac{\sqrt{15}}{3}$$ Simplify: $\sqrt{9} = 3$. The denominator is now the rational number 3.

Thus, $\frac{\sqrt{5}}{\sqrt{3}} = \frac{\sqrt{15}}{3}$. Since there is no radical in the denominator and $\sqrt{15}$ cannot be simplified, the expression $\frac{\sqrt{15}}{3}$ is in simplest form, and the division is complete.

Success Tip As an informal check, we can use a calculator to evaluate each expression.

$$\frac{\sqrt{5}}{\sqrt{3}} \approx 1.290994449$$

$$\frac{\sqrt{15}}{3} \approx 1.290994449$$

EXAMPLE 6

Rationalize each denominator: **a.** $\sqrt{\frac{20}{7}}$ **b.** $\frac{4}{\sqrt[3]{2}}$

Strategy In part a, we will examine the radicand in the denominator and ask, "By what must we multiply it to obtain a perfect square?" In part b, we will examine the radicand in the denominator and ask, "By what must we multiply it to obtain a perfect cube?"

WHY The answers to those questions will determine what form of 1 we use to rationalize each denominator.

Solution

a. This radical expression is not in simplified form, because the radicand contains a fraction. We begin by writing the square root of the quotient as the quotient of two square roots:

$$\sqrt{\frac{20}{7}} = \frac{\sqrt{20}}{\sqrt{7}}$$ Apply the division property of radicals: $\sqrt[n]{\frac{a}{b}} = \frac{\sqrt[n]{a}}{\sqrt[n]{b}}$.

Self Check 6

Rationalize each denominator:

a. $\sqrt{\frac{24}{5}}$ **b.** $\frac{5}{\sqrt[4]{3}}$

Now Try **Problems 52 and 56**

Self Check 6 Answers

a. $\frac{2\sqrt{30}}{5}$ b. $\frac{5\sqrt[4]{27}}{3}$

Teaching Example 6 Rationalize each denominator:

a. $\sqrt{\frac{12}{11}}$ b. $\frac{7}{\sqrt[3]{75}}$

Answers:

a. $\frac{2\sqrt{33}}{11}$ b. $\frac{7\sqrt[3]{45}}{15}$

To rationalize the denominator, we proceed as follows:

$$\frac{\sqrt{20}}{\sqrt{7}} = \frac{\sqrt{20}}{\sqrt{7}} \cdot \frac{\sqrt{7}}{\sqrt{7}}$$ Multiply by the form of 1 to rationalize the denominator.

$$= \frac{\sqrt{140}}{\sqrt{49}}$$ Multiply the radicals. This radicand is now a perfect square.

$$= \frac{2\sqrt{35}}{7}$$ Simplify: $\sqrt{140} = \sqrt{4 \cdot 35} = \sqrt{4}\sqrt{35} = 2\sqrt{35}$ and $\sqrt{49} = 7$.

b. Here, we must rationalize a denominator that is a cube root. We multiply the numerator and the denominator by a number that will give a perfect cube under the radical sign. Since $2 \cdot 4 = 8$ is a perfect cube, $\sqrt[3]{4}$ is such a number.

$$\frac{4}{\sqrt[3]{2}} = \frac{4}{\sqrt[3]{2}} \cdot \frac{\sqrt[3]{4}}{\sqrt[3]{4}}$$ Multiply by a form of 1 to rationalize the denominator.

$$= \frac{4\sqrt[3]{4}}{\sqrt[3]{8}}$$ Multiply the radicals in the denominator. This radicand is now a perfect cube.

$$= \frac{4\sqrt[3]{4}}{2}$$ Simplify: $\sqrt[3]{8} = 2$.

$$= 2\sqrt[3]{4}$$ Simplify: $\frac{4\sqrt[3]{4}}{2} = \frac{\overset{1}{\cancel{2}} \cdot 2\sqrt[3]{4}}{\underset{1}{\cancel{2}}} = 2\sqrt[3]{4}$.

Self Check 7

Rationalize the denominator: $\frac{\sqrt{4ab^3}}{\sqrt{2a^2b^2}}$

Assume that $a > 0$ and $b > 0$. $\frac{\sqrt{2ab}}{a}$

Now Try **Problem 62**

Teaching Example 7 Rationalize the denominator: $\frac{\sqrt{6a^2b^5}}{\sqrt{3a^3b}}$

Answer: $\frac{b^2\sqrt{2a}}{a}$

EXAMPLE 7 Rationalize the denominator: $\frac{\sqrt{5xy^2}}{\sqrt{xy^3}}$

Assume that x and y are positive numbers.

Strategy We will begin by using the quotient rule for radicals in reverse $\frac{\sqrt[n]{a}}{\sqrt[n]{b}} = \sqrt[n]{\frac{a}{b}}$.

WHY When the radicals are written under a single radical symbol, the result is a rational expression. Our hope is that the rational expression can be simplified, which could possibly make rationalizing the denominator easier.

Solution

There are two methods we can use to rationalize the denominator. In each method, we simplify the expression first.

Method 1

$$\frac{\sqrt{5xy^2}}{\sqrt{xy^3}} = \sqrt{\frac{5xy^2}{xy^3}}$$

$$= \sqrt{\frac{5}{y}}$$

$$= \frac{\sqrt{5}}{\sqrt{y}}$$

$$= \frac{\sqrt{5}}{\sqrt{y}} \cdot \frac{\sqrt{y}}{\sqrt{y}}$$ Multiply outside the radical.

$$= \frac{\sqrt{5y}}{y}$$

Method 2

$$\frac{\sqrt{5xy^2}}{\sqrt{xy^3}} = \sqrt{\frac{5xy^2}{xy^3}}$$

$$= \sqrt{\frac{5}{y}}$$

$$= \sqrt{\frac{5}{y} \cdot \frac{y}{y}}$$ Multiply within the radical.

$$= \frac{\sqrt{5y}}{\sqrt{y^2}}$$

$$= \frac{\sqrt{5y}}{y}$$

EXAMPLE 8 Rationalize the denominator and assume $q > 0$: $\sqrt{\frac{11}{20q^5}}$

Strategy We will begin by using the quotient rule for radicals $\sqrt[n]{\frac{a}{b}} = \frac{\sqrt[n]{a}}{\sqrt[n]{b}}$.

WHY When the radicals are written under separate radicals, our hope is that the radical in the denominator can be simplified, which could possibly make rationalizing the denominator easier.

Solution

We write the expression as a quotient of two radicals. Then we simplify the radical in the denominator before rationalizing.

$$\sqrt{\frac{11}{20q^5}} = \frac{\sqrt{11}}{\sqrt{20q^5}}$$ The square root of a quotient is the quotient of the square roots.

$$= \frac{\sqrt{11}}{\sqrt{4q^4 \cdot 5q}}$$ To simplify $\sqrt{20q^5}$, write it as $\sqrt{4q^4 \cdot 5q}$.

$$= \frac{\sqrt{11}}{2q^2\sqrt{5q}}$$ Simplify: $\sqrt{4q^4 \cdot 5q} = \sqrt{4q^4}\sqrt{5q} = 2q^2\sqrt{5q}$.

$$= \frac{\sqrt{11}}{2q^2\sqrt{5q}} \cdot \frac{\sqrt{5q}}{\sqrt{5q}}$$ To rationalize the denominator, multiply by $\frac{\sqrt{5q}}{\sqrt{5q}} = 1$.

$$= \frac{\sqrt{55q}}{2q^2(5q)}$$ Multiply the radicals: $\sqrt{5q}\sqrt{5q} = 5q$.

$$= \frac{\sqrt{55q}}{10q^3}$$ Multiply in the denominator.

Self Check 8

Rationalize the denominator: $\sqrt[3]{\frac{1}{16h^4}}$ $\frac{\sqrt[3]{4h^2}}{4h^2}$

Now Try Problem 65

Teaching Example 8 Rationalize the denominator: $\sqrt{\frac{7}{18x}}$

Answer: $\frac{\sqrt{84x^2}}{6x}$

EXAMPLE 9 Rationalize the denominator: $\frac{\sqrt[3]{5}}{\sqrt[3]{9m}}$

Strategy We will examine the radicand in the denominator and ask, "By what must we multiply it to obtain a perfect cube?"

WHY The answers to those questions will determine what form of 1 we use to rationalize each denominator.

Solution

We multiply the numerator and the denominator by $\sqrt[3]{3m^2}$, which will produce a perfect cube, $27m^3$, under the radical sign in the denominator.

$$\frac{\sqrt[3]{5}}{\sqrt[3]{9m}} = \frac{\sqrt[3]{5}}{\sqrt[3]{9m}} \cdot \frac{\sqrt[3]{3m^2}}{\sqrt[3]{3m^2}}$$ Multiply by the form of 1 to rationalize the denominator.

$$= \frac{\sqrt[3]{15m^2}}{\sqrt[3]{27m^3}}$$ Multiply the radicals. This radicand is now a perfect cube.

$$= \frac{\sqrt[3]{15m^2}}{3m}$$ Simplify the denominator: $\sqrt[3]{27m^3} = 3m$.

Self Check 9

Rationalize the denominator: $\frac{\sqrt{5}}{\sqrt{17b}}$ $\frac{\sqrt{85b}}{17b}$

Now Try Problem 70

Teaching Example 9 Rationalize the denominator: $\frac{\sqrt[3]{2}}{\sqrt[3]{25a^2}}$

Answer: $\frac{\sqrt[3]{10a}}{5a}$

4 Rationalize denominators that have two terms.

So far, we have rationalized denominators that had only one term. We will now discuss a method to rationalize denominators that have two terms.

One-term denominators	Two-term denominators
$\frac{\sqrt{5}}{\sqrt{3}}$, $\frac{11}{\sqrt{20q^5}}$, $\frac{4}{\sqrt[3]{2}}$	$\frac{1}{\sqrt{2}+1}$, $\frac{\sqrt{x}+\sqrt{2}}{\sqrt{x}-\sqrt{2}}$

To rationalize a denominator of $\frac{1}{\sqrt{2}+1}$, for example, we multiply the numerator and denominator by $\sqrt{2}-1$, because the product $(\sqrt{2}+1)(\sqrt{2}-1)$ contains no radicals.

$$\begin{aligned}(\sqrt{2}+1)(\sqrt{2}-1) &= (\sqrt{2})^2 - (1)^2 \quad \text{Use a special product formula.}\\ &= 2-1\\ &= 1\end{aligned}$$

Radical expressions that involve the sum and difference of the same two terms, such as $\sqrt{2}+1$ and $\sqrt{2}-1$, are called **conjugates.**

Self Check 10

Rationalize the denominator:

a. $\frac{2}{\sqrt{3}+1}$ **b.** $\frac{\sqrt{x}-\sqrt{5}}{\sqrt{x}+\sqrt{5}}$

Self Check 10 Answers

a. $\sqrt{3}-1$ b. $\frac{x-2\sqrt{5x}+5}{x-5}$

Now Try **Problems 74 and 80**

Teaching Example 10 Rationalize the denominator:

a. $\frac{3}{\sqrt{5}-1}$ b. $\frac{\sqrt{x}-\sqrt{3}}{\sqrt{x}+\sqrt{3}}$

Answers:

a. $\frac{3\sqrt{5}+3}{4}$ b. $\frac{x-2\sqrt{3x}+3}{x-3}$

EXAMPLE 10 Rationalize the denominator: **a.** $\frac{1}{\sqrt{2}+1}$ **b.** $\frac{\sqrt{x}+\sqrt{2}}{\sqrt{x}-\sqrt{2}}$

Strategy We will rationalize the denominator by multiplying the numerator and the denominator by the conjugate of the denominator.

WHY Multiplying the denominator by its conjugate will produce a new denominator that does not contain radicals.

Solution

a. We multiply the numerator and denominator of the fraction by $\sqrt{2}-1$, which is the conjugate of the denominator.

$$\begin{aligned}\frac{1}{\sqrt{2}+1} &= \frac{1}{(\sqrt{2}+1)} \cdot \frac{(\sqrt{2}-1)}{(\sqrt{2}-1)}\\ &= \frac{\sqrt{2}-1}{2-1} \quad \text{In the denominator, multiply the binomials: } (\sqrt{2}+1)(\sqrt{2}-1) = \sqrt{2}\sqrt{2}-\sqrt{2}+\sqrt{2}-1 = 2-1.\\ &= \sqrt{2}-1 \quad \text{Simplify: } \frac{\sqrt{2}-1}{2-1} = \frac{\sqrt{2}-1}{1} = \sqrt{2}-1.\end{aligned}$$

b. We multiply the numerator and denominator by $\sqrt{x}+\sqrt{2}$, which is the conjugate of $\sqrt{x}-\sqrt{2}$, and simplify.

$$\begin{aligned}\frac{\sqrt{x}+\sqrt{2}}{\sqrt{x}-\sqrt{2}} &= \frac{(\sqrt{x}+\sqrt{2})(\sqrt{x}+\sqrt{2})}{(\sqrt{x}-\sqrt{2})(\sqrt{x}+\sqrt{2})}\\ &= \frac{x+\sqrt{2x}+\sqrt{2x}+2}{x-2} \quad \text{In the numerator and denominator, use the FOIL method.}\\ &= \frac{x+2\sqrt{2x}+2}{x-2} \quad \text{In the numerator, combine like radicals.}\end{aligned}$$

5 Rationalize numerators.

In calculus, we sometimes have to rationalize a numerator by multiplying the numerator and denominator of the fraction by the conjugate of the numerator.

EXAMPLE 11 Rationalize the numerator: $\dfrac{\sqrt{x}-3}{\sqrt{x}}$

Strategy To rationalize the numerator, we will multiply the numerator and the denominator by the conjugate of the numerator.

WHY After rationalizing the numerator, we can simplify the expression. Although the result will not be in simplified form, this nonsimplified form is often desirable in calculus.

Solution

We multiply the numerator and denominator by $\sqrt{x}+3$, which is the conjugate of the numerator.

$$\frac{\sqrt{x}-3}{\sqrt{x}} = \frac{\sqrt{x}-3}{\sqrt{x}} \cdot \frac{\sqrt{x}+3}{\sqrt{x}+3}$$ Multiply by a form of 1 to rationalize the numerator.

$$= \frac{\left(\sqrt{x}\right)^2-(3)^2}{x+3\sqrt{x}}$$ Multiply the numerators using a special-product rule. Multiply the denominators.

$$= \frac{x-9}{x+3\sqrt{x}}$$

Self Check 11

Rationalize the numerator: $\dfrac{\sqrt{x}+3}{\sqrt{x}}$ $\dfrac{x-9}{x-3\sqrt{x}}$

Now Try **Problem 82**

Teaching Example 11 Rationalize the numerator: $\dfrac{\sqrt{x}+5}{\sqrt{x}}$

Answer: $\dfrac{x-25}{x-5\sqrt{x}}$

ANSWERS TO SELF CHECKS

1. a. $-20\sqrt{7}$ **b.** $18x\sqrt[4]{2x}$ **2.** $12\sqrt{10}-32$ **3.** $-1+\sqrt{15}$ **4.** $x-2\sqrt{x}-3$ **5. a.** 11 **b.** $108y$ **c.** $x-10\sqrt{x-8}+17$ **6. a.** $\frac{2\sqrt{30}}{5}$ **b.** $\frac{5\sqrt[4]{27}}{3}$ **7.** $\frac{\sqrt{2ab}}{a}$ **8.** $\frac{\sqrt[3]{4h^2}}{4h^2}$ **9.** $\frac{\sqrt{85b}}{17b}$ **10. a.** $\sqrt{3}-1$ **b.** $\frac{x-2\sqrt{5x}+5}{x-5}$ **11.** $\frac{x-9}{x-3\sqrt{x}}$

SECTION 8.4 STUDY SET

VOCABULARY

Fill in the blanks.

1. To multiply $\left(\sqrt{3}+\sqrt{2}\right)\left(\sqrt{3}-2\sqrt{2}\right)$, we can use the FOIL method.
2. To multiply $2\sqrt{5}\left(3\sqrt{8}+\sqrt{3}\right)$, use the distributive property to remove parentheses.
3. The denominator of the fraction $\dfrac{4}{\sqrt{5}}$ is an irrational number.
4. The conjugate of $\sqrt{x}+1$ is $\sqrt{x}-1$.
5. To rationalize the denominator of $\dfrac{4}{\sqrt{5}}$, we multiply the numerator and denominator by $\sqrt{5}$.
6. To obtain a perfect cube under the radical in the denominator of $\dfrac{\sqrt[3]{7}}{\sqrt[3]{5n}}$, we multiply the numerator and denominator by $\sqrt[3]{25n^2}$.

CONCEPTS

Perform each operation, if possible.

7. $4\sqrt{6}+2\sqrt{6}$ $6\sqrt{6}$
8. $4\sqrt{6}\left(2\sqrt{6}\right)$ 48
9. $3\sqrt{2}-2\sqrt{3}$ can't be simplified
10. $3\sqrt{2}\left(-2\sqrt{3}\right)$ $-6\sqrt{6}$

Perform each operation, if possible.

11. $5+6\sqrt[3]{6}$ can't be simplified
12. $5\left(6\sqrt[3]{6}\right)$ $30\sqrt[3]{6}$
13. $\dfrac{30\sqrt[3]{15}}{5}$ $6\sqrt[3]{15}$
14. $\dfrac{\sqrt[3]{15}}{5}$ can't be simplified
15. Consider $\dfrac{\sqrt{3}}{\sqrt{7}}=\dfrac{\sqrt{3}\sqrt{7}}{\sqrt{7}\sqrt{7}}$. Explain why the expressions on the left-hand side and the right-side side of the equation are equal.
When the numerator and the denominator of a fraction are multiplied by the same nonzero number, the value of the fraction is not changed.

16. To rationalize the denominator of $\frac{\sqrt[3]{2}}{\sqrt[3]{3}}$, why wouldn't we multiply the numerator and denominator by $\frac{\sqrt[3]{3}}{\sqrt[3]{3}}$?
We don't get a perfect-cube factor under the radical in the denominator.

17. Explain why $\frac{\sqrt[3]{12}}{\sqrt[3]{5}}$ is not in simplified form.
A radical appears in the denominator.

▶ **18.** Explain why $\sqrt{\frac{3a}{11k}}$ is not in simplified form.
The radicand contains a fraction.

NOTATION

Fill in the blanks.

19. Multiply: $5\sqrt{8} \cdot 7\sqrt{6}$

$$5\sqrt{8} \cdot 7\sqrt{6} = 5(7)\sqrt{8}\sqrt{6}$$
$$= 35\sqrt{48}$$
$$= 35\sqrt{16 \cdot 3}$$
$$= 35(4)\sqrt{3}$$
$$= 140\sqrt{3}$$

▶ **20.** Rationalize the denominator: $\frac{9}{\sqrt[3]{4a^2}}$

$$\frac{9}{\sqrt[3]{4a^2}} = \frac{9 \cdot \sqrt[3]{2a}}{\sqrt[3]{4a^2} \cdot \sqrt[3]{2a}}$$
$$= \frac{9\sqrt[3]{2a}}{\sqrt[3]{8a^3}}$$
$$= \frac{9\sqrt[3]{2a}}{2a}$$

GUIDED PRACTICE

Perform each multiplication and simplify. All variables represent positive numbers. See Example 1.

21. $\sqrt{5}\sqrt{10}$ $5\sqrt{2}$

22. $\sqrt{7}\sqrt{35}$ $7\sqrt{5}$

23. $4\sqrt{5a}(3\sqrt{8a})$ $24a\sqrt{10}$

24. $-5\sqrt{8b}(4\sqrt{3b})$ $-40b\sqrt{6}$

25. $3\sqrt[3]{2}\sqrt[3]{12}$ $6\sqrt[3]{3}$

▶ **26.** $\sqrt[3]{3}(4\sqrt[3]{18})$ $12\sqrt[3]{2}$

27. $(3\sqrt[3]{9a^2})(2\sqrt[3]{3a})$ $18a$

28. $(2\sqrt[3]{16b^2})(-\sqrt[3]{4b^4})$ $-8b^2$

Perform each multiplication and simplify. See Example 2.

29. $3\sqrt{5}(4 - \sqrt{5})$ $12\sqrt{5} - 15$

30. $2\sqrt{7}(3\sqrt{7} - 1)$ $42 - 2\sqrt{7}$

31. $3\sqrt{2}(4\sqrt{6} + 2\sqrt{7})$ $24\sqrt{3} + 6\sqrt{14}$

▶ **32.** $-\sqrt{3}(\sqrt{7} - \sqrt{15})$ $-\sqrt{21} + 3\sqrt{5}$

Perform each multiplication and simplify. See Example 3.

33. $(\sqrt{2} + 1)(\sqrt{2} - 3)$ $-1 - 2\sqrt{2}$

34. $(2\sqrt{3} + 1)(\sqrt{3} - 1)$ $5 - \sqrt{3}$

35. $(\sqrt{5} + \sqrt{3})(\sqrt{5} - 2\sqrt{3})$ $-1 - \sqrt{15}$

▶ **36.** $(\sqrt{6} + 3\sqrt{5})(\sqrt{6} - 4\sqrt{5})$ $-54 - \sqrt{30}$

Perform each multiplication and simplify. All variables represent positive numbers. See Example 4.

37. $(\sqrt{5z} + \sqrt{3})(\sqrt{5z} + \sqrt{3})$ $5z + 2\sqrt{15z} + 3$

38. $(\sqrt{3p} - \sqrt{2})(\sqrt{3p} + \sqrt{2})$ $3p - 2$

39. $(\sqrt{5b} - \sqrt{3})(\sqrt{2b} + \sqrt{6})$ $b\sqrt{10} + \sqrt{30b} - \sqrt{6b} - 3\sqrt{2}$

▶ **40.** $(\sqrt{3y} - \sqrt{2})(\sqrt{2y} - \sqrt{3})$ $y\sqrt{6} - 5\sqrt{y} + \sqrt{6}$

Perform each multiplication and simplify. All variables represent positive numbers. See Example 5.

41. $(\sqrt{7})^2$ 7

42. $(\sqrt{23})^2$ 23

43. $(3\sqrt{2x})^2$ $18x$

44. $(2x\sqrt{5})^2$ $20x^2$

45. $(3\sqrt[3]{5x^2})^3$ $135x^2$

▶ **46.** $(-2\sqrt[3]{9y^2})^3$ $-72y^2$

47. $(\sqrt{x-2} + 3)^2$ $x + 6\sqrt{x-2} + 7$

48. $(\sqrt{x+1} - 2)^2$ $x - 4\sqrt{x+1} + 5$

Rationalize each denominator. See Example 6.

49. $\sqrt{\frac{1}{7}}$ $\frac{\sqrt{7}}{7}$

50. $\sqrt{\frac{5}{3}}$ $\frac{\sqrt{15}}{3}$

51. $\sqrt{\frac{36}{30}}$ $\frac{\sqrt{30}}{5}$

52. $\sqrt{\frac{64}{10}}$ $\frac{4\sqrt{10}}{5}$

53. $\frac{1}{\sqrt[3]{2}}$ $\frac{\sqrt[3]{4}}{2}$

▶ **54.** $\frac{2}{\sqrt[3]{6}}$ $\frac{\sqrt[3]{36}}{3}$

55. $\frac{3}{\sqrt[3]{9}}$ $\sqrt[3]{3}$

56. $\frac{-5}{\sqrt[3]{10}}$ $-\frac{\sqrt[3]{100}}{2}$

57. $\frac{\sqrt[3]{2}}{\sqrt[3]{9}}$ $\frac{\sqrt[3]{6}}{3}$

58. $\frac{\sqrt[3]{9}}{\sqrt[3]{54}}$ $\frac{\sqrt[3]{36}}{6}$

59. $\frac{1}{\sqrt[4]{8}}$ $\frac{\sqrt[4]{2}}{2}$

60. $\frac{1}{\sqrt[5]{2}}$ $\frac{\sqrt[5]{16}}{2}$

Rationalize each denominator. Assume all variables represent positive numbers. See Example 7.

61. $\frac{\sqrt{8}}{\sqrt{xy}}$ $\frac{2\sqrt{2xy}}{xy}$

62. $\frac{\sqrt{9xy}}{\sqrt{3x^2y}}$ $\frac{\sqrt{3x}}{x}$

63. $\dfrac{\sqrt{10xy^2}}{\sqrt{2xy^3}}$ $\dfrac{\sqrt{5y}}{y}$

▶ 64. $\dfrac{\sqrt{5ab^2c}}{\sqrt{10abc}}$ $\dfrac{\sqrt{2b}}{2}$

Rationalize each denominator. Assume all variables represent positive numbers. See Example 8.

65. $\sqrt{\dfrac{7}{8a^3}}$ $\dfrac{\sqrt{14a}}{4a^2}$

66. $\sqrt{\dfrac{5}{2b^5}}$ $\dfrac{\sqrt{10b}}{2b^3}$

67. $-\sqrt{\dfrac{13}{5p^7}}$ $-\dfrac{\sqrt{65p}}{5p^4}$

▶ 68. $-\sqrt{\dfrac{2}{3t}}$ $-\dfrac{\sqrt{6t}}{3t}$

Rationalize each denominator. Assume all variables represent positive numbers. See Example 9.

69. $\dfrac{\sqrt[3]{4a^2}}{\sqrt[3]{2ab}}$ $\dfrac{\sqrt[3]{2ab^2}}{b}$

▶ 70. $\dfrac{\sqrt[3]{9x}}{\sqrt[3]{3xy}}$ $\dfrac{\sqrt[3]{3y^2}}{y}$

71. $\dfrac{\sqrt[3]{7}}{\sqrt[3]{4p}}$ $\dfrac{\sqrt[3]{14p^2}}{2p}$

72. $\dfrac{\sqrt[3]{5p^2}}{\sqrt[3]{9q}}$ $\dfrac{\sqrt[3]{15p^2q^2}}{3q}$

Rationalize each denominator. Assume all variables represent positive numbers. See Example 10.

73. $\dfrac{1}{\sqrt{2}-1}$ $\sqrt{2}+1$

74. $\dfrac{3}{\sqrt{3}-1}$ $\dfrac{3(\sqrt{3}+1)}{2}$

75. $\dfrac{\sqrt{2}}{\sqrt{5}+3}$ $\dfrac{3\sqrt{2}-\sqrt{10}}{4}$

76. $\dfrac{\sqrt{3}}{\sqrt{3}-2}$ $-3-2\sqrt{3}$

77. $\dfrac{\sqrt{3}+1}{\sqrt{3}-1}$ $2+\sqrt{3}$

78. $\dfrac{\sqrt{2}-1}{\sqrt{2}+1}$ $3-2\sqrt{2}$

79. $\dfrac{\sqrt{x}-\sqrt{y}}{\sqrt{x}+\sqrt{y}}$ $\dfrac{x-2\sqrt{xy}+y}{x-y}$

▶ 80. $\dfrac{\sqrt{x}+\sqrt{y}}{\sqrt{x}-\sqrt{y}}$ $\dfrac{x+2\sqrt{xy}+y}{x-y}$

Rationalize each numerator. Assume all variables represent positive numbers. See Example 11.

81. $\dfrac{\sqrt{a}-2}{\sqrt{a}}$ $\dfrac{a-4}{a+2\sqrt{a}}$

82. $\dfrac{\sqrt{p}+3}{\sqrt{p}}$ $\dfrac{p-9}{p-3\sqrt{p}}$

83. $\dfrac{3+\sqrt{b}}{\sqrt{b}}$ $\dfrac{9-b}{3\sqrt{b}-b}$

▶ 84. $\dfrac{2-\sqrt{p}}{\sqrt{p}}$ $\dfrac{4-p}{2\sqrt{p}+p}$

TRY IT YOURSELF

Simplify each radical expression. Assume that all variables represent positive numbers.

85. $\sqrt{11}\sqrt{11}$ 11

86. $\sqrt{35}\sqrt{35}$ 35

87. $\sqrt{2}\sqrt{8}$ 4

88. $\sqrt{3}\sqrt{27}$ 9

89. $2\sqrt{3}\sqrt{6}$ $6\sqrt{2}$

90. $-3\sqrt{11}\sqrt{33}$ $-33\sqrt{3}$

91. $\sqrt[3]{5}\sqrt[3]{25}$ 5

92. $-\sqrt[3]{7}\sqrt[3]{49}$ -7

93. $(-2\sqrt{2})^2$ 8

94. $(-3\sqrt{10})^2$ 90

95. $\sqrt{ab^3}\sqrt{ab}$ ab^2

96. $\sqrt{8x}\sqrt{2x^3y}$ $4x^2\sqrt{y}$

97. $\sqrt{5ab}\sqrt{5a}$ $5a\sqrt{b}$

▶ 98. $\sqrt{15rs^2}\sqrt{10r}$ $5rs\sqrt{6}$

99. $-4\sqrt[3]{5r^2s}(5\sqrt[3]{2r})$ $-20r\sqrt[3]{10s}$

100. $-\sqrt[3]{3xy^2}(-\sqrt[3]{9x^3})$ $3x\sqrt[3]{xy^2}$

▶ 101. $\sqrt{x(x+3)}\sqrt{x^3(x+3)}$ $x^2(x+3)$

102. $\sqrt{y^2(x+y)}\sqrt{(x+y)^3}$ $y(x+y)^2$

▶ 103. $-2\sqrt{5x}(4\sqrt{2x}-3\sqrt{3})$ $-8x\sqrt{10}+6\sqrt{15x}$

104. $3\sqrt{7t}(2\sqrt{7t}+3\sqrt{3t^2})$ $42t+9t\sqrt{21t}$

105. $(\sqrt{3x}-\sqrt{2y})(\sqrt{3x}+\sqrt{2y})$ $3x-2y$

▶ 106. $(\sqrt{3m}+\sqrt{2n})(\sqrt{3m}+\sqrt{2n})$ $3m+2\sqrt{6mn}+2n$

107. $(2\sqrt{3a}-\sqrt{b})(\sqrt{3a}+3\sqrt{b})$ $6a+5\sqrt{3ab}-3b$

▶ 108. $(5\sqrt{p}-\sqrt{3q})(\sqrt{p}+2\sqrt{3q})$ $5p+9\sqrt{3pq}-6q$

▶ 109. $(3\sqrt{2r}-2)^2$ $18r-12\sqrt{2r}+4$

110. $(2\sqrt{3t}+5)^2$ $12t+20\sqrt{3t}+25$

111. $-2(\sqrt{3x}+\sqrt{3})^2$ $-6x-12\sqrt{x}-6$

112. $3(\sqrt{5x}-\sqrt{3})^2$ $15x-6\sqrt{15x}+9$

Simplify each radical expression by rationalizing the denominator. All variables represent positive real numbers.

113. $\dfrac{\sqrt{5}}{\sqrt{8}}$ $\dfrac{\sqrt{10}}{4}$

114. $\dfrac{\sqrt{3}}{\sqrt{50}}$ $\dfrac{\sqrt{6}}{10}$

115. $\dfrac{\sqrt{8}}{\sqrt{2}}$ 2

116. $\dfrac{\sqrt{27}}{\sqrt{3}}$ 3

117. $\dfrac{1}{\sqrt[5]{16}}$ $\dfrac{\sqrt[5]{2}}{2}$

118. $\dfrac{4}{\sqrt[4]{32}}$ $\sqrt[4]{8}$

119. $\dfrac{\sqrt{7}-\sqrt{2}}{\sqrt{2}+\sqrt{7}}$ $\dfrac{9-2\sqrt{14}}{5}$

▶ 120. $\dfrac{\sqrt{3}+\sqrt{2}}{\sqrt{3}-\sqrt{2}}$ $5+2\sqrt{6}$

121. $\dfrac{2}{\sqrt{x}+1}$ $\dfrac{2(\sqrt{x}-1)}{x-1}$

▶ 122. $\dfrac{3}{\sqrt{x}-2}$ $\dfrac{3\sqrt{x}+6}{x-4}$

123. $\dfrac{2z-1}{\sqrt{2z}-1}$ $\sqrt{2z}+1$

124. $\dfrac{3t-1}{\sqrt{3t}+1}$ $\sqrt{3t}-1$

APPLICATIONS

▶ 125. STATISTICS An example of a normal distribution curve, or *bell-shaped* curve, is shown in the illustration. A fraction that is part of the equation that models this curve is

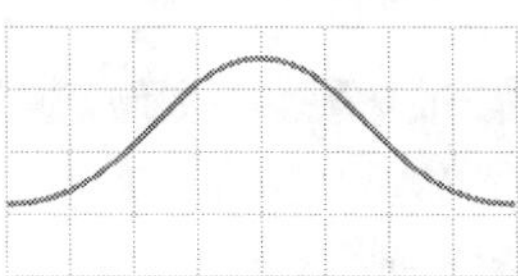

$$\frac{1}{\sigma\sqrt{2\pi}}$$

where σ is a letter from the Greek alphabet. Rationalize the denominator of the fraction. $\dfrac{\sqrt{2\pi}}{2\pi\sigma}$

126. ANALYTIC GEOMETRY The length of the perpendicular segment drawn from $(-2, 2)$ to the line with equation $2x - 4y = 4$ is given by

$$L = \frac{|2(-2) + (-4)(2) + (-4)|}{\sqrt{(2)^2 + (-4)^2}}$$

Find L. Express the result in simplified radical form. Then give an approximation to the nearest tenth. $\frac{8\sqrt{5}}{5} \approx 3.6$

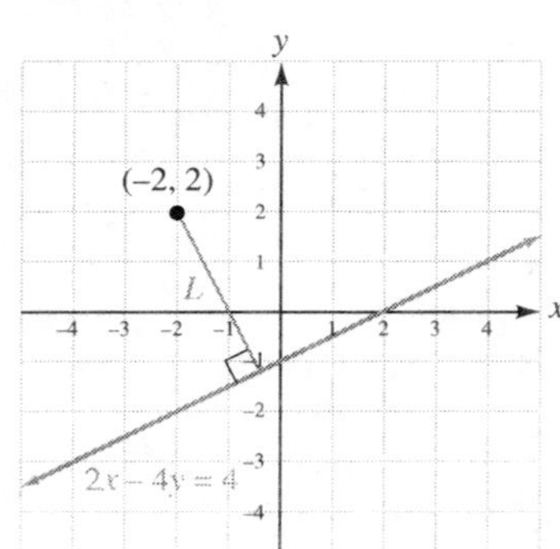

127. TRIGONOMETRY In trigonometry, we must often find the ratio of the lengths of two sides of right triangles. Use the information in the illustration to find the ratio

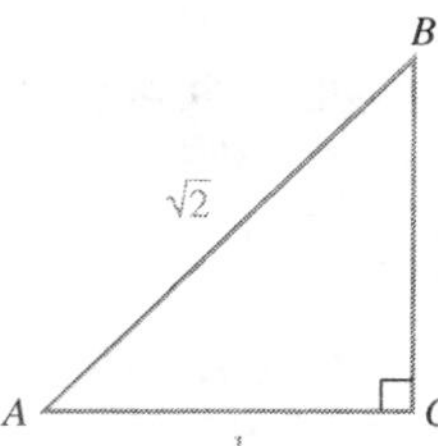

$$\frac{\text{length of side } AC}{\text{length of side } AB}$$

Write the result in simplified radical form. $\frac{\sqrt{2}}{2}$

128. MECHANICAL ENGINEERING A measure of how fast the block shown in the next column will oscillate when the system is set in motion is given by the formula

$$\omega = \sqrt{\frac{k_1 + k_2}{m}}$$

where k_1 and k_2 indicate the stiffness of the springs and m is the mass of the block. Rationalize the right-hand side and restate the formula. $\omega = \frac{\sqrt{(k_1 + k_2)m}}{m}$

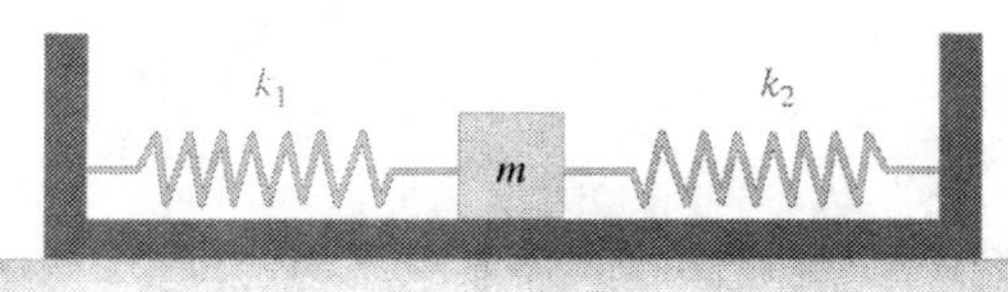

129. The period of a pendulum is the time required for the pendulum to swing back and forth to complete one cycle. The period (in seconds) is a function given by

$$f(L) = 2\pi\sqrt{\frac{L}{32}}$$

Rationalize the right-hand side and restate the formula. $f(L) = \frac{\pi\sqrt{2L}}{4}$

130. ELECTRONICS A formula that is used when designing AC (alternating current) circuits is

$$f_0 = \frac{1}{2\pi}\sqrt{\frac{1}{LC}}$$

Rationalize the right-hand side and restate the formula. $f_0 = \frac{\sqrt{LC}}{2\pi LC}$

WRITING

131. Explain why $\sqrt{m} \cdot \sqrt{m} = m$ but $\sqrt[3]{m} \cdot \sqrt[3]{m} \neq m$. (Assume that $m > 0$.)

132. Explain why the product of $\sqrt{m} + 3$ and $\sqrt{m} - 3$ does not contain a radical.

REVIEW

Solve each equation.

133. $\frac{2}{3 - a} = 1$ 1

134. $5(s - 4) = -5(s - 4)$ 4

135. $\frac{8}{b - 2} + \frac{3}{2 - b} = -\frac{1}{b}$ $\frac{1}{3}$

136. $\frac{2}{x - 2} + \frac{1}{x + 1} = \frac{1}{(x + 1)(x - 2)}$ $\frac{1}{3}$

Objectives

1. Solve equations containing one radical.
2. Solve equations containing two radicals.
3. Solve formulas containing radicals.

SECTION 8.5
Solving Radical Equations

Many situations can be modeled by equations that contain radicals. In this section, we will develop techniques to solve such equations.

1 Solve equations containing one radical.

Radical equations contain a radical expression with a variable radicand. Some examples are

$$\sqrt{x + 3} = 4 \qquad \sqrt[3]{x} = 2 \qquad \sqrt{x} - \sqrt{x + 1} = -1$$

To solve equations containing radicals, we will use the **power rule.**

The Power Rule

If we raise two equal quantities to the same power, the results are equal quantities.

If x, y, and n represent real numbers and $x = y$, then

$$x^n = y^n$$

If we raise both sides of an equation to the same power, the resulting equation might not be equivalent to the original equation. For example, if we square both sides of the equation

(1) $x = 3$

with a solution set of {3}, we obtain the equation

(2) $x^2 = 9$

with a solution set of {3, −3}.

Equations 1 and 2 are not equivalent, because they have different solution sets, and the solution −3 of Equation 2 does not satisfy Equation 1. Since raising both sides of an equation to the same power can produce an equation with solutions that don't satisfy the original equation, we must always check each proposed solution in the original equation and discard any **extraneous solutions.**

When we use the power rule to solve square root radical equations, it produces expressions of the form $(\sqrt{a})^2$. We have seen that when this expression is simplified, the radical symbol is removed.

The Square of a Square Root

For any nonnegative real number a,

$$(\sqrt{a})^2 = a$$

EXAMPLE 1 Solve: $\sqrt{x+3} = 4$

Strategy We will use the power rule and square both sides of the equation.

WHY Squaring both sides will produce, on the left side, the expression $(\sqrt{x+3})^2$ that simplifies to $x + 3$. This step clears the equation of the radical.

Solution

To eliminate the radical, we apply the power rule by squaring both sides of the equation and proceed as follows:

$\sqrt{x+3} = 4$ This is the equation to solve.

$(\sqrt{x+3})^2 = (4)^2$ To clear the equation of the square root, square both sides.

$x + 3 = 16$ Perform the operations on each side.

$x = 13$ Subtract 3 from both sides.

We must check the proposed solution 13 to see whether it satisfies the original equation.

Self Check 1

Solve: $\sqrt{a-2} = 3$ 11

Now Try **Problem 22**

Teaching Example 1 Solve: $\sqrt{x-6} = 5$

Answer: 31

Evaluate the left side. Do not square both sides when checking!

Check:

$$\sqrt{x+3} = 4 \quad \text{This is the original equation.}$$

$$\sqrt{13+3} \stackrel{?}{=} 4 \quad \text{Substitute 13 for } x.$$

$$\sqrt{16} \stackrel{?}{=} 4$$

$$4 = 4 \quad \text{True.}$$

Since 13 satisfies the original equation, it is the solution. ■

The method used in Example 1 to solve a radical equation containing a radical can be generalized as follows.

Solving an Equation Containing Radicals

1. Isolate one radical expression on one side of the equation.
2. Raise both sides of the equation to the power that is the same as the index of the radical.
3. Solve the resulting equation. If it still contains a radical, go back to step 1.
4. Check the results to eliminate extraneous solutions.

Self Check 2

AMUSEMENT PARK RIDES In Example 2, how long a vertical drop is needed if the riders are to free fall for 3.5 seconds? 196 ft

***Now Try* Problem 28**

Teaching Example 2 AMUSEMENT PARK RIDES In Example 2, how long a vertical drop is needed if the riders are to free fall for 4 seconds?
Answer:
256 ft

EXAMPLE 2 *Amusement Park Rides* The distance d in feet that an object will fall in t seconds is given by the formula

$$t = \sqrt{\frac{d}{16}}$$

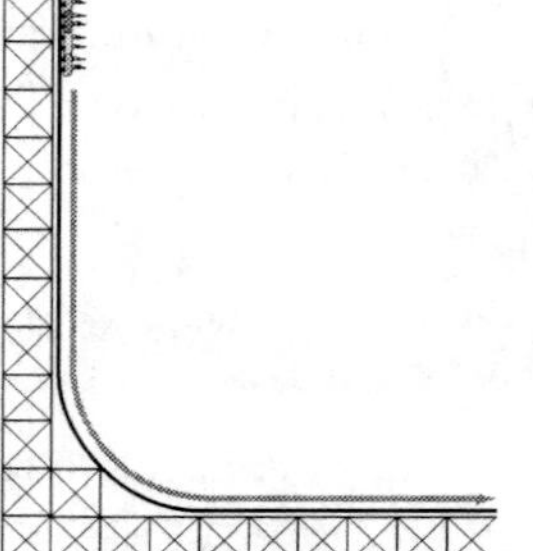

If the designers of the amusement park attraction shown to the right want the riders to experience 3 seconds of vertical free fall, what length of vertical drop is needed?

Strategy We will begin by substituting 3 for the time t in the formula.

WHY We can then solve the resulting radical equation in one variable to find the unknown distance d.

Solution

We substitute 3 for t in the formula and solve for d.

$$t = \sqrt{\frac{d}{16}}$$

$$3 = \sqrt{\frac{d}{16}} \quad \text{Here the radical is isolated on the right-hand side.}$$

$$(3)^2 = \left(\sqrt{\frac{d}{16}}\right)^2 \quad \text{Raise both sides to the second power.}$$

$$9 = \frac{d}{16} \quad \text{Simplify.}$$

$$144 = d \quad \text{Solve the resulting equation by multiplying both sides by 16.}$$

The amount of vertical drop needs to be 144 feet. ■

EXAMPLE 3 Solve: $\sqrt{3x+1}+1=x$

Strategy Since 1 is added outside the square root symbol, there are two terms on the left side of the equation. To isolate the radical, we will subtract 1 from both sides.

WHY This will put the equation in the form where we can square both sides to clear the radical.

Solution

We first subtract 1 from both sides to isolate the radical. Then, to eliminate the radical, we square both sides of the equation and proceed as follows:

$$\sqrt{3x+1}+1=x$$

$\sqrt{3x+1}=x-1$ Subtract 1 from both sides.

$\left(\sqrt{3x+1}\right)^2=(x-1)^2$ Square both sides to eliminate the square root.

$3x+1=x^2-2x+1$ On the right-hand side, $(x-1)^2=(x-1)(x-1)=x^2-x-x+1=x^2-2x+1$.

$0=x^2-5x$ Subtract 3x and 1 from both sides. This is a quadratic equation. Use factoring to solve it.

$0=x(x-5)$ Factor x^2-5x.

$x=0$ or $x-5=0$ Set each factor each to 0.

$x=0$ | $x=5$

We must check each proposed solution to see whether it satisfies the original equation.

Check:

This is the check for 0:	This is the check for 5:
$\sqrt{3x+1}+1=x$	$\sqrt{3x+1}+1=x$
$\sqrt{3(0)+1}+1\stackrel{?}{=}0$	$\sqrt{3(5)+1}+1\stackrel{?}{=}5$
$\sqrt{1}+1\stackrel{?}{=}0$	$\sqrt{16}+1\stackrel{?}{=}5$
$2\neq 0$	$5=5$

Since 0 does not check, it must be discarded. The only solution of the original equation is 5.

Self Check 3

Solve: $\sqrt{4x+1}+1=x$

Now Try **Problem 29**

Self Check 3 Answer

6, 0 is extraneous

Teaching Example 3 Solve: $\sqrt{2x+4}+2=x$

Answer:

6, 0 is extraneous

Using Your CALCULATOR Solving Equations Containing Radicals

To find approximate solutions for $\sqrt{3x+1}+1=x$ with a graphing calculator, we use window settings of $[-5, 10]$ for x and $[-2, 8]$ for y and graph the functions $f(x)=\sqrt{3x+1}+1$ and $g(x)=x$. We then use the INTERSECT feature to approximate the point of intersection of the graphs. See the figure to the right. The intersection point of (5, 5) implies that 5 is a solution of the radical equation. Check this result.

Intersection
X=5 Y=5

EXAMPLE 4 Solve: $\sqrt[3]{x^3+7}=x+1$

Strategy Note that the index of the radical is 3. We will use the power rule and cube both sides of the equation.

WHY Cubing both sides will produce, on the left side, the expression $\left(\sqrt[3]{x^3+7}\right)^3$ that simplifies to x^3+7. This step clears the equation of the radical.

Self Check 4

Solve: $\sqrt[3]{x^3+8}=x+2$ 0, −2

Now Try **Problem 34**

Teaching Example 4 Solve: $\sqrt[3]{x^3+27}=x+3$

Answer:

0, −3

Solution

$\sqrt[3]{x^3 + 7} = x + 1$	This is the equation to solve.
$\left(\sqrt[3]{x^3 + 7}\right)^3 = (x + 1)^3$	Cube both sides to eliminate the cube root.
$x^3 + 7 = x^3 + 3x^2 + 3x + 1$	$(x + 1)^3 = (x + 1)(x + 1)(x + 1)$.
$0 = 3x^2 + 3x - 6$	Subtract x^3 and 7 from both sides.
$0 = x^2 + x - 2$	Divide both sides by 3. To solve this quadratic equation, use factoring.
$0 = (x + 2)(x - 1)$	Factor the trinomial.

$$x + 2 = 0 \quad \text{or} \quad x - 1 = 0$$
$$x = -2 \qquad\qquad x = 1$$

We check each proposed solution to see whether it satisfies the original equation.

Check:

$$\sqrt[3]{x^3 + 7} = x + 1 \qquad\qquad \sqrt[3]{x^3 + 7} = x + 1$$
$$\sqrt[3]{(-2)^3 + 7} \stackrel{?}{=} -2 + 1 \qquad\qquad \sqrt[3]{1^3 + 7} \stackrel{?}{=} 1 + 1$$
$$\sqrt[3]{-8 + 7} \stackrel{?}{=} -1 \qquad\qquad \sqrt[3]{1 + 7} \stackrel{?}{=} 2$$
$$\sqrt[3]{-1} \stackrel{?}{=} -1 \qquad\qquad \sqrt[3]{8} \stackrel{?}{=} 2$$
$$-1 = -1 \qquad\qquad 2 = 2$$

Both -2 and 1 are solutions of the original equation.

Self Check 5

Let $g(x) = \sqrt[5]{10x + 1}$. For what value(s) of x is $g(x) = 1$? 0

Now Try **Problem 39**

Teaching Example 5 Let $f(x) = \sqrt[3]{4x - 4}$. For what value(s) of x is $f(x) = 2$?
Answer:
3

EXAMPLE 5 Let $f(x) = \sqrt[4]{2x + 1}$. For what value(s) of x is $f(x) = 5$?

Strategy We will substitute 5 for $f(x)$ and solve the equation $5 = \sqrt[4]{2x + 1}$. To do so, we will raise both sides of the equation to the fourth power.

WHY Raising both sides to the fourth power will produce, on the right side, the expression $\left(\sqrt[4]{2x + 1}\right)^4$ that simplifies to $2x + 1$. This step clears the equation of the radical.

Solution

To find the value(s) where $f(x) = 5$, we substitute 5 for $f(x)$ and solve for x.

$$f(x) = \sqrt[4]{2x + 1}$$
$$5 = \sqrt[4]{2x + 1} \qquad \text{This is the equation to solve.}$$

Since the equation contains a fourth root, we raise both sides to the fourth power to solve for x.

$(5)^4 = \left(\sqrt[4]{2x + 1}\right)^4$	Use the power rule to eliminate the radical.
$625 = 2x + 1$	Perform the operations on each side.
$624 = 2x$	To solve the resulting equation, subtract 1 from both sides.
$312 = x$	Divide both sides by 2.

If $x = 312$, then $f(x) = 5$. Verify this by evaluating $f(312)$.

2 Solve equations containing two radicals.

Self Check 6

Solve: $\sqrt{x - 4} = 2\sqrt{x - 16}$ 20

Now Try **Problem 43**

EXAMPLE 6 Solve: $\sqrt{5x + 9} = 2\sqrt{3x + 4}$

Strategy We will square both sides to clear the equation of both radicals.

WHY We can immediately square both sides since each radical is isolated on one side of the equation.

Solution

$\sqrt{5x+9} = 2\sqrt{3x+4}$ This is the equation to solve.

$\left(\sqrt{5x+9}\right)^2 = \left(2\sqrt{3x+4}\right)^2$ Square both sides.

$5x + 9 = 4(3x+4)$ On the right-hand side: $\left(2\sqrt{3x+4}\right)^2 = 2^2\left(\sqrt{3x+4}\right)^2 = 4(3x+4)$.

$5x + 9 = 12x + 16$ Distribute the multiplication by 4.

$-7 = 7x$ Subtract 5x and 16 from both sides.

$-1 = x$ Divide both sides by 7.

We check the proposed solution by substituting -1 for x in the original equation.

$\sqrt{5x+9} = 2\sqrt{3x+4}$ This is the original equation.

$\sqrt{5(-1)+9} \stackrel{?}{=} 2\sqrt{3(-1)+4}$ Substitute -1 for x.

$\sqrt{4} \stackrel{?}{=} 2\sqrt{1}$

$2 = 2$ True

The solution is -1.

Teaching Example 6 Solve: $\sqrt{3x+21} = 3\sqrt{x-5}$
Answer: 11

When more than one radical appears in an equation, it is often necessary to apply the power rule more than once.

EXAMPLE 7

Solve: $\sqrt{x} + \sqrt{x+2} = 2$

Strategy We will isolate $\sqrt{x+2}$ on the left side of the equation and square both sides to eliminate it. After simplifying the resulting equation, we will isolate the remaining radical term and square both sides a second time to eliminate it.

WHY Each time that we square both sides, we are able to clear the equation of one radical.

Solution

To remove the radicals, we must square both sides of the equation. This is easier to do if one radical is on each side of the equation. So we subtract $\sqrt{x}$ from both sides to isolate $\sqrt{x+2}$ on the left-hand side of the equation.

$\sqrt{x} + \sqrt{x+2} = 2$

$\sqrt{x+2} = 2 - \sqrt{x}$ Subtract $\sqrt{x}$ from both sides.

$\left(\sqrt{x+2}\right)^2 = \left(2-\sqrt{x}\right)^2$ Square both sides to eliminate the square root.

$x + 2 = 4 - 2\sqrt{x} - 2\sqrt{x} + x$ $\left(2-\sqrt{x}\right)^2 = \left(2-\sqrt{x}\right)\left(2-\sqrt{x}\right) = 4 - 2\sqrt{x} - 2\sqrt{x} + x$.

$x + 2 = 4 - 4\sqrt{x} + x$ Combine like radicals: $-2\sqrt{x} - 2\sqrt{x} = -4\sqrt{x}$.

$2 = 4 - 4\sqrt{x}$ Subtract x from both sides.

$-2 = -4\sqrt{x}$ Subtract 4 from both sides.

$\frac{1}{2} = \sqrt{x}$ Divide both sides by -4 and simplify.

$\frac{1}{4} = x$ Square both sides.

Self Check 7

Solve: $\sqrt{a} + \sqrt{a+3} = 3$ 1

Now Try **Problem 46**

Teaching Example 7 Solve: $\sqrt{9x+16} + \sqrt{9x} = 8$
Answer: 1

Check:

$$\sqrt{x} + \sqrt{x+2} = 2 \quad \text{This is the original equation.}$$

$$\sqrt{\frac{1}{4}} + \sqrt{\frac{1}{4} + 2} \stackrel{?}{=} 2 \quad \text{Substitute } \tfrac{1}{4} \text{ for } x.$$

$$\frac{1}{2} + \sqrt{\frac{9}{4}} \stackrel{?}{=} 2 \quad \text{Think of 2 as } \tfrac{8}{4} \text{ and add: } \tfrac{1}{4} + \tfrac{8}{4} = \tfrac{9}{4}.$$

$$\frac{1}{2} + \frac{3}{2} \stackrel{?}{=} 2 \quad \text{Evaluate } \sqrt{\tfrac{9}{4}}.$$

$$2 = 2 \quad \text{True}$$

The solution is $\frac{1}{4}$.

Using Your CALCULATOR Solving Equations Containing Radicals

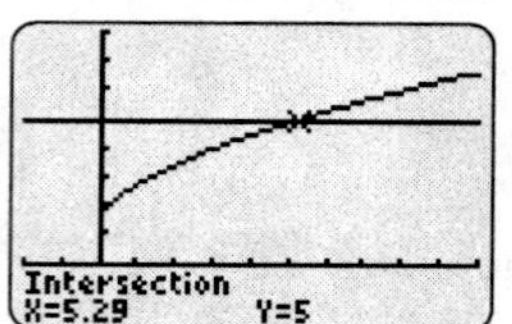

To find approximate solutions for $\sqrt{x} + \sqrt{x+2} = 5$ (an equation similar to that in Example 7) with a graphing calculator, we can use window settings of $[-2, 10]$ for x and $[-2, 8]$ for y and graph the functions $f(x) = \sqrt{x} + \sqrt{x+2}$ and $g(x) = 5$.

The figure shows that the INTERSECT feature gives the approximate coordinates of the point of intersection of the two graphs as (5.29, 5). Therefore, an approximate solution of the radical equation is 5.29. Check its reasonableness.

3 Solving formulas containing radicals.

To *solve a formula for a variable* means to isolate that variable on one side of the equation, with all other quantities on the other side.

Self Check 8

STATISTICS A formula used in statistics to determine the necessary size of a sample to obtain the desired degree of accuracy is

$$e = z_0\sqrt{\frac{pq}{n}}$$

Solve the formula for n. $n = \frac{z_0^2 pq}{e^2}$

Now Try **Problem 54**

Teaching Example 8 STATISTICS A formula used in statistics to determine the necessary size of a sample to obtain the desired degree of accuracy is

$$E = \frac{Z_c\sigma}{\sqrt{n}}$$

Solve the formula for n.
Answer:
$n = \left(\frac{Z_c\sigma}{E}\right)^2$

EXAMPLE 8 *Depreciation Rates* A piece of office equipment that is now worth V dollars originally cost C dollars 3 years ago. The rate r at which it has depreciated (lost value) is given by

$$r = 1 - \sqrt[3]{\frac{V}{C}}$$

Solve the formula for C.

Strategy To isolate the radical, we will subtract 1 from both sides. We can then eliminate the radical by cubing both sides.

WHY Cubing both sides will produce, on the right, the expression $\left(-\sqrt[3]{\frac{V}{C}}\right)^3$ that simplifies to $-\frac{V}{C}$. This step clears the equation of the radical.

Solution

We begin by isolating the cube root on the right-hand side of the equation.

$$r = 1 - \sqrt[3]{\frac{V}{C}}$$

$$r - 1 = -\sqrt[3]{\frac{V}{C}} \quad \text{Subtract 1 from both sides.}$$

$$(r-1)^3 = \left[-\sqrt[3]{\frac{V}{C}}\right]^3 \quad \text{Cube both sides.}$$

$$(r-1)^3 = -\frac{V}{C} \quad \text{Simplify the right-hand side.}$$

$$C(r-1)^3 = -V \quad \text{Multiply both sides by } C.$$

$$C = -\frac{V}{(r-1)^3} \quad \text{Divide both sides by } (r-1)^3.$$

ANSWERS TO SELF CHECKS

1. 11 **2.** 196 ft **3.** 6, 0 is extraneous **4.** 0, −2 **5.** 0 **6.** 20 **7.** 1 **8.** $n = \frac{z_0^2 pq}{e^2}$

SECTION 8.5 STUDY SET

VOCABULARY

Fill in the blanks.

1. Equations such as $\sqrt{x+4} - 4 = 5$ and $\sqrt[3]{x+1} = 12$ are called radical equations.

2. When solving equations containing radicals, try to isolate one radical expression on one side of the equation.

3. Squaring both sides of an equation can introduce extraneous solutions.

▶ **4.** To check a proposed solution means to substitute it into the original equation and see whether a true statement results.

CONCEPTS

What is the first step in solving each equation?

5. $\sqrt{x+4} = 5$ Square both sides.

6. $\sqrt[3]{x+4} = 2$ Cube both sides.

Simplify each expression. Assume all variables represent positive numbers.

7. $(\sqrt{x})^2$ x

8. $(\sqrt{x-5})^2$ $x-5$

9. $(4\sqrt{2x})^2$ $32x$

10. $(-\sqrt{x+3})^2$ $x+3$

Simplify each expression. Assume all variables represent positive numbers.

▶ **11.** $(\sqrt[3]{x})^3$ x

▶ **12.** $(\sqrt[4]{x})^4$ x

▶ **13.** $(-\sqrt[3]{2x})^3$ $-2x$

▶ **14.** $(2\sqrt[3]{x+3})^3$ $8x+24$

▶ **15.** Fill in the blank to make a true statement. $\sqrt{x}$ represents the number that, when squared, gives x.

16. Find the error.

$$\sqrt{x+1} - 3 = 8$$
$$\sqrt{x+1} = 11$$
$$(\sqrt{x+1})^2 = 11$$
$$x + 1 = 11$$
$$x = 10$$

Only one side of the equation was squared.

▶ **17.** Solve $\sqrt{x-2} + 2 = 4$ graphically, using the graphs at the right. 6

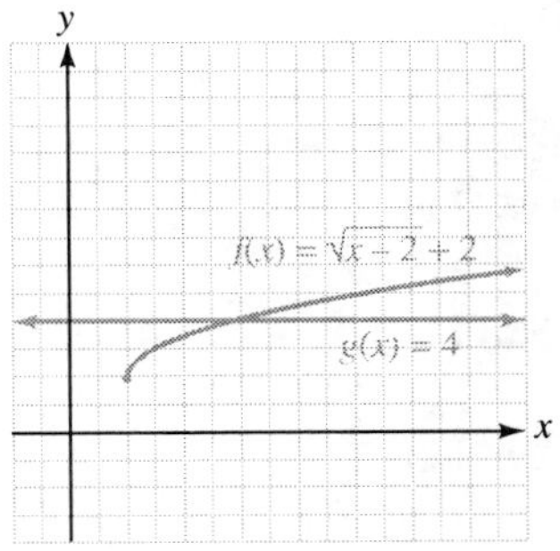

18. Use your own words to restate the power rule: If x, y, and n represent real numbers and $x = y$ then $x^n = y^n$. If we raise two equal quantities to the same power, the results are equal quantities.

NOTATION

Complete each solution to solve the equation.

19.
$$2\sqrt{x-2} = 4$$
$$(2\sqrt{x-2})^2 = 4^2$$
$$4(x-2) = 16$$
$$4x - 8 = 16$$
$$4x = 24$$
$$x = 6$$

▶ Selected exercises available online at **www.webassign.net/brookscole**

▶ **20.** $\sqrt{1-2x} = \sqrt{x+10}$

$(\sqrt{1-2x})^2 = (\sqrt{x+10})^2$

$1-2x = x+10$

$-3x = 9$

$x = -3$

GUIDED PRACTICE

Solve each equation. See Example 1.

21. $\sqrt{5x-6} = 2$ 2

22. $\sqrt{7x-10} = 12$ 22

23. $\sqrt{6x+1} = 5$ 4

▶ **24.** $\sqrt{6x+13} = 7$ 6

Use the formula $t = \sqrt{\frac{d}{16}}$ to find the indicated value. See Example 2.

25. If $d = 16$, find t. 1

26. If $d = 32$, find t. $\sqrt{2}$

27. If $t = 2$, find d. 64

▶ **28.** If $t = 4$, find d. 256

Solve each equation. Cross out any extraneous solutions. See Example 3.

29. $\sqrt{2r-3} + 9 = r$ 14, ~~6~~

30. $-s - 3 = 2\sqrt{5-s}$ -11, ~~1~~

31. $\sqrt{y+2} = 4 - y$ 2, ~~7~~

▶ **32.** $\sqrt{-x+2} + 2 = x$ 2, ~~1~~

Solve each equation. See Example 4.

33. $\sqrt[3]{x^3-7} = x - 1$ 2, -1

34. $\sqrt[3]{x^3+56} = x + 2$ 2, -4

35. $\sqrt[3]{b^3-63} = b - 3$ 4, -1

▶ **36.** $\sqrt[3]{m^3+26} = m + 2$ 1, -3

See Example 5.

37. Let $f(x) = \sqrt[3]{3x-6}$. For what value(s) of x is $f(x) = -3$? -7

▶ **38.** Let $f(x) = \sqrt{2x^2-7x}$. For what value(s) of x is $f(x) = 2$? $-\frac{1}{2}$, 4

39. Let $f(x) = \sqrt[4]{3x+1}$. For what value(s) of x is $f(x) = 4$? 85

40. Let $f(x) = \sqrt[5]{4x-4}$. For what value(s) of x is $f(x) = -2$? -7

Solve each equation. See Example 6.

41. $2\sqrt{x} = \sqrt{5x-16}$ 16

42. $3\sqrt{x} = \sqrt{3x+54}$ 9

43. $2\sqrt{4x+1} = \sqrt{x+4}$ 0

▶ **44.** $\sqrt{3(x+4)} = \sqrt{5x-12}$ 12

Solve each equation. See Example 7.

45. $\sqrt{x-5} + \sqrt{x} = 5$ 9

46. $\sqrt{x-7} + \sqrt{x} = 7$ 16

47. $\sqrt{z+3} - \sqrt{z} = 1$ 1

▶ **48.** $\sqrt{x+12} + \sqrt{x} = 6$ 4

Solve each equation for the indicated variable. See Example 8.

49. $v = \sqrt{2gh}$ for h $h = \frac{v^2}{2g}$

▶ **50.** $d = 1.4\sqrt{h}$ for h $h = \frac{d^2}{1.96}$

51. $T = 2\pi\sqrt{\frac{l}{32}}$ for l $l = \frac{8T^2}{\pi^2}$

52. $d = \sqrt[3]{\frac{12V}{\pi}}$ for V $V = \frac{\pi d^3}{12}$

53. $r = \sqrt[3]{\frac{A}{P}} - 1$ for A $A = P(r+1)^3$

▶ **54.** $r = \sqrt[3]{\frac{A}{P}} - 1$ for P $P = \frac{A}{(r+1)^3}$

55. $L_A = L_B\sqrt{1 - \frac{v^2}{c^2}}$ for v^2 $v^2 = c^2\left(1 - \frac{L_A^2}{L_B^2}\right)$

56. $R_1 = \sqrt{\frac{A}{\pi} - R_2^2}$ for A $A = \pi R_1^2 + \pi R_2^2$

TRY IT YOURSELF

Solve each equation. Cross out all extraneous solutions.

57. $\sqrt[3]{7n-1} = 3$ 4

58. $\sqrt[3]{12m+4} = 4$ 5

59. $\sqrt[4]{10p+1} = \sqrt[4]{11p-7}$ 8

60. $\sqrt[4]{10y+6} = 2\sqrt[4]{y}$ 1

61. $x = \frac{\sqrt{12x-5}}{2}$ $\frac{5}{2}, \frac{1}{2}$

62. $x = \frac{\sqrt{16x-12}}{2}$ 1, 3

63. $\sqrt{x+2} - \sqrt{4-x} = 0$ 1

64. $\sqrt{6-x} - \sqrt{2x+3} = 0$ 1

65. $\sqrt{-5x+24} = 6 - x$ 4, 3

▶ **66.** $\sqrt{22y+86} = y + 9$ 5, -1

67. $\sqrt[4]{x^4+4x^2-4} = -x$ -1, ~~1~~

68. $\sqrt[4]{8x+8} + 2 = 0$ ~~1~~

69. $\sqrt[4]{12t+4} + 2 = 0$ ~~1~~

▶ **70.** $u = \sqrt[4]{u^4 - 6u^2 + 24}$ 2

71. $\sqrt{x+5} + \sqrt{x-3} = 4$ 4

72. $\sqrt{b+7} - \sqrt{b-5} = 2$ 9

73. $\sqrt{2y+1} = 1 - 2\sqrt{y}$ 0, ~~4~~

74. $\sqrt{u} + 3 = \sqrt{u-3}$ ~~4~~

75. $\sqrt{y+7} + 3 = \sqrt{y+4}$ ~~-3~~

▶ **76.** $1 + \sqrt{z} = \sqrt{z+3}$ 1

77. $2 + \sqrt{u} = \sqrt{2u+7}$ 1, 9

78. $5r + 4 = \sqrt{5r + 20} + 4r$ 1, −4

79. $\sqrt{6t + 1} - 3\sqrt{t} = -1$ 4, ~~0~~

80. $\sqrt{4s + 1} - \sqrt{6s} = -1$ 6, ~~0~~

81. $\sqrt{2x + 5} + \sqrt{x + 2} = 5$ 2, ~~142~~

82. $\sqrt{2x + 5} + \sqrt{2x + 1} + 4 = 0$ ~~$\frac{5}{8}$~~

83. $\sqrt{x - 5} - \sqrt{x + 3} = 4$ ∅

84. $\sqrt{x + 8} - \sqrt{x - 4} = -2$ ~~8~~

APPLICATIONS

85. HIGHWAY DESIGNS A curved concrete road will accommodate traffic traveling s mph if the radius of the curve is r feet, according to the formula $s = 3\sqrt{r}$. If engineers expect 40-mph traffic, what radius should they specify? Give the result to the nearest foot. 178 ft

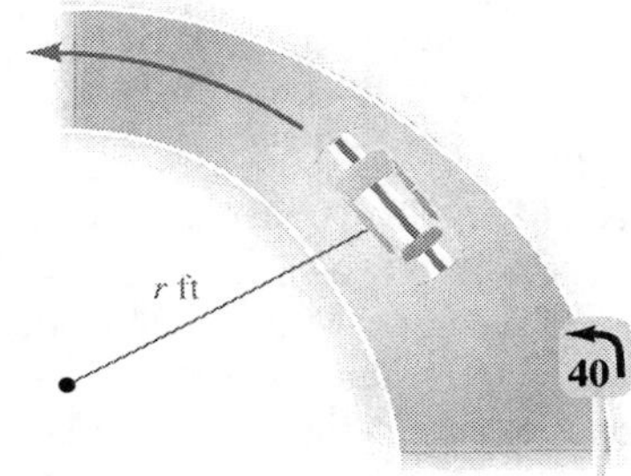

86. FORESTRY The higher a lookout tower is built, the farther an observer can see. That distance d (called the *horizon distance*, measured in miles) is related to the height h of the observer (measured in feet) by the formula $d = 1.4\sqrt{h}$. How tall must a lookout tower be to see the edge of the forest, 25 miles away? (Round to the nearest foot.) 319 ft

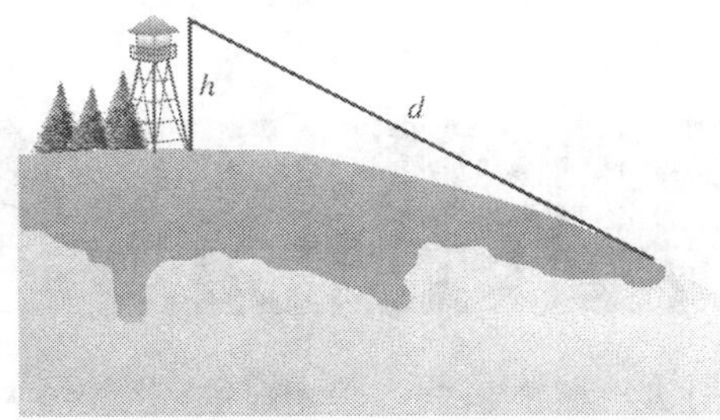

87. WIND POWER The power generated by a certain windmill is related to the velocity of the wind by the formula

$$v = \sqrt[3]{\frac{P}{0.02}}$$

where P is the power (in watts) and v is the velocity of the wind (in mph). Find how much power the windmill is generating when the wind is 29 mph. about 488 watts

88. DIAMONDS The *effective rate of interest r* earned by an investment is given by the formula

$$r = \sqrt[n]{\frac{A}{P}} - 1$$

where P is the initial investment that grows to value A after n years. If a diamond buyer got \$4,000 for a 1.73-carat diamond that he had purchased 4 years earlier, and earned an annual rate of return of 6.5% on the investment, what did he originally pay for the diamond? \$3,109

89. THEATER PRODUCTIONS The ropes, pulleys, and sandbags shown are part of a mechanical system used to raise and lower scenery for a stage play. For the scenery to be in the proper position, the following formula must apply:

$$w_2 = \sqrt{w_1^2 + w_3^2}$$

If $w_2 = 12.5$ lb and $w_3 = 7.5$ lb, find w_1. 10 lb

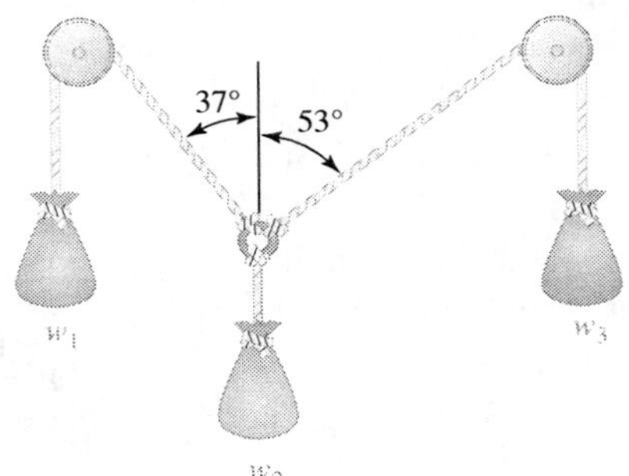

90. CARPENTRY During construction, carpenters often brace walls as shown, where the length of the brace is given by the formula

$$\ell = \sqrt{f^2 + h^2}$$

If a carpenter nails a 10-ft brace to the wall 6 feet above the floor, how far from the base of the wall should he nail the brace to the floor? 8 ft

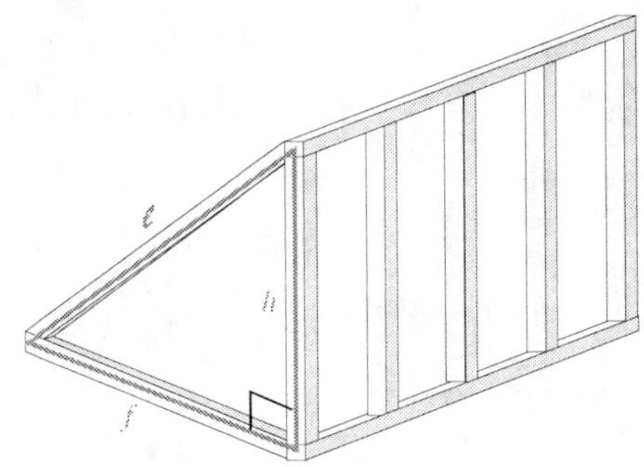

91. SUPPLY AND DEMAND The number of wrenches that will be produced at a given price can be predicted by the formula $s = \sqrt{5x}$, where s is the supply (in thousands) and x is the price (in dollars). The demand d for wrenches can be predicted by the formula $d = \sqrt{100 - 3x^2}$. Find the equilibrium price; that is, find the price at which supply will equal demand. \$5

▶ **92.** SUPPLY AND DEMAND The number of mirrors that will be produced at a given price can be predicted by the formula $s = \sqrt{23x}$, where s is the supply (in thousands) and x is the price (in dollars). The demand d for mirrors can be predicted by the formula $d = \sqrt{312 - 2x^2}$. Find the equilibrium price—that is, find the price at which supply will equal demand. \$8

WRITING

93. If both sides of an equation are raised to the same power, the resulting equation might not be equivalent to the original equation. Explain.

▶ **94.** Explain how the radical equation $\sqrt{2x - 1} = x$ can be solved graphically.

95. Explain how the table on the right can be used to solve $\sqrt{4x - 3} - 2 = \sqrt{2x - 5}$ if $Y_1 = \sqrt{4x - 3} - 2$ and $Y_2 = \sqrt{2x - 5}$.

X	Y1	Y2
2	.23607	ERROR
3	1	1
4	1.6056	1.7321
5	2.1231	2.2361
6	2.5826	2.6458
7	3	3
8	3.3852	3.3166

X=2

96. Explain how to use the graph shown on the right to approximate the solution of $\sqrt[3]{x - 0.5} = 1$.

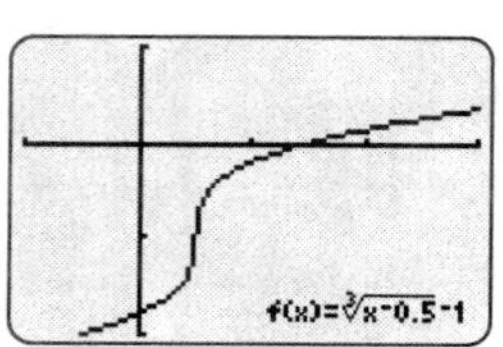

REVIEW

97. LIGHTING The intensity of the light reaching you from a light bulb varies inversely as the square of your distance from the bulb. If you are 5 feet away from a light bulb and the intensity is 40 foot-candles, what will the intensity be if you move 20 feet away from the bulb? 2.5 foot-candles

98. COMMITTEES What type of variation is shown below? As the number of people on this committee increased, what happened to its effectiveness? inverse; it decreased

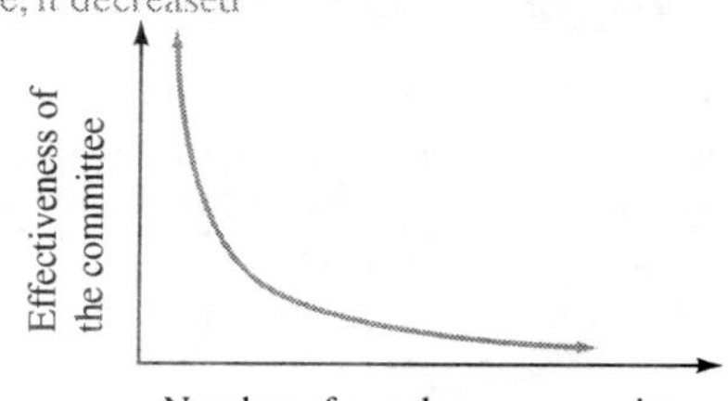

99. TYPESETTING If 12-point type is 0.166044 inch tall, how tall is 30-point type? 0.41511 in.

▶ **100.** GUITAR STRINGS The frequency of vibration of a string varies directly as the square root of the tension and inversely as the length of the string. Suppose a string 2.5 feet long, under a tension of 16 pounds, vibrates 25 times per second. Find k, the constant of variation. 15.625

Objectives

1. Use the quadratic formula to solve quadratic equations.
2. Identify quadratic equations with no real-number solutions.
3. Determine the most efficient method to solve a quadratic equation.
4. Solve problems modeled by quadratic equations.

SECTION 8.6

Solving Quadratic Equations: The Quadratic Formula

We can solve any quadratic equation by completing the square, but the work is often lengthy and involved. In this section, we will develop a formula, called the *quadratic formula,* that will enable us to solve quadratic equations with much less effort.

1 Use the quadratic formula to solve quadratic equations.

We can solve the **general quadratic equation** $ax^2 + bx + c = 0$, where $a \neq 0$, by completing the square.

$$ax^2 + bx + c = 0$$

$$\frac{ax^2}{a} + \frac{bx}{a} + \frac{c}{a} = \frac{0}{a} \quad \text{Divide both sides by } a \text{ so that the coefficient of } x^2 \text{ is 1.}$$

$$x^2 + \frac{b}{a}x + \frac{c}{a} = 0$$ Simplify $\frac{ax^2}{a} = x^2$. Write $\frac{bx}{a}$ as $\frac{b}{a}x$.

$$x^2 + \frac{b}{a}x = -\frac{c}{a}$$ Subtract $\frac{c}{a}$ from both sides.

Since the coefficient of x is $\frac{b}{a}$, we can complete the square on $x^2 + \frac{b}{a}x$ by adding

$$\left(\frac{1}{2} \cdot \frac{b}{a}\right)^2, \quad \text{which is} \quad \frac{b^2}{4a^2}$$

to both sides:

$$x^2 + \frac{b}{a}x + \frac{b^2}{4a^2} = \frac{b^2}{4a^2} - \frac{c}{a}$$

After factoring the perfect-square trinomial on the left-hand side, we have

$$\left(x + \frac{b}{2a}\right)\left(x + \frac{b}{2a}\right) = \frac{b^2}{4a^2} - \frac{4ac}{4aa}$$ The lowest common denominator on the right-hand side is $4a^2$. Build the second fraction.

$$\left(x + \frac{b}{2a}\right)^2 = \frac{b^2 - 4ac}{4a^2}$$ Subtract the numerators and write the difference over the common denominator.

The resulting equation can be solved by the square root method to obtain

$$x + \frac{b}{2a} = \sqrt{\frac{b^2 - 4ac}{4a^2}} \quad \text{or} \quad x + \frac{b}{2a} = -\sqrt{\frac{b^2 - 4ac}{4a^2}}$$

$$x + \frac{b}{2a} = \frac{\sqrt{b^2 - 4ac}}{\sqrt{4a^2}} \qquad x + \frac{b}{2a} = -\frac{\sqrt{b^2 - 4ac}}{\sqrt{4a^2}}$$

$$x = -\frac{b}{2a} + \frac{\sqrt{b^2 - 4ac}}{2a} \qquad x = -\frac{b}{2a} - \frac{\sqrt{b^2 - 4ac}}{2a}$$

$$x = \frac{-b + \sqrt{b^2 - 4ac}}{2a} \qquad x = \frac{-b - \sqrt{b^2 - 4ac}}{2a}$$

These solutions are usually written in one formula called the **quadratic formula.**

The Quadratic Formula

The solutions of the quadratic equation $ax^2 + bx + c = 0$ are

$$x = \frac{-b \pm \sqrt{b^2 - 4ac}}{2a} \quad \text{where } a \neq 0$$

Caution! When you write the quadratic formula, draw the fraction bar so that it includes the complete numerator. Do not write

$$x = -b \pm \frac{\sqrt{b^2 - 4ac}}{2a}$$

Self Check 1

Solve: $x^2 + 6x + 5 = 0$ $-1, -5$

Now Try **Problem 29**

EXAMPLE 1 Solve: $x^2 + 5x + 6 = 0$

Strategy We will compare the given equation to the general quadratic equation $ax^2 + bx + c = 0$ to identify a, b, and c.

Teaching Example 1 Solve: $x^2 + 13x + 12 = 0$

Answer:

$-1, -12$

WHY To use the quadratic formula, we need to know what numbers to substitute for a, b, and c in $x = \dfrac{-b \pm \sqrt{b^2 - 4ac}}{2a}$.

Solution

The equation is written in $ax^2 + bx + c = 0$ form with $a = 1$, $b = 5$, and $c = 6$.

$$\begin{array}{l} 1x^2 + 5x + 6 = 0 \\ \uparrow \quad\;\; \uparrow \quad\;\; \uparrow \\ ax^2 + bx + c = 0 \end{array}$$

To find the solutions, we substitute these values into the quadratic formula and evaluate the right-hand side.

$$x = \frac{-b \pm \sqrt{b^2 - 4ac}}{2a}$$ This is the quadratic formula.

$$= \frac{-5 \pm \sqrt{5^2 - 4(1)(6)}}{2(1)}$$ Substitute 1 for a, 5 for b, and 6 for c.

$$= \frac{-5 \pm \sqrt{25 - 24}}{2}$$ Evaluate the power and multiply within the radical symbol.

$$= \frac{-5 \pm \sqrt{1}}{2}$$ Perform the subtraction within the radical symbol.

$$x = \frac{-5 \pm 1}{2}$$ $\sqrt{1} = 1$.

This notation represents two solutions. We simplify them separately, first using the + sign and then using the − sign.

$$x = \frac{-5 + 1}{2} \quad \text{or} \quad x = \frac{-5 - 1}{2}$$

$$x = \frac{-4}{2} \qquad\qquad x = \frac{-6}{2}$$

$$x = -2 \qquad\qquad x = -3$$

The solutions are −2 and −3.

> ***Success Tip*** In Example 1, you may have noticed that we could have solved $x^2 + 5x + 6 = 0$ by factoring.

Self Check 2

Solve: $4x^2 - 11x = 3$ $3, -\frac{1}{4}$

Now Try **Problem 33**

Teaching Example 2 Solve: $5x^2 = -2x + 3$
Answer: $-1, \frac{3}{5}$

EXAMPLE 2 Solve: $2x^2 = 5x + 3$

Strategy We will use the subtraction property of equality to get 0 on the right side of the equation. Then we will compare the resulting equation to the general quadratic equation $ax^2 + bx + c = 0$ to identify a, b, and c.

WHY To use the quadratic formula, we need to know what numbers to substitute for a, b, and c in $x = \dfrac{-b \pm \sqrt{b^2 - 4ac}}{2a}$.

Solution

$$2x^2 = 5x + 3$$ This is the equation to solve.

$$2x^2 - 5x - 3 = 0$$ Subtract 5x and 3 from both sides.

In this equation, $a = 2$, $b = -5$, and $c = -3$. To find the solutions, we substitute these values into the quadratic formula and evaluate the right-hand side.

$$x = \frac{-b \pm \sqrt{b^2 - 4ac}}{2a}$$ This is the quadratic formula.

$$= \frac{-(-5) \pm \sqrt{(-5)^2 - 4(2)(-3)}}{2(2)}$$ Substitute 2 for a, -5 for b, and -3 for c.

$$= \frac{5 \pm \sqrt{25 - (-24)}}{4}$$ $-(-5) = 5$. Evaluate the power and multiply within the radical symbol.

$$= \frac{5 \pm \sqrt{49}}{4}$$ Perform the subtraction within the radical symbol: $25 - (-24) = 25 + 24 = 49$.

$$= \frac{5 \pm 7}{4}$$ $\sqrt{49} = 7$.

Thus,

$$x = \frac{5 + 7}{4} \quad \text{or} \quad x = \frac{5 - 7}{4}$$

$$x = \frac{12}{4} \qquad x = \frac{-2}{4}$$

$$x = 3 \qquad x = -\frac{1}{2}$$

The solutions are 3 and $-\frac{1}{2}$. Check each one in the original equation.

EXAMPLE 3 Solve $3x^2 = 2x + 4$. Round each solution to the nearest hundredth.

Strategy We will use the subtraction property of equality to get 0 on the right side of the equation. Then we will compare the resulting equation to the general quadratic equation $ax^2 + bx + c = 0$ to identify a, b, and c.

WHY To use the quadratic formula, we need to know what numbers to substitute for a, b, and c in $x = \frac{-b \pm \sqrt{b^2 - 4ac}}{2a}$.

Solution

We begin by writing the given equation in $ax^2 + bx + c = 0$ form.

$$3x^2 = 2x + 4$$ This is the equation to solve.

$$3x^2 - 2x - 4 = 0$$ Subtract 2x and 4 from both sides.

In this equation, $a = 3$, $b = -2$, and $c = -4$. To find the solutions, we substitute these values into the quadratic formula and evaluate the right-hand side.

$$x = \frac{-b \pm \sqrt{b^2 - 4ac}}{2a}$$ This is the quadratic formula.

$$= \frac{-(-2) \pm \sqrt{(-2)^2 - 4(3)(-4)}}{2(3)}$$ Substitute 3 for a, -2 for b, and -4 for c.

$$= \frac{2 \pm \sqrt{4 + 48}}{6}$$ $-(-2) = 2$. Simplify within the radical symbol.

$$= \frac{2 \pm \sqrt{52}}{6}$$ Perform the addition within the radical symbol.

Self Check 3

Solve $2x^2 - 1 = 2x$. Round each solution to the nearest hundredth.

Now Try **Problem 37**

Self Check 3 Answer

$\frac{1 + \sqrt{3}}{2} \approx 1.37, \frac{1 - \sqrt{3}}{2} \approx -0.37$

Teaching Example 3 Solve: $3x^2 - 1 = 5x$. Round each solution to the nearest hundredth.

Answer:

$\frac{5 + \sqrt{37}}{6} \approx 1.85, \frac{5 - \sqrt{37}}{6} \approx -0.18$

$$= \frac{2 \pm 2\sqrt{13}}{6}$$ $\sqrt{52} = \sqrt{4 \cdot 13} = 2\sqrt{13}$.

$$= \frac{\overset{1}{\cancel{2}}(1 \pm \sqrt{13})}{\underset{1}{\cancel{2}} \cdot 3}$$ In the numerator, factor out 2: $2 \pm 2\sqrt{13} = 2(1 \pm \sqrt{13})$. Write 6 as $2 \cdot 3$. Then remove the common factor of 2.

$$x = \frac{1 \pm \sqrt{13}}{3}$$ Simplify.

The solutions are $\frac{1 \pm \sqrt{13}}{3}$. We can use a calculator to approximate each of them. To the nearest hundredth,

$$\frac{1 + \sqrt{13}}{3} \approx 1.54 \qquad \frac{1 - \sqrt{13}}{3} \approx -0.87$$

2 Identify quadratic equations with no real-number solutions.

The next example shows that some quadratic equations have no real-number solutions.

Self Check 4

Does the equation

$$2x^2 + x + 1 = 0$$

have any real-number solutions? no

***Now Try* Problem 41**

Teaching Example 4 Does the equation
$4x^2 - 3x + 2 = 0$
have any real-number solutions?
Answer:
no

EXAMPLE 4 Does the equation $x^2 + 2x + 5 = 0$ have any real-number solutions?

Strategy We will compare the given equation to the general quadratic equation $ax^2 + bx + c = 0$ to identify a, b, and c.

WHY To use the quadratic formula, we need to know what numbers to substitute for a, b, and c in $x = \frac{-b \pm \sqrt{b^2 - 4ac}}{2a}$.

Solution

In this equation $a = 1$, $b = 2$, and $c = 5$. We substitute these values into the quadratic formula.

$$x = \frac{-b \pm \sqrt{b^2 - 4ac}}{2a}$$ This is the quadratic formula.

$$= \frac{-2 \pm \sqrt{2^2 - 4(1)(5)}}{2(1)}$$ Substitute 1 for a, 2 for b, and 5 for c.

$$= \frac{-2 \pm \sqrt{4 - 20}}{2}$$ Evaluate the power and multiply within the radical symbol.

$$x = \frac{-2 \pm \sqrt{-16}}{2}$$ Perform the subtraction within the radical symbol. The result is a negative number, -16.

Since $\sqrt{-16}$ is not a real number, there are no real-number solutions.

3 Determine the most efficient method to solve a quadratic equation.

We have discussed four methods that are used to solve quadratic equations. The following table shows some advantages and disadvantages of each method.

Method	Advantages	Disadvantages	Examples
Factoring and the zero-factor property	It can be very fast. When each factor is set equal to 0, the resulting equations are usually easy to solve.	Some polynomials may be difficult to factor and others impossible.	$x^2 - 2x - 24 = 0$ $4a^2 + a = 0$
Square root property	It is the fastest way to solve equations of the form $ax^2 = n$ or $(ax + b)^2 = n$, where n is a number.	It only applies to equations that are in these forms.	$x^2 = 27$ $(2y + 3)^2 = 25$
Completing the square*	It can be used to solve any quadratic equation. It works well with equations of the form $x^2 + bx = n$, where b is even.	It involves more steps than the other methods. The algebra can be cumbersome if the leading coefficient is not 1.	$t^2 - 14t = 9$ $x^2 + 4x + 1 = 0$
Quadratic formula	It can be used to solve any quadratic equation.	It involves several computations where sign errors can be made. Often the result must be simplified.	$x^2 + 3x - 33 = 0$ $4s^2 - 10s + 5 = 0$

*The quadratic formula is just a condensed version of completing the square and is usually easier to use. However, you need to know how to complete the square because it is used in more advanced mathematics courses.

To determine the most efficient method for a given equation, we can use the following strategy.

Strategy for Solving Quadratic Equations

1. See whether the equation is in a form such that the **square root method** is easily applied.
2. See whether the equation is in a form such that the **completing the square method** is easily applied.
3. If neither Step 1 nor Step 2 is reasonable, write the equation in $ax^2 + bx + c = 0$ form.
4. See whether the equation can be solved using the **factoring method.**
5. If you can't factor, solve the equation by the **quadratic formula.**

4 Solve problems modeled by quadratic equations.

The equation solving methods discussed in this section can be used to solve a variety of real-world applications that are modeled by quadratic equations.

Self Check 5

A rectangular garden is 4 feet longer than it is wide. If the garden has an area of 96 square feet, find the garden's length and width. width: 8 ft, length: 12 ft

Now Try **Problem 69**

Teaching Example 5 An architect needs to design a trianglar-shaped window that has an area of 100 in.^{2} If the height is 10 in. less than the base, find the base and height.
Answer:
base: 20 in., height: 10 in.

EXAMPLE 5 *Sailing* The height of a triangular sail is 4 feet more than the length of the base. If the sail has an area of 30 square feet, find the length of its base and the height.

Analyze

- The height of the sail is 4 feet more than the length of the base.
- The area of the sail is 30 ft^2.
- Find the length of the base and height of the sail.

Form If we let b = the length of the base in feet of the triangular sail, then $b + 4$ = the height in feet. We can use the formula for the area of a triangle, $A = \frac{1}{2}bh$, to form an equation.

$\frac{1}{2}$	times	the length of the base	times	the height	equals	the area of the triangle.
$\frac{1}{2}$	$\cdot$	b	$\cdot$	$(b + 4)$	=	30

Success Tip It is usually easier to clear quadratic equations of fractions before attempting to solve them.

Solve

$$\frac{1}{2}b(b + 4) = 30$$

$$b(b + 4) = 60$$ To clear the equation of the fraction, multiply both sides by 2.

$$b^2 + 4b = 60$$ Distribute the multiplication by b.

Since the coefficient of the b-term is the even number 4, this equation can be solved quickly by completing the square.

$$b^2 + 4b = 60$$

$$b^2 + 4b + 4 = 60 + 4$$ Complete the square: $\frac{1}{2}(4) = 2$ and $(2)^2 = 4$. Add 4 to both sides.

$$(b + 2)^2 = 64$$ On the left side, factor the perfect-square trinomial. On the right, add.

$$b + 2 = \pm\sqrt{64}$$ Use the square root property.

$$b = -2 \pm 8$$ To isolate b, subtract 2 from both sides. Evaluate: $\sqrt{64} = 8$.

$$b = -2 + 8 \quad \text{or} \quad b = -2 - 8$$ To find the solutions, perform the calculation using a + symbol and then using a − symbol.

$$b = 6 \quad \Big| \quad b = -10$$ Discard the solution −10. The length of the base cannot be negative.

State The length of the base of the sail is 6 feet. Since the height is given by $b + 4$, the height of the sail is $6 + 4 = 10$ feet.

Check A height of 10 feet is 4 feet more than the length of the base, which is 6 feet. Also, the area of the triangle is $\frac{1}{2}(6)(10) = 30$ ft^2. The results check.

EXAMPLE 6 ***Televisions*** A television's screen size is measured diagonally. For the 42-inch plasma television shown in the illustration, the screen's height is 16 inches less than its length. What are the height and length of the screen?

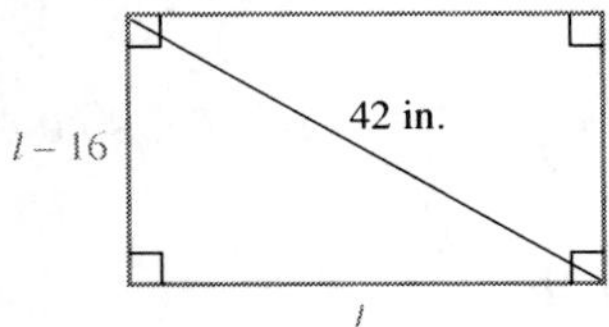

Analyze A sketch of the screen shows that two adjacent sides and the diagonal form a right triangle. The length of the hypotenuse is 42 inches.

Form If we let l = the length of the screen in inches, then $l - 16$ represents the height of the screen in inches. We can use the Pythagorean theorem to form an equation.

$a^2 + b^2 = c^2$ — This is the Pythagorean theorem.

$l^2 + (l - 16)^2 = 42^2$ — Substitute l for a, $l - 16$ for b, and 42 for c.

$l^2 + l^2 - 32l + 256 = 1{,}764$ — Find $(l - 16)^2$ and 42^2.

$2l^2 - 32l - 1{,}508 = 0$ — To get 0 on the right side of the equation, subtract 1,764 from both sides.

$l^2 - 16l - 754 = 0$ — Divide both sides of the equation by 2: $\frac{2l^2}{2} - \frac{32l}{2} - \frac{1{,}508}{2} = \frac{0}{2}$.

Solve Because of the large constant term, -754, we will not attempt to solve this quadratic equation by factoring. Instead, we will use the quadratic formula, with $a = 1, b = -16$, and $c = -754$.

$l = \frac{-b \pm \sqrt{b^2 - 4ac}}{2a}$ — In the quadratic formula, replace x with l.

$l = \frac{-(-16) \pm \sqrt{(-16)^2 - 4(1)(-754)}}{2(1)}$ — Substitute 1 for a, -16 for b, and -754 for c.

$l = \frac{16 \pm \sqrt{256 - (-3{,}016)}}{2}$ — Evaluate the power and multiply within the radical. Multiply in the denominator.

$l = \frac{16 \pm \sqrt{3{,}272}}{2}$ — Subtract within the radical.

We can use a calculator to approximate each one to the nearest tenth. The negative solution is discarded because the length of the screen cannot be negative.

$$\frac{16 + \sqrt{3{,}272}}{2} \approx 36.6 \quad \text{or} \quad \frac{16 - \sqrt{3{,}272}}{2} \approx -20.6$$

State The length of the television screen is approximately 36.6 inches. Since the height is $l - 16$, the height is approximately $36.6 - 16$ or 20.6 inches.

Check The sum of the squares of the lengths of the sides is $(36.6)^2 + (20.6)^2 = 1{,}763.92$. The square of the length of the hypotenuse is $42^2 = 1{,}764$. Since these are approximately equal, the results seem reasonable.

Self Check 6

Find the height and the length of the screen of a laptop if the diagonal measurement is 15.4 inches and its length is 4.5 inches more than its width. Round to the nearest hundredth.

Now Try **Problem 72**

Self Check 6 Answer
width: 8.40 in., length: 12.90 in.

Teaching Example 6 A strong wind holds a kite at the end of a 50-foot string. If the kites's height above the ground is 10 feet less than its position across the ground how high is the kite above Earth?
Answer:
30 ft

ANSWERS TO SELF CHECKS
1. $-1, -5$ **2.** $3, -\frac{1}{4}$ **3.** $\frac{1+\sqrt{3}}{2} \approx 1.37, \frac{1-\sqrt{3}}{2} \approx -0.37$ **4.** no
5. width: 8 ft, height: 12 ft **6.** width: 8.40 in., length: 12.90 in.

SECTION 8.6 STUDY SET

VOCABULARY

Fill in the blanks.

1. To solve a quadratic equation means to find all the values of the variable that make the equation true.
2. $\sqrt{-16}$ is not a real number.
3. The general quadratic equation is $ax^2 + bx + c = 0$.
4. The formula $x = \frac{-b \pm \sqrt{b^2 - 4ac}}{2a}$ is called the quadratic formula.

CONCEPTS

Fill in the blanks.

5. In the quadratic equation $ax^2 + bx + c = 0$, $a \neq 0$.
6. Before we can determine a, b, and c for $x = 3x^2 - 1$, we must write the equation in quadratic (general) form.
7. In the quadratic equation $3x^2 - 5 = 0$, $a = 3$, $b = 0$, and $c = -5$
8. In the quadratic equation $-4x^2 + 8x = 0$, $a = -4$, $b = 8$, and $c = 0$
9. The formula for the area of a rectangle is $A = lw$, and the formula for the area of a triangle is $A = \frac{1}{2}bh$.
10. If a, b, and c are three sides of a right triangle and c is the hypotenuse, then $c^2 = a^2 + b^2$.
11. In evaluating the numerator of $\frac{-5 \pm \sqrt{5^2 - 4(2)(1)}}{2(2)}$ what operation should be performed first? Evaluate 5^2
12. Consider the expression $\frac{3 \pm 6\sqrt{2}}{3}$
    a. How many terms does the numerator contain? 2
    b. What common factor do the terms have? 3
    c. Simplify the expression. $1 \pm 2\sqrt{2}$
13. A student used the quadratic formula to solve an equation and obtained $x = \frac{-3 \pm \sqrt{15}}{2}$
    a. How many solutions does the equation have? 2
    b. What are they exactly? $\frac{-3+\sqrt{15}}{2}, \frac{-3-\sqrt{15}}{2}$
    c. Approximate them to the nearest hundredth. 0.44, −3.44

14. The solutions of a quadratic equation are $x = 2 \pm \sqrt{3}$. Graph them on the number line.

$2-\sqrt{3}$ $2+\sqrt{3}$
−4 −3 −2 −1 0 1 2 3 4

NOTATION

Complete each solution.

15. Solve: $x^2 - 5x - 6 = 0$

$$x = \frac{-b \pm \sqrt{b^2 - 4ac}}{2a}$$
$$= \frac{-(-5) \pm \sqrt{(-5)^2 - 4(1)(-6)}}{2(1)}$$
$$= \frac{5 \pm \sqrt{25 + 24}}{2}$$
$$= \frac{5 \pm \sqrt{49}}{2}$$
$$x = \frac{5 \pm 7}{2}$$
$$x = \frac{5+7}{2} = 6 \quad \text{or} \quad x = \frac{5-7}{2} = -1$$

16. Solve: $3x^2 + 2x - 2 = 0$

$$x = \frac{-b \pm \sqrt{b^2 - 4ac}}{2a}$$
$$= \frac{-2 \pm \sqrt{2^2 - 4(3)(-2)}}{2(3)}$$
$$= \frac{-2 \pm \sqrt{4 + 24}}{6}$$
$$= \frac{-2 \pm \sqrt{28}}{6}$$
$$= \frac{-2 \pm 2\sqrt{7}}{6}$$
$$= \frac{2(-1 \pm \sqrt{7})}{2 \cdot 3}$$
$$x = \frac{-1 \pm \sqrt{7}}{3}$$

Selected exercises available online at
www.webassign.net/brookscole

17. What is wrong with the following work?

Solve: $x^2 + 4x - 5 = 0$

$$x = -4 \pm \frac{\sqrt{16 - 4(1)(-5)}}{2}$$

The fraction bar is not extended to underline the complete numerator.

18. In reading $\frac{-b \pm \sqrt{b^2 - 4ac}}{2a}$ we say, "the opposite (negative) of b, plus or minus the square root of b squared minus 4 times a times c, all over $2a$."

GUIDED PRACTICE

Change each equation into quadratic form, if necessary, and find the values of a, b, and c. Do not solve the equation. See Example 1.

19. $x^2 + 4x + 3 = 0$ $a = 1, b = 4, c = 3$

20. $x^2 - x - 4 = 0$ $a = 1, b = -1, c = -4$

21. $3x^2 - 2x + 7 = 0$ $a = 3, b = -2, c = 7$

22. $4x^2 + 7x - 3 = 0$ $a = 4, b = 7, c = -3$

23. $4y^2 = 2y - 1$ $a = 4, b = -2, c = 1$

24. $2x = 3x^2 + 4$ $a = 3, b = -2, c = 4$

25. $x(3x - 5) = 2$ $a = 3, b = -5, c = -2$

26. $y(5y + 10) = 8$ $a = 5, b = 10, c = -8$

Use the quadratic formula to find all real solutions. See Example 1.

27. $x^2 - 5x + 6 = 0$ $2, 3$

28. $x^2 + 5x + 4 = 0$ $-1, -4$

29. $x^2 + 7x + 12 = 0$ $-3, -4$

30. $x^2 - x - 12 = 0$ $-3, 4$

Use the quadratic formula to find all real solutions. See Example 2.

31. $2x^2 - x = 1$ $1, -\frac{1}{2}$

32. $2x^2 + 3x = 2$ $-2, \frac{1}{2}$

33. $3x^2 + 2 = -5x$ $-1, -\frac{2}{3}$

34. $3x^2 + 1 = 4x$ $1, \frac{1}{3}$

Use the quadratic formula to find all real solutions. Round each solution to the nearest hundredth. See Example 3.

35. $x^2 - 2x - 1 = 0$ $1 \pm \sqrt{2}$; $-0.41, 2.41$

36. $b^2 = 18$ $\pm 3\sqrt{2}$; ± 4.24

37. $2x^2 + x = 5$ $\frac{-1 \pm \sqrt{41}}{4}$; $-1.85, 1.35$

38. $3x^2 - x = 1$ $\frac{1 \pm \sqrt{13}}{6}$; $-0.43, 0.77$

Does each equation have any real-number solutions. If so, find them. See Example 4.

39. $3m^2 - 2m + 5 = 0$ no

40. $4n^2 + 12n - 3 = 0$ yes, $\frac{-3 \pm 2\sqrt{3}}{2}$

41. $2d^2 + 8d + 5 = 0$ yes, $\frac{-4 \pm \sqrt{6}}{2}$

42. $9c^2 - 2c + 4 = 0$ no

Use the most convenient method to find all real solutions. If a solution contains a radical, give the exact solution and then approximate it to the nearest hundredth. See Objective 3.

43. $(2y - 1)^2 = 25$ $-2, 3$

44. $m^2 + 14m + 49 = 0$ $-7, -7$

45. $2x^2 - x + 2 = 0$ no real solutions

46. $x^2 + 2x + 7 = 0$ no real solutions

47. $x^2 - 2x - 35 = 0$ $-5, 7$

48. $x^2 + 5x + 3 = 0$ $\frac{-5 \pm \sqrt{13}}{2}$; $-4.30, -0.70$

49. $4c^2 + 16c = 0$ $-4, 0$

50. $t^2 - 1 = 0$ ± 1

51. $18 = 3y^2$ $\pm\sqrt{6}$; ± 2.45

52. $25x - 50x^2 = 0$ $0, \frac{1}{2}$

TRY IT YOURSELF

Determine a, b, and c.

53. $7(x^2 + 3) = -14x$ $a = 7, b = 14, c = 21$

54. $(2a + 3)(a - 2) = (a + 1)(a - 1)$ $a = 1, b = -1, c = -5$

Use the quadratic formula to find all real solutions.

55. $4x^2 + 4x - 3 = 0$ $\frac{1}{2}, -\frac{3}{2}$

56. $4x^2 + 3x - 1 = 0$ $\frac{1}{4}, -1$

57. $x^2 + 3x + 1 = 0$ $\frac{-3 \pm \sqrt{5}}{2}$

58. $x^2 + 3x - 2 = 0$ $\frac{-3 \pm \sqrt{17}}{2}$

59. $3x^2 - x = 3$ $\frac{1 \pm \sqrt{37}}{6}$

60. $5x^2 = 3x + 1$ $\frac{3 \pm \sqrt{29}}{10}$

61. $x^2 + 5 = 2x$ no real solutions

62. $2x^2 + 3x = -3$ no real solutions

63. $x^2 = 1 - 2x$ $-1 \pm \sqrt{2}$

64. $x^2 = 4 + 2x$ $1 \pm \sqrt{5}$

65. $3x^2 = 6x + 2$ $\frac{3 \pm \sqrt{15}}{3}$

66. $3x^2 = -8x - 2$ $\frac{-4 \pm \sqrt{10}}{3}$

Solve each equation. Round each solution to the nearest tenth.

67. $2.4x^2 - 9.5x + 6.2 = 0$ $0.8, 3.1$

68. $-1.7x^2 + 0.5x + 0.9 = 0$ $-0.6, 0.9$

APPLICATIONS

69. HEIGHT OF A TRIANGLE The triangle shown has an area of 30 square inches. Find its height. 6 in.

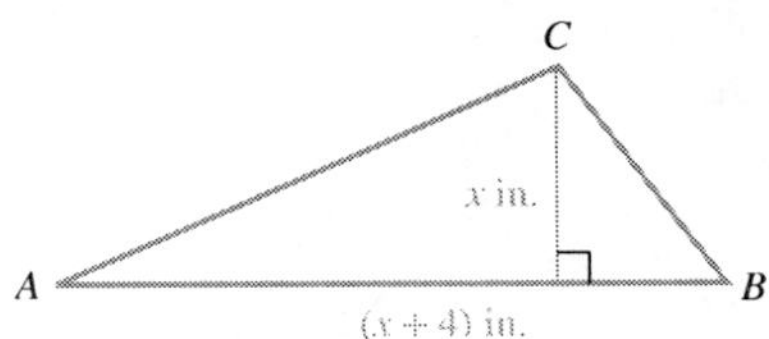

70. A poster that shows former UCLA basketball coach John Wooden's Pyramid of Success has an area of 80 square inches. The base of the triangular-shaped poster is 6 inches longer than the height. Find the length of the base and the height of the poster. 16 in., 10 in.

from Campus to Careers
Graphic Designer

© iStockphoto.com/Chris Schmidt

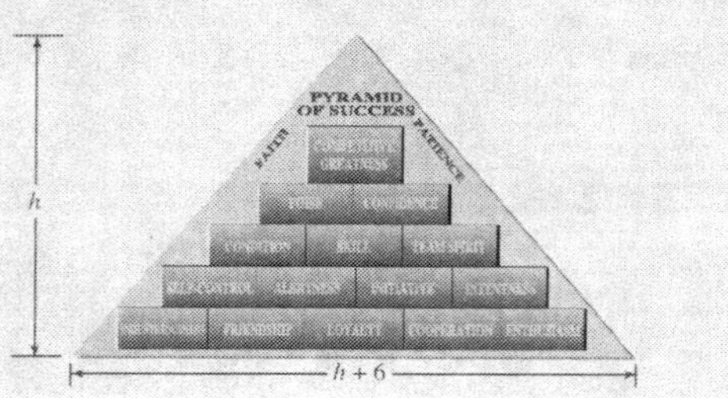

71. KITCHEN FLOOR PLANS To minimize the number of steps that a cook must take when preparing meals, designers carefully plan the *kitchen work triangle* (the area between the sink, refrigerator, and range). The one leg of the work triangle shown is 2 feet longer than the other leg, and the area covered is 24 ft^2. Find the length of each leg of the triangle. 6 ft, 8 ft

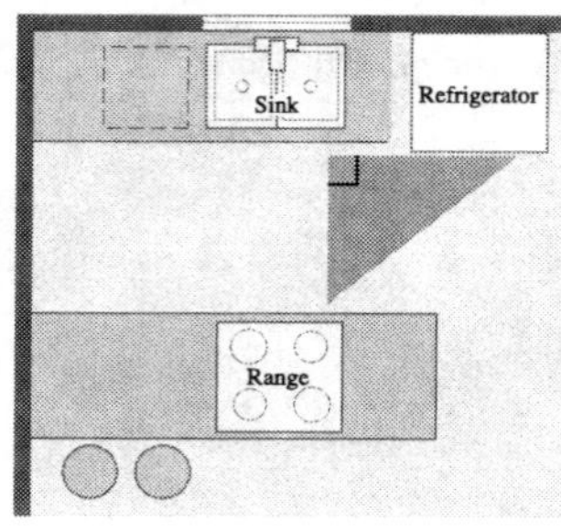

72. EARTHQUAKES After an earthquake, a store owner nailed a 50-inch-long board across a broken window. Find the height and length of the window if the height is 10 inches less than the length. 30 in., 40 in.

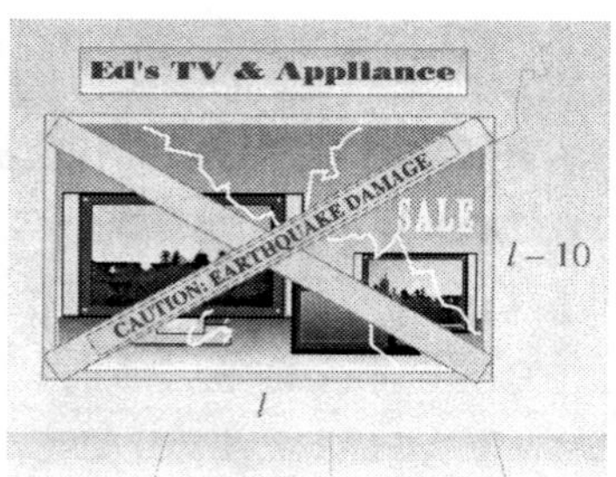

73. FLAGS According to the *Guinness Book of World Records 1998,* the largest flag flown from a flagpole was a Brazilian national flag, a rectangle having an area of 3,102 ft^2. If the flag is 19 feet longer than it is wide, find its width and length. 47 ft by 66 ft

74. COMICS See the illustration. A comic strip occupies 96 square centimeters of space in a newspaper. The length of the rectangular space is 4 centimeters more than twice its width. Find its dimensions. 6 cm by 16 cm

75. COMMUNITY GARDENS See the illustration. Residents of a community can work their own 16 ft × 24 ft plot of city-owned land if they agree to the following stipulations:

- The area of the garden cannot exceed 180 square feet.
- A path of uniform width must be maintained around the garden.

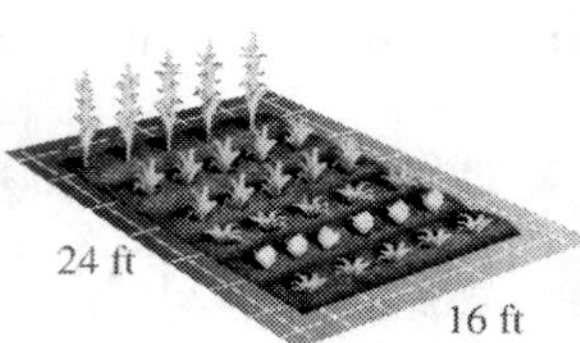

Find the dimensions of the largest possible garden. 10 ft by 18 ft

76. DECKING The owner of the pool shown below wants to surround it with a concrete deck of uniform width (shown in gray). If he can afford 368 square feet of decking, how wide can he make the deck? 4 ft

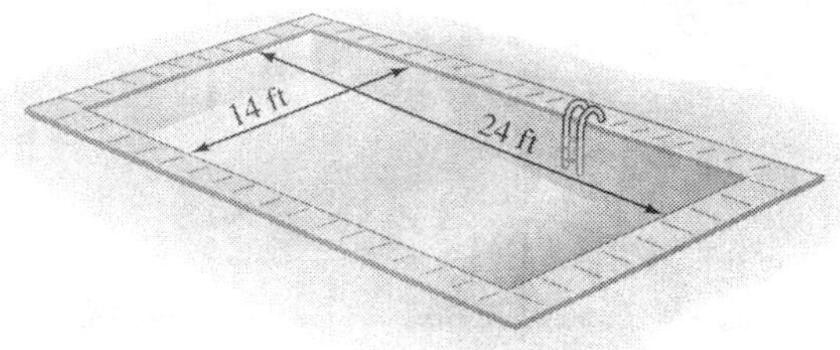

77. FALLING OBJECTS A tourist drops a penny from the observation deck of a skyscraper 1,377 feet above the ground. How long will it take for the penny to hit the ground? about 9.3 sec

78. ABACUS The Chinese abacus shown consists of a frame, parallel wires, and beads that are moved to perform arithmetic computations. If the frame is 21 centimeters wider than it is high, find its dimensions. 15 cm by 36 cm

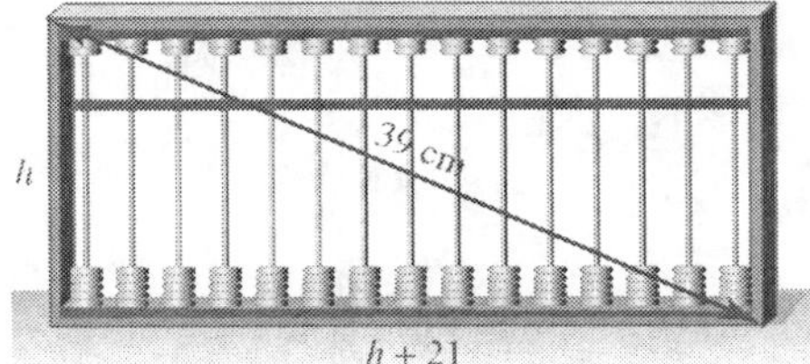

79. SIDEWALKS A 170-meter-long sidewalk from the mathematics building M to the student center C is shown in red in the illustration. However, students prefer to walk directly from M to C. How long are the two segments of the existing sidewalk? 50 m and 120 m

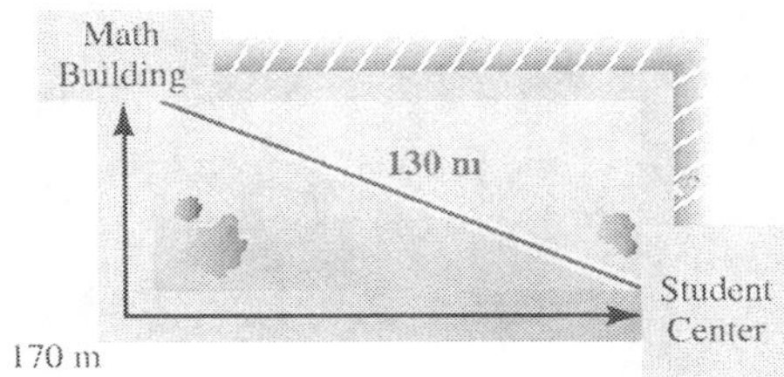

80. NAVIGATION Two boats leave port at the same time, one sailing east and one sailing south. If one boat sails 10 nautical miles more than the other and they are then 50 nautical miles apart, how far does each boat sail? 30 and 40 nautical mi

81. NAVIGATION One plane heads west from an airport, flying at 200 mph. One hour later, a second plane heads north from the same airport, flying at the same speed. When will the planes be 1,000 miles apart? 3 hr after the second plane takes off

82. INVESTING We can use the formula $A = P(1 + r)^2$ to find the amount \$$A$ that \$$P$ will become when invested at an annual rate of r% for 2 years. What interest rate is needed to make \$5,000 grow to \$5,724.50 in 2 years? 7%

83. INVESTING What interest rate is needed to make \$7,000 grow to \$8,470 in 2 years? (See Exercise 82.) 10%

84. MANUFACTURING A firm has found that its revenue for manufacturing and selling x television sets is given by the formula $R = -\frac{1}{6}x^2 + 450x$. How much revenue will be earned by manufacturing 600 television sets? \$210,000

85. RETAILING When a wholesaler sells n CD players, his revenue R is given by the formula $R = 150n - \frac{1}{2}n^2$. How many players would he have to sell to receive \$11,250? (*Hint:* Multiply both sides of the equation by -2.) 150

86. METAL FABRICATION A square piece of tin, 12 inches on a side, is to have four equal squares cut from its corners, as shown. If the edges are then to be folded up to make a box with a floor area of 64 square inches, find the depth of the box. 2 in.

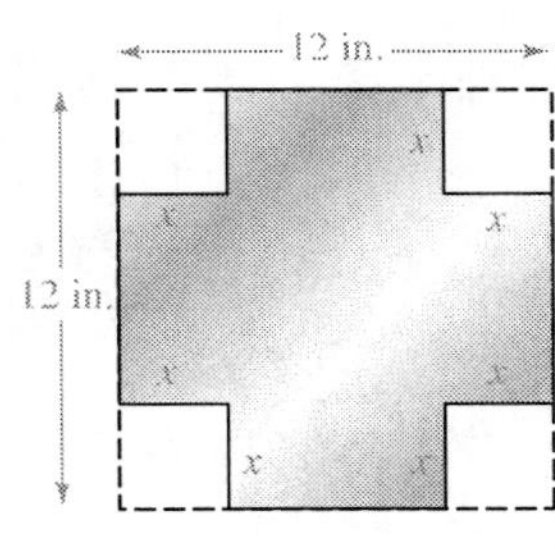

87. MAKING GUTTERS A piece of sheet metal, 18 inches wide, is bent to form the gutter shown. If the cross-sectional area is 36 square inches, find the depth of the gutter. 3 in. or 6 in.

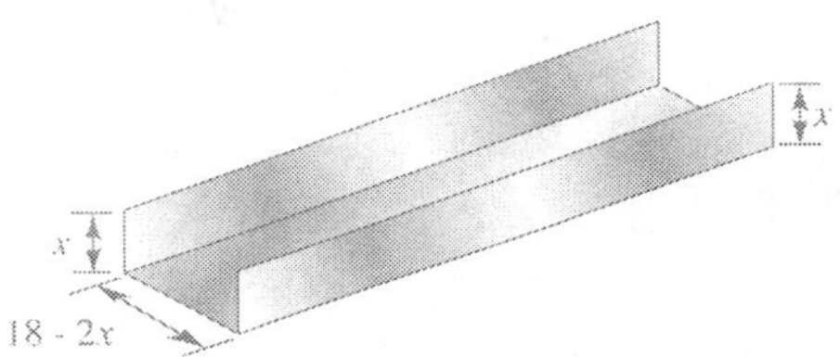

WRITING

88. Do you agree with the following statement? Explain your answer.

The quadratic formula is the easiest method to use to solve quadratic equations.

89. Explain the meaning of the ± symbol.

90. Use the quadratic formula to solve $x^2 - 2x - 4 = 0$. What is an exact solution, and what is an approximate solution of this equation? Explain the difference.

91. Rewrite in words:

$$x = \frac{-b \pm \sqrt{b^2 - 4ac}}{2a}$$

REVIEW

Solve each equation for the indicated variable.

92. $A = p + prt$, for r $r = \frac{A - p}{pt}$

93. $F = \frac{GMm}{d^2}$, for M $M = \frac{Fd^2}{Gm}$

APPENDIX I

Addition and Multiplication Facts

SECTION I.1 Addition Table and One Hundred Addition and Subtraction Facts

Table of Basic Addition Facts

+	0	1	2	3	4	5	6	7	8	9
0	0	1	2	3	4	5	6	7	8	9
1	1	2	3	4	5	6	7	8	9	10
2	2	3	4	5	6	7	8	9	10	11
3	3	4	5	6	7	8	9	10	11	12
4	4	5	6	7	8	9	10	11	12	13
5	5	6	7	8	9	10	11	12	13	14
6	6	7	8	9	10	11	12	13	14	15
7	7	8	9	10	11	12	13	14	15	16
8	8	9	10	11	12	13	14	15	16	17
9	9	10	11	12	13	14	15	16	17	18

Fifty Addition Facts

1. 3 + 2 = 5	2. 1 + 1 = 2	3. 2 + 5 = 7	4. 5 + 4 = 9
5. 7 + 7 = 14	6. 1 + 8 = 9	7. 6 + 6 = 12	8. 9 + 4 = 13
9. 3 + 8 = 11	10. 0 + 4 = 4	11. 6 + 3 = 9	12. 5 + 1 = 6
13. 2 + 8 = 10	14. 4 + 7 = 11	15. 1 + 6 = 7	16. 7 + 2 = 9
17. 8 + 9 = 17	18. 4 + 3 = 7	19. 7 + 0 = 7	20. 1 + 3 = 4
21. 4 + 6 = 10	22. 8 + 6 = 14	23. 9 + 9 = 18	24. 5 + 9 = 14
25. 0 + 8 = 8	26. 2 + 2 = 4	27. 7 + 6 = 13	28. 8 + 8 = 16
29. 1 + 2 = 3	30. 4 + 2 = 6	31. 4 + 4 = 8	32. 5 + 6 = 11
33. 3 + 3 = 6	34. 9 + 7 = 16	35. 2 + 6 = 8	36. 6 + 9 = 15
37. 0 + 6 = 6	38. 8 + 5 = 13	39. 7 + 3 = 10	40. 5 + 5 = 10
41. 1 + 0 = 1	42. 4 + 1 = 5	43. 3 + 5 = 8	44. 8 + 4 = 12
45. 9 + 2 = 11	46. 3 + 9 = 12	47. 7 + 8 = 15	48. 1 + 9 = 10
49. 5 + 7 = 12	50. 7 + 1 = 8		

Fifty Subtraction Facts

1. 8 − 5 = 3	2. 8 − 7 = 1	3. 4 − 2 = 2	4. 4 − 3 = 1
5. 7 − 3 = 4	6. 14 − 7 = 7	7. 12 − 8 = 4	8. 11 − 5 = 6
9. 12 − 3 = 9	10. 10 − 8 = 2	11. 18 − 9 = 9	12. 8 − 6 = 2
13. 10 − 4 = 6	14. 6 − 3 = 3	15. 15 − 9 = 6	16. 9 − 5 = 4
17. 2 − 0 = 2	18. 10 − 5 = 5	19. 15 − 7 = 8	20. 10 − 1 = 9
21. 17 − 8 = 9	22. 7 − 1 = 6	23. 13 − 6 = 7	24. 9 − 0 = 9
25. 16 − 8 = 8	26. 12 − 5 = 7	27. 7 − 5 = 2	28. 11 − 7 = 4
29. 14 − 5 = 9	30. 16 − 7 = 9	31. 5 − 0 = 5	32. 6 − 4 = 2
33. 12 − 6 = 6	34. 14 − 6 = 8	35. 5 − 3 = 2	36. 11 − 3 = 8
37. 13 − 8 = 5	38. 7 − 0 = 7	39. 9 − 1 = 8	40. 2 − 1 = 1
41. 3 − 2 = 1	42. 9 − 3 = 6	43. 13 − 9 = 4	44. 11 − 2 = 9
45. 10 − 3 = 7	46. 6 − 1 = 5	47. 4 − 0 = 4	48. 8 − 4 = 4
49. 9 − 2 = 7	50. 5 − 4 = 1		

SECTION I.2

Multiplication Table and One Hundred Multiplication and Division Facts

Table of Basic Multiplication Facts

×	**0**	**1**	**2**	**3**	**4**	**5**	**6**	**7**	**8**	**9**
0	**0**	0	0	0	0	0	0	0	0	0
1	0	**1**	2	3	4	5	6	7	8	9
2	0	2	**4**	6	8	10	12	14	16	18
3	0	3	6	**9**	12	15	18	21	24	27
4	0	4	8	12	**16**	20	24	28	32	36
5	0	5	10	15	20	**25**	30	35	40	45
6	0	6	12	18	24	30	**36**	42	48	54
7	0	7	14	21	28	35	42	**49**	56	63
8	0	8	16	24	32	40	48	56	**64**	72
9	0	9	18	27	36	45	54	63	72	**81**

Fifty Multiplication Facts

1. $\begin{array}{r}4\\ \times 4\\ \hline 16\end{array}$	**2.** $\begin{array}{r}1\\ \times 4\\ \hline 4\end{array}$	**3.** $\begin{array}{r}6\\ \times 3\\ \hline 18\end{array}$	**4.** $\begin{array}{r}9\\ \times 7\\ \hline 63\end{array}$
5. $\begin{array}{r}5\\ \times 7\\ \hline 35\end{array}$	**6.** $\begin{array}{r}0\\ \times 8\\ \hline 0\end{array}$	**7.** $\begin{array}{r}5\\ \times 2\\ \hline 10\end{array}$	**8.** $\begin{array}{r}1\\ \times 2\\ \hline 2\end{array}$
9. $\begin{array}{r}7\\ \times 8\\ \hline 56\end{array}$	**10.** $\begin{array}{r}4\\ \times 0\\ \hline 0\end{array}$	**11.** $\begin{array}{r}3\\ \times 3\\ \hline 9\end{array}$	**12.** $\begin{array}{r}9\\ \times 3\\ \hline 27\end{array}$
13. $\begin{array}{r}5\\ \times 6\\ \hline 30\end{array}$	**14.** $\begin{array}{r}7\\ \times 2\\ \hline 14\end{array}$	**15.** $\begin{array}{r}3\\ \times 5\\ \hline 15\end{array}$	**16.** $\begin{array}{r}8\\ \times 8\\ \hline 64\end{array}$
17. $\begin{array}{r}1\\ \times 8\\ \hline 8\end{array}$	**18.** $\begin{array}{r}3\\ \times 2\\ \hline 6\end{array}$	**19.** $\begin{array}{r}0\\ \times 7\\ \hline 0\end{array}$	**20.** $\begin{array}{r}6\\ \times 4\\ \hline 24\end{array}$
21. $\begin{array}{r}8\\ \times 6\\ \hline 48\end{array}$	**22.** $\begin{array}{r}9\\ \times 9\\ \hline 81\end{array}$	**23.** $\begin{array}{r}6\\ \times 0\\ \hline 0\end{array}$	**24.** $\begin{array}{r}1\\ \times 3\\ \hline 3\end{array}$
25. $\begin{array}{r}4\\ \times 8\\ \hline 32\end{array}$	**26.** $\begin{array}{r}8\\ \times 2\\ \hline 16\end{array}$	**27.** $\begin{array}{r}9\\ \times 1\\ \hline 9\end{array}$	**28.** $\begin{array}{r}7\\ \times 7\\ \hline 49\end{array}$
29. $\begin{array}{r}9\\ \times 6\\ \hline 54\end{array}$	**30.** $\begin{array}{r}1\\ \times 5\\ \hline 5\end{array}$	**31.** $\begin{array}{r}9\\ \times 0\\ \hline 0\end{array}$	**32.** $\begin{array}{r}4\\ \times 5\\ \hline 20\end{array}$
33. $\begin{array}{r}8\\ \times 3\\ \hline 24\end{array}$	**34.** $\begin{array}{r}7\\ \times 6\\ \hline 42\end{array}$	**35.** $\begin{array}{r}6\\ \times 2\\ \hline 12\end{array}$	**36.** $\begin{array}{r}7\\ \times 1\\ \hline 7\end{array}$
37. $\begin{array}{r}5\\ \times 8\\ \hline 40\end{array}$	**38.** $\begin{array}{r}4\\ \times 3\\ \hline 12\end{array}$	**39.** $\begin{array}{r}7\\ \times 4\\ \hline 28\end{array}$	**40.** $\begin{array}{r}1\\ \times 1\\ \hline 1\end{array}$
41. $\begin{array}{r}9\\ \times 5\\ \hline 45\end{array}$	**42.** $\begin{array}{r}2\\ \times 2\\ \hline 4\end{array}$	**43.** $\begin{array}{r}7\\ \times 3\\ \hline 21\end{array}$	**44.** $\begin{array}{r}2\\ \times 4\\ \hline 8\end{array}$
45. $\begin{array}{r}6\\ \times 6\\ \hline 36\end{array}$	**46.** $\begin{array}{r}9\\ \times 2\\ \hline 18\end{array}$	**47.** $\begin{array}{r}5\\ \times 5\\ \hline 25\end{array}$	**48.** $\begin{array}{r}6\\ \times 1\\ \hline 6\end{array}$
49. $\begin{array}{r}8\\ \times 9\\ \hline 72\end{array}$	**50.** $\begin{array}{r}9\\ \times 4\\ \hline 36\end{array}$		

Fifty Division Facts

1. $\begin{array}{r}5\\ 4\overline{)20}\end{array}$	**2.** $\begin{array}{r}7\\ 8\overline{)56}\end{array}$	**3.** $\begin{array}{r}2\\ 3\overline{)6}\end{array}$	**4.** $\begin{array}{r}8\\ 1\overline{)8}\end{array}$
5. $\begin{array}{r}5\\ 9\overline{)45}\end{array}$	**6.** $\begin{array}{r}6\\ 7\overline{)42}\end{array}$	**7.** $\begin{array}{r}5\\ 5\overline{)25}\end{array}$	**8.** $\begin{array}{r}8\\ 3\overline{)24}\end{array}$
9. $\begin{array}{r}1\\ 5\overline{)5}\end{array}$	**10.** $\begin{array}{r}3\\ 7\overline{)21}\end{array}$	**11.** $\begin{array}{r}9\\ 9\overline{)81}\end{array}$	**12.** $\begin{array}{r}0\\ 3\overline{)0}\end{array}$
13. $\begin{array}{r}4\\ 8\overline{)32}\end{array}$	**14.** $\begin{array}{r}3\\ 6\overline{)18}\end{array}$	**15.** $\begin{array}{r}0\\ 9\overline{)0}\end{array}$	**16.** $\begin{array}{r}5\\ 2\overline{)10}\end{array}$
17. $\begin{array}{r}2\\ 4\overline{)8}\end{array}$	**18.** $\begin{array}{r}9\\ 3\overline{)27}\end{array}$	**19.** $\begin{array}{r}1\\ 1\overline{)1}\end{array}$	**20.** $\begin{array}{r}5\\ 6\overline{)30}\end{array}$
21. $\begin{array}{r}7\\ 1\overline{)7}\end{array}$	**22.** $\begin{array}{r}4\\ 4\overline{)16}\end{array}$	**23.** $\begin{array}{r}9\\ 7\overline{)63}\end{array}$	**24.** $\begin{array}{r}0\\ 5\overline{)0}\end{array}$
25. $\begin{array}{r}5\\ 7\overline{)35}\end{array}$	**26.** $\begin{array}{r}1\\ 3\overline{)3}\end{array}$	**27.** $\begin{array}{r}3\\ 5\overline{)15}\end{array}$	**28.** $\begin{array}{r}6\\ 8\overline{)48}\end{array}$
29. $\begin{array}{r}0\\ 7\overline{)0}\end{array}$	**30.** $\begin{array}{r}8\\ 2\overline{)16}\end{array}$	**31.** $\begin{array}{r}3\\ 3\overline{)9}\end{array}$	**32.** $\begin{array}{r}2\\ 6\overline{)12}\end{array}$
33. $\begin{array}{r}8\\ 9\overline{)72}\end{array}$	**34.** $\begin{array}{r}0\\ 8\overline{)0}\end{array}$	**35.** $\begin{array}{r}7\\ 4\overline{)28}\end{array}$	**36.** $\begin{array}{r}8\\ 8\overline{)64}\end{array}$
37. $\begin{array}{r}4\\ 6\overline{)24}\end{array}$	**38.** $\begin{array}{r}9\\ 6\overline{)54}\end{array}$	**39.** $\begin{array}{r}7\\ 7\overline{)49}\end{array}$	**40.** $\begin{array}{r}2\\ 7\overline{)14}\end{array}$
41. $\begin{array}{r}6\\ 6\overline{)36}\end{array}$	**42.** $\begin{array}{r}9\\ 1\overline{)9}\end{array}$	**43.** $\begin{array}{r}4\\ 3\overline{)12}\end{array}$	**44.** $\begin{array}{r}9\\ 4\overline{)36}\end{array}$
45. $\begin{array}{r}2\\ 2\overline{)4}\end{array}$	**46.** $\begin{array}{r}5\\ 8\overline{)40}\end{array}$	**47.** $\begin{array}{r}1\\ 2\overline{)2}\end{array}$	**48.** $\begin{array}{r}4\\ 1\overline{)4}\end{array}$
49. $\begin{array}{r}2\\ 9\overline{)18}\end{array}$	**50.** $\begin{array}{r}1\\ 6\overline{)6}\end{array}$		

APPENDIX II

Polynomials

Objectives

1 Know the vocabulary for polynomials.

2 Evaluate polynomials.

SECTION II.1 Introduction to Polynomials

1 Know the vocabulary for polynomials.

Recall that an **algebraic term,** or simply a **term,** is a number or a product of a number and one or more variables, which may be raised to powers. Some examples of terms are

$$17, \quad 5x, \quad 6t^2, \quad \text{and} \quad -8z^3$$

The *coefficients* of these terms are 17, 5, 6, and −8, in that order.

Polynomials

A **polynomial** is a single term or a sum of terms in which all variables have whole-number exponents and no variable appears in the denominator.

Some examples of polynomials are

$$141, \quad 8y^2, \quad 2x + 1, \quad 4y^2 - 2y + 3, \quad \text{and} \quad 7a^3 + 2a^2 - a - 1$$

The polynomial $8y^2$ has one term. The polynomial $2x + 1$ has two terms, $2x$ and 1. Since $4y^2 - 2y + 3$ can be written as $4y^2 + (-2y) + 3$, it is the sum of three terms, $4y^2$, $-2y$, and 3.

We classify some polynomials by the number of terms they contain. A polynomial with one term is called a **monomial.** A polynomial with two terms is called a **binomial.** A polynomial with three terms is called a **trinomial.** Some examples of these polynomials are shown in the table below.

Monomials	Binomials	Trinomials
$5x^2$	$2x - 1$	$5t^2 + 4t + 3$
$-6x$	$18a^2 - 4a$	$27x^3 - 6x + 2$
29	$-27z^4 + 7z^2$	$32r^2 + 7r - 12$

Self Check 1

Classify each polynomial as a monomial, a binomial, or a trinomial:

a. $8x^2 + 7$ binomial

b. $5x$ monomial

c. $x^2 - 2x - 1$ trinomial

Now Try **Problems 5, 7, and 11**

EXAMPLE 1 Classify each polynomial as a monomial, a binomial, or a trinomial: **a.** $3x + 4$ **b.** $3x^2 + 4x - 12$ **c.** $25x^3$

Strategy We will count the number of terms in the polynomial.

WHY The number of terms determines the type of polynomial.

Solution

a. Since $3x + 4$ has two terms, it is a binomial.

b. Since $3x^2 + 4x - 12$ has three terms, it is a trinomial.

c. Since $25x^3$ has one term, it is a monomial.

Teaching Example 1 Classify each polynomial as a monomial, a binomial, or a trinomial:
a. $x^5 + x^3 - 10$
b. $t^{15} + 6$
c. $-4n$

Answers:
a. trinomial
b. binomial
c. monomial

The monomial $7x^3$ is called a **monomial of third degree** or a **monomial of degree 3,** because the variable occurs three times as a factor.

- $5x^2$ is a monomial of degree 2. Because the variable occurs two times as a factor: $x^2 = x \cdot x$.
- $-8a^4$ is a monomial of degree 4. Because the variable occurs four times as a factor: $a^4 = a \cdot a \cdot a \cdot a$.
- $\frac{1}{2}m^5$ is a monomial of degree 5. Because the variable occurs five times as a factor: $m^5 = m \cdot m \cdot m \cdot m \cdot m$.

We define the degree of a polynomial by considering the degrees of each of its terms.

Degree of a Polynomial

The **degree of a polynomial** is the same as the degree of its term with largest degree.

For example,

- $x^2 + 5x$ is a binomial of degree 2, because the degree of its term with largest degree (x^2) is 2.
- $4y^3 + 2y - 7$ is a trinomial of degree 3, because the degree of its term with largest degree ($4y^3$) is 3.
- $\frac{1}{2}z + 3z^4 - 2z^2$ is a trinomial of degree 4, because the degree of its term with largest degree ($3z^4$) is 4.

Self Check 2

Find the degree of each polynomial:

a. $3p^3$ 3

b. $17r^4 + 2r^8 - r$ 8

c. $-2g^5 - 7g^6 + 12g^7$ 7

Now Try **Problems 13, 15, and 17**

Teaching Example 2 Find the degree of each polynomial:
a. $100 - 8x$
b. $7a^4 + 5a^3 + 4a$
c. $x - x^2 + x^3 - x^6$
Answers:
a. 1 b. 4 c. 6

EXAMPLE 2 Find the degree of each polynomial:

a. $-2x + 4$ **b.** $5t^3 + t^4 - 7$ **c.** $3 - 9z + 6z^2 - z^3$

Strategy We will determine the degree of each term of the polynomial.

WHY The term with the highest degree gives the degree of the polynomial.

Solution

a. Since $-2x$ can be written as $-2x^1$, the degree of the term with largest degree is 1. Thus, the degree of the polynomial $-2x + 4$ is 1.

b. In $5t^3 + t^4 - 7$, the degree of the term with largest degree (t^4) is 4. Thus, the degree of the polynomial is 4.

c. In $3 - 9z + 6z^2 - z^3$, the degree of the term with largest degree ($-z^3$) is 3. Thus, the degree of the polynomial is 3.

2 Evaluate polynomials.

When a number is substituted for the variable in a polynomial, the polynomial takes on a numerical value. Finding this value is called **evaluating the polynomial.**

EXAMPLE 3 Evaluate each polynomial for $x = 3$:

a. $3x - 2$ **b.** $-2x^2 + x - 3$

Strategy We will substitute the given value for each x in the polynomial and follow the order of operations rule.

WHY To *evaluate a polynomial* means to find its numerical value, once we know the value of its variable.

Solution

a. $3x - 2 = 3(3) - 2$ Substitute 3 for x.
$= 9 - 2$ Multiply: 3(3) = 9.
$= 7$ Subtract.

b. $-2x^2 + x - 3 = -2(3)^2 + 3 - 3$ Substitute 3 for x.
$= -2(9) + 3 - 3$ Evaluate the exponential expression.
$= -18 + 3 - 3$ Multiply: $-2(9) = -18$.
$= -15 - 3$ Add: $-18 + 3 = -15$.
$= -18$ Subtract: $-15 - 3 = -15 + (-3) = -18$.

Self Check 3

Evaluate each polynomial for $x = -1$:

a. $-2x^2 - 4$ −6

b. $3x^2 - 4x + 1$ 8

Now Try **Problems 23 and 31**

Teaching Example 3 Evaluate each polynomial for $a = -6$.
a. $-2a^2 + 2$ b. $a^3 - 7a + 1$
Answers:
a. −70 b. −173

EXAMPLE 4 *Height of an Object* The polynomial $-16t^2 + 28t + 8$ gives the height (in feet) of an object t seconds after it has been thrown into the air. Find the height of the object after 1 second.

Strategy We will substitute 1 for t and evaluate the polynomial.

WHY The variable t represents the time since the object was thrown into the air.

Solution

To find the height at 1 second, we evaluate the polynomial for $t = 1$.

$-16t^2 + 28t + 8 = -16(1)^2 + 28(1) + 8$ Substitute 1 for t.
$= -16(1) + 28(1) + 8$ Evaluate the exponential expression.
$= -16 + 28 + 8$ Multiply: $-16(1) = -16$ and $28(1) = 28$.
$= 12 + 8$ Add: $-16 + 28 = 12$.
$= 20$ Add.

At 1 second, the height of the object is 20 feet.

Self Check 4

Refer to Example 4. Find the height of the object after 2 seconds. 0 ft

Now Try **Problems 35 and 37**

Teaching Example 4 PROJECTILES The polynomial $-16t^2 + 30t + 10$ gives the height (in feet) of an object t seconds after it has been thrown into the air. Find the height of the object after 2 seconds.
Answer:
6 ft

ANSWERS TO SELF CHECKS

1. a. binomial **b.** monomial **c.** trinomial **2. a.** 3 **b.** 8 **c.** 7 **3. a.** −6 **b.** 8 **4.** 0 ft

SECTION II.1 STUDY SET

VOCABULARY

Fill in the blanks.

1. A polynomial with one term is called a monomial.
2. A polynomial with three terms is called a trinomial.
3. A polynomial with two terms is called a binomial.
4. The degree of a polynomial is the same as the degree of its term with largest degree.

CONCEPTS

Classify each polynomial as a monomial, a binomial, or a trinomial.

5. $3x^2 - 4$ binomial
6. $5t^2 - t + 1$ trinomial
7. $17e^4$ monomial
8. $x^2 + x + 7$ trinomial
9. $25u^2$ monomial
10. $x^2 - 9$ binomial
11. $q^5 + q^2 + 1$ trinomial
12. $4d^3 - 3d^2$ binomial

Find the degree of each polynomial.

13. $5x^3$ 3

14. $3t^5 + 3t^2$ 5

15. $2x^2 - 3x + 2$ 2

16. $\frac{1}{2}p^4 - p^2$ 4

17. $2m$ 1

18. $7q - 5$ 1

19. $25w^6 + 5w^7$ 7

20. $p^6 - p^8$ 8

NOTATION

Complete each solution.

21. Evaluate $3a^2 + 2a - 7$ for $a = 2$.

$$\begin{aligned} 3a^2 + 2a - 7 &= 3(2)^2 + 2(2) - 7 \\ &= 3(4) + 4 - 7 \\ &= 12 + 4 - 7 \\ &= 16 - 7 \\ &= 9 \end{aligned}$$

22. Evaluate $-q^2 - 3q + 2$ for $q = -1$.

$$\begin{aligned} -q^2 - 3q + 2 &= -(-1)^2 - 3(-1) + 2 \\ &= -(1) - 3(-1) + 2 \\ &= -1 + 3 + 2 \\ &= 2 + 2 \\ &= 4 \end{aligned}$$

PRACTICE

Evaluate each polynomial for the given value.

23. $3x + 4$ for $x = 3$ 13

24. $\frac{1}{2}x - 3$ for $x = -6$ −6

25. $2x^2 + 4$ for $x = -1$ 6

26. $-\frac{1}{2}x^2 - 1$ for $x = 2$ −3

27. $0.5t^3 - 1$ for $t = 4$ 31

28. $0.75a^2 + 2.5a + 2$ for $a = 0$ 2

29. $\frac{2}{3}b^2 - b + 1$ for $b = 3$ 4

30. $3n^2 - n + 2$ for $n = 2$ 12

31. $-2s^2 - 2s + 1$ for $s = -1$ 1

32. $-4r^2 - 3r - 1$ for $r = -2$ −11

APPLICATIONS

The height h (in feet) of a ball shot straight up with an initial velocity of 64 feet per second is given by the equation $h = -16t^2 + 64t$. Find the height of the ball after the given number of seconds.

33. 0 second 0 ft

34. 1 second 48 ft

35. 2 seconds 64 ft

36. 4 seconds 0 ft

The number of feet that a car travels before stopping depends on the driver's reaction time and the braking distance. For one driver, the stopping distance d is given by the equation $d = 0.04v^2 + 0.9v$, where v is the velocity of the car. Find the stopping distance for each of the following speeds.

37. 30 mph 63 ft

38. 50 mph 145 ft

39. 60 mph 198 ft

40. 70 mph 259 ft

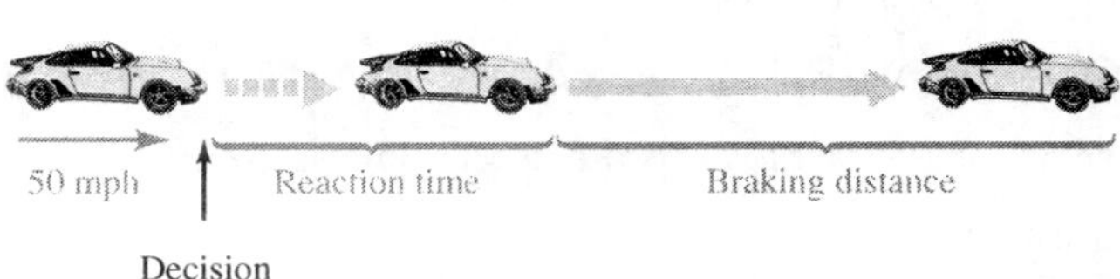

WRITING

41. Explain how to find the degree of the polynomial $2x^3 + 5x^5 - 7x$.

42. Explain how to evaluate the polynomial $-2x^2 - 3$ for $x = 5$.

REVIEW

Perform the operations.

43. $\frac{2}{3} + \frac{4}{3}$ 2

44. $\frac{36}{7} - \frac{23}{7}$ $\frac{13}{7} = 1\frac{6}{7}$

45. $\frac{5}{12} \cdot \frac{18}{5}$ $\frac{3}{2} = 1\frac{1}{2}$

46. $\frac{23}{25} \div \frac{46}{5}$ $\frac{1}{10}$

Solve each equation.

47. $x - 4 = 12$ 16

48. $4z = 108$ 27

49. $2(x - 3) = 6$ 6

50. $3(a - 5) = 4(a + 9)$ −51

Objectives

1 Add polynomials.

2 Subtract polynomials.

SECTION II.2 Adding and Subtracting Polynomials

Polynomials can be added, subtracted, and multiplied just like numbers in arithmetic. In this section, we show how to find sums and differences of polynomials.

1 Add polynomials.

Recall that like terms have exactly the same variables and the same exponents. For example, the monomials

$3z^2$ and $-2z^2$ are like terms — Both have the same variable (z) with the same exponent (2).

However, the monomials

$7b^2$ and $8a^2$ are not like terms — They have different variables.

$32p^2$ and $25p^3$ are not like terms — The exponents of p are different.

Also recall that we use the distributive property in reverse to simplify a sum or difference of like terms. We **combine like terms** by adding their coefficients and keeping the same variables and exponents. For example,

$$2y + 5y = (2 + 5)y \qquad \text{and} \qquad -3x^2 + 7x^2 = (-3 + 7)x^2$$
$$= 7y \qquad\qquad\qquad\qquad = 4x^2$$

These examples suggest the following rule.

Adding Polynomials

To add polynomials, combine their like terms.

EXAMPLE 1 Add: $5x^3 + 7x^3$

Strategy We will use the distributive property in reverse and add the coefficients of the terms.

WHY $5x^3$ and $7x^3$ are like terms and therefore can be added.

Solution

$5x^3 + 7x^3 = 12x^3$ — Think: $(5 + 7)x^3 = 12x^3$.

Self Check 1

Add: $7y^3 + 12y^3$ $19y^3$

Now Try **Problems 15 and 19**

Teaching Example 1 Add: $15x^5 + 5x^5$
Answer:
$20x^5$

EXAMPLE 2 Add: $\frac{3}{2}t^2 + \frac{5}{2}t^2 + \frac{7}{2}t^2$

Strategy We will use the distributive property in reverse and add the coefficients of the terms.

WHY $\frac{3}{2}t^2$, $\frac{5}{2}t^2$, and $\frac{7}{2}t^2$ are like terms and therefore can be added.

Solution

Since the three monomials are like terms, we add the coefficients and keep the variables and exponents.

$$\frac{3}{2}t^2 + \frac{5}{2}t^2 + \frac{7}{2}t^2 = \left(\frac{3}{2} + \frac{5}{2} + \frac{7}{2}\right)t^2$$
$$= \frac{15}{2}t^2$$

To add the fractions, add the numerators and keep the denominator: $3 + 5 + 7 = 15$.

Self Check 2

Add:
$\frac{1}{9}a^3 + \frac{2}{9}a^3 + \frac{5}{9}a^3$ $\frac{8}{9}a^3$

Now Try **Problem 21**

Teaching Example 2
Add: $\frac{1}{16}c^2 + \frac{7}{16}c^2 + \frac{3}{16}c^2$
Answer:
$\frac{11}{16}c^2$

To add two polynomials, we write a + sign between them and combine like terms.

EXAMPLE 3 Add: $2x + 3$ and $7x - 1$

Strategy We will reorder and regroup to get the like terms together. Then we will combine like terms.

WHY To add polynomials means to combine their like terms.

Self Check 3

Add:
$5y - 2$ and $-3y + 7$ $2y + 5$

Now Try **Problem 27**

Teaching Example 3
Add: $11n + 4$ and $6n - 3$
Answer:
$17n + 1$

Solution

$(2x + 3) + (7x - 1)$ — Write a + sign between the binomials.

$= (2x + 7x) + (3 - 1)$ — Use the associative and commutative properties to group like terms together.

$= 9x + 2$ — Combine like terms.

The binomials in Example 3 can be added by writing the polynomials so that like terms are in columns.

$$\begin{array}{r} 2x + 3 \\ +\ \underline{7x - 1} \\ 9x + 2 \end{array}$$

Add the like terms, one column at a time.

Self Check 4

Add: $(2b^2 - 4b) + (b^2 + 3b - 1)$ $3b^2 - b - 1$

Now Try **Problem 33**

Teaching Example 4
Add: $(6t^2 - 5t) + (t^2 + 2t - 9)$
Answer:
$7t^2 - 3t - 9$

EXAMPLE 4 Add: $(5x^2 - 2x + 4) + (3x^2 - 5)$

Strategy We will combine the like terms of the trinomial and binomial.

WHY To add polynomials, we combine like terms.

Solution

$(5x^2 - 2x + 4) + (3x^2 - 5)$

$= (5x^2 + 3x^2) + (-2x) + (4 - 5)$ — Use the associative and commutative properties to group like terms together.

$= 8x^2 - 2x - 1$ — Combine like terms.

The polynomials in Example 4 can be added by writing the polynomials so that like terms are in columns.

$$\begin{array}{r} 5x^2 - 2x + 4 \\ +\ \underline{3x^2 \qquad - 5} \\ 8x^2 - 2x - 1 \end{array}$$

Add the like terms, one column at a time.

Self Check 5

Add: $(s^2 + 1.2s - 5) + (3s^2 - 2.5s + 4)$ $4s^2 - 1.3s - 1$

Now Try **Problem 37**

Teaching Example 5 Add:
$(m^2 + 3.7m - 7) + (8m^2 - 4.8m + 2)$
Answer:
$9m^2 - 1.1m - 5$

EXAMPLE 5 Add: $(3.7x^2 + 4x - 2) + (7.4x^2 - 5x + 3)$

Strategy We will combine the like terms of the two trinomials.

WHY To add polynomials, we combine like terms.

Solution

$(3.7x^2 + 4x - 2) + (7.4x^2 - 5x + 3)$

$= (3.7x^2 + 7.4x^2) + (4x - 5x) + (-2 + 3)$ — Use the associative and commutative properties to group like terms together.

$= 11.1x^2 - x + 1$ — Combine like terms.

The trinomials in Example 5 can be added by writing them so that like terms are in columns.

$$\begin{array}{r} 3.7x^2 + 4x - 2 \\ +\ \underline{7.4x^2 - 5x + 3} \\ 11.1x^2 - \ \ x + 1 \end{array}$$

Add the like terms, one column at a time.

2 Subtract polynomials.

To subtract one monomial from another, we add the opposite of the monomial that is to be subtracted. In symbols, $x - y = x + (-y)$.

EXAMPLE 6 Subtract: $8x^2 - 3x^2$

Strategy We will add the opposite of $3x^2$ to $8x^2$.

WHY To subtract monomials, we add the oppostie of the monomial that is to be subtracted.

Solution

$8x^2 - 3x^2 = 8x^2 + (-3x^2)$ Add the opposite of $3x^2$.

$= 5x^2$ Add the coefficients and keep the same variable and exponent. Think: $[8 + (-3)]x^2 = 5x^2$

Self Check 6

Subtract: $6y^3 - 9y^3$ $-3y^3$

Now Try **Problem 47**

Teaching Example 6
Subtract: $10b^2 - 12b^2$
Answer:
$-2b^2$

Recall from Chapter 1 that we can use the distributive property to find the opposite of several terms enclosed within parentheses. For example, we consider $-(2a^2 - a + 9)$.

$-(2a^2 - a + 9) = -1(2a^2 - a + 9)$ Replace the − symbol in front of the parentheses with −1.

$= -2a^2 + a - 9$ Use the distributive property to remove parentheses.

This example illustrates the following method of subtracting polynomials.

Subtracting Polynomials

To subtract two polynomials, change the signs of the terms of the polynomial being subtracted, drop the parentheses, and combine like terms.

EXAMPLE 7 Subtract: $(3x - 4.2) - (5x + 7.2)$

Strategy We will change the signs of the terms of $5x + 7.2$, drop the parentheses, and combine like terms.

WHY This is the method for subtracting two polynomials.

Solution

$(3x - 4.2) - (5x + 7.2)$

$= 3x - 4.2 - 5x - 7.2$ Change the signs of each term of $5x + 7.2$ and drop the parentheses.

$= -2x - 11.4$ Combine like terms: Think: $(3 - 5)x = -2x$ and $(-4.2 - 7.2) = -11.4$.

Self Check 7

Subtract:
$(3.3a - 5) - (7.8a + 2)$ $-4.5a - 7$

Now Try **Problem 51**

Teaching Example 7
Subtract: $(1.7d - 2) - (0.9d + 11)$
Answer:
$0.8d - 13$

The binomials in Example 7 can be subtracted by writing them so that like terms are in columns.

$$\begin{array}{r} 3x - 4.2 \\ -\underline{(5x + 7.2)} \end{array} \longrightarrow \begin{array}{r} 3x - 4.2 \\ + \underline{-5x - 7.2} \\ -2x - 11.4 \end{array}$$

Change signs and add, column by column.

Self Check 8

Subtract: $2y^2 - 6y + 3$

$(5y^2 - 4y + 2) - (3y^2 + 2y - 1)$

Now Try **Problem 59**

Teaching Example 8 Subtract: $(9x^2 - 4x + 1) - (8x^2 + x - 8)$

Answer: $x^2 - 5x + 9$

EXAMPLE 8 Subtract: $(3x^2 - 4x - 6) - (2x^2 - 6x + 12)$

Strategy We will change the signs of the terms of $2x^2 - 6x + 12$, drop the parentheses, and combine like terms.

WHY This is the method for subtracting two polynomials.

Solution

$(3x^2 - 4x - 6) - (2x^2 - 6x + 12)$

$= 3x^2 - 4x - 6 - 2x^2 + 6x - 12$ Change the signs of each term of $2x^2 - 6x + 12$ and drop the parentheses.

$= x^2 + 2x - 18$ Combine like terms: Think: $(3 - 2)x^2 = x^2$, $(-4 + 6)x = 2x$, and $(-6 - 12) = -18$.

The trinomials in Example 8 can be subtracted by writing them so that like terms are in columns.

$$\begin{array}{r} 3x^2 - 4x - 6 \\ -(2x^2 - 6x + 12) \\ \hline \end{array} \longrightarrow \begin{array}{r} 3x^2 - 4x - 6 \\ + \; -2x^2 + 6x - 12 \\ \hline x^2 + 2x - 18 \end{array}$$

Change signs and add, column by column.

ANSWERS TO SELF CHECKS

1. $19y^3$ **2.** $\frac{8}{9}a^3$ **3.** $2y + 5$ **4.** $3b^2 - b - 1$ **5.** $4s^2 - 1.3s - 1$ **6.** $-3y^3$ **7.** $-4.5a - 7$ **8.** $2y^2 - 6y + 3$

SECTION II.2 STUDY SET

VOCABULARY

Fill in the blanks.

1. If two algebraic terms have exactly the same variables and exponents, they are called __like__ terms.
2. $3x^3$ and $3x^2$ are __unlike__ terms.

CONCEPTS

Fill in the blanks.

3. To add two monomials, we add the __coefficients__ and keep the same __variables__ and exponents.
4. To subtract one monomial from another, we add the __opposite__ of the monomial that is to be subtracted.

Determine whether the monomials are like terms. If they are, combine them.

5. $3y, 4y$ yes, $7y$
6. $3x^2, 5x^2$ yes, $8x^2$
7. $3x, 3y$ no
8. $3x^2, 6x$ no
9. $3x^3, 4x^3, 6x^3$ yes, $13x^3$
10. $-2y^4, -6y^4, 10y^4$ yes, $2y^4$
11. $-5x^2, 13x^2, 7x^2$ yes, $15x^2$
12. $23, 12x, 25x$ no

NOTATION

Complete each solution.

13. $(3x^2 + 2x - 5) + (2x^2 - 7x)$
$= (3x^2 + \boxed{2x^2}) + (2x - \boxed{7x}) + (-5)$
$= \boxed{5x^2} + (-5x) - 5$
$= 5x^2 - 5x - 5$

14. $(3x^2 + 2x - 5) - (2x^2 - 7x)$
$= (3x^2 + 2x - 5) + [-(\boxed{2x^2} - 7x)]$
$= (3x^2 + 2x - 5) + (\boxed{-2x^2 + 7x})$
$= (\boxed{3x^2 - 2x^2}) + (2x + 7x) + (-5)$
$= x^2 + 9x - 5$

PRACTICE

Add the polynomials.

15. $4y + 5y$ $9y$
16. $-2x + 3x$ x
17. $8t^2 + 4t^2$ $12t^2$
18. $15x^2 + 10x^2$ $25x^2$
19. $3s^2 + 4s^2 + 7s^2$ $14s^2$
20. $-2a^3 + 7a^3 - 3a^3$ $2a^3$

21. $\frac{1}{8}a + \frac{3}{8}a + \frac{5}{8}a$ $\frac{9}{8}a$

22. $\frac{1}{4}b + \frac{3}{4}b + \frac{1}{4}b$ $\frac{5}{4}b$

23. $\frac{2}{3}c^2 + \frac{1}{3}c^2 + \frac{2}{3}c^2$ $\frac{5}{3}c^2$

24. $\frac{4}{9}d^3 + \frac{1}{9}d^3 + \frac{3}{9}d^3$ $\frac{8}{9}d^3$

25. Add: $3x + 7$ and $4x - 3$ $7x + 4$

26. Add: $2y - 3$ and $4y + 7$ $6y + 4$

27. Add: $2x^2 + 3$ and $5x^2 - 10$ $7x^2 - 7$

28. Add: $-4a^2 + 1$ and $5a^2 - 1$ a^2

29. $(5x^3 - 42x) + (7x^3 - 107x)$ $12x^3 - 149x$

30. $(-43a^3 + 25a) + (58a^3 - 10a)$ $15a^3 + 15a$

31. $(3x^2 + 2x - 4) + (5x^2 - 17)$ $8x^2 + 2x - 21$

32. $(5a^2 - 2a) + (-2a^2 + 3a + 4)$ $3a^2 + a + 4$

33. $(7y^2 + 5y) + (y^2 - y - 2)$ $8y^2 + 4y - 2$

34. $(4p^2 - 4p + 5) + (6p - 2)$ $4p^2 + 2p + 3$

35. $(3x^2 - 3x - 2) + (3x^2 + 4x - 3)$ $6x^2 + x - 5$

36. $(4c^2 + 3c - 2) + (3c^2 + 4c + 2)$ $7c^2 + 7c$

37. $(2.5a^2 + 3a - 9) + (3.6a^2 + 7a - 10)$ $6.1a^2 + 10a - 19$

38. $(1.9b^2 - 4b + 10) + (3.7b^2 - 3b - 11)$ $5.6b^2 - 7b - 1$

39. $(3n^2 - 5.8n + 7) + (-n^2 + 5.8n - 2)$ $2n^2 + 5$

40. $(-3t^2 - t + 3.4) + (3t^2 + 2t - 1.8)$ $t + 1.6$

41.
$$\begin{array}{r} 3x^2 + 4x + 5 \\ +\ \underline{2x^2 - 3x + 6} \\ 5x^2 + x + 11 \end{array}$$

42.
$$\begin{array}{r} 2x^2 - 3x + 5 \\ +\ \underline{-4x^2 - x - 7} \\ -2x^2 - 4x - 2 \end{array}$$

43.
$$\begin{array}{r} -3x^2 \qquad - 7 \\ +\ \underline{-4x^2 - 5x + 6} \\ -7x^2 - 5x - 1 \end{array}$$

41.
$$\begin{array}{r} 4x^2 - 4x + 9 \\ +\ \underline{9x - 3} \\ 4x^2 + 5x + 6 \end{array}$$

45.
$$\begin{array}{r} -3x^2 + 4x + 25.4 \\ +\ \underline{5x^2 - 3x - 12.5} \\ 2x^2 + x + 12.9 \end{array}$$

46.
$$\begin{array}{r} -6x^3 - 4.2x^2 + 7 \\ +\ \underline{-7x^3 + 9.7x^2 - 21} \\ -13x^3 + 5.5x^2 - 14 \end{array}$$

Subtract the polynomials.

47. $32u^3 - 16u^3$ $16u^3$

48. $25y^2 - 7y^2$ $18y^2$

49. $18x^5 - 11x^5$ $7x^5$

50. $17x^6 - 22x^6$ $-5x^6$

51. $(30x^2 - 4) - (11x^2 + 1)$ $19x^2 - 5$

52. $(5x^3 - 8) - (2x^3 + 5)$ $3x^3 - 13$

53. $(3x^2 - 2x - 1) - (-4x^2 + 4)$ $7x^2 - 2x - 5$

54. $(7a^2 + 5a) - (5a^2 - 2a + 3)$ $2a^2 + 7a - 3$

55. $(4.5a + 3.7) - (2.9a - 4.3)$ $1.6a + 8$

56. $(5.1b - 7.6) - (3.3b + 5.9)$ $1.8b - 13.5$

57. $(2b^2 + 3b - 5) - (2b^2 - 4b - 9)$ $7b + 4$

58. $(3a^2 - 2a + 4) - (a^2 - 3a + 7)$ $2a^2 + a - 3$

59. $(5p^2 - p + 71) - (4p^2 + p + 71)$ $p^2 - 2p$

60. $(m^2 - m - 5) - (m^2 + 5.5m - 75)$ $-6.5m + 70$

61. $(3.7y^2 - 5) - (2y^2 - 3.1y + 4)$ $1.7y^2 + 3.1y - 9$

62. $(t^2 - 4.5t + 5) - (2t^2 - 3.1t - 1)$ $-t^2 - 1.4t + 6$

63.
$$\begin{array}{r} 3x^2 + 4x - 5 \\ -\ \underline{(-2x^2 - 2x + 3)} \\ 5x^2 + 6x - 8 \end{array}$$

64.
$$\begin{array}{r} 3y^2 - 4y + 7 \\ -\ \underline{(6y^2 - 6y - 13)} \\ -3y^2 + 2y + 20 \end{array}$$

65.
$$\begin{array}{r} -2x^2 - 4x + 12 \\ -\ \underline{(10x^2 + 9x - 24)} \\ -12x^2 - 13x + 36 \end{array}$$

66.
$$\begin{array}{r} 25x^3 - 45x^2 + 31x \\ -\ \underline{(12x^3 + 27x^2 - 17x)} \\ 13x^3 - 72x^2 + 48x \end{array}$$

67.
$$\begin{array}{r} 4x^3 - 3x + 10 \\ -\ \underline{(5x^3 - 4x - 4)} \\ -x^3 + x + 14 \end{array}$$

68.
$$\begin{array}{r} 3x^3 + 4x^2 + 12 \\ -\ \underline{(-4x^3 + 6x^2 - 3)} \\ 7x^3 - 2x^2 + 15 \end{array}$$

APPLICATIONS

In Exercises 69–72, recall that the perimeter of a figure is equal to the sum of the lengths of its sides.

69. THE RED CROSS In 1891, Clara Barton founded the Red Cross. Its symbol is a white flag bearing a red cross. If each side of the cross has length x, write an expression that represents the perimeter of the cross. $12x$

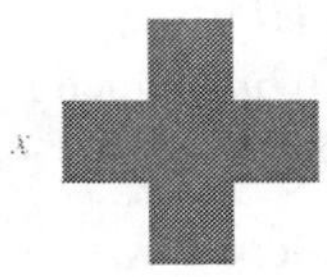

70. BILLIARDS Billiard tables vary in size, but all tables are twice as long as they are wide.

a. If the billiard table is x feet wide, write an expression that represents its length. $2x$ ft

b. Write an expression that represents the perimeter of the table. $6x$ ft

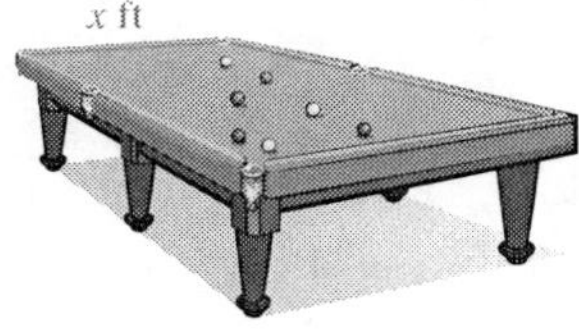

71. PING-PONG Write an expression that represents the perimeter of the Ping-Pong table. $(4x + 8)$ ft

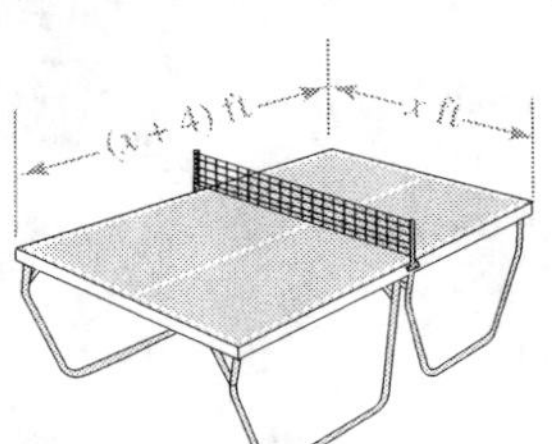

72. SEWING Write an expression that represents the length of the yellow trim needed to outline a pennant with the given side lengths. $(5x - 30)$ cm

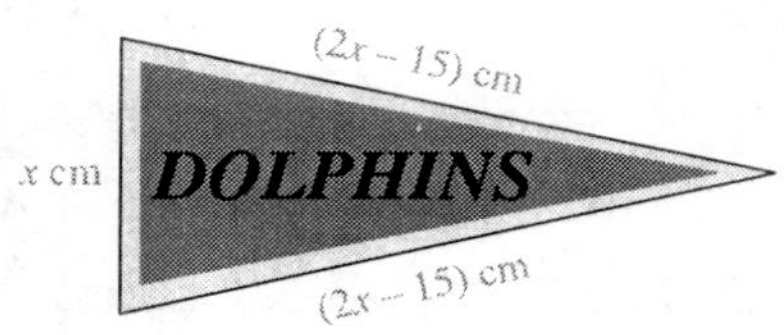

WRITING

73. What are *like terms?*

74. Explain how to add two polynomials.

75. Explain how to subtract two polynomials.

76. When two binomials are added, is the result always a binomial? Explain.

REVIEW

77. BASKETBALL SHOES Use the following information to find how much lighter the Kevin Garnett shoe is than the Michael Jordan shoe. 0.8 oz

Nike Air Garnett III	Air Jordan XV
Synthetic fade mesh and leather. Sizes $6\frac{1}{2}$–18 Weight: 13.8 oz	Full grain leather upper with woven pattern. Sizes $6\frac{1}{2}$–18 Weight: 14.6 oz

78. AEROBICS The number of calories burned when doing step aerobics depends on the step height. How many more calories are burned during a 10-minute workout using an 8-inch step instead of a 4-inch step? 19 calories

Step height (in.)	Calories burned per minute
4	4.5
6	5.5
8	6.4
10	7.2

Source: *Reebok Instructor News* (Vol. 4, No. 3, 1991)

79. THE PANAMA CANAL A ship entering the Panama Canal from the Atlantic Ocean is lifted up 85 feet to Lake Gatun by the Gatun Lock system. See the illustration. Then the ship is lowered 31 feet by the Pedro Miguel Lock. By how much must the ship be lowered by the Miraflores Lock system for it to reach the Pacific Ocean water level? 54 ft

80. CANAL LOCKS What is the combined length of the system of locks in the Panama Canal? Express your answer as a mixed number and as a decimal, rounded to the nearest tenth. $3\frac{1}{3}$ mi, 3.3 mi

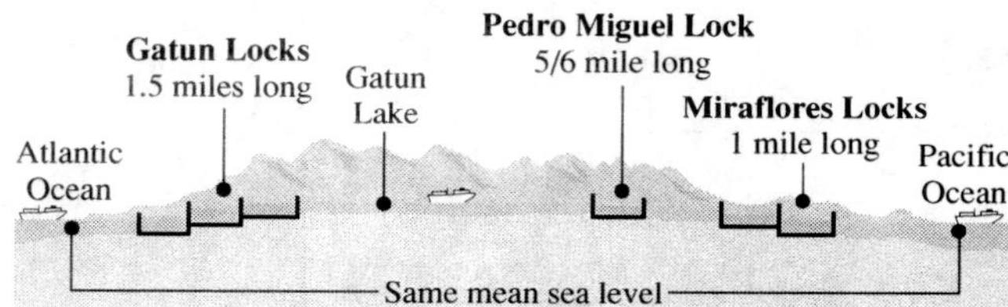

Objectives

1 Multiply monomials.

2 Multiply a polynomial by a monomial.

3 Multiply binomials.

4 Multiply polynomials.

SECTION II.3 Multiplying Polynomials

We now discuss how to multiply polynomials. We will begin with the simplest case—finding the product of two monomials.

1 Multiply monomials.

To multiply $4x^2$ by $2x^3$, we use the commutative and associative properties of multiplication to reorder and regroup the factors.

$$(4x^2)(2x^3) = (4 \cdot 2)(x^2 \cdot x^3)$$ Group the coefficients together and the variables together.

$$= 8x^5$$ Simplify: $x^2 \cdot x^3 = x^{2+3} = x^5$.

This example suggests the following rule.

Multiplying Two Monomials

To multiply two monomials, multiply the numerical factors (the coefficients) and then multiply the variable factors.

EXAMPLE 1 Multiply: **a.** $3y \cdot 6y$ **b.** $-3x^5(2x^5)$

Strategy We will multiply the numerical factors and then multiply the variable factors.

WHY The commutative and associative properties of multiplication enable us to reorder and regroup factors.

Solution

a. $3y \cdot 6y = (3 \cdot 6)(y \cdot y)$ Group the numerical factors and group the variables.

$= 18y^2$ Multiply: $3 \cdot 6 = 18$ and $y \cdot y = y^2$.

b. $(-3x^5)(2x^5) = (-3 \cdot 2)(x^5 \cdot x^5)$ Group the numerical factors and group the variables.

$= -6x^{10}$ Multiply: $-3 \cdot 2 = -6$ and $x^5 \cdot x^5 = x^{5+5} = x^{10}$.

Self Check 1

Multiply: $-7a^3 \cdot 2a^5$ $-14a^8$

Now Try **Problem 15**

Teaching Example 1
Multiply: $-9f^3 \cdot 4f^7$
Answer:
$-36f^{10}$

2 Multiply a polynomial by a monomial.

To find the product of a polynomial and a monomial, we use the distributive property. To multiply $x + 4$ by $3x$, for example, we proceed as follows:

$3x(x + 4) = 3x(x) + 3x(4)$ Use the distributive property.

$= 3x^2 + 12x$ Multiply the monomials: $3x(x) = 3x^2$ and $3x(4) = 12x$.

The results of this example suggest the following rule.

Multiplying Polynomials by Monomials

To multiply a polynomial by a monomial, multiply each term of the polynomial by the monomial.

EXAMPLE 2 Multiply: **a.** $2a^2(3a^2 - 4a)$ **b.** $8x(3x^2 + 2x - 3)$

Strategy We will multiply each term of the polynomial by the monomial.

WHY We use the distributive property to multiply a monomial and a polynomial.

Solution

a. $2a^2(3a^2 - 4a)$

$= 2a^2(3a^2) - 2a^2(4a)$ Use the distributive property.

$= 6a^4 - 8a^3$ Multiply: $2a^2(3a^2) = 6a^4$ and $2a^2(4a) = 8a^3$.

b. $8x(3x^2 + 2x - 3)$

$= 8x(3x^2) + 8x(2x) - 8x(3)$ Use the distributive property.

$= 24x^3 + 16x^2 - 24x$ Multiply: $8x(3x^2) = 24x^3$, $8x(2x) = 16x^2$, and $8x(3) = 24x$.

Self Check 2

Multiply:

a. $3y(5y^3 - 4y)$ $15y^4 - 12y^2$

b. $5x(3x^2 - 2x + 3)$ $15x^3 - 10x^2 + 15x$

Now Try **Problem 29**

Teaching Example 2 Multiply:
a. $4x(7x^2 - 3x)$ b. $6t(3t^2 - 5t + 11)$
Answers:
a. $28x^3 - 12x^2$ b. $18t^3 - 30t^2 + 66t$

3 Multiply binomials.

The distributive property can also be used to multiply binomials. For example, to multiply $2a + 4$ and $3a + 5$, we think of $2a + 4$ as a single quantity and distribute it over each term of $3a + 5$.

$$(2a + 4)(3a + 5) = (2a + 4)3a + (2a + 4)5$$
$$= (2a + 4)3a + (2a + 4)5$$
$$= (2a)3a + (4)3a + (2a)5 + (4)5$$ Distribute the multiplication by 3a and by 5.
$$= 6a^2 + 12a + 10a + 20$$ Multiply the monomials.
$$= 6a^2 + 22a + 20$$ Combine like terms.

In the third line of the solution, notice that each term of $3a + 5$ has been multiplied by each term of $2a + 4$. This example suggests the following rule.

Multiplying Binomials

To multiply two binomials, multiply each term of one binomial by each term of the other binomial, and then combine like terms.

We can use a shortcut method, called the **FOIL method,** to multiply binomials. FOIL is an acronym for **F**irst terms, **O**uter terms, **I**nner terms, **L**ast terms. To use the FOIL method to multiply $2a + 4$ by $3a + 5$, we

1. multiply the **F**irst terms $2a$ and $3a$ to obtain $6a^2$,
2. multiply the **O**uter terms $2a$ and 5 to obtain $10a$,
3. multiply the **I**nner terms 4 and $3a$ to obtain $12a$, and
4. multiply the **L**ast terms 4 and 5 to obtain 20.

Then we simplify the resulting polynomial, if possible.

Outer
First
Inner
Last

F O I L

$$(2a + 4)(3a + 5) = 2a(3a) + 2a(5) + 4(3a) + 4(5)$$
$$= 6a^2 + 10a + 12a + 20$$ Multiply the monomials.
$$= 6a^2 + 22a + 20$$ Combine like terms.

The Language of Algebra An *acronym* is an abbreviation of several words in such a way that the abbreviation itself forms a word. The *acronym* FOIL helps us remember the order to follow when multiplying two binomials: First, Outer, Inner, Last.

EXAMPLE 3 Multiply: **a.** $(x + 5)(x + 7)$ **b.** $(3x + 4)(2x - 3)$

Strategy We will use the FOIL method.

WHY In each case we are to find the product of two binomials, and the FOIL method is a shortcut for multiplying two binomials.

Solution

a.

$$(x + 5)(x + 7) = x(x) + x(7) + 5(x) + 5(7)$$
$$= x^2 + 7x + 5x + 35 \quad \text{Multiply the monomials.}$$
$$= x^2 + 12x + 35 \quad \text{Combine like terms.}$$

b.

$$(3x + 4)(2x - 3) = 3x(2x) + 3x(-3) + 4(2x) + 4(-3)$$
$$= 6x^2 - 9x + 8x - 12 \quad \text{Multiply the monomials.}$$
$$= 6x^2 - x - 12 \quad \text{Combine like terms.}$$

Self Check 3

Multiply:

a. $(y + 3)(y + 1)$ $y^2 + 4y + 3$

b. $(2a - 1)(3a + 2)$ $6a^2 + a - 2$

Now Try **Problems 35 and 39**

Teaching Example 3 Multiply:
a. $(p + 4)(p + 3)$ **b.** $(6r - 1)(2r + 9)$
Answers:
a. $p^2 + 7p + 12$ **b.** $12r^2 + 52r - 9$

EXAMPLE 4 Find: $(5x - 4)^2$

Strategy We will write the base, $5x - 4$, as a factor twice, and perform the multiplication.

WHY In the expression $(5x - 4)^2$, the binomial $5x - 4$ is the base and 2 is the exponent.

Solution

$$(5x - 4)^2 = (5x - 4)(5x - 4) \quad \text{Write the base as a factor twice.}$$
$$= 5x(5x) + 5x(-4) + (-4)(5x) + (-4)(-4)$$
$$= 25x^2 - 20x - 20x + 16 \quad \text{Multiply the monomials.}$$
$$= 25x^2 - 40x + 16 \quad \text{Combine like terms.}$$

Self Check 4

Find: $(5x + 4)^2$ $25x^2 + 40x + 16$

Now Try **Problem 41**

Teaching Example 4
Find: $(8x + 5)^2$
Answer:
$64x^2 + 80x + 25$

Caution! A common error when squaring a binomial is to square only its first and second terms. For example, it is incorrect to write

$$(5x - 4)^2 = (5x)^2 - (4)^2$$
$$= 25x^2 - 16$$

The correct answer is $25x^2 - 40x + 16$.

4 Multiply polynomials.

To develop a general rule for multiplying any two polynomials, we will find the product of $2x + 3$ and $3x^2 + 3x + 5$. In the solution, the distributive property is used four times.

$$(2x + 3)(3x^2 + 3x + 5)$$
$$= (2x + 3)3x^2 + (2x + 3)3x + (2x + 3)5 \quad \text{Distribute.}$$
$$= (2x + 3)3x^2 + (2x + 3)3x + (2x + 3)5$$
$$= (2x)3x^2 + (3)3x^2 + (2x)3x + (3)3x + (2x)5 + (3)5 \quad \text{Distribute.}$$
$$= 6x^3 + 9x^2 + 6x^2 + 9x + 10x + 15 \quad \text{Multiply the monomials.}$$
$$= 6x^3 + 15x^2 + 19x + 15 \quad \text{Combine like terms.}$$

In the third line of the solution, note that each term of $3x^2 + 3x + 5$ has been multiplied by each term of $2x + 3$. This example suggests the following rule.

Multiplying Polynomials

To multiply two polynomials, multiply each term of one polynomial by each term of the other polynomial, and then combine like terms.

Self Check 5

Multiply:
$(3a^2 - 1)(2a^4 - a^2 - a)$
$6a^6 - 5a^4 - 3a^3 + a^2 + a$

Now Try **Problem 49**

Teaching Example 5 Multiply:
$(3x^2 + 1)(2x^2 - 3x + 1)$
Answer:
$6x^4 - 9x^3 + 5x^2 - 3x + 1$

EXAMPLE 5 Multiply: $(7y + 3)(6y^2 - 8y + 1)$

Strategy We will multiply each term of the trinomial, $6y^2 - 8y + 1$, by each term of the binomial, $7y + 3$.

WHY To multiply two polynomials, we must multiply each term of one polynomial by each term of the other polynomial.

Solution

$$(7y + 3)(6y^2 - 8y + 1)$$
$$= 7y(6y^2) + 7y(-8y) + 7y(1) + 3(6y^2) + 3(-8y) + 3(1)$$
$$= 42y^3 - 56y^2 + 7y + 18y^2 - 24y + 3 \quad \text{Multiply the monomials.}$$
$$= 42y^3 - 38y^2 - 17y + 3 \quad \text{Combine like terms.}$$

Caution! The FOIL method cannot be applied here—only to products of two binomials.

It is often convenient to multiply polynomials using a **vertical form** similar to that used to multiply whole numbers.

Success Tip Multiplying two polynomials in vertical form is much like multiplying two whole numbers in arithmetic.

```
   347
 ×  25
 1 735
+6 940
 8,675
```

Self Check 6

Multiply using vertical form:

a. $(3x + 2)(2x^2 - 4x + 5)$
$6x^3 - 8x^2 + 7x + 10$

b. $(-2x^2 + 3)(2x^2 - 4x - 1)$
$-4x^4 + 8x^3 + 8x^2 - 12x - 3$

Now Try **Problem 63**

EXAMPLE 6 Multiply using vertical form:

a. $(3a^2 - 4a + 7)(2a + 5)$ **b.** $(6y^3 - 5y + 4)(-4y^2 - 3)$

Strategy First, we will write one polynomial underneath the other and draw a horizontal line beneath them. Then, we will multiply each term of the upper polynomial by each term of the lower polynomial.

WHY *Vertical form* means to use an approach similar to that used in arithmetic to multiply two whole numbers.

Solution

a. Multiply:

$$\begin{array}{rl} 3a^2 - 4a + 7 & \\ \times \quad 2a + 5 & \\ \hline 15a^2 - 20a + 35 & \text{Multiply } 3a^2 - 4a + 7 \text{ by } 5. \\ 6a^3 - 8a^2 + 14a \quad & \text{Multiply } 3a^2 - 4a + 7 \text{ by } 2a. \\ \hline 6a^3 + 7a^2 - 6a + 35 & \text{In each column, combine like terms.} \end{array}$$

b. With this method, it is often necessary to leave a space for a missing term to vertically align like terms.

Multiply:

$$\begin{array}{rl} 6y^3 - 5y + 4 & \\ \times \quad - 4y^2 - 3 & \\ \hline -18y^3 \quad + 15y - 12 & \text{Multiply } 6y^3 - 5y + 4 \text{ by } -3. \\ -24y^5 + 20y^3 - 16y^2 \quad & \text{Multiply } 6y^3 - 5y + 4 \text{ by } -4y^2. \\ \hline -24y^5 + 2y^3 - 16y^2 + 15y - 12 & \text{Leave a space for any missing powers of } y. \\ & \text{In each column, combine like terms.} \end{array}$$

Teaching Example 6 Multiply using vertical form:
a. $(x^2 - 2x + 1)(x + 2)$
b. $(x^3 + 5x^2 - 4x - 4)(x^2 - 8)$
Answers:
a. $x^3 - 3x + 2$
b. $x^5 + 5x^4 - 12x^3 - 44x^2 + 32x + 32$

ANSWERS TO SELF CHECKS

1. $-14a^8$ **2. a.** $15y^4 - 12y^2$ **b.** $15x^3 - 10x^2 + 15x$ **3. a.** $y^2 + 4y + 3$ **b.** $6a^2 + a - 2$ **4.** $25x^2 + 40x + 16$ **5.** $6a^6 - 5a^4 - 3a^3 + a^2 + a$ **6. a.** $6x^3 - 8x^2 + 7x + 10$ **b.** $-4x^4 + 8x^3 + 8x^2 - 12x - 3$

SECTION II.3 STUDY SET

VOCABULARY

Fill in the blanks.

1. $(2x^3)(3x^4)$ is the product of two monomials.
2. $(2a - 4)(3a + 5)$ is the product of two binomials.
3. In the acronym FOIL, F stands for first terms, O for outer terms, I for inner terms, and L for last terms.
4. $(2a - 4)(3a^2 + 5a - 1)$ is the product of a binomial and a trinomial.

CONCEPTS

Fill in the blanks.

5. To multiply two polynomials, multiply each term of one polynomial by each term of the other polynomial, and then combine like terms.
6. Label each arrow using one of the letters F, O, I, or L. Then fill in the blanks.

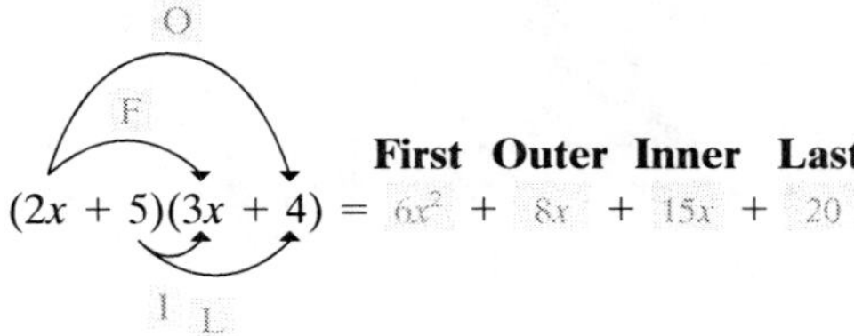

First Outer Inner Last
$(2x + 5)(3x + 4) = 6x^2 + 8x + 15x + 20$

7. Simplify each polynomial by combining like terms.
   a. $6x^2 - 8x + 9x - 12$ $6x^2 + x - 12$
   b. $5x^4 + 3ax^2 + 5ax^2 + 3a^2$ $5x^4 + 8ax^2 + 3a^2$
8. a. Add: $(x - 4) + (x + 8)$ $2x + 4$
   b. Subtract: $(x - 4) - (x + 8)$ -12
   c. Multiply: $(x - 4)(x + 8)$ $x^2 + 4x - 32$

NOTATION

Complete each solution.

9. $(9n^3)(8n^2) = (9 \cdot 8)(n^3 \cdot n^2) = 72n^5$
10. $7x(3x^2 - 2x + 5) = 7x(3x^2) - 7x(2x) + 7x(5)$
    $= 21x^3 - 14x^2 + 35x$
11. $(2x + 5)(3x - 2) = 2x(3x) - 2x(2) + 5(3x) - 5(2)$
    $= 6x^2 - 4x + 15x - 10$
    $= 6x^2 + 11x - 10$
12. $$\begin{array}{r} 3x^2 + 4x - 2 \\ 2x + 3 \\ \hline 9x^2 + 12x - 6 \\ 6x^3 + 8x^2 - 4x \quad \\ \hline 6x^3 + 17x^2 + 8x - 6 \end{array}$$

PRACTICE

Multiply.

13. $(3x^2)(4x^3)$ $12x^5$

14. $(-2a^3)(3a^2)$ $-6a^5$

15. $(3b^2)(-2b)$ $-6b^3$

16. $(3y)(-y^4)$ $-3y^5$

17. $(-2x^2)(3x^3)$ $-6x^5$

18. $(-7x^3)(-3x^3)$ $21x^6$

19. $\left(-\frac{2}{3}y^5\right)\left(\frac{3}{4}y^2\right)$ $-\frac{1}{2}y^7$

20. $\left(\frac{2}{5}r^4\right)\left(\frac{3}{5}r^2\right)$ $\frac{6}{25}r^6$

21. $3(x + 4)$ $3x + 12$

22. $-3(a - 2)$ $-3a + 6$

23. $-4(t + 7)$ $-4t - 28$

24. $6(s^2 - 3)$ $6s^2 - 18$

25. $3x(x - 2)$ $3x^2 - 6x$

26. $4y(y + 5)$ $4y^2 + 20y$

27. $-2x^2(3x^2 - x)$ $-6x^4 + 2x^3$

28. $4b^3(2b^2 - 2b)$ $8b^5 - 8b^4$

29. $2x(3x^2 + 4x - 7)$ $6x^3 + 8x^2 - 14x$

30. $3y(2y^2 - 7y - 8)$ $6y^3 - 21y^2 - 24y$

31. $-p(2p^2 - 3p + 2)$ $-2p^3 + 3p^2 - 2p$

32. $-2t(t^2 - t + 1)$ $-2t^3 + 2t^2 - 2t$

33. $3q^2(q^2 - 2q + 7)$ $3q^4 - 6q^3 + 21q^2$

34. $4v^3(-2v^2 + 3v - 1)$ $-8v^5 + 12v^4 - 4v^3$

35. $(a + 4)(a + 5)$ $a^2 + 9a + 20$

36. $(y - 3)(y + 5)$ $y^2 + 2y - 15$

37. $(3x - 2)(x + 4)$ $3x^2 + 10x - 8$

38. $(t + 4)(2t - 3)$ $2t^2 + 5t - 12$

39. $(2a + 4)(3a - 5)$ $6a^2 + 2a - 20$

40. $(2b - 1)(3b + 4)$ $6b^2 + 5b - 4$

Square each binomial.

41. $(2x + 3)^2$ $4x^2 + 12x + 9$

42. $(2y + 5)^2$ $4y^2 + 20y + 25$

43. $(2x - 3)^2$ $4x^2 - 12x + 9$

44. $(2y - 5)^2$ $4y^2 - 20y + 25$

45. $(5t - 1)^2$ $25t^2 - 10t + 1$

46. $(6a - 3)^2$ $36a^2 - 36a + 9$

47. $(9b - 2)$ $81b^2 - 36b + 4$

48. $(7m - 2)^2$ $49m^2 - 28m + 4$

Multiply.

49. $(2x + 1)(3x^2 - 2x + 1)$ $6x^3 - x^2 + 1$

50. $(x + 2)(2x^2 + x - 3)$ $2x^3 + 5x^2 - x - 6$

51. $(x - 1)(x^2 + x + 1)$ $x^3 - 1$

52. $(x + 2)(x^2 - 2x + 4)$ $x^3 + 8$

53. $(x + 2)(x^2 - 3x + 1)$ $x^3 - x^2 - 5x + 2$

54. $(x + 3)(x^2 + 3x + 2)$ $x^3 + 6x^2 + 11x + 6$

55. $(r^2 - r + 3)(r^2 - 4r - 5)$ $r^4 - 5r^3 + 2r^2 - 7r - 15$

56. $(w^2 + w - 9)(w^2 - w + 3)$ $w^4 - 7w^2 + 12w - 27$

Multiply.

57. $\begin{array}{r} 4x + 3 \\ \underline{x + 2} \end{array}$ $4x^2 + 11x + 6$

58. $\begin{array}{r} 5r + 6 \\ \underline{2r - 1} \end{array}$ $10r^2 + 7r - 6$

59. $\begin{array}{r} 4x - 2 \\ \underline{3x + 5} \end{array}$ $12x^2 + 14x - 10$

60. $\begin{array}{r} 6r + 5 \\ \underline{2r - 3} \end{array}$ $12r^2 - 8r - 15$

61. $\begin{array}{r} x^2 - x + 1 \\ \underline{x + 1} \end{array}$ $x^3 + 1$

62. $\begin{array}{r} 4x^2 - 2x + 1 \\ \underline{2x + 1} \end{array}$ $8x^3 + 1$

63. $\begin{array}{r} 4x^2 + 3x - 4 \\ \underline{3x + 2} \end{array}$ $12x^3 + 17x^2 - 6x - 8$

64. $\begin{array}{r} 5r^2 + r + 6 \\ \underline{2r - 1} \end{array}$ $10r^3 - 3r^2 + 11r - 6$

APPLICATIONS

65. GEOMETRY Find a polynomial that represents the area of the rectangle (*Hint:* Recall that the area of a rectangle is the product of its length and width). $(x^2 - 4)$ ft²

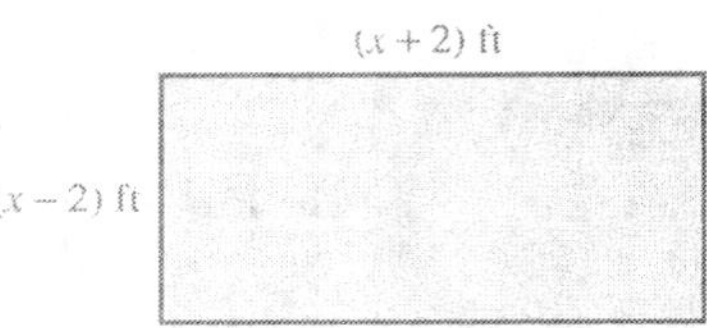

66. SAILING The height h of the triangular sail is $4x$ feet, and the base b is $(3x - 2)$ feet. Find a polynomial that represents the area of the sail. (*Hint:* The area of a triangle is given by the formula $A = \frac{1}{2}bh$.) $(6x^2 - 4x)$ ft²

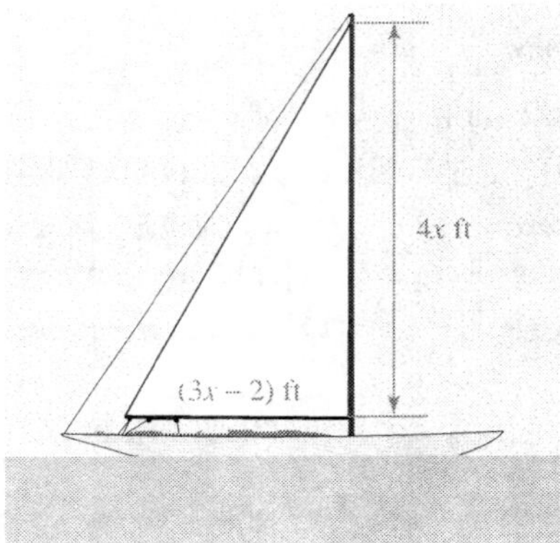

67. STAMPS Find a polynomial that represents the area of the stamp. $(6x^2 + x - 1)$ cm²

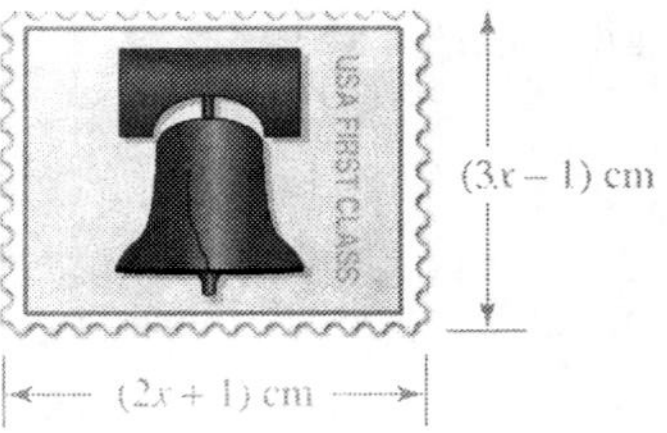

68. PARKING Find a polynomial that represents the total area of the van-accessible parking space and its access aisle. $(2x^2 + 20x)$ ft^2

69. TOYS Find a polynomial that represents the area of the Etch-A-Sketch. $(35x^2 + 43x + 12)$ in.^{2}

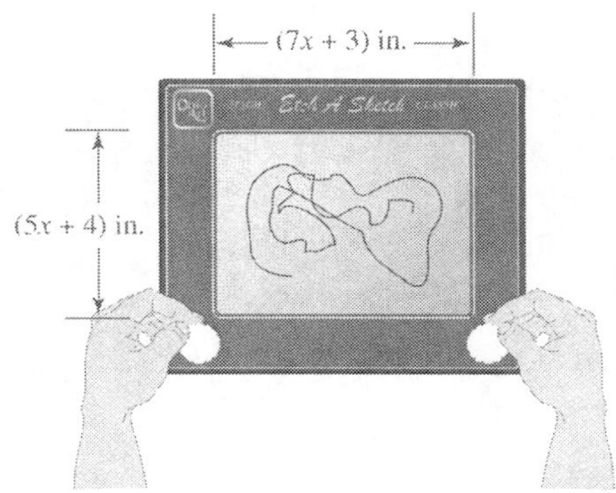

70. PLAYPENS Find a polynomial that represents the area of the floor of the playpen. $(x^2 + 12x + 36)$ in.^{2}

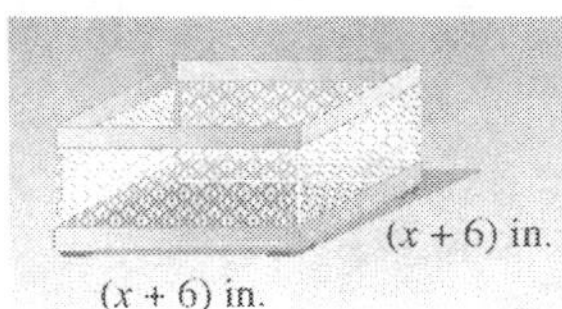

WRITING

71. Explain how to multiply two binomials.

72. Explain how to find $(2x + 1)^2$.

73. Explain why $(x + 1)^2 \neq x^2 + 1^2$. (Read $\neq$ as "is not equal to.")

74. If two terms are to be added, they have to be like terms. If two terms are to be multiplied, must they be like terms? Explain.

REVIEW

75. THE EARTH It takes 23 hours, 56 minutes, and 4.091 seconds for the Earth to rotate on its axis once. Write 4.091 in words.
four and ninety-one thousandths

76. TAKE-OUT FOOD The sticker shows the amount and the price per pound of some spaghetti salad that was purchased at a delicatessen. Find the total price of the salad. \$3.08

77. Write $\frac{7}{64}$ as a decimal. 0.109375

78. Write $-\frac{6}{10}$ as a decimal. -0.6

79. Evaluate: $56.09 + 78 + 0.567$ 134.657

80. Evaluate: $-679.4 - (-599.89)$ -79.51

81. Evaluate: $\sqrt{16} + \sqrt{36}$ 10

82. Find: $103.6 \div 0.56$ 185

Inductive and Deductive Reasoning

Objectives

1 Use inductive reasoning to solve problems.

2 Use deductive reasoning to solve problems.

SECTION III.1
Inductive and Deductive Reasoning

To reason means to think logically. The objective of this appendix is to develop your problem-solving ability by improving your reasoning skills. We will introduce two fundamental types of reasoning that can be applied in a wide variety of settings. They are known as *inductive reasoning* and *deductive reasoning.*

1 Use inductive reasoning to solve problems.

In a laboratory, scientists conduct experiments and observe outcomes. After several repetitions with similar outcomes, the scientist will generalize the results into a statement that appears to be true:

- If I heat water to 212°F, it will boil.
- If I drop a weight, it will fall.
- If I combine an acid with a base, a chemical reaction occurs.

When we draw general conclusions from specific observations, we are using **inductive reasoning.** The next examples show how inductive reasoning can be used in mathematical thinking. Given a list of numbers or symbols, called a *sequence,* we can often find a missing term of the sequence by looking for patterns and applying inductive reasoning.

Self Check 1

Find the next number in the sequence $-3, -1, 1, 3, \ldots$. 5

Now Try **Problem 11**

Teaching Example 1 Find the next number in the sequence 2, 8, 14, 20, ...
Answer:
26

EXAMPLE 1 Find the next number in the sequence 5, 8, 11, 14, ...

Strategy We will find the *difference* between pairs of numbers in the sequence.

WHY This process will help us discover a pattern that we can use to find the next number in the sequence.

Solution

The numbers in the sequence 5, 8, 11, 14, . . . are increasing. We can find the difference between each pair of successive numbers as follows:

$8 - 5 = 3$ Subtract the first number, 5, from the second number, 8.

$11 - 8 = 3$ Subtract the second number, 8, from the third number, 11.

$14 - 11 = 3$ Subtract the third number, 11 from the fourth number, 14.

The difference between each pair of numbers is 3. This means that each number in the sequence is 3 greater than the previous one. Thus, the next number in the sequence is $14 + 3$, or 17.

EXAMPLE 2 Find the next number in the sequence $-2, -4, -6, -8, \ldots$.

Strategy The terms of the sequence are decreasing. We will determine how each number differs from the previous number.

WHY This type of examination helps us discover a pattern that we can use to find the next number in the sequence.

Self Check 2

Find the next number in the sequence $-0.1, -0.3, -0.5, -0.7, \ldots$. -0.9

Now Try **Problem 15**

Solution

Since each successive number is 2 less than the previous one, the next number in the sequence is $-8 - 2$, or -10.

-2	,	-4	,	-6	,	-8	,	....
		This number is 2 less than the previous number.		This number is 2 less than the previous number.		This number is 2 less than the previous number.		

Self Check 3

Find the next letter in the sequence B, G, D, I, F, K, H, ... M

Now Try **Problem 19**

Teaching Example 2 Find the next number in the sequence $-5, -8, -11, -14, \ldots$.
Answer:
-17

Teaching Example 3 Find the next letter in the sequence A, F, D, I, G, L, J, ...
Answer:
O

EXAMPLE 3 Find the next letter in the sequence A, D, B, E, C, F, D, ...

Strategy We will create a letter–number correspondence and rewrite the sequence in an equivalent numerical form.

WHY Many times, it is easier to determine the pattern if we examine a sequence of numbers instead of letters.

Solution

The letter A is the 1st letter of the alphabet, D is the 4th letter, B is the 2nd letter, and so on. We can create the following letter–number correspondence:

Letter		Number	
A	→	1	Add 3.
D	→	4	Subtract 2.
B	→	2	Add 3.
E	→	5	Subtract 2.
C	→	3	Add 3.
F	→	6	Subtract 2.
D	→	4	

The numbers in the sequence 1, 4, 2, 5, 3, 6, 4, ... alternate in size. They change from smaller to larger, to smaller, to larger, and so on.

We see that 3 is added to the first number to get the second number. Then 2 is subtracted from the second number to get the third number. To get successive numbers in the sequence, we alternately add 3 to one number and then subtract 2 from that result to get the next number.

Applying this pattern, the next number in the given numerical sequence would be $4 + 3$, or 7. The next letter in the original sequence would be G, because it is the 7th letter of the alphabet.

Self Check 4

Find the next shape in the sequence below.

Now Try **Problem 23**

EXAMPLE 4 Find the next shape in the sequence below.

Strategy To find the next shape in the sequence, we will focus on the changing positions of the dots.

WHY The star does not change in any way from term to term.

Solution

We see that each of the three dots moves from one point of the star to the next, in a counterclockwise direction. This is a circular pattern. The next shape in the sequence will be the one shown here.

EXAMPLE 5 Find the next shape in the sequence below.

Strategy To find the next shape in the sequence, we must consider two changing patterns at the same time.

WHY The shapes are changing and the number of dots within them are changing.

Solution

The first figure has three sides and one dot, the second figure has four sides and two dots, and the third figure has five sides and three dots. Thus, we would expect the next figure to have six sides and four dots, as shown to the right.

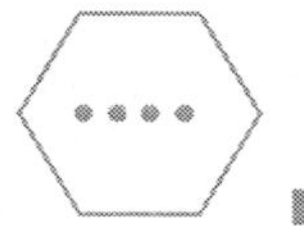

Self Check 5

Find the next shape in the sequence below.

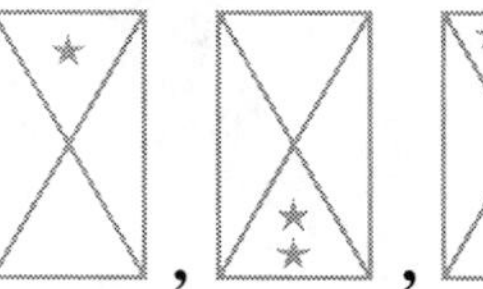

Now Try **Problem 27**

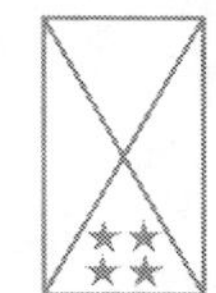

2 Use deductive reasoning to solve problems.

As opposed to inductive reasoning, deductive reasoning moves from the general case to the specific. For example, if we know that the sum of the angles in any triangle is 180°, we know that the sum of the angles of $\triangle ABC$ shown in the right margin is 180°. Whenever we apply a general principle to a particular instance, we are using deductive reasoning.

A deductive reasoning system is built on four elements:

1. **Undefined terms:** terms that we accept without giving them formal meaning
2. **Defined terms:** terms that we define in a formal way
3. **Axioms** or **postulates:** statements that we accept without proof
4. **Theorems:** statements that we can prove with formal reasoning

Many problems can be solved by deductive reasoning. For example, suppose a student knows that his college offers algebra classes in the morning, afternoon, and evening and that Professors Anderson, Medrano, and Ling are the only algebra instructors at the school. Furthermore, suppose that the student plans to enroll in a morning algebra class. After some investigating, he finds out that Professor Anderson teaches only in the afternoon and Professor Ling teaches only in the evening. Without knowing anything about Professor Medrano, he can conclude that she will be his algebra teacher, since she is the only remaining possibility.

The following examples show how to use deductive reasoning to solve problems.

EXAMPLE 6 *Scheduling Classes* An online college offers only one calculus course, one algebra course, one statistics course, and one trigonometry course. Each course is to be taught by a different professor. The four professors who will teach these courses have the following course preferences:

1. Professors A and B don't want to teach calculus.
2. Professor C wants to teach statistics.
3. Professor B wants to teach algebra.

Who will teach trigonometry?

Strategy We will construct a table showing all the possible teaching assignments. Then we will cross off those classes that the professors do not want to teach.

Now Try **Problem 31**

WHY The best way to examine this much information is to describe the situation using a table.

Solution
The following table shows each course, with each possible instructor.

Calculus	Algebra	Statistics	Trigonometry
A	A	A	A
B	B	B	B
C	C	C	C
D	D	D	D

Since Professors A and B don't want to teach calculus, we can cross them off the calculus list. Since Professor C wants to teach statistics, we can cross her off every other list. This leaves Professor D as the only person to teach calculus, so we can cross her off every other list. Since Professor B wants to teach algebra, we can cross him off every other list. Thus, the only remaining person left to teach trigonometry is Professor A.

Calculus	Algebra	Statistics	Trigonometry
~~A~~	A	A	A
~~B~~	B	B	~~B~~
~~C~~	~~C~~	C	~~C~~
D	~~D~~	~~D~~	~~D~~

Self Check 7

USED CARS Of the 50 cars on a used-car lot, 9 are red, 31 are foreign models, and 6 are red, foreign models. If a customer wants to buy an American model that is not red, how many cars does she have to choose from? 16

***Now Try* Problem 35**

EXAMPLE 7 ***State Flags*** The graph below gives the number of state flags that feature an eagle, a star, or both. How many state flags have neither an eagle nor a star?

Has an eagle	10
Has a star	27
Has an eagle and a star	5

Strategy We will use two intersecting circles to model this situation.

WHY The intersection is a way to represent the number of state flags that have both an eagle and a star.

Solution
In figure (a) on the following page, the intersection (overlap) of the circles shows that there are 5 state flags that have both an eagle and a star. If an eagle appears on a total of 10 flags, then the red circle must contain 5 more flags outside of the

intersection, as shown in figure (b). If a total of 27 flags have a star, the blue circle must contain 22 more flags outside the intersection, as shown.

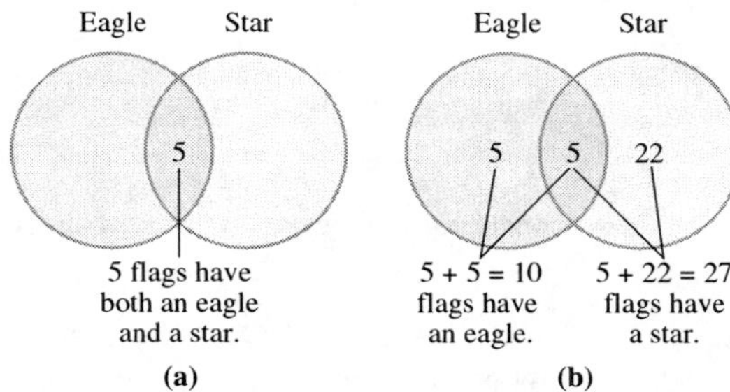

From figure (a), we see that $5 + 5 + 22$, or 32 flags have an eagle, a star, or both. To find how many flags have neither an eagle nor a star, we subtract this total from the number of state flags, which is 50.

$50 - 32 = 18$

There are 18 state flags that have neither an eagle nor a star.

ANSWERS TO SELF CHECKS

1. 5 **2.** −0.9 **3.** M **4.**  **5.** **7.** 16

APPENDIX III STUDY SET

VOCABULARY

Fill in the blanks.

1. Inductive reasoning draws general conclusions from specific observations.

2. Deductive reasoning moves from the general case to the specific.

CONCEPTS

Tell whether the pattern shown is increasing, decreasing, alternating, or circular.

3. 2, 3, 4, 2, 3, 4, 2, 3, 4, . . . circular

4. 8, 5, 2, −1, . . . decreasing

5. −2, −4, 2, 0, 6, . . . alternating

6. 0.1, 0.5, 0.9, 1.3, . . . increasing

7. a, c, b, d, c, e, . . . alternating

8.  . . . circular

9. ROOM SCHEDULING From the chart, determine what time(s) on a Wednesday morning a practice room in a music building is available. The symbol X indicates that the room has already been reserved. 10 A.M.

	M	T	W	Th	F
9 A.M.	X		X		X
10 A.M.	X	X			X
11 a.m.		X	X	X	

10. COUNSELING QUESTIONNAIRE A group of college students were asked whether they were taking a mathematics course and whether they were taking an English course. The results are displayed below.

a. How many students were taking a mathematics course and an English course? 11 students

b. How many students were taking an English course but not a mathematics course? 18 students

c. How many students were taking a mathematics course? 21 students

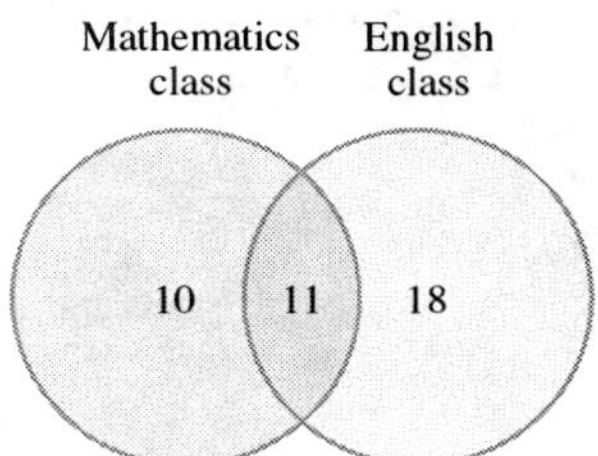

GUIDED PRACTICE

Find the number that comes next in each sequence.
See Example 1.

11. 1, 5, 9, 13, . . . 17

12. 11, 20, 29, 38, . . . 47

13. 5, 9, 14, 20, . . . 27

14. 6, 8, 12, 18, . . . 26

Find the number that comes next in each sequence.
See Example 2.

15. 15, 12, 9, 6, . . . 3

16. 81, 77, 73, 69, . . . 65

17. $-3, -5, -8, -12, \ldots$ -17

18. $1, -8, -16, -25, -33, \ldots$ -42

Find the letter that comes next in each sequence.
See Example 3.

19. E, I, H, L, K, O, N, . . . R

20. C, H, D, I, E, J, F, . . . K

21. c, b, d, c, e, d, f, . . . e

22. z, w, y, v, x, u, w, . . . t

Find the figure that comes next in each sequence.
See Example 4.

23.

24.
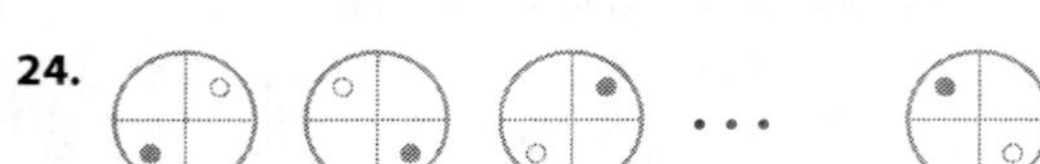

25.
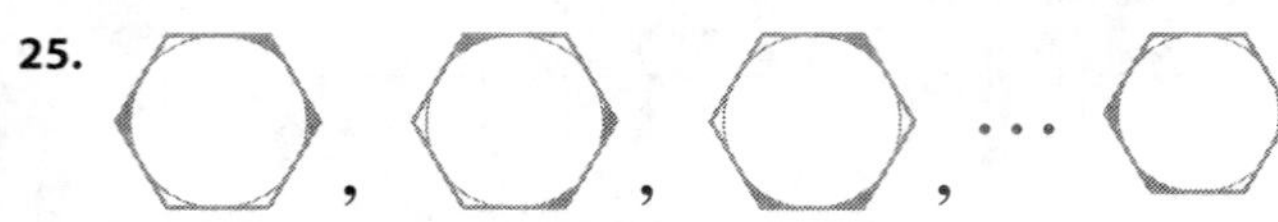

26.
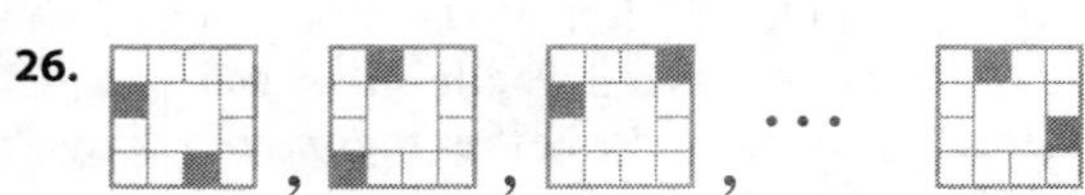

Find the figure that comes next in each sequence.
See Example 5.

27.
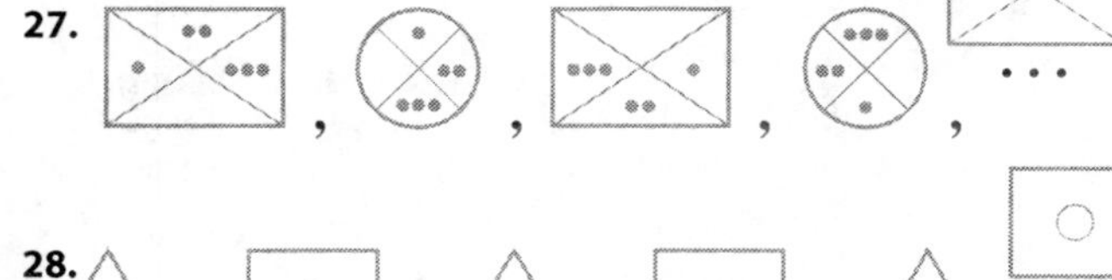

28.
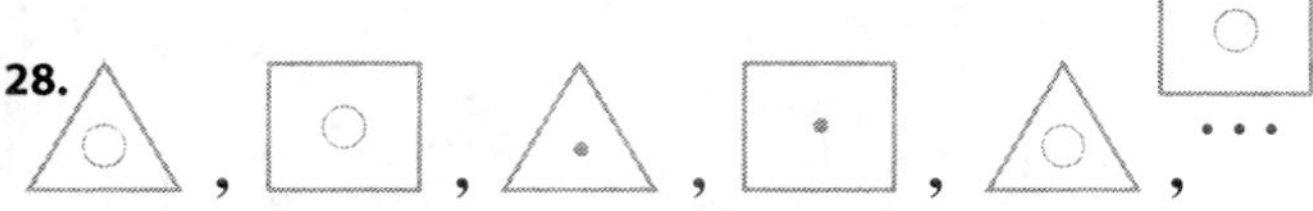

29.
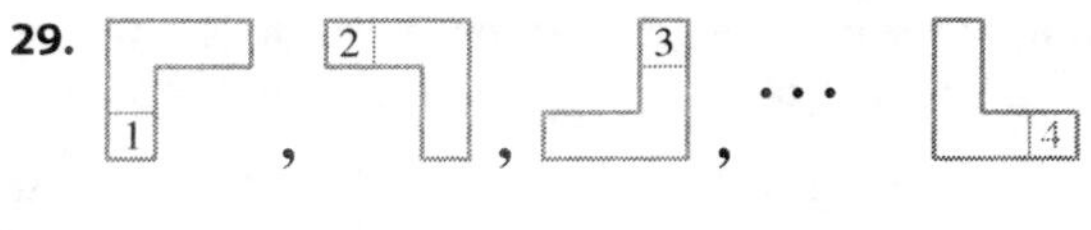

30.

What conclusion can be drawn from each set of information?
See Example 6.

31. TEACHING SCHEDULES A small college offers only one biology course, one physics course, one chemistry course, and one zoology course. Each course is to be taught by a different adjunct professor. The four professors who will teach these courses have the following course preferences:

1. Professors B and D don't want to teach zoology.
2. Professor A wants to teach biology.
3. Professor B wants to teach physics.

Who will teach chemistry? D

32. DISPLAYS Four companies will be displaying their products on tables at a convention. Each company will be assigned one of the displays shown below. The companies have expressed the following preferences:

1. Companies A and C don't want display 2.
2. Company A wants display 3.
3. Company D wants display 1.

Which company will get display 4? C

33. OCUPATIONS Four people named John, Luis, Maria, and Paula have occupations as teacher, butcher, baker, and candlestick maker.

1. John and Paula are married.
2. The teacher plans to marry the baker in December.
3. Luis is the baker.

Who is the teacher? Maria

34. PARKING A Ford, a Buick, a Dodge, and a Mercedes are parked side by side.

1. The Ford is between the Mercedes and the Dodge.
2. The Mercedes is not next to the Buick.
3. The Buick is parked on the left end.

Which car is parked on the right end? the Mercedes

Use a circle diagram to solve each problem. See Example 7.

35. EMPLOYMENT HISTORY One hundred office managers were surveyed to determine their employment backgrounds. The survey results are shown below. How many office managers had neither sales nor manufacturing experience? 6 office managers

Sales experience	63
Manufacturing experience	47
Both	16

36. PURCHASING TEXTBOOKS Sixty college sophomores were surveyed to determine where they purchased their textbooks during their freshman year. The survey results are shown below. How many students did not purchase a book at a bookstore or online? 8 students

Online	23
Bookstore	35
Both	6

37. SIBLINGS When 27 children in a first-grade class were asked, "How many of you have a brother?" 11 raised their hands. When asked, "How many have a sister?" 15 raised their hands. Eight children raised their hands both times. How many children didn't raise their hands either time? 9 children

38. PETS When asked about their pets, a group of 35 sixth-graders responded as follows:

- 21 said they had at least one dog.
- 11 said they had at least one cat.
- 5 said they had at least one dog and at least one cat.

How many of the students do not have a dog or a cat? 8 students

TRY IT YOURSELF

Find the next letter or letters in the sequence.

39. A, c, E, g, . . . I

40. R, SS, TTT, . . . UUUU

41. Z, A, Y, B, X, C, . . . W

42. B, N, C, N, D, . . . N

Find the missing figure in each sequence.

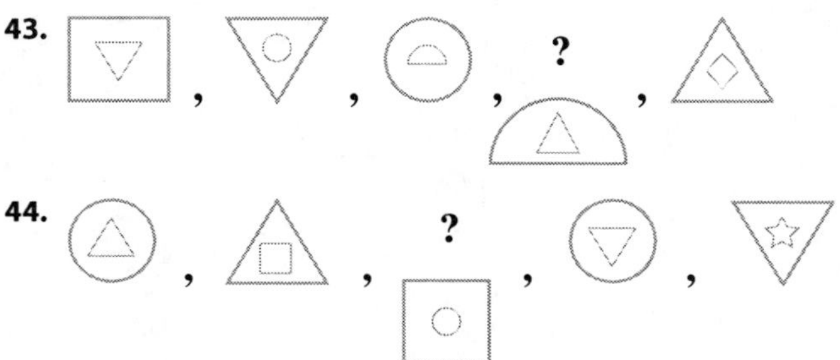

Find the next letter in the sequence.

45. C, B, F, E, I, H, L, . . . K

46. d, h, g, k, j, n, . . . m

Find the next number in the sequence.

47. $-7, 9, -6, 8, -5, 7, -4, \ldots$ 6

48. $2, 5, 3, 6, 4, 7, 5, \ldots$ 8

49. $9, 5, 7, 3, 5, 1, \ldots$ 3

50. $1.3, 1.6, 1.4, 1.7, 1.5, 1.8, \ldots$ 1.6

51. $-2, -3, -5, -6, -8, -9, \ldots$ -11

52. $8, 5, 1, -4, -10, -17, \ldots$ -25

53. $6, 8, 9, 7, 9, 10, 8, 10, 11, \ldots$ 9

54. $10, 8, 7, 11, 9, 8, 12, 10, 9, \ldots$ 13

55. ZOOS In a zoo, a zebra, a tiger, a lion, and a monkey are to be placed in four cages numbered from 1 to 4, from left to right. The following decisions have been made:

1. The lion and the tiger should not be side by side.
2. The monkey should be in one of the end cages.
3. The tiger is to be in cage 4.

In which cage is the zebra? cage 3

56. FARM ANIMALS Four animals—a cow, a horse, a pig, and a sheep—are kept in a barn, each in a separate stall.

1. The cow is in the first stall.
2. Neither the pig nor the sheep can be next to the cow.
3. The pig is between the horse and the sheep.

What animal is in the last stall? the sheep

57. OLYMPIC DIVING Four divers at the Olympics finished first, second, third, and fourth.

1. Diver B beat diver D.
2. Diver A placed between divers D and C.
3. Diver D beat diver C.

In which order did they finish? B, D, A, C

58. FLAGS A green, a blue, a red, and a yellow flag are hanging on a flagpole.

1. The only flag between the green and yellow flags is blue.
2. The red flag is next to the yellow flag.
3. The green flag is above the red flag.

What is the order of the flags from top to bottom? green, blue, yellow, red

APPLICATIONS

59. JURY DUTY The results of a jury service questionnaire are shown below. Determine how many of the 20,000 respondents have served on neither a criminal court nor a civil court jury. 18,935 respondents

Jury Service Questionnaire

997	Served on a criminal court jury
103	Served on a civil court jury
35	Served on both

60. ELECTRONIC POLL For the Internet poll shown below, the first choice was clicked on 124 times, the second choice was clicked on 27 times, and both the first and second choices were clicked on 19 times. How many times was the third choice, "Neither" clicked on? 46 times

Internet Poll	You may vote for more than one.	
What would you do if gasoline reached $5.50 a gallon?	◉ Cut down on driving ◉ Buy a more fuel-efficient car ◉ Neither	
	Number of people voting	178

61. THE SOLAR SYSTEM The graph below shows some important characteristics of the nine planets in our solar system. How many planets are neither rocky nor have moons? 0 planets

Rocky planets	4
Planets with moons	7
Rocky planets with moons	2

62. WORKING TWO JOBS Andres, Barry, and Carl each have a completely different pair of jobs from the following list: jeweler, musician, painter, chauffeur, barber, and gardener. Use the facts below to find the two occupations of each man.

1. The painter bought a ring from the jeweler.
2. The chauffeur offended the musician by laughing at his mustache.
3. The chauffeur dated the painter's sister.
4. Both the musician and the gardener used to go hunting with Andres.
5. Carl beat both Barry and the painter at monopoly.
6. Barry owes the gardener $100.

Andres: painter and barber; Barry: jeweler and musician; Carl: chauffer and gardener

WRITING

63. Describe deductive reasoning and inductive reasoning.

64. Describe a real-life situation in which you might use deductive reasoning.

65. Describe a real-life situation in which you might use inductive reasoning.

66. Write a problem in such a way that the diagram below can be used to solve it.

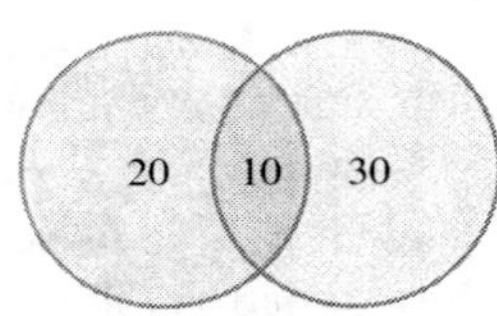

APPENDIX IV

Roots and Powers

n	n^2	$\sqrt{n}$	n^3	$\sqrt[3]{n}$	n	n^2	$\sqrt{n}$	n^3	$\sqrt[3]{n}$
1	1	1.000	1	1.000	51	2,601	7.141	132,651	3.708
2	4	1.414	8	1.260	52	2,704	7.211	140,608	3.733
3	9	1.732	27	1.442	53	2,809	7.280	148,877	3.756
4	16	2.000	64	1.587	54	2,916	7.348	157,464	3.780
5	25	2.236	125	1.710	55	3,025	7.416	166,375	3.803
6	36	2.449	216	1.817	56	3,136	7.483	175,616	3.826
7	49	2.646	343	1.913	57	3,249	7.550	185,193	3.849
8	64	2.828	512	2.000	58	3,364	7.616	195,112	3.871
9	81	3.000	729	2.080	59	3,481	7.681	205,379	3.893
10	100	3.162	1,000	2.154	60	3,600	7.746	216,000	3.915
11	121	3.317	1,331	2.224	61	3,721	7.810	226,981	3.936
12	144	3.464	1,728	2.289	62	3,844	7.874	238,328	3.958
13	169	3.606	2,197	2.351	63	3,969	7.937	250,047	3.979
14	196	3.742	2,744	2.410	64	4,096	8.000	262,144	4.000
15	225	3.873	3,375	2.466	65	4,225	8.062	274,625	4.021
16	256	4.000	4,096	2.520	66	4,356	8.124	287,496	4.041
17	289	4.123	4,913	2.571	67	4,489	8.185	300,763	4.062
18	324	4.243	5,832	2.621	68	4,624	8.246	314,432	4.082
19	361	4.359	6,859	2.668	69	4,761	8.307	328,509	4.102
20	400	4.472	8,000	2.714	70	4,900	8.367	343,000	4.121
21	441	4.583	9,261	2.759	71	5,041	8.426	357,911	4.141
22	484	4.690	10,648	2.802	72	5,184	8.485	373,248	4.160
23	529	4.796	12,167	2.844	73	5,329	8.544	389,017	4.179
24	576	4.899	13,824	2.884	74	5,476	8.602	405,224	4.198
25	625	5.000	15,625	2.924	75	5,625	8.660	421,875	4.217
26	676	5.099	17,576	2.962	76	5,776	8.718	438,976	4.236
27	729	5.196	19,683	3.000	77	5,929	8.775	456,533	4.254
28	784	5.292	21,952	3.037	78	6,084	8.832	474,552	4.273
29	841	5.385	24,389	3.072	79	6,241	8.888	493,039	4.291
30	900	5.477	27,000	3.107	80	6,400	8.944	512,000	4.309
31	961	5.568	29,791	3.141	81	6,561	9.000	531,441	4.327
32	1,024	5.657	32,768	3.175	82	6,724	9.055	551,368	4.344
33	1,089	5.745	35,937	3.208	83	6,889	9.110	571,787	4.362
34	1,156	5.831	39,304	3.240	84	7,056	9.165	592,704	4.380
35	1,225	5.916	42,875	3.271	85	7,225	9.220	614,125	4.397
36	1,296	6.000	46,656	3.302	86	7,396	9.274	636,056	4.414
37	1,369	6.083	50,653	3.332	87	7,569	9.327	658,503	4.431
38	1,444	6.164	54,872	3.362	88	7,744	9.381	681,472	4.448
39	1,521	6.245	59,319	3.391	89	7,921	9.434	704,969	4.465
40	1,600	6.325	64,000	3.420	90	8,100	9.487	729,000	4.481
41	1,681	6.403	68,921	3.448	91	8,281	9.539	753,571	4.498
42	1,764	6.481	74,088	3.476	92	8,464	9.592	778,688	4.514
43	1,849	6.557	79,507	3.503	93	8,649	9.644	804,357	4.531
44	1,936	6.633	85,184	3.530	94	8,836	9.695	830,584	4.547
45	2,025	6.708	91,125	3.557	95	9,025	9.747	857,375	4.563
46	2,116	6.782	97,336	3.583	96	9,216	9.798	884,736	4.579
47	2,209	6.856	103,823	3.609	97	9,409	9.849	912,673	4.595
48	2,304	6.928	110,592	3.634	98	9,604	9.899	941,192	4.610
49	2,401	7.000	117,649	3.659	99	9,801	9.950	970,299	4.626
50	2,500	7.071	125,000	3.684	100	10,000	10.000	1,000,000	4.642